Finding the leading antique centres in London is as simple as ABC.

Antiquarius

135/141 Kings Rd. Chelsea London SW3
Open Monday to Saturday 10am to 6pm

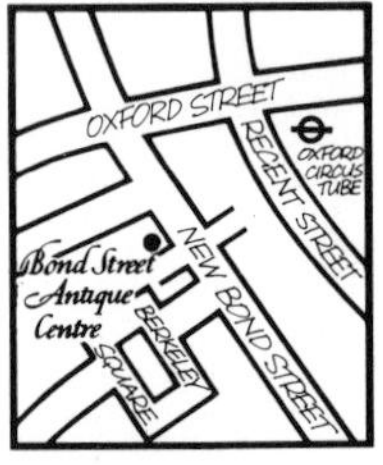

Bond Street

124 New Bond Street London W1
Open Monday to Friday 10am to 5.45pm

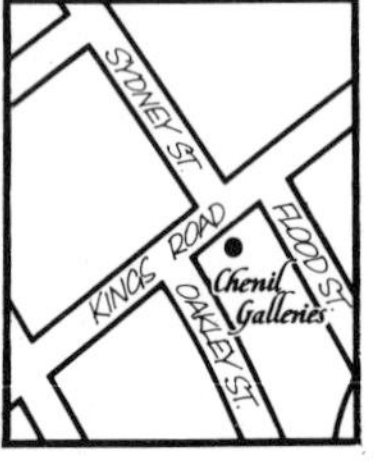

Chenil Galleries

181/183 Kings Rd. Chelsea London SW3
Open Monday to Saturday 10am to 6pm

and the world famous Bermondsey antique market

On the corner of Long Lane and Bermondsey Street London SE1
Open Friday mornings 5am to 2pm

ABC antique centres 15 Flood St Chelsea London SW3. For further information telephone: 01-351 5353

MILLER'S
ANTIQUES
PRICE GUIDE
1984
(Volume V)

Compiled and Edited by

Martin and Judith Miller

SBN 0–905879–77–5

While every care has been exercised in the compilation of this guide, neither the authors or publishers accept any liability for any financial or other loss incurred by reliance placed on the information contained in Miller's Price Guide.

Printed and bound in Great Britain by William Clowes (Beccles) Limited, Beccles and London

PUBLISHED BY M.J.M. PUBLICATIONS LTD.
THE GRANGE · BENENDEN · CRANBROOK · KENT
Telephone Cranbrook (0580) 240454

COLIN DYTE

Colin Dyte & OCL

International antique dealer and exporter to the world. That is the high distinction of Colin Dyte, who has built up one of Britain's busiest export operations specialising in antique furniture.

Colin Dyte Exports Ltd. enjoys a well earned reputation across four continents. His valuable cargoes are shipped to Australia, New Zealand, South Africa, United States, Canada and most of the European countries.

By using the modern facilities of the OCL fleet of door to door container transport he knows his valuable cargoes will reach their destination in the same condition as when they were packed.

The Highbridge company site attracts a constant flow of overseas antique buyers. Situated just a mile off the M5 motorway, the company is within 90 minutes of Heathrow Airport and surrounded by a wide variety of accommodation to meet every need of the flying visitor.

The company is so well known now that the buyers cable to advise of their imminent needs, expecting — and receiving — most of their requirements.

Five years ago Colin Dyte moved into his present premises at Highbridge having previously been in Bridgwater for some 20 years. From the outset he has been a constant believer in the facility afforded by OCL's containerisation. He was one of the first to use the through transport system to the United States — expanding his business to new areas as the system itself was established worldwide.

The container system is ideal for the shipment of delicate cargo and the regularity of the sailings provided by the operators ensures a constant turnaround of shipments.

Antique exporting is a non stop business these days — empty containers are delivered as the full container is collected from Colin Dyte's extensive premises and it was only recently that Colin Dyte despatched his 4000th container.

Fortunately, for lovers of good, old and well made furniture, the United Kingdom appears to have an inexhaustible supply — and the services of Colin Dyte Exports Ltd. to meet the demand.

Of the many shipping companies used by Colin Dyte OCL in particular are proud to associate themselves with a continually expanding concern such as Colin Dyte Exports Ltd.

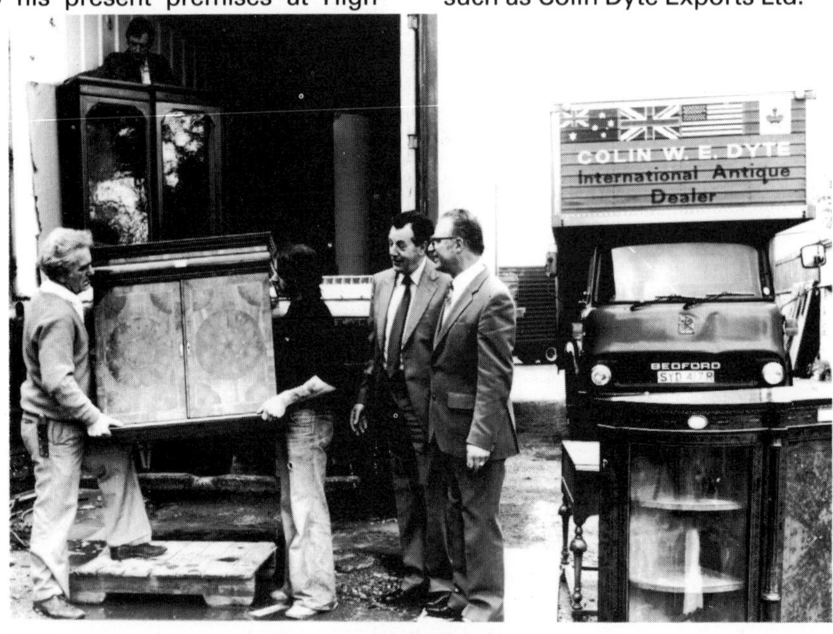

See page 642 for news about another Egon Ronay 1984 Guide.

Introduction

STATE OF THE MARKET

by Anne Bouillot

Interaction between the real estate and personal property markets, where buoyant conditions rarely seem to coincide, can be a positive asset to the antique collector with time to attend provincial auctions run by firms engaged in both markets.

This has been especially true in the last year or two; real estate operations have tended to support antique auctions at which as much as a third has been returned unsold. In other words, it has been a buyer's market, and the collector has had the opportunity to determine the price at which an antique has entered the market.

The adverse effect of this interaction has been particularly marked among some firms without property connections and, if they failed to get their own real estate right, they went to the wall.

Even the country's leading firm of auctioneers, Sothebys, has been forced to divest itself of properties which were causing too big a drain on its finances: Belgravia in London, Rainbow in Torquay (which has now reverted to the Bearne partnership) and Duke Street in Chester.

Dramatic — but fortunately not universal — examples of the sort of overhead some antique dealers have to face before they can even think of trading occur in London's Kensington Church Street. There, premiums of around £5,800 per year are sought for each year of an unexpired lease on shops as small as 210 square feet, with an equivalent amount of basement storage. Annual rents for properties of that size are in the region of £6,500, rates are about £1,250 and the tenant is responsible for all repairs and insurance — making the minimum outlay for such premises about £14,000 p.a.

Alternatively, to buy the freehold would cost about £115,000, but the rates, repairs, insurance charges — and generally the mortgage repayments as well — still have to be met.

It is no wonder that, under such circumstances, an increasing number of dealers are working from home or seeking cheaper outlets through a proliferation of fairs and markets, because they know full well there is a limit to the mark-up collectors are prepared to pay.

This limit was also the reason why dealers, who account for 80% of the purchases at auction, were so opposed to the introduction of the buyer's premium, but when the case was put to the Office of Fair Trading several years ago, the Director felt unable to intervene.

PREMIUMS DOWN

In this last year, Christie's have managed to cut their buyer's premium from 10% to 8%, and Wingett and Son of Wrexham, who have no real estate connection, have dropped theirs altogether, but have re-adjusted the vendor's commission on antiques to 15%.

In order for the salerooms to remain profitable while serving the best interests of the trade as a whole, it is essential that they attract the largest possible number of prospective buyers. This means encouraging new buyers from the ranks of the general public and those collectors who normally prefer to do business with antiques dealers. To this end, saleroom staff are generally encouraged to give all the help and guidance they can to any prospective buyer who may be unacquainted with saleroom procedure.

The excuse of being at work during the day is no longer as valid as it once was because an increasing number of auctioneers hold sales in the evening. If anything, though, attendance at 'the view' is even more important, and that frequently takes place in the evening too.

To try and get by without a catalogue is a false economy. It will not only give a description of each lot on offer, but should also indicate if an article is damaged or incomplete (a.f. — as found or all faults).

The practice of giving pre-sale estimates, which can be bound into the catalogue, posted on the wall or available from the porters, has grown considerably. This should not, however, preclude a talk with the auctioneer for it will give him a chance to recognise a new face, and the prospective purchaser the opportunity of learning more about an item of special interest and sorting out bank references if he is tempted to buy.

Auctioneers usually sell at a steady rate of 100 lots an hour or 36 seconds per lot, so if the auction starts at 10.00 a.m., Lot 250 will be sold around 12.30. Dealers sometimes object to other people knowing what they are interested in and so they do use signals, but a member of the public should indicate his bid promptly in a clear voice or raise his catalogue.

If a collector cannot attend a sale, then he must fill in a bidding slip with the help of the auctioneer at the view. The conditions of sale in the catalogue will explain how delivery is effected after payment is made.

The premium position should also be checked in the catalogue; a bid of £100 frequently means a bill of £111.50 (£100 plus 10% buyer's premium of £10 and 15% V.A.T. on the premium).

As each week passes, opportunities for the amateur collector to secure a bargain become more restricted. Even before the General Election, all the major auctioneers confirmed that confidence was returning to the market and the recession-induced period of catharsis culminating in Sotheby's making its first-ever loss had finally been weathered.

While the cliff-hanging serial of the shareholders' battle for control of the firm continued, Sotheby's managed to secure one of the most prestigious sales of the year in conjunction with Savills, the real estate agents, another example of the close liaison between real and personal property worlds.

RECORD PRICES

Together they had valued the castle and contents comprising the Hever Castle Estate where Henry VIII courted Anne Boleyn, at £13.5m, £10.5m for the property and £3m for the contents, the purchaser of the Castle having right of first refusal of the contents.

In the event, Broadland Properties acquired the Castle, Estate and the major part of the furniture and furnishing, leaving Sotheby's to auction two impressive collections: one of arms and armour, the other of Gothic, Renaissance and Baroque ivories, together with tapestries, metalwork, ships' models and musical instruments. Even without the furniture, Sotheby's raised £9.63 million, not perhaps having realised to what extent the market was eager for fresh stock and the amount it was prepared to pay for 'provenance'.

Star of the whole sale, which had been announced a year in advance, was the three-quarter armour made for Henri II by Giovanni Paolo Negroli, c. 1540-45, which was expected to fetch over £500,000. With provenance that could be traced all the way from Henri II to Lord Astor's father and world-wide media interest, the 'combat suit' was eventually bought with a telephone bid from America for £1.75m or £1.925m with premium.

Christie's meticulously researched and beautifully presented catalogue, which itself cost £12, bears out the old adage of always buying the best one can afford, advice the previous owners took to heart.

A Transitional commode by Leonard Boudin, which was ordered for the Comte de Provence at a cost of 2,340 livres in 1771, went way past the £25,000/£35,000 estimate to realise £59,400, the same price given for four George I scarlet and gold lacquer dining-chairs, while at the same estimate, a pair of George II giltwood mirrors in the Kent style, on which the Duchess of Kent raised £262.10s. at Christie's in 1947, sold for £45,360.

Even Christie's were not prepared to put an estimate on the most important item in the sale, a late 15th century Gothic tapestry, which eventually achieved £140,440.

SILVER

Another prestigious sale that Christie's held during the year — this time at their Glasgow branch — was the dispersal of Scottish silver collected by Major Ian Shaw, Chief of Clan Shaw, with one of only nine known Scottish monteiths, 74 oz., fetching £23,000 and one of the earliest known Scottish cake baskets on record, 62 oz., securing a bid of £21,000.

During the year, the melt value of silver rose from £2.75 per oz. to £7.20, falling back to £6.60 at the end and, by rule-of-thumb, antique silver of no special provenance or rarity value is supposed to be worth five times the melt value by ounce, but rules are always made to be broken.

As a spin-off from silver, electro-plate is doing quite well as Sheffield Plate always has because it is in limited supply, but pewter has been in decline on the metal market.

Best price for the firearms was the £50,000 given by a German dealer for a mid-16th century Augsburg breech loading, self-spanning wheellock holster pistol with exceptional technical innovations.

From Augsburg, too, but a century later, came the 4 in. high circular ivory tankard holder, by Bernard Strauss, which realised £41,800.

The most important ivory, however, was the 3 in. high 14th century French Gothic casket thought to have been acquired by James I on his accession and expected to realise over £120,000. Noteworthy for its fine carvings of scenes from the Legend of St. Eustace, it actually sold for £418,000 to a London dealer.

Ivory collectors who find these prices too rich for their pockets may be interested to know that small ornamental groups came in for their fair share of attention during the decorative-minded recession and 3 in. high late 19th century Japanese carvings now fetch on average £100. Japanese goods were unknown in the West before the Paris Exhibition in 1867 so much 19th century Japanese ware is of necessity late.

PROVENANCE

The provenance factor definitely accounted for a substantial percentage of the £3,681,783 which Christie's raised on the sale of the contents of Godmersham Park, making it their best house sale since 1945, which will contribute in part to their next set of results which they already describe as extremely encouraging.

On the death of the owner of Godmersham Park, Christie's were instructed to sell the contents while Hobbs & Parker sold the estate to the Sunley family for close on £3m, which was undoubtedly far in excess of what it was worth when Edward Austen Knight, Jane Austen's brother, inherited it in 1797.

Jane Austen paid frequent visits to the house and is reputed to have modelled Mansfield Park on it. In fact, one of the first editions of *Pride and Prejudice*, collected by the previous owners, which it was thought would sell for £300/£400, went to a bid of £1,800.

AIRCRAFT TAKE OFF

While a major house sale may have eluded Phillips, they more than made up for it by the amount of interest the media showed in their other sales: Billy Butlin's pictures, Wing Commander James Nicholson's V.C., which was bid up to £110,000 by two benefactors both intending to give it to the Battle of Britain Museum, and the sale of the contents of The Historic Aircraft Museum in Southend conducted jointly with Weatherall Green & Smith.

More than 2,000 people were attracted to the sale in Southend where £34,000 was paid for a Hawker Sea Fury, £28,000 for a De Havilland Dragon and £200 for a porcelain tile decorated with a view of a hot air balloon flying over the Eiffel Tower, 1889.

While on the subject of Phillips, it is worth mentioning the success they have had with Royal Doulton character jugs this year because these jugs — and figurines too — are on the move again, £120 being an average price for jugs that are not particularly scarce, while two examples of *Hatless Drake*, a pilot production that was never actually marketed, realised £2,000 and £1,500 respectively.

THEME SALES

Bonhams meanwhile have been successfully pursuing their Theme Sales designed to coincide with the Smithfield Show, Cowes Week, Crufts, etc., and a competitive coterie of collectors anxiously waited to see what fishing reels would be on offer at the special auction devoted to that subject. In the event, they paid £160 for an Illingworth No. 1 casting reel, £130 for a Hardy 4 in. Perfect fly reel and £380 for an ivory fisherman's tackle winder and holder, c. 1800-25. Dreweatt Watson & Barton also sold a Hardy 3 in. Perfect for £105 while a salmon fly reel from the same manufacturer fetched £150 at their annual sale timed to coincide with the opening of the season.

Bonham's earlier sale of a tole peinte iron framed bedstead at £400 underlines the market's continual quest for unusual materials, shape or decorative effect. Tole peinte sounds better than japanned tinwear, a cheap and cheerful material with an inbuilt discard factor. Rarity value therefore comes into play when it survives in good condition for over a century.

Beds also provide good examples of shape and decorative effect with the former embodied in the French 19th century bateau lit, framed in mahogany with swan's head finials and gilt mounts raised on carved wood and gilt griffin legs, which made £1,000 at W. H. Lane & Son of Plymouth.

For sheer spectacular effect, it would be hard to beat the 19th century domed canopy bed with headboard, footboard and frame of ebony inlaid overall with brass and tortoiseshell boulle-work and continuous spirals of ormolu foliage growing up spiral ebony columns sold for £8,100 in Carmarthen by John Francis, Thomas Jones & Son.

CLOCKS AND WATCHES

Another interesting piece to be sold by the same auctioneers was an 18th century pocket watch bought on 15th August, 1789, for £57.15s. The white enamel dial was set round with split pearls while the rim of the gold case was decorated with diamond chips. Complete with winding key, fob and original receipt, it sold for £2,200.

A rough and ready calculation would seem to indicate that that particular watch had not kept pace with inflation and, even at Godmersham Park, the fine Louis XV ormolu mantel clock, by Morel Aine a Lyon, supported on the back of a boar, which sold for £9,180, failed to reach the pre-sale estimate, whereas the Louis XV bronze and ormolu mantel clock, by Vulliamy, London, went over the £6,000/£8,000 estimate by £2,800. Vulliamy is perhaps the better-known maker, but that clock was supported on the back of an elephant-and elephants, in whatever form, are now very collectable.

When the same English dial timepiece with verge escapement by William Ward of Bloomsbury, c. 1775, went through Reeds Rains saleroom for the second time in two years, they saw a 26% price increase from £820 to £1,060, but the escapement was rare and, by and large, the clock and watch market is still patchy with some areas reporting downright difficulty in selling.

So this is obviously one area where scope still exists for the amateur collector interested in horology and prepared to work at it.

A good place to start would be with a perfect understanding of the mechanism of the eight-day longcase clock, which had become fairly standardised by the time George III came to the throne. This will familiarise the collector with the anchor escapement and will ultimately lead on to an appreciation of the rarity of the verge escapement.

For the theory, E. J. Tyler's books can be recommended, but the practical is a more difficult proposition; visiting museums and buying old movements for study is one answer, but the demise of Kingston Antiques, the well-known clock dealers, is to be regretted. Restaurants like the one that now occupies their former premises are not too hard to come by, whereas clock dealers who make the amateur feel it is their privilege to be able to explain to them the finest horological details are at a premium.

OPTIMISM

Fortunately, there is a new, if still somewhat guarded, feeling of optimism within the trade and, despite the political capital to be made out of our current mass unemployment, it is a fact that people with money to spend tend to have more than they did a year ago — and are more inclined to invest a fair proportion of it in quality items.

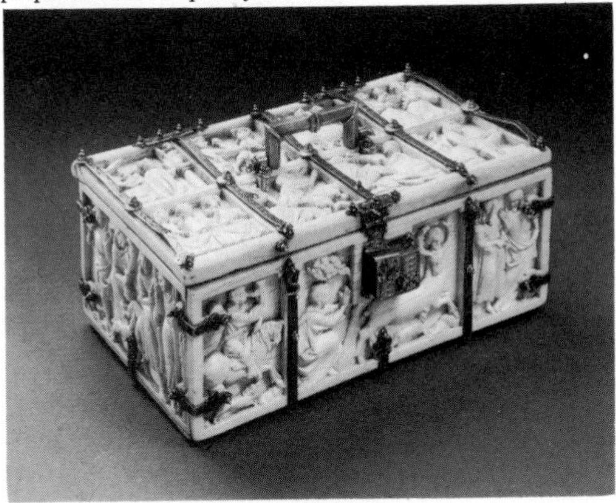

EDITORS' FOREWORD

Martin and Judith Miller

As each new edition of Miller's Guide is planned, a great deal of thought is devoted to finding ways of extending its scope, increasing its reliability and generally improving its effectiveness as Britain's leading price guide. Its content must be reassessed for balance each year, with new categories being introduced, while others recieve greater or less emphasis according to their treatment in previous editions for, although each annual volume is complete in itself, it is also very much a part of a continuing process. So great has been the demand for information contained in back issues that these have now been reprinted to satisfy the demands of dealers and collectors anxious to build their libraries volume by volume.

DIRECTORY OF SPECIALISTS

The Directory of Specialist Services proved so successful in last year's book that we have extended it and added a Directory of Auctioneers. Since the purpose of Miller's (apart from the price guide aspect) is to help stimulate the antiques trade in every way possible, this has been introduced in the expectation that it will be of benefit to users of the book. The intention is to expand both directories in forthcoming editions.

Regular users of Miller's will notice two further differences in this edition; it is larger by almost 40 pages, and it contains about 30 pages of advertising.

RELIABLE PRICES

Naturally, one of the areas requiring greatest care involves the determination of accurate and reliable price estimates. It is a fact that all of the objects selected for inclusion in Miller's are derived from auction houses or dealers stocks in the year prior to publication.

It is the function of a responsibly produced price guide to reconcile differences in price by arriving at a valuation that will be accepted as 'reasonable' by the trade at large.

Since it is clearly impossible to attribute a precise value to any antique, a price range is given which, in the opinion of the editors and independent consultants, may fairly be taken as an indication of its worth on the open market.

COMPREHENSIVE INDEX

In the compilation of a book as comprehensive as Miller's, which is used by the broadest possible cross section of people from those with considerable antiques knowledge and experience to others with virtually none, there sometimes arise problems of classification. Taking porcelain as an example, there are a number of possible methods which might logically be employed. One such would be to group items first under the factory of manufacture and then according to types of article. In order that the book should be of most use to most people, the opposite system has been adopted; plates (for example) are brought together in a section which is then sub-divided into factory groupings.

In the case of, say, a clock in an elaborate porcelain case classification becomes rather more difficult. In such a case, the editors will place the object in the category which is likely to have the greatest influence on the price of the piece in question. To simplify matters, great care has been taken over the index which is exhaustive and fully cross referenced.

Acknowledgements

The publishers would like to acknowledge the great assistance given by our consultant editors:

POTTERY: **David Clark,** *Elias Clark Antiques Ltd., 1 The Cobbles, High Street, Bletchingly, Surrey.*
Jonathan Horne, *66b & c Kensington Church Street, London W8.*

PORCELAIN: **Gordon Lang,** *Sotheby Parke Bernet & Co., 34 & 35 New Bond Street, London W1.*
Nicholas Long, *Studio Antiques, Bourton on the Water, Glos.*

GOSS & CRESTED WARE: **Nicholas Pine,** *Goss & Crested China Ltd., 62 Murray Road, Horndean, Hants.*

FURNITURE: **Richard Davidson,** *Richard Davidson Antiques, Lombard Street, Petworth, Sussex.*

CLOCKS: **Roy Clements,** *Coppelia Antiques, Holford Lodge, Plumley Moor Road, Plumley, Cheshire.*

GLASS: **Wing Cdr. R. G. Thomas,** *Somervale Antiques, 6 Radstock Road, Midsomer Norton, Bath.*

ART NOUVEAU & ART DECO: **Gordon Lang,** *Sotheby Park Bernet & Co., 34 & 35 New Bond Street, London W1.*

ARMS & ARMOUR: **Roy Butler,** *Wallis & Wallis, Regency House, Albion Street, Lewes, E. Sussex.*

CRAFTS: **Lady Gloria Dale,** *The Grange, Benenden, Kent.*

Key to illustrations

Each illustration and descriptive caption is accompanied by a letter-code. By reference to the following list of Auctioneers (denoted by ⋆) and Dealers (•); the source of any item may be immediately determined. In no way does this constitute or imply a contract or binding offer on the part of any of our contributors to supply or sell the goods illustrated, or similar articles, at the prices stated.

A ⋆ Aldridges of Bath Ltd., The Auction Galleries, 130-132 Walcot St., Bath. Tel: 0225 62830/9
Ad • Adams Antiques, 47 Chalk Farm Road, NW1 8AJ. Tel: 01-267 9241
AG ⋆ Anderson & Garland, Anderson House, Market Street., Newcastle-upon-Tyne. Tel: 0632 326278
AGG ⋆ Arthur G. Griffiths & Sons, 57 Foregate Street, Worcester WR1 1DZ. Tel: 0905 26464
AGr ⋆ Andrew Grant, 59/60 Foregate Street, Worcester. Tel: 0905 52310
AH • Abbotts House Antiques (Pauline & Dick Newby), 25 White Hart Street, Aylsham, Norfolk. Tel: 026-373 4182
AL • Ann Lingard, T/A Rope Walk Antiques, Rye, Sussex. Tel: 0797 223486
AS ⋆ Andrew Sharpe & Partners, Ilkley Auction Galleries, Riddings Road, Ilkley, W. Yorkshire. Tel: 0943 600456
B ⋆ Boardman, Station Road Corner, Haverhill, Suffolk. Tel: 0440 703784
BA ⋆ T. Bannister & Co., Market Place, Haywards Heath, W. Sussex. Tel: 0444 412402
Bea ⋆ Bearnes, Rainbow, Avenue Road, Torquay, Devon. Tel: 0803 26277
BD ⋆ Burrows & Day, 39-41 Bank Street, Ashford, Kent TN23 1DJ. Tel: 0233 674485
BHA • Bull House Antiques (Z. Walker), High Street, Burford, Oxon. Tel: 099 382 3284
BHW • Butler & Hatch Waterman, High Street, Tenterden, Kent. Tel: 05806 3233. Also High Street, Hythe, Kent.
Bon • Bonhams, Montpelier Galleries, Montpelier Street, Knightsbridge, London S.W.7. Tel: 01-584 9161
BP • Bell Passage Antiques, 38 High Street, Wickwar, Wotton-under-Edge, Glos. Tel: 045424 251
BS ⋆ Banks & Silvers, 66 Foregate Street, Worcester. Tel: 0905 23456
BW ⋆ Burtenshaw Walker, 66 High Street, Lewes, E. Sussex. Tel: 079 16 4225
C ⋆ Christie's, Manson & Woods Ltd., 8 King Street, London S.W.1. Tel: 01-839 9060
CA • Charterhouse Antiques, 14 Birds Hill, Heath & Reach, Beds. Tel: 052 523 379 (See Miller's 1983)
CC • Christopher Clarke, The Fosse Way, Stow-on-the-Wold, Glos. Tel: 0451 30476
CCC • Cornfield Carriage Co., 10 Cornfield Lane, Eastbourne, Sussex. Tel: 0323 30167
CDC ⋆ Capes, Dunn & Co., The Auction Galleries, 38 Charles Street, Manchester. Tel: 061-273 6060
CDE • Colin Dyte Export Ltd., Huntspill Road, Highbridge, Somerset. Tel: 0278 788590/788605
CEd ⋆ Christie's & Edmiston's Ltd., 164-166 Bath Street, Glasgow. Tel: 041-332 8134/7
CGC ⋆ Cheffins, Grain & Chalk, 49-53 Regent Street, Cambridge. Tel: 0223 358721
CH ⋆ Chancellors & Co., 31 High Street, Ascot, Berks. Tel: 0990 20101
CKK ⋆ Coles, Knapp & Kennedy, Tudor House, High Street, Ross-on-Wye, Hereford. Tel: 0989 63553/4
Also: Georgian Rooms, Ross-on-Wye. Tel: 0989 62225
CLA • Country Life Antiques, Sheep Street, Stow-on-the-Wold, Glos. Tel: 0451 30776/30192
CLG ⋆ Clarke Gammon, 45 High Street, Guildford, Surrey. Tel: 0483 72266
CoH ⋆ Cooper Hirst, F.R.I.C.S., Goldlay House, Parkway, Chelmsford, Essex. Tel: 0245 58141
CSK ⋆ Christie's South Kensington, 85 Old Brompton Road, London, S.W.7. Tel: 01-581 2231
DA ⋆ Dee & Atkinson, The Exchange, Driffield, E. Yorkshire. Tel: 0377 43151
DDM ⋆ Dickinson, Davy & Markham, 10 Wrawby Street, Brigg, S. Humberside. Tel: 0652 53666
DL • Dunsdale Lodge Antiques, Brasted Road, Westerham, Kent. Tel: 0959 62160
DM ⋆ Diamond, Mills & Co., 117 Hamilton Road, Felixstowe. Tel: 03942 2281/2
DS ⋆ Daniel Smith, Fine Art & Auction Dept., 24/26 Dover Road, Folkestone, Kent. Tel: 0303 41967

DSH	⋆	Dacre, Son & Hartley, 1-5 The Grove, Ilkley, W. Yorkshire. Tel: 0943 600655
DWB	⋆	Dreweatt, Watson & Barton, Donnington Priory, Donnington, Newbury, Berks. Tel: 0635 31234
EBB	⋆	Edwards, Bigwood & Bewlay, The Old School, Tiddington, Stratford-upon-Avon. Tel: 0789 69415
EC	•	Elias Clark Antiques Ltd., 1 The Cobbles, High Street, Bletchingley, Surrey. Tel: 0883 843714
EEW	⋆	Eldon E. Worrall, 15 Seel Street, Liverpool. Tel: 051-0709 2950
EH	⋆	Edgar Horn, 47 Cornfield Road, Eastbourne, E. Sussex. Tel: 0323 22801/2/3
Far	•	The Farmhouse, The Fourth Avenue, The Covered Market, Oxford. Tel: 0865 247084
FD	•	Flora Dora Antiques, Dales House, Lombard Street, Petworth, W. Sussex. Tel: 0798 43109
FF	•	Franfam Ltd., High Street, Moreton-in-Marsh, Glos. Tel: 0608 50648
FHF	⋆	Frank H. Fellows & Sons, Bedford House, 88 Hagley Road, Edgbaston, Birmingham. Tel: 021-454 1261 & 1219
Fr	⋆	Fryer's Auction Galleries, Terminus Road, Bexhill-on-Sea. Tel: 0424 212994
G	⋆	Golding, Auctioneers, 45 High Street, Grantham, Lincs. Tel: 0476 5456
GC	⋆	Geering & Colyer, Auctioneers, Highgate, Hawkhurst, Kent. Tel: 05805 3463/3181
GCA	•	Gerald Clark Antiques Ltd., 1 High Street, Mill Hill Village, London N.W.7. Tel: 01-906 0342
G&CC	•	Goss & Crested China Ltd., 62 Murray Road, Horndean, Hants. PO8 9JL. Tel: 0705 597440
GH	⋆	Giles Haywood, The Auction House, St. Johns Road, Stourbridge, W. Midlands. Tel: 03843 70891
GM	⋆	George Mealy & Sons, The Square, Castlecomer, Co. Kilkenny. Tel: 056 41229
Gor	⋆	Gorringes Auction Galleries, 15 North Street, Lewes. Tel: 07916 2503 or 2382
GR	⋆	Green & Co., 33 Market Place, Wantage, Oxon. Tel: 02357 3561/2
GSP	⋆	Graves, Son & Pilcher, 71 Church Road, Hove, E. Sussex. Tel: 0273 735266
HA	•	House of Antiques, 4 College Street, Petersfield, Hampshire. Tel: 0730 2172
HAD	•	Hadlow Antiques, No. 1 The Pantiles, Tunbridge Wells, Kent. Tel: 0892 29858
HAL	•	Hallidays Antiques Ltd., The Old College, Dorchester-on-Thames, Oxon. Tel: 0865 340028/68
HB	•	Heath-Bullock, 8 Meadrow, Godalming, Surrey. Tel: 048 68 22562
HFM	⋆	Hothersall, Forrest, McKenna & Son, Bank Salerooms, Clitheroe, Lancashire. Tel: 0200 25446 & 22695
HP	⋆	Hoddell Pritchard, Six Ways, Clevedon, Avon. Tel: 0272 876011
HSS	⋆	Henry Spencer & Sons, 20 The Square, Retford, Notts. Tel: 0777 706767
HW	⋆	Hanbury Williams, 34 Church Street, Cromer. Tel: 0263 513247
HWO	⋆	Hall, Wateridge & Owen, Welsh Bridge Salerooms, Shrewsbury, Shropshire. Tel: 0743 60212
HyD	⋆	Hy. Duke & Son, 40 South Street, Dorchester, Dorset. Tel: 0305 65080
IAT	•	It's About Time, 863 London Road, Westcliff, Essex. Tel: 0702 72574
IHA	•	Ivy House Antiques, High Street, Brasted, Kent. Tel: 0959 64581
IMC	⋆	Ibbett, Mosely, Card & Co., 125 High Street, Sevenoaks, Kent. Tel: 0732 452246
JD	⋆	Julian Dawson, 66 High Street, Lewes, Sussex. Tel: 07916 78221
JF	⋆	John Francis, Thomas Jones & Sons, King Street, Carmarthen. Tel: 0267 33456/7
JH	⋆	Jacobs & Hunt, Lavant Street, Petersfield, Hants. Tel: 0730 2744/5
JHo	•	Jonathan Horne, 66 b & c, Kensington Church Street, London W.8. Tel: 01-221 5658
JHR	⋆	John H. Raby & Son, The Estate Office, 21 St. Mary's Road, Bradford. Tel: 0274 491121
JHS	⋆	John Hogbin & Son, 53 High Street, Tenterden, Kent. Tel: 05806 3200
JMW	⋆	J. M. Welch & Son, The Old Town Hall, Dunmow, Essex. Tel: 0371 2117
JS	⋆	Jackson-Stops & Staff, 25 Nicholas Street, Chester. Tel: 0244 28361
JSm	⋆	John Smale & Co., 19 Cross Street, Barnstaple, Devon. Tel: 0271 2000 2916
KHD	⋆	K. Hugh Dodd & Partners, Victoria Auction Galleries, Chester Street, Mold, Clwyd. Tel: 0352 2552
KS	⋆	Kent Sales, Kent House, 4 New Road, South Darenth, Kent. Tel: 0322 864919
L	⋆	Lawrence's, South Street, Crewkerne, Somerset. Tel: 0460 73041
Lan	⋆	Langlois, Don Street, St. Helier, Jersey, Channel Isles. Tel: 0534 22441
Lay	⋆	David Lay, A.S.V.A., 7 Morrab Road, Penzance, Cornwall. Tel: 0736 68308
LE	⋆	Locke & England, The Auction Rooms, Walton House, 11 The Parade, Royal Leamington Spa. Tel: 0926 27988
LeG	⋆	Le Gallais & Sons, Bath Street, St. Helier, Jersey, Channel Isles. Tel: 0534 30202
LG	•	Lloyd & Greenwood Antiques, High Street, Burford, Oxon. Tel: 099 382 2359
LS	⋆	Lacy Scott, 1a Angel Hill, Bury St. Edmunds, Suffolk. Tel: 0284 63531
LT	⋆	Louis Taylor & Sons, Percy Street, Hanley, Stoke-on-Trent. Tel: 0782 260222
M	⋆	Morphets of Harrogate, 4-6 Albert Street, Harrogate, N. Yorks. Tel: 0423 502282
McCMB	⋆	McCartney, Morris & Barker, 25 Corve Street, Ludlow, Shropshire. Tel: 0584 2636
Mea	⋆	Meads of Brighton, St. Nicholas Road, Brighton, Sussex. Tel: 0273 202997/8
MMB	⋆	Messenger, May, Baverstock, Fine Art Salerooms, 93 High Street, Godalming, Surrey. Tel: 048 68 23567
MPA	⋆	Market Place Antiques, 35 Market Place, Henley-on-Thames, Oxon. Tel: 049 12 2387
Ms	⋆	Messenger & Son, Pevensey House Salerooms, Manorsfield Road, Bicester, Oxon. Tel: 08692 45985
N	⋆	Neales of Nottingham, The Nottingham Salerooms, 192 Mansfield Road, Nottingham. Tel: 0602 624141
NC	•	Nigel Coleman Antiques, High Street, Brasted, Kent. Tel: 0959 64042
NDA	⋆	Noel D. Abel, 32 Norwich Road, Watton, Norfolk. Tel: 0953 881204
Nes	⋆	Nesbit & Co., 7 Clarendon Road, Southsea, Hants. Tel: 0705 820785
NML	•	Nicholas Marchant-Lane, Pound Cottage, Pound Place, Petworth, W. Sussex. Tel: 0798 42838
NP	•	North Parade Antiques, 75 Banbury Road, Oxford OX2 6PE. Tel: 0865 59816
NSF	⋆	Neal Sons & Fletcher, 26 Church Street, Woodbridge, Suffolk. Tel: 039 43 2263/4 *Also* 33 Market Hill, Framlingham. Tel: 0728 723877
NSN	•	Mrs. M. K. Nielsen Antiques, Seaford House, High Street, Moreton-in-Marsh, Glos. Tel: 0608 50448
O	⋆	Olivers, 23-24 Market Hill, Sudbury, Suffolk. Tel: 0787 72247
OL	⋆	Outhwaite & Litherland, Kingsway Galleries, Fontenoy Street, Liverpool. Tel: 051-236 6561
OT	⋆	Osmond, Tricks & Son, Regent Street Auction Rooms, Clifton, Bristol. Tel: 0272 737201
P	⋆	Phillips, Blenstock House, 7 Blenheim Street, New Bond Street, London W.1. Tel: 01-629 6602
PB	⋆	Phillips, inc. Brooks, 39 Park End Street, Oxford. Tel: 0865 723524
PC		Private Collector
PE	⋆	Peter Eley, F.S.V.A. Western House, 98-100 High Street, Sidmouth, Devon. Tel: 03955 2552/3
Pea	⋆	Pearsons, Walcote Chambers, High Street, Winchester, Hants. Tel: 0962 64444
PFW	⋆	Peter F. Windibank, Auctioneer, 18-20 Reigate Road, Dorking, Surrey. Tel: 0306 884556
Ph	•	Phelps Ltd., 129-135 St. Margaret's Road, East Twickenham, Middlesex. Tel: 01-892 1778
PK	⋆	Phillips (Knowle), The Old House, Station Road, Knowle, Solihull, W. Midlands. Tel: 056 45 6151

PM • The Pine Merchants, High Street, Great Missenden, Bucks. Tel: 02406 2002

PSH ★ J. R. Parkinson, Son & Hamer, The Auction Rooms, Rochdale Road, Bury. Tel: 061 761 1612

PWC ★ Parsons, Welch & Cowell, 129 High Street, Sevenoaks, Kent. Tel: 0732 451211/4

Px ★ Phillips in Exeter, Alphin Brook Road, Alphington, Exeter. Tel: 0392 39025/6

RBB ★ Russell, Baldwin & Bright, Auctioneers, Ryelands Road, Leominster, Herefordshire. Tel: 0568 3897

RD • Richard Davidson Antiques, Lombard Street, Petworth, Sussex. Tel: 0798 42508

RdeR • Rogers de Rin, 76 Royal Hospital Road, Chelsea, London S.W.3. Tel: 01-352 9007

RVA • Rye Vaults Antiques, 8 Market Street, Rye, East Sussex. Tel: 0797 223407

S ★ Sotheby, Parke, Bernet & Co., 34-35 New Bond Street, London W.1. Tel: 01-493 8080

SA • Studio Antiques Ltd., Bourton-on-the-Water, Glos. Tel: 0451 20352

SC ★ Sotheby's, Chester, Booth Mansions, Watergate Street, Chester. Tel: 0244 315531.

SH • Sheila Hines Antiques, St. Mary's Cottage, Church Street, Petworth, Sussex. Tel: 0798 42408

SI ★ Sotheby's in Ireland, Slane Castle, Slane, Navan, Co. Meath. Tel: 041 24401

SL ★ Simmons & Lawrence, 32 Bell Street, Henley-on-Thames, Oxon. Tel: 049 12 78301

Som • Somervale Antiques 6 Radstock Road, Midsomer Norton, Bath, Avon. Tel: 0761 412686

SOU ★ Southam & Sons, Corn Exchange, Thrapston, Kettering, Northants. Tel: 08012 2409

SS ★ Sotheby's in Sussex, Station Road, Pulborough, W. Sussex. Tel: 07982 3831

STR • Strawsons Antiques, The Pantiles, Tunbridge Wells, Kent. Tel: 0892 30607

SWO ★ Sworders, G. E. & Sons, Chequers, 19 North Street, Bishops Stortford, Herts. Tel: 0279 52441

SWHB ★ Stanilands, William H. Brown, 28 Netherhall Road, Doncaster. Tel: 0302 67766 & 27121

SZ ★ Sotheby, Parke, Bernet, A.G., Bleicherweg 20, 8022 Zurich, Switzerland.

T ★ Tennant's, 26-27 Market Place, Leyburn, N. Yorkshire. Tel: 0969 23451

TA • Tilings Antiques, High Street, Brasted, Kent. Tel: 0959 64735

TM ★ Thos. Mawer & Son, 63 Monks Road, Lincoln. Tel: 0522 24984/22215

TP • Times Past Antiques Ltd., 59 High Street, Eton, Berkshire. Tel: 075 35 57018

TW ★ Thomas Watson & Son, Northumberland Street, Darlington, Co. Durham. Tel: 0325 62555 & 62559

V ★ Vidler & Co., Rye Auction Galleries, Cinque Ports Street, Rye, E. Sussex. Tel: 0797 222124/5

W • Woodstock, Pine Furniture, 1565 London Road, Norbury, London S.W.16. Tel: 01-764 0270

WAT ★ Watson, Edwin & Son, 1 Market Street, Saffron Walden, Essex. Tel: 0799 22058

WD ★ Weller & Dufty Ltd., 141 Bromsgrove Street, Birmingham. Tel: 021-692 1414

WHA • Wych House Antiques, Wych House, Wych Hill, Woking, Surrey. Tel: 04862 64636/65152

WHB ★ William H. Brown, Westgate Hall, Westgate, Grantham, Lincs. Tel: 0476 68861

WHL ★ W. H. Lane & Son, Central Auction Rooms, Penzance, Cornwall. Tel: 0736 61447/8
Also Central Auction Rooms, Kinterbury House, Plymouth, Devon. Tel: 0752 669298

Wor ★ Worsfold's (Canterbury), 40 Station Road West, Canterbury, Kent. Tel: 0227 68984

WSH ★ Warner, Sheppard & Wade (The Warner Auction Rooms), 16-18 Halford Street, Leicester. Tel: 0533 21613

WSW ★ Wyatt & Son, 59 East Street, Chichester, Sussex. Tel: 0243 786581

WW ★ Woolley & Wallis, The Castle Auction Mart, Castle Street, Salisbury, Wilts. Tel: 0722 27405

WWW • W.W. Warner (Antiques) Ltd., The Green, Brasted, Nr. Westerham, Kent. Tel: 0959 63698

A27 ANTIQUES WAREHOUSE

DITTONS ROAD INDUSTRIAL ESTATE
A27 TRUNK ROAD
POLEGATE, EAST SUSSEX
Tel: (03212) 7167

11,000 square feet period Victorian and shipping furniture and quality stripped pine. Re-finishing and upholstery service container packing and shipping.

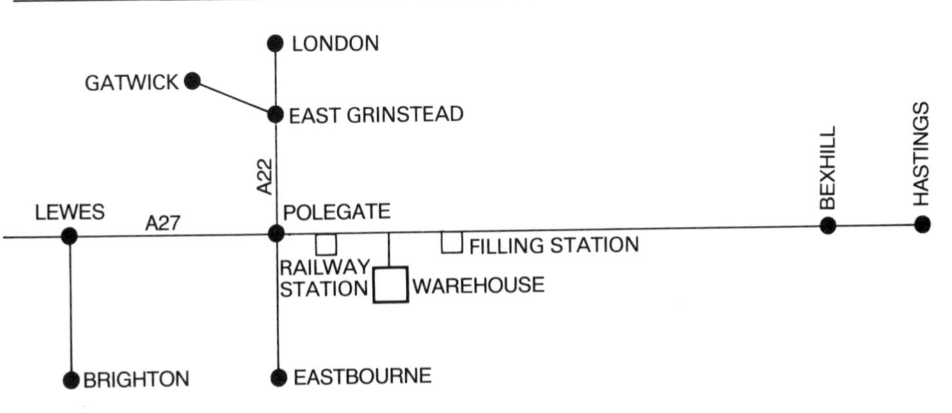

THE HERTS & ESSEX ANTIQUES CENTRE

AT THE MALTINGS, STATION ROAD, SAWBRIDGEWORTH, HERTFORDSHIRE.
TEL BISHOP'S STORTFORD (0279) 725809

OVER 30 ANTIQUE SHOPS

AND EIGHTY SHOWCASES UNDER ONE ROOF

The quality stock of more than one hundred professional dealers displayed on three floors of clean, carpeted and well lit showrooms

OPEN EVERY DAY
(Except Mondays)
10·30am-6pm
INCLUDING MOST BANK HOLIDAYS

ON SITE CAR PARKING • BISTRO AND COFFEE SHOP • SALES STAFF ARE ALWAYS AVAILABLE TO ASSIST YOU IF REQUIRED
Access, Barclaycard, American Express, Diners Club and most other major credit and charge card accepted.

THE HERTS & ESSEX ANTIQUES CENTRE

IS SITUATED OPPOSITE SAWBRIDGEWORTH RAILWAY STATION (ON THE LIVERPOOL STREET TO CAMBRIDGE LINE)
EASY ACCESS FROM M11 MOTORWAY, JUNCTIONS 7 OR 8. CONVENIENT FOR HARWICH, FELIXSTOWE & STANSTED AIRPORT
FOR ENQUIRIES & LETTINGS PLEASE PHONE BISHOP'S STORTFORD (0279) 725809

POTTERTON BOOKS

We specialise in buying and selling important classic reference works in most branches of

ANTIQUES & COLLECTING

Browsers are welcome to visit our Bookroom, at **8 Montpellier Parade, Harrogate, telephone Harrogate (0423) 521439.**

Catalogues bi-monthly — Free book search service

ATTIC ANTIQUE FAIRS

Reputable, Reliable
and Well Established Antique Fairs

Monthly Fairs currently organised in

BERKSHIRE
Twyford, near Reading
Hungerford Farnham Royal
near Slough

HAMPSHIRE
Alton Hartley Wintney

DEVON
South Coast

ANNUAL FAIRS
Henley Regatta (2 days early July)
Twyford (3 days late July)

A Granny's Attic Calendar giving full details of all Fairs is available. Please telephone:
Bridget Fraser, Marlow (06284) 3658
or Georgina Whiting, Bratton Clovelly (083 787) 285
for Devon Fairs.

Gloucester's Antique Centre

Good quality 18th and 19th century furniture, silver, ceramics, oils, watercolours, clocks, etc.

Services available:
Coffee Shop
Wine Bar
Courier Service
Accommodation:
Bed and Breakfast

Opening Times
Mon.-Fri. 8 a.m.–5 p.m.
Saturday 9.00 a.m.–4.30 p.m.
Sunday 1.00 p.m.–4.30 p.m.

Good Parking

Severn Road, Gloucester GL1 2LE
Telephone: Gloucester (0452) 29716

Antiques in the capital city of Wales

PENYLAN ANTIQUES

110 ALBANY ROAD
CARDIFF

(0222) 483927

also at **37 PENYLAN ROAD**
CARDIFF

The best call in Cardiff for all Private & Trade Buyers

BRITAIN'S BIGGEST ANTIQUE MARKET

1-7 DAVIES MEWS & 58 DAVIES STREET
LONDON W1 01-629 7034

(By Bond Street Station)

OPEN MONDAY TO FRIDAY 10.00 a.m. to 6.00 p.m.

KIRKBY ANTIQUES LTD.

"HEAD OFFICE"
HIGHFIELD
KIRKBY ON BAIN
WOODHALL SPA

AND AT
19 MARKET PLACE
TATTERSHALL

LINCOLNSHIRE

TELEPHONE: (0526) 52119 53461 42225

VOLUME ANTIQUE WHOLESALERS
WE CAN GENUINELY OFFER GOODS TO SUIT ALL MARKETS FROM OUR LARGE WAREHOUSES

AMPLE PARKING AND LOADING FACILITIES

NEATLY DISPLAYED CENTRALLY HEATED WAREHOUSING

TRADE BUYERS – WELCOME – A CALL NOT TO BE MISSED

INTERESTING AND UNUSUAL ITEMS ALWAYS STOCKED

QUANTITIES OF FRESH GOODS ARRIVING DAILY

UNQUESTIONABLY THE LARGEST STOCK IN THE AREA

EVERY KIND OF ANTIQUE AND SHIPPING GOODS STOCKED

SERVICES: RESTORATION FACILITIES, CONTAINER PACKING, CLIENTS COLLECTED BY CAR

As one would expect, packing is considered somewhat of an art at B.A.E. and David Gilbert, the director in charge of the works, ensures that each piece will reach its final destination in the condition a customer would wish. B.A.E. set a very high standard and, as a further means of improving each container load David Gilbert, who also deals with customer/container liaison, invites each customer to return detailed information on the saleability of each piece in the container thereby ensuring successful future shipments. This feedback of information is the all important factor which guarantees the profitability of future containers. "By this method" Mr. Lefton explains, "we have established that an average £7000 container will immediately it is unpacked at its final destination realise in the region of £10000 to £14000 for our clients selling the goods on a quick wholesale turnover basis". When visiting the warehouses various container loads can be seen in the course of completion. The intending buyer can then judge for himself which type of container load would best be suited to his market. In an average 20-foot container B.A.E. put approximately 150 to 200 pieces carefully selected to suit the particular destination. There are always at least 10 outstanding or unusual items in each shipment, but every piece included looks as though it has something special about it.

Based at Burgess Hill 7 miles from Brighton and on a direct rail link with London 39 miles (only 40 minutes journey) the Company is ideally situated to ship containers to all parts of the world. The showrooms, restoration and packing departments are open to overseas buyers and no visit to purchase antiques for re-sale in other countries is complete without a visit to their Burgess Hill premises where a welcome is always found.

CONTENTS

Armour made for Henri II by Giovanni Paolo Negroli, c. 1540-45, which was expected to fetch over £500,000, was eventually bought with a telephone bid from America for £1.75m or £1.95m with premium. *S*

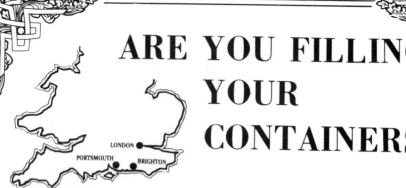

ARE YOU FILLING YOUR CONTAINERS ?

VISIT PORTSMOUTH ON YOUR NEXT INTERNATIONAL BUYING TRIP..

JUST 90 MINUTES FROM LONDON
50 MINUTES FROM BRIGHTON

TONY AMOS ANTIQUES

239 Albert Road, Southsea,
Portsmouth.
Tel: (0705) 750152 & 736818
Trade Warehouse at
152 Haslemere Road, Southsea.

CANADIANA EXPORTS (U.K.)

B.R.S. Depot, Haslemere Road,
Southsea. Tel: (0705) 734173
Trade Warehouse at
139 Goldsmith Avenue,
Southsea. Tel: (0705) 816278.

RODNEY DODSON ANTIQUES

85 Fawcett Road, Southsea.
Tel: (0705) 829481 (07014) 2226
Trade Warehouse B.R.S. Depot,
Haslemere Road, Southsea.
Tel: (0705) 734173

W.R. PRIDDY ANTIQUES

57 Fawcett Road, Southsea,
Portsmouth.
Tel: (0705) 826135
738906

INVITE YOU TO VISIT THEIR SHIPPING WAREHOUSES

- CONTAINER FACILITIES - SHIPPING
- CONTINUOUS STOCK VARIATION
- DOCUMENTATION ARRANGED
- PACKING - COLLECTION
- SPECIALIST GOODS FOR USA
- FRANCE - HOLLAND
- ITALY - GERMANY
- JAPAN - SOUTH AFRICA
- AND AUSTRALASIAN MARKETS.

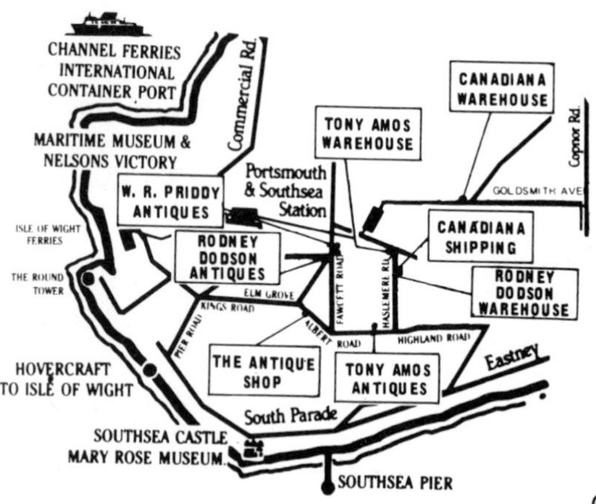

PORTSMOUTH
THE ANTIQUES CENTRE OF THE SOUTH

INTRODUCTION

One of the main problems with a general price guide is the lack of space when dealing with as diverse subjects as 16th Century Italian maiolica and late 19th Century Martin Brothers stoneware. Although the basic material may be similar a section could quite justifiably be devoted to each separate ware. This section includes:—

Tin glaze earthenware: Italian maiolica, French faience, German delft or faience, Dutch Delft, English delft.

Stonewares:—
Rhenish,
English — Fulham, Nottingham
Doulton, Martin Bros.

Lead glaze earthenwares:—
Staffordshire slipwares, Whieldon, Wedgwood and related types up to 1780.

Creamware:
Pearlware and Prattware.

Later ironstone
Transfer printed pottery
English maiolica

Some market trends in Pottery:

It is always interesting to note the way the currency market influences prices in antiques. When the American dollar is high the traditional favourites of the American buyers obviously show significant price increases. This has certainly helped English delft with some exceptionally high prices paid for good quality items. English delft has also been helped by the three major Lipski sales held by Sotheby's and a general increased awareness and regard for our native delft. As always, and this applies to every category of pottery and antiques in general, rare and important pieces have seen substantial increases in price and tend to sell quickly.

Dutch Delft is still quite weak and could possibly be a good buy, particularly if you can afford to wait for the upturn. German faience has also been down and Italian maiolica hasn't moved much. French faience has tended to be quite erratic in price, with some record prices seen in an otherwise very flat sale. German stoneware followed delft and has been weaker than it was 2 years ago: may again be the time to buy.

English figures:
* 'interesting' figures selling well
* Walton, Sherratt, Ralph Wood and Whieldon are good, especially pieces with early coloured glazes
* military figures, particularly Victorian Staffordshire, are at last much stronger
* square based figures and groups have seen substantial rise in price.

Pottery has often been thought of as 'poor man's porcelain' and this misconception has meant that much 18th Century pottery was greatly undervalued. There has been a steady growing interest and awareness which has caused substantial price increases in all areas. Pottery can still be a good investment but even more an interesting study of social history.

A Wedgwood creamware basket with cover, 9 in. high, c. 1750-1800. **£250-350** *BP*

A creamware pierced dish and saucer, 9½ in. wide, c. 1800. **£70-£80** *TA*

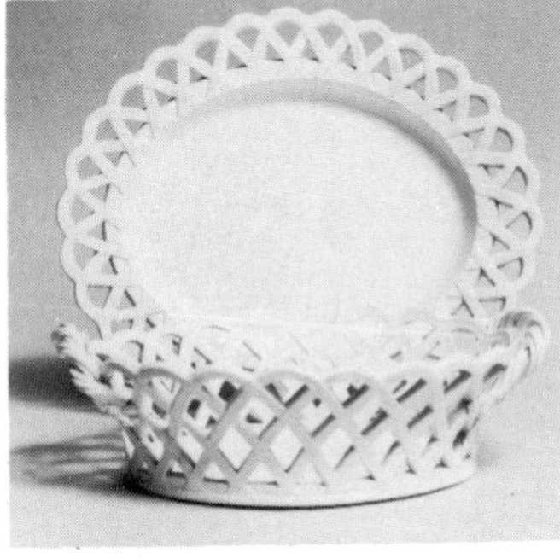

A Leeds creamware basket and stand, 10 in. wide, c. 1800. **£175-£200** *EC*

A 17th C. German bellarmine, 16 in. high. **£180-200** *FF*

A Cologne stoneware bellarmine, sprigged with vine and leaf motifs, with medallions showing bearded heads, 26 cm., 16th C., minor chips and hair cracks. **£2,650-3,000** *S*

A late 17th C. German bellarmine, 9 in. **£190-210** *JHo*

A Lambeth bottle decorated in blue, 9 in., mid 18th C., lip damaged. (L.L.). **£200-250** *S*

L.L. denotes a piece sold at the Louis Lipski sale in March 1983.

A bottle decorated in blue with a continuous chinoiserie landscape, Bristol or Liverpool, 9½ in., mid 18th C., top damaged, patch of glaze missing. (L.L.). **£90-120** *S*

A Lambeth bottle decorated in blue, 10¾ in., second half 18th C., some chips. (L.L.). **£280-360** *S*

In this guide we are discussing what a BUYER may expect to pay for a piece similar to that in the photograph. If one is looking to sell a piece it would be fair to assume our price range minus 30%. If a reader has a piece to sell it may well be worth taking a photograph of it and sending this to two auctioneers, one in the locality and one in London and also sending a copy of the photograph to a specialist dealer listed in the directory at the back of this volume. In most cases one would expect to get a better offer from a specialist dealer rather than a general dealer as he will almost certainly have top collectors among his customers and be more aware of current market values.

A Deruta bowl, the central ochre medallion reserved in white enamel with a latin cross and COM monogram within a blue ovolo surround, the reverse decorated in blue with a 3-headed monster and the date ? 1514, 19 cm. diam. **£2,200-2,500** *C*

Similar chequer-pattern borders are to be found on a variety of pieces given to Deruta.
Provenance: A. Imbert, Rome No. 895.

An unusual small London bowl painted in dark blue, 6⅜ in., late 17th C., minor hair cracks and chips. (L.L). **£280-360** *S*

The style of decoration is rare on bowls.

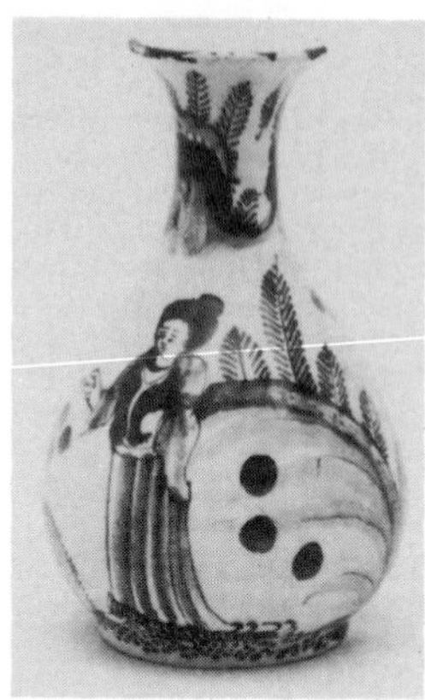

Two Liverpool bottles, decorated in shades of inky-blue, 4¾ in., c. 1760, rims chipped and rubbed. (L.L.). **£600-700** *S*

A London delft blue and white dated 2-handled bowl and cover, the shoulder with the initials and date R.F., 1695 (finial damaged), 15.5 cm. wide. **£5,500-6,500** *C*

The nodular scroll handles would appear to derive from contemporary Venetian style glassware. Note also the painted scrolling foliage on the shoulder — almost a direct copy of the 'Karakusa' vine scroll or 'octupus' design on late 17th C. Japanese (Arita) ware, a motif introduced from T'ang China.

A Lambeth delft blue and white dated bleeding bowl, cracked, 17.5 cm. wide, 1696. **£1,500-1,600** *C*

A Dutch Delft polychrome fluted octagonal bowl, minor rim chips, iron-red VE monogram of Lambertus van Eenhoorn, 28 cm. wide, c. 1700. **£400-500** *C*

A Lambeth polychrome powder bowl with Royal initials, 8½ in. diam., c. 1710. **£1,000-1,200** *JHo*

A Bristol bowl, painted in blue, 10 in., 1740-50, rim chips. **£350-£400** *S*

A Staffordshire saltglaze bowl with strapwork enriched in gilding, 14 cm. diam., c. 1750. **£250-300** *C*

Virtually the same applied motifs are to be found on contemporary Staffordshire red ware.

A Sunderland purple lustre box, with black transfer print, 'To Hornsey Market', 6 in., c. 1850. **£270-320** *DL*

A pair of maiolica salts, each painted with a classical portrait above 4 winged females, 6½ in. high. **£150-250** *CEd*

A dated Dutch Delft blue and white deep bowl with the initials S*S*E and the date 1718, hair cracks, rim chips, blue monogram mark of Lambertus van Eenhoorn, 34.5 cm. diam. **£400-600** *C*

A delft bowl sketchily painted in tones of greyish blue with a forlorn Chinaman, numeral 2 on the reverse, Bristol or possibly Brislington, 9¾ in., early 18th C., riveted. (L.L). **£180-220** *S*

A Castelli small bowl, the interior painted with the Virgin and Child against an aureol background, inscribed 'EX PULVERE PARIETU, & EX AQUA SACRA SCUTELLA ALMA DOMUS LAURETANA 1720', 10.7 cm. **£1,000-1,200** *P*

A Moorcroft box and cover, slip-trailed in white with the 'Hazeldene' pattern in shades of olive, blue and plum, handle cracked, impressed Moorcroft Burslem, painted signature in green, 16.7 cm., c. 1915. **£220-260** *S*

A shallow bowl painted in blue, Brislington or Bristol, 8½ in., early 18th C., chips (L.L.). **£400-500** *S*

A Bristol delft powdered manganese bowl, 25.5 cm. diam., c. 1740. **£3,100-3,300** *C*

A Bristol delft blue and white dated punch bowl, the base with the initials and date HC:E, 1764, crack to base, 35 cm. diam. **£400-£500** *C*

Use the Index!

Because certain items might fit easily into any of a number of categories, the quickest and surest method of locating any entry is by reference to the index at the back of the book. This has been fully cross-referenced for absolute simplicity.

A Royal Doulton Titanian shallow bowl, internally decorated with a black dragon with gilt and silver scales, c.m.l. & c. 'Titanian', 37 cm. **£180-240** *P*

(l.) A German faience pear-shaped jug, painted in the Oriental style, minor chips to glaze, probably Ansbach, 18 cm. high, c. 1740. **£200-300** *C*

(c). A Holics pear-shaped coffee pot and cover, cracks in body, chips to glaze, mark in black HH in monogram, 22.5 cm. high, c. 1775. **£400-600** *C*

(r.) A Bayreuth (Pfeiffer) pear-shaped coffee pot and cover, painted in manganese monochrome, cover damaged, BP mark, 21.5 cm. high, c. 1765. **£250-300** *C*

A Minton 'Majolica' centrepiece, glazed in shades of brown, green and flesh pink, stem holder cracked, impressed M and date code for 1859, 27.5 cm. **£550-650** *S*

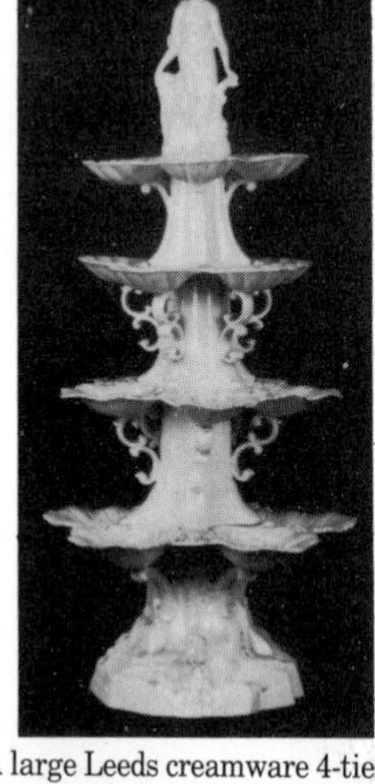

A large Leeds creamware 4-tier centrepiece, crack to base, 5 shells damaged, 75 cm. high, c. 1775. **£600-700** *C*

An unusual Minton 'Majolica' centrepiece in typical 'majolica' glazes, minor damage, impressed ermine mark and date code for 1859, 48 cm. **£350-450** *S*

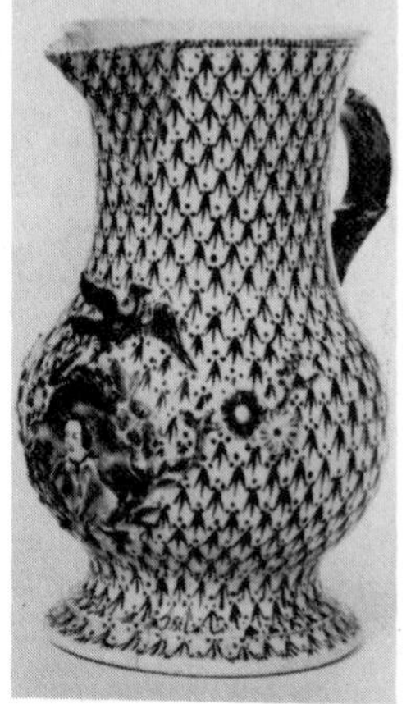

A rare Staffordshire saltglaze baluster jug, applied with the head of Frederick the Great, within a flower wreath and surmounted by an eagle, brightly coloured, on an overall black ermine diaper ground, 18 cm. **£1,300-1,500** *P*

Although the subject is well known in saltglaze, the relief decoration is much more unusual.

A Leeds creamware baluster jug, transfer printed in iron-red with a portrait medallion of George III, inscribed March 17th 1789, with the verse 'Britons Rejoice, Cheer Up and Sing, and Drink this Health, Long Live the King', 17.5 cm. high. **£400-500** *C*

Made to commemorate the restoration to health of King George III in 1789.

A rare Admiral Nelson/Captain Berry jug, 5 in., c. 1790. **£165-195** *GCA*

A pearlware pottery commemorative jug in Pratt colours showing the 'Royal Sufferers' and the Duke of York, 7¾ in., c. 1798. **£400-450** *EC*

Marie Antoinette, Louis XVI and the Dauphin were known as The Royal Sufferers.

A Liverpool polychrome creamware jug, transfer printed, dated 1793, inscribed 'God speed the plough', and 8 Liverpool Volunteers, slight repair, 9½ in. **£250-270** Perfect **£320-350** *JHo*

A Pratt jug with unusual battle scene, 5¾ in. high, c. 1800. **£140-£150** *JHo*

A Lord Wellington/General Hill commemorative jug, 5 in. high, c. 1820. **£65-95** *GCA*

A jug commemorating the coronation of William IV and Queen Adelaide printed in purple, 7 in. high, c. 1830. **£150-200** *CSK*

A rare pearlware jug and cover commemorating the French retreat from Moscow in 1812 modelled as a muzzled Russian bear squeezing a figure of Napoleon caricatured as a monkey, 10¼ in. high. **£650-750** *CSK*

A very rare Liverpool creamware plaque, printed with a bust portrait of George III, inscribed 'George III in the 51st year of his reign', 6¾ in. high. **£270-350** *CSK*

cf J & J May p. 23 which records this print as appearing only on a creamware jug and associates it with the series of 1809 commemorative prints produced by Dixon and potted at Herculaneum, which feature the 1807 Jubilee monument erected in Liverpool showing an equestrian George III.

A rare creamware mug printed in red with a cartoon of Napoleon and John Bull, 4¾ in. high. **£190-250** *CSK*

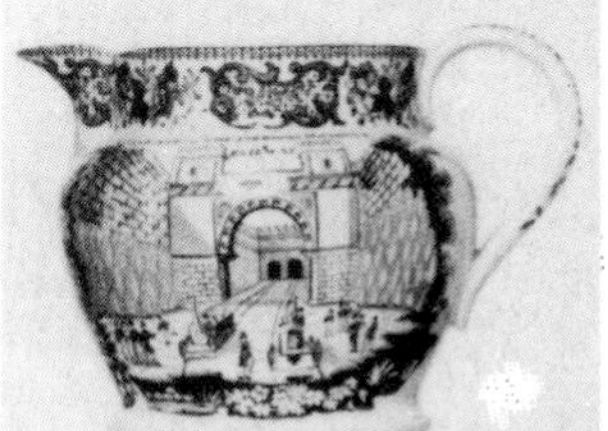

A rare oviform jug printed in purple with the entrance to the Liverpool and Manchester Railway, 4¼ in. high. **£95-125** *CSK*

A pottery mug commemorating the death of Nelson, the reverse with the ship Victory in battle, after a design by Fenton, printed Royal Doulton mark, number 367 of 600, 10¼ in. high. **£300-350** *CSK*

A nursery plate brown-printed with a crowned bust for Princess Charlotte, In Memoriam, inscribed and dated, 5¼ in. high. **£120-180** *CSK*

A rare Hartley Greens & Co. creamware black printed plate, inscribed 'George IV Crowned July 1821', the back with impressed numeral 10, 9 in. diam. **£280-360** *CSK*

A nursery plate printed with named portraits of Victoria and Albert. **£70-90** *CSK*

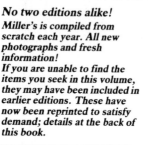

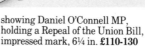

(1) A commemorative plate, made to commemorate the marriage of Queen Victoria and Prince Albert, blue printed with title and portrait of the royal couple, with pink edge line, 7½ in. **£60-70** *PWC*

(2) A commemorative dish, black printed with title and portrait of William The Fourth King of Great Britain, 5 in. **£50-60** *PWC*

(3) A commemorative plate, black printed with head profile of Queen Caroline wearing a feathered hat, entitled 'Long Live Queen Caroline', 6½ in. **£60-70** *PWC*

(4) A hexagonal commemorative dish by Francis Dillon of Cobridge, the centre black printed and showing Daniel O'Connell MP, holding a Repeal of the Union Bill, impressed mark, 6¼ in. **£110-130** *PWC*

(5) A commemorative plate, printed in black and showing the young Prince of Wales upon a horse within the grounds of Windsor, entitled 'England's Hope, Prince of Wales', 6¾ in. **£50-60** *PWC*

(6) A good 19th C. oval dish, printed in puce with a ballooning scene within a fruiting vine border, bead scalloped edge, 13 in. **£120-£160** *PWC*

(7) A Wesleyan commemorative dish, the centre printed in colours with a portrait of John Wesley, 6¼ in. **£60-70** *PWC*

A blue and white plate printed with a portrait of Caroline, 6½ in. high. **£65-85** *CSK*

cf J & J May pl. 55.

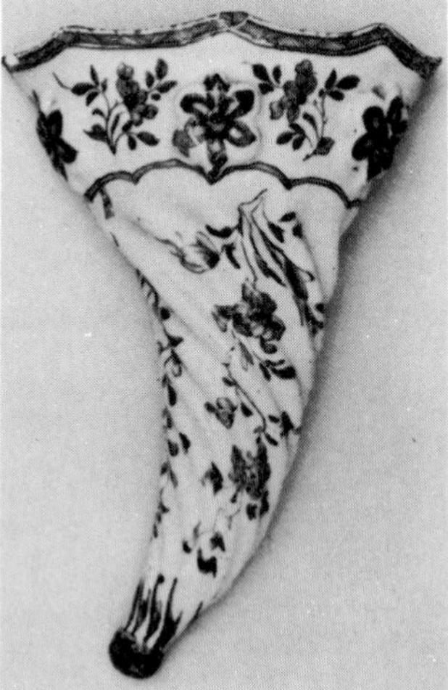

An inscribed and dated Liverpool wall-pocket, painted in bright blue, inscribed on the reverse 'G/II' and dated 1748, pierced for suspension, chips, small hair cracks, 8 in. (L.L.). **£750-850** *S*

The majority of cornucopia wall-pockets of rococo silver-shape were manufactured at the Liverpool factory from the late 1740's until the neo classical period around 1770.

Lund's Bristol and Worcester factory produced similar cornucopiae in the early 1750's in porcelain.

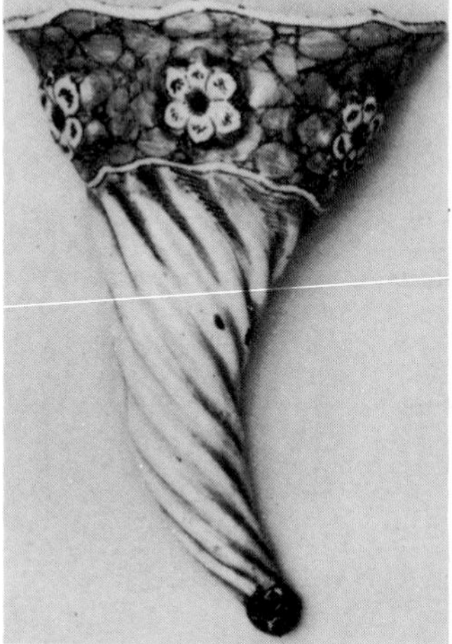

A Liverpool wall pocket, reserved on a blue 'cracked ice' ground, pierced for suspension, small chips, 8 in., c. 1750. (L.L.). **£180-250** *S*

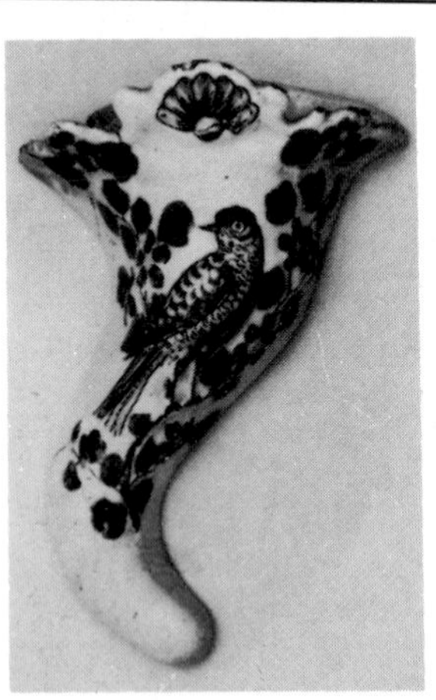

A pair of Liverpool wall pockets of cornucopia shape, moulded in relief and brightly painted in green, yellow, red, brown and manganese, one with rim repaired and chipped, drilled on reverse, the other restored and damaged, 8¼ in., c. 1760. (L.L.). **£200-300** *S*

A Liverpool wall pocket coloured in yellow, green and blue, the tapering body terminating in a satyr mask picked out in blue, pierced for suspension, crack, chips, 9½ in., c. 1760-70. **£280-360** *S*

An unusual Staffordshire castle spill holder, 8 in. wide, c. 1825. **£95-£125** *GCA*

A Staffordshire cottage money box, 4 in. high, c. 1830. **£65-95** *GCA*

A Leeds pottery gazebo pastille burner, 5 in., c. 1835. **£245-295** *GCA*

A 'Gothick' cottage pastille burner, on blue glazed rock moulded base, minor chips, 14 cm., mid 19th C. **£400-500** *SS*

A Yorkshire pottery church, 10¼ in., c. 1790. **£420-460** *DL*

STAFFORDSHIRE COTTAGES

- **best cottages made from 1810-1840**
- **very early Prattware cottages c.1800 command good prices**
- **quality varied tremendously**
- **after the 1850s cottages tended to be of lesser quality**
- **the rarer subjects are much sought after**
- **prices of more common examples are often high in non-specialist outlets**
- **the cottages often have other uses – money boxes, pastille burners, inkwells, spill vases**
- **condition is very important although minor damage, say a crack on the base or slight damage to the bocage, may not substantially affect the price**
- **the cottage will be worth much less if it is not decorated all round**
- **applied sheep, figures, flowers, dogs all add to value**
- **severe damage to cottage or flowers can halve the value**
- **watch for fakes – the glaze on modern examples is normally too shiny, the crackle is often too perfect, the glaze on originals often pools, the colours often don't have the depth of 19th century examples**

A Staffordshire castle spill holder, 5½ in. high, c. 1840. **£65-95** *GCA*

A Staffordshire pottery pastille burner, 5 in. high, c. 1830. **£120-£145** *GCA*

A Staffordshire cottage pastille burner, 5 in., c. 1830. **£150-175** *GCA*

A Yorkshire pottery cottage money box, 4½ in. wide, c. 1840. **£60-70** *EC*

A Staffordshire watch holder/spill vase, 10 in. high, c. 1845. **£95-£125** *GCA*

A Staffordshire cottage pastille burner, with a detachable pyramidal roof edged in green shredding, 11 cm., mid 19th C. **£450-550** *SS*

A rare Yorkshire pottery cow creamer, 7½ in., c. 1800. **£350-£400** *EC*

A Swansea pottery cow creamer, 7¼ in., c. 1810. **£210-250** *EC*

A pair of cow creamers and covers of large size, 8 in., early 19th C., covers chipped **£500-700** *S*

No two editions alike!
Miller's is compiled from scratch each year. All new photographs and fresh information!
If you are unable to find the items you seek in this volume, they may have been included in earlier editions. These have now been reprinted to satisfy demand; details at the back of this book.

An early English pottery cow creamer, 6¼ in., c. 1770. **£325-£375** *EC*

POTTERY: COW CREAMERS

The price of cow creamers depends upon age, type and complexity. Whieldon cow creamers are probably the most expensive. They are thinly potted and readily damaged and consequently few survive. They are to be distinguished by their rich tortoiseshell lead glaze coloured by the inclusion of different metallic oxides. These early cow creamers have a glassy appearance, the later Staffordshire and North of England products have a more primitive look, the potters relying on sponging simple high fixed oxides for decorative effect. Generally speaking neatness of potting and a harmonious colouring make a piece expensive. Other considerations are the presence of a milkmaid – 'hobbled' legs also add to value.

A Staffordshire church spill vase, 13½ in., c. 1850. **£95-125** *GCA*

A Pratt cow creamer with calf, 6½ in. long, c. 1780. **£325-375** *GCA*

A Swansea lustre cow creamer, 7 in. long, c. 1810. **£195-235** *GCA*

A London fuddling cup painted in blue with stylised flower-sprigs, 3½ in., mid 17th C., chips, glaze flaking, restored chips. (L.L.). **£900-£1,100** *S*

A rare Lambeth fuddling cup formed of 3 vessels linked by entwined handles, each painted in blue, 3¾ in., c. 1680, chips, one neck restored. **£500-600** *S*

A Lambeth cup, decorated in manganese, 3 in., c. 1700. **£625-£650** *JHo*

Cups or tankards of the same form were made in Dehua 'Blanc-de-Chine'.

A Bayreuth stoneware tea bowl and saucer, 'yellow ware' body decorated in silver (oxidised), Knöller period, 1728-44. **£2,000-£2,300** *S*

A loving cup and cover, painted in blue, base marked 'B', probably Bristol, repaired, glaze flaking, 9½ in. overall, c. 1720. (L.L.). **£300-£400** *S*

A Laterza faience cup and saucer, decorated in brown, yellow, blue and green, 18th C. **£500-600** *S*

An unusually large Lambeth cup decorated in blue, 3¼ in.; and another blue and white Lambeth coffee cup, 2¼ in., c. 1720-30, both cracked and chipped. (L.L.). **£400-£500** *S*

Two rare tea bowls, each painted in iron-red, olive-green and blue, Bristol or Lambeth, c. 1730-40, chips, one cracked. (L.L.). **£420-£500** *S*

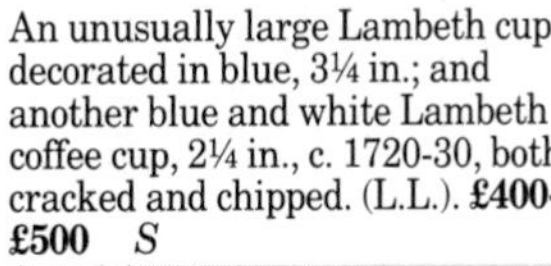

A Lambeth blue and white coffee cup, c. 1740, small chips, hair-crack. (L.L.). **£300-350** *S*

A matched English polychrome delftware tea bowl and saucer, with some damage, saucer 4½ in. diam., c. 1750. As is **£350-400**
Perfect **£800-900** *JHo*

Two rare miniature tea bowls painted in manganese, red, yellow and green, both probably Bristol, both chipped, the second cracked; and a Liverpool miniature saucer painted in blue, chips, c. 1740-50. (L.L.). **£250-300** *S*

A Staffordshire salt-glaze flared coffee cup, 6.5 cm. high, c. 1750. **£150-180** *C*

A rare bell-shaped cup painted in dark blue, iron-red and gilding, mid 18th C., handle replaced, crack. (L.L.). **£95-125** *S*

A Bristol coffee cup painted and 'pencilled' in blue, c. 1750, hair-crack, small chips. (L.L.). **£350-£400** *S*

A pair of white salt-glaze cups by Thomas and John Wedgwood, 6.5 cm., mid 18th C., firing crack to one handle. **£280-360** *Bea*

A pearlware harvest loving cup, 5 in., c. 1810. **£110-120** *EC*

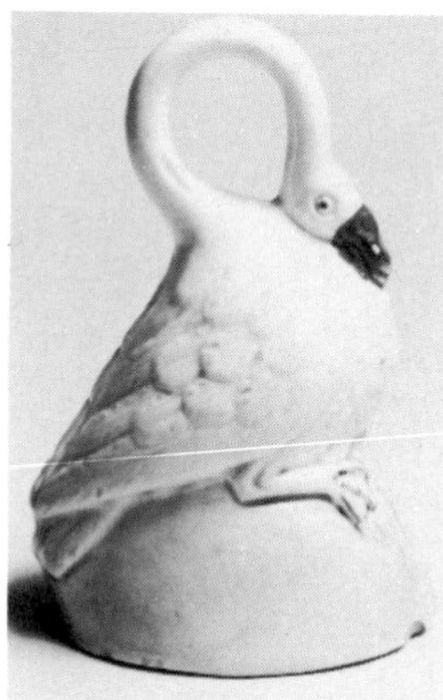
An unusual pottery swan stirrup cup, 4 in. high, c. 1790. **£300-350** *EC*

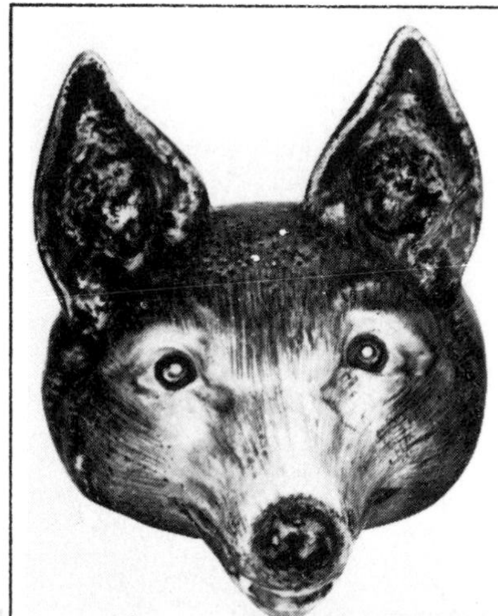
A Staffordshire foxhead stirrup cup, its fur delineated in brown, 6 in.; and another in the form of a hound's head, its features picked out in black, 4½ in., early 19th C. **£180-240** *SC*

A pearlware loving cup, 6 in., c. 1810. **£110-125** *EC*

A German stoneware baluster ewer decorated with running wolves and foliage on a blue ground, 16½ in. high. **£150-250** *CEd*

A limited edition loving cup titled 'The Apothecary' moulded in low relief, incise moulded signature 'Fenton', 15 cm., printed lion, crown and circle title and verse, numbered 593 from a 600 edition. **£120-160** *Bon*

A good Minton 'Majolica' ewer with blue-ground body, 46 cm., impressed mark and date code for 1872. **£500-600** *S*

A pair of Cantagalli ewers, painted in lustrous glazes against a blue ground, 20 in. (51 cm.), painted cockerel mark, late 19th C., one restored. **£280-340** *S*

DUTCH DELFT

Production of tin-glazed earthenware was established in the Low Countries at the beginning of the 16th century. The earliest wares were influenced by Italian maiolica doubtless introduced by migrant craftsmen. In the early 17th century with the arrival of Chinese Kraak porselein polychrome wares lost favour and the blue and white Chinese style gained the ascendancy. Chinese or chinoiserie themes remained dominant throughout the entire life of the Delft factories. Many Netherlandish protestant potters fled their native countries to escape religious persecution and many took up residence in England. The earliest English delftware factory was in fact started by two such immigrant potters.

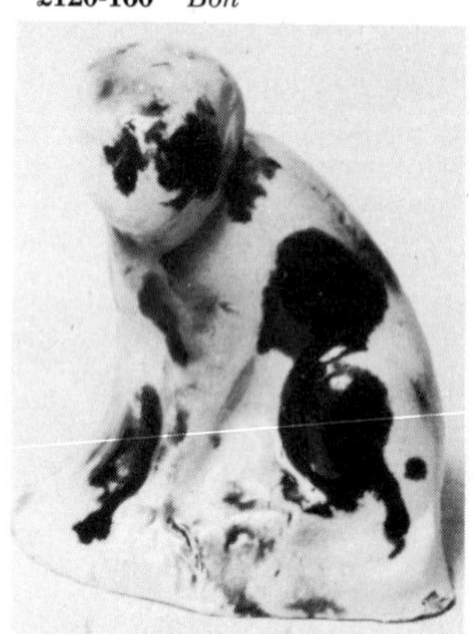
A Whieldon monkey, 2¾ in., c. 1760. **£225-275** *GCA*

A pair of Dutch Delft polychrome recumbent cows (restoration to horns, ears and fore-legs), blue AP mark of Adriaen Pijnacker, 17.5 cm. wide, early 18th C. **£1,000-£1,200** *C*

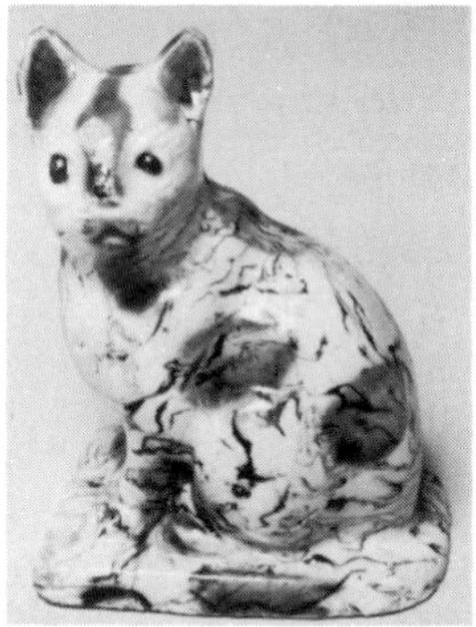
A Staffordshire agateware cat, 4½ in., c. 1755. **£400-450** *JHo*

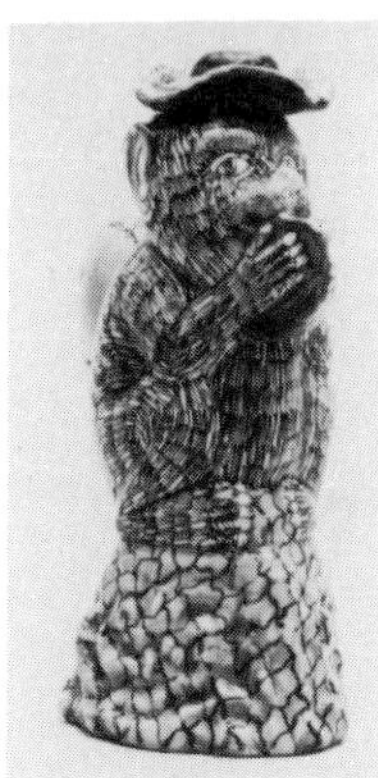

A Dutch Delft 'monkey' ewer and cover, its fur stencilled in blue, a tricorn hat in manganese and yellow forming the cover, 17 cm., factory mark in red, mid 18th C. **£500-600** *S*

A Whieldon-type pottery lion, 4 in., c. 1760. **£240-270** *EC*

A rare white salt-glaze model of a lion, 14.5. cm., restored. **£800-900** *P*

An 18th C. pottery dalmation, 3½ in. wide, c. 1770. **£165-195** *GCA*

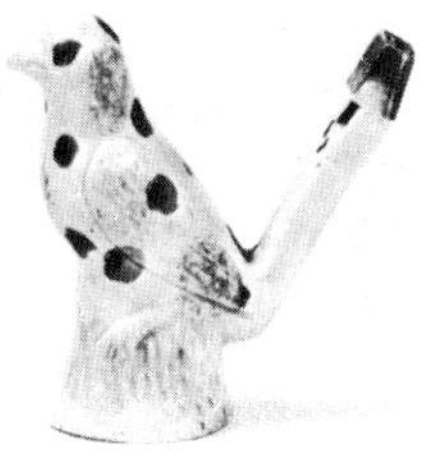

A Whieldon-type bird whistle in the form of an ochre spotted yellow finch upon a green mound base, 7 cm., c. 1770. **£280-360** *SS*

A Ralph Wood seated setter (firing crack to back and chest of dog), 18 cm., high, c. 1775. **£1,000-£1,200** *C*

Dogs are still one of the most desirable subjects — this piece is also helped by the maker Ralph Wood.

A Ralph Wood pottery monkey whistle in coloured glazes, 3 in. high, c. 1770. **£300-350** *EC*

A Ralph Wood lion and fox spill vase group, 5 in. high, c. 1775. **£850-950** *EC*

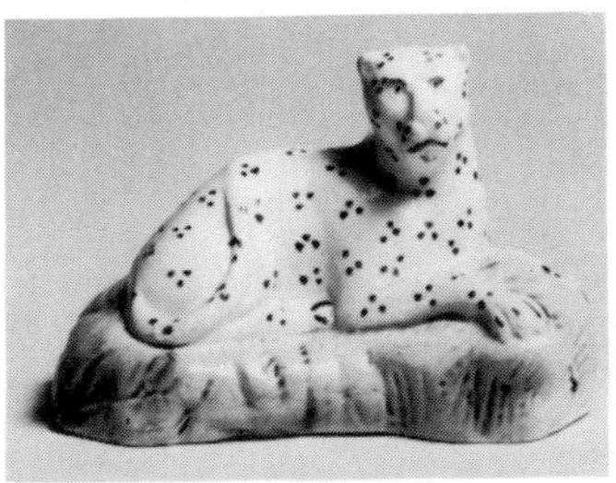

An early English pottery leopard, 3½ in., c. 1775. **£220-240** *EC*

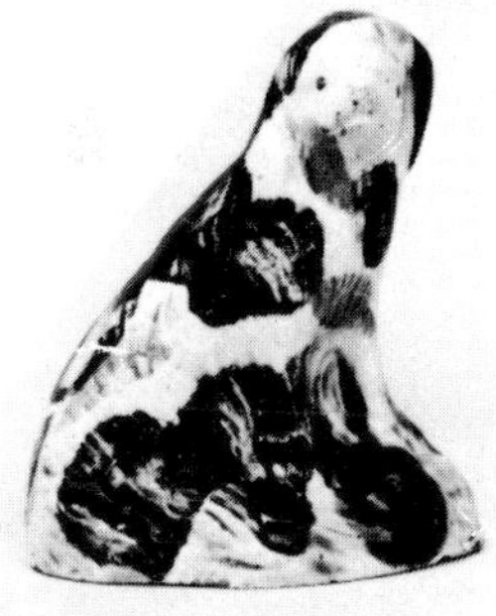

A small figure of a seated dog, splashed in brown and ochre, 2¾ in. (7 cm.), late 18th C. **£90-£120** *S*

POTTERY FIGURES

The market for English pottery figures has, despite the recession, remained buoyant, with prices in general showing increases virtually across the board. Not the least contributing factor has been the continuing interest shown by American buyers and collectors, some of whom are paying record prices for exceptional pieces.

- **Most popular are theatrical groups, very elaborate circus groups and animals.**
- **Obadiah Sheratt humorous rural groups — very good.**
- **Best of the Toby Jugs are unusual, 18th C. examples based on characters such as Admiral Howe, and small, Dr. Johnson jugs.**
- **Good cottages and pastille burners gaining in popularity (some worthwhile examples can still be found under £100).**
- **Best investment for under £100 are square-based early Staffordshire figures.**
- **Mantel dogs have risen 300-400% over the past two years — are unlikely to rise much further.**

A small Prattware figure of a seated pug dog, spotted in brown and ochre, with pale green glazed base, 3 in. (7.5 cm.), c. 1780-90. **£200-250** *S*

A Prattware lioness, 4 in., c. 1790. **£250-280** *EC*

A Yorkshire cow group, on a green-glazed base, picked out in a typical 'sponged' palette, 6 in. (15 cm.), late 18th/early 19th C., one horn restored and damaged, hair-crack in base. **£500-600** *S*

An early English pottery ram and lamb spill-holder, indistinctly signed on base, 6 in., c. 1795. **£150-£185** *GCA*

A Prattware figure of a cockerel, brightly coloured in brown, green and blue, 3¾ in. (9.5 cm.), 1780-90, small chips on base. **£300-400** *S*

A Ralph Wood-type figure of a recumbent ram with brown eyes, horns and hooves, 6 in. (15 cm.), c. 1790, one horn restored. **£150-£200** *S*

A Yorkshire figure of a shire horse sponged in ochre and with brown mane and tail, minor crack to chest, resoration to tail, ears and base, 17 cm. wide, c. 1800. **£950-£1,400** *C*

A Walton Group of 'Friendship', inscribed 'FRIENDSHIP' on a label, 7 in., impressed WALTON on a label, c. 1820, bocage and one hand restored. **£250-300** *S*

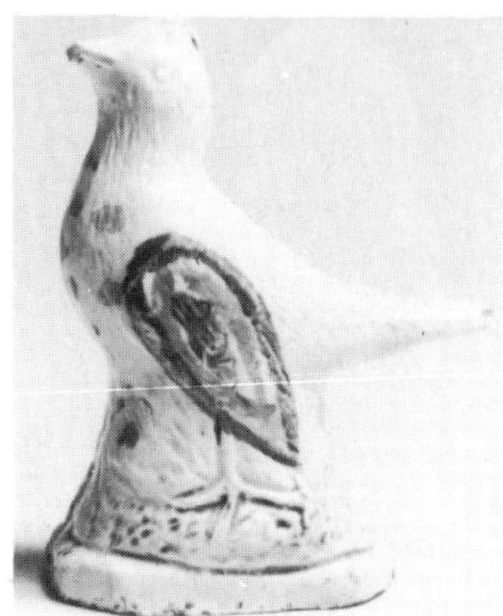

A Prattware pottery bird, 3½ in. high, c. 1790. **£200-230** *EC*

A pottery pug dog, 4 in. high, c. 1790. **£275-310** *EC*

A Prattware model of a lion, typically coloured in ochre, brown and blue, 25 cm. high, late 18th C., one tooth missing. **£700-800** *SS*

A pair of ochre coloured Yorkshire pottery cow groups, 5¾ in., c. 1790. **£1,400-1,600** *DL*

An early pottery bull baiting group, 9½ in. wide, c. 1790. **£425-£475** *EC*

A Yorkshire cow group, 5¾ in. (14.5 cm.), late 18th/early 19th C., crack in base. **£500-600** *S*

A large Yorkshire bull-baiting group, 12 in. wide, c. 1800. **£2,500-£2,800** *JHo*

A figure of a cow, patched in russet, the beast being attacked by a green snake, the base picked out in bright colours, 7⅛ in. (19.5 cm.), early 19th C., some restoration. **£200-£250** *S*

An early 19th C. Staffordshire bull-baiting group, 5½ in. high. **£350-£380** *JHo*

Make the most of Miller's

Every care has been taken to ensure the accuracy of descriptions and estimated valuations.
Where an attribution is made within inverted commas (e.g. 'Chippendale') or is followed by the word 'style' (e.g. early Georgian style) it is intended to convey that, in the opinion of the publishers, the piece concerned is a later – though probably still antique – reproduction of the style so designated.
Unless otherwise stated, any description which refers to 'a set' or 'a pair' includes a valuation for the entire set or the pair, even though the illustration may show only a single item.

An early 19th C. unusual Staffordshire fox group, 6 in. **£350-£400** *JHo*

(c.) A Staffordshire group of 5 lambs, 6¾ in., early 19th C. **£100-£120** *WW*
(l. & r.) A pair of Staffordshire recumbent sheep, 4¾ in. high, early 19th C. **£120-140** *WW*

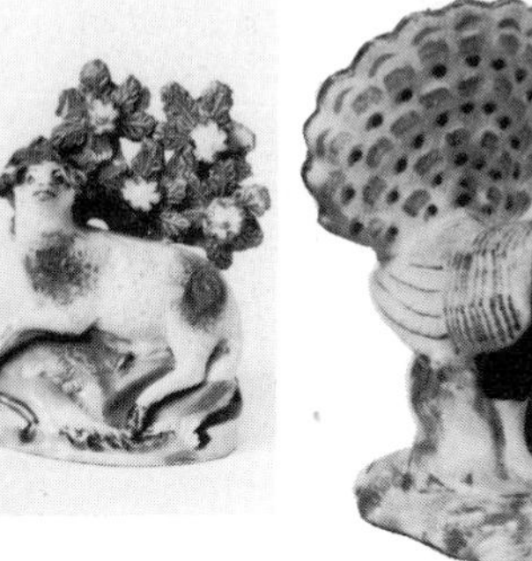

A figure of a peacock standing on a grassy mound, 4⅛ in. (10.5 cm.), early 19th C. **£70-90** *S*

A pottery sheep and lamb group, 4½ in. high, 1800-10. **£75-95** *EC*

A rare brightly coloured figure of a lion standing on a shaped gilt-lined base, 4½ in. high, early 19th C. **£220-280** *CSK*

A large figure of a brown hound the features vigorously modelled 16½ in. (42 cm.), early 19th C. **£650-850** *S*

An early Staffordshire bull-baiting group, 9 in. wide, c. 1810. **£650-£700** *DL*

An early English pottery dog, 6½ in. long, c. 1800. **£195-225** *GCA*

A pottery spaniel, 3½ in. high, c. 1810. **£200-225** *EC*

A pair of small pottery leopards with bocage, 3½ in. high, c. 1820. **£450-500** *EC*

A Wood and Caldwell lion, 5 in. wide, c. 1820. **£225-250** *GCA*

JOHN WALTON

- **John Walton worked from c. 1805-1850**
- **is known mainly for sentimental figures with bocage backgrounds**
- **bocage tended to support the figures in the kiln**
- **uses some excellent vivid colours**
- **work is often marked with an impressed name on a scroll at the rear**
- **any animal groups with amusing lions are very desirable**

A pair of Walton cows, 6 in. high, c. 1820. **£325-375** *EC*

A Walton pottery stag, 4 in. high, c. 1820. **£75-95** *EC*

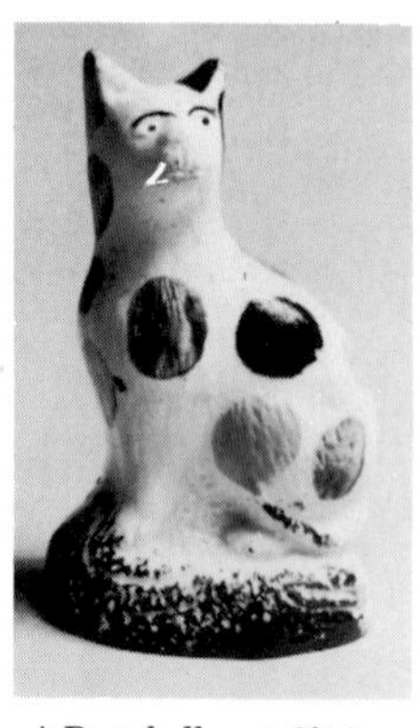

A Portobello cat, 3¾ in., c. 1815. **£200-225** *EC*

A rare pair of cats, sitting on iron-red gilt-lined cushioned bases, 7½ in. high. **£300-350** *CSK*

A fine pair of Victorian Staffordshire spill vases, 8½ in., c. 1845. **£145-175** *GCA*

An Obadiah Sherratt model of a cow standing before a flowering tree and painted with brown patches, the base with multi-coloured decoration, slight restoration, 20 cm., c. 1820. **£200-£250** *P*

An unusual figure of a rat-catcher, probably 'Billy', untitled, small chip, 16 cm., c. 1840. **£150-200** *S*

A rare pair of Staffordshire tiger figures, 4 in. over base, c. 1845. **£350-400** *DL*

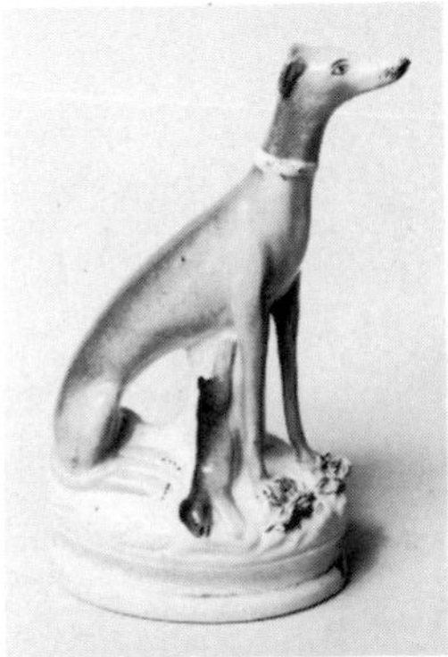

A Victorian Staffordshire greyhound with hare, 7½ in. high, c. 1850. **£45-65** *GCA*

A Victorian Staffordshire horse, by a stream, 10½ in., c. 1850. **£85-110** *GCA*

A Staffordshire figure of a zebra attacked by a snake (originally one of a pair), 10½ in., c. 1840-60. **£90-£120** Pair **£250-350** *PC*

A rare Victorian Staffordshire dairy window display 'Milk sold here', 14 in., c. 1850. **£275-325** *GCA*

A pair of well modelled dogs with black markings and gilt collars sitting on oval coloured and gilt bases, 7 in. high, mid 19th C. **£400-£500** *CSK*

A pair of Victorian Staffordshire lion spill-holders, 6½ in. high, c. 1850. **£345-395** *GCA*

A pair of Victorian Staffordshire fretted poodles, 7 in., c. 1860. **£125-£145** *GCA*

A pair of Staffordshire fretted dog groups on underglaze blue bases, 4½ in. high, c. 1850. **£85-110** *GCA*

A pair of Staffordshire mantel dogs, 9½ in., c. 1855. **£95-125** *GCA*

A Victorian Staffordshire 'Royal coat of arms' clock group, 9½ in., c. 1845. **£120-150** *GCA*

An early pair of Staffordshire dogs, decorated with underglaze black, 10 in., c. 1840-60. **£85-100** *PC*

A rare pair of Staffordshire porcellaneous figures of lions and lambs, with brown coats and shredded clay manes, minor damage, 3¾ in. and 4 in. (9.5 cm. and 10.2 cm.), mid 19th C. **£450-£550** *S*

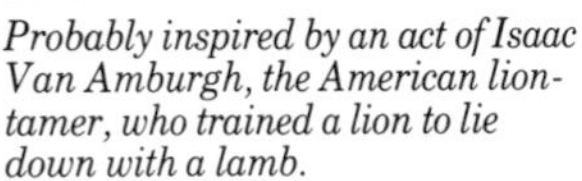

Probably inspired by an act of Isaac Van Amburgh, the American lion-tamer, who trained a lion to lie down with a lamb.

A pair of Staffordshire spaniel spill vases, 13 in., c. 1860. **£125-150** *GCA*

A pair of Staffordshire 'Whippets', rare combination of turquoise enamel and underglaze black, 10½ in. high, c. 1855. **£360-400** *DL*

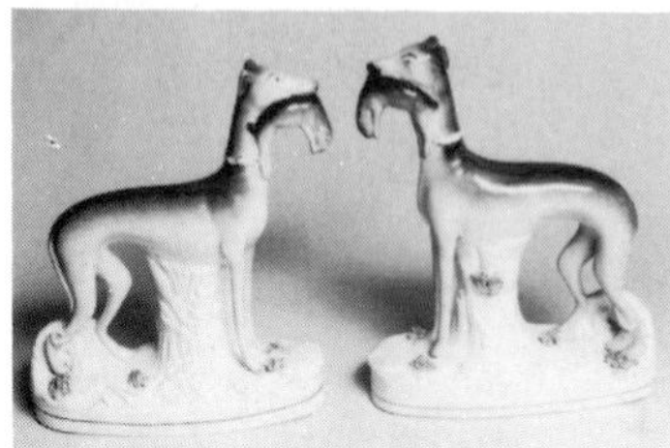

A made up pair of Staffordshire whippets, 11½ in. high, left figure c. 1840-60, right figure c. 1880-1900, early pair **£180-240,** late pair **£100-120** *PC*

A late pair of Staffordshire dogs, 13 in., c. 1900-10. **£30-40** *PC*

A Staffordshire horse and foal spill vase, 11½ in., c. 1860. **£110-135** *GCA*

A Staffordshire figure of a stag attacked by a snake (originally one of a pair), 10½ in., c. 1870-80. **£50-£60** Pair **£130-150** *PC*

A pair of Staffordshire black and white cats, 3½ in., c. 1860. **£140-£170** *DL*

A pair of Staffordshire bronze lustre dogs, 10 in., c. 1880-1920. **£25-30** *PC*

A pair of Staffordshire pug dogs, 11 in. high, c. 1900. **£200-250** *PC*

A pair of Staffordshire lions, 12 in. wide, c. 1910. **£70-100** *PC*

Figures fitted with glass eyes are always 20th C.

A C. H. Brannam Barum-ware cat, the green coat combed with brown details and with feathery pale-blue 'bib' and blue tail, yellow glass eyes, minor chips, incised marks, Rd.44561 and artist's initials, dated 1910, 33.3 cm. **£180-220** *S*

A French faience cat, seated, its yellow coat painted with blue hearts, with inset glass eyes, painted marks, 12¾ in. (32.4 cm.), 20th C. **£150-200** *S*

A Bretby model of a black cat, seated, inset glass eyes, base repaired, impressed mark, 12 in. (30.5 cm.), c. 1900. **£65-95** *S*

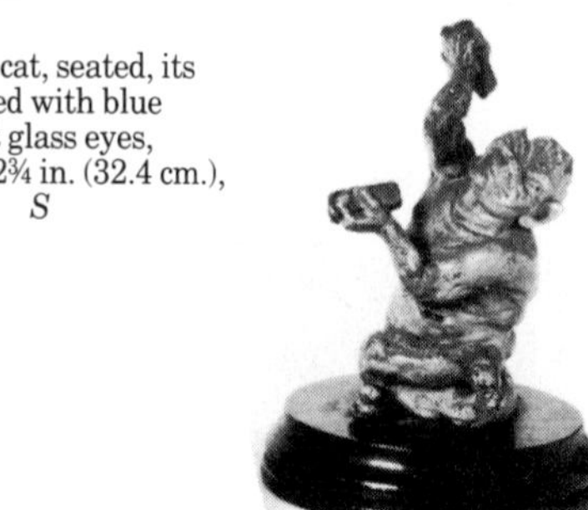

A Martin Brothers stoneware imp musician beating a tambourine with his feet, signed 'R.W. Martin & Bros., London & Southall, 8-1890', 12 cm. high, and another playing castanets, signed 'Martin Bros., London', 15.5 cm. high. **£250-£300** *P*

A Martin Brothers stoneware imp musician playing a mandolin, signed on instrument 'Martin', 12.5 cm. high. **£350-400** *P*

A Martin Brothers stoneware imp musician holding a large book of musical scores, signed on book 'Martin Bros.', 12.5 cm. high and another playing pan pipes, signed 'Martin, London', 13 cm. high. **£500-600** *P*

A Martin Brothers stoneware bird, in tones of pale blue, brown and green, signed on base 'Martin Bros., London & Southall, 12-1900', and on head 'R.W. Martin & Bros., London & Southall, 3. 1902', 22.5 cm. high. **£1,000-1,200** *P*

A rare Whieldon group modelled as a grinning Chinese boy reclining on the back of a fabulous beast, glazed in brown and green, crack on reverse, small chips, 5 in., c. 1750. **£350-450** *S*

Boy on a buffalo; a theme borrowed from Chinese pottery and porcelain.

A Martin Brothers bird glazed in deep-green and buff, base repaired, the head and base with incised marks and dated 9.1.1907, fixed wood stand, 24.4. cm. **£700-800** *S*

A Whieldon figure of a Turk, 5¾ in., c. 1755. **£2,400-2,800** *EC*

A rare Schrezheim figure of Christ crucified, on a wooden cross, the faience 41.5 cm., 77 cm. overall, 1770-80. **£1,300-1,700** *S*

A Ralph Wood figure of a shepherdess, 9 in., c. 1765. **£475-£525** *EC*

A pair of pottery figures of Elijah and the Widow, in coloured glazes, by Ralph Wood, 8 in., c. 1780. **£230-£260** *EC*

An unusual figure of a female harvester, 8 in., c. 1780. **£220-£260** *EC*

An amusing and unusual Prattware model of St. George and the dragon, the saint in typical Roman-style costume, but unusually astride a tree trunk and not a horse, in yellow, ochre and blue, all on a rocky base, restored, 25.5 cm. **£650-750** *P*

A rare pair of Neale & Co. figures of musicians, impressed mark, 8 in. high, c. 1785. **£650-700** *DL*

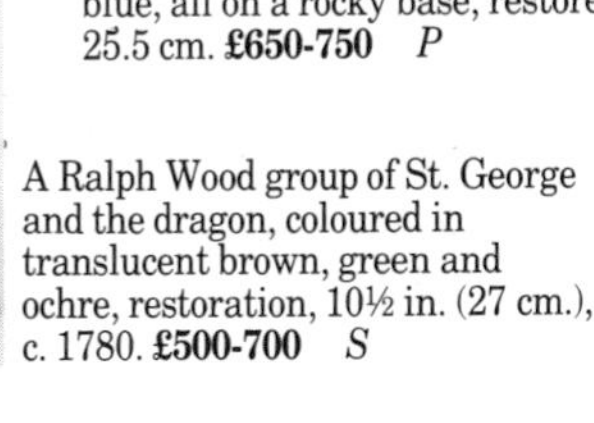

A Ralph Wood group of St. George and the dragon, coloured in translucent brown, green and ochre, restoration, 10½ in. (27 cm.), c. 1780. **£500-700** *S*

A Ralph Wood (younger) group of St. George and the dragon, 11½ in., c. 1790. **£450-520** *DL*

A Ralph Wood group of St. George and the dragon, 27 cm., c. 1770-80. **£1,200-1,400** *P*

A Prattware model of St. George and the dragon, in yellow, blue, brown and ochre tunic and helmet, the green dragon lying on the translucent green glazed rocky base, restored. **£550-650** *P*

A Staffordshire group of St. George and the dragon, after the model by Ralph Wood, he wears a bright blue sash over a green scale cuirass, restored, 27 cm., late 18th C. **£350-£450** *P*

A pair of Ralph Wood white figures of Venus and Neptune, Neptune lacks spear, both with chips to base, about 28 cm. high, 1780-90. **£200-£300** *C*

A late 18th C. brightly coloured Yorkshire or Portobello model of St. George and the dragon, with green and blue borders, 33 cm., restored. **£450-550** *P*

A pair of Ralph Wood (younger) figures of Neptune and Venus, enamelled and coloured glaze, 8½ in., c. 1790. **£450-520** *DL*

THE WOOD FAMILY	
Ralph Wood senior	1715-72
Ralph Wood junior	1748-95
Aaron Wood	
(brother of R. Wood snr.)	1717-85
Enoch Wood	
(son of A. Wood)	1759-1840

A Ralph Wood (younger) figure of a gardener, 7¾ in., c. 1790. **£120-£140** *DL*

This figure is sometimes known as Earth.

A Prattware money box modelled as a longcase clock flanked by 2 soldiers, in ochre, blue, yellow, black, green and raspberry pink, restored, 22 cm., c. 1790. **£400-£500** *SS*

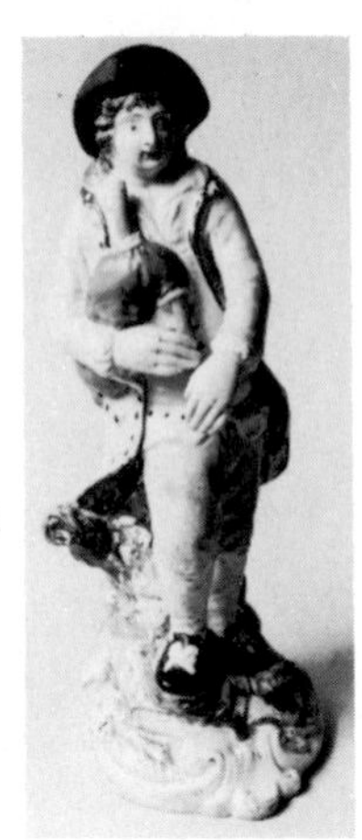
A fine Enoch Wood bagpiper, 8½ in., c. 1795. **£210-260** *GCA*

A pair of late 18th C. Staffordshire earthenware square base figures titled Flemish Music and Partner, in bright enamel colours, both upon grassy mounds, the male figure restored, 23 cm. **£200-250** *Bon*

Two North Country pottery figures from The Four Seasons, 'Autumn' and 'Winter' in a yellow cape over manganese waistcoat and blue breeches, 17 cm., late 18th C. **£200-£300** *SS*

A Pratt type figure of a lady, 3⅜ in. (8.5 cm.), c. 1800. **£160-220** *S*

A pair of early Staffordshire figures of a gardener and his mate, 23 cm., late 18th C., slight restoration. **£500-600** *P*

A bust of Voltaire, named on the reverse, probably Wood and Caldwell, socle restored, 6½ in. (16.5 cm.), c. 1800. **£60-80** *S*

A bust of Rousseau, probably Wood and Caldwell, minor chip on base, 6½ in. (16.5 cm.), c. 1800. **£100-£150** *S*

An Enoch Wood group, 'Liberty and Matrimony', 13½ in., c. 1800. **£350-420** *DL*

A rare Leeds figure of a soldier, 8 in., c. 1800. **£450-500** *JHo*

A Yorkshire money box in the form of a clock, 8½ in., c. 1800. **£475-£575** *JHo*

A fine early English pottery tithe pig group, 6 in., c. 1800. **£300-350** *GCA*

A fine early English pottery sweetmeat group, 7½ in. high, c. 1800. **£250-350** *GCA*

A Leeds figure of Venus, 6 in. high, c. 1800. **£80-100** *JHo*

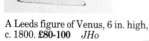

An early English pottery rural group, 7½ in., c. 1800. **£250-350** *GCA*

An early English pottery musicians group, 7 in., c. 1800. **£225-275** *GCA*

A Prattware musician group, 8½ in. high, c. 1800. **£450-475** *JHo*

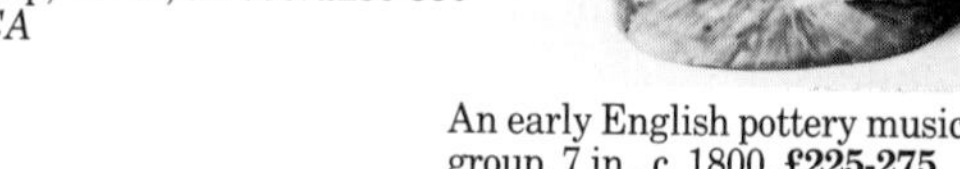

An early 19th C. Staffordshire Elephant and Castle group, 9 in. high. **£1,000-1,200** *JHo*

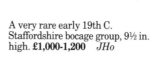

A Prattware watch stand, decorated in red, blue, green and ochre, all on a red and black sponged rectangular base, 10¾ in., c. 1800. **£250-300** *S*

An early Staffordshire group 'The Dandies', 9 in., c. 1800. **£250-300** *DL*

A very rare early 19th C. Staffordshire bocage group, 9½ in. high. **£1,000-1,200** *JHo*

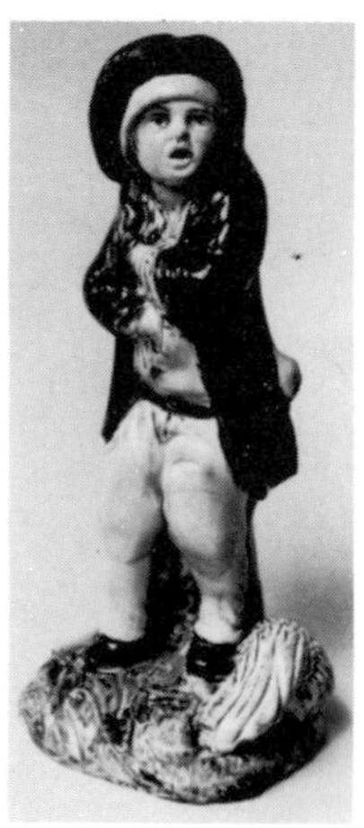

An Enoch Wood figure of a chimney sweep, 7 in., c. 1800. **£200-250** *GCA*

A group 'Perswaition', on a scroll moulded base, inscribed with the foregoing on a small plaque, some restoration, 7 in. (18 cm.), early 19th C. **£300-350** *S*

A pair of Walton well coloured groups of 'the Flight and Return to Egypt', on oval green mound base applied with flower sprays and entitled in black capitals, impressed marks, 8 in. high. **£540-£600** *CSK*

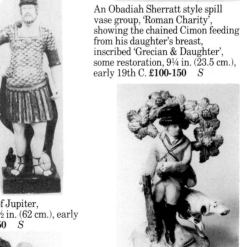

An unusual early Staffordshire figure of a fisherwoman, in green, ochre, red and blue, 22.5 cm. **£120-£160** *P*

Two Walton groups, almost a pair, one emblematic of Friendship, the other with 3 children squabbling, both with flowering bocages, impressed Walton, slight restoration, 20 cm., early 19th C. **£350-400** *P*

An Obadiah Sherratt style spill vase group, 'Roman Charity', showing the chained Cimon feeding from his daughter's breast, inscribed 'Grecian & Daughter', some restoration, 9¼ in. (23.5 cm.), early 19th C. **£100-150** *S*

A large figure of Jupiter, restoration, 24½ in. (62 cm.), early 19th C. **£100-150** *S*

An early English sportsman group, 7 in., c. 1810. **£165-195** *GCA*

An equestrian group of a centurion, the rectangular base moulded with black and red stiff leaves, some enamel on horse degraded, 8½ in. (21.5 cm.), early 19th C. **£500-£600** *S*

An interesting Staffordshire pottery figural group, in bright enamel colours, all upon an oval base and before a 3-branch tree, vase and toll booth cottage, 18 cm., early 19th C. **£550-650** *Bon*

An early English Walton figure of St. John, 7½ in., c. 1810. **£225-£275** *GCA*

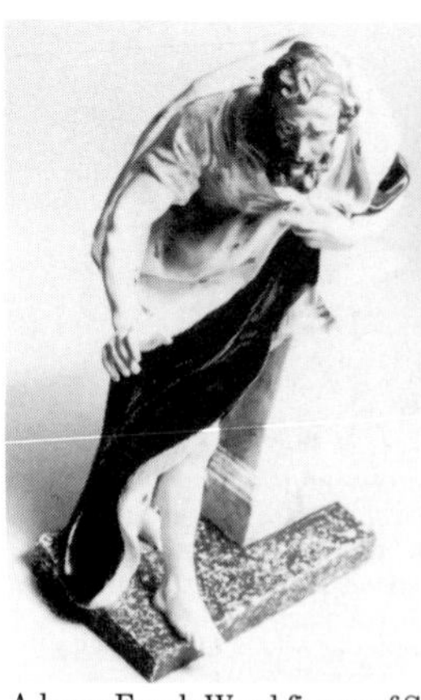

A large Enoch Wood figure of St. Paul preaching at Athens, 18½ in., c. 1810. **£475-525** *EC*

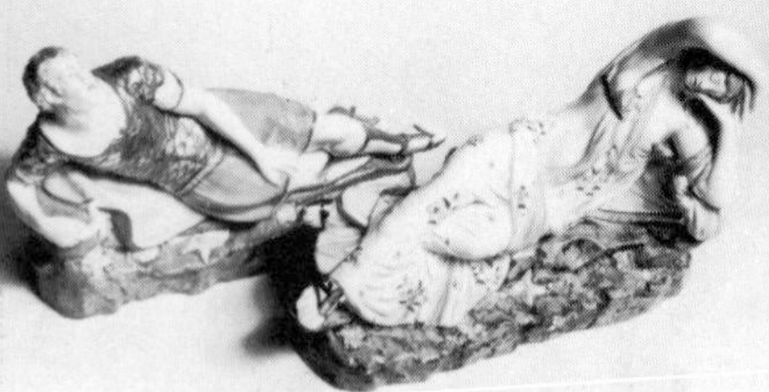

A pair of Enoch Wood figures of Antony and Cleopatra, 12 in. long, c. 1810. **£775-825** *EC*

A rare pair of Yorkshire pottery figures in Prattware colours, 8 in., c. 1810. **£550-600** *EC*

A pair of rural pastime groups, 7¾ in., c. 1820. **£440-480** *EC*

A pair of Enoch Wood figures of the elements, Earth and Water, 8 in., c. 1810. **£345-375** *EC*

A rare early Staffordshire figure of 'Harlequin', 5 in., c. 1820. **£140-£170** *DL*

A Walton type group, 'Remus and Romulus', 8½ in., c. 1820. **£450-£520** *DL*

An unusual figure of a rural trumpeter by Walton, 6¼ in., c. 1820. **£185-210** *EC*

A Portobello figure of a seated Turk, 3¼ in., c. 1815-20. **£110-£130** *EC*

An early Staffordshire figure of Elijah with unusual bocage, 9½ in., c. 1820. **£150-180** *DL*

A fine figure of a female archer modelled by Ralph Salt, with Salt scroll on reverse, 7 in., c. 1820. **£200-225** *EC*

A bocage figure of a girl playing a tambourine, 7¼ in., c. 1820. **£145-£165** *EC*

A marked Walton figure of a boy and a dog, 5½ in., c. 1820. **£90-£110** *EC*

A rare Tittensor crucifixion group, the 2 soldiers carrying crosses, one missing, on an oval green glazed mound base, impressed mark, hair crack in base, slight damage, 7½ in. (19.5 cm.), c. 1820. **£500-£600** *S*

An almost matched pair of early Staffordshire figures, 'Departure' and 'Return', 9 in., c. 1825. **£260-£320** *DL*

An Obadiah Sherratt figure of Neptune, 10 in. high, c. 1825. **£250-£320** *DL*

Obadiah Sherratt figures of Elijah and the Widow, enamel colours, small amount of purple lustre, 11½ in. high, c. 1825. **£350-420** *DL*

An early Staffordshire Obadiah Sherratt-type shepherd group, 6¾ in. high, c. 1825. **£350-390** *DL*

A Portobello group of fisherwomen, 9½ in., c. 1845. **£110-140** *GCA*

A rare pair of Minton 'Majolica' figures, glazed in streaky turquoise and brown, chips, impressed mark and date code for 1864, 32 and 37 cm. **£500-600** *S*

A pottery figure of St. Paul, 8¼ in., c. 1825. **£150-175** *EC*

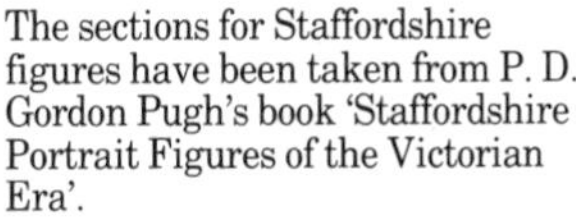

The sections for Staffordshire figures have been taken from P. D. Gordon Pugh's book 'Staffordshire Portrait Figures of the Victorian Era'.

Section A: British and Foreign Royalty
B: Statesmen and Politicians
C: Naval, Military and Exploration
D: Religious
E: Theatre, Opera, Ballet and Circus
F: Sport
G: Crime
H: Authors, Poets, Composers, etc.
I: Miscellaneous

VICTORIAN STAFFORDSHIRE PORTRAIT FIGURES

This section contains that distinctive type of earthenware portrait figures introduced during the 1840's.

They are to be distinguished from their immediate predecessors by their method of construction. They are mainly made from three part moulds. The more detailed figures do, however, have one or more subsidiary moulds for outstretched arms or legs. They are usually supported on concave oval bases.

Figures made throughout the 1840's and 50's are usually well coloured and particularly noticeable is the widespread use of a brilliant cobalt blue and a rich orange. Other colours are utilised but perhaps (with some exceptions) tend to be confined to detail painting.

Figures produced from the 60's onwards are typified by the more sparing use of colour with perhaps just the application of flesh tones to highlight the face and gilding to pick out the dress and title, if there is one.

(l.) A group of the Empress Eugenie and the Prince Imperial, untitled, 18.5 cm., c. 1856. **£80-130** *S*

(c.) Two figures of Queen Victoria, untitled, both necks repaired, 27 and 27.5 cm., c. 1840. **£120-180** *S*

(r.) A box and cover in the form of Queen Victoria, 17 cm., mid 19th C. **£70-100** *S*

A Staffordshire pair of Prince Alfred and the Prince of Wales, 10½ in., 1858 (A61/188, 189). **£250-£350** *PC*

Singles: Prince of Wales **£80-100**
Prince Alfred **£150-170**

An English porcellaneous figure of the Princess Royal on a goat, 3¾ in., c. 1845. **£85-110** *GCA*

A very rare pair of Staffordshire figures of Prince of Wales and Prince Alfred, 11½ in., 1858 (A62/192, 193). **£350-450** *PC*

Coloured **£450+**

A Staffordshire figure of the Prince of Wales and his dog, 14½ in., c. 1862 (A60/186), coloured **£140-£180**, white **£90-120** *PC*

A pair of Staffordshire figures, probably the Prince of Wales and the Princess Royal, 7½ in., c. 1850. **£70-100** *PC*

Miller's is a price GUIDE Not a price LIST.

The price ranges given reflect the average price a purchaser should pay for similar items. Condition, rarity of design or pattern, size, colour, provenance, restoration and many other factors must be taken into account when assessing values.

A Staffordshire group of the Prince of Wales and the Princess Royal, 7½ in., c. 1840's. **£200-240** *PC*

A similar group with a goat replacing the pony — add **£100**

Known Manufacturers of Staffordshire Figures
The 'Alpha' Factory, 1845-51 (named by Balston)
Geo. Baguley or Baggaley, c. 1851
H (?) Bentley, Hanley, 1840's
Lancaster & Sons, Hanley, c. 1900
Ridgway & Robey, 1837-39
James Sadler & Sons, Burslem, c. 1900
Samson Smith, Longton, 1853-78
then as Adderley & Tams until 1888
The Shelton Factory (John & Rebecca Lloyd), 1834-52
Obadiah and Martha Sherratt, 1820-34 ?
Joseph Unwin, 1877-1926

Whilst all of these are known to have been involved in the production of Staffordshire figures during the 19th Century it is certain that there were a great many other producers who have vanished into obscurity.

Bibliography

Staffordshire Portrait Figures. P. D. Gordon Pugh, Barrie & Jenkins, 1981.
Staffordshire Pottery, The Tribal Art of England. Anthony Oliver, Heinemann, 1981.
Of interest to collectors but now dated:
Staffordshire Chimney Ornaments, R. G. Haggar, Phoenix House, 1955.
Staffordshire Portrait Figures of the Victorian Age. Thomas Balston, Faber & Faber, 1958.

A Staffordshire figure of (probably) the Princess Royal mounted on a stag, severely damaged, 10 in., c. 1855. **£15-20** Perfect **£60-80** *PC*

A pair of late Staffordshire figures of Charles I and Cromwell, 11 in., 1900-20 (A96/258, 259). **£25-35** *PC*

Note the typically flat nature of the late figures — with sparse use of colour.

A Staffordshire figure of the Princess Royal, 8 in. high, 1855-65. **£40-50** *PC*

An early Parr factory Staffordshire pair of figures, the Prince of Wales and the Princess Royal, 9 in., 1840-60 (A54/160, 161). **£250-350** *PC*

William Kent repro. **£80-90**

A Staffordshire figure of Sir Robert Peel, 8½ in., c. 1845 (B1/2). **£195-£245** *GCA*

A rare Staffordshire figure of Sir Robert Peel, 12 in. high, 1850 (B.7/31). **£400-500** *PC*

Version with right arm outstretched **£1,500+**

The figure commemorates the tragic riding accident which caused Peel's death in 1850.

A figure of Garibaldi, the patriot, wearing an orange shirt, standing by a white horse with red-brown mane and tail, sword chipped, 22 cm., c. 1860 (C.97/282). **£150-£200** *CSK*

A rare white and gilt figure of the Duke of Wellington, 11¾ in. high, c. 1852 (B3/23). **£110-140** *CSK*

This figure is certainly of Wellington in old age. He died in an armchair in Walmer Castle, Kent.

An arbour group of Uncle Tom and Little Eva, 6 in. high, c. 1850 (B26/79). **£100-125** *GCA*

A Staffordshire figure of Garibaldi, 9 in., c. 1861 (C97/282). **£160-200** *PC*

A Staffordshire figure of Daniel O'Connell, 16 in., c. 1850 (B2/16). **£450-600** *PC*

This is generally regarded as one of the best pieces made in the Potteries (see Pugh).

A figure of Benjamin Franklin standing in long blue coat holding a black tricorn hat, 14 in. high, c. 1850's (B21/66). **£350-400** *CSK*

The figures in brackets denote the figure coding in Pugh.

A Victorian Staffordshire group of Uncle Tom and Little Eva, 11½ in. high, c. 1852. **£110-135** *GCA*

Taken from the anti-slavery novel 'Uncle Tom's Cabin' published in 1852.

A Staffordshire figure of Robert Napier, 9 in. high, c. 1867 (C.104/283). **£200-240** *PC*

A Staffordshire figure of Garibaldi, 12 in. (C102/299). **£90-110** *PC*
Coloured **£140-180**

A Staffordshire figure of Garibaldi, 15 in., 1840-60 (C101/294). **£120-£180** *PC*

A Staffordshire 'Alliance' group of Napoleon and Albert in underglaze blue and colours, 12 in., c. 1854 (C77/223). **£150-200** *PC*

A pair of William Kent reproductions of earlier Parr Staffordshire figures: Garibaldi and Victor Emmanuel, 15 in., 1890-1900 (C103/302, 303). **£250-£350** Originals **£1,000+** *PC*

A Staffordshire 'Alliance' group of Napoleon and Prince Albert, 14 in., c. 1854 (C78/227). **£110-140** *PC*

A pair of Staffordshire figures of Campbell and Havelock, 10½ in., c. 1857. **£220-280** *PC*

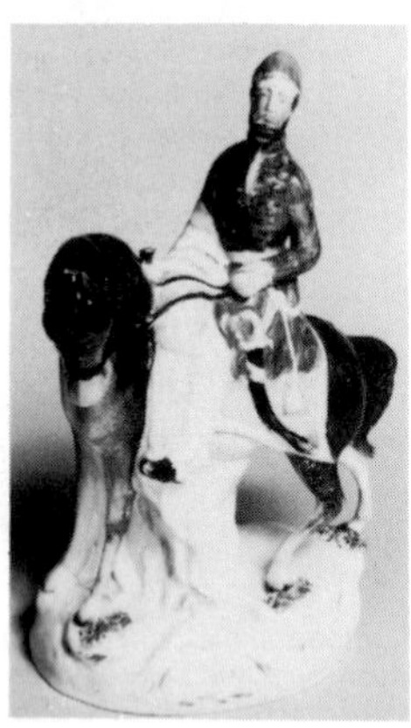

A Staffordshire Parr factory figure of Omar Pasha, 11 in. high, c. 1854 (C63/163). **£180-220** *PC*

STAFFORDSHIRE FIGURES

- **made as chimney ornaments**
- **figures characteristic of the Victorian era became established in the 1840's**
- **body actually whiter than earlier Staffordshire figures**
- **made in 3 part moulds**
- **base typically flat and oval**
- **1840-60 — strong colours, note particularly cobalt blue**
- **early pieces well moulded and decorated to imitate porcelain**
- **later flat-back figures much simplified**
- **c. 1860's there was a development away from the strong colours to a lighter, more sparse colouring with more gilt decoration**
- **1870's virtual disappearance of underglaze blue**
- **Victorian Staffordshire figures show immense interest in:—**
  a. Royalty
  b. great interest in war
  c. politically most figures tend to be left-wing
  d. religious tend to be nonconformist (possibly caused by northern cottage interest — way of expressing dissatisfaction with ruling classes)
- **up to 1880 mercuric gold used on figures — tended to rub off**
- **in the 1880's 'Bright Gold' used — much harsher in appearance**
- **reproductions have none of the spontaneity of the Victorian figures**
- **late figures modelling not sharp**
- **most desirable figures tend to be the highly coloured prior to 1860!**
- **the Crimean war period (1854-56) was probably the high point — both of production and quality**
- **theatre, crime and sport seem to be the three collecting areas which hold their price and frequently astound estimators with some record prices**
- **collectors should beware of description in sale catalogues which state 'rare' as this is frequently incorrect**

A Staffordshire figure of a Crimean War General (General Sir James Simpson), 18 in. high, c. 1854, restored (C44/109). **£350-400** Perfect **£550+** *PC*

Four of a rare series of 10 Staffordshire figures of Boer War Commanders, 11 in., c. 1900. **£60-£80** each (C124/345, 346, 347) *PC*

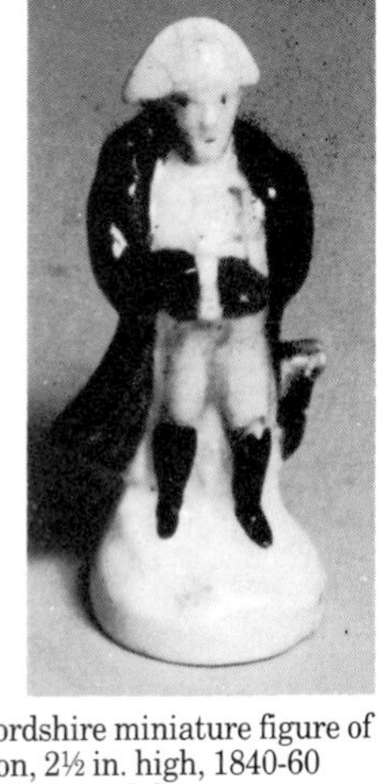

A Staffordshire miniature figure of Napoleon, 2½ in. high, 1840-60 (C23/62). **£1-5** *PC*

Such miniatures are now becoming widely collected, and it is certainly an area worth considering as prices seem certain to rise.

Make the most of Miller's

When buying or selling, it must always be remembered that prices can be greatly affected by the condition of any piece. Unless otherwise stated, all goods shown in Miller's are of good merchantable quality, and the valuations given reflect this fact. Pieces offered for sale in exceptionally fine condition or in poor condition may reasonably be expected to be priced considerably higher or lower respectively than the estimates given herein.

A pair of Staffordshire figures of Greenwich Hospital Pensioners, 7½ in., 1840-60 (C76/221, 222). **£250-350** *PC*

A pair of Staffordshire figures of a sailor and his wife (she is previously unrecorded), 9½ in., 1840-60 (C.85/250). **£180-220** *PC*

A Staffordshire figure of a Vivandiere, 13 in., c. 1840 (C.83/237). **£150-200** *PC*

A Victorian Staffordshire group of sailor and midshipman, 11 in., c. 1850. **£110-135** *GCA*

A Staffordshire bust of Wesley, reproduced from earlier figure, 11¾ in., c. 1880 (D8/15). **£70-90** *PC*

A Staffordshire figure of a Highland soldier, 17 in., 1840-60 (C.83/238). **£220-280** *PC*

This figure has no titled equivalent.

A pair of Staffordshire Parr factory figures of Sankey and Moody, 13 in., c. 1873 (D.5/10(a)). **£160-£220** *PC*

Sankey and Moody were American evangelists who visited England in 1873 and 1883.

A Derby Stevenson and Hancock figure of Billy Waters, marked, 3¾ in., c. 1870 (E36L). **£80-110** *DL*

Billy Waters was a well known busker outside London theatres of the period.

A rare figure of Billy Waters, 8 in., c. 1830 (E.35/70). **£575-635** *EC*

A pottery figure with its porcelain equivalent.

A Staffordshire figural group, 'Mazeppa on a horse', 9 in. high, c. 1864 (E.107/213). **£70-90** *PC*

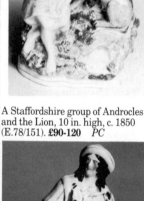

A Staffordshire group 'Paul et Virginie', repair to spill vase, 12 in. high, c. 1850. **£40-50** Perfect **£60-£80** *PC*

Based on a romance by Bernardin de St. Pierre, published in 1787.

A figure of 'Falstaff' from the Alpha factory, possibly as Luigi Lablanche in the role, entitled, 16 cm., c. 1845. **£250-£300** *S*

A theatrical figure, possibly Mrs. Siddons as Lady Macbeth, 18.8 cm., c. 1845 (E fig. 10). **£100-150** *S*

A Staffordshire group of Androcles and the Lion, 10 in. high, c. 1850 (E.78/151). **£90-120** *PC*

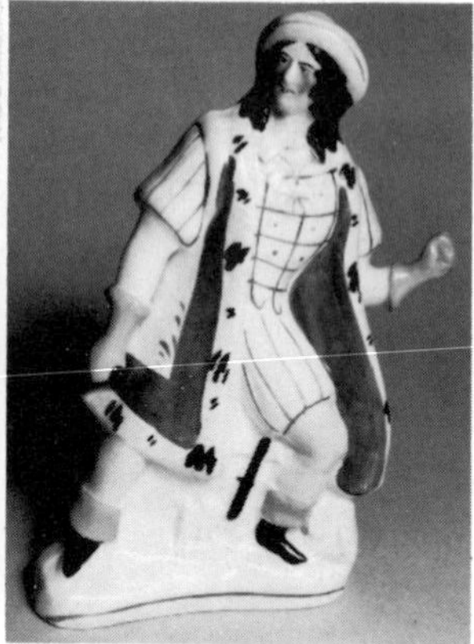

A Staffordshire figure of Edmund Kean as Richard III, originally one of a pair, 11 in. (E14/34). **£70-90** For pair **£200-250** *PC*

A pair of Staffordshire figures of an American horse trainer called Rarey, 7½ in. high, c. 1860 (E.77/148). **£130-170** If named **£500+** *PC*

John Soloman Rarey arrived in England in 1857. He gave a demonstration of his horse training in front of the Queen and Prince Albert. He toured Europe and returned to America in 1860.

A pair of Staffordshire figures, MacReady as James V and unidentified actress, 8½ in., 1846 (E7/20). **£250-350** *PC*

This unidentified actress may well have been made by potters merely to balance MacReady.

A rare pair of Parr factory Staffordshire figures of Jessica and Lorenzo, 11 in. high, c. 1850. **£240-£280** *PC*

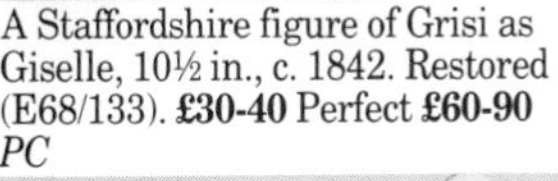

A Staffordshire figure of Grisi as Giselle, 10½ in., c. 1842. Restored (E68/133). **£30-40** Perfect **£60-90** *PC*

A very rare pair of Staffordshire equestrian figures, probably of Astley's Circus, one repaired, 10½ in., c. 1850. **£300-350** Perfect **£350+** *PC*

A pair of Staffordshire figures of a drummer boy and girl, 10½ in., c. 1840-60 (E72/144). **£90-100** *PC*

The girl was previously thought to be Jenny Lind — see Pugh, but the discovery of her male partner throws doubt on this. As was she fetched £90-100. Now she is a decorative, as opposed to a portrait figure, her value has halved . . . a cautionary tale for all those who buy merely for investment! The reverse can also occur when the origin of a 'decorative' figure is found which turns it into a portrait figure, the price rises, sometimes dramatically.

A Staffordshire porcellaneous theatrical figure, 5½ in., c. 1840-60. **£40-60** *PC*

A Staffordshire musicians group in remarkably fine condition, 15½ in., c. 1840-60 (E.138/286). **£180-220** *PC*

A rare Staffordshire figure of a clown, in iron-red jacket, on shaped gilt lined base, 6¾ in. high (E100/199). **£300-400** *CSK*

A pair of Staffordshire circus performers, 9½ in., c. 1850. **£145-£175** *GCA*

A pair of Staffordshire figures of dancers, probably Perrott and Grisi, 8½ in., c. 1840-60 (E68/134, 135). **£70-90** *PC*

A Staffordshire figure of 'The Blind Fiddler', one coloured, one white and gilt, 12 in. high, c. 1840-60. Coloured **£90-120** White **£70-90** *PC*

A Staffordshire circus group, 10½ in., c. 1850 (E68/131). **£120-£160** *PC*

A Victorian Staffordshire theatrical group, 11 in., c. 1845. **£145-175** *GCA*

MARKET TRENDS

Prices have continued to increase as, contrary to popular belief, very few portrait figures in pristine condition have survived and those that do appear are much sought after. Condition is all important. For instance, a badly coloured damaged Victory (Pugh C185) recently made under £200 at auction, however, a perfect well moulded and coloured Victory would fetch over £1,000. To be called pristine, a figure in order of importance must be:—

a) PERFECT (i.e. no damage, restoration, chips, not stained or heavily crazed).

b) NAMED

c) WELL MODELLED (i.e. early from the mould, with sharp features and details).

d) COLOURED (enamels not flaked or faded, preferably with underglaze blue).

To the items above there must be considered two other important factors, which are RARITY and, finally, DESIRABILITY.

It is figures meeting all the above criteria that fetch record prices, and will continue to do so.

One of a pair of Staffordshire figures, 12 in., c. 1850. **£250-300** pair, single **£90-£130** *PC*

A pair of Staffordshire figures of musicians, 8¼ in. high, c. 1850. **£90-120** *PC*

A Staffordshire figure 'The Blind Harpist', 14½ in., c. 1850. **£150-250** *PC*

A matched pair of Staffordshire figures, Fanny Elssler and her sister, castanet dancing, 8 in. high, c. 1850 (E72/139 and 140). One figure imperfect. As is **£120-150** Perfect pair **£150-200** *PC*

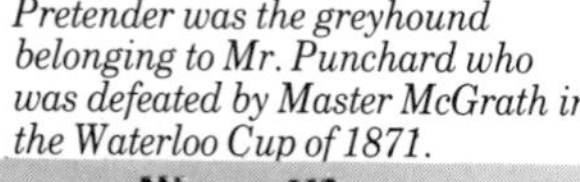

A rare figure of 'Pretender', named in gilt capitals, 9½ in. high, c. 1871 (F.7/21). **£250-300** *CSK*

Pretender was the greyhound belonging to Mr. Punchard who was defeated by Master McGrath in the Waterloo Cup of 1871.

A Staffordshire figure of a mounted jockey, 11 in., c. 1900. **£20-30** *PC*

Bright gilding dates a piece after 1880.

A Staffordshire figure of a mounted jockey, 6¾ in., c. 1850-70 (F7/18). **£60-80** *PC*

'Stanfield Hall' scene of the murder of Mr. Isaac Jermy by James Rush, 7½ in. wide, c. 1850 (G20/46). **£120-150** *EC*

A Staffordshire crime group of Smith and Collier, 13½ in., c. 1866 (G27/54). **£110-150** *PC*

Thomas Smith was shot by William Collier when he discovered him poaching. Collier was found guilty of murder and was the last person to be publicly executed at Stafford Gaol.

A Staffordshire pair of figures, Tom King and Dick Turpin, 9½ in., c. 1840-60. Repairs to both figures (G8/25, 26). **£80-100** Perfect **£120-£180** *PC*

A Staffordshire figure of Dick Turpin, originally one of a pair, 10 in., c. 1840-60 (G.4/13). **£40-50** *PC*

A pair of Staffordshire figures of Dick Turpin and Tom King, 12 in., c. 1840-60 (G4/15, 16). **£100-140** *PC*

Underglaze blue suggests a date before 1863.

A pair of figures of Tam O'Shanter and Souter Johnny, each seated in a grey chair set on a green rectangular base 'sponged' in red and black, possibly Scottish, 6¼ in. (16 cm.) and 7 in. (17.7 cm.), c. 1830. **£300-400** *S*

A Staffordshire figure of Eliza Cook, the poetess, wearing a blue jacket and rose sprigged skirt, base titled in gilding, some crazing, 10¼ in., 1860's (H.10/36). **£140-£200** *SC*

A well coloured group of Shakespeare standing in long iron-red cloak, flanked by Hamlet and Lady Macbeth, 10½ in. high (H.5/14). **£180-240** *CSK*

A pair of rare figures of Shakespeare and Milton (one figure illustrated), 12 in. high (H.5/11, 12). **£200-250** *CSK*

A Staffordshire porcellaneous figure of Walter Scott and his dog, 9¼ in., c. 1840-60 (H.18/57). **£100-£120** *PC*

Larger — 14 in. **£140-180**

(l.) A Staffordshire figure of Paxton (?), 10 in. high (I.23/59). **£120-150** *PC*

(r.) A Staffordshire figure of Paxton, incorrectly restored, 10 in. high (I.23/59). **£70-90** *PC*

This merely points out the effect poor quality restoration can have on the value of Staffordshire figures. Obviously on a very rare specimen some damage may be excused but poor restoration, such as above, will always severely affect the price.

A Staffordshire group 'Tam O'Shanter and Souter Johnny', 10¼ in., c. 1840-60 (H.20/64). **£150-£200** *PC*

A 'Highland Huntsman', 14 in. high, c. 1890. **£20-30** *PC*

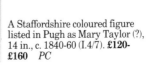

A pair of Staffordshire figures of huntsmen with dog and stag, 10½ in., c. 1840-60. **£120-150**
Singles **£40-50** *PC*

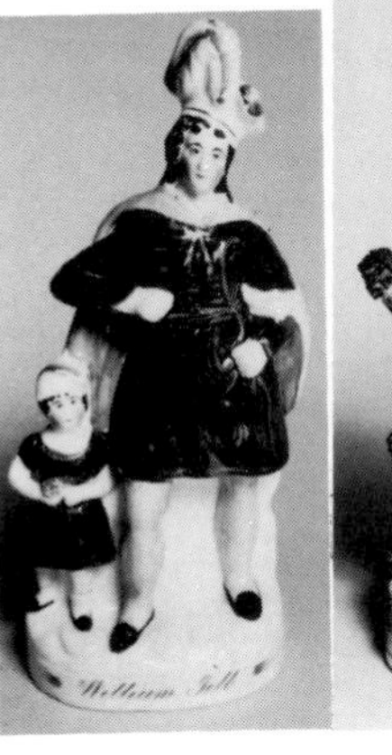

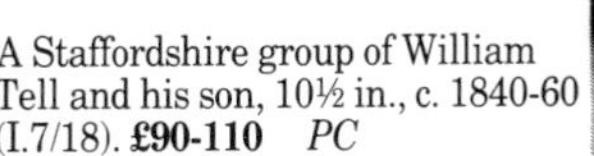

A Staffordshire group of William Tell and his son, 10½ in., c. 1840-60 (I.7/18). **£90-110** *PC*

A Staffordshire coloured figure listed in Pugh as Mary Taylor (?), 14 in., c. 1840-60 (I.4/7). **£120-£160** *PC*

A Staffordshire figure of a falconer and his dog, 15 in., c. 1840-60. **£120-160** *PC*

A pair of well coloured 'Highland Huntsman' figures, 14 in. high, c. 1840. **£250-350** *PC*

Single figure **£90-100**

Note: *A pair will fetch considerably more than 2 singles.*

A Staffordshire group of 2 huntsmen with stags, 13¼ in., c. 1840-60. **£140-160** *PC*

A Staffordshire group of 2 huntsmen, 13 in., c. 1860-70. **£25-£30** *PC*

A Staffordshire figure of the Falconer and his lass, 11 in. high, c. 1840-60. **£40-60** *PC*

An unusual figure of St. John, from the Alpha factory, in a deep blue and purple robe, 18 cm., mid 19th C. **£120-180** *S*

A Staffordshire decorative figure of a huntsman, 13 in., c. 1840-60. **£80-£100** *PC*

A Staffordshire porcellaneous figure of Grandfather having his tea, hands restored, 7 in., c. 1840-60. **£50-60** Perfect **£100-£120** *PC*

A Staffordshire candle snuffer modelled as a 'blue coat boy', 3¾ in., c. 1840-60 (I.33). **£35-45** *PC*

A well coloured Staffordshire figure of a man in Eastern dress, on a shaped gilt lined base, 7¼ in. **£50-£70** *CSK*

A Staffordshire figure of a Welsh woman, 12 in. tall, c. 1840-60. **£70-90** *PC*

A very rare pair of Staffordshire figures of 'The Falconers', 14 in. high, c. 1850. **£250-350** *PC*

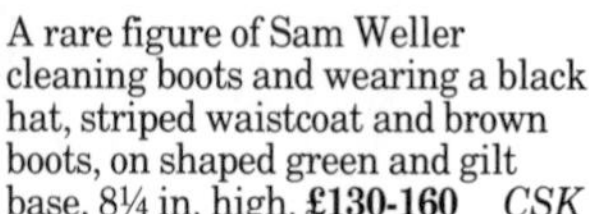

A rare figure of Sam Weller cleaning boots and wearing a black hat, striped waistcoat and brown boots, on shaped green and gilt base, 8¼ in. high. **£130-160** *CSK*

A Parr factory figure group of the Lover and his Lass, 11 in. high, c. 1850. **£70-90** *PC*

'The Orphans', a Thomas Parr group, coloured in pale pink and yellow, 20 cm., c. 1850. **£100-150** *S*

A rare 'Family Act' Staffordshire group, 15 in., c. 1850. **£180-220** *PC*

A Staffordshire figure of 'Arabia', originally one of a pair, 7½ in., c. 1850. **£70-90** *PC*

A Staffordshire figure, originally one of a pair, 9½ in., c. 1840-60. **£60-80** Pair **£180-200** *PC*

A pair of Staffordshire figures, 9¼ in. high, c. 1850. **£80-100** *PC*

A rare Parr factory Staffordshire figure of Lady Godiva, foot restored, left arm a potter's error, 9½ in., c. 1850. **£300-400** Perfect **£400+** *PC*

A pair of Parr factory Staffordshire figures of fruit sellers, 14 in. high, c. 1840-60. **£100-140** *PC*

A pair of very late Staffordshire figures of the Gardener and his wife, 12 in. high, c. 1920. **£8-10** *PC*

A pair of Staffordshire figures, 'pure water fountains', 9¼ in., c. 1850. **£90-120** *PC*

A rare Pratt flask with portrait of George and his family, the reverse with portrait of Admiral Jarvis, 5½ in. high, c. 1790. **£295-335** *GCA*

A rare Prattware flask, moulded in relief on either side with a profile bust-portrait of George Augustus Eliot, First Baron Heathfield, sparsely picked out in blue, ochre and yellow splashes, 6½ in. (16.5 cm.), c. 1790. **£200-250** *S*

Eliot was a naval commander and governor of Gibraltar. He was awarded the Order of the Bath by George III and created Lord Heathfield. He died in 1790 at Aix-la-Chapelle, France.

A Hispano Moresque copper lustre armorial dish, repaired, 47.5 cm. diam., late 15th C. **£500-600** *C*

A Deruta blue and gold lustre charger, riveted, c. 1520. **£2,200-£2,500** *C*

A Gubbio Coppa Amatoria painted in gold and copper lustre and blue, rim chips, 17 cm. diam., c. 1520. **£4,000-5,000** *C*

A Deruta circular dish, reserved in blue on a copper lustre ground, cracked and repainted, 20.5 cm. diam., c. 1520. **£1,000-1,200** *C*

ITALIAN MAIOLICA

Tinglazed earthenware made in Italy from the end of the 15th century. The term derives from Majorca from whence the Spanish lustre pottery was shipped into Italy.

The earliest Maiolica used predominantly floral designs then portraits and from about 1520, the 'Istoriato' of figural subjects based largely upon mythological or Biblical sources.

A Deruta polychrome large charger painted in blue, yellow, ochre and turquoise, inscribed 'non bene pro toto liberta vedi Laura', cracked and slightly restored, 40 cm. diam., c. 1520. **£1,200-1,500** *C*

The Latin inscription may be loosely translated 'liberty, Laura, is not good for everybody'.

A Faenza (Casa Pirota) dark Berrettino ground dish of cardinal's hat form painted in green, yellow and white, cracked, some restoration, 20 cm. diam., c. 1530. **£950-1,150** *C*

A Deruta polychrome charger, in turquoise, lined in yellow and blue brocade, extensively damaged, 41 cm. diam., c. 1525. **£700-800** *C*

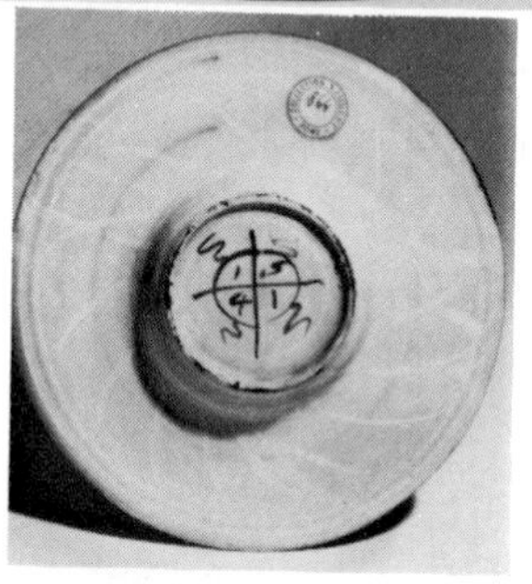

A Casteldurante dish, the border painted in bianco-sopra-bianco and with turquoise rim, the reverse with the date 1541, minor restorations to rim, 19 cm. diam. **£10,000-12,000** *C*

A Rimini Istoriato dish painted with Diana, rim chips, hair crack, 26.5 cm. diam., c. 1560. **£3,000-£4,000** *C*

A Venice Istoriato dish, the reverse inscribed 'cir cire all tempio per far sachreficio', repaired, 29.5 cm. diam., c. 1550. **£600-800** *C*

An Istoriato dish of cardinal's hat form painted with Dejanira offering the poisoned shirt to Hercules, the reverse inscribed in blue 'Dionira a presen/la fatatta camisa, Duchy of Urbino, cracked and repaired, 22.5 cm. diam., c. 1555. **£700-800** *C*

Dejanira gave Hercules a shirt dipped in the blood of the centaur Nessus to restore his affections; it was in fact fatally poisoned.

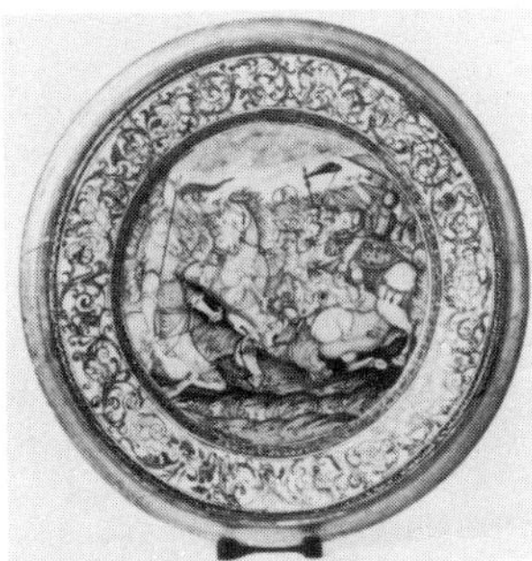

A Castelli circular dish, painted by Francesco Grue, with an extensive equestrian battle scene after an engraving by Antoine Tempesta, 41 cm. framed. **£1,000-1,200** *P*

An Istoriato dish, the centre with Venus recumbent, surrounded with other Gods and Goddesses, the reverse with inscription in blue 'Venera' above a C in a square, Duchy of Urbino, cracked and chipped, 22.4 cm. diam., late 16th C. **£450-550** *C*

An Urbino Istoriato large circular dish from the Fontana workshop, the reverse inscribed in blue 'Quando fu asediato la cita di Ardea', repaired and cracked, 37.5 cm. diam., c. 1555. **£4,000-£5,000** *C*

Ardea was a city of the 'Latin league' loyal to Rome which withstood a long siege during the Punic War (Livy Book 4, ch. 37). It is therefore most probable that the present dish formed part of the Guido baldo service though it is not numbered and the inscription on the reverse is not poetic. The treatment of the subject is totally anachronistic although it is a delightful portrait of Renaissance warfare.

A Montelupo charger, on a yellow ground, cracked, 31.5 cm. diam., early 17th C. **£800-900** *C*

A Montelupo plate painted in strong tones of ochre, yellow, blue, manganese and green, cracked and chipped, 26 cm., early 17th C. **£450-£550** *S*

A small Montelupo dish painted with a man in blue and ochre striped suit holding a similarly striped flag, cracked, 24.5 cm. diam., early 17th C. **£400-500** *C*

An Urbino Istoriato plate with 3 scenes from the story of Neptune, the reverse inscribed in blue 'Netuno mutato/in dalphino' Fontana workshop, cracked, 23.5 cm. diam., c. 1550. **£1,800-£2,000** *C*

An Urbino Istoriato dish painted with Apollo's musical contest with Marsyas, repaired, 26.5. cm. diam., c. 1560. **£600-700** *C*

A Montelupo charger, repaired, 32 cm. diam., early 17th C. **£650-£750** *C*

A Montelupo dated dish decorated in pale ochre and blue, the border inscribed 'Manus mea lavabo inocentes' and dated 1578, riveted crack, 24.5 cm. diam. **£700-800** *C*

A Montelupo dish, painted in ochre, manganese, green and greyish blue, with a man standing in a landscape, 32 cm. **£650-750** *P*

A rare Netherlands 'Maiolica' plate, possibly Haarlem, painted in ochre, yellow, blue and manganese, 21 cm., early 17th C. **£500-600** *P*

Identical border designs are found on tiles of this period attributed to Haarlem.

A Montelupo circular charger painted with a man in striped yellow and blue suit holding a yellow, blue and manganese banner, 31 cm. diam., 17th C. **£320-£400** *C*

A Netherlands maiolica dish in yellow, manganese and blue, restored, 39 cm. diam., 17th C. **£300-400** *C*

A Lambeth delft 'blue dash' tulip charger, painted in copper-green, blue, yellow and ochre, riveted cracks, restored chips on reverse, 13½ in., late 17th C. **£450-500** *S*

A Lambeth delft 'blue dash' charger, painted in bright copper-green, blue and pale yellow, with a 'blue dash' rim, firing defect, cracked, 13¾ in., c. 1680. **£350-£400** *S*

A set of 6 delft blue and white octagonal 'Merryman' plates, painted with the verse: '1. What is a merry man, 2. Lett him doe what hee can, 3. to entertaine his guesse, 4. with wine and merry jests, 5. but if his wife doe frowne, 6. All merryment goe's downe,' numbers 1, 3 and 4 cracked across and restuck, minor glaze flaking, London or Holland, 19.5 cm. wide, c. 1690. **£4,000-5,000** *C*

A Bristol polychrome William and Mary plate, 8½ in., c. 1690. **£2,300-£2,500** *JHo*

A Castelli plate probably painted by Carlo Antonio Grue, yellow rim, 17 cm., 17th/18th C. **£400-500** *S*

A London delft royal portrait plate or saucer dish painted in blue, cracked, 8½ in., c. 1690. **£1,000-£1,300** *S*

A Brislington delft portrait charger painted in blue and manganese, damaged and riveted, 13¼ in., c. 1680-90. **£1,400-1,600** *S*

The features are very similar to those of King William on a dish in the Glaisher Collection in the FitzWilliam Museum. However in that instance the king is crowned and is flanked by the initials K.W.

A London octagonal plate painted in manganese and bright yellow, glaze chips, some wear, 7½ in., late 17th C. (L.L). **£750-950** *S*

Locate the source

The source of each illustration in Miller's can be found by checking the code letters below each caption with the list of contributors on page 12. In view of the undoubted differences in price structures from region to region, this information could be extremely valuable to everyone who buys and sells antiques.

An unusual Bristol dish of saucer shape, crudely painted in muddy blue, red and green, the reverse with numeral 6 in blue, chips and wear on rim, 10 in., late 17th C. (L.L). **£650-750** *S*

A London charger boldly painted in blue with a geometric pattern, typical flaking on rim, 13⅝ in., late 17th C. (L.L.). **£400-500** *S*

A London blue and white charger painted with 2 bands of stylised foliage, cracks, 13 in., late 17th C. (L.L.). **£400-500** *S*

A rare London blue and white charger, painted with an amusing figure of a Chinaman, crack, 13¼ in., late 17th C. (L.L.). **£2,300-£3,000** *S*

A painted 'oak leaf' charger, with turquoise-green, blue and yellow, 13¼ in., late 17th C. **£800-900** *S*

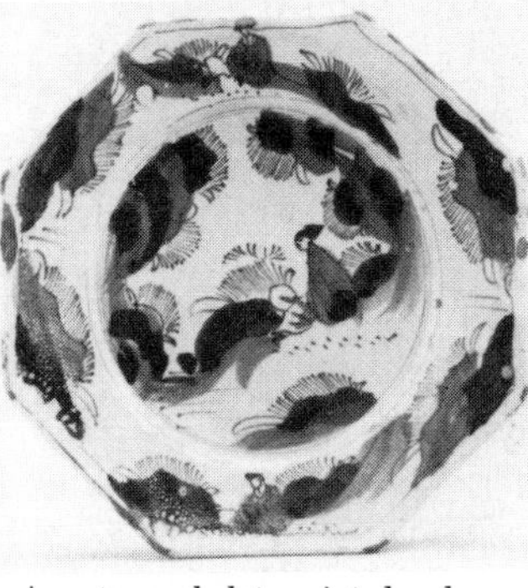

An octagonal plate painted and 'pencilled' in blue, probably Bristol, chips, 7½ in., late 17th C. (L.L.). **£400-500** *S*

A London delft blue-dash Adam and Eve charger, the couple in blue and ochre and manganese, flanking a blue and green tree with ochre fruits, cracked, 33.5 cm. diam., c. 1670. **£400-600** *C*

A London delft polychrome blue-dash Adam and Eve charger, on an ochre, green, blue and manganese shaded mound, within a concentric blue and yellow line and blue-dash rim, 2 small areas of rim repair and small crack, 41 cm. diam., c. 1670. **£2,500-3,000** *C*

An English delft Adam and Eve charger with blue-dash rim, painted in dark and pale manganese, blue, copper-green and ochre, 34 cm., c. 1680-90. **£650-£750** *P*

A Bristol delftware Adam and Eve charger, the tree laden with manganese fruit among green foliage, blue sponged border, repaired, c. 1700. **£350-450** *SS*

ENGLISH DELFT

Tin-glazed earthenware was first produced in this country by two Antwerp potters, Jasper Andries and Jacob Janson. The earliest wares were mainly influenced by Italian and French pottery. Later as with their Dutch counterparts, English potters drew inspiration from the late Ming blue and white wares imported into Europe at the beginning of the 17th century. Whilst producing such obviously derivative wares, English painters also innovated their own styles and themes. The 'blue-dash' Adam and Eve and portrait dishes are almost exclusively an English preserve. Commemorative events were popular such as the Seven Years War, the Jacobite Rebellion, the American War of Independence and even the first Balloon ascent (1784). With the invention of creamware, the days of English delft were numbered. The last factory to close was Lambeth at the beginning of the 19th century.

A Bristol delft blue-dash Adam and Eve charger, the couple with manganese hair flanking a green boughed tree with sponged blue foliage and red striped yellow fruits, rim chip, 34.5 cm. diam., early 18th C. **£1,100-1,300** *C*

A Bristol delft blue-dash Adam and Eve charger, 34 cm. diam., c. 1710. **£1,800-2,000** *C*

A Bristol delft blue-dash Adam and Eve charger, with a manganese boughed blue sponged tree with 5 striped yellow fruits, rim flaking and minor crack, 34.5 cm. diam., c. 1720-30. **£800-1,000** *C*

An Adam and Eve 'blue-dash' charger, the figures with manganese hair, probably Bristol, crack, 14⅛ in., mid 18th C. **£700-£800** *S*

An English delft Adam and Eve charger painted in blue, ochre, yellow and manganese, possibly Bristol, extensively damaged and repaired, 13¼ in., early 18th C. **£200-300** *S*

An Adam and Eve charger painted in blue, green, ochre and yellow, possibly Bristol, cracked and restored on rim, 13¼ in., early 18th C. **£300-350** *S*

An Adam and Eve charger, crudely painted in manganese, copper-green, blue and yellow, sponged blue trees in the background, 'blue-dash' rim, probably Bristol, repaired, 13 in., mid 18th C. (L.L.). **£400-500** *S*

A Lambeth delft Adam and Eve blue-dash charger, crudely painted in blue, pale turquoise and yellow, with a 'blue-dash' rim, repaired, 14 in., early 18th C. **£400-450** *S*

A Bristol delft blue-dash Adam and Eve charger, the couple taking iron-red fruit from the blue sponged tree, with a blue serpent hidden in its branches, minor cracks, 2 small chips to underside of rim and minor glaze flaking, 34 cm. diam., c. 1710-20. **£600-£700** *C*

An interesting polychrome saucer dish inspired by a metal prototype, painted in yellow, red, blue and green, the rim moulded, probably Bristol, damaged, 10½ in., c. 1710. **£300-350** *S*

A large Angarano dish, painted in blue and manganese with the triumph of Neptune, the border marbled in manganese, 49 cm. diam., c. 1700. **£1,200-1,500** *C*

A Savona blue and white tazza, the reverse with scrolling foliage, minor rim chips, 33.5 cm. diam., early 18th C. **£1,050-1,250** *C*

A 'Tulip' dish painted in blue, green, red and yellow, probably Bristol, chips on rim, 13 in., early 18th C. (L.L). **£750-950** *S*

Formerly in the W.L. Little Collection.

A delft 'Tulip' charger, painted in a palette of blue, green, red and yellow, the rim 'sponged' in blue, probably Bristol, cracked, restored, 13⅜ in., early 18th C. **£350-400** *S*

A Frankfurt blue and white dish, minor rim chips, 38 cm. diam., early 18th C. **£300-400** *C*

A Hanau blue and white dish, minor rim chips, 39 cm. diam., early 18th C. **£300-400** *C*

A Dutch Delft blue and white dish, 34 cm. diam., early 18th C. **£160-£200** *C*

The compartmented design derives from the Chinese export ware or Kraak porselein style which appeared in Western Europe over 100 years prior to the present Delft example.

A Netherlandish fluted flared dish painted in yellow, ochre and blue, minor rim chips, 30.5 cm. diam., early 18th C. **£150-200** *C*

A Dutch Delft blue and white dish, rim chips, 35 cm. diam., early 18th C. **£110-150** *C*

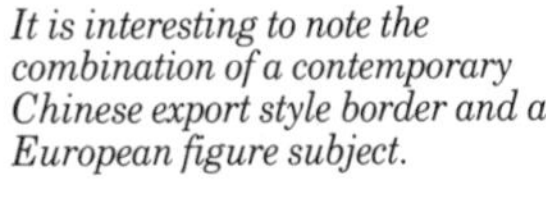

It is interesting to note the combination of a contemporary Chinese export style border and a European figure subject.

A London blue and white dish, painted with a central 'sunflower' motif, chips on rim, 11½ in., early 18th C. (L.L.). **£150-200** *S*

A rare 'Union' plate painted in blue with a stylised rose and thistle, below a crown flanked by the initials 'GR', probably Lambeth, chips, crack, 8⅝ in., c. 1715. (L.L.). **£1,300-1,600** *S*

Although the twenty-five Articles of Union were drawn up in 1707, thus uniting England and Scotland under one parliament, wares commemorating this event were still being made early in the reign of King George I.

A plate painted with a bird delineated in blue and with a red head and wing feathers, its body and the tree foliage 'sponged' in greyish green, within a blue 'loop-and-dash' border, Lambeth or Bristol, flaking on rim, 8¾ in., c. 1720. (L.L.). **£800-900** *S*

Two Bristol delft polychrome dishes painted in underglaze blue, green and overglaze iron-red, minor rim flaking, 32.5 cm. diam., c. 1730. **£350-400** *C*

A large Bristol 'Royal Portrait' dish painted in blue, red and green with, in the centre, a portrait of King George I with initials 'G R', within a 'three-brick' and whorl border, the reverse with crosses and dashes in blue, numeral 4 within the footrim, restored, 13⅜ in., c. 1720. (L.L.). **£1,900-£2,200** *S*

Formerly in the Freeth Collection.

A Bristol dish, painted in blue, red and green with an 'acrobatic' bird in flight, the reverse with crosses and dashes in blue, chips, some wear, 13½ in., c. 1730-40. (L.L.). **£350-450** *S*

A Lambeth 'Merryman' plate, 8½ in., c. 1730. **£320-350** *JHo*

A Bristol dish, freely painted in blue, red and green, the reverse with crosses and dashes in blue, typical flaking on rim, 13¼ in., c. 1730-40. (L.L.). **£300-400** *S*

A Bristol dish of saucer shape, painted in pale blue, chips on rim, some wear, 11¾ in., c. 1720-30. (L.L.). **£180-240** *S*

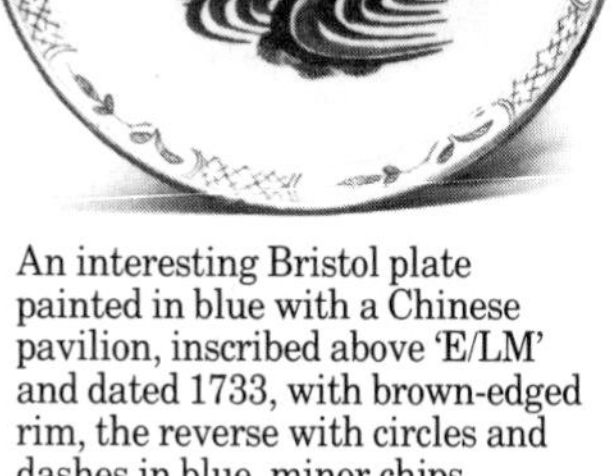

An interesting Bristol plate painted in blue with a Chinese pavilion, inscribed above 'E/LM' and dated 1733, with brown-edged rim, the reverse with circles and dashes in blue, minor chips, 8⅝ in. (L.L.). **£450-500** *S*

See Britton p. 155, no. 10.33 for another example from this set. The author attributes the plate to Joseph Taylor of Redcliff Pottery. The plates commemorate the marriage of Lot Evans to Mary Bayly on 18th August 1733; the bondsman was Joseph Taylor.

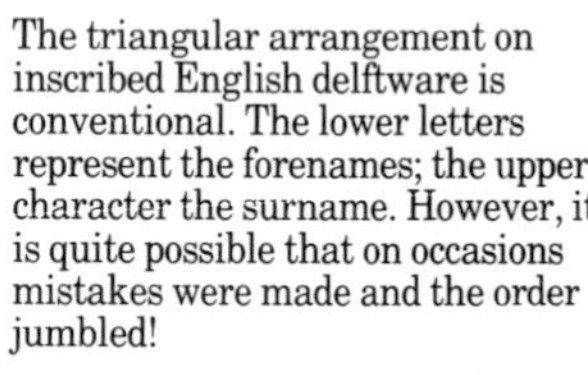

The triangular arrangement on inscribed English delftware is conventional. The lower letters represent the forenames; the upper character the surname. However, it is quite possible that on occasions mistakes were made and the order jumbled!

A Bristol saucer shaped dish unusually painted in blue, chips on rim, 11¾ in., c. 1720-30. (L.L.) **£180-240** *S*

Formerly in the W.L. Little Collection.

A blue and white salver or tea pot stand, the base washed in blue, probably Bristol, chips on rim, 5 in., c. 1720-30. (L.L.). **£700-800** *S*

Salvers of this type are more commonly raised on tripod feet.

A Bristol delft polychrome plate painted with a parrot, the wings and feathers enriched in green and yellow, within a blue line rim, chip to underside of rim, minor rim chips, 23.5 cm. diam., c. 1740. **£2,500-3,000** *C*

A pair of Bristol delft polychrome plates, painted in iron-red, green, yellow and blue, within blue line rims, one slightly stained, rim chips, 22.5 cm. diam., c. 1740. **£800-£900** *C*

A Bristol dish painted in yellow, blue, pale green and red, rim chips, 13 in., mid 18th C. and another, painted in blue, green and red, cracked, small repair, 13¼ in., c. 1740. **£220-280** *S*

Two small plates painted in blue, with 'sponged' trees and buildings in the background, one damaged, Wincanton or possibly Lambeth, 7⅝ in., c. 1740. (L.L). **£550-650** *S*

Compare this scene to the plate illustrated in Garner and Archer, pl. 123A, which has a similar bridge and tree arrangement, mounds in the middle-ground and birds flying in the same formation.

A set of 4 English delft plates, each with an octagonal panel, the rim with 'A.H.T.' and dated 1740, all in underglaze blue with a powder manganese ground, probably Wincanton, glaze chips to rim, 22.5 cm. **£1,800-2,200** *Bea*

A document attached to one of the plates claims they were made for a family with the name of Taunton. Following the convention regarding the arrangement or order of the letters and also the fact that family histories are all too frequently apocryphal, it is more likely that the surname begins with the letter 'A'. That the family came from Taunton would seem more plausible.

An inscribed and dated Lambeth plate painted in blue, inscribed and dated 1733, the border 'scratched' with C-scrolls, repaired, 8½ in., 1733. **£250-300** *S*

A Bristol blue and white dish, chip on rim, 13¼ in., c. 1740-50. **£150-£200** *S*

A plate painted in blue with a rural landscape with 'sponged' trees and a building in the background, minor hair-crack on rim, possibly Wincanton or Lambeth, 9 in., c. 1740-50. (L.L). **£400-500** *S*

This figure appears to be a mirror image of a lady seen on a plate illustrated in Garner and Archer, pl. 123A and is probably taken from a print.

An inscribed and dated Bristol plate painted in tones of blue, inscribed 'T/IE' and dated 1748, the reverse with dashes and crosses in blue, chips and slight restoration on rim, 9 in., 1748. (L.L). **£400-£500** *S*

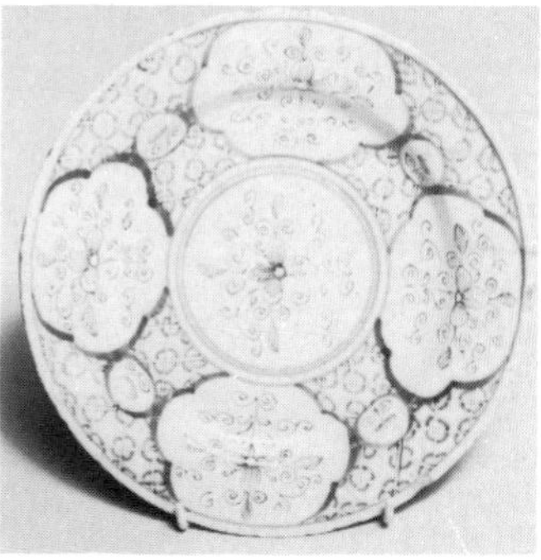

A mid 18th C. monochrome delft plate, 8½ in. **£60-75** *JHo*

A Lambeth plate painted in green, manganese, blue, red and green, rim chips, 9 in., mid 18th C. **£300-£400** *S*

A 'Fazackerly' plate, probably Liverpool, restoration, 9⅛ in.; and a Lambeth polychrome plate typically decorated with a seated Chinaman in a hilly landscape, cracked, chipped, 9 in.; both mid 18th C. (L.L). **£160-200** *S*

An English polychrome plate, 9 in., mid 18th C. **£100-120** *JHo*

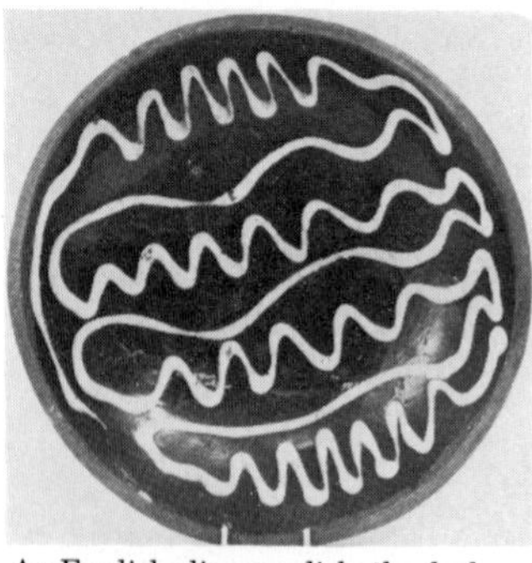

An English slipware dish, the dark-brown ground trailed with a continuous line and meander design in cream, unglazed back, 34.8 cm., 18th/19th C. **£650-750** *SS*

A large Bristol dish painted in bright blue, chips, 17¼ in., c. 1750. (L.L). **£1,100-1,300** *S*

A rare Irish octagonal dish 'pencilled' and painted in blue, the yellow-edged lobed rim with a demi-floret and trellis border, chips, some wear, 19⅝ in., mid 18th C. **£250-350** *S*

The design closely follows a 'Compagnie-des-Indes' original.

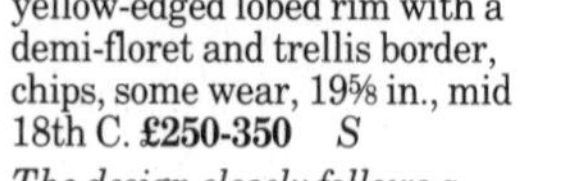

A Liverpool plate painted in sage-green, iron-red, purple, blue and yellow, the reverse inscribed 'B/H*M' and dated 1754, the under-rim with blue 'herbal sprigs', hair-crack around base, chips on rim, 8¾ in., 1754. (L.L). **£500-600** *S*

An English polychrome plate, 8¾ in., c. 1750. **£200-220** *JHo*

An unusual 'mimosa' pattern dish, painted in blue, red and green, Bristol or possibly Wincanton, typical wear on rim, 11⅞ in.; and a blue and white 'mimosa' pattern dish, probably Lambeth, small chips, small hair-crack, 12¼ in.; both mid 18th C. (L.L). **£200-250** *S*

An 18th/19th C. Staffordshire slipware dish, 13 in. diam. **£400-£500** *JHo*

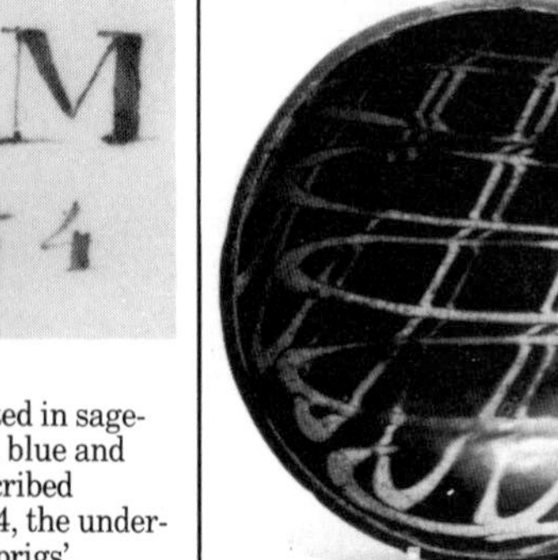

A slipware shallow circular dish, the dark-brown ground decorated in cream slip, 27.5 cm., 18th/19th C. **£500-600** *C*

Three blue and white octagonal plates, the first two probably Liverpool with 'herbal sprig' markings on the reverse, the third probably Lambeth, painted with radiating petal-shaped panels and a 'whorl' border, chips, the first cracked, the last crazed, 8¼ in. to 8⅝ in., all mid 18th C. (L.L). **£220-£280** *S*

A Bristol landscape plate, 8¾ in., c. 1750. **£140-165** *JHo*

A Staffordshire slipware shallow circular dish, the cream ground naïvely decorated in dark-brown slip with a stylised cockerel, crack to rim, 28.5 cm. diam., 18th/19th C. **£2,600-3,000** *C*

Two rare Dublin octagonal plates painted in blue, one monogrammed 'NE' on the reverse, the other marked 'K', chips, 9¼ in., Henry Delamain's factory, c. 1755. (L.L). **£350-450** *S*

A Savona (Albissola) sponged-manganese circular tazza, repaired, manganese eagle and F mark of Folco, 33.5 cm. diam., c. 1760. **£300-£350** *C*

A rare Dublin pierced oval dish, the interior lightly moulded with trellis and basket-work and pierced with 4 trellis panels, painted in blue, marked 'R' in blue, chips, 9½ in., and another dish of similar form, marked 'W' (?) in blue, Dublin or possibly Liverpool, riveted, 10⅜ in., both c. 1755. (L.L). **£450-550** *S*

The pierced borders are derived from contemporary silver forms.

A 'Fazackerly' plate, Bristol or Liverpool, chips, 9 in., and another, painted with a central flower spray, cross in manganese on the reverse, Liverpool, large chip, 9 in., c. 1760. (L.L). **£140-180** *S*

A Liverpool delft polychrome dish, painted in tones of green, blue and yellow and outlined in manganese, glaze flaking and minor chips to rim, 34.5 cm. diam., c. 1760. **£500-£600** *C*

A Liverpool delft polychrome dish, boldly painted in tones of green, yellow, blue and manganese, minor glaze flaking and small chips to rim, 34 cm. diam., c. 1760. **£950-£1,050** *C*

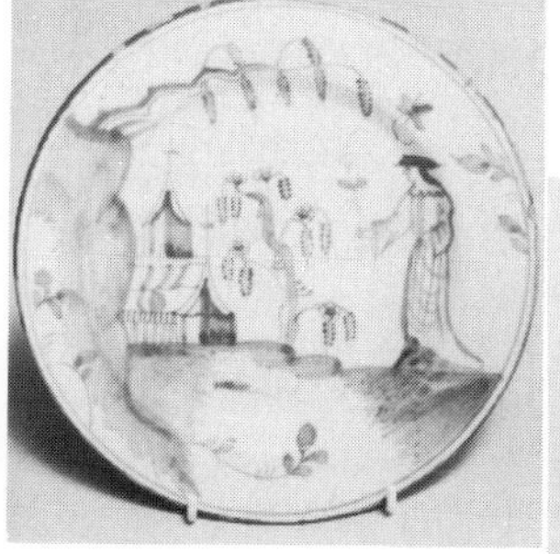

A Liverpool blue and white plate, 8½ in., c. 1760. **£75-85** *JHo*

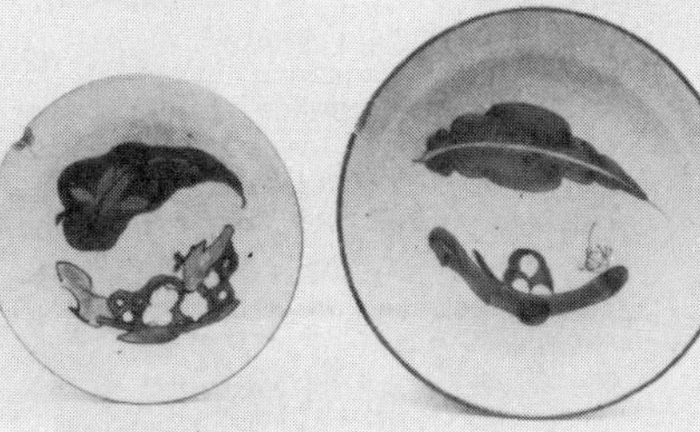

An unusual saucer dish of Chinese inspiration, glazed in pale blue and painted in blue, brown-edged rim, probably Lambeth, 10¼ in., c. 1760, crazed, chips, and a Chinese saucer dish, with similar decoration, four character commendation mark, Transitional, chips, small repair, 8¼ in., c. 1670. (L.L). **£380-480** *S*

An English delft plate decorated in the Ann Gomm pattern, 8¾ in., c. 1760. **£85-95** *JHo*

A polychrome Liverpool plate, 12 in., c. 1760. **£250-300** *JHo*

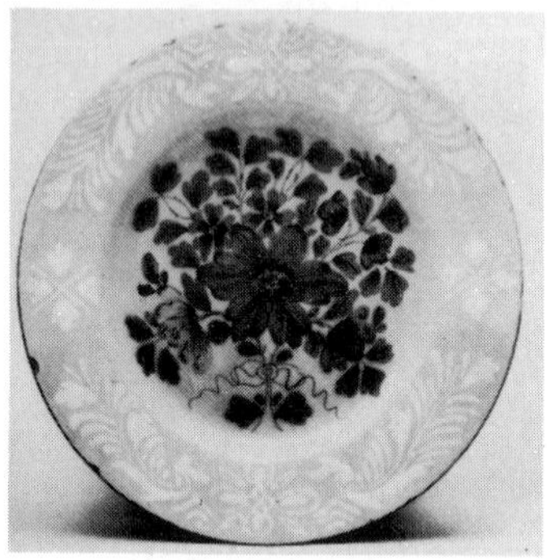
A 'bianco-sopra-bianco' plate painted in 'Fazackerly' style, Bristol or Liverpool, chips, 8⅞ in., c. 1760. (L.L). **£400-500** *S*

A delft chinoiserie dish painted in pale blue, Bristol or perhaps Liverpool, riveted crack, 12¾ in., c. 1760. (L.L). **£120-180** *S*

Compare with a plate illustrated in Garner and Archer pl. 95B, which is dated 1760 and shows a similar mound on the left with a spiky plant and an almost identical single-leafed stem growing from a fence on the right-hand side.

A blue and white plate, probably Bristol, c. 1760. **£400-450** *AG*

An English delft monochrome dish, cracked ice pattern, 13¾ in. diam., c. 1760. **£180-200** *JHo*

A Liverpool plate, painted in manganese, blue, green and yellow, 13½ in., c. 1760. **£250-350** *S*

A very rare 'Royal Portrait' marriage plate painted in blue and manganese with a profile bust-portrait of George III wearing a sash and Garter star, probably Lambeth, chips on rim, 8¾ in., c. 1761. (L.L). **£4,000-5,000** *S*

This plate commemorates the marriage of King George III and Queen Charlotte. This monarch is rarely depicted on delftware.

A dated Bristol 'bianco-sopra-bianco' plate painted in blue, inscribed above 'ASTM' and dated 1761 below, chips on rim, 8⅞ in., 1761. (L.L). **£280-360** *S*

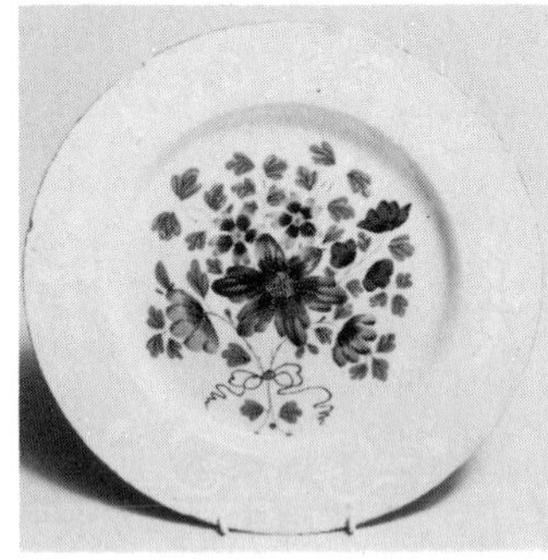
A polychrome plate with 'bianco-sopra-bianco' border, 11¾ in., c. 1760. **£240-260** *JHo*

A Bristol dish painted in blue, the rim in 'bianco-sopra-bianco', 13⅛ in., c. 1760. **£150-250** *S*

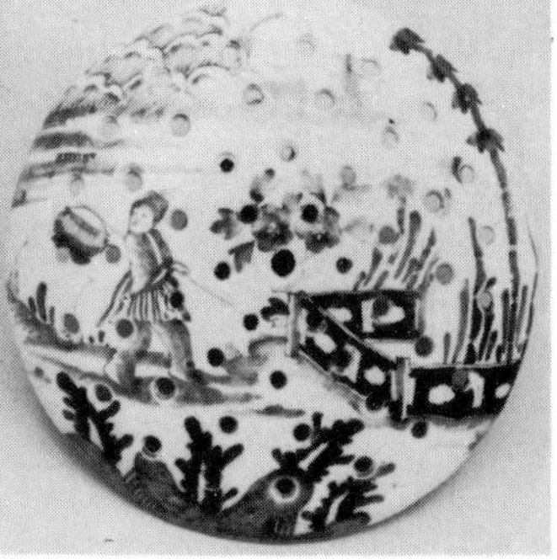
A circular drainer with overall perforations, painted in dark blue, probably Lambeth, chips under rim, 7½ in., c. 1760. (L.L). **£520-£620** *S*

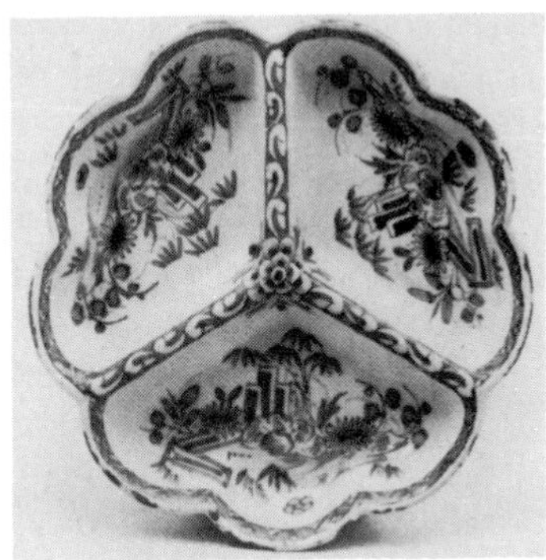

A Liverpool sweetmeat dish painted in blue with an Oriental garden scene, small hair cracks, typical wear on rim, 6¾ in., c. 1760. (L.L). **£220-280** *S*

Formerly in the Lane Collection.

An unusual octagonal 'powder blue' plate of small size, probably Lambeth, chipped, 6⅜ in., c. 1760-65. **£500-600** *S*

The decoration compares almost exactly with Bow porcelain 'powder blue' wares of this period.

A rare 'black enamel' plate, the underside with 3 blue 'whiplashes' and a central single leaf, probably Liverpool, chips on rim, 8¾ in., c. 1760. (L.L). **£400-500** *S*

A Liverpool plate painted in a 'Fazackerly' palette, in manganese, sage green, blue and pale yellow, wear on rim, 8½ in., c. 1760. (L.L). **£180-220** *S*

Louis Lipski Collection: Part III The initials (L.L.) have been included after pieces sold at the above sale on 1st March 1983. The editors felt it was important to single these pieces out as this collection has stimulated great interest and hence prices may not always be regarded as totally representative. It was felt nonetheless that this highly important sale should be documented as it assists with the identification of some rare examples of the great delft factories in this country.

A Liverpool plate, the reverse inscribed 'C, & E, Birdsall' and dated '14th Jany., 1765', the under rim with blue herbal sprigs, small chips on rim, 9 in., 1765. (L.L). **£650-750** *S*

A Whieldon plate, 9 in., c. 1765. **£100-125** *JHo*

A rare delftware plate transfer printed in black by Sadler with a fanciful coat-of-arms for a huntsman, damaged, 9 in., c. 1760-70. (L.L). **£1,600-2,000** *S*

From the Ernest Allman Collection. Delftware decorated with transfer prints is rare.

Two Lambeth blue and white dishes, within a border of whorl motifs, small chips, 10½ in., c. 1760-70. (L.L). **£250-350** *S*

A large Irish octagonal dish painted in inky tones of blue, riveted, hair crack, 22½ in., c. 1760-70. **£300-400** *S*

The unusually 'busy' design following a Chinese pattern immediately suggests an Irish provenance.

CREAMWARE

A type of fine pottery originated in the late 1740's but was not fully developed until 1765 when Wedgwood produced a superior body for which he coined the term Queen's ware in honour of Queen Charlotte. This pottery proved so successful that it was responsible for the demise of most European factories producing tin-glaze earthenware.

A Derbyshire creamware plate, 7½ in., c. 1765. **£55-60** *JHo*

A pair of Zurich faience plates, painted in purple, the rims with traces of dentil gilding, 20.5 cm. diam., c. 1775. **£1,200-1,600** *C*

A Wedgwood/Whieldon dish with pierced lattice-work rim, picked out in rich translucent green, yellow and aubergine glazes, 11 in., 1770's. **£400-500** *SC*

A Lambeth delft blue and white dated dish, the centre with the initials RSC 1776, 34.5 cm. diam. **£250-350** *C*

A polychrome delft plate decorated to commemorate Lunardi's balloon ascent, Lambeth, 1784, 11¾ in. **£600-650** *AG*

An inscribed and dated Lambeth plate painted in inky blue inscribed 'Thos. Stevens' and dated 1784, 9 in., 1784, and a shallow bowl decorated en suite but without the inscription and date, 8¾ in., c. 1784, both with small rim chips. (L.L). **£300-350** *S*

A pair of English pearlware plates with feathered edges, impressed mark of Don pottery, 10 in., c. 1800. **£30-35** each *JHo*

A blue and white transfer printed tureen base with 'The Hop Pickers', 8½ in., c. 1810-20. **£50-60** *SH*

A pair of Leeds pottery transfer printed plates, 8 in., c. 1800. **£140-£165** *EC*

A Leeds blue and white transfer printed plate, 'Great Wall of China', impressed mark, 14 in., c. 1800-10. **£280-300** *SH*

A blue and white transfer printed meat plate, 'The Bee Master', 17 in. wide, c. 1825. **£250-300** *SH*

A set of 8 Mason's ironstone dessert dishes and a fruit stand, printed and painted in Oriental taste, printed crown and pelmet mark, c. 1830. **£350-450** *S*

Use the Index!

Because certain items might fit easily into any of a number of categories, the quickest and surest method of locating any entry is by reference to the index at the back of the book.

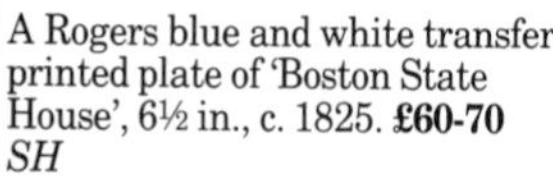

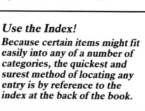

A Rogers blue and white transfer printed plate of 'Boston State House', 6½ in., c. 1825. **£60-70** *SH*

Made for the American market.

An Italian painted charger, 24 in. diam., c. 1850. **£200-250** *IHA*

A Wedgwood creamware dish painted by E. Lessore, signed, ochre-lined rim, impressed mark and date code for 1861, 21.8 cm. **£250-330** *S*

A large Minton 'Limoges Enamels' tazza painted by Thos. Allen, signed and dated, the reverse gilt against the black ground, painted mark, 1862, 18½ in. **£300-350** *S*

A rare Nevers faience campana-shaped jardiniere, picked out in blue and manganese, the foot rim with a border of stiff leaves, also in blue and manganese, restored, 38.5 cm., late 17th C. **£300-400** *P*

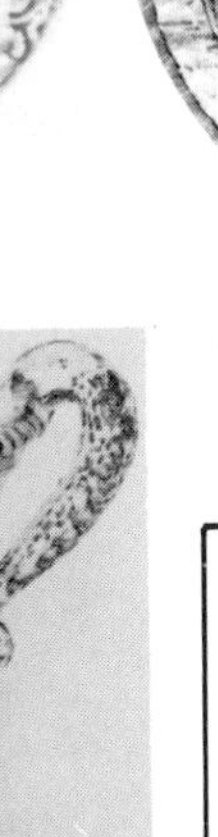

FRENCH FAIENCE

Production began in the 16th century mostly following the Italian styles. The term itself derives from a corruption of the word Faenza (a town in North East Italy). For most of the 17th century Chinese themes were popular but towards the end of the century an indigenous style was developed. This formal style was based on contemporary metalwork or silverwork which evolved into the STYLE RAYONNANT which is perhaps most strongly identified with Rouen.

From about the middle of the 18th century after another marriage to the contemporary Chinese 'famille verte' porcelain French painters introduced a new sophisticated style under the influence of the Lowenfinck brothers. Low fired or *petit feu* enamels were used to decorate faience. The celebrated *fleurs de Strasbourg* are a product of this period. Faience like Delft suffered a fatal blow as a result of the introduction of creamware pottery.

A rare Bristol plant pot decorated in blue with Chinese ruyi head borders, damaged, 6 in., mid 18th C. (L.L). **£250-300** *S*

A pair of Minton 'Majolica' jardinieres, each painted in brightly coloured glazes, impressed mark, one handle chipped, 15½ in., c. 1870. **£700-800** *S*

A large Minton 'Majolica' jardiniere and stand, in typical colours, rim crack, 154 cm. overall, c. 1865. **£650-850** *S*

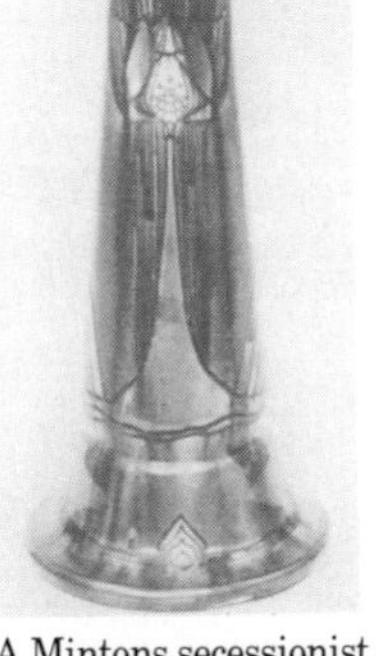

A Mintons secessionist jardiniere and stand, tube lined in green with streaked ochre and green against a ruby-red ground, chips to foot rims, printed mark, No. 72, incised shape numbers 3472 and 3469, impressed mark and date code for 1910, 101 cm. overall. **£750-850** *S*

A Minton 'majolica' Jardinière, glazed in blue, green, ochre and brown, the interior lilac, 10½ in., impressed mark, shape number and date code for 1864, glaze chips. **£300-350** *S*

A Caffaggiolo waisted albarello for Micreta, on a blue ground incised in white and ochre, repair to neck, chip to foot, c. 1520. **£650-750** *C*

Two Castel Durante small albarelli for Pilole stomance and Il Pile Agregative, damages, 14.5 cm. high, c. 1550. **£2,000-2,300** *C*

A Faenza a Quartieri armorial albarello painted in the bottega of Virgiliotto Calamelli, reserved in yellow and ochre on a blue ground, chips to neck and foot, 29 cm. high, c. 1550. **£1,200-1,400** *C*

Two albarelli from the same pharmacy are in the British Museum.

A pair of Venice albarelli painted with wild boar, a hare, and ostrich-like birds, one with hole in base, 15.5 cm. high, mid 16th C. **£1,300-£1,600** *C*

A Deruta armorial wet-drug jar for Diamoronne, dated 1562, chips to glaze, 24.5 cm. high. **£800-900** *C*

A rare dated Westerwald jar, grey stoneware body incised with stripes, diamond pattern, and sprigged with a panel bearing the inscription and date: 'OF.HI.NIT.ENIS/VAIA IVDAS.GE/SLECHT.1.5.9.1', 20.4 cm., 1591. **£850-1,050** *S*

A Naples armorial waisted albarello, minor rim chips and hair cracks, 19.5 cm. high, late 17th C. **£250-350** *C*

A Venice oviform jar on a blue ground reserved with marshal trophies, crack in base, 26 cm. high, perhaps late 16th C. **£1,500-£2,000** *C*

Miller's is a price GUIDE Not a price LIST.

The price ranges given reflect the average price a purchaser should pay for similar items. Condition, rarity of design or pattern, size, colour, provenance, restoration and many other factors must be taken into account when assessing values.

A rare dated London slipware jardiniere or jar, in dark red earthenware, decorated in cream slip with the initials and date 'W : B : M 1686', covered with a straw coloured glaze which ends unevenly around the foot, chipping, 10¾ in. diam., 1686. **£2,800-£3,400** *S*

The initials are almost certainly those of the people for whom it was made — possibly as a wedding gift.

A Lambeth delft blue and white wet-drug jar for HISSOPO. S named on a cartouche with a cherub's head above, glaze flaking to rim and spout, 18 cm. high, c. 1690. **£500-600** *C*

Cf. F. H. Garner and Michael Archer, op. cit. pl. 37 for an example dated 1684.

A Venice albarello with portrait medallions, on a dark blue ground, cracked, 16 cm., late 16th C. **£800-£900** *S*

A London wet-drug jar, decorated in blue below the spout with a label inscribed 'S. PECTOR', handle missing, foot and spout chipped, 7 in., late 17th C. (L.L). **£220-280** *S*

A pair of Lambeth delft dry-drug jars painted in shades of blue, the labels inscribed 'U:SAMBUC' and 'U:POPULN', glaze cracks, one with small chip on rim, 7 in., c. 1700. **£1,100-1,300** *S*

A London wet-drug jar, decorated in blue with a label inscribed 'S. PECTOR', spout missing, 7½ in., c. 1700. (L.L). **£180-250** *S*

A pair of Lambeth delft dry-drug jars painted in shades of blue, the labels inscribed 'C:RUTAE' and 'C:MALVAE', glaze cracks, one with cracks, 7 in., c. 1700. **£1,600-£1,800** *S*

An early 18th C. English delftware wet-drug jar, 6¾ in. **£420-450** *JHo*

A Lambeth delft inscribed and dated blue and white oviform drug jar, for C:CYNOSBAT, with initials and date WI 1738, body cracked, chip to rim and minor glaze flaking, 18 cm. high. **£1,100-£1,300** *C*

Twelve Lambeth delft blue and white small cylindrical drug jars, 5 with rim chips, 10 with painted tin tops, 9 cm. high, c. 1720. **£5,000-£6,000** *C*

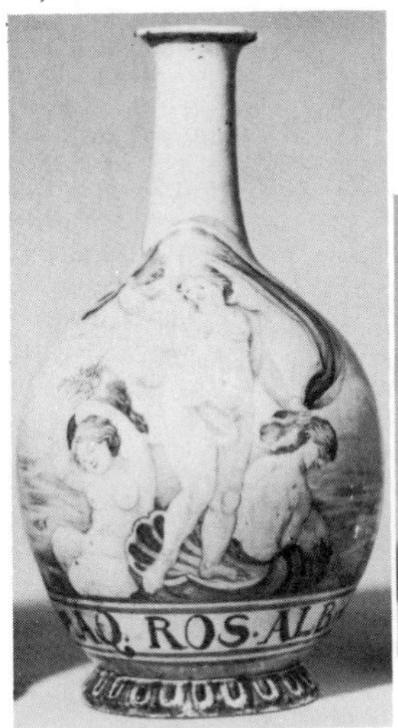

A Castelli drug jar painted in the Grue workshop, named contents AQ.ROS.ALB. and painted gadrooned foot, chip to foot and rim, 34 cm. high, c. 1750. **£700-£800** *C*

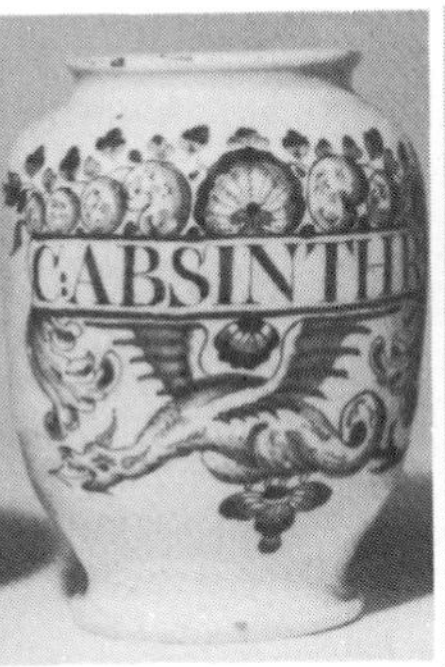

A Lambeth delft blue and white drug jar, for C:ABSINTHR, small hole to bottom, minor glaze flaking and crack, 18 cm. high, c. 1720. **£400-500** *C*

A dated Tuscan waisted albarello for Cofetioneame dated on the reverse 1624, 22.5 cm. high. **£350-£450** *C*

A large delft blue and white globular drug jar and a cover for E:MITHRIDATI, large chips to rim and foot rim, glaze flaking and cover extensively damaged, London or Bristol, the jar 31 cm. high, c. 1720-40. **£1,200-1,500** *C*

An early 18th C. blue and white English drug pot, 3¼ in. high. **£60-£75** *JHo*

A pair of Urbino Istoriato albarelli for Antidotus Enag and Diantos, rim chips to neck, 20 cm. high, mid 18th C. **£1,200-1,500** *C*

A rare blue and white English small pill pot, 3½ in., c. 1760. **£220-£240** *JHo*

A rare Lambeth jar in Chinese style, decorated in blue, rim chipped, 7¾ in., c. 1760. (L.L). **£400-500** *S*

A very close copy of Compagnie-des-Indes blue and white original but with the addition of a European style house.

A Dutch Delft blue and white tobacco jar, inscribed Marteniek, brass lid, 12½ in. high, 18th C., and another similar, inscribed St. Domingo, 10½ in. high. **£450-550** *CEd*

An early 19th C. Westerwald stoneware storage jar, 18½ in. **£140-150** *FF*

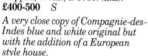

A blue ground wet-drug jar, inscribed SVDIVIOLATO RATO COL, 7½ in. high. **£200-300** *CEd*

A Moorcroft MacIntyre Florian-ware bonbonniere and cover, painted with iron-red and blue flowers on a salmon pink and deep blue ground enriched with gilding, printed MacIntyre mark, M.2412, 8½ in. high. **£180-240** *CSK*

A Westerwald stoneware jug, having a crowned 'G.R.' on a foliate ground in tones of blue below a manganese neck, 19.5 cm., early 18th C. **£200-250** *Bea*

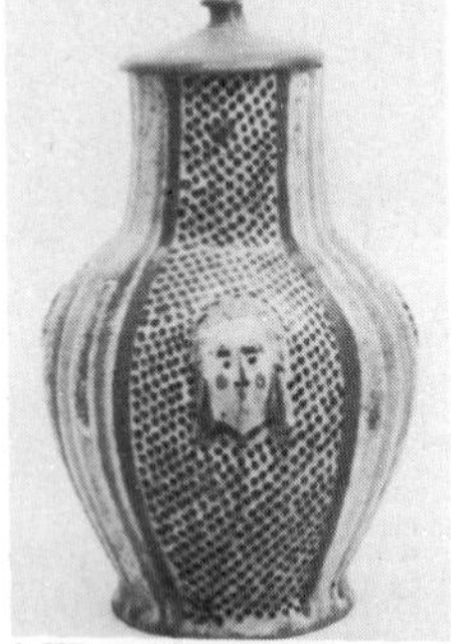

A Winterthur Hafnerware jug, probably from the workshop of the Reinhardt family, lead glaze applied with a mask and florettes, palette of ochre, green, blue and yellow, hinged pewter cover, some wear, 19 cm., late 16th C. **£450-£550** *S*

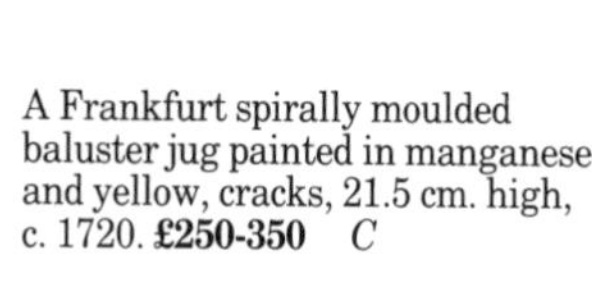

A Frankfurt spirally moulded baluster jug painted in manganese and yellow, cracks, 21.5 cm. high, c. 1720. **£250-350** *C*

A French polychrome faience puzzle jug, painted with a yellow flowerhead growing on a spray of blue leaves, probably Le Croisic, 16.4 cm., 18th C. **£60-80** *SS*

A Nottingham saltglaze stoneware bear jug, 9 in. high, c. 1745. **£400-£450** *JHo*

A Siegburg stoneware silver-mounted baluster jug, the neck moulded with 3 masks, dated 1624, minor chip to foot, the stoneware c. 1600, 16 cm. high. **£900-1,000** *C*

A Liverpool puzzle jug, one nozzle damaged, glaze chips, 7 in., c. 1750-60. **£250-300** *S*

An Erfurt baluster jug with hinged pewter cover, with a sponged manganese ground, minor chips to rim, 32 cm. high, c. 1760. **£400-£500** *C*

A Pratt hunting jug, 5 in., c. 1780. **£125-150** *GCA*

A creamware inscribed and dated baluster jug inscribed in the manner of David Rhodes in black beneath the spout A: CORNS 1767, probably Yorkshire, 18 cm. high, c. 1767. **£750-850** *C*

An 18th C. large Dorset pottery cider jug, 18½ in. **£90-120** *FF*

A West Country harvest jug, red earthenware body decorated in cream slip, 10¾ in., late 18th C. **£500-600** *S*

A Liverpool pearlware jug with chinoiserie transfer decoration, 4¾ in. high, c. 1800. **£45-55** *JHo*

A Prattware jug, 'mischievous sports, sporting innocence', 6 in., c. 1800. **£85-95** *EC*

A Pratt sportive innocence jug, 6 in., c. 1780. **£125-150** *GCA*

The open-ended reference system
Miller's Antiques Price Guide builds up year by year to form the most comprehensive photo-reference system available. The first four volumes contain photographs of over 30,000 stock items!

A pair of Proskau jugs modelled as parrots, painted with yellow and green plumage, restorations, 26.5 cm. high, late 18th C. **£1,200-£1,600** *C*

A creamware jug showing the Cooper's Arms on reverse, 9¾ in., c. 1805. **£385-425** *EC*

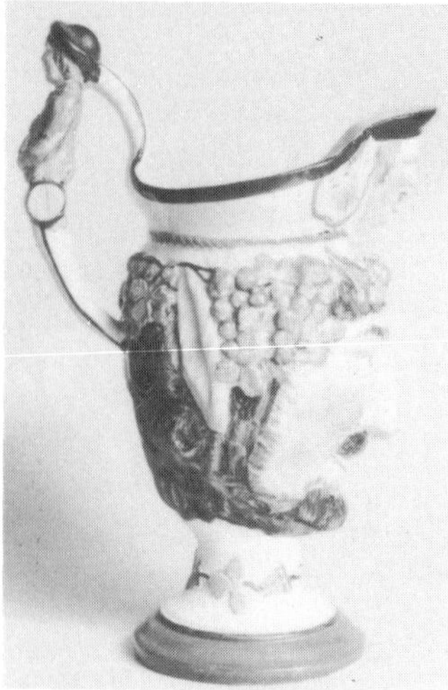

An Enoch Wood satyr jug, 10 in., c. 1800. **£120-150** *DL*

A Lambeth saltglazed stoneware 'Union' jug, moulded with the Royal Arms and various horticultural motifs, the glaze shading from deep brown to beige, incised 'Published According to Act of Parliament by T. Wetherill, Modler (sic), No. 1 Cleaver Street, Lambeth, London', 9¾ in. (24.8 cm.), early 19th C. **£150-£200** *S*

A rare Masonic Staffordshire jug, 9 in. high, c. 1826. Restored **£300-£350** Perfect **£600-900** *BP*

A Sunderland lustre pottery jug, 6 in. high, c. 1830. **£50-60** *WWW*

A large Staffordshire earthenware jug, 38 cm., mid 19th C. **£200-250** *SS*

A 19th C. Sunderland lustre jug, 9½ in. **£110-120** *TA*

A Doulton Lambeth stoneware jug decorated by George Tinworth, impressed mark, 1887, assistant's initials M.T., chipped spout, 18 cm. **£100-140** *Bon*

A Whieldon Toby jug, 9½ in., c. 1770. **£350-450** *JHo*

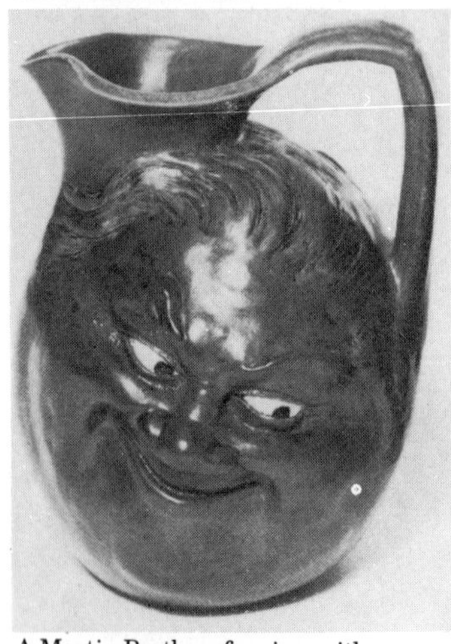

A Martin Brothers face jug, with a broadly grinning countenance beneath a shock of hair, glazed deep brown with white eyes, incised mark and dated 8-1903, 20 cm. **£500-600** *S*

An early Doulton jug incised by Hannah Barlow, minor rim chip, impressed mark, incised artist's monogram, dated 1873, 23.5 cm. **£200-£300** *S*

A Toby jug with unusual leaf motif base, 9½ in., c. 1770. **£365-435** *GCA*

(l.) A Ralph Wood Toby jug decorated in pastel colours, 9½ in., c. 1780. **£500-560** *DL*

(r.) A Ralph Wood Toby jug, with grey jacket and green waistcoat, 9½ in., c. 1780. **£540-620** *DL*

A Yorkshire Lord Howe jug, in brown, green and yellow, right hand and handle restored, 24.5 cm. high, c. 1790. **£750-850** *C*

(l.) A Prattware Toby jug, 7½ in. high, c. 1790. **£160-200** *DL*
(r.) A Prattware Toby jug, 9 in., c. 1790. **£280-340** *DL*

A 'Hearty Good Fellow' Toby jug, the whole coloured in Pratt palette, restored tricorn and mug with flaked enamels, 28.5 cm., late 18th C. **£300-400** *SS*

A late 18th C. Pratt 'Hearty Good Fellow' Toby jug, 11 in. **£375-450** *GCA*

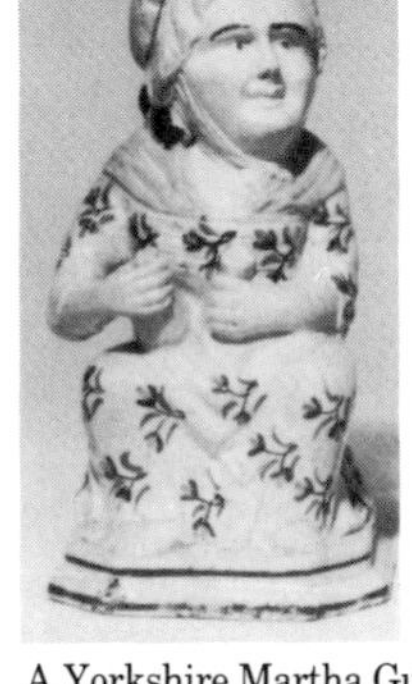

A Yorkshire Martha Gunn jug, the grotesque woman in olive hat, yellow scarf and flowered dress, holding a flask and glass, 27.5 cm. high, c. 1800. **£600-700** *C*

A Staffordshire miniature Toby jug of conventional type in brown hat, blue jacket and yellow breeches, 16.5 cm. high, c. 1800. **£450-500** *C*

A Sunderland Toby jug, 7 in., c. 1830. **£80-110** *FF*

A small mug, decorated in blue, London or Bristol, glaze crazed, 3¾ in., late 17th C. (L.L). **£1,200-£1,500** *S*

A set of 11 Wilkinson Ltd. First World War Toby jugs, each designed by Sir F. Carruthers Gould, one rim repaired, printed crowned lion mark, facsimile signature, retailer's mark for Soane & Smith, 1914-18, 25 to 33 cm. **£1,200-1,500** *S*

All but four of the set are sold with their original certificates.

A rare Lambeth cylindrical mug, painted in two shades of blue, chips and glaze cracks, 3½ in., early 18th C. (L.L.). **£800-900** *S*

A Whieldon octagonal baluster agateware small mug, striated with brown slip on a cream ground, rim chip, 6.5 cm. high, c. 1745. **£1,000-1,200** *C*

An 18th C. Fulham stoneware mug, 3¼ in. **£40-50** *FF*

A child's pottery mug, 2½ in. high, c. 1825. **£30-35** *EC*

A Leeds creamware Masonic mug, 5½ in., c. 1800. **£155-175** *EC*

A Castelli rectangular plaque, painted with an angel leading a young man away from a group of figures, ochre rim, slight restoration, 27.5 by 21 cm., 18th C. **£450-550** *P*

A Staffordshire saltglaze Jacobite baluster mug painted in colours with a portrait of The Young Pretender, with the inscription 'Our Prince is Brave, His Cause is Just, in God Alone, we put our trust', 13 cm. high, c. 1745. **£4,500-£5,500** *C*

No similar example would appear to be recorded.

A Castelli plaque painted with a scene from the life of Judas Maccabaeus, Grue workshop, ebonised and giltwood frame, 26 by 33 cm., c. 1740. **£1,600-2,000** *C*

A Castelli mythological plaque painted with Bacchus crowning Ariadne, Grue workshop, ebonised and giltwood frame, 25 by 32 cm., c. 1740. **£1,800-2,200** *C*

A Castelli rectangular plaque painted in the Gentile workshop, chip to top right hand corner, 18.5 by 26 cm., second half 18th C. **£850-£950** *C*

An unusual Castelli plaque, chip to lower left hand corner, 18 by 24 cm., mid 18th C. **£1,300-1,500** *C*

A child's pottery mug, 2¾ in. high, c. 1835. **£30-35** *EC*

A pink lustre mug, probably Staffordshire, dated 1852, 3½ in. **£50-60** *FF*

A Castelli plaque depicting St. Roch painted in muted enamel colours, slight glaze chip, in carved giltwood frame, 21.5 by 14 cm., mid 18th C. **£150-200** *Bea*

A pair of Castelli rectangular plaques, bearing reversed N and OE marks, 22 by 28.5 cm., perhaps 18th C., framed. **£900-1,100** *C*

A well modelled and well coloured Staffordshire plaque of a woman, within a black framed border outlined in yellow, 9½ in. high. **£650-750** *JHo*

A pair of Pratt circular plaques, 5¾ in. **£700-800** *DWB*

An early English pottery wall plaque, 6 in. wide, c. 1800. **£225-£275** *GCA*

A Prattware oval plaque with Ceres holding a scythe in one hand and a sheaf of corn in the other, in brown and ochre, the moulded rim washed in brown, 33 cm. **£300-£350** *P*

A pair of pottery plaques with unusual coloured borders, 7 in., c. 1835. **£200-230** *EC*

A Mexborough pottery plaque of Sir Toby Phillpot dated 1834 on reverse, 9¼ in. diam. **£225-250** *EC*

An English pottery wall plaque 'Teetotal Society', 7 in., c. 1840. **£80-110** *GCA*

A pair of Dutch Delft polychrome plaques, painted in underglaze blue, the rococo borders painted in enamel colours, 39 cm., 19th C. **£180-£230** *Bea*

A Sunderland lustre wall plaque impressed Dixon & Co., 9 in., c. 1855. **£75-95** *GCA*

A Sunderland lustre wall plaque, 9 in. wide, c. 1855. **£45-60** *GCA*

These tend to be less valuable with heavily religious sentiments.

A Wedgwood blue Jasperware plaque sprigged in white, impressed Wedgwood, cracks, framed and glazed, 15.5 by 59 cm., mid to late 19th C. **£150-200** *S*

A Wedgwood blue Jasperware plaque modelled in white relief with 'The Choice of Hercules', impressed Wedgwood, framed, 15 by 46 cm., 3rd quarter of the 19th C. **£200-250** *S*

Originally modelled in 1777 by William Hackwood.

A Dutch pottery plaque, painted and signed by Springer, framed, impressed mark, Joost Thoopt & Labouchèr, 19¾ by 14½ in., late 19th C. **£350-450** *SC*

A pair of earthenware plaques probably Copeland, painted by W. Yale, signed, with 'The Waning Year', or 'Ivy Bridge, Plymouth', 45.8 by 36 cm., c. 1800. **£400-500** *S*

A late 19th C. painted pottery wall plaque by Julius Richard, Milan, painted by Magna, in high relief, 21 by 16 in. **£250-300** *A*

A cylindrical posset pot painted in shades of blue, between blue-line borders, the double strap handles and the spout with 'blue dashes', probably London, cracks, 4⅜ in. high, late 17th C. (L.L). **£200-250** *S*

A Lambeth posset pot, unusually raised on three ball feet painted with blue dashes, painted overall in blue, green, red and yellow, restored, 8¼ in., late 17th/early 18th C. **£300-400** *S*

A posset pot and a cover 'trekked' in manganese and painted in dark blue, the cover with a 'mushroom' knop, probably Bristol, glaze flaking and restoration, 8 in. overall, early 18th C. (L.L). **£250-£350** *S*

It should be noted that when an auction house state 'and a cover' they are implying they believe the cover was not originally with the lower part.

A pair of Mettlach plaques, each decorated and signed by C. Warth, with girls allegorical of Spring and Autumn, incised and picked out in coloured enamels, impressed marks and numeral 1489, slight chips, 16⅝ by 10⅞ in. (42.3 by 27.7 cm.), late 19th C. **£250-300** *SC*

A 17th C. London blue and white posset pot, 10 in. wide, c. 1690. **£800-1,000** *JHo*

A Lambeth blue and white posset pot decorated with chinoiserie figures, 8½ in. high, c. 1700. **£520-£550** *JHo*

An early 18th C. Lambeth blue and white posset pot, 9 in. high. **£420-£450** *JHo*

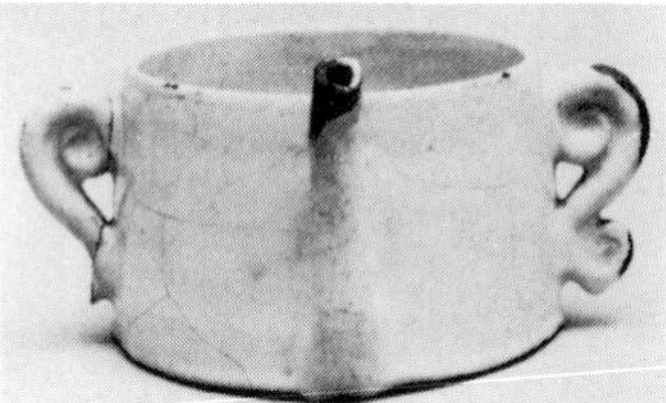
A London posset pot in the white, the thick tin-glaze with a pinkish tinge, one handle damaged and repaired, glaze flaking, cracks, 6⅜ in., c. 1670-80. (L.L). **£450-£550** *S*

A posset pot and a cover, washed in tones of blue and 'trekked' in manganese with Chinese figures, probably London, restoration and glaze flaking, cover damaged, 8½ in. overall, late 17th C. (L.L). **£400-500** *S*

A posset pot and cover, painted in dark blue, the pot with part of rim missing and flaked glaze, the cover damaged and repaired, probably Lambeth, 10½ in. overall, early 18th C. (L.L). **£300-400** *S*

A posset pot and cover painted in blue, probably Bristol, some damage, 9 in. overall, c. 1720-30. (L.L). **£300-400** *S*

A Bristol blue and white posset pot, handles repaired, and a cover, repaired and restored, c. 1720-30. (L.L). **£120-180** *S*

A Bristol posset pot painted in blue, red and green, cracks, slight restoration, 5½ in., c. 1730. (L.L). **£350-400** *S*

An inscribed and dated Bristol posset pot, 'pencilled' and painted in pale blue, inscribed 'Elizabeth Taylor' above the date 1743, restored, 6½ in. high. (L.L). **£750-£850** *S*

'Hauling in the Trawl', untitled, rope-twist border, 4 in. diam. (Ball 53). **£50-70** *N*

A rare earthenware posset pot, with a dark brown-lead glaze, incised with the initials and date 'IBM' 174-, spout damaged, perhaps Essex, 8¾ in., 1740-49. **£400-500** *S*

'England's Pride', titled, black background and beaded border, 4¼ in. diam. (Ball 149). **£95-115** *N*

'Fair Sports Woman', untitled, 4 in. diam. (Ball 250). **£50-70** *N*

'A Race for Derby Day', untitled, 4 in. diam. (Ball 257). **£60-80** *N*

'Pretty Kettle of Fish', untitled, square window panes, 4 in. diam. (Ball 48). **£60-80** *N*

'The Farriers', untitled, 4¾ in. diam. (Ball 324). **£30-40** *N*

'The Snowdrift', titled, 4¼ in. diam. (Ball 276). **£65-85** *N*

'The Blue Boy', untitled, 5 in. diam. (Ball 174). **£50-60** *N*

The late Prince Consort, a medium lid (Ball 153). **£55-65** *S*

'A Letter from the Diggings', titled, 4¼ in. diam. (Ball 360). **£60-70** *N*

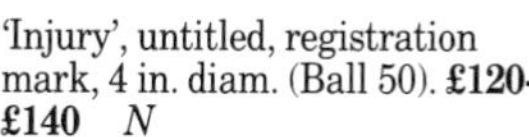

Allied Generals, a large lid, slight crack (Ball 168). **£80-100** *S*

'Injury', untitled, registration mark, 4 in. diam. (Ball 50). **£120-£140** *N*

'Embarking for the East', titled, line and scroll border, 4 in. diam. (Ball 206). **£50-60** *N*

Prince and Princess of Wales on their marriage in 1863, a medium lid (Ball 157). **£130-180** *S*

A Leeds creamware duck sauceboat, his tail forming the lip, cracked, 19.5 cm., c. 1770. **£350-£400** *C*

A Whieldon type 'duck' sauce boat, painted in manganese, green and ochre, crack, 7½ in. (19 cm.), c. 1770. **£200-250** *S*

A Spode Copeland's dessert service, painted by F. Furnivall, signed, with a royal blue ground border, comprising: 12 plates, 4 tazze and 2 fruit stands, printed mark, painted pattern number R3639, impressed date codes, mainly for 1908, one plate repaired, plate 23.4 cm. **£500-£600** *S*

An Ashworth's 37-piece dinner service, in underglaze blue, red, green and ochre enamels, plates 26.2 cm., mid 19th C. **£300-350** *Bea*

A Prattware dessert service, each piece bearing a print of 'The Mountain Stream', 'Landscape and River Scene' or 'The Two Anglers' (Ball 423, 416 or 432), comprising: 9 plates, 8 dishes and a fruit stand, some wear, plate 23.4 cm., c. 1860. **£300-400** *S*

A creamware 'dolphin' sauce boat, moulded with scales and edged in green, small chips, 8½ in. (21.5 cm.), c. 1780. **£150-200** *S*

An extensive Spode 'New Stone' dinner service of 81 pieces, in underglaze blue, iron-red and gilding, impressed marks SPODES/ NEW STONE and pattern no. 3504 in iron-red, 10 pieces slightly damaged, c. 1820. **£2,000-2,500** *S*

An extensive 117-piece Herculaneum earthenware dinner and dessert service, transfer printed in sepia and painted in colours, impressed 'Liver Bird' mark, pattern number 1917, some damage, c. 1835. **£1,500-2,000** *S*

A rare Wrotham Tyg by Henry Ifield, initialled 'HI' below the date 1668, the whole covered in a yellowed transparent lead-glaze, handle missing, some damage, 6⅝ in., 1668. **£1,200-1,500** *S*

A pair of extremely rare and fine Liverpool or Dublin delft sauce boats, painted in a pale blue with flowers in Chinese style, chip on rim of one, 8½ in., c. 1750. **£850-£950** *S*

This shape was also made in porcelain at Worcester.

A 20-piece Masons ironstone dinner service, impressed mark, c. 1820. **£280-360** *SS*

A Robinson & Wood blue and white 'Venetian Scenery' pattern 49-piece dinner service, transfer printed in blue, printed mark incorporating title, 1832-36, minor damage, dinner plate 26.5 cm. **£300-400** *S*

A Minton's 58-piece pottery service, each piece printed in bright blue, picked out with iron-red, registration mark for 1853, impressed marks, late 19th C. **£450-550** *SS*

A Westerwald stoneware tankard with a blue ground and blue and grooved line borders, 17.3 cm., c. 1700. **£400-500** *S*

A Liverpool delftware tankard, 5 in. high, dated 1745, some repair. **£750-850** *JHo*

A Bunzlau green-glazed melon-shaped tankard with pewter mounts and engraved A.E.R., 1756, minor glaze chips, 19 cm. high, late 17th C. **£1,000-1,200** *C*

A Thuringian faience tankard, manganese ground with blue and yellow line borders, hinged pewter cover incised 'No. 1/D/1768', minor chips and haircracks, 25 cm., mid 18th C. **£500-600** *S*

A Hanover pewter-mounted tankard, decorated in pale-blue with the horse of Hanover on a powdered manganese ground, the hinged pewter cover inscribed 'Jochim Breck, Wolt, 1757', chip, cracked, 8¼ in. (21 cm.), c. 1757. **£300-400** *SC*

A German faience cylindrical pewter-mounted blue and white tankard inscribed J.J.H. 1747, hair cracks, rim chip, 24 cm. high. **£900-£1,000** *C*

A Bayreuth faience pewter-mounted tankard with powdered lilac ground, dated 1756, struck 3 times with the mark of Peter Eschenbach (entered in 1730), 27.5 cm. high. **£900-1,000** *C*

SALTGLAZE STONEWARE

First manufactured in Europe from about the 14th century, the main centre of production being in the Rhine Valley at Cologne, Sieburg and Raeren. Similar ware was made in England at Fulham and later in Nottingham and Staffordshire. Although overtaken by other pottery such as creamware it nevertheless remained in continuous production almost everywhere.

It enjoyed a revival in England in the second half of the 19th century primarily through the efforts of Doulton and the Martin Bros.

A Liverpool stoneware tankard, marked Herculaneum, impressed, c. 1800. **£220-240** *JHo*

(l.) A Whieldon tea caddy by Greatbach, 5 in., c. 1760. **£420-£480** *DL*

(r.) A Whieldon tea caddy moulded with a bust of Flora, 6¼ in., c. 1760. **£550-600** *DL*

A Thuringian faience tankard painted with an oriental dancing, between manganese lambrequins with large green leaves, minor repair, 18.4 cm., late 18th C. **£400-£500** *S*

A Mortlake saltglaze stoneware tankard, the sides moulded with a scene after Teniers above a fox hunt, the rim silver mounted, makers' mark TR to the mount, foot chipped, 7 in. (18.5 cm.), late 18th C. **£60-80** *S*

A rare Whieldon chinoiserie tea pot and cover, the matching cover with griffin finial, all splashed in predominantly green and yellow glazes, picked out in blue and manganese, cover damaged, 16.5 cm., early 1750's. **£1,000-1,200** *SS*

Geoffrey Godden (British Pottery p. 101, fig. 125) illustrates a similar tea pot excavated from the Whieldon factory site at Fenton Vivian.

A Leeds creamware arched rectangular tea-caddy moulded with portraits of George III, 15 cm. high, c. 1765. **£350-400** *C*

A Staffordshire white saltglaze stoneware tea pot, 5½ in. high, c. 1750, slight damage **£255-265**, perfect **£430-450** *JHo*

Make the most of Miller's

When buying or selling, it must always be remembered that prices can be greatly affected by the condition of any piece. Unless otherwise stated, all goods shown in Miller's are of good merchantable quality, and the valuations given reflect this fact.

Pieces offered for sale in exceptionally fine condition or in poor condition may reasonably be expected to be priced considerably higher or lower respectively than the estimates given herein.

A Whieldon pottery tea pot, 4½ in. high, c. 1760. **£600-700** *EC*

A saltglaze stoneware enamel decorated tea pot, 4¾ in. high, c. 1755, minor damage **£450-500**, perfect **£640-660** *JHo*

A saltglaze tea pot, restored, 5 in., c. 1760. **£150-200** *DL*

(l.) A Whieldon brown glazed tea pot, 3½ in. high, c. 1770. **£300-£330** *DL*

(r.) An English coloured saltglaze tea pot, 3½ in., c. 1755. **£620-680** *DL*

A Wedgwood creamware tea pot, 6 in. high, c. 1770. **£425-450** *JHo*

A Whieldon tea pot, 5 in., c. 1770. **£320-360** *DL*

A small Prattware tea pot, 5 in. high, late 18th C. **£145-165** *EC*

A William Greatbach creamware cylindrical tea pot and cover, painted in the manner of David Rhodes, with Aurora in her chariot, chip to spout and rim, cover damaged, 21 cm. wide, c. 1775. **£300-350** *C*

A rare 'Popish Plot' tile, decorated in blue with 'The Execution of the 5 Iesuitts' (sic), London, possibly from the factory of Jan Ariens van Hamme, chipped, cracked, 4⅞ in. square, c. 1680. **£1,000-1,200** *S*

From the Hodgkin Collection. In 1679 five prominent members of the Jesuit Order were hanged for their alleged part in the 'plot'. This scene appears on the Three of Spades.

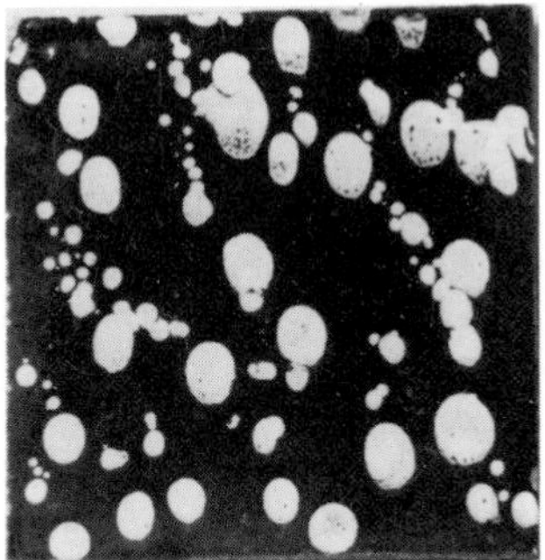

A Lambeth tile splashed in white on a 'bleu persan' ground in the manner of Nevers faience, 5 in. square, first quarter 18th C. (L.L). **£220-300** *S*

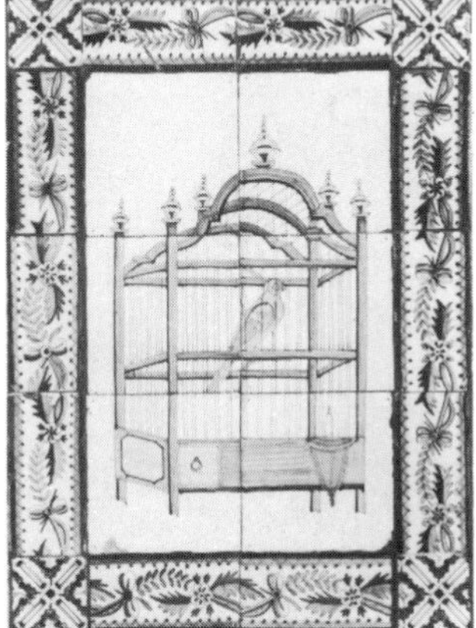

A pair of Dutch Delft polychrome tile pictures painted with yellow birds perched in bird cages, 2 tiles cracked, some minor chips, 53 by 40 cm. each, first half of the 18th C. **£400-600** *C*

Four Liverpool tiles, decorated with a blue, yellow and manganese bird with a bright red tail, blue leaf corners, damaged, approx. 5 in. square, 1750-75. (L.L). **£120-180** *S*

A blue and white Liverpool tile, rubbed, approx. 5 in. square, 1750-75. (L.L). **£70-90** *S*

A rare 'Popish Plot' tile painted in blue with 'The Plot first hatcht at Rome by the pope and Cardinalls' (sic), London, possibly from the factory of Jan Ariens van Hamme, one corner chipped, slightly rubbed, 4⅞ in. square, c. 1680. (L.L). **£1,300-1,500** *S*

From the Hodgkin Collection. The decoration of these 'Popish Plot' tiles is taken from a set of playing cards engraved in 1679 to commemorate the imaginary conspiracy by the Catholics against Charles II in 1678. This tile is taken from the Ace of Hearts.

A rare 'green ground' tile in red, green and blue, the corners with red carnation-heads, London, chipped, some mortar adhering to back, 5⅛ in. square, second quarter 18th C. (L.L). **£200-250** *S*

Two Biblical tiles decorated in blue with 'The Mocking of Elisha' and 'Tobias and the Angel', reserved on a powder blue ground, Liverpool, approx. 5 in. square, 1740-60. (L.L). **£150-200** *S*

These tiles belong to a very small group with biblical subjects reserved on a blue ground.

A London tile decorated in red, blue and green, reserved on a bright blue ground with red carnation-head corners, minor chips, 5⅛ in. square, second quarter 18th C. (L.L). **£90-120** *S*

Eighteen Dutch Delft tiles, each trekked in manganese and washed in blue with Biblical, pastoral or shipping scenes, ten in frames, 12.5 cm. square, 17th/18th C. **£400-£500** *SS*

Two London tiles decorated in blue, reserved on a powdered blue ground, minor chips, approx. 5 in. square, first half 18th C. (L.L). **£90-£120** *S*

A pair of Dutch Delft tile pictures of a cat and a dog, both painted in manganese, each made up of 6 tiles, 38.5 by 26 cm., restoration, late 18th C. **£450-550** *S*

Two Liverpool tiles decorated in blue, manganese, yellow and green, one corner missing, one tile damaged, approx. 5 in. square, 1750-75. (L.L). **£70-90** *S*

The decoration is probably derived from The Ladies Amusement, pl. 162.

Two Liverpool tiles decorated in blue, numerals in manganese, minor chips, approx. 5 in. square, second half 18th C. **£180-240** *S*

A Liverpool tile transfer printed in lilac by Sadler, chipped, another Liverpool tile transfer printed in black, damaged, and another Liverpool tile similarly decorated with the print in black and the glaze stained blue, one corner chipped, all approx. 5 in. square, c. 1760. (L.L). **£150-250** *S*

A rare Liverpool delft tile painted with a blue, yellow and brown auricula, wood frame, approx. 5 in. square, c. 1750-75. **£400-450** *S*

A Liverpool tile decorated in colours, chipped, 5 in. square, 1755-75. (L.L). **£250-300** *S*

This particular design is taken from the John Bowles drawing book of 24th November 1756.

Two Liverpool tiles, decorated in blue, numerals in manganese, minor chips, one cracked, approx. 5 in. square, second half 18th C. (L.L). **£100-130** *S*

A rare tile painted in sombre colours with a butterfly, possibly Bristol, 5 in. square, mid 18th C. (L.L). **£380-460** *S*

Two rare Liverpool tiles, decorated in blue, the panels showing a rearing horse on one and two cows on the other, minor chips, approx. 5 in. square, 1760-70. (L.L). **£200-£250** *S*

Two Liverpool tiles, one with a manganese rose on a green and blue stem, the other with a blue flower and 2 smaller red flowers, the first marked 6, the other 4, minor chips, approx. 5 in. square, mid 18th C. (L.L). **£250-320** *S*

Two Liverpool polychrome tiles, numerals in manganese, minor chips, one tile slightly pitted, approx. 5 in. square, second half 18th C. (L.L). **£280-360** *S*

Four Liverpool tiles, decorated in colours, some chips, approx. 5 in. square, second half 18th C. (L.L). **£200-250** *S*

Three Liverpool tiles each painted in blue, and reserved on a manganese ground, one with numeral in manganese, one chipped, approx. 5 in. square, second half 18th C. (L.L). **£100-£150** *S*

A Liverpool tile transfer printed in black with the glaze coloured slightly blue, signed 'Sadler Liverpl', and another Liverpool tile transfer printed in sepia with the same design, first tile pitted and chipped, second tile damaged, approx. 5 in. square, c. 1760. (L.L.). **£120-200** *S*

Two rare Liverpool tiles decorated in blue, on one 2 stags and the other 2 hounds, minor chips, 5 in. square, c. 1760-70. (L.L.). **£220-£260** *S*

The 2 stags are adapted from pl. III of The Ladies Amusement, and the 2 hounds from pl. 112.

Two tiles decorated in blue, possibly Bristol, one tile cut down, approx. 5¼ in. square, c. 1760-70. (L.L.). **£110-150** *S*

Two Liverpool tiles transfer printed in black by Sadler, one damaged, one chipped, c. 1760; and another Liverpool tile transfer printed in black, signed 'Green', chipped, all approx. 5 in. square, c. 1775. (L.L.). **£150-200** *S*

The print on the third tile is taken from Pillemont's Petits Parasols Chinois published in 1774. This print is the only one known with the signature 'Green'.

Two rare chinoiserie tiles, each painted in the centre in manganese, within bianco-sopra-bianco borders, Bristol, chips, approx. 5 in. square, second half 18th C. (L.L). **£220-£280** *S*

Both figures are after Pillemont and appear on p. 57 of The Ladies Amusement.

A Liverpool tile transfer printed by Sadler in black lightly stained in blue, a Liverpool tile transfer printed in grey by Sadler, minor chips, another Liverpool tile transfer printed in black by Sadler, rubbed minor chips, a Liverpool tile transfer printed in sepia, signed 'J.Sadler', edges cut down, and 3 other Liverpool tiles transfer printed by Sadler, all damaged, all approx. 5 in. square, c. 1760-70. (L.L.). **£200-250** *S*

See Ray III nos. 654, 653, 656, 635, 655, 634 and 644. We are sometimes asked why we include damaged pieces in this guide. The answer is simply because a large amount of available antiques are also damaged and perfect prices may well mislead.

A Liverpool tile transfer printed in sepia, signed 'J.Sadler Liverpl'; a Liverpool tile transfer printed in brownish black, signed 'Sadler, Liverpool'; and another Liverpool tile transfer printed in black by Sadler, minor chips, both approx. 5 in. square, c. 1760. (L.L.). **£100-£140** *S*

Four Liverpool tiles transfer printed in black by Sadler, chips, 2 tiles rubbed, approx. 5 in. square, c. 1760-70. (L.L.). **£150-200** *S*

Two Bristol tiles, with bianco-sopra-bianco borders, and another Bristol tile similar, one cut down, approx. 5 in. square, 1760-70. (L.L.). **£120-£160** *S*

Two tiles, both decorated in blue, possibly Bristol, one tile cut down, 5⅛ in. square, c. 1760-70. (L.L.). **£150-200** *S*

Four Delft polychrome tiles, painted with river scenes with boats, swans, churches and other buildings, on manganese grounds with blue trellis and scrolls in the spandrels, Friesian, 13 cm., 18th C. **£100-150** *L*

A blue and white tile picture, some tiles repaired, probably Portuguese, mounted in 3 panels, 148 by 221 cm. overall, 18th C. **£400-600** *C*

A William De Morgan 'Persian Style' tile panel, painted in bright blues, turquoise and greens against white, mounted in ebonised frame, each tile 15 cm. square. **£450-500** *P*

A Spode blue and white transfer printed tureen, base and ladle, with a pattern from Aesops Fables, c. 1830-33. **£180-220** *SH*

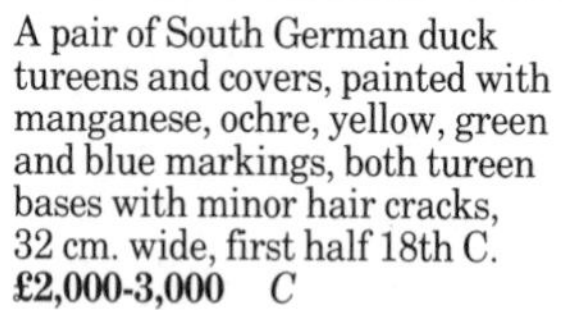

A pair of South German duck tureens and covers, painted with manganese, ochre, yellow, green and blue markings, both tureen bases with minor hair cracks, 32 cm. wide, first half 18th C. **£2,000-3,000** *C*

A Davenport creamware dish and cover, decorated inside, 10½ in. wide, c. 1805. **£45-60** *FF*

A creamware decorated small tureen, cover and ladle, 8 in. wide, c. 1790. **£165-185** *EC*

A pair of Frankfurt faience baluster vases, painted in Chinese Transitional style, 29 cm., late 17th C. **£320-380** *SS*

A Mason's ironstone tureen and cover painted in 'famille rose' colours, 12½ in. **£700-800** *DWB*

A Minton majolica game dish, painted in muted colours, impressed mark and date code for 1866, 34 cm. wide. **£300-350** *Bea*

A Dutch Delft ovoid vase decorated in blue with bands of 'mimosa' pattern, damaged, 9¾ in., c. 1750. **£120-180** *S*

A pair of Mason's ironstone sauce tureens and covers, decorated in underglaze blue, iron-red and gilding, in Oriental taste, impressed mark, 19.8 cm., c. 1825. **£200-300** *S*

A Savona two-handled baluster vase, rim chips, star mark, 19 cm. high, first half 18th C. **£200-300** *C*

A North German faience vase and cover, restoration to cover, rim, probably Berlin, 39.5 cm., c. 1760. **£900-1,300** *S*

A rare Bristol vase and cover, painted in blue with tall chinoiserie figures in a fantastic garden, damaged, 13¼ in., mid 18th C. (L.L.). **£350-450** *S*

A Wedgwood & Bentley black basalt oviform two-handled vase, the body moulded with The Dancing Hours, impressed Wedgwood & Bentley Etruria within a circle mark, minor damage to stem, 37.5 cm. high, c. 1775. **£1,000-1,200** *C*

A Wedgwood blue jasper-dip Portland vase, impressed mark, foot rim ground, 26 cm., early to mid 19th C. **£200-300** *S*

A Minton vase decorated with the 'Old Bogey' design by Dr. Christopher Dresser, printed, enamelled and gilt on a cream ground, restored, 28.7 cm., c. 1870. **£800-900** *S*

A Minton 'Majolica' 'Marine' vase, glazed in shades of turquoise-green, brown and sandy-pink, impressed Minton and numerals, date code for 1862, rim restored, 42.2 cm. **£150-£220** *S*

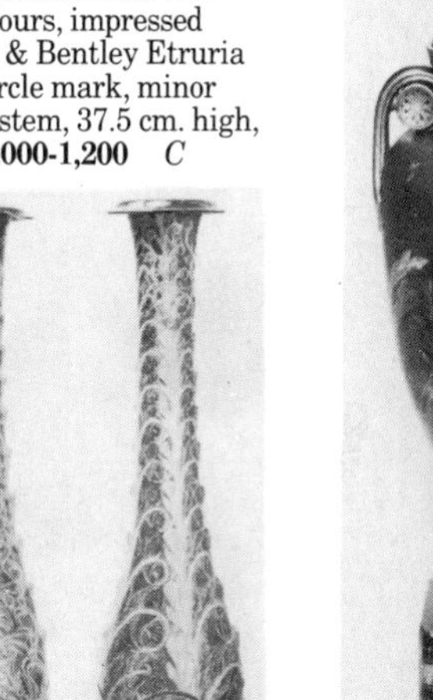

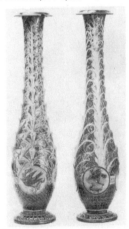

A large pair of Martinware vases, moulded, incised and painted in brown, green and deep blue enamels, incised with the serial No. 16 or 17 and R.W. Martin, London 2-1876, damage to one rim, 76.5 cm. **£500-700** *Bea*

A Minton's vase and cover painted by W. Mussill, signed, against a rust-brown ground, the rim, handles and foot gilt, impressed Mintons 1656, date code for 1876, knop repaired, gilding rubbed, 24¾ in. **£200-£250** *S*

A massive Rookwood earthenware vase, painted with 3 diagonal panels, divided by textured gilt painted ribbons, impressed Rookwood 1883 G. 54 cm. high. **£2,000-2,300** *C*

ROOKWOOD POTTERY

- **American factory producing art pottery**
- **founded by Maria Nichols in 1880 in Cincinnati**
- **employed painter Albert R. Valentien (1862-1925) to decorate wares**
- **only purely decorative wares produced**
- **much influenced by Japanese art**
- **early pieces, particularly those with a 'tiger-eye' crystalline glaze are particularly in demand**
- **some excellent Art Nouveau pieces produced**
- **factory still exists**

A pair of unusual Doulton vases decorated by Harry Barnard, impressed Lambeth mark, incised artists' monogram, 188 and 193, painted assistants' initials of Jane Hurst and Emily Welch, dated 1882, 28.5 cm. **£400-500** *S*

The artist and assistants are extremely important when valuing Doulton.

A pair of Wedgwood 'Three Colour' pot pourri vases and covers, the covers pierced, the white jasper body sprigged with lilac and sage green, impressed Wedgwood marks, 7⅝ in., 19th C. **£850-900** *SC*

A pair of Doulton vases decorated by Hannah Barlow, incised and glazed in ashen white and brown with foot and neck glazed olive green, impressed Lambeth mark, incised artist's and assistants' initials and numerals, 24.5 cm., 1890's. **£300-350** *S*

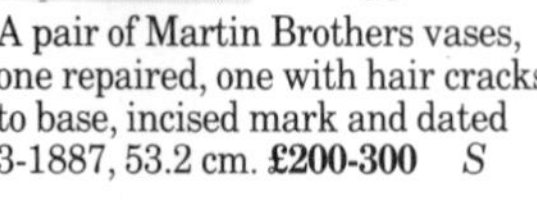

A pair of Martin Brothers vases, one repaired, one with hair cracks to base, incised mark and dated 3-1887, 53.2 cm. **£200-300** *S*

A pair of Doulton vases, by Hannah Barlow, impressed Lambeth mark, incised artist's monogram, 663 and assistants' initials of Louisa Russell and Bessie Newbery, one rim restored, 43.5 cm., 1890's. **£400-500** *S*

A pair of unusual Moorcroft Macintyre 'Florian ware' vases, with leaves rising from a blue decorated base, Florian mark and incised 'W. Moorcroft', 20.5 cm. high. **£300-350** *P*

A pair of Doulton vases decorated by Eliza Simmance, Lambeth mark, incised artist's monogram, 141 and assistant's initials of Mary Aitken, one foot chipped, 45 and 45.5. cm., c. 1895. **£450-550** *S*

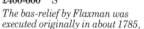

A large Wedgwood black jasper-dip vase and cover, one handle restored, knop repaired, 50 cm., late 19th C. **£400-600** *S*

The bas-relief by Flaxman was executed originally in about 1785,

A large Martin Brothers stoneware vase, with a blue glaze and sgraffito dragons in combat, their scales and feathery wings incised, signed on base 'Martin Brothers, London & Southall' and dated '1-1898', 46 cm. high. **£1,400-£1,600** *P*

A William De Morgan pottery vase with turquoise neck, decorated by Edward Porter, on a cream ground, impressed oval mark 'De Morgan, Merton Abbey', 23.5 cm. **£170-£200** *P*

A Martin Brothers vase, glazed in nut-brown on a brown ground, incised mark and dated 9-1899, 22.9 cm. **£300-350** *S*

A Della Robbia vase decorated by Charles Collis and Hannah Jones, in shades of green, pink, brown and yellow with hydrangea blooms, incised galleon mark and C. Collis, painted monogram of Hannah Jones, neck restored, 29.5 cm., c. 1900. **£350-400** *S*

A Della Robbia vase, decorated by Tom Hall and May Furniss, shades of green, yellow and red, incised mark, painted artists' initials, 29.5 cm., c. 1900. **£180-£220** *S*

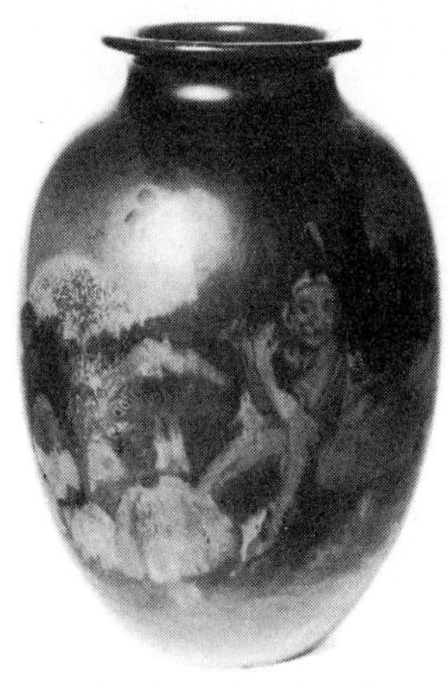

A Royal Doulton 'Flambe' oviform vase, probably decorated by A. Eaton, picked out in vivid 'Sung' colours of ruby, ochre, rose, violet and blue, c.m.l. & c. and 'Flambe' on base, 31 cm. high. **£650-850** *P*

A Pilkingtons Royal Lancastrian pottery vase, designed by Gordon M. Forsyth with a silvered classical design entitled POSEIDON, on royal blue ground, impressed standard and artists' mark and Roman numerals for 1909 and No. 2640, 17½ in. high. **£550-650** *GSP*

A Royal Doulton 'Flambe' vase, decorated on a ruby ground streaked with mottled blue, ochre, rose pink and pale green, c.m.l. & c. and 'Flambe' on base, 17 cm. high. **£80-100** *P*

A Doulton Lambeth 'Carrara' ware vase, decorated by Josephine Durtnall, in green and gilt, painted in panels by Ada Dennis, r.m. Carrara mark, A.D. and J.D. initials for artists, restoration on neck, 40.5 cm. high. **£280-320** *P*

A good Royal Doulton stoneware vase by Harry Simeon, decorated around the shoulders in browns, green and white, against a blue ground above a celadon glazed lower body, c.m. & l. initial 'H.S.' and number '520', 23 cm. high. **£140-180** *P*

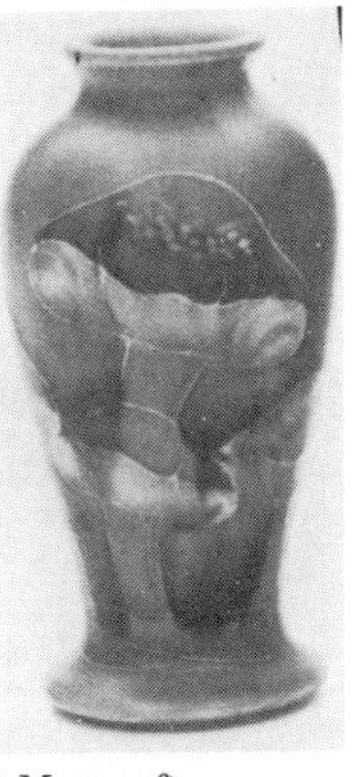

A Moorcroft miniature 'Claremont' vase, tube-lined in white with mauve, blue, yellow and olive, impressed Moorcroft Burslem, 10 cm., c. 1915. **£200-250** *S*

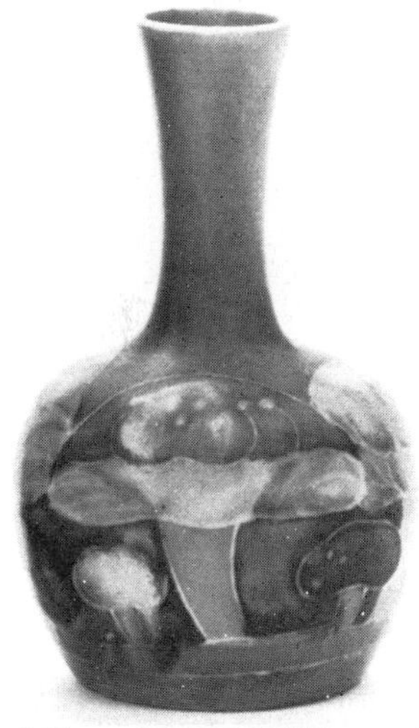

A Moorcroft miniature 'Claremont' vase, tube-lined in white with toadstools coloured in deep rose, mauve and yellow against an olive ground, impressed Moorcroft Burslem, painted initials in green, 9.4 cm., c. 1915. **£200-250** *S*

A large Wedgwood vase painted by Alfred Powell, in tones of green and blue, signed in cipher and 340, impressed mark, chipped and cracked, 28½ in., dated 1915. **£700-800** *S*

This was probably one of a set of vases designed by Powell for Sir Hugh Bell's house at Rounton, Yorkshire.

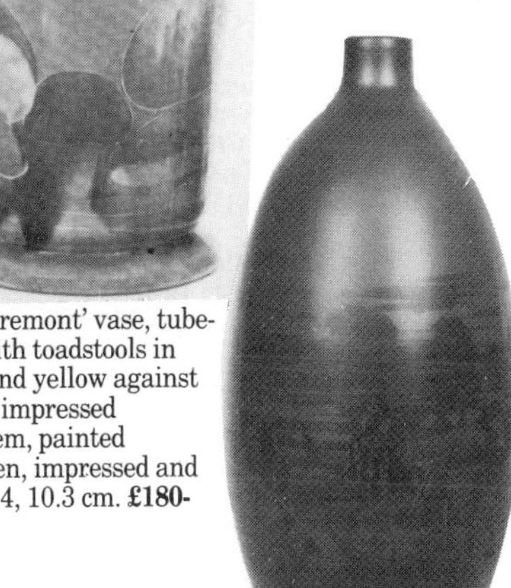

A Moorcroft 'Claremont' vase, tube-lined in white with toadstools in deep rose, blue and yellow against an olive ground, impressed Moorcroft Burslem, painted signature in green, impressed and painted date 1914, 10.3 cm. **£180-220** *S*

A Doulton Flambe vase, printed in black, reserved on a rich translucent red ground, black printed marks, 17 in., c. 1920. **£200-300** *SC*

A Moorcroft vase decorated in muted colours against an olive ground, facsimile signature, Royal mark and signed W.M., 31.5 cm. high. **£150-200** *P*

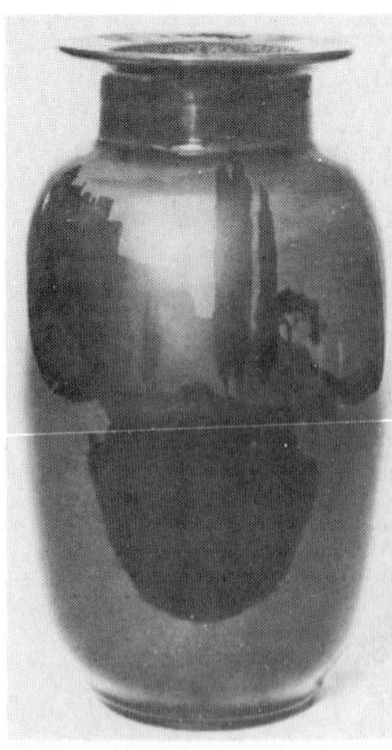

A Royal Doulton 'Sung' vase decorated by Noke and A. Eaton, signed, printed lion, crown and circle, Flambe, impressed Doulton, 7903, incised date 7-29, 38 cm. **£900-1,100** *S*

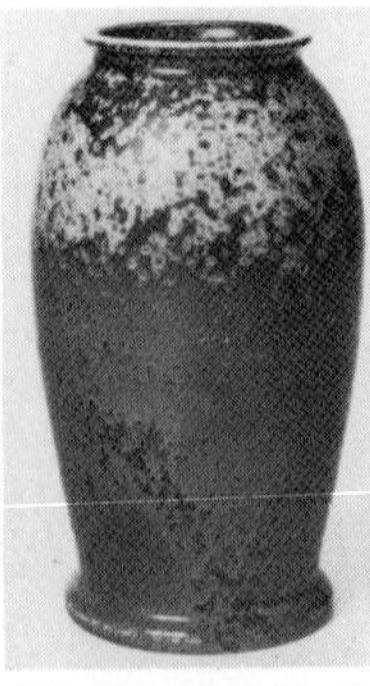

A Ruskin 'High Fired' vase, impressed, dated 1933, also signed 'W. Howson Taylor', 25.5 cm. **£250-300** *P*

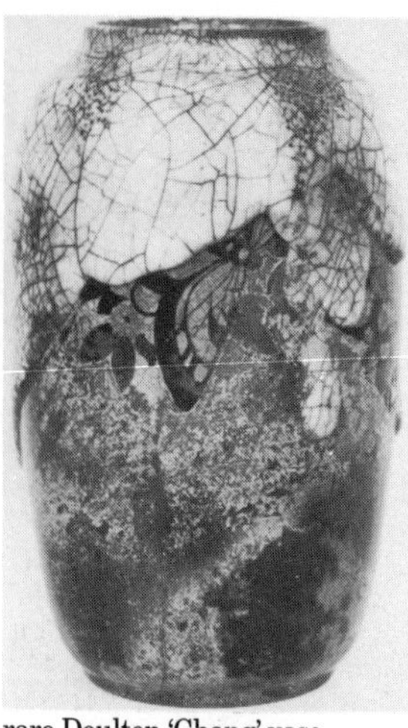

A rare Doulton 'Chang' vase, inscribed DOULTON, slight chip, 10 in., 1930's. **£600-700** *SC*

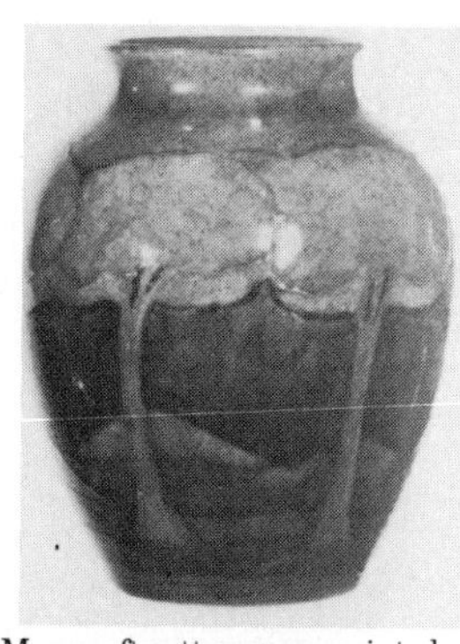

A Moorcroft pottery vase painted with the Hazeldene Moonlit Blue design, green and blue trees against a turquoise and deep blue ground, impressed Moorcroft mark, signed in green, W. Moorcroft, c. 1924, 8¼ in. high. **£450-550** *CSK*

A rare pair of Wedgwood crimson jasper-dip Portland vases, impressed mark, chips to reliefs, 15 cm., c. 1930. **£400-500** *S*

Crimson jasper dip was first produced experimentally in 1910, then attempted again in 1925-32. It proved a difficult colour, often 'bleeding' into the white reliefs, and was consequently used only for this short time.

A large late 19th C. sponged Wemyss pig, impressed mark Wemyss ware, 'R.H. & S.' (Robt. Heron & Son), 18½ in. **£300-600** *RdeR*

A Scottish Wemyss ware ink stand, impressed mark, 10½ in. wide, c. 1900. **£150-250** *RdeR*

WEMYSS WARE, c. 1883-1930

Robert Methven Heron introduced a group of continental artists into his Fife pottery in the 1880's. The very characteristic nature of Wemyss derives from their influence although roses, apples and cherries had been stiffly painted before.

Most of the artists returned home but Karel Nekola remained. Wemyss was always wanted by the rich and the ware was well supported by Scottish lairds.

Wemyss was fired at low temperatures to produce a biscuit body which would absorb the delicate brush strokes. Then it was dipped in a soft lead glaze and fired again at a low temperature. This accounts for the fragility of Wemyss and the relative rarity of exceptional quality pieces.

Nekola trained James Sharp, David Grinton, John Brown, Hugh and Christina McKinnon and they were later joined by Nekola's sons Carl and Joseph.

Karel Nekola tended to paint the large important pieces and also the commemorative pieces from Queen Victoria's Jubilee in 1897 until the Coronation of George V in 1911. He died in 1915.

Edwin Sandiland became chief decorator in 1916. The change in public taste after the First World War, with the introduction of the Art Deco movement, saw a move away from the traditional Wemyss designs. Various new designs were tried but by the time Edwin Sandiland died in 1928, the end was in sight. The Fife Pottery closed in 1930.

The Bovey Tracy pottery in Devon bought the rights and moulds of the Fife pottery and gave employment to Joseph Nekola, who continued the familiar decorations to a high standard until his death in 1952. Royal Doulton subsequently acquired the rights.

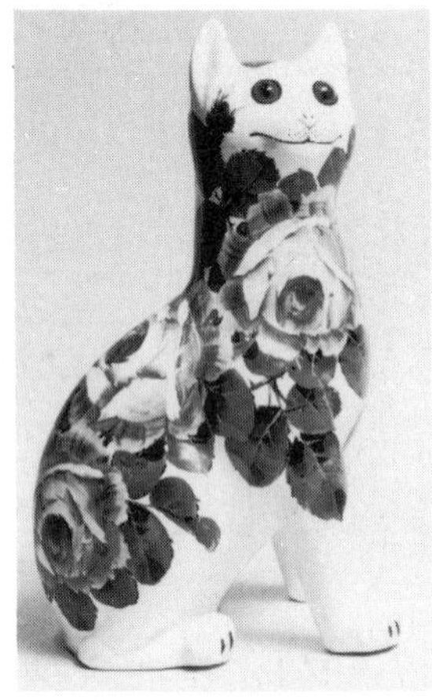

A Bovey Tracey Wemyss ware cat painted by Joseph Nekola, 13½ in., c. 1930. **£300-700** *RdeR*

The quality of the painting is of prime importance when discussing the price of Wemyss ware.

A small Bovey Tracey Wemyss pig decorated with thistles, painted by Joseph Nekola, 5½ in. long, c. 1930. **£150-250** *RdeR*

A Scottish Wemyss ware ink stand, 7 in. **£100-250** *RdeR*

A Scottish Wemyss ware inkwell, 6 in. diam. **£150-200** *RdeR*

A Scottish Wemyss ware mug, impressed marks, 5½ in. high, c. 1900. **£150-250** *RdeR*

A late 19th C. Scottish coombe flower pot, impressed Wemyss, 11½ in. diam. **£100-150** *RdeR*

A Scottish Wemyss ware Stuart pot, 8½ in. high, c. 1900. **£150-£250** *RdeR*

A Scottish Wemyss ware quaiche 11 in. wide, c. 1895. **£150-250** *RdeR*

A Scottish Wemyss ware goblet to commemorate Queen Victoria's Silver Jubilee, 5½ in., 1897. **£250-£350** *RdeR*

A Kenmore vase, Scottish Wemyss ware, impressed marks, 14 in. high, c. 1900. **£300-500** *RdeR*

A large late 19th/early 20th C. Scottish Wemyss ware loving cup, 9½ in. high. **£150-300** *RdeR*

An English Wemyss ware commemorative cup, made by Royal Doulton for Queen Elizabeth, the Queen Mother, 1980 (limited edition), 7½ in. wide. **£250** *RdeR*

A Scottish Wemyss ware Grosvenor vase, impressed marks, 8 in. high. **£40-60** *RdeR*

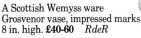

A Scottish Wemyss ware plate, impressed marks, 6½ in., c. 1900. **£40-75** *RdeR*

A Scottish Wemyss plaque, impressed marks, 5½ in. wide, c. 1900. **£75-150** *RdeR*

A late 19th C. rare Scottish Wemyss ware jug and basin painted with a mallard duck, impressed Wemyss and R.H. & S., bowl 15½ in. diam. **£300-400** *RdeR*

The price of Wemyss ware varies dramatically according to rarity and quality of painting.

A late 19th C. Scottish Wemyss ware bucket, impressed marks, 13 in. wide. **£100-200** *RdeR*

WEMYSS VALUE POINTS

- **price relevant to the quality of painting**
- **Karel Nekola's work highly prized**
- **skill of the painter's free-flowing approach paramount in discussing price**
- **certain shapes rare and desirable — such as Karel Nekola's 'carp'**
- **late pieces which were produced just to keep the factory going less desirable**
- **chips can be acceptable, particularly in well painted piece, but cracks do substantially affect price**

A Scottish Wemyss ware Japan vase, 9 in. **£50-75** *RdeR*

A Scottish Wemyss ware biscuit barrel, 5½ in. diam., c. 1930. **£50-£75** *RdeR*

A Scottish Wemyss ware basket, impressed mark, c. 1920. **£200-£350** *RdeR*

A Scottish Wemyss ware Gordon plate, impressed mark, 8 in., c. 1900. **£75-150** *RdeR*

A Scottish Wemyss ware preserve pot, impressed Wemyss, c. 1900. **£25-40** *RdeR*

A Scottish Wemyss ware tea pot, 7 in. **£75-150** *RdeR*

Our thanks to Victoria de Rin for her assistance in compiling this section.

A pair of Scottish Wemyss ware Kintore candlesticks, impressed marks, 9¾ in., c. 1920. **£100-250** depending on painting *RdeR*

A rare Dublin delft spirit barrel, probably the Delamain factory, slight chipping, wooden stand, 9¼ in., c. 1755. **£700-800** *S*

Delftware spirit barrels appear to be unique to the Dublin factories.

A pair of Bristol spirit barrels decorated by W. Fifield, 5½ in. high, c. 1835. **£285-310** *EC*

A rare Lambeth bird-feeder decorated in blue, inscribed 'FGiles' with the date, June 7 1792, cup missing, 3¾ in. (L.L.). **£650-750** *S*

A Clews blue and white transfer printed bedpan, c. 1817-25. **£240-£260** *SH*

A Staffordshire pottery bust of Minerva probably by Enoch Wood, the thick off-white glaze tinged with pale enamel colours, slight damage, 35.5 cm., early 19th C. **£120-180** *Bea*

A pair of blue and white busts of Louis XVI and Marie Antoinette, probably Dutch, 12½ and 11 in. high, c. 1815. **£250-300** *AG*

A Wedgwood parian bust titled Zetland, impressed WEDGWOOD, EDGE and PROOF, incised 'Registered 11th Dec'r, 1868', 20 in. **£250-300** *SC*

PRATT COLOURS

So-called Pratt ware and related types used a range of high temperature opaque colours derived from different metal oxides: green, ochre, brown, black and blue.

A blue and white transfer printed chamber stick, 3¼ in., early 19th C. **£100-120** *SH*

A documentary William Turner inscribed pearlware candlestick enriched in Pratt colours, the reverse inscribed Wm. Turner, Burslem, Staffordshire, 26 cm. high, c. 1800. **£350-400** *C*

An early Staffordshire clock case, modelled with a classical lady leaning upon a celestial globe with multi-coloured marble decoration, 18 cm. **£200-250** *P*

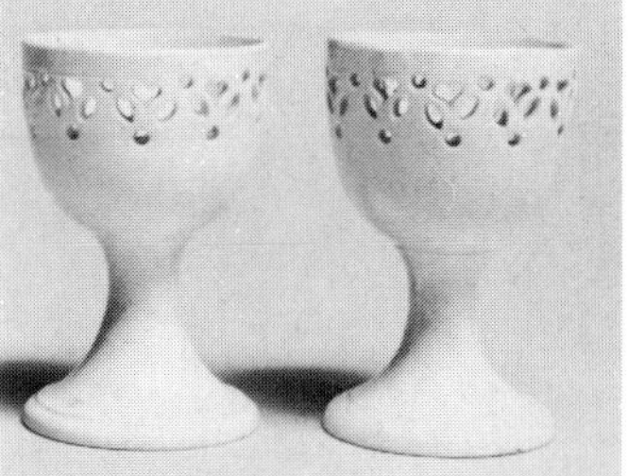

A pair of Leeds creamware egg cups, 2¾ in., c. 1790. **£175-200** *EC*

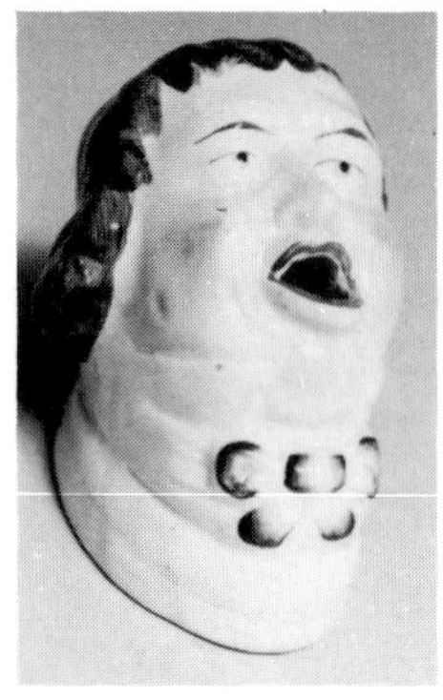

A Staffordshire inkwell modelled as the head of Charles Ridgway, a potter, originally one of a pair, with his wife's head as the other, 3½ in., c. 1830-40. **£70-90** Pair **£220-250** *PC*

These were issued by a rival potter.

A 'majolica' honeycomb dish and cover, probably George Jones, coloured in typical 'majolica' glazes of ochre, green, brown and turquoise, minor chip, painted pattern number, indistinct P.O.D.R. mark, 34.3 cm., c. 1870. **£250-350** *S*

A pair of Lambeth 'flower' bricks, each painted in blue, chips, 6 in., mid 18th C. **£350-400** *S*

A Spode blue transfer 2-handled footbath of the Caramanian series, c. 1810. **£340-400** *A*

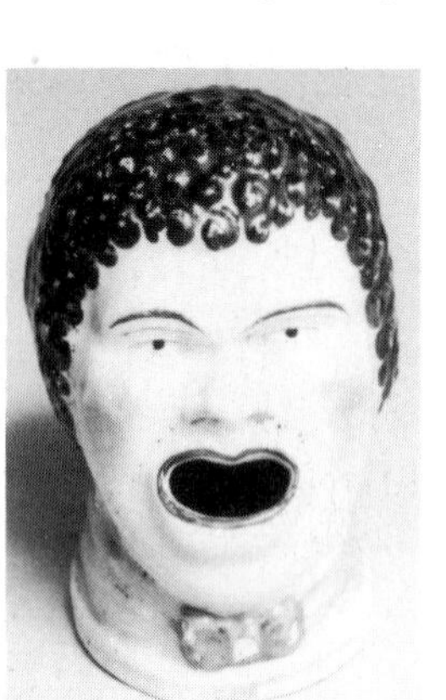

A Staffordshire inkwell, modelled as a portrait head of the Prince Regent, 3 in., c. 1830-40. **£50-60** *PC*

A Liverpool delft blue and white flower-brick, slight rim chips, 18.5 cm. wide, c. 1760. **£400-450** *C*

An unusual 'flower' brick modelled in the form of a flat casket, the sides painted in blue, probably Liverpool, feet damaged, chips, 5 in., c. 1760. (L.L.). **£250-300** *S*

This type of 'brick' is rare. The known examples are all compartmented, as in this case, and it is conjectured that they were intended as inkwells and not flower-holders.

A blue and white transfer printed foot bath, c. 1840-50. **£250-275** *SH*

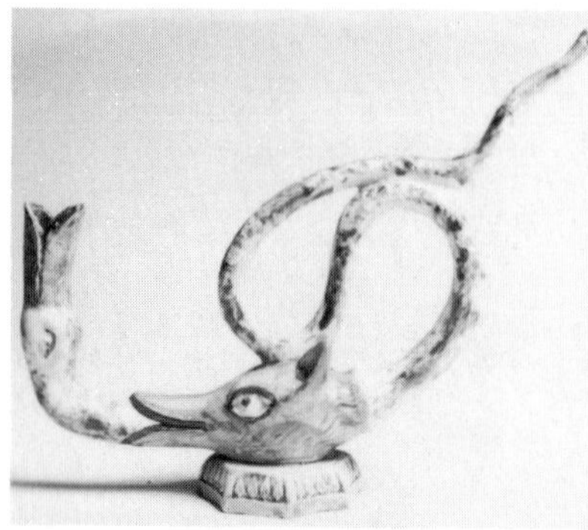

A rare Prattware 'fox and goose' pipe, 7½ in. wide, c. 1795. **£400-£450** *EC*

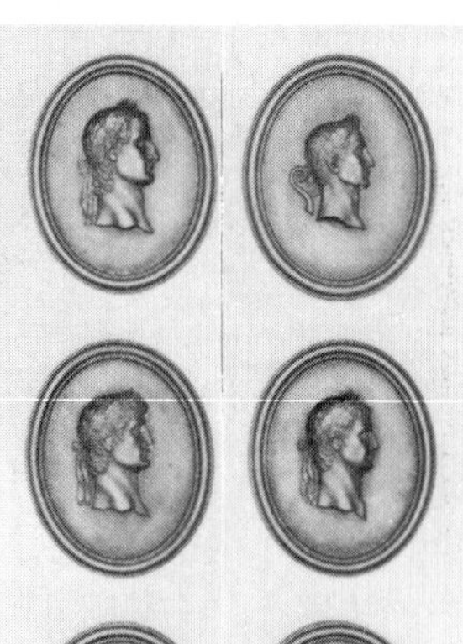

A rare collection of 72 black basaltes oval portrait medallions including 'The Twelve Caesars' and 'Kings and Illustrious Persons of Asia, Egypt and Greece', in a contemporary cabinet, impressed Wedgwood and Bentley and Wedgwood marks, some named, some with incised class reference numbers, one repaired, 2⅞ and 2⅛ in., c. 1775-90. **£1,800-2,400** *S*

An extremely rare English polychrome delft salt, 2½ in. high, c. 1740. **£900-1,000** *JHo*

A Lambeth delft blue and white shoe, 5 in. high, c. 1710. **£1,600-£1,800** *JHo*

A rare Brislington salt, painted in green, red and blue, foot chipped, glaze chips, 2⅞ in. high, early 18th C. (L.L.). **£1,100-1,300** *S*

A pair of 'Malachite' garden seats, probably Mintons, the ground simulating green striations, one repaired, 18½ in., c. 1870. **£700-£800** *S*

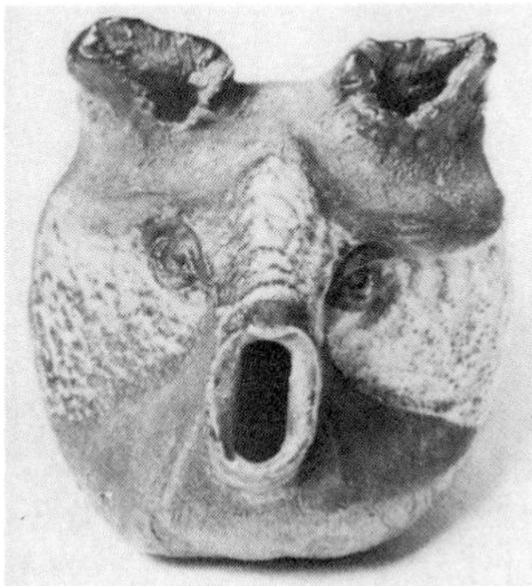

An unusual Martin Brothers grotesque spoon-warmer, roughly textured and part glazed in brown, incised marks, minor chip to mouth, 9.5 cm. width, 1880's. **£300-£400** *S*

A Martinware spoon-warmer, in typical muted enamel colours, signed Martin, London & Southall, indistinctly dated, 15.5 cm. diam. **£90-110** *Bea*

A Minton 'Majolica' tazza, glazed in shades of turquoise, green, blue, pink and ochre, impressed Minton, 758, and date code for 1868, 44 cm. **£550-650** *S*

A Dutch Delft blue and white Louis XV style miniature salon suite, signed Vevk 38, 34, etc., length of settee 8 in. **£200-250** *AGr*

A blue and white transfer printed sucrier and cover with unusual print of llamas, early 19th C. **£35-£40** *SH*

PORCELAIN

A rare early Worcester cream boat, of flared hexagonal shape, painted in underglaze blue with chinoiserie scenes within scroll-moulded panels, the spout moulded with a geranium leaf on the underside, the interior painted with flowers and foliage, painter's mark on the interior, 4½ in., c. 1755-58. Sold for **£1,950** in May 1983 by Sotheby's.

Since February 1983 there has been a general upward trend in the market for European porcelain. This has been particularly evident in English early blue and white wares. Hand-painted pieces with rare patterns and in good condition command top prices. There has been an interesting development over the past few years in the prices of damaged blue and white porcelain. Collectors once dictated that only perfect pieces were acceptable and hence damage rendered a piece virtually unsaleable. As the rarer patterns are now in such demand this has been superseded and some of the more astonishing percentage increases have been seen in damaged wares.

Another area of great interest is 19th Century porcelain plaques which have seen a great increase in value over the last year. Once again, the subject is of great importance; diaphanously clad sad-eyed ladies are still favourite. They seem to be the passion of Japanese buyers and some record prices have been paid, both in London and New York. Condition is absolutely vital, helped by a full mark and signature. Relgious subjects are not so popular unless containing a serene young maiden.

Certainly prices seem very steady and hints of the longed for recovery seem abundant.

A Belleek basket and cover, with a creamy iridescent glaze, minor chips, impressed mark on applied ribbon, 28.5 cm., late 19th C. **£1,000-1,300** *S*

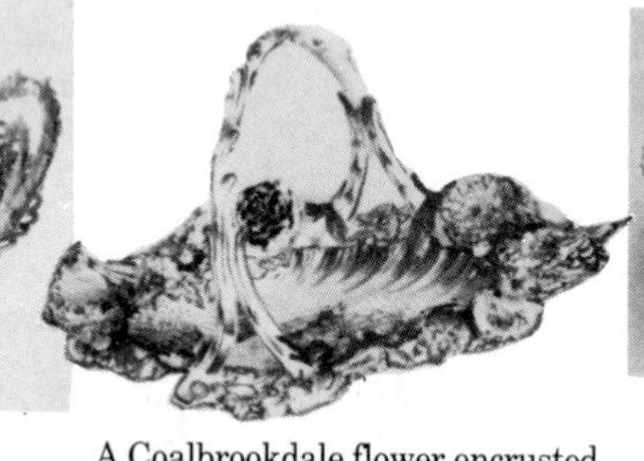

A Coalbrookdale flower encrusted basket, slight chips, 12 in., early 19th C. **£300-350** *SC*

A Derby basket applied with blue and yellow flower-heads, small crack on rim restored, 11 in., c. 1760-65. **£550-650** *S*

A first period Worcester blue and white basket, with the pine cone pattern, 6¾ in., c. 1770. **£330-350** *WWW*

A Coalbrookdale basket with stiff overhead rustic branch handle, painted with flower sprays within the flower encrusted rim, the exterior green ground, slight chipping, 6¼ in., early 19th C. **£300-350** *SC*

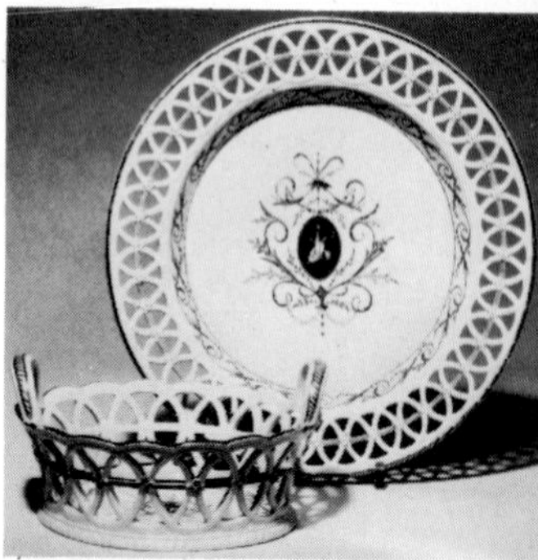

A Fürstenberg neo-classical two-handled basket, 19 cm. wide; a circular dish en suite, 27.5 cm. diam.; an oval dish en suite, 38.5 cm. wide; and a circular dish en suite, 34.5 cm. diam., blue script F marks, c. 1790. **£800-900** *C*

A pair of unusual Worcester blue and white baskets, painted on the inside and applied with florets on the exterior, small open crescent marks, one restored and cracked, 7½ in., c. 1760-65. **£450-550** *S*

A Royal Worcester peach ground basket, 4½ in. wide, 1906. **£65-75** *NSN*

A Longton Hall blue and white flared conical bowl painted with a tall figure walking by a pyramid, the interior with a flower-spray, blue line mark, 11 cm. diam., c. 1755. **£600-700** *C*

An ormolu mounted 'Sevres' bowl with a 'bleu-celeste' ground, the ormolu mounts with loose ring handles, 11½ in. (29 cm.), late 19th C. **£400-500** *SC*

A 'Vienna' pedestal centre bowl, well painted by Wagner, signed, with two panels of playful cherubs against a cream ground, shield in underglaze blue, painted titles, base and bowl detached, 17 in. (43 cm.) width, late 19th C. **£1,450-£1,650** *S*

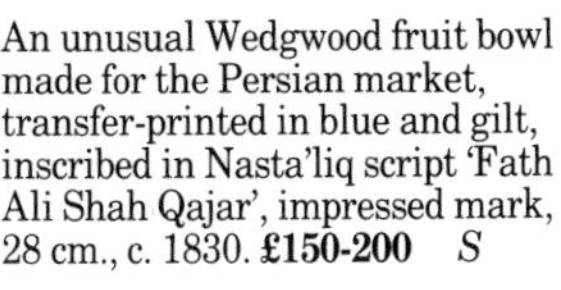

An unusual Wedgwood fruit bowl made for the Persian market, transfer-printed in blue and gilt, inscribed in Nasta'liq script 'Fath Ali Shah Qajar', impressed mark, 28 cm., c. 1830. **£150-200** *S*

A pair of Coalport bottles and stoppers, printed in underglaze blue, reserved on a burnished gilt ground, green printed marks, slight hairline cracks at neck, gilding slightly rubbed, 20 in., 1900's. **£550-650** *SC*

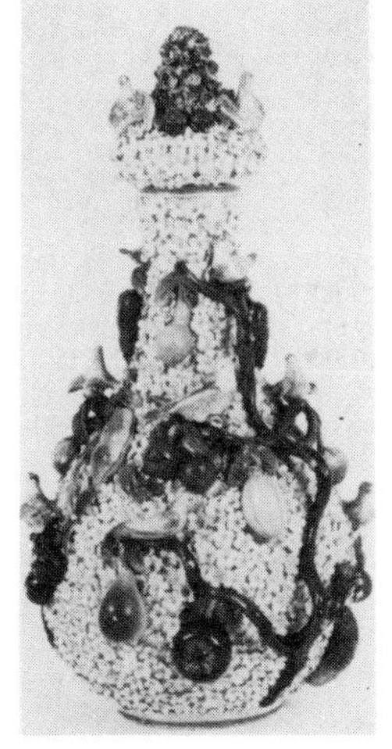

A pair of German 'schneeballen' bottles and stoppers of pear shape, tightly packed white florets in high relief with branches and birds, pseudo-swords in blue, incised numerals, some chipping, 13¾ in. (34.8 cm.), late 19th C. **£180-240** *SC*

A rare Chelsea peach scent bottle, with pale pinky lilac shading, neck formed as a branch with green leaves, gilt mounted neck and stopper, 2¼ in., c. 1755. **£1,500-£1,700** *S*

A Coalport posy bowl, with deep blue and gilt decoration, 3¼ in. high, c. 1880-90. **£175-200** *NSN*

A Tournai slop-bowl painted by Joseph Duvivier, gilt foot rim, 16.5 cm. diam., c. 1770. **£1,700-£2,000** *C*

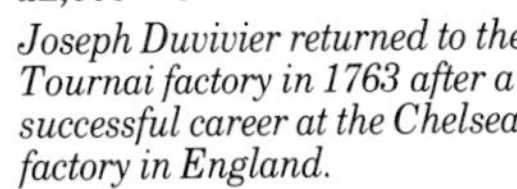

Joseph Duvivier returned to the Tournai factory in 1763 after a successful career at the Chelsea factory in England.

A Wedgwood fairyland lustre bowl, the exterior printed in gilding with 'Woodland Bridge', the interior with a profusion of fairy folk amongst trees, printed Portland vase mark, in gilding, inscribed Z4968 in black, 7 in., 1920's. **£300-£400** *SC*

A good Wedgwood fairyland lustre bowl with the 'Woodland Bridge' variation of the 'Woodland Elves' pattern and the 'Poplar Trees' design, printed urn mark, Z4968, ebonised hardwood stand, 11 in., 1920's. **£700-900** *S*

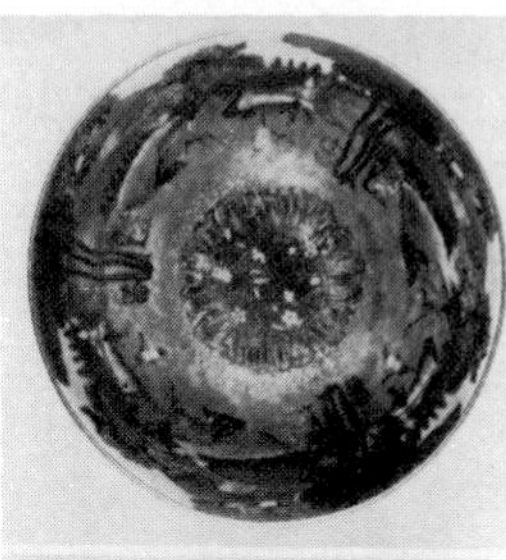

A Wedgwood fairyland lustre bowl decorated on the interior with the 'Picnic by a River' pattern, the exterior with the 'Woodland Bridge — Variation 1' design, slight rubbing to exterior gilding, printed urn mark, Z4968, 21 cm., 1920's. **£450-550** *S*

A fine and early Dr. Wall Worcester bowl, with decoration of Chinese ladies and the fishermen, known as Pu Tai, 6¼ in. **£320-£380** *SA*

A Royal Worcester bowl of campana form, with a royal blue ground, printed crowned circle mark, shape number 2130, Rd. No. 365542, retailer's mark for James Green, 26 cm., indistinct date code, c. 1900. **£250-350** *S*

FAIRYLAND LUSTRE

- The Wedgwood factory had been experiencing serious financial difficulties during the closing years of the 19th C.
- Daisy Makeig-Jones helped bring about a total reversal with the introduction of her 'Fairyland Lustre'
- the patterns for 'The First Ten Lustre Decorations' Z4823 were published in October 1914
- the butterflies of the First Series tended to be of the 'solid' variety, which were normally printed in gold
- the butterflies of the Second Series were 'open' and were filled with various colours
- in 1917 perhaps the most successful of Daisy's natural lustre subjects — The Hummingbird, was perfected
- the 'Fairy' lustre subjects now command high prices at auction, particularly the more unusual lustre colour combinations

An early Worcester bowl, the outside painted in enamels in oriental style with an exotic bird on a branch by a triangular fence, the reverse with a solitary insect, 15.8 cm. diam., c. 1755. **£350-400** *P*

A first period Worcester blue and white paté pan, 'bare tree and speared bird pattern', with workman's mark, 4½ in. diam., c. 1758. Restored **£150-165** Perfect **£200-250** *WWW*

This pattern, which was produced from 1758-65, has a workman's mark on early examples and an open crescent on later pieces.

A Wedgwood fairyland lustre bowl of flared squat campana shape, the exterior with a band of pixies by toadstools, printed Portland vase mark, slight rubbing, 10¼ in., 1920's. **£800-900** *SC*

A Wedgwood fairyland lustre bowl, printed in gilding with the 'Castle on a road' design, printed Portland vase mark and Z5125 in puce, gilding slightly rubbed, 9 in., 1920's. **£500-550** *SC*

A good Wedgwood daylight fairyland lustre 'K'ang Hsi' bowl with the 'striped pants' version of the 'Woodland Elves' pattern and the 'Woodland Bridge — Variation 11' design, printed urn mark, Z4968, 8 in., 1920's. **£550-650** *S*

A Worcester covered bowl and stand painted in puce, iron-red, mauve, yellow and green, with apple-green basket moulded borders, gilt rose knop, 13 cm., c. 1770. **£200-250** *SS*

Basket moulding as a decorative feature was originated by the Meissen factory in the 1730's and later adopted by other continental and English factories.

A Royal Worcester bowl with shaped gilt edge, the inside with blackberry and autumnal decoration on an ivory ground, signed K. Blake, 11½ in. diam. **£120-150** *OL*

A Royal Worcester bowl painted by Jas. Stinton, signed, hair crack, 21.5 cm., printed crowned circle mark and date code for 1917. **£300-£400** *S*

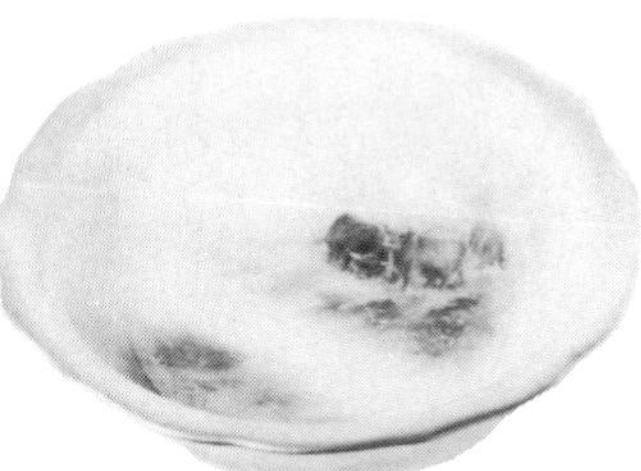

A Royal Worcester bowl by Harry Stinton, 11½ in. diam., 1920. **£500-£600** *NSN*

A Royal Worcester bowl with wavy everted rim, boldly painted by Horace Price in warm enamel colours between gold rims, 23.2 cm. diam., printed mark and date code for 1937. **£400-500** *NSN*

WORCESTER PORCELAIN DATES

1751-1783	**First Period**
1751-1774	**'Dr. Wall' Period**
1776-1792	**Davis/Flight Period**
1783-1792	**Flight Period**
1792-1804	**Flight and Barr Period**
1804-1813	**Barr, Flight and Barr**
1813-1840	**Flight, Barr and Barr**
1788-1840	**Chamberlain — Worcester**
1840-1852	**Chamberlain and Company**
1852-1862	**Kerr and Binns (W. H. Kerr & Company)**
1862-	**Worcester Royal Porcelain Company**

A pair of late 19th C. Minton ewers, signed M. Dudley, 11 in. **£750-850** *NSN*

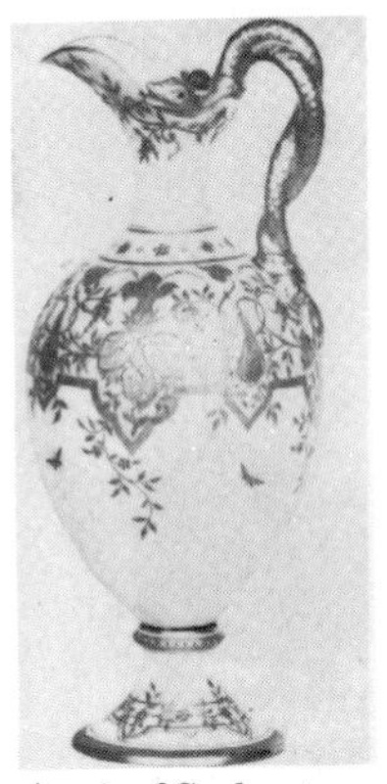

A pair of Coalport ewers, elaborately decorated with a complex band of raised gilt scrolling foliage reserved on a shaped seeded green ground band, on a pale ivory reserve, green printed marks, both slightly cracked, 10⅝ in., c. 1910. **£250-£300** *SC*

A Zurich porcelain bowl, the interior sparsely painted with leaves, all in natural colours below a gold rim, 17.2 cm., mid 18th C. **£550-650** *Bea*

A pair of Belleek ewers, marked County Fermanagh, 9 in. high, c. 1910. **£400-440** pair *NSN*

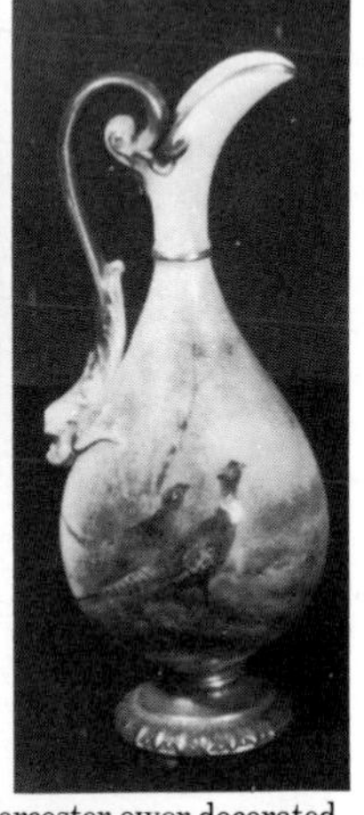

A Royal Worcester ewer decorated by James Stinton, printed mark for 1911. **£300-350** *DWB*

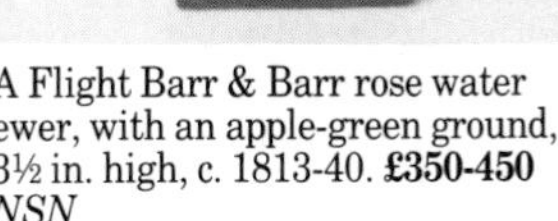

A Flight Barr & Barr rose water ewer, with an apple-green ground, 3½ in. high, c. 1813-40. **£350-450** *NSN*

A Royal Worcester ewer with apple-green ground, centre painted by W. A. Hawkins, pattern no. of vase 1742, 17½ in., 1909. **£1,400-£1,600** *SA*

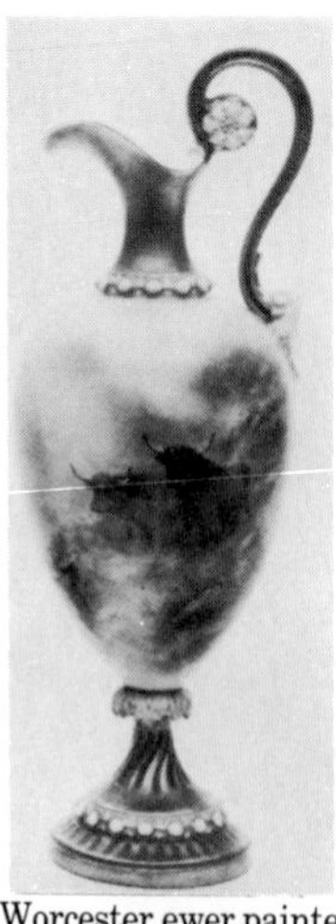

A Royal Worcester ewer painted by H. Stinton, signed, the gilding by Henry Bright, printed crowned circle mark, painted gilder's initials, shape number 2464, 11¾ in., date code for 1913. **£600-£700** *S*

A Royal Worcester ewer painted after Claude, probably by Harry Davis, on a black ground, shape 2464, 10¾ in. high, date code 1920. **£250-350** *N*

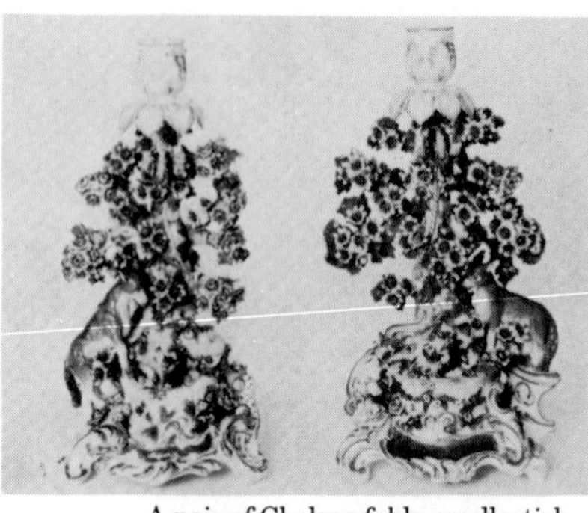

A pair of Chelsea fable candlestick groups with later nozzles, both with gold anchor marks and period, restored, 27 cm. **£400-500** *P*

A pair of Minton candlestick figures dressed in elaborate 18th C. costume, the whole well coloured and detailed in gilt, some damage, 22.5 cm., c. 1830. **£450-500** *SS*

A fine and large 19th C. Paris porcelain casket, 11½ in. wide. **£350-400** *PWC*

A Dresden casket painted with 18th C. lovers within pink-scale-ground panels, the interior of the cover similarly painted, 7 in. (17.8 cm.) wide, mid to late 19th C. **£500-600** *S*

A Dresden porcelain centrepiece, 19½ in., c. 1870's. **£200-250** *IHA*

A Royal Worcester reticulated two-handled casket and cover by George Owen, of bombé form, enriched with gilt dots within pale turquoise beaded cartouches, incised signature to the base, gilt marks and pattern no. 2416, 16 cm. wide, date code for 1910. **£4,000-£5,000** *C*

A pair of Meissen candelabra groups, crossed swords in blue, chipped, 25 cm., 2nd half 19th C. **£450-550** *SS*

A French gilt-metal and porcelain jewel casket, silk lined, 7¼ in. (18.7 cm.) long, unmarked, c. 1865, key and detached printed paper label: 'Aumont St. Bernard/Voisin/ 23/Passage Les Panochines/Paris'. **£300-350** *S*

A Meissen comport, crossed swords in blue, 38 cm., late 19th C. **£400-£500** *SS*

A Naples centrebasket, crowned N mark in blue, slight damage, 18¾ in. (47.6 cm.), late 19th C. **£150-200** *SC*

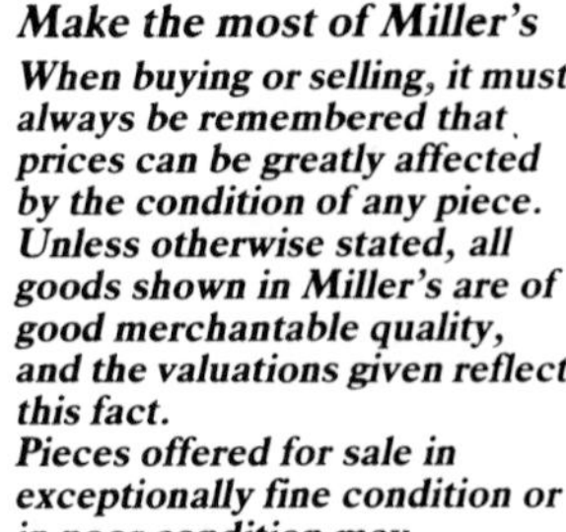

Make the most of Miller's

When buying or selling, it must always be remembered that prices can be greatly affected by the condition of any piece. Unless otherwise stated, all goods shown in Miller's are of good merchantable quality, and the valuations given reflect this fact.
Pieces offered for sale in exceptionally fine condition or in poor condition may reasonably be expected to be priced considerably higher or lower respectively than the estimates given herein.

A pair of Meissen centrepiece baskets, underglaze blue crossed swords, incised 'D.196', minor chips, 33 cm., last half 19th C. **£950-1,050** *SS*

A Royal Worcester sweetmeat dish, in Hadley style, 8 in., 1913. **£260-£290** *NSN*

A Meissen clock case modelled as a child, lacking dial and movement, crossed swords in underglaze blue, chips, 10 in. (25.4 cm.), late 19th C. **£800-900** *S*

A Meissen porcelain mantel clock, lavishly encrusted with flowers, painted in blue enamel and gold, slight damage, 46 cm., late 19th C. **£1,050-1,250** *Bea*

An English porcelain 2-piece house pastille burner, 5 in. high, c. 1830. **£275-350** *GCA*

A Paris porcelain cased clock and stand, 41 cm., c. 1840. **£400-500** *SS*

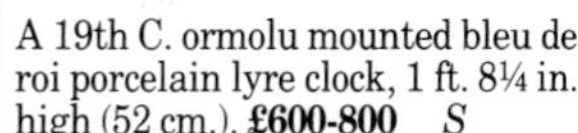

A 19th C. ormolu mounted bleu de roi porcelain lyre clock, 1 ft. 8¼ in. high (52 cm.). **£600-800** *S*

An English porcelain 2-piece cottage pastille burner, 4 in. high, c. 1825. **£375-450** *GCA*

An English porcelain octagonal cottage pastille burner, 5½ in., c. 1830. **£145-185** *GCA*

A Paris porcelain clock, 20 in. high, c. 1870. **£500-550** *IHA*

A Staffordshire porcelain pastille burner, moulded as a 'Gothick' church, chipped flowers, 15 cm., c. 1830-40. **£600-700** *SS*

A porcelain cottage pastille burner, 5½ in. high, c. 1840. **£150-200** *EC*

A fine Staffordshire porcelain pagoda pastille burner, 6 in., c. 1835. **£265-325** *GCA*

A Staffordshire porcelain pastille burner, detachable chimney, 12.5 cm., 2nd quarter 19th C. **£700-£800** *SS*

A small porcelain umbrella cottage pastille burner, 3 in. high, c. 1840. **£155-175** *EC*

A John Rose Coalport cup and saucer, c. 1820. **£75-85** *NSN*

A Chelsea fluted tea bowl and saucer, softly painted scalloped gilt-dentil rims, red anchor marks, minor wear on saucer, c. 1754-56. **£750-850** *S*

A pair of Chelsea Derby caudle cups, covers and stands, probably painted by Richard Askew on a ruby ground, one cover cracked. **£800-900** *WHL*

A Coalport loving cup painted on one side with an ostrich, the reverse inscribed in gilding 'John & Elizabeth Eyre 1852', 5¼ in., 1852. **£200-250** *SC*

A Chelsea white tea plant beaker (cracked down one side), crown and trident mark in underglaze blue, 1745-49, 7 cm. high. **£1,100-1,300** *C*

Although this form of beaker is not particularly unusual, less than a dozen trident marked examples have so far been recorded.

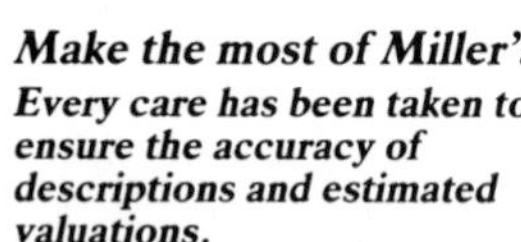

Make the most of Miller's

Every care has been taken to ensure the accuracy of descriptions and estimated valuations.

Where an attribution is made within inverted commas (e.g. 'Chippendale') or is followed by the word 'style' (e.g. early Georgian style) it is intended to convey that, in the opinion of the publishers, the piece concerned is a later – though probably still antique – reproduction of the style so designated.

Unless otherwise stated, any description which refers to 'a set' or 'a pair' includes a valuation for the entire set or the pair, even though the illustration may show only a single item.

A Chelsea octagonal beaker painted with a bouquet, raised anchor mark, 7 cm. high, c. 1750. **£400-500** *C*

A Derby cup and saucer, c. 1810. **£90-100** *NSN*

A Crown Derby chocolate cup, saucer and cover, 1901. **£65-75** *NSN*

A Doccia Alla Sassonia tea cup and a saucer, handle repaired, c. 1755. **£300-400** *C*

A Höchst tea cup and saucer painted 'en camaieu rose' with landscapes with gilt rims, blue wheel marks and W1 impressed, c. 1760. **£200-300** *C*

A Royal Crown Derby triple-handled loving cup, painted and signed by A. F. Wood with a turquoise band and reserved on a rich gros-bleu ground, 7⅛ in., red printed marks including date code for 1899. **£400-450** *SC*

A Royal Crown Derby double-handled cup, painted with pink rose panels on a burnished gilt oval medallion, 7 in., red printed mark including date code for 1902. **£50-£70** *SC*

A Crown Derby cup and saucer, 1912. **£30-35** *NSN*

A Frankenthal coffee cup and saucer, blue rampant lion mark, the cup with 5K, the saucer with 3, 1756-59. **£600-750** *C*

A Doccia Alla Sassonia coffee cup and saucer with purple, gilt and iron-red foliage cartouches, the saucer with impressed star mark, 18th C. **£250-300** *C*

A pair of Doccia tea cups and saucers decorated con basso relievo istoriato, moulded in low relief with an istoriato subject, c. 1755. **£1,000-1,200** *C*

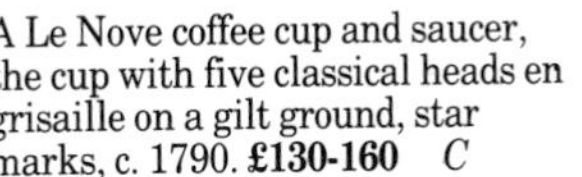

A Le Nove coffee cup and saucer, the cup with five classical heads en grisaille on a gilt ground, star marks, c. 1790. **£130-160** *C*

A Longton Hall blue and white cylindrical coffee can, small rim chip, minor hair crack, c. 1756. **£400-500** *S*

A Liverpool white cup, the flared upper part with uneven fluting, on an indented quatrefoil foot (minute rim chips), William Reid's factory, 6.5 cm. high, c. 1755. **£650-700** *C*

Although attributed here to the Liverpool factory of William Reid, these wares remain the subject of considerable discussion, the Shelton factory of John Baddeley and the Pomona Works at Newcastle-under-Lyme must be considered as possible alternatives.

A Meissen chinoiserie tea bowl and a saucer within iron-red Böttger-lustre and gilt quatrefoil Laub-und-Bandelwerk cartouches, the tea bowl with minute chip, gilder's marks 18 and K, c. 1730. **£800-£900** *C*

A Meissen tea bowl and saucer decorated in Kakiemon style with prunus, bamboo and pine, crossed swords in blue enamel, Johanneum number N=243/W, c. 1730. **£1,500-£1,800** *S*

A Meissen beaker painted in the manner of Dannhoffer, enriched with gilding, minor rim chips, the porcelain c. 1730. **£500-600** *C*

Three early Meissen chinoiserie two-handled beakers painted in the workshop of J. G. Herold, within Böttger lustre, gold, puce and iron-red Laub-und-Bandelwerk cartouches, one with small restored rim chip, gilt 2 marks, c. 1725. **£1,000-1,300** *C*

A Meissen yellow ground cup and saucer, probably decorated by A. F. von Löwenfinck, brown and gilt rims, crossed swords in underglaze blue, II incised, 1730-35. **£1,300-£1,800** *S*

The chinoiserie painting is executed in a derivative Kakiemon style utilising a 'famille verte' palette.

MEISSEN

- **in 1709, J. F. Böttger produced a white hard-paste porcelain**
- **wares often decorated by outside decorators (Hausmaler)**
- **in 1720, kilnmaster Stozel came back to Meissen bringing with him J. G. Herold**
- **from this time Meissen was supreme in enamelling hard-paste porcelain**
- **crossed swords factory mark started in 1723**
- **many port scenes painted by C. F. Herold**
- **finest Meissen figures modelled by J. J. Kändler from 1731**
- **cut-flower decoration (Schnittblumen) often associated with J. G. Klinger**
- **from 1755 the rococo style became very popular, especially as a base for figures**
- **this period saw softer colours used with a great deal of gilding**

A Meissen cup and saucer decorated with panels on a yellow ground, gilt-scroll borders, crossed swords in underglaze blue, minor chip on rim of cup, c. 1730-40. **£500-£600** *S*

The panelled style of decoration and the quatre lobed form of the ware was extensively copied in the second half of the 19th century principally by Dresden manufacturers, such as Helena Wolfsohn, who invariably added a spurious AR (Augustus Rex) monogram.

A rare Meissen double-handle yellow ground cup and saucer painted probably by A. F. von Löwenfinck, in colours and gilding, crossed swords in underglaze blue, II incised, restored chip to saucer, 1730-35. **£1,500-1,800** *S*

A Meissen chinoiserie tea bowl and a saucer within shaped iron-red, puce, Böttger-lustre and gilt Laub- und-Bandelwerk cartouches, on a chequered iron-red ground, blue crossed swords marks, the tea bowl with gilder's mark z., the saucer with zi., tea bowl cracked, both with minor chips, c. 1735. **£400-£500** *C*

A pair of Meissen yellow-ground cups and saucers, crossed swords in underglaze blue, some wear, incised 23, 1735-40. **£2,000-3,000** *S*

A Meissen gold ground tea bowl and saucer painted by B. G. Hauer, the reverse of the saucer with indianische Blumen, blue crossed swords mark and incised double star, gilder's mark R., c. 1745. **£1,500-1,600** *C*

An early Meissen tea bowl painted in the manner of J. G. Heintze, the interior painted with a spray of indianische Blumen, crossed swords mark in underglaze blue, gilder's initial 'B', 8 cm. **£300-350** *SS*

A Meissen tulip-flower cup and saucer moulded and decorated in puce and cream, blue crossed swords mark, chip to foot rim of saucer, c. 1765. **£400-500** *C*

A rare Dr. Wall Worcester tea cup and saucer, painted in bright polychrome enamels. **£360-400** *SA*

An unusual pair of Meissen cups and saucers each painted in strong colours, crossed swords in underglaze blue, minor damage, c. 1745-50. **£600-700** *S*

A Du Paquier beaker and saucer, each painted in iron-red, purple and gilding, restoration to one, minor chip, incised N., c. 1730. **£850-950** *S*

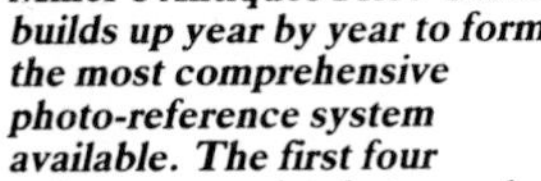

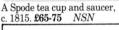

A Spode tea cup and saucer, c. 1815. **£65-75** *NSN*

The open-ended reference system
Miller's Antiques Price Guide builds up year by year to form the most comprehensive photo-reference system available. The first four volumes contain photographs of over 30,000 stock items!

A first period Worcester blue and white fluted tea bowl and saucer, 'hollow rock lily' pattern, 5½ in., c. 1765. **£135-145** *WWW*

A Dr. Wall Worcester blue and white 'Long Eliza' tea bowl and saucer, c. 1770. **£200-250** *SA*

A pair of Worcester (Grainger & Co.) tomato-red ground flared beakers, painted in sepia with views of Worcester, one with script mark in gold, 9.5 cm. high, c. 1805. **£500-600** *C*

The bucket form was most fashionable from about 1805-15.

A Chamberlain Worcester trio, late 18th C. **£100-120** *NSN*

Marked wares have to be treated with caution as many factories in the 18th C. copied more successful factory marks. Closer attention should be paid to the body, glaze and shape in order to ascertain the factory. The mark should only be used as a final check. Many recent discoveries have changed previously held beliefs, e.g. the disguised numeral mark, once held to be Caughley and now known to be Worcester. It is also true that a large number of 18th C. wares were unmarked. Many English factories adopted mock Oriental marks in order to compete with imported Chinese porcelain.

A Worcester tea bowl and saucer in Imari style, painted in underglaze blue and overglaze iron-red and gilding, c. 1770. **£350-450** *C*

A pair of Chamberlain's Worcester mauve ground cups and saucers painted with named views of Luscombe, Devon, Killerton, Devonshire, Sherbourn, Oxfordshire and Beechworth, within gilt quatrefoil borders, script marks, c. 1815. **£800-900** *C*

A Flight, Barr & Barr tea cup and saucer, 1813-40. **£85-95** *NSN*

A rare Flight, Barr & Barr cabinet cup and stand, printed and painted with portraits of Fath Ali Shah, King of Persia, and his son, full script mark in sepia on the cup, c. 1830. **£250-350** *S*

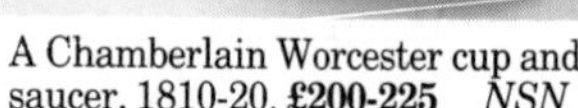

A Chamberlain Worcester cup and saucer, 1810-20. **£200-225** *NSN*

A Chamberlain Worcester cup and saucer, cracked ice pattern, c. 1840. **£120-145** *NSN*

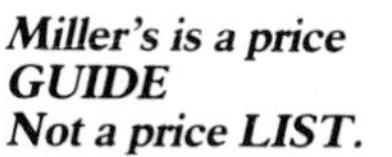

Miller's is a price GUIDE Not a price LIST.

The price ranges given reflect the average price a purchaser should pay for similar items. Condition, rarity of design or pattern, size, colour, provenance, restoration and many other factors must be taken into account when assessing values.

A Flight, Barr & Barr tea cup and saucer, c. 1820. **£90-110** *NSN*

A Flight, Barr & Barr trio, c. 1830. **£180-220** *NSN*

A Chamberlain Worcester cup and saucer, slightly rubbed, c. 1830. **£65-100** *NSN*

A set of 6 Royal Worcester coffee cups and saucers, painted by Jas. Stinton, signed, saucer: 9.8 cm., printed crowned circle mark, date code for 1923; and 6 silver coffee spoons, Wakely & Wheeler, London, fitted case, 1914. **£600-£700** *S*

A set of 6 Royal Worcester coffee cups and saucers, painted by H. Stinton, signed, saucer: 9.8 cm., printed mark, date code for 1913; and 6 silver-gilt coffee spoons, fitted case, H. J. Hulbert & Co. Ltd., London, 1923. **£800-900** *S*

A Belleek croaking frog, eyes and feet with black details, body glazed, in lustrous yellow, printed dog and harp mark, 4½ in., c. 1900. **£300-£400** *S*

A Bow figure of a tabby cat with a greyish purple striped coat, ears chipped, 8 cm. high, c. 1758. **£850-£950** *C*

A Flight, Barr & Barr trio, c. 1813-40. **£120-130** *NSN*

A Grainger Worcester cup and saucer, c. 1850. **£65-80** *NSN*

A Royal Worcester cabinet cup and saucer painted and signed by T. Lockyer with still-life of fruit, purple printed mark including date code for 1921. **£150-200** *SC*

A pair of well painted continental porcelain cups and stands, each cup 8.1 cm. high, 'Flensburg' in gilt Gothic script, incised 'M', mid 19th C. **£500-600** *SS*

A rare pair of Bow figures of a cow and a bull, extensively damaged, 8¾ in., c. 1755-60. **£500-600** *S*

A Royal Worcester loving cup by Rushton, 5¼ in., 1912. **£400-450** *NSN*

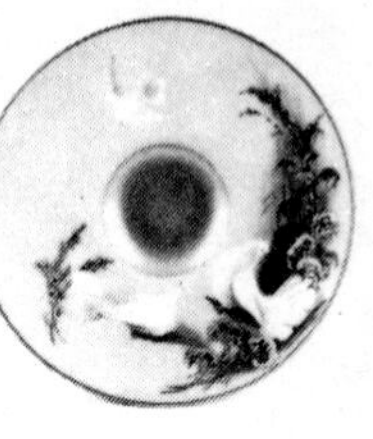
A Royal Worcester demi tasse and saucer, painted and signed by Rushton, with doves by raised foliage, on a sky-blue ground, purple printed marks with date code for 1921. **£150-200** *SC*

A set of 6 Royal Worcester coffee cups and saucers, painted by M. Hunt, signed, with red and pink cabbage roses against a shaded ground, saucer: 9.8 cm., printed crowned circle, painted pattern number C275, date code for 1940, fitted case. **£650-750** *S*

A Chelsea group of 2 goats, their coats lightly incised and marked in black and brown, the base with coloured flowers, repairs and restorations, a firing crack, raised red anchor mark, 11 cm. wide, c. 1750. **£850-1,050** *C*

A Coalbrookdale horse group, 12½ in., 1862. **£345-395** *NSN*
Made for the Exhibition.

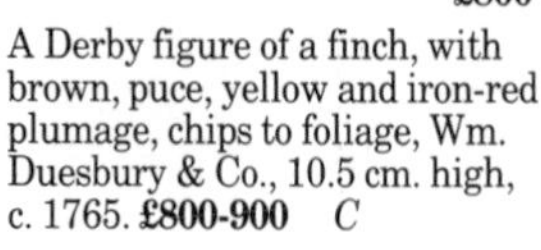

A Derby figure of a finch, with brown, puce, yellow and iron-red plumage, chips to foliage, Wm. Duesbury & Co., 10.5 cm. high, c. 1765. **£800-900** *C*

A pair of Derby dry edge figures of a sheep and ram, the sheep broken away from the base and re-stuck, the ram with minor chips to horn and flowers, Andrew Planche period, 9.5 cm. wide, c. 1753. **£600-£800** *C*

A pair of Derby white and gilt squirrels, 3¼ in., c. 1780. **£450-£480** *DL*

A Derby porcelain squirrel, 3 in. high, c. 1790. **£275-300** *EC*

A pair of Derby bullfinches, 2½ in., c. 1800. **£420-460** *DL*

A white and gilt English porcelain pepper pot, possibly Derby, 3¼ in., c. 1845. **£80-100** *DL*

A Derby porcelain greyhound, 3 in. high, c. 1820. **£225-265** *EC*

A Derby white mouse with green nose and iron-red whiskers, on a lime-green mound with gilding, ears restored, printed Bloor Derby mark within a circle twice, Robert Bloor & Co., 6.5 cm. wide, c. 1830. **£250-300** *C*

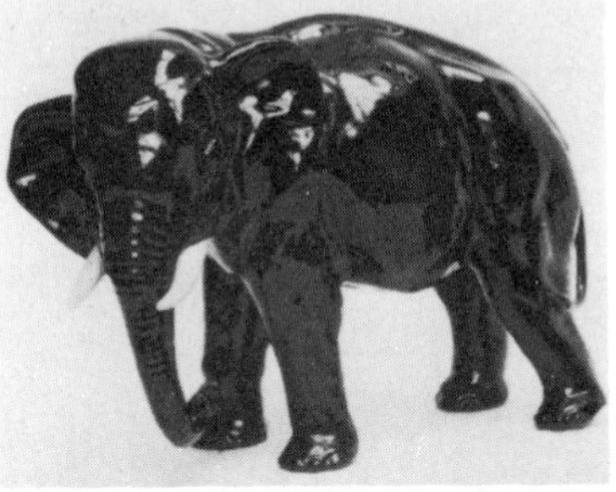

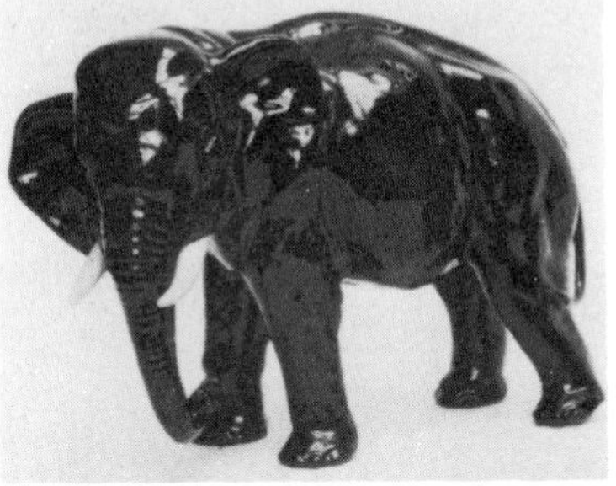

A fine Royal Doulton flambe figure of an elephant, 13 in. high. **£400-£500** *LT*

A Royal Doulton figure, 'Tiger on Rock', HN2639, 16 in. long. **£240-£280** *LT*

A Royal Dux group of a pointer and a setter, on an oval grassy mound, painted in pale enamel and gold, 39 cm. wide. **£180-240** *Bea*

A Royal Doulton figure 'Matador and Bull', HN2324, Noted Large Group, designer Margaret Davies, 16 in. high. **£1,100-1,300** *LT*

A mid 19th C. Meissen mongrel, 6½ in. high. **£180-220** *IHA*

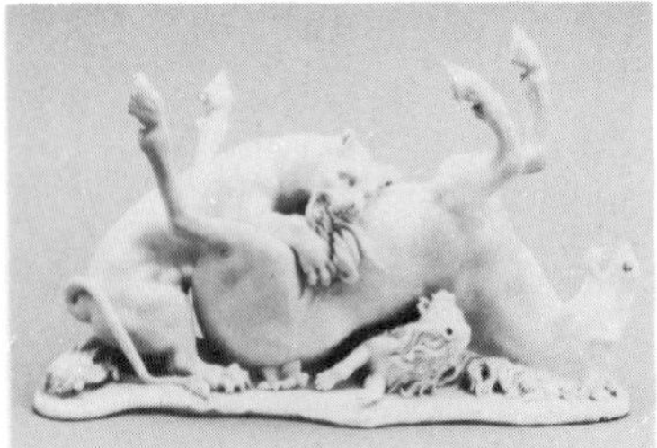

A rare Nymphenburg animal group by Dominikus Auliczek, in white, some restoration, 23 cm., c. 1770. **£1,000-1,300** *S*

A pair of Meissen figures of eagles, decorated in colours, underglaze blue crossed swords mark and incised 836 numerals, chips to foliage and one with minute chip to beak, 31.5 cm. high, c. 1880. **£500-£600** *C*

A large Samson figure of a cockerel, its plumage coloured in brown and black and its tail feathers in orange, yellow, green and mauve, crossed swords in underglaze blue, some restoration, 28¼ in. (72 cm.), late 19th C. **£600-£700** *S*

A Rockingham crouching white hare with gilt collar, chewing green leaves, impressed Rockingham Works Brameld, incised No. 110 and C1.2 in iron-red, ears restored, chips to leaves, 7 cm. wide, 1826-30. **£450-550** *C*

A white and gilt Chamberlain's Worcester deer, marked, 3 in. wide, c. 1825. **£150-180** *DL*

An English porcellanous mouse, 3 in., c. 1835. **£70-80** *DL*

A Royal Worcester model of a 'Dairy Shorthorn Bull', modelled by Doris Linder, No. 368 of a limited edition of 500, complete with wood stand and certificate. **£200-250** *Bea*

An English porcelain dog, 3 in. high, c. 1830. **£100-125** *EC*

A rare Bow figure of a sphinx, in the white, slight damage, 4¾ in., c. 1750. **£500-600** *S*

The modelling of the head is reputed to have been taken from a portrait of the actress Peg Woffington; however the source is far more likely to be a French bronze or engraving.

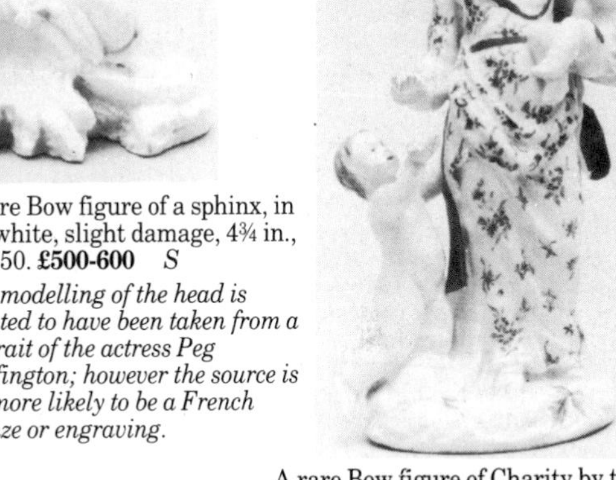
A rare Bow figure of Charity by the Muses Modeller, hands restored, 10 in., c. 1752-55. **£600-700** *S*

A rare Bow figure of a fishergirl after a Meissen original, 6 in., c. 1758. **£600-700** *S*

Formerly in the McMurrin Collection, Vancouver. It is important to note when a piece has come from an important collection as this frequently reflects in the price range.

A Bow figure of Scapin, in puce washed cape, white jacket with gilt frogging and pale yellow breeches, minor restoration to right foot, nose, hand and mask, 12.5 cm. high, 1750-52. **£1,500-1,800** *C*

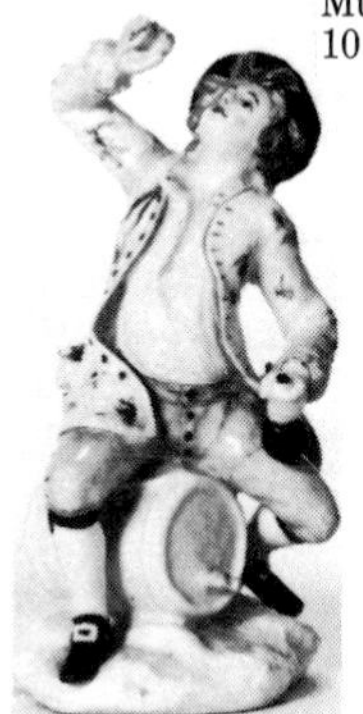
A rare early Bow figure of a Toper after a Meissen original, dressed in puce breeches and black hat, his white jacket painted with floral sprigs, restored, 14.5 cm., c. 1760. **£400-500** *P*

A Bow figure of Polyhymnia by the Muses Modeller, damage to hilt of one sword, 18 cm. high, 1750-52. **£800-1,000** *C*

A good Bow figure group of 2 putti and a goat, the irregular rocky base applied with a profusion of brightly coloured vines, impressed T. for John Toulouse, painted numeral 2, 14.5 cm. **£400-500** *P*

A rare Bow Commedia Del'Arte group of Harlequin and Columbine, restored, 17 cm. **£450-550** *P*
If perfect **£1,000-1,200**

A pair of Bow figures of a shepherd and shepherdess, both on turquoise and gilt pierced scroll bases, some restoration, 6¾ and 7 in., c. 1765. **£400-500** *S*

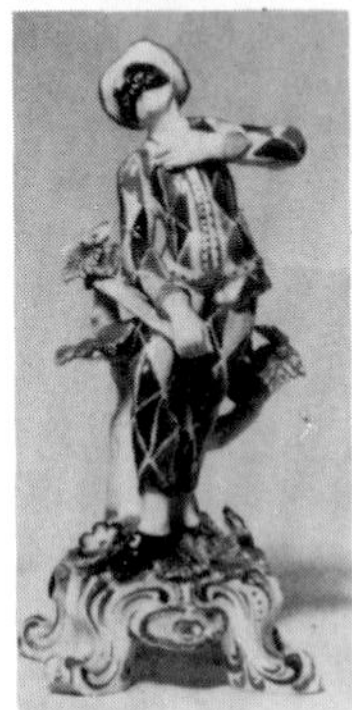

A pair of Bow figures of Harlequin and Columbine, wearing brightly chequered puce, blue, yellow and black clothes, he restored, she with minor chipping to flowers and slapstick, 19 and 19.5 cm., c. 1765. **£900-1,000** *C*

A Bow figure of Harlequin in a chequered pink, green, grey and yellow and black suit edged in gold, chips to leaves, 18.5 cm. high, c. 1765. **£700-800** *C*

A pair of Bow figures of a musician and a flower seller, modelled after Meissen originals, iron-red anchor and dagger mark, the man with some restoration, 15.5 cm., mid 18th C. **£400-450** *Bea*

Miller's is a price GUIDE Not a price LIST.
The price ranges given reflect the average price a purchaser should pay for similar items. Condition, rarity of design or pattern, size, colour, provenance, restoration and many other factors must be taken into account when assessing values.

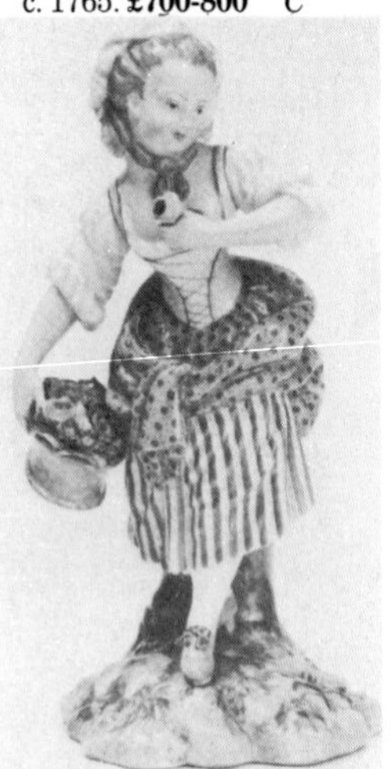

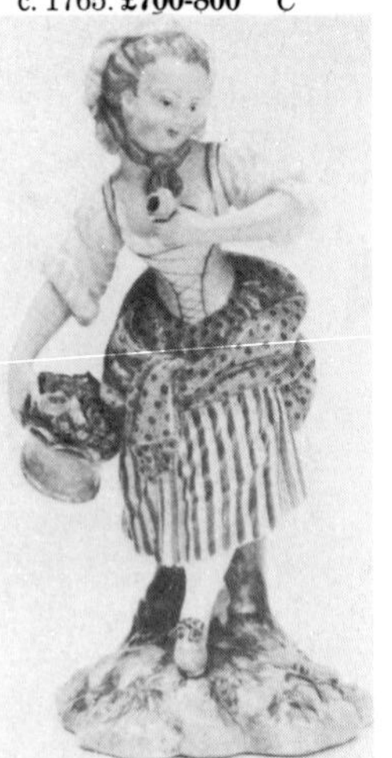

A Royal Copenhagen figure of 'Summer', 19.5 cm., late 18th/early 19th C. **£130-180** *SS*

A pair of Demartial & Tallandier, Limoges, biscuit figures wearing colourful traditional robes, painted initials, mark and numerals, minor damage, 38 cm., c. 1880. **£300-£400** *S*

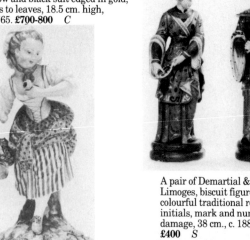

A Bow bocage group, painted in typical enamel colours and embellished in gold, painted sword and anchor mark, some restoration, 20 cm., c. 1760-70. **£300-350** *Bea*

A large pair of Derby figures of Mars and Minerva in plumed helmets, the decoration disguising firing faults in the bases, Mars inscribed Marsicus non Musecum and with the initials FE (?), Minerva with restorations to raised arm, cloak and neck, Wm. Duesbury & Co., 22 and 24.5 cm. high, c. 1756. **£1,600-2,000** *C*

A near pair of rare Derby candlestick figures of a gardener and his companion, chipped, 23.5 cm., c. 1760. **£450-550** *SS*

A pair of Copeland parian figures titled 'Young England' and 'Young England's Sister', modelled by C. Halse, incised marks, impressed Copeland, 16 in., late 19th C. **£250-£300** *SC*

A Derby figure of Mars in gilt cuirass, cracks, slight restoration, 13½ in., c. 1765. **£180-220** *S*

A very rare Derby porcelain group, 8½ in., c. 1765. **£450-500** *DL*

A Derby figure of Minerva, bocage restored, finger missing, 12½ in., c. 1765. **£200-250** *S*

A rare Derby classical group of Hector and Andromache standing beneath a statue to Diana, in bright turquoise and yellow scattered with puce Indian flowers, incised No. 37, patch marks, restored, 37 cm., late 18th C. **£300-£400** *SS*

A Derby figure of Harlequin wearing a green yellow, iron-red, black and white chequered suit, incised No. 199, Wm. Duesbury & Co., minor chips to tree stump, 15 cm. high, c. 1775. **£550-650** *C*

A large Derby figure of Britannia, flanked by a shield and a flag, some damage, 14¼ in., 18th C. **£200-£300** *WHL*

A Derby figure of the goddess Minerva, painted in bright enamel colours, slight damage, 37 cm., late 18th C. **£250-300** *Bea*

A Derby figure of Neptune, incised No. 299, damaged, 10½ in., c. 1785. **£250-300** *S*

A Derby figure of a young woman playing a lute, painted in bright enamel colours and gold, slight damage, 16.5 cm., late 18th C. **£150-200** *Bea*

A Derby figure, slight restoration, 5 in., 1790-1810. **£45-65** *NSN*

A pair of Derby groups depicting 'The Welsh Tailor and his Wife', painted in naturalistic enamel colours and gold, painted mark, some damage and restoration, 2nd quarter 19th C. **£500-550** *Bea*

A Doccia pastoral group painted with enamel colours, the features in typical dotted iron-red, damaged, 17 cm., mid 18th C. **£650-750** *Bea*

A good Doulton figure of a 'Jester' modelled by C. J. Noke, wearing lilac and black costume, script signature, title and HN55, green printed marks and impressed date for 1923, 10 in. **£500-550** *SC*

A Derby group of a gallant and his maid, minor damage, incised No. 81, 17.8 cm., c. 1840. **£300-400** *S*

A Royal Doulton figure of a 'Jester', after a model by C. J. Noke, moulded signature, printed lion and crown mark, painted mark, title and HN71, impressed date code for 1920, 24 cm. **£250-350** *S*

An early Doulton figure of Guy Fawkes in a long red cloak, green printed mark title in red script with HN98 above CN, impressed date 1.3.29., 10 in. **£300-350** *SC*

A Royal Doulton figure entitled 'The Balloon Seller', after the original by Leslie Harradine, HN583, withdrawn 1949. **£150-£200** *Bea*

A Royal Doulton figure of 'Anthea', printed mark and title, painted mark, title and HN 1527, impressed date code for 1933, 6¼ in. **£130-180** *S*

A Royal Doulton figure of 'Captain MacHeath', designed by L. Harradine, HN464, potted by Doulton, impressed date 8.32, introduced 1921, withdrawn 1949, c.m.l. & c., 18.5 cm. high. **£250-£300** *P*

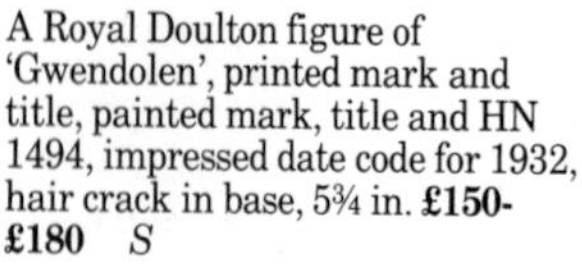
A Royal Doulton figure of 'The Bride', printed mark and title, painted HN 1600, impressed date code for 1935, hair cracks, 8¾ in. **£100-150** *S*

A Royal Doulton figure of 'The Bather', printed lion, crown and circle mark, painted mark, title and HN 687, impressed date code for 1929, 7½ in. **£400-500** *S*

A Royal Doulton figure of 'Modena', printed mark, painted title and HN 1845, impressed date code for 1938, 7¼ in. **£400-500** *S*

A Royal Doulton figure of 'Gwendolen', printed mark and title, painted mark, title and HN 1494, impressed date code for 1932, hair crack in base, 5¾ in. **£150-£180** *S*

A Royal Doulton figure of 'Irene', printed mark and title, painted HN 1621, impressed date code for 1936, 6½ in. **£160-190** *S*

A Royal Doulton figure of 'Eleanore', printed mark, painted title and HN 1754, impressed date code for 1936, hair crack, 7¼ in. **£110-140** *S*

A Royal Doulton figure of 'Mendicant', coloured in mottled black, ochre and blue, printed lion, crown and circle, title and HN 1365, date code for 1931, 20.8 cm. **£150-200** *S*

A Royal Doulton figure of 'Maisie', with a shaded crimson dress, printed lion, crown and circle, title and registration number, painted HN 1619, printed date code for 1935, 15.6 cm. **£150-200** *S*

A Royal Doulton figure titled 'The Cobbler', picked out in bright coloured glazes, printed mark in black, script title and HN 1283 in black, impressed date 1.1.30, 9 in. **£120-150** *SC*

A Royal Doulton figure entitled 'Kathleen', designed by L. Harradine, HN 1253, c.m. & l., introduced 1927, withdrawn 1938, 19.5 cm. high. **£200-250** *P*

A Royal Doulton figure entitled 'Celia', designed by L. Harradine, HN 1727, c.m.l. & c. date code for 1936, introduced 1935, withdrawn 1949, 29.5 cm. high. **£450-500** *P*

A pair of Royal Doulton figures entitled 'Darby' and 'Joan', HN 2024 and HN 2023, each withdrawn in 1959. **£200-250** *Bea*

A Doulton figure 'Top o' the Hill', HN 1833, 7 in. **£120-140** *NSN*

(l.) A Royal Doulton figure of 'Sunshine Girl', printed lion, crown and circle mark, painted title and HN 1344, impressed date code for 1929, 5 in. **£500-600** *S*

The figure may have been inspired by the musical comedy The Sunshine Girl, first performed at the Gaiety Theatre on 24 February 1912. It concerned the love affair of the girl Delia Dale, played by Phyllis Dare, from the Port Sunlight soap factory, and the factory owner.

(r.) A Royal Doulton figure of 'Dulcinia' (sic), printed lion, crown and circle mark, painted title and HN 1419, impressed date code for 1930, 5½ in. **£500-600** *S*

A Doulton figure, 'The Orange Lady', HN 1953, 8¼ in. **£95-110** *NSN*

ROYAL DOULTON FIGURES

- **since 1913 2,000 different models have been produced by the Royal Doulton factory**
- **basically thought of as a modern day Staffordshire figure revival**
- **since 1920's figures mainly designed by Peggy Davies, Leslie Harradine and Mary Nicoll**
- **the HN numbering sequence was introduced with Charles Vyse 'Darling' HN 1 (which is still in production today)**
- **since 1938 new figures are introduced only to replace ones which are to be withdrawn and so at any one time there are only 200-300 figures in production**
- **any figure which is unsuccessful is withdrawn – and those are the ones most sought after by collectors**
- **this section is ordered in HN number sequence**

A Royal Doulton figure of St. George, designed by Stanley Thorogood, A.R.A.C., printed mark and titled, HN 2067, 39.7 cm., 1950-76. **£700-800** *S*

A Doulton figure, 'School Marm', HN 2223, 7 in. **£100-120** *NSN*

A Dresden group of a fallen woman reproached by an elderly companion, crossed swords and star in underglaze blue, one hand missing, chips, 24 cm., late 19th C. **£250-300** *S*

A Royal Doulton figure, 'Memories', designed by L. Harradine, HN 2030, c.m.l. & c., introduced 1949, withdrawn 1959, 15.5 cm. high. **£120-150** *P*

A Royal Doulton figure, 'Standing Beefeater', holding a facsimile of the first edition of the Illustrated London News, c.m. & l. impressed date 10.28, introduced approximately 1924, withdrawn 1938, 19.5 cm. high. **£650-750** *P*

A Royal Dux porcelain group of young boy with pink tunic with 2 white stallions, on green and gilt rocky ground, 17¼ in. high, 16¼ in. long. **£450-550** *DSH*

A pair of Royal Dux busts, coloured in pastel tones of pink, green and brown, applied and impressed pink triangle mark, minor chips, 40 and 41 cm., c. 1910. **£500-600** *S*

An unrecorded Royal Doulton figure of a kitchen maid, printed lion crown and circle mark, painted marks, HN 2213, 13.5 cm., c. 1960. **£250-350** *Bon*

Royal Doulton are without details for this figure which is probably a pilot model. The present production model using this HN number is a completely different model.

A Royal Dux group, all picked out in pale colours and gilding, oval base, applied triangle mark, impressed 1725, 19¾ in. (52 cm.), c. 1900. **£400-500** *SC*

A pair of Royal Dux porcelain figures of lady in pink dress with plumed hat, and gentleman in a green frockcoat holding a rose, 22½ in. high, c. 1900. **£450-550** *DSH*

A Frankenthal figure of a hurdygurdy player in green hat, black cape, chequered jacket and maroon breeches, blue rampant lion mark and interlaced monogram of Joseph-Adam-Hannong and impressed repairers mark HAE2, 1756-59, minor restoration, 16 cm. high. **£900-£1,100** *C*

A Frankenthal white figure of a boy disguised as L'Abbé modelled by Johann Friedrich Lück, blue rampant lion mark and incised JH.1. of Joseph Hannong, minor repairs, 17 cm. high, c. 1759. **£1,000-1,200** *C*

A rare Fürstenberg figure of a girl in a yellow and black cap, orange bodice and purple striped skirt, marked F in blue, 14.5 cm., c. 1770. **£700-800** *S*

A Frankenthal figure of a baker's wife, blue rampant lion mark and monogram of Joseph-Adam-Hannong, minor chips, 19.5 cm. high, c. 1760. **£800-1,000** *C*

A Frankenthal figure of a beggar man modelled by K. G. Lück, blue crowned CT mark and the date 1776, minor repairs, 15.5 cm. high. **£650-850** *C*

A rare allegorical Frankenthal group modelled by Adam Bauer, all painted in sombre colours heightened in gilding, incised numerals, firing crack, slight damage, 29.5 cm., c. 1777. **£1,700-£2,000** *S*

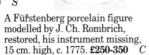

FRANKENTHAL

- **Paul A. Hannong started producing porcelain in Frankenthal in 1755, under the patronage of the Elector Carl Theodor**
- **glaze has a quite distinctive quality as it tends to 'soak in' the enamel colours**
- **high quality porcelain produced under Modellmeister J. W. Lanz, who favoured striped gilt grounds and green and crimson**
- **K. G. Lück and his brother or cousin J. F. Lück came to Frankenthal from Meissen in 1758**
- **K. G. Lück's work tends to be quite fussy and often on grassy mounds, with rococo edges picked out in gilding**
- **in the late 18th C. a fine range of figures produced by J. P. Melchior and A. Bauer**
- **Melchior's figures tend to have a rather severe look**
- **Frankenthal utility ware is noted for the quality of the painting**
- **factory closed in 1799**
- **moulds from the factory were used in many other 19th C. German factories**

An interesting Fürstenberg figure of a fisherman, probably modelled by J. Ch. Rombrich, covered in a creamy glaze, F in underglaze blue, incised a/No. 14/LB, minute chips, 7.8 cm., c. 1775. **£300-400** *S*

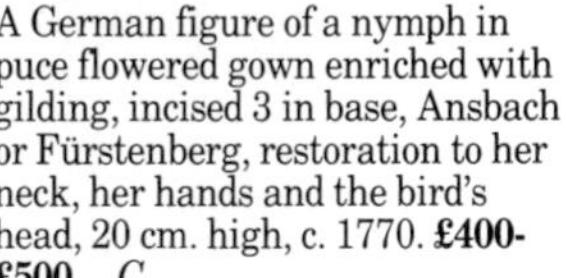

A German figure of a nymph in puce flowered gown enriched with gilding, incised 3 in base, Ansbach or Fürstenberg, restoration to her neck, her hands and the bird's head, 20 cm. high, c. 1770. **£400-£500** *C*

The modelling and colouring resembles the figures produced at Fürstenberg by Anton Carl Luplau and Simon Feilner.

A Fürstenberg porcelain figure modelled by J. Ch. Rombrich, restored, his instrument missing, 15 cm. high, c. 1775. **£250-350** *C*

A Fürstenberg figure of a miner after the original model by Simon Feilner, blue script F mark, repair to the end of his hammer and his neck, 17 cm. high, c. 1790. **£400-£500** *C*

A biscuit porcelain figure by Gardner of an old man wearing a white blouse and blue trousers, maker's mark in red and incised, numbered 21, 6¼ in. (16 cm.), late 19th C. **£250-300** *S*

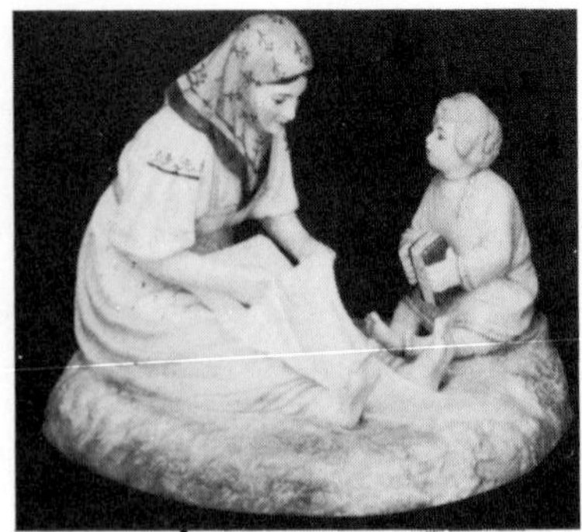

A biscuit porcelain group by Gardner, of a laundress and child, maker's mark in red and incised, numbered 132, 4½ in. (11.5 cm.), late 19th C. **£500-600** *S*

A Höchst figure of a tailor, iron-red wheel mark and painter's mark C, believed to be the mark of Lothar Sharlot, some restorations to the horns, damage to the scissors and iron, 17 cm. high, c. 1760. **£4,000-£5,000** *C*

Unrecorded in Röder.

A Höchst group of a Chinese boy and a girl modelled by J. P. Melchior, blue crowned wheel mark, his topknot chipped and restored, 17.5 cm. high, c. 1770. **£1,200-1,500** *C*

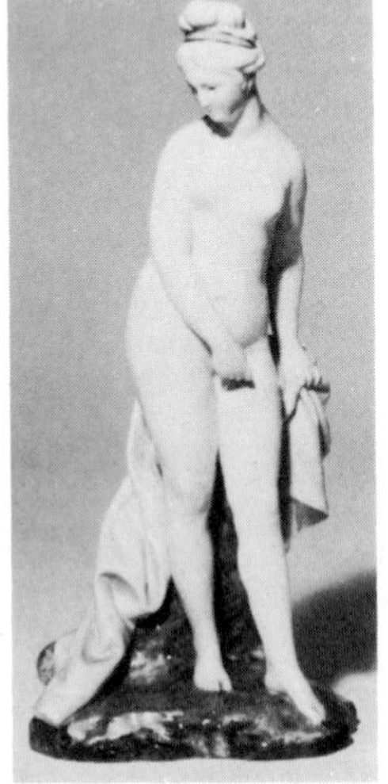

A Höchst figure of Venus, before a tree stump draped in a pink and yellow cloth, blue wheel mark, incised marks S71N14, 19 cm. high, c. 1770. **£3,000-3,500** *C*

A pair of Holics groups of a shepherd and shepherdess, one with H mark in manganese, both with some restoration, 22.5 cm. high, c. 1750. **£1,500-2,500** *C*

A Le Nove figure of a young man, in brown, red and yellow, restoration to his left arm and the end of the tree stump, 12.5 cm. high, c. 1770. **£600-800** *C*

A Hutschenreuther porcelain figure of a dancer, wearing a short yellow dress, marked 'Hutschenreuther, Selt, Germany, Kunstabteilung', 28 cm. high. **£200-250** *P*

A Limbach figure of a Sultan in yellow, white and iron-red turban, iron-red ermine-trimmed cloak, puce LB mark, right arm missing, repair to topknot, neck and hand, 20 cm. high, c. 1775. **£300-400** *C*

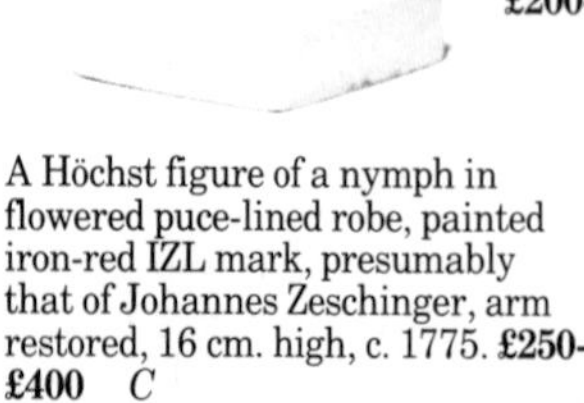

A Höchst figure of a nymph in flowered puce-lined robe, painted iron-red IZL mark, presumably that of Johannes Zeschinger, arm restored, 16 cm. high, c. 1775. **£250-£400** *C*

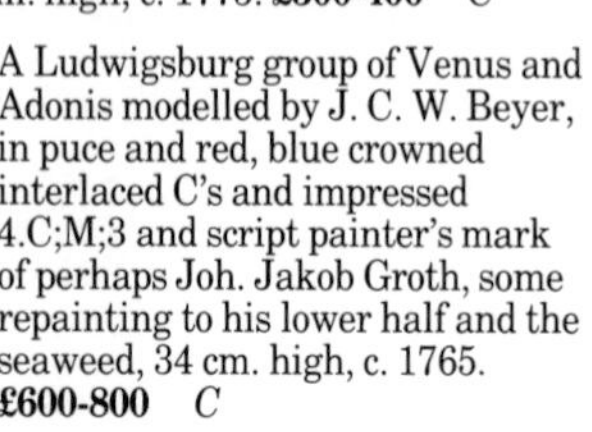

A Ludwigsburg group of Venus and Adonis modelled by J. C. W. Beyer, in puce and red, blue crowned interlaced C's and impressed 4.C;M;3 and script painter's mark of perhaps Joh. Jakob Groth, some repainting to his lower half and the seaweed, 34 cm. high, c. 1765. **£600-800** *C*

HÖCHST MARK

Wheelmark, incised, impressed, in blue or in coloured enamels, c.1750-96

A Ludwigsburg group of rearing horses with Turkish groom modelled by J. J. Lovis, blue crowned CC monogram and incised 3T.F. N;3L and iron-red painter's mark S of Sausenhofer, the horses forequarters, neck and head restored, other minor repairs and chips, c. 1765. **£2,000-2,500** *C*

A Ludwigsburg figure of a peasant woman, blue crowned interlaced C's and H incised, damage to her hat and staff, 19 cm. high, c. 1765. **£600-800** *C*

A Meissen group of seated lovers modelled by J. F. Eberlein, repair to her neck, her left leg and his left foot, 15.5 cm. high, c. 1745. **£1,200-£1,600** *C*

First modelled by Eberlein in 1740.

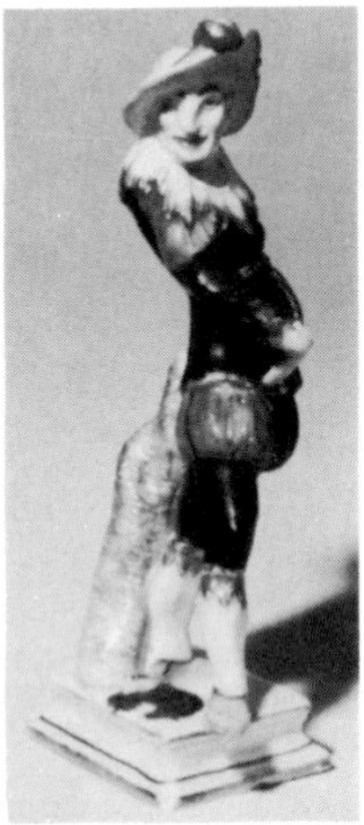

A Meissen Italian Comedy figure of Harlequin, in puce, black and iron-red, blue crossed swords mark, chips to hat, his left lower arm missing, minor chips to base, 17 cm. high, c. 1730. **£4,000-£6,000** *C*

A Meissen figure of a seated bear modelled by J. J. Kändler, traces of blue crossed swords mark, 10 cm. high, the porcelain, c. 1745. **£900-£1,200** *C*

This model is unrecorded in Albiker.

A Meissen equestrian figure of a man, blue crossed swords mark, restored, 21 cm. wide, c. 1745. **£700-800** *C*

A Meissen figure of a miner (Bergmann) modelled by J. J. Kändler and P. Reinicke, blue crossed swords mark at back and painter's mark in puce of a T bisecting an O, chip to end of his baton, 20.5 cm. high, c. 1750. **£3,000-4,000** *C*

A Meissen figure of Harlequin with a birdcage, modelled by Johan Friederick Eberlein, slight restoration, 13.5 cm. **£1,200-£1,500** *P*

Modelled by Eberlein in August 1743.

A Meissen figure of a dancing girl, in puce, white and green, blue crossed swords mark and Pressnummer 24, restored, 11.5 cm. high, c. 1760. **£350-450** *C*

A Meissen group of a Pole and companion, 10 cm. high, c. 1755. **£500-600** *C*

A Meissen figure of a Bacchanalian putto in a puce and blue cloak, blue crossed swords mark, minor chips, 13 cm. wide, c. 1760. **£300-400** *C*

A Meissen crinoline group 'Der Kuss' by J. J. Kändler, traces of crossed swords in blue, restored, 12 cm., c. 1746-50. **£700-800** *S*

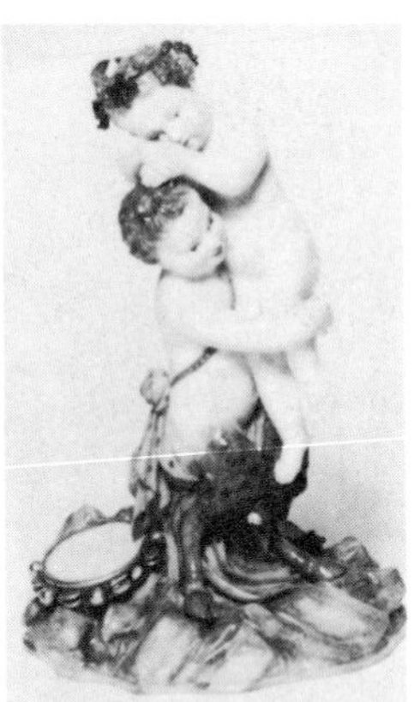

A Meissen group modelled as a baby satyr and cherub, crossed swords in underglaze blue, incised D28, minor chips, 6¾ in. (17.5 cm.), mid 19th C. **£300-400** *S*

A Meissen group emblematic of Marriage, blue crossed swords mark, 19 cm. high, c. 1760. **£1,300-£1,500** *C*

A Meissen group of a young girl, blue crossed swords mark and Pressnummer 13, 12.5 cm. high, c. 1760. **£650-750** *C*

A Meissen figure of a young woman admiring a rose, painted in bright enamel colours, some damage, 15.5 cm., mid 18th C. **£500-600** *Bea*

A set of 5 late Meissen figures emblematic of the Senses, modelled by von Schönheit, crossed swords mark and incised E1 to E5, 12 to 14 cm. high. **£1,400-1,600** *P*

A late Meissen group, modelled by Acier, depicting Frederick the Great, crossed swords mark, 45 cm. **£800-900** *P*

A pair of Meissen figures from the 'Senses' set, one with slight damage, 5½ in., c. 1870-80. **£500-£600** *NSN*

A Meissen figure of Europa on the bull, 9 in. high, c. 1870. **£375-420** *TA*

A Meissen drinking group, their clothes decorated in colours and enriched in gilding, blue crossed swords marks, incised C65 and impressed numerals, chips to foliage, 21.5 cm. high, c. 1880. **£550-650** *C*

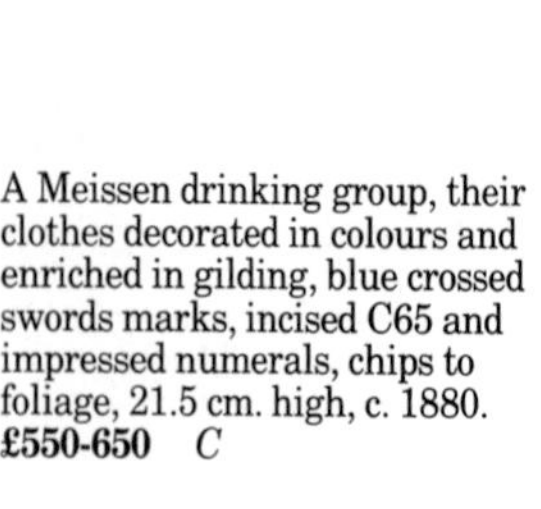

A pair of Meissen figures of a chorister and a triangle player from a monkey band, blue crossed swords mark, 5¾ and 4¾ in., 19th C. **£225-250** *WW*

A large Meissen group of 'Lessons in Love', crossed swords in underglaze blue, incised F74, minor damage, 11¼ in. (28.5 cm.), mid 19th C. **£1,000-1,200** *S*

A Meissen outside decorated pagoda figure, after J. J. Kändler, wearing a yellow-lined robe painted with Indianische Blumen, outstretched hands, head and tongue pivoted to rock rhythmically, cancelled crossed swords in underglaze blue, incised 2883, 12½ in. (31.5 cm.), mid 19th C. **£2,800-3,000** *S*

A Meissen group of 2 young flower-sellers, underglaze blue crossed swords, single score mark, late 19th C., 16 cm. **£350-400** *Bon*

A Meissen group of 'The Good Mother' after the original by von Schönheit, their clothes decorated in colours and enriched with gilding, blue crossed swords marks, incised E69 and impressed numerals, boy's arm chipped and restored, chips to feathers of child's hat, 21.5 cm. high, c. 1880. **£700-£800** *C*

A pair of Meissen figures of baby satyrs, each playing a tambourine or cymbals and dancing, crossed swords in underglaze blue, incised D49 and D50, chips, 7 and 6¾ in. (17.5 and 17.2 cm.), mid to late 19th C. **£300-400** *S*

A Meissen group of youthful lovers, the mound base with a formal border, crossed swords in underglaze blue, incised F91, 5½ in. (14 cm.), late 19th C. **£500-£600** *S*

A large Meissen figure of Count Bruhl's tailor, after J. J. Kändler, crossed swords in underglaze blue, incised 107, minor damage, 16½ in. (42 cm.), mid 19th C. **£2,000-£2,500** *S*

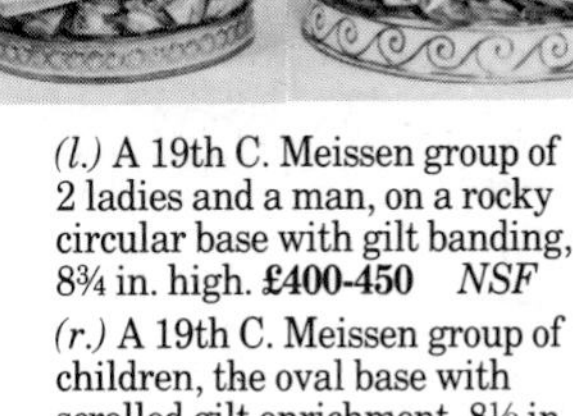

(l.) A 19th C. Meissen group of 2 ladies and a man, on a rocky circular base with gilt banding, 8¾ in. high. **£400-450** *NSF*

(r.) A 19th C. Meissen group of children, the oval base with scrolled gilt enrichment, 8½ in. high. **£500-550** *NSF*

A Meissen figure titled 'Je les ramêne' depicting Cupid holding aloft a floral garland, crossed swords and dot mark. **£250-300** *Bon*

A pair of Meissen figural table salts, encrusted and painted with flower sprays, underglaze blue crossed swords mark, the maid with one ankle repaired, length 18 cm. **£400-500** *Bon*

A Meissen group of child vintagers, in 18th C. style rustic dress, cancelled crossed swords in underglaze blue, incised G93, chips, 6 in. (15.5 cm.), late 19th C. **£500-600** *S*

A Meissen group, crossed swords in underglaze blue and incised numerals 2654, some damage, 6¼ in., late 19th C. **£90-140** *WHL*

A Meissen figure of a young girl wearing lace-trimmed clothes, crossed swords in underglaze blue, incised F32, chips, 5¾ in. (14.8 cm.), c. 1880. **£400-500** *S*

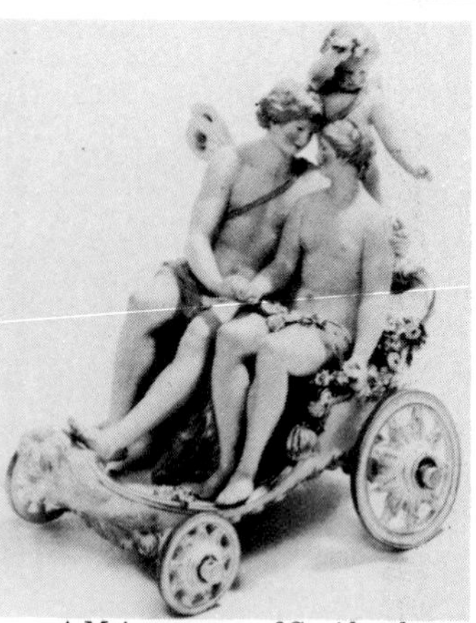

A Meissen group of Cupid and Psyche, cancelled crossed swords in underglaze blue, chips, 23.5 cm., c. 1880. **£550-650** *S*

A Meissen group of amorous gardeners, crossed swords in underglaze blue, incised B17, 10 in. (25.2 cm.), late 19th C. **£600-£700** *S*

A pair of Meissen nodding mandarin figures, with deutsche-Blumen sprigged drapery, with articulated heads, hands and tongues, swords mark in blue, incised numeral, 7½ in. (19 cm.), late 19th C. **£800-900** *SC*

A Meissen group, crossed swords in underglaze blue and incised numerals 2685, some damage, 6½ in., late 19th C. **£100-140** *WHL*

A pair of Meissen figures of a gardener and companion, crossed swords marks in underglaze blue, impressed numerals, girls basket damaged, 5¼ in., late 19th C. **£300-£400** *SC*

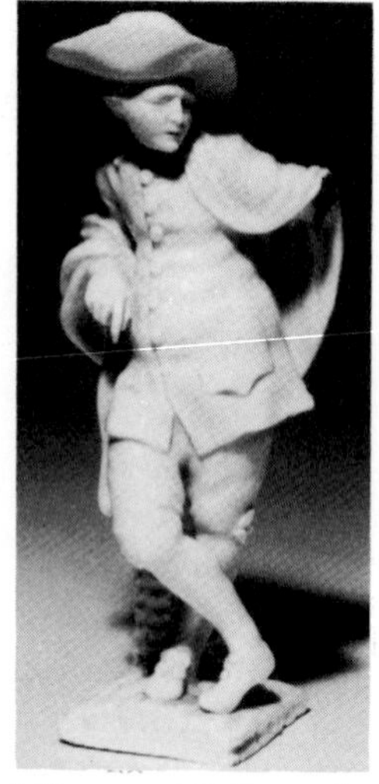

A Mennecy white figure of a young man, left arm missing, 17.5 cm. high, c. 1740. **£250-350** *C*

A Meissen rustic group, enriched in turquoise, pink and with gilding, blue crossed swords mark, incised J93 and impressed numerals, minor chips, 15.5 cm. high, c. 1900. **£500-600** *C*

A rare pair of Minton sweetmeat dishes, 5½ in. high, c. 1835. Restored **£350-400** Perfect **£700-£800** *DL*

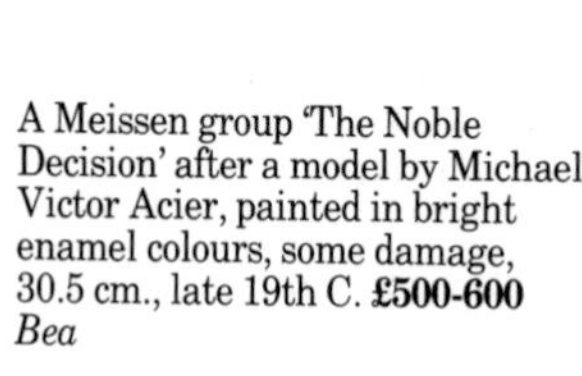

A Meissen group 'The Noble Decision' after a model by Michael Victor Acier, painted in bright enamel colours, some damage, 30.5 cm., late 19th C. **£500-600** *Bea*

A Minton pair of candlestick figures, 9 in., c. 1835. **£750-800** *DL*

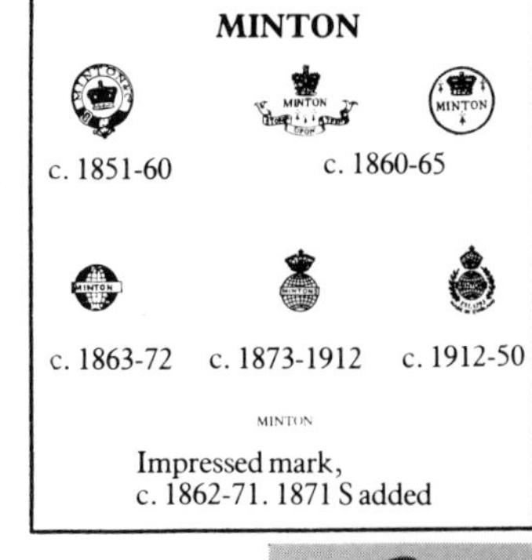
MINTON

c. 1851-60 c. 1860-65

c. 1863-72 c. 1873-1912 c. 1912-50

MINTON

Impressed mark, c. 1862-71. 1871 S added

A Minton white biscuit porcelain figure in the form of a Meissen original representing 'Hearing', 14 cm., mid 19th C. **£120-150** *Bea*

Two Plymouth figures of Summer and Autumn, Summer in blue and iron-red and Autumn in puce, on scroll moulded bases enriched in puce and turquoise, William Cookworthy's Factory, Summer with restoration to right arm and sickle, with minor chipping, 12 and 12.5 cm. high, c. 1770. **£350-400** *C*

A pair of Nymphenburg figures of Bavarians, he with impressed Bavarian shield mark and inscribed Bl, chip to her hat, 18.5 cm. high, c. 1820. **£300-400** *C*

A Russian Imperial Porcelain factory figure of a young boy wearing a blue shirt and striped trousers, 8½ in. (22 cm.) high, c. 1817. **£1,000-1,200** *S*

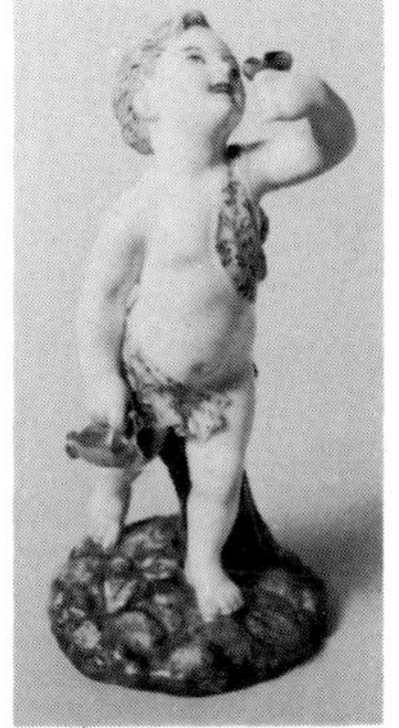
A Royal Worcester figure, 6¾ in., 1874. **£180-220** *NSN*

A Royal Worcester figure of 'The Chinaman', 6¼ in., 1886. **£100-£120** *NSN*

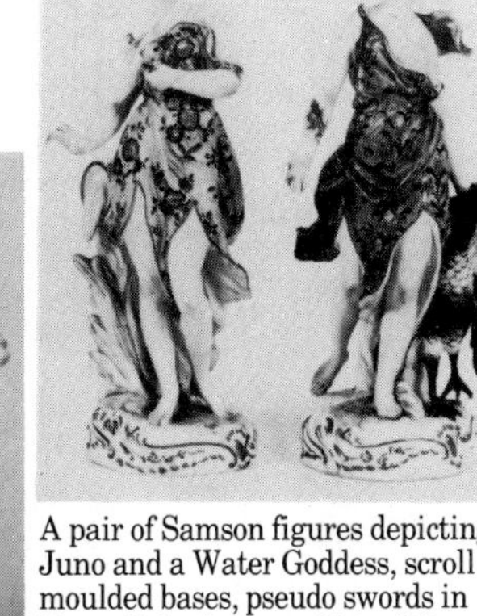
A pair of Samson figures depicting Juno and a Water Goddess, scroll moulded bases, pseudo swords in blue, slight damage, 11 in. (28 cm.), late 19th C. **£160-240** *SC*

Make the most of Miller's
Every care has been taken to ensure the accuracy of descriptions and estimated valuations.
Where an attribution is made within inverted commas (e.g. 'Chippendale') or is followed by the word 'style' (e.g. early Georgian style) it is intended to convey that, in the opinion of the publishers, the piece concerned is a later – though probably still antique – reproduction of the style so designated.
Unless otherwise stated, any description which refers to 'a set' or 'a pair' includes a valuation for the entire set or the pair, even though the illustration may show only a single item.

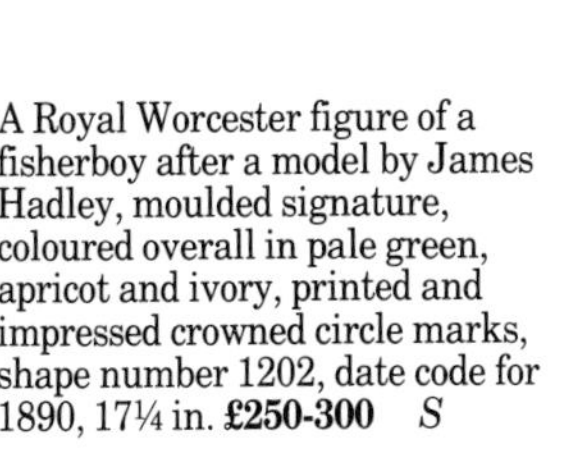
A Royal Worcester figure of a fisherboy after a model by James Hadley, moulded signature, coloured overall in pale green, apricot and ivory, printed and impressed crowned circle marks, shape number 1202, date code for 1890, 17¼ in. **£250-300** *S*

A Royal Worcester porcelain figure, small repair, 15⅞ in. high. **£180-240** *GC*

A Royal Worcester figure wearing a pink and gilt robe, green printed mark including date code probably for 1897, 13 in. **£250-300** *SC*

A pair of Royal Worcester enamelled figures, 8½ in., c. 1900. **£450-500** *NSN*

A Royal Worcester figure of a Water Goddess, wearing a greenish gilt drapery, purple printed mark including date code for 1912, slight crack, 9½ in. **£150-200** *SC*

A Royal Worcester figure of a Cairo Water Carrier, wearing gilt and green drapery, green printed mark with date code for 1912, 10 in. **£200-250** *SC*

A pair of Royal Worcester figures of Bringaree Indians, printed crowned circle mark, shape number 1243 and date code for 1916, one cracked, 8¾ in. **£300-400** *S*

A rare Royal Worcester figure of a Puritan, picked out in coloured sprigs and gilding, purple printed marks including date code for 1918, gilding slightly rubbed, 7¼ in. **£180-260** *SC*

A Royal Worcester figure of a Grecian Water Carrier, wearing gilt flowing drapery, purple printed mark with date code for 1919, fingers damaged, 9¾ in. **£100-£140** *SC*

A Royal Worcester figure, 'Colleen', 6¼ in., 1931. **£100-150** *NSN*

A Royal Worcester equestrian figure of the Duke of Marlborough, after a model by Bernard Winskill, printed crowned circle mark, title, facsimile signature, numbered 111 from an edition of 350, 1974, numbered certificate, brass-banded rosewood stand, 17¾ in. **£950-£1,050** *S*

A Royal Worcester figure of 'Louisa', after a model by Ruth van Ruyckveldt, printed crowned circle mark, title, facsimile signature and dated 1961, fitted box, certificate numbered 260 from an edition of 500, 18.4 cm. **£400-500** *S*

A Royal Worcester figure of 'Rebecca' after an original by Ruth van Ruyckveldt, printed crowned circle mark, title, facsimile signature and dated 1961, fitted box, certificate numbered 206 from an edition of 500, 19.8 cm. **£500-£600** *S*

A Royal Worcester figure of 'Melanie', after a model by Ruth van Ruyckveldt, printed crowned circle mark, title, facsimile signature and dated 1964, fitted box, certificate numbered 22 from an edition of 500, 20.3 cm. **£500-£600** *S*

A Zurich figure of a clarinetist in pink and yellow, Z in underglaze blue, slight damage to clarinet, 15 cm., c. 1770. **£2,600-2,900** *S*

A Royal Worcester figure of 'Elizabeth', after a model by Ruth van Ruyckveldt, printed crowned circle mark, title, facsimile signature and dated 1967, fitted box, certificate numbered 112 from an edition of 500, 21.2 cm. **£250-£300** *S*

An early English porcelain girl playing with mice, 5 in., c. 1835. **£45-65** *GCA*

A pair of continental coloured biscuit figures, coloured in a pastel palette with gilt details, mounted as lamp bases, 14¾ and 15 in. (37.5 and 38 cm.) excluding fittings, mid 19th C. **£480-560** *S*

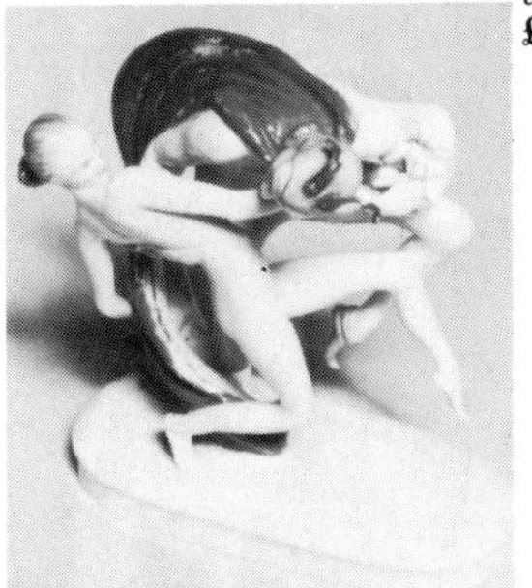

A German porcelain 'devil and dancer' group, 7 in. wide, c. 1930's. **£150-200** *IHA*

An Aynsley plate, not signed, impressed mark, 9 in., c. 1870-80. **£65-75** *NSN*

A pair of Royal Worcester moon flasks, on a blue ground gilt with overlapping diaper mon and ferns, the foot simulating a giltwood stand, printed crowned circle mark and date code for 1875, 25.3 cm. **£300-400** *S*

A pair of Derby pilgrim flasks, turquoise blue ground, 11½ in., c. 1870. **£1,000-1,200** *NSN*

An Aynsley plate, signed by Robert Keeling, 9 in., c. 1870-80. **£120-£140** *NSN*

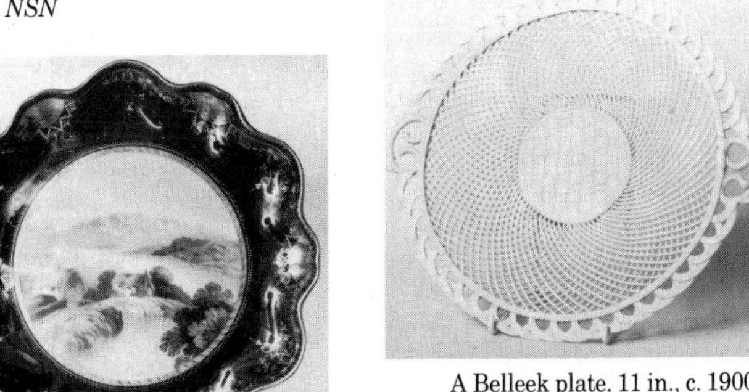

A Belleek plate, 11 in., c. 1900. **£180-200** *NSN*

A Charles Bourne plate, 8½ in., c. 1820. **£100-120** *NSN*

A Caughley plate with blue and gilt decoration, 8 in., c. 1790, marked Salopian. **£110-130** *NSN*

A rare Belleek 'Chinese tea ware' tray moulded with a dragon, in lilac and pale yellow lustre, printed dog and harp mark and P.O.D.R. mark for 1872, chipped, 15¼ in. **£350-400** *S*

A Chelsea leaf dish, moulded as a full blown chrysanthemum with over-lapping leaf, the details painted in mauve and blue, red anchor mark, chipped, 23 cm., c. 1755. **£450-500** *SS*

A fine pair of Chelsea claret ground dishes with feather moulded rims edged in turquoise and gilding, within gilt floral and trellis borders, gold anchor marks, one with old chip on footrim, 13½ in., c. 1760. **£700-800** *WHL*

A Chelsea botanical plate painted with purple lily with foliage in tones of green, firing crack to well, minor rubbing, 24 cm. diam., c. 1755. **£700-800** *C*

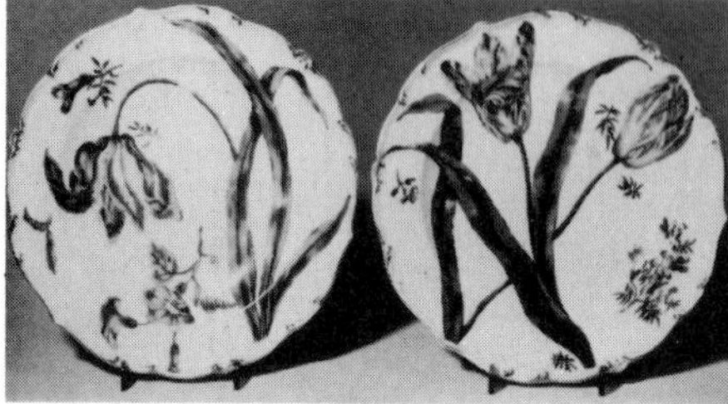

A pair of Chelsea plates painted in the botanical style within moulded gilt C-scroll borders, gold anchor marks, 21 cm. diam., c. 1758. **£1,000-1,300** *C*

Chelsea like most contemporary European factories were influenced by the prevailing Meissen fashion. The present examples are akin to the deutsche-Blumen style; the botanical studies dominate the surface in contrast to Meissen wares which were less boldly conceived.

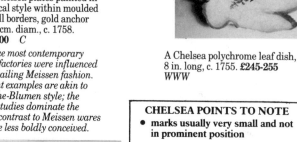

A Chelsea polychrome leaf dish, 8 in. long, c. 1755. **£245-255** *WWW*

A pair of Chelsea shaped oval dishes painted with bouquets and sprays of garden flowers within a moulded border, red anchor marks, 29 cm. wide, c. 1755. **£600-800** *C*

CHELSEA POINTS TO NOTE

- **marks usually very small and not in prominent position**
- **paste varies from white to greenish when seen by transmitted light**
- **on red anchor ware, look out for 'moons' caused by frit in the kiln, also seen by transmitted light**
- **three spur marks often found on the base, left by kiln supports, also a feature of Arita porcelain (not to be confused with Derby pad marks)**
- **glaze on early pieces is reasonably opaque, this later becomes clearer and more glassy. Later still it becomes thicker when it tends to craze**

A Coalport plate on deep blue ground, with raised gilding, 8¾ in., c. 1820. **£100-130** *NSN*

A Coalport plate with yellow ground, c. 1900-10. **£130-160** *NSN*

A pair of oval Chelsea dishes, painted in bright colours with fruit and butterflies, brown anchor mark, slightly rubbed on the interior, 10⅞ in., c. 1755. **£350-400** *S*

Right

A Coalport plate, 9¼ in., c. 1820. **£120-160** *NSN*

A Coalport plate by P. Simpson, 9 in., c. 1910-15. **£140-150** *NSN*

A Coalport plate, with deep blue ground and brightly painted birds, 9 in., c. 1910. **£55-65** *NSN*

A Copeland jewelled plate, deep blue ground, 8¼ in., c. 1851-85. **£130-150** *NSN*

A Davenport plate, painted with flowers, 9 in., 1837-45. **£85-100** *NSN*

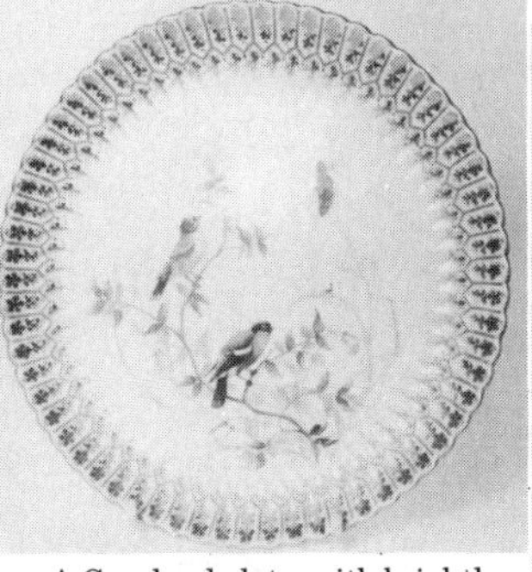
A Copeland plate, with brightly coloured birds, 8¼ in., c. 1870. **£120-160** *NSN*

A good Derby dessert plate, well painted by Richard Dodson, finely painted border of blossom and butterflies, gilt edged rim, crown, crossed batons and script D mark in iron-red, 8¾ in., early 19th C. **£300-350** *SC*

DAVENPORT

- **factory ran from 1793-1887**
- **early porcelain of a hard-paste variety**
- **any Davenport marked 'Longport' is quite rare**
- **high quality wares produced, particularly in the 1840's-1860's.**
- **on botanical wares if the flowers are named it can add 50% to the value**
- **high quality Davenport often wrongly classified as Rockingham.**
- **Davenport produced the Imari styles better known on Royal Crown Derby; this is rarer than Derby but not as highly collectable.**

A Davenport plate, on deep blue ground, with gilding, 8¾ in., c. 1840. **£120-150** *NSN*

A Davenport plate, with landscape scene and pink ground, 9 in., c. 1870. **£120-150** *NSN*

A Derby 'Botanical' plate probably by 'Quaker' Pegg, named on reverse, pattern no. 141, crown, crossed batons and D in blue enamel, impressed M, minor wear, 8¾ in., c. 1796-1800. **£450-550** *S*
and
A Derby sauce tureen and cover from the same service, specimens named, pattern no. 141, crown, crossed batons and D in blue enamel, 19 in red, 6 in blue, hair crack in handle on cover, 7½ in., c. 1796-1800. **£450-550** *S*

A Derby named-view plate painted with a landscape medallion; 'on the Dove near Tutbury, Staffordshire', marks in blue including pattern no. 364, slight rubbing, 9¼ in., late 18th C. **£350-400** *SC*

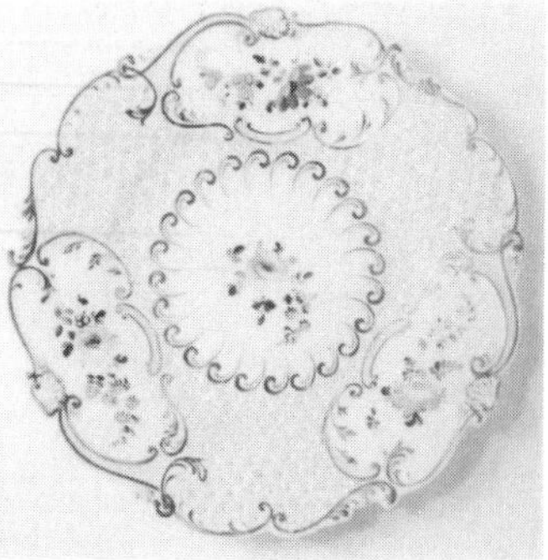
A Daniel plate with pink ground, 8½ in., c. 1839-45. **£100-140** *NSN*

A Derby plate, with view of Yellow Tower Trim, 1800-25. **£150-175** *NSN*

A fine Derby plate painted by William Billingsley, with deep blue enamel and gold, crown, cross baton and D mark in puce, pattern no. 100, 22 cm. **£200-250** *P*

A Stevenson and Hancock plate painted and signed by James Rouse senior, crown, crossed batons, D flanked by SH in iron-red, hairline crack, 9½ in., c. 1870. **£250-300** *SC*

A Derby plate, painted and signed by James Rouse junior with a scene titled 'Making Nets', titled in gilding, cracked, 9¾ in., c. 1870. **£50-70** *SC*

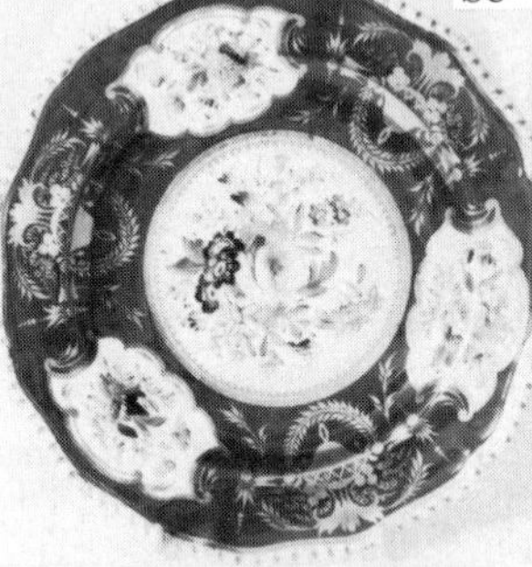

A Bloor Derby plate, on deep blue ground, 8½ in., 1825-40. **£130-£150** *NSN*

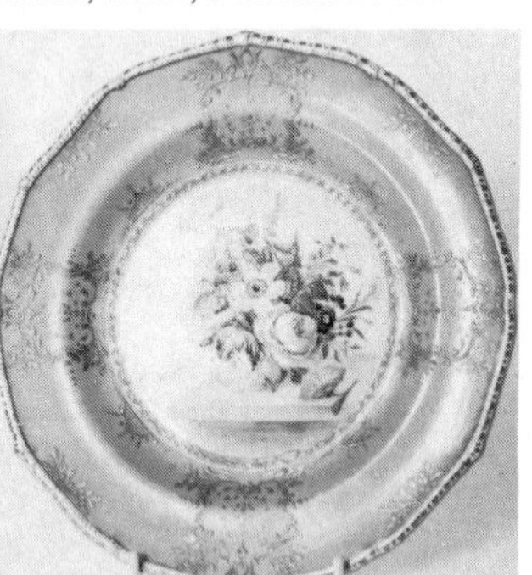

A Derby plate with apple-green ground, by H. S. Hancock, 9 in., 1880. **£300-350** *NSN*

A good Derby plate painted and signed by James Rouse senior with a still-life of colourful flowers, solid green border, gilt rim, 9 in., late 19th C. **£150-200** *SC*

A Derby dessert plate, possibly by Maclachlan, 9 in. diam. **£200-250** *PK*

A Derby dish by Zachariah Boreman, blue crown, cross batons and 'D' mark inscribed 'Bally Fin Queens County Ireland', 12 in. across. **£350-400** *PK*

A Derby plate, 9 in., c. 1880-90. **£135-155** *NSN*

A Royal Crown Derby dessert dish, painted by W. E. J. Dean, the border painted in gold on a green ground, printed mark and date code for 1902, 28 cm. **£200-300** *Bea*

A good Stevenson & Hancock Derby plate painted and signed by James Rouse senior, crown, crossed batons and script D mark in iron-red, 10 in., late 19th C. **£200-300** *SC*

A Crown Derby dish, 1128 pattern, 10¾ in., c. 1914. **£100-120** *NSN*

A Royal Crown Derby plate painted and signed by J. Wale with a thatched cottage, gros-bleu border, decorated with raised gilt vines, printed mark in iron-red including date code for 1920, 8¾ in. **£130-180** *SC*

A Derby Gregory plate, signed, 8½ in., 1934. **£300-350** *NSN*

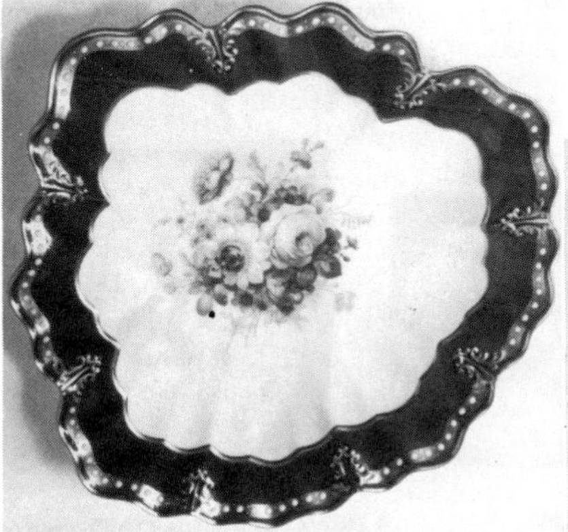

A Derby dish painted by Gregory, 9½ in., c. 1937. **£300-350** *NSN*

DERBY MARKS

Painted anchor in red, brown or gold, c. 1760-80, normally a Chelsea mark.

Incised mark, c. 1770-80.

Chelsea Derby marks, c. 1769-75, usually painted in gold

Painted mark, c. 1770-82.

Painted mark in colours, puce, blue and black, c. 1782-1800, red, c. 1800-25.

Printed or painted, surmounted by a crown or in an oval, c. 1830-40.

BLOOR DERBY

Printed mark, c. 1820-40.

Printed mark in red, c. 1825-40.

Printed mark in red, c. 1830-48.

King Street Factory, 1861-1935.

Printed mark, c. 1878-90. Year ciphers occur below this mark.

A Crown Derby tazza, 9¼ in., 1920. **£180-200** *NSN*

A Royal Crown Derby plate, well painted and signed by Albert Gregory, with a flower spray enclosed by a gros-bleu border and gilt pie-crust rim, printed marks in iron-red including date code for 1905, 8¾ in. **£190-240** *SC*

A good Royal Crown Derby plate painted and signed by C. Gresley with a panel, 'Scone Palace Scotland', enclosed by green and raised gilt borders, pie-crust rim, printed marks in iron-red including date code for 1920, 9 in. **£140-180** *SC*

A Royal Crown Derby plate, painted and signed by W. E. J. Dean, gros-bleu and gilt scroll border, printed marks in iron-red including date code for 1929, 10¼ in. **£150-180** *SC*

Three Doccia plates, decorated in underglaze blue and coloured enamels, underglaze blue borders in Chinese style, 23.5 cm., and 3 similar plates, 2 plates cracked, some chips, c. 1750-55. **£400-£600** *S*

A Le Nove shaped dish of silver form, blue star and V mark, minor glaze chips, 59 cm. diam., c. 1820. **£600-700** *C*

Imperial Porcelain Factory. A porcelain dinner plate in the style of Liotard, marked with the cypher of Nicholas I., 26 cm. diam., c. 1830. **£650-750** *S*

A Doccia plate probably painted by G. B. Fanciullacci, 'en camaieu rose', the blue border with 3 panels within gilt edged C-scroll shells, 24 cm. diam., c. 1770. **£450-550** *C*

A Lockett, Baggulay and Cooper plate, 9 in., c. 1855. **£45-55** *NSN*

A Meissen chinoiserie saucer with Böttger-lustre, gilt, iron-red and brown foliage surround, gilder's mark 10, c. 1728. **£500-600** *C*

A fine Chaffers plate, painted in underglaze blue, workman's numeral 15 on base, 21 cm. **£280-£340** *P*

The painting shows close affinities to delft decoration.

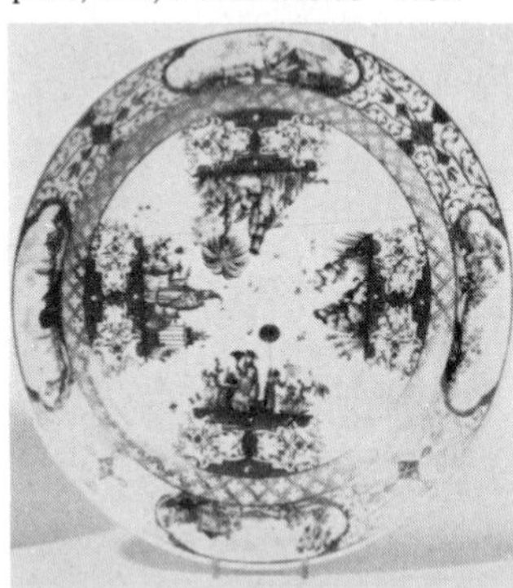

A large Meissen chinoiserie circular dish painted by C. F. Herold on Böttger-lustre, gold and chocolate Gitterwerk supports enriched with scrolls in puce and iron-red, blue crossed swords mark and impressed Dreher's mark, crazing in the glaze, 44.5 cm., c. 1735. **£3,500-4,500** *C*

A Meissen Hausmalerei saucer, decorated in the atelier of Franz Ferdinand Mayer of Pressnitz in iron-red palette, titled, gilt line rim, crossed swords in blue, impressed '17', 13.7 cm., mid 18th C. **£300-400** *SS*

A pair of Meissen plates, the borders painted with a goat, hedgehogs and birds within gilt rims, blue crossed swords mark and pressnummer 22, one with rim chip, 24.5 cm. diam., c. 1750. **£500-£600** *C*

A Meissen ornithological plate with an ozier border and gilt rim, blue crossed swords mark and pressnummer 22, 23.5 cm., c. 1760. **£350-450** *C*

A pair of Meissen ornithological plates, blue crossed swords mark and pressnummer 61, 24 cm. diam., c. 1760. **£700-800** *C*

A pair of Meissen fabeltiere plates, blue crossed swords mark and pressnummer 16, 24 cm. diam., c. 1740. **£1,200-1,500** *C*

Twelve Meissen plates painted with scattered deutsche-Blumen within ozier moulded borders, blue crossed swords and dot mark, one with rim chip, 24 cm. diam., c. 1770. **£700-900** *C*

A Meissen plate, with deep blue ground and gilding, 8½ in., c. 1880. **£180-200** *NSN*

A set of 12 Meissen dinner plates and 12 Meissen soup plates en suite, the shaped rims lightly moulded with basket weave panels and painted with a green scale border and gilt with foliate scrolls, cancelled crossed swords in underglaze blue, various incised numerals, small chips, 10¼ and 10 in. (26.5 and 26 cm.), mid to late 19th C. **£1,400-1,600** *S*

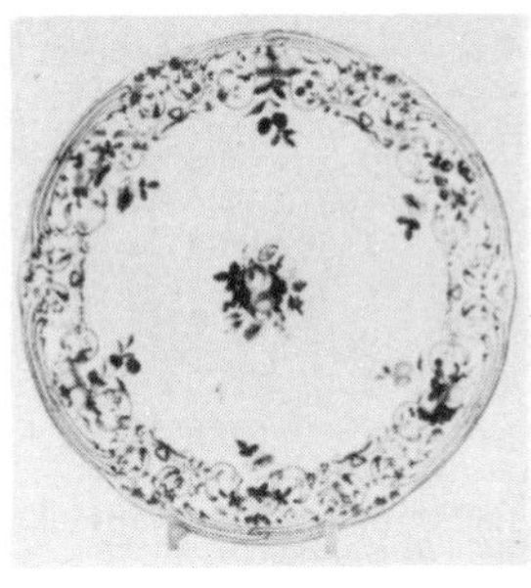

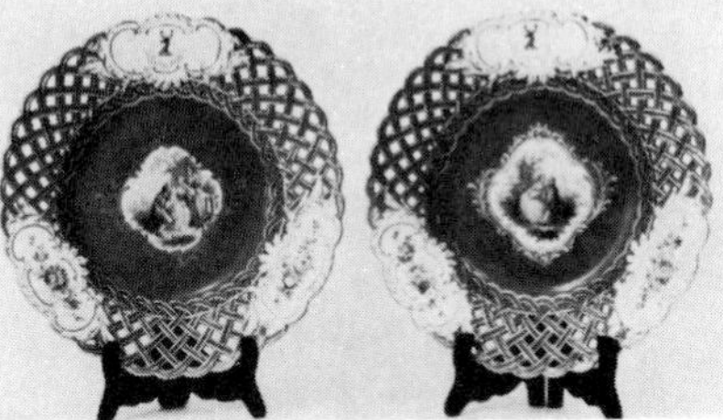

Six Meissen dessert plates, the centres with bouquets of Manier Blumen, enriched in pink and gold, blue crossed swords and dot mark, pressnummer 10, 24 cm. diam., c. 1765. **£1,800-2,000** *C*

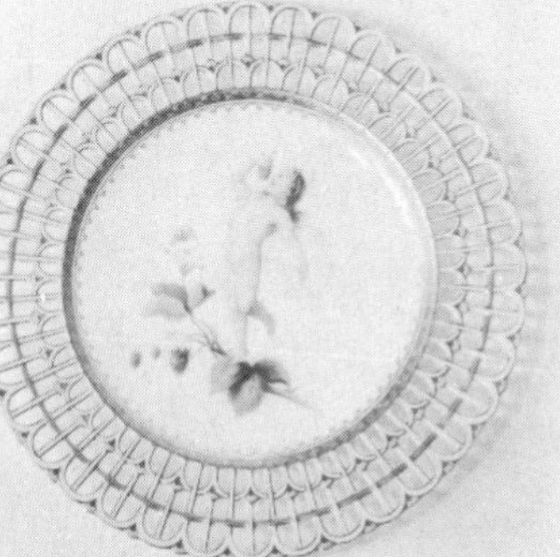

A set of 18 cerise ground Meissen dessert plates, the central panels decorated with romantic figures in landscapes, and a matching set of 18 coffee cups and saucers, blue crossed swords and impressed numerals, late 19th C. **£3,000-£3,500** *WW*

A Minton plate by Boullemier, 9¼ in., 1863-72. **£400-450** *NSN*

A set of 18 Mintons dessert plates, with a gilt border, impressed mark, painted pattern number G1416, impressed date code for 1873, 24 cm. **£350-450** *S*

A Nantgarw plate with foliate scroll moulded rim, finely painted with fruit and flowers within a foliate border, heightened in gilding, impressed Nantgarw C.W., slight rubbing, 9¾ in., 1813-22. **£250-300** *SC*

A pair of Meissen shaped ornithological plates, within ozier moulded border and gilt rim, blue crossed swords and dot marks, pressnummer 29, 24 cm. diam., c. 1770. **£600-700** *C*

A pair of Meissen (Marcolini) ornithological soup plates, blue crossed swords and star marks, pressnummer 54, 23 cm. diam., c. 1775. **£500-700** *C*

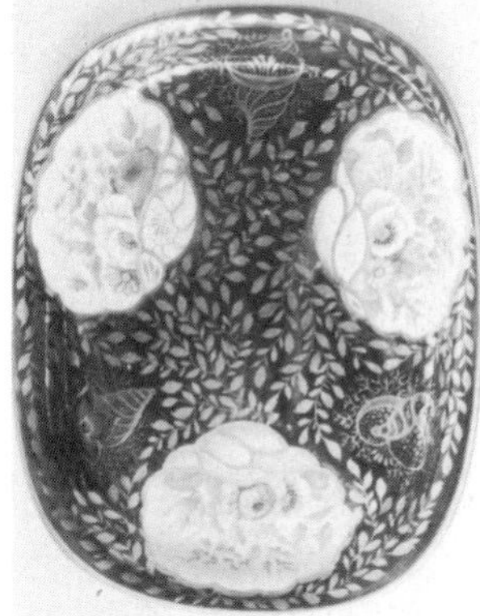

A Minton tea pot stand, Sevres mark, 7½ in. wide, c. 1820. **£200-£250** *NSN*

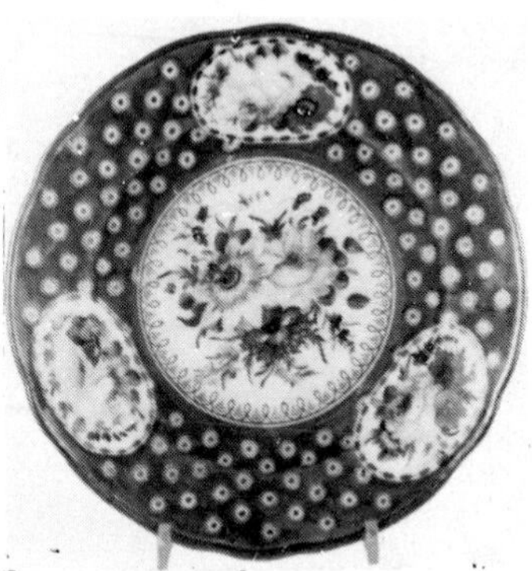

A Nantgarw plate painted with a central spray of coloured flowers, reserved on a green 'œil de perdix' ground, impressed Nantgarw C.W., and a breakfast cup and saucer en suite, saucer repaired, 9¼ in., 1813-22. **£700-800** *SC*

A Nantgarw London decorated blue ground plate, the blue border reserved with oval panels of flowers and gilt 'œil de perdrix', impressed Nantgarw C.W. mark, 21.5 cm. diam., c. 1820. **£800-1,000** *C*

cf. John (W.D.): Nantgarw Porcelain Album, pl. 9 and Nantgarw Porcelain, p. 105 where the decoration is tentatively attributed to T. Martin Randall.

A Nantgarw plate from the MacIntosh service, the centre with an exotic finch, the indented rim edged with sawtooth trim, impressed marks Nantgarw C.W., 23.5 cm., c. 1820. **£1,000-1,200** *Bon*

A Nantgarw pink ground plate from the green meadow service, painted by Thomas Pardoe with named botanical specimens of purple stock, white rose and love in a mist named in iron-red, impressed Nantgarw C.W. mark, 22 cm. diam., c. 1820. **£500-700** *C*

Painted for Wyndham Lewis, M.P., of Green Meadow, Glamorganshire.

A Ridgway dish, on deep blue ground with gilding, 8 in. wide, c. 1840-45. **£95-110** *NSN*

A Nantgarw London decorated plate, with a shaded brown ground within a gilt well and a lobed 'feuille de choux' and gilt line rim, impressed Nantgarw C.W. mark, 23.5 cm. diam., c. 1820. **£800-£1,000** *C*

A Nantgarw plate, painted in London, impressed Nantgarw C.W., 24 cm., c. 1820. **£350-450** *P*

A set of 8 'Sèvres' plates, within a 'bleu de roi' ground rim and tooled gilt foliate scrolls, printed gilt Louis Philippe crowned monogram, 23.7 cm., late 19th C. **£700-800** *S*

A Samson armorial plate, 18 in. diam., c. late 19th C. **£120-150** *IHA*

A Nantgarw London decorated plate, the border moulded with C-scrolls and wreaths of flowers, within a lobed gilt dentil rim, impressed Nantgarw C.W. mark, 24.5 cm. diam., c. 1820. **£700-£800** *C*

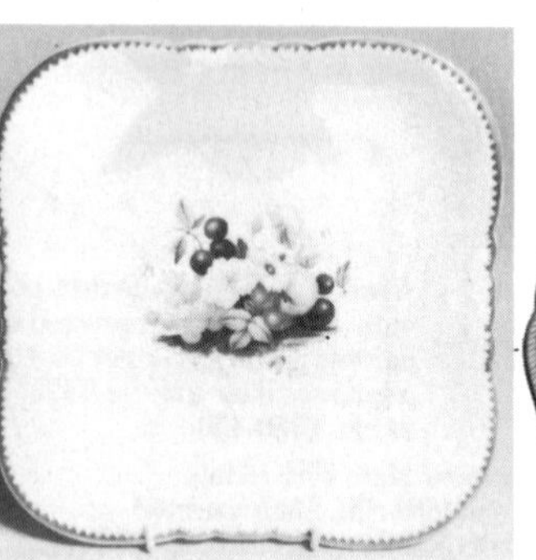

A Rockingham dish decorated by Steel, in coloured enamels, with gilt rim, 9 in., c. 1830. **£235-245** *WWW*

A Ridgway plate, 9 in., c. 1841-45. **£100-120** *NSN*

A set of 6 Staffordshire plates, pattern number 1985 in underglaze blue, 9 in., mid 19th C. **£200-300** *S*

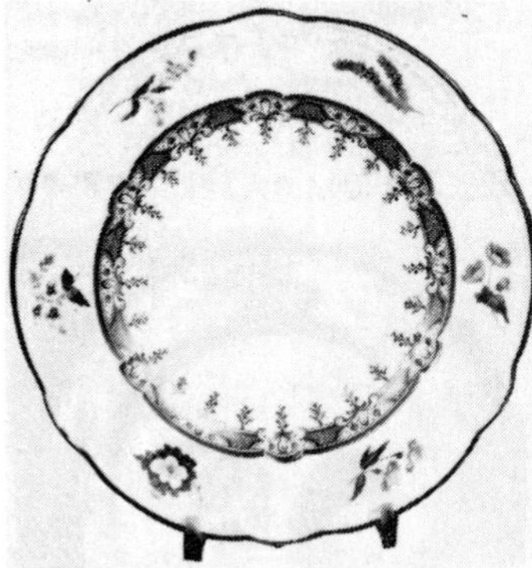

A Swansea plate crisply moulded with scrolls and foliage, stencilled SWANSEA in iron-red, gilding slightly rubbed, 8¼ in., 1814-22. **£180-260** *SC*

A Swansea plate painted by William Pollard, the border moulded with C scrolls and wreaths of flowers, divided by feathered gilt foliage, 21 cm. diam., c. 1815. **£700-800** *C*

A Swansea dish from the Burdett Coutts service, the rim with full-blown pink roses, gilt dentil rim, impressed SWANSEA, gilding rubbed, 10¼ in., 1814-22. **£300-£400** *SC*

A Swansea double handled dessert dish, painted probably by Henry Morris, within a gilt rim, 12½ in., 1813-22. **£250-300** *SC*

SWANSEA PORCELAIN

- **factory produced high quality soft-paste porcelain from 1814-17**
- **factory started by Dillwyn, Billingsley and Walker**
- **superb translucent body, excellent glaze**
- **in many ways one of the best English porcelain bodies**
- **also noted for delicacy of flower painting, usually attributed to Billingsley although much was obviously done by other decorators**
- **a close study of marked pieces will give one an idea of Billingsley's work but unless actually signed by him pieces should be marked 'possibly by Billingsley'**
- **with Swansea flatware the moulding usually appears on the underside**
- **especially notable are figures and birds by T. Baxter**
- **the Swansea mark often faked**
- **in 1816 Billingsley left to start up again at Nantgarw**
- **many pieces were decorated in London studios and the added 'kudos' increases their value**
- **at Swansea blanks were decorated until the early 1820's**

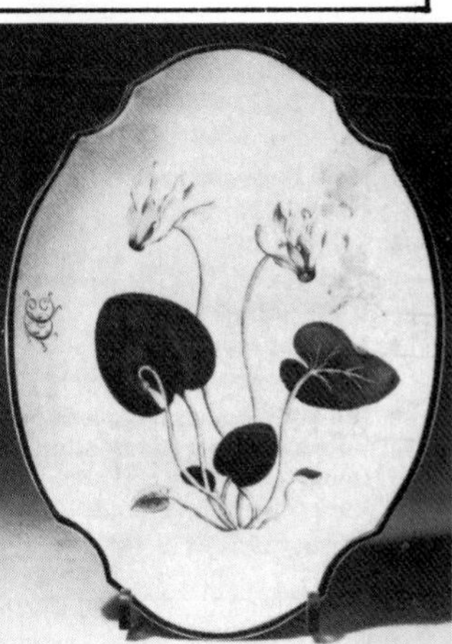

A Swansea botanical dish painted by Thomas Pardoe with a large specimen of 'Persian Cyclamen', impressed Swansea, 25 cm. **£250-£300** *P*

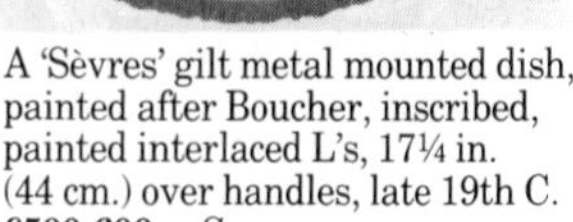

A 'Sèvres' gilt metal mounted dish, painted after Boucher, inscribed, painted interlaced L's, 17¼ in. (44 cm.) over handles, late 19th C. **£500-600** *S*

A 'Swansea' plate with foliate scroll moulded rim and a green and gilt border, stencilled SWANSEA in green, rubbed, 8⅜ in. **£160-200** *SC*

A Swansea armorial cruciform plate painted by Henry Morris with the motto 'Frangas non Flectes' within a border of green urns, red stencil mark, 21.5 cm. diam., 1815-20. **£700-800** *C*

The Arms are those of Hereford impaling Parkinson.

A pair of Tournai plates decorated with the coat-of-arms of Comte de Spaare, gilt and pale green feathered rim, rubbed, 23.5 cm., c. 1770. **£400-500** *S*

A Vienna plate painted in the Imari palette, the reverse with three flower sprays, impressed beehive mark and 6, 24.5 cm. diam., 1744-49. **£400-500** *C*

A Venice (Cozzi) shell shaped dish, the blue border gilt with zig-zags, red anchor mark, 19 cm. wide, c. 1775. **£200-250** *C*

A good Vienna plate painted and indistinctly signed with a scene showing three monks, elaborate 'gros bleu' and raised gilt foliate scroll border, shield mark in underglaze blue, scene titled in black script 'Vesper', 9⅝ in. (24.4 cm.), late 19th C. **£250-300** *SC*

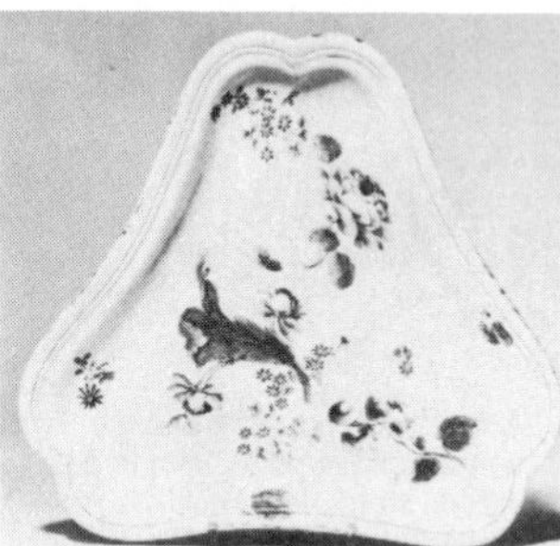

A Vienna trefoil dish painted with carefully drawn Holzschnitt Blumen, impressed beehive mark, 30.5 cm. wide, c. 1745. **£250-350** *C*

A 'Vienna' circular dish painted by C. Weber with Die Entführung der Orythia after the original in the Belvedere, Vienna, with pale blue, pink, green and purple panels within a gilt band, signed, underglaze blue beehive mark, 46 cm. diam., c. 1880. **£850-950** *C*

A Vienna plate painted in the 'famille verte' manner on iron-red cell-pattern grounds between black and gilt bands, blue beehive mark, 24 cm. diam., c. 1760. **£250-300** *C*

A Royal Vienna plate, 'PSYCHE-AM-WASSER' No. 21650, late 19th C. **£250-300** *HFM*

VIENNA

- **factory founded by C. I. du Paquier in 1719 with the help of Stolzel and Hunger from Meissen**
- **the body of du Paqûier wares has a distinctive smoky tone**
- **decoration tends to cover much of the body and is more elaborate than Meissen**
- **the style of this period was baroque, with scrollwork and lattice-like gilding**
- **the 'State' period of the factory ran from 1744-84**
- **plain bases were used from mid 1760's**
- **excellent figure modelling was undertaken by J. J. Niedermayer from 1747-84**
- **Konrad von Sorgenthal became director from 1784-1804**
- **the style became far less based on rococo and much simpler in taste, but with good strong colours and raised gilding**
- **factory closed in 1864**

A Vienna plate painted in the du Paquier manner, blue beehive and painter's marks, impressed numbers for 1809, minor chips to foot rim, 25 cm. diam. **£180-240** *C*

A good Vienna plate painted and signed by Wagner with a portrait named on the reverse 'Helena', elaborate 'gros bleu' and raised gilt border, shield mark in underglaze blue, titled in black script, 9½ in. (24.2 cm.), late 19th C. **£250-300** *SC*

A Vienna (du Paquier) dish, painted with Holzschnitt Blumen, the border painted in iron-red, blue, puce and gilt, 37.5 cm. diam., c. 1730. **£1,200-1,600** *C*

A 'Vienna' plate painted and signed by T. Koller with Ruth within a gilt panelled border reserved on claret, pink and yellow borders, shield in blue enamel, titled in black script, 9½ in. (24.2 cm.), late 19th C. **£80-£110** *SC*

A 'Vienna' cabinet plate painted by Wagner, signed, with 'Favorite', painted shield in blue, painted title, 24.8 cm., c. 1900. **£500-600** *S*

A 'Vienna' plate painted within a blue and gilt border, shield mark in blue enamel, scene titled in black script, title rubbed, 9½ in. (24.2 cm.), late 19th C. **£80-100** *SC*

VIENNA MARKS

Shield mark in blue or impressed, 1744- onwards.

A 'Vienna' wall dish painted by C. Heer, signed, after Poussin, with 'Shepherds in Arcadie', within a ruby red ground border, printed shield in blue, impressed numerals, 40 cm., c. 1900. **£350-400** *S*

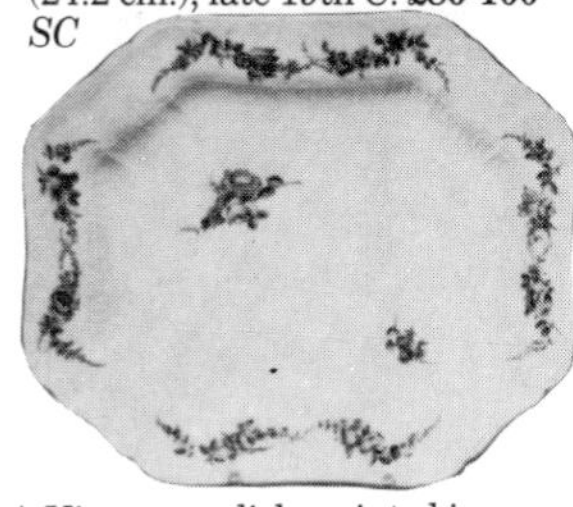

A Vincennes dish, painted in colours with swags of flowers, blue interlaced L marks enclosing the date letter A for 1753, painter's mark of Sioux jeune, 28 cm. wide. **£300-400** *C*

A 'Vienna' deep plate painted with 'The Judgment of Paris', blue and gilt border, shield in underglaze blue, titled in black script, slight rubbing, 9⅝ in. (24.4 cm.), late 19th C. **£160-190** *SC*

The somewhat formal panelled border is typical of 19th C. 'Vienna' porcelain.

A rare, early Worcester small saucer dish painted in underglaze blue with 'The Romantic Rocks' pattern after a drawing by Pillement, workman's marks, 6¾ in., c. 1754-55. **£650-750** *S*

This rare pattern is more usually found on octagonal tea bowls and saucers.

A Worcester 'famille verte' plate painted in green, blue, iron-red and yellow with a bird perched on a prunus tree flanked by bamboo, 23 cm. diam., c. 1754. **£2,000-£2,500** *C*

Only three examples of this rare pattern are recorded. One is on display in the Bristol City Art Gallery.

A first period Worcester hand painted blue and white plate, c. 1760. **£350-450** *SA*

Powder blue ground wares were also made at Bow and Lowestoft. For an English delftware version see the pottery section.

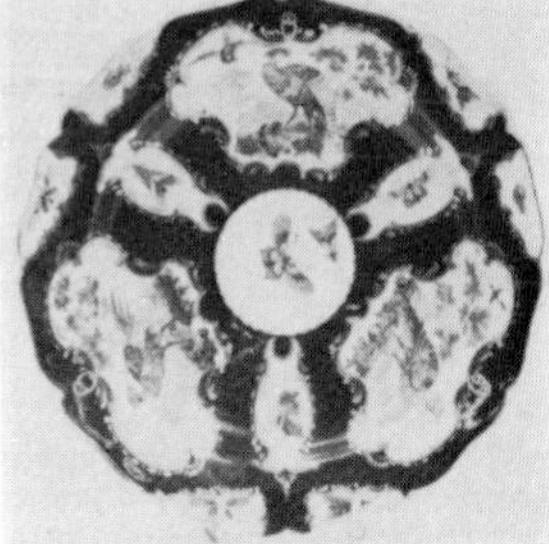

A pair of Worcester blue scale ground plates, each painted in the manner of Giles, pseudo seal marks in underglaze blue, 22.7 cm., 1760's. **£650-750** *SS*

A Bishop Sumner Worcester plate painted in 'famille-verte' palette, crescent mark in gilding, very slight wear, 8¾ in., c. 1765-70. **£450-550** *S*

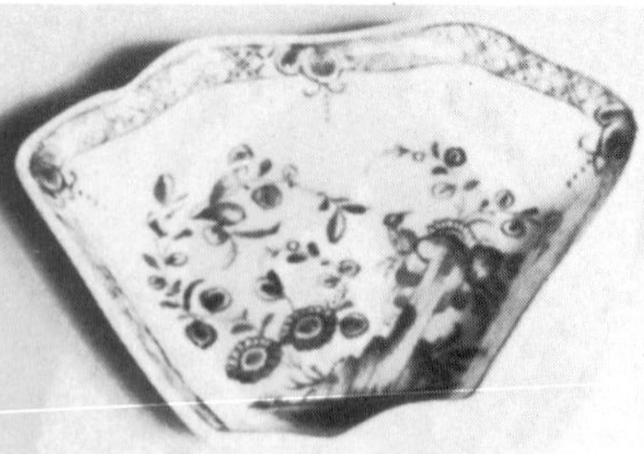
A first period Worcester blue and white hors d'oeuvres dish, 'willow rock bird' pattern, 3½ in., c. 1765. **£165-175** *WWW*

This would have been part of a six piece hors d'oeuvres set.

A Worcester 'brocade pattern' plate with fluted rim, decorated in Imari style in underglaze blue and coloured enamels, pseudo character marks, slightly rubbed, 7⅝ in., c. 1765. **£300-400** *S*

The use of complex diaper or brocade design is a derivative of the 'Shibuemon' Arita style dating from around 1700.

A first period Worcester vine leaf pickle dish, 3½ in., c. 1768. **£125-£135** *WWW*

A pair of Worcester 'Blind Earl' plates boldly painted in the atelier of James Giles with scattered butterflies and insects, one with small firing crack to rim, 19 cm. diam., c. 1768. **£850-950** *C*

A Worcester plate with fluted rim, painted in a bright Kakiemon style palette in the Sir Joshua Reynolds pattern, crescent mark in underglaze blue, 7½ in., c. 1770. **£250-350** *S*

A pair of Worcester fluted plates with coloured flowers within a gilt border on a 'gros bleu' ground, pseudo seal marks in underglaze blue, 7½ in., c. 1770. **£300-400** *S*

A first period Worcester blue and white pine cone pattern cress dish and stand, 9 in. diam., c. 1770. **£350-375** *WWW*

A first period Worcester blue and white cabbage leaf dish, pine cone pattern, 9½ in. **£245-265** *WWW*

A pair of Worcester blue and white cushion shaped dishes with central scrolling foliage medallion, blue emblem mark within a double circle, 8½ in., c. 1770-75. **£500-£600** *SA*

This is a similar design to the K'ang Hsi Lotus pattern.

A Flight Barr and Barr plate, 8½ in., c. 1813-40. **£150-200** *NSN*

A Flight Barr and Barr plate, c. 1813-40. **£220-250** *NSN*

A pierced Worcester plate, slight restoration, impressed mark, 8½ in., c. 1880. **£400-450** *NSN*

A Chamberlain Worcester small dish, with green ground, 5¼ in. wide, c. 1847. **£200-250** *NSN*

A set of 5 Worcester cabinet plates, painted by H. Ayrton or Freeman, signed, printed crowned circle mark, 22.5 cm., post 1956. **£600-£700** *S*

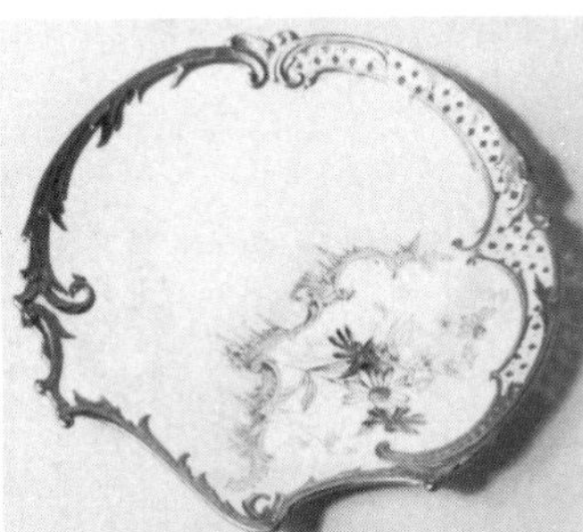

A Royal Worcester Empress shape plate, on peach ground, 8½ in., 1890. **£75-95** *NSN*

A pair of Royal Worcester plates painted and signed by Freeman, within a broad pale ivory ground band, printed in gilding, black printed marks, 10½ in. **£130-180** *SC*

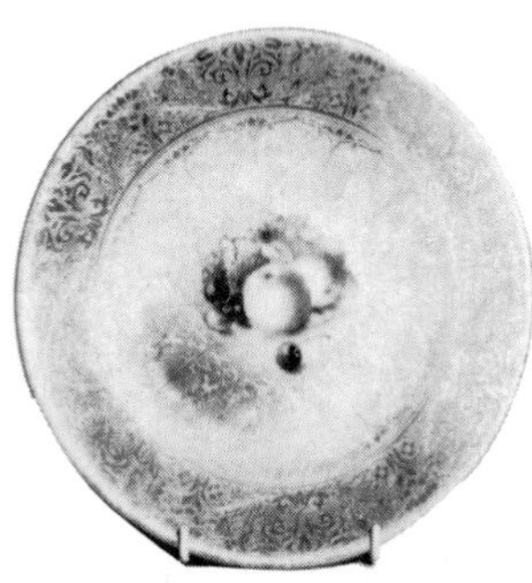

A pair of Royal Worcester plates, finely gilt overall and acid-etched with burnished strapwork, by J. Freeman, signed, printed mark in gilt, 9¼ in. diam., date code 1956. **£300-400** *N*

A Royal Worcester dish with royal blue ground, 11½ in., c. 1897. **£70-£80** *NSN*

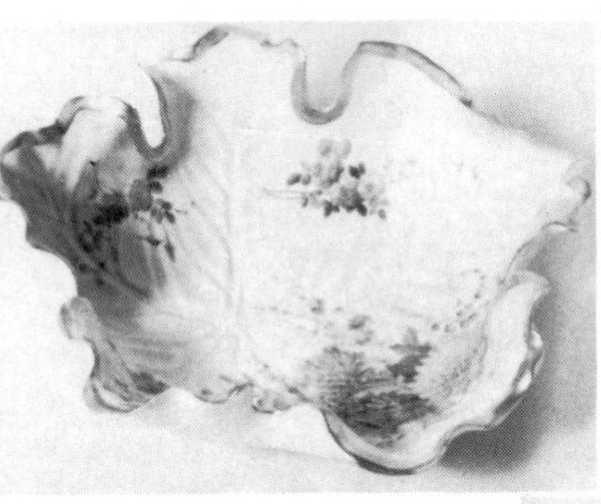

A Royal Worcester peach ground leaf dish, 9½ in., c. 1904. **£150-£175** *NSN*

A porcelain inkstand, probably Coalport, 15 in., c. 1840. **£190-£220** *IHA*

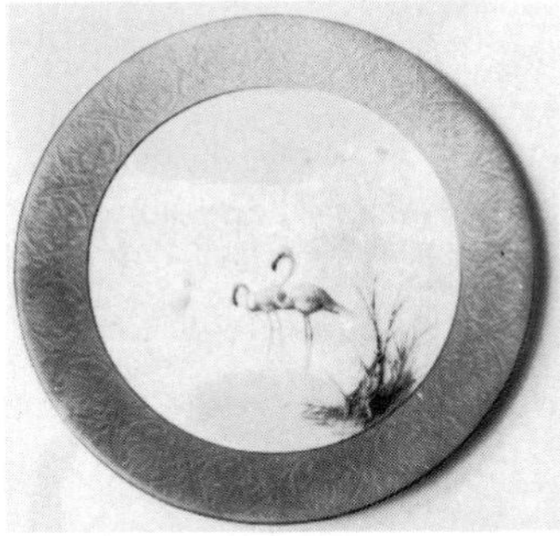

A Royal Worcester flamingo plate painted by William Powell, 9¼ in. **£350-400** *SA*

Right:
A rare Kloster Veilsdorf inkstand on scroll-edged base picked out in green and purple, restored, 15 cm., late 18th C. **£500-600** *S*

A Louis XV ormolu and Meissen porcelain encrier fitted with a square sander and inkpot, the stand with ormolu handle terminating in a taper-stick holder, the base with nib compartment and 'Nashiji' lacquer inset, 4½ in. (11.5 cm.) wide, the porcelain c. 1750. **£1,400-1,600** *C*

A Paris porcelain encrier, 11½ in. wide, c. 1880. **£100-140** *IHA*

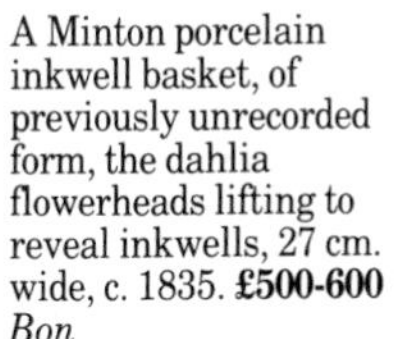

A Minton porcelain inkwell basket, of previously unrecorded form, the dahlia flowerheads lifting to reveal inkwells, 27 cm. wide, c. 1835. **£500-600** *Bon*

A pair of Sèvres later-decorated turquoise-ground jardinieres enriched in gilding, the rims gilt, the decoration 19th C., 24 cm. wide. **£700-800** *C*

A Royal Worcester peach ground jardiniere, 8 in., 1907. **£320-380** *NSN*

A Royal Worcester jardiniere painted by Sedgley, signed, with printed crowned circle mark, 10¾ in., shape number H295 and date code for 1924. **£450-550** *S*

A rare early Bow cream jug painted in pale blue, mark of three dots arranged in a triangle on the base, small chip, 3⅛ in., c. 1753. **£400-£500** *S*

A Royal Worcester 'rose jar', cover and lid, painted by H. Davis, signed, with a view of 'St. Nicholas Cathedral, Newcastle', cover damaged, printed crowned circle mark, shape number 2048, painted title, 34 cm., date code for 1912. **£350-450** *S*

A Royal Worcester pot-pourri jar painted by Edward I. Raby with flowers, in muted enamel colours on an apricot and ivory ground, 33 cm., printed mark and date code for 1896. **£600-700** *Bea*

A Caughley blue and white inscribed and dated cabbage-leaf moulded mask-jug transfer-printed in a dark-blue with 'The Fisherman Pattern', the inscription 'MANLOVE VERNON LAWRENCE 1782', firing crack at base of handle, blue S mark, 23.5 cm. high, c. 1780. **£600-700** *C*

A Sèvres jardiniere (cuvette courteille) finely painted in colours, the edges picked out in blue and gilding, marked in blue with interlaced L's, 24.5 cm., date letter for 1768, painter's mark of Francois Aloncle, 1768. **£1,200-1,400** *S*

Francois Aloncle was employed at Sèvres from 1758 until 1781.

A Royal Worcester 'oval jardiniere' with a shaded apricot ground within green and gilt borders, printed crowned circle mark, shape number 2053, Rd. No. 338641, 47 cm., date code for 1899. **£500-£600** *S*

A Royal Worcester peach ground jardiniere, 7 in. high, 1920. **£500-£600** *NSN*

A Salopian toy milk jug with sparrow-beak spout, painted in underglaze blue with a Chinese river scene, the inside with a narrow diaper border, S mark in blue, 4 cm. **£280-340** *L*

'The Red Haired Clown'. A Royal Doulton character jug designed by H. Fenton, c.m.l. & c., Rd. No. 810520, introduced 1937, withdrawn 1942, 15 cm. high. **£1,800-2,100** *P*

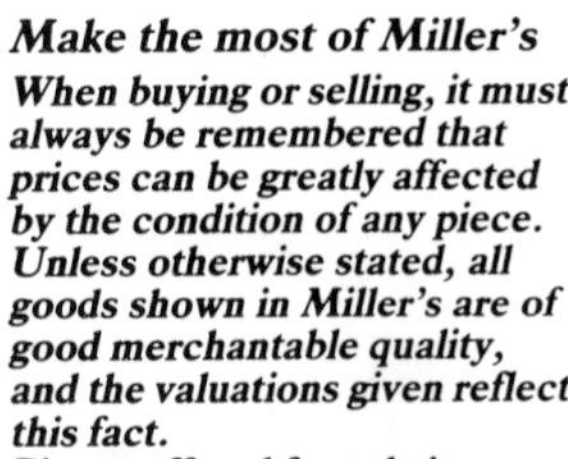

Make the most of Miller's

When buying or selling, it must always be remembered that prices can be greatly affected by the condition of any piece. Unless otherwise stated, all goods shown in Miller's are of good merchantable quality, and the valuations given reflect this fact.

Pieces offered for sale in exceptionally fine condition or in poor condition may reasonably be expected to be priced considerably higher or lower respectively than the estimates given herein.

A Meissen purple-ground cream jug and cover (Milchtopf) with white and gilt rococo scroll handle, painted in Kakiemon style on a rich purple ground, crossed swords mark in underglaze blue, cover and spout restored, 14 cm., c. 1730. **£550-650** *S*

'Smuts'. A Royal Doulton character jug designed by H. Fenton, c.m.l. & c., inscription, introduced 1946, withdrawn 1948, 17 cm. high. **£800-1,000** *P*

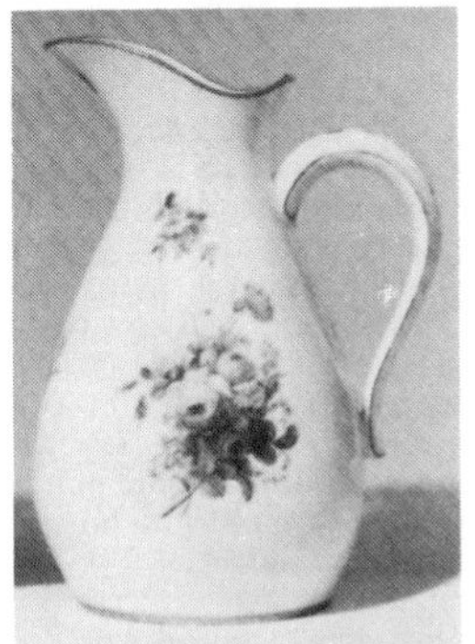

A Sèvres jug (broc ordinaire) blue interlaced L marks and date letter for 1773 and painter's mark of Theodore, 23 cm. high. **£250-350** *C*

'Drake' (Hatless). A rare Royal Doulton character jug designed by H. Fenton, c.m.l. & c., date code for 1940, 15 cm. high. **£1,700-2,000** *P*

This early version without a hat was piloted but never actually released for general production.

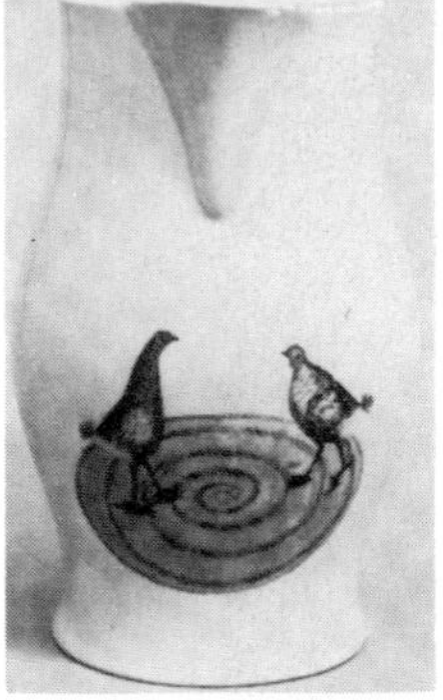

A rare Chaffer's Liverpool jug painted with a scene of two cocks trimmed for the pit, firing crack running into hair crack, small chip, 9 in., c. 1760-62. **£300-400** *S*

HOCHST

- **factory was founded in 1746 by the painter A. F. von Löwenfinck**
- **porcelain was produced from 1750**
- **milk-white in colour**
- **early wares tended to have poor translucency and be somewhat heavy**
- **from 1758-65 the style reminiscent of the French 'Louis Seize' style came into fashion**
- **this style was continued and developed by J. P. Melchior who was chief modeller 1767-79**
- **the base of figures from 1765 tends to be in the form of a grassy mound**
- **the factory closed in 1796**

A Höchst baluster hot-milk jug and cover painted in the 'famille verte' manner, chips to spout and foot rim, impressed IH, 14.5 cm. high, c. 1760. **£300-400** *C*

A Meissen baluster hot-milk jug and hinged cover with French silver-gilt mount, painted in iron-red and gilt, cover chipped, spout repaired, blue crossed swords mark and gilder's mark H. to each piece, 16 cm. high, c. 1735, the mount with the décharge for 1738-44. **£900-1,000** *C*

A Spode jug decorated in enamels and gilt, 4½ in., c. 1810. **£50-60** *BP*

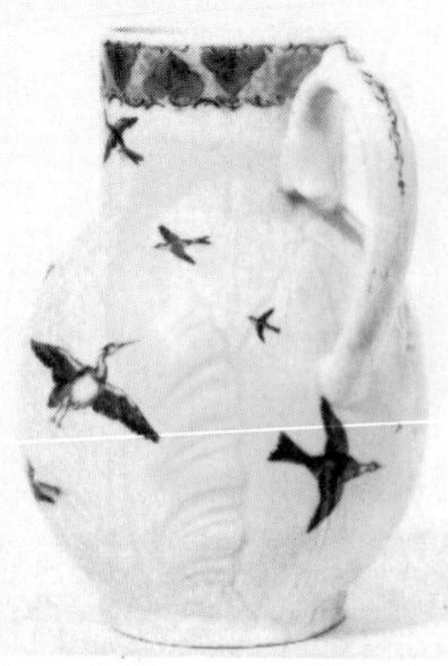

An early Worcester cabbage leaf jug, by James Rogers, finely painted in colours with a pair of billing birds perched on the ruins of a wall watched by another bird on a dilapidated fence, a mallard, a heron and other fancy birds in flight, 20 cm., c. 1757. **£4,000-£5,500** *P*

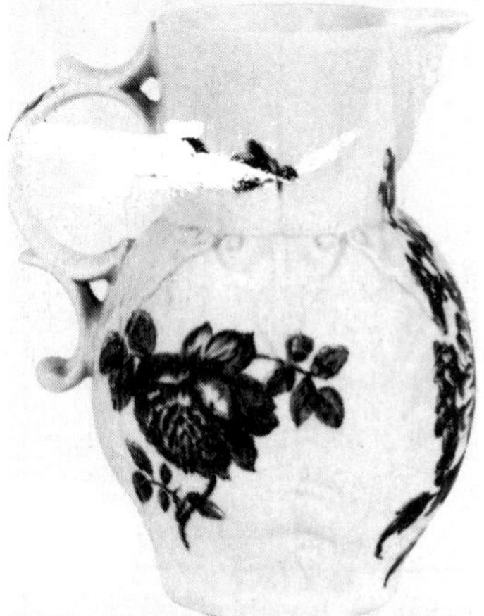

A Worcester blue and white 'Cabbage Leaf' mask jug, painter's mark in underglaze blue, 8¼ in., c. 1760. **£400-450** *SC*

A Royal Worcester peach ground flat backed jug, 8 in., 1908. **£160-£180** *NSN*

A porcelain milk-jug, the creamy white body decorated in Holland, damage to spout, perhaps Weesp, 10 cm., mid 18th C. **£400-500** *S*

Marked wares have to be treated with caution as many factories in the 18th C. copied more successful factory marks. Closer attention should be paid to the body, glaze and shape in order to ascertain the factory. The mark should only be used as a final check. Many recent discoveries have changed previously held beliefs, e.g. the disguised numeral mark, once held to be Caughley and now known to be Worcester. It is also true that a large number of 18th C. wares were unmarked. Many English factories adopted mock Oriental marks in order to compete with imported Chinese porcelain.

A Coalport mug, with gilt inscription, claret red ground, 3½ in. high, dated 1866. **£120-150** *NSN*

A Royal Worcester peach ground claret jug, 9 in., 1915. **£170-£190** *NSN*

A Vienna jug with masked lip, signed LCF, 8½ in. high, c. 1920. **£150-200** *IHA*

A Worcester hunting jug, probably by Humphrey Chamberlain, salmon ground, 7 in., c. 1800. **£2,200-2,400** *SA*

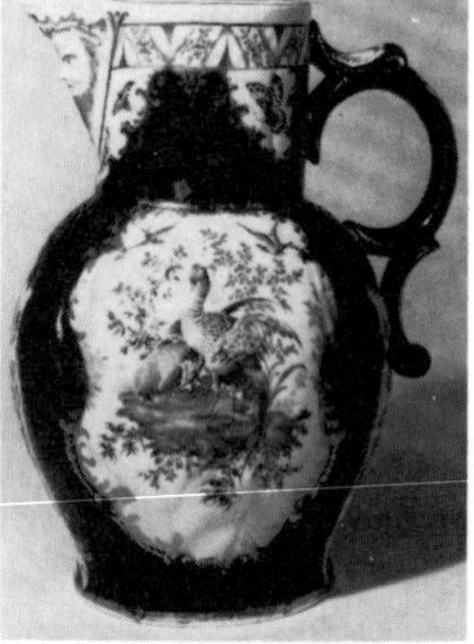

A Worcester blue-scale cabbage-leaf moulded mask jug, the neck with a band of stiff leaves edged in green, blue square seal mark, 29.5 cm. high, c. 1770. **£1,300-1,600** *C*

A graduated set of 3 Royal Worcester jugs, body moulded with stylised leaf design and applied with elephant head handles, impressed mark, 19, 16.8 and 15 cm., late 19th C. **£150-200** *Bea*

A Royal Worcester peach ground jug, 8¾ in., 1908. **£180-220** *NSN*

A rare early Worcester 'Scratch Cross' type mug painted in pale underglaze blue with the 'Question-Mark Island' pattern, the design entirely delineated in red enamel, workman's mark in blue, 9.3 cm., c. 1754-56. **£400-500** *P*

This is the only Worcester blue pattern where red enamel was used and archaeological evidence has shown the enamelling to be contemporary.

A first period Worcester blue and white jug with mask spout, Gilliflower pattern, 6½ in. **£145-£165** *WWW*

This pattern was derived from the continental factories, particularly Chantilly, and was produced by a large number of other English factories.

A Worcester blue and white bell shape mug, 'Long Eliza' pattern, cracked ice ground, 6 in., c. 1770. **£800-900** *SA*

Very rare in blue and white, nearly always in colour.

A Worcester polychrome mug, painted with flowers within a cartouche on a scale blue ground, 'square' mark in underglaze blue within a wide unglazed foot rim, 8.8 cm., mid 18th C. **£200-250** *Bea*

BERLIN

- **a second factory was started in 1761 by J. E. Gotzkowsky**
- **many artists came from Meissen including F. E. Meyer**
- **porcelain has a distinctly creamy tone**
- **painting was in the restrained rococo manner**
- **pieces with Mosaic (or scale pattern) borders and delicate flower painting**
- **from 1770 the porcelain has a much colder more brilliant white tone**
- **the factory became influenced by the Neo-classical movement**
- **figure modelling was perfected by the brothers Friedrich Elias Meyer and Wilheim Christian Meyer — note the characteristic small heads and elongated bodies**
- **c.1775 figure bases became more architectural in design, notably oval and square pedestals**
- **in the early 19th C. the 'Empire' style of Sèvres was copied**
- **as the 19th C. progressed Berlin tended to follow the prevailing trends**

A Berlin plaque painted by R. Perling Stettin and dated 24 Mai 1859, with Christopher Columbus before the King and Queen of Spain, slight chip to bottom left-hand corner underside, impressed eagle and P7, 20.5 by 18 cm., 1859. **£240-280** *C*

A Berlin plaque painted by C. A. Lippold after Correggio with The Penitent Magdalen, inscribed, signed and dated 1848 on the reverse, impressed sceptre and KPM marks, 24.5 by 30.5 cm., 1848. **£1,100-1,300** *C*

A Berlin plaque indistinctly signed with 'The Evening Prayer', impressed KPM and sceptre, incised numerals, 13 by 8 in. (33 by 20 cm.), mid 19th C. **£2,200-2,400** *S*

A Berlin plaque framed, impressed KPM beneath a sceptre, 6 by 4⅝ in. (15.2 by 11.7 cm.). **£200-300** *SC*

A late 19th C. Berlin porcelain plaque, 6½ by 9¾ in. **£500-600** *PWC*

A Berlin rectangular plaque, impressed sceptre and KPM marks, 40 by 26 cm., c. 1880. **£1,800-£2,000** *C*

A set of 4 19th C. Capo-di-Monte oval porcelain relief pictures 'The Four Seasons' in ebonised frames. **£150-200** *DA*

A 19th C. Capo-di-Monte octagonal porcelain relief picture of 'The Devil with two attendants and a Goat', mounted in a brass and ebonised frame set with 8 semi-precious stones and ormolu mount. **£200-250** *DA*

A pair of Copeland plaques, printed mark, both framed, 84 by 22.5 cm., c. 1860. **£200-300** *S*

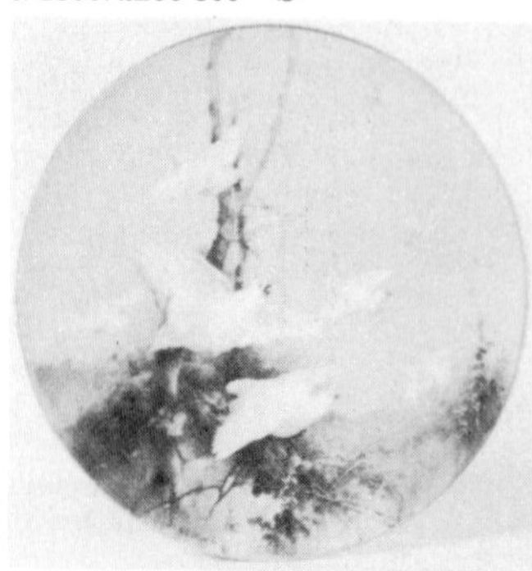

A Berlin rectangular plaque painted by Wagner with Hagar and her son Ishmael, signed, impressed sceptre and KPM marks, carved giltwood frame, 18.5 by 31.5 cm., late 19th C. **£750-850** *C*

A Berlin plaque painted and signed by R. Dittrich 'nach Ritscher' titled on the reverse 'Der Escuh bei der Amme', impressed KPM and sceptre mark, framed, 16 by 12 in. (40.7 by 30.5 cm.), late 19th C. **£2,000-2,500** *SC*

A Derby plaque by C. Gresley, 6 by 4½ in., 1910. **£280-340** *NSN*

A Franz Dörfl, Vienna, porcelain plaque, painted by F. Koeller, signed, with 'Shakespeare at the Court of Queen Elizabeth', printed shield mark and inscribed title in German, 49.8 cm., last quarter 19th C. **£750-850** *SS*

A Royal Worcester circular wall plaque painted by Charley Baldwyn, signed, with eight ptarmigan in winter plumage against a matt blue ground, the rim gilt, 30 cm., date code for 1900. **£800-1,000** *P*

A Berlin plaque painted in Vienna by F. Wagner after M. Ring, with a scantily draped maiden, inscribed on the reverse Loreley n. U. Ring, signed, impressed KPM marks, ebonised and giltwood frame, 33 by 20 cm., c. 1880. **£2,500-3,000** *C*

A Berlin oval plaque painted by Wagner, signed, with 'The Queen of Roses', impressed sceptre and KPM printed mark, framed 17.2 cm., c. 1905. **£800-900** *S*

A Vienna plaque painted in colours in a gilt wooden frame, 17.5 by 22.5 cm., 19th C. **£1,000-1,500** *S*

A large Werdau porcelain plaque, painted within a key fret design, the rim within decorative gold borders, 45.8 cm., late 19th C. **£400-450** *Bea*

A pair of Royal Worcester oval plaques, painted by J. Stinton, signed, one damaged, printed crowned circle mark, painted title, framed and glazed, 32.5 cm., date code for 1919. **£1,600-1,900** *S*

A fine Royal Worcester oval plaque, painted in rich colours by Richard Sebright, signed, framed, 16 by 24.5 cm., date code for 1910. **£450-550** *P*

A Royal Worcester plaque painted and signed by John Stinton, framed, 4⅛ in., purple printed mark including date code for 1915. **£250-300** *SC*

An Austrian plaque painted with a panel depicting 'Peace and Prosperity', reserved within a band of vine leaves on a gold ground, painted mark, 42 cm., late 19th C. **£450-550** *Bea*

A topographical plaque painted with a view of Constantinople, framed, 24 by 24.5 cm., c. 1835. **£550-650** *S*

A German porcelain plaque painted after Rubens with 'The Rape of the Sabines', with wood frame, 23.5 by 18.5 cm., last quarter of the 19th C. **£1,000-£1,200** *C*

A decorative plaque painted by F. G. Adlard, signed and dated 1884, 38.6 by 30.5 cm., 1884. **£250-£350** *S*

An English porcelain scenic plaque, 8¾ in., c. 1840. **£245-295** *GCA*

A pair of Booth silicon flowerpots, extremely rare complete with liners, purchased by Worcester in the white, decorated in blue and white with the 'Pine Cone' pattern, c. 1770. **£780-860** pair *SA*

A Caughley butter pail and stand, with the 'Fence' pattern, c. 1775. **£780-860** *SA*

A Höchst pot pourri vase and domed cover enriched in gilding, the cover with repair, blue wheel mark and incised Former's marks, 18.5 cm. high, c. 1765. **£600-700** *C*

A pair of Crown Derby pots with covers, 3 in. high, 1936. **£120-140** *NSN*

A rare Saint Cloud porcelain pot pourri basket and cover in the white, set with ormolu handles, chipping, 29 cm. long, 1730's. **£450-£550** *SS*

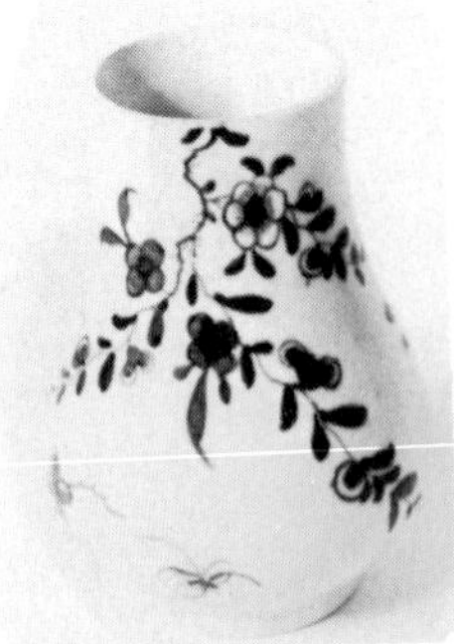

A Worcester blue and white base of a dry mustard pot, the prunus root pattern, minus cover, 3½ in. **£180-£220** With top **£1,000** *SA*

It is staggering to realise the difference in price in this piece due to the loss of the cover.

A Paris porcelain pot pourri painted and gilt on green ground, 8½ in., mid 19th C. **£200-250** *IHA*

A Wedgwood fairyland lustre 'Malfrey pot' and cover, decorated with the 'Bubbles 11' pattern in tones of deep purple, blue and green with orange and red details, printed urn mark, Z5257, 18 cm., 1920's. **£2,000-2,500** *S*

A Royal Worcester peach ground pot pourri with pierced cover, 7 in. wide, 1909. **£95-120** *NSN*

ROYAL WORCESTER

Some Royal Worcester artists and their specialities
C. Baldwyn — birds, particularly swans
George Johnson — exotic birds
James Stinton — game birds
John Stinton — highland cattle
Harry Stinton — highland cattle (more vivid colours than father)
R. Rushton — landscapes
R. Sebright — fruit and flowers
H. Price — fruit
J. Stanley — hunting scenes
E. Barker — sheep
Kitty Blake — blackberries and autumnal leaves

A Royal Worcester peach ground pot pourri vase, cover and liner, 8 in., 1900. **£200-240** *NSN*

A Royal Worcester pot pourri vase and covers, painted and signed by H. Davis, picked out in pale green and gilding, restored cover, purple printed mark including date code for 1913, 18½ in. **£1,300-1,500** *SC*

A Royal Worcester pot pourri vase and covers, painted and signed by Freeman with a still-life of fruit, black printed marks, 13½ in. **£500-£600** *SC*

A Derby sauceboat, 7¼ in., c. 1765. Damaged **£85-95** Perfect **£170-£185** *WWW*

A pair of Vincennes small pots and covers painted in colours, interlaced L marks and painter's mark of a star, 7.5 cm. high, 1752-55. **£400-500** *C*

A pair of Grainger's & Co. Worcester pot pourri vases and covers painted with a named view of 'Dover' on one and 'Abbotsford' on the other, marbled pedestal bases, script marks in iron-red, some repair, 12¼ in., c. 1815. **£400-£500** *SC*

A pair of Staffordshire porcelain sauceboats and covers, probably Davenport, 6 in. high, c. 1805. **£235-265** *EC*

A Coalport 'Japan pattern' 45-piece dinner service, brightly painted, some damage, c. 1805. **£3,000-£3,500** *S*

A very rare small first period Worcester, blue and white, cream boat, with the 'Bare Tree Pagoda' pattern, 4½ in., c. 1760. Damaged **£250-265** Perfect **£350-400** *WWW*

A small first period Worcester sauceboat, with blue and white 'Two-porter landscape' pattern, 5½ in., c. 1770. Damaged **£90-100** Perfect **£180-200** *WWW*

A Caughley tea service, printed in underglaze blue with the 'Cormorant fisherman' pattern, gilt line borders, comprising: tea pot, cover and stand, sucrier and cover, tea caddy and cover, milk jug, 4 tea bowls and saucers, and a saucer dish, S marks in underglaze blue, one saucer cracked, one tea bowl chipped, both saucer dishes cracked, 1785-90. **£300-350** *SC*

BOW MARKS

Most Bow porcelain is unmarked.

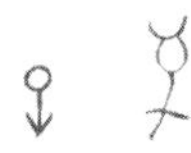

Incised marks, c. 1750

painted anchor and dagger marks, c. 1760-76.

A rare Bow toy 22-piece tea and coffee service, painted in Chinese 'famille rose' style with flowering tree peonies within brown-edged rims. **£3,500-4,500** *L*

A Caughley doll's tea service, each piece painted in underglaze blue comprising: tea pot and cover, jug, sucrier and cover, slop bowl and 6 tea bowls and stands, 'S' in underglaze blue, some cracked, last quarter 18th C. **£1,100-1,400** *SS*

A 61-piece Coalport dinner service decorated in blue and gilt with floral banding, central rose motif. **£1,000-1,200** *TM*

A 31-piece Coalport topographical 'Union' dessert service, painted in autumnal palette, incised numerals, 2 lozenge dishes cracked, some pieces badly rubbed, c. 1826. **£600-700** *SC*

A good and unusual Victorian silver and Coalport porcelain coffee set. **£500-600** *PWC*

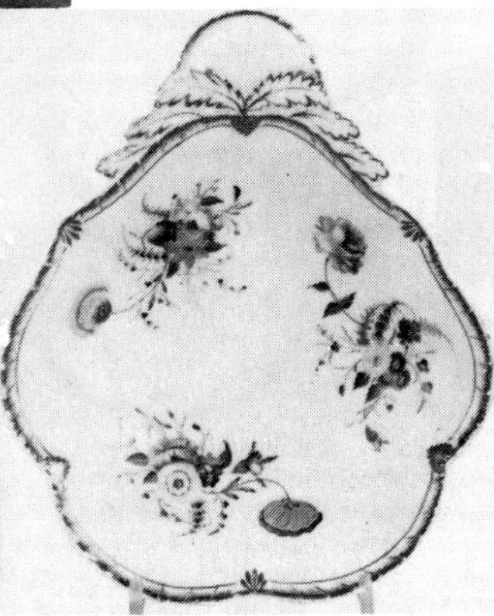

A 32-piece dessert service, pattern no. 237 in gilding, probably Coalport, slight rubbing, one plate cracked, c. 1815-20. **£500-600** *SC*

An English porcelain 32-piece tea and coffee service, the details picked out in magenta and green on an apricot and gilt seed ground, pattern no. 5/1730, probably Coalport, c. 1845-50. **£200-250** *SS*

A 45-piece tea and coffee service, picked out in 'gros bleu', pale yellow and gilding, pattern no. 722 in gilding, probably Coalport, some damaged, c. 1830. **£1,000-1,500** *SC*

A Coalport china dessert service painted with roses by F. Howard comprising 9 plates and a pair of 2-handled dishes (No. 5351 P in gilt), 10 pieces signed, c. 1910. **£1,500-1,700** *GSP*

A Derby 44-piece tea service decorated in blue, worn red and gilt in the Japan pattern, some pieces damaged and repaired, c. 1820. **£500-600** *WHL*

A Derby tea set decorated with a 'Japan' pattern in underglaze blue, iron-red, green and gilding, comprising: a tea pot, cover and stand, a sugar bowl and cover, a milk jug, a slop bowl and stand, 7 tea cups, 10 coffee cans and 12 saucers, 2 cups cracked, some wear, painted crowned crossed batons and D, various numerals, saucer: 14 cm., c. 1815-25. **£700-800** *S*

A Davenport dessert service, the centres painted with bouquets of flowers in shaped panels on a cobalt blue ground with gold beaded ornaments and scrolls, printed mark in green Davenport Longport Staffordshire below a crown, 2 plates and a dish with the earlier mark in blue, Davenport on a scroll above an anchor, 1870-86. **£1,100-1,400** *L*

A Royal Crown Derby 43-piece Imari pattern coffee service, red printed marks including date code for 1889 and 1923. **£450-500** *SC*

A Meissen 21-piece coffee service, painted in oriental taste with iron-red ground panels, crossed swords in underglaze blue, 8¾ in. (22 cm.), mid to late 19th C. **£1,200-1,400** *S*

The design is based on a late 17th century Kakiemon design.

A Crown Derby 'Lazy Susan' tea service on revolving plinth, 18 in., c. 1880. **£350-400** *IHA*

MEISSEN MARKS

crossed swords mark in underglaze blue, introduced 1723

crossed swords mark of the Marcolini period 1774-1814

crossed swords mark of 'Dot Period' 1763-74

Augustus Rex mark in blue

An assembled outside-decorated Meissen and Berlin yellow-ground tête-à-tête, each piece painted with 18th C. lovers, cancelled crossed swords and obliterated sceptre marks, minor damage, 15 in. (38.4 cm.), late 19th C. **£700-800** *S*

A Höchst 51-piece dinner service in the Meissen style, one oval deep dish cracked, 5 dinner plates with rim chips, blue crowned wheel marks, c. 1765. **£9,000-10,000** *C*

A Meissen 'onion pattern' service, each piece decorated in underglaze blue with a typical design of stylised flowers and fruits, 102 pieces in all, some pieces damaged, crossed swords in underglaze blue, dinner plate: 9¾ in. (24.8 cm.), c. 1900. **£3,500-4,000** *S*

A Minton porcelain 60-piece part dinner service, each piece painted with a bright light blue band within gold ribbons, some damage, impressed mark, late 19th C. **£500-£600** *Bea*

A good New Hall 43-piece tea service of London shape, the pale blue ground with gilt sprig borders, pattern no. 1092. **£1,500-1,800** *P*

A 21-piece Spode ornithological dessert service, each piece with named bird specimens, each inscribed en grisaille with the name of the bird and SPODE, above pattern no. 2059, early 19th C. **£2,500-3,000** *SC*

A royal blue ground part dinner service, probably Ridgways, comprising: 4 soup plates, 19 dinner plates, 10 side plates and a soup tureen and cover, damages, dinner plate: 24.3 cm., c. 1825. **£150-200** *S*

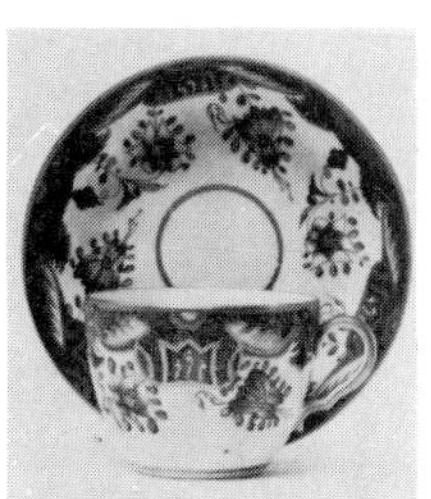

A Spode tea set with 'Imari' patterned border comprising: a tea pot, cover and stand, a milk jug, a sugar bowl and cover, a slop bowl, 11 cups, 12 saucers and a cake plate, some damage, saucer: 14.2 cm., painted mark and pattern number 1645, c. 1825. **£500-600** *S*

A combined Spode pottery and porcelain 27-piece dinner service, printed in black and picked out in rich green and gilding, printed marks 'en grisaille', pattern no. 1653 in iron-red, 8¼ in., early 19th C. **£200-250** *SC*

A Staffordshire topographical dessert service, with a deep-turquoise ground rim and formal gilt borders, comprising: 11 plates, 2 footed circular dishes and 2 fruit stands, some damage and wear, plate: 22.2 cm., painted title and pattern number 148, c. 1860. **£250-£300** *S*

A Staffordshire dessert service, probably Ridgway, with an apricot-ground border and a shaped and pierced rim, comprising 12 plates, 4 dishes and a fruit stand, minor damage and staining, painted pattern no. 3/36, 22.7 cm., mid 19th C. **£300-400** *S*

A Flight, Barr and Barr Worcester 36-piece dessert service painted in the style of Baxter, on a turquoise ground, one oval dish and one plate damaged, impressed marks, c. 1852-62, plates c. 1813-20. **£3,500-4,000** *S*

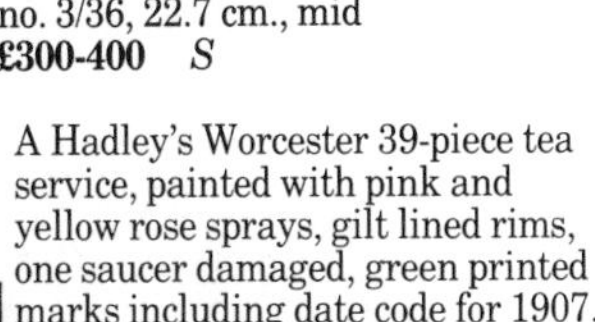

A Hadley's Worcester 39-piece tea service, painted with pink and yellow rose sprays, gilt lined rims, one saucer damaged, green printed marks including date code for 1907. **£250-300** *SC*

A rare Royal Worcester cabaret service, made for the Australian market, painted in colours and raised enamels with various Australian birds, the tray 45 cm., date codes for 1906. **£1,000-1,200** *P*

Almost certainly the work of Reginald or Walter Austin.

A Vinovo porcelain part tea-service painted 'en camaieu rose' comprising: tea pot and cover, milk jug and cover, sugar bowl and cover, 5 cups and saucers, crack to neck of milk jug, c. 1780. **£2,000-£3,000** *C*

A Chantilly quail pattern Kakiemon sugar bowl and cover painted in the Japanese style, iron-red hunting horn mark, rim chips to body, 8.5 cm. diam., 1735-40. **£180-240** *C*

The Chantilly factory was founded by the Prince de Conde, an avid collector of Japanese porcelain, particularly Kakiemon. His taste was manifest in the wares his factory produced. His own massive collection was dispensed, probably at the time of the Revolution.

A 19th C. dessert service, 36 pieces. **£250-300** *DWB*

A 128-piece dinner and dessert service, each piece brightly painted with a 'Japan' pattern and heightened in gilding, some damage, pattern no. 3116 in red, c. 1820-30. **£5,000-6,000** *S*

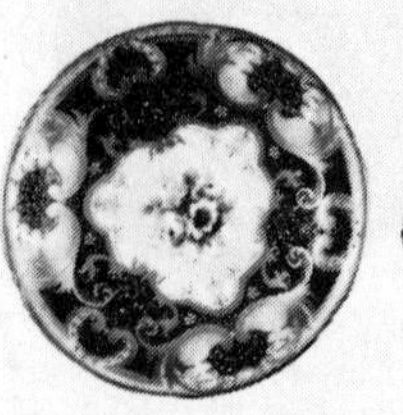

A good Royal Worcester tea service, each piece painted and signed by J. Stanley, within elaborate stylised scroll borders in gros bleu and tooled and raised gilding, purple printed marks with date code for 1926. **£850-950** *SC*

An Ansbach sugar bowl and cover, with landscapes in colours, gilt scroll brackets, incised Z, slight damage to knop, 12.6 cm., c. 1765-70. **£700-800** *S*

A Coalport felspar sucrier and cover, 6½ in. wide, 1830-45. **£90-£100** *NSN*

A Meissen sugar box and cover painted in underglaze blue with overglaze enamels and gilt, the rim of the cover with traces of Böttger-lustre, blue crossed swords mark and blue 8, impressed X, 12 cm. wide, c. 1735. **£600-800** *C*

A Worcester dry blue sucrier, with gilding, 6 in. high, c. 1780. **£185-£195** *WWW*

A Minton sucrier and cover, 6½ in. wide, c. 1830. **£130-150** *NSN*

A Chamberlain's Worcester sugar bowl, 7½ in., c. 1815. **£60-70** *IHA*

The English and Continental porcelain section is ordered in alphabetical category order, each category is then divided into alphabetical factory order and each factory is chronologically ordered.

A first period Worcester tankard by Hancock, with black transfer print of 'King of Prussia', 5 in. high, c. 1760. Slight fault **£200-225** Perfect **£300-350** *WWW*

A first period Worcester blue and white bell shaped tankard, 'The Plantation Print' pattern, 6 in. high, c. 1765. **£285-295** *WWW*

A Dresden tankard, 5¾ in., c. 1860. **£80-100** *IHA*

A jewelled Coalport tea pot, with pink ground, 5 in., c. 1900-10. **£180-£200** *NSN*

An early Meissen tea pot with Dutch decoration and Dutch Delft cover, chips to rim of cover, 13 cm. wide, the porcelain c. 1722. **£1,000-£1,500** *C*

A Meissen tea pot and cover painted in colours with gilt scrolling borders, flower knop, crossed swords and a dot in underglaze blue, 11.5 cm., c. 1760. **£450-550** *S*

A Crown Derby miniature tea pot, 1909. **£130-145** *NSN*

A Lowestoft toy tea pot and cover, painted in underglaze blue with Chinese river scenes below a husk border, numeral 17 mark on the foot rim, 7.5 cm. **£300-350** *L*

An important Meissen cock tea pot and cover modelled by J. J. Kändler in the form of a fabulous bird resembling a cockerel, the spout set in the bird's blue breast, its head painted in black and iron-red with yellow beak and gold comb, the finial formed as a frog with open mouth, 15 cm. long, c. 1740. **£4,000-4,500** *P*

A Ludwigsburg coffee pot and cover painted in colours, interlaced C's below a crown in underglaze blue, incised numerals, painter's mark in iron-red, restored, 23.5 cm., c. 1770. **£500-600** *S*

A Meissen chinoiserie globular tea pot and domed cover, painted in the manner of J. E. Stadler, with gilt and Böttger-lustre Laub-und-Bandelwerk, with gilt metal chain attachment, minor repair to rim and tip of spout, 15.5 cm. wide, c. 1735. **£1,400-1,700** *C*

A first period Worcester blue and white tea pot, 'The Bird in a Ring' pattern, 5½ in. high, c. 1765. **£200-£225** *WWW*

This design was almost certainly exclusive to Worcester.

(l.) A Sèvres oviform tea pot and cover with seeded blue borders, blue interlaced L marks enclosing illegible date letter, painter's mark of Thevenet, 11.5 cm. high, c. 1755. **£200-250** *C*

(c.) A Sèvres oviform tea pot and cover with green ground, painted with chocolate ribbons enclosing pink medallions with gilt rosettes, finial restored, 12 cm. high, c. 1770. **£120-150** *C*

(r.) A Sèvres hard-paste oviform tea pot and cover, puce crowned interlaced L mark and painter's mark of Dutanda, 12 cm. high, c. 1775. **£120-180** *C*

SÈVRES MARKS

2nd Empire period, red, 1852-70

First Republic period, blue, 1793-1800

Cypher mark, blue and various colours, used 1753-93. Includes letter code for year. B denotes 1754

A rare Worcester tea pot and cover, printed in underglaze blue with the the 'Two Quail' pattern (I.C.15), crescent mark, 14.5 cm., c. 1775. **£450-550** *P*

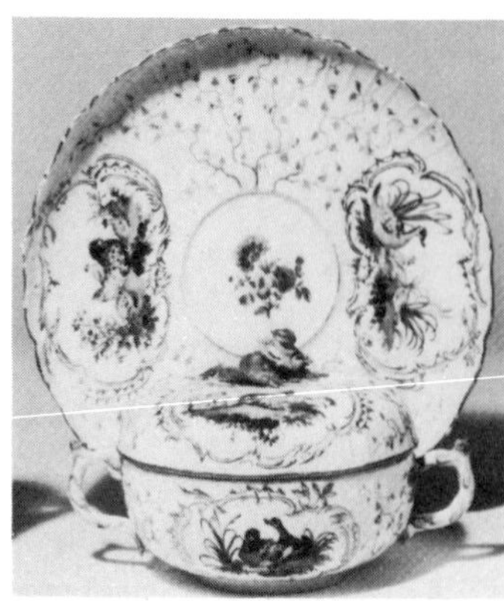
A Berlin two-handled ecuelle, cover and stand, the rims gilt, blue sceptre mark, repair to finial and both handles, stand chipped, the stand 22 cm. diam., c. 1770. **£500-£600** *C*

A Meissen ecuelle, cover and stand, Böttger-lustre grounds, the centre of the cover painted with further puce chinoiseries, blue crossed swords mark, finial restored, the stand 23.7 cm. diam., c. 1735. **£4,500-5,500** *C*

A fine Dr. Wall period Worcester tureen, lid and stand, painted with English flowers, c. 1770. **£1,700-£1,900** *SA*

A pair of Belleek vases covered in a nacreous glaze, impressed Belleek Co. Fermanagh, one with slight damage, 25.8 cm., late 19th C. **£200-300** *Bea*

A first period Worcester blue and white coffee pot, with butterflies and flowers, 10 in. **£360-440** *SA*

A Longton Hall cos-lettuce tureen, cover and stand, painted with scattered insects, the cover with cauliflower finial, the stand 33 cm. long, c. 1755. **£3,500-4,500** *C*

No complete example with a cauliflower finial would appear to be recorded.

A Vincennes bleu lapis small two-handled ecuelle and stand, on mottled 'bleu lapis' ground, interlaced L marks in underglaze blue, minute rim chip to cup, the stand 12.5 cm. diam., c. 1752. **£250-£350** *C*

Use the Index!
Because certain items might fit easily into any of a number of categories, the quickest and surest method of locating any entry is by reference to the index at the back of the book. This has been fully cross-referenced for absolute simplicity.

A Derby porcelain sauce tureen, 6½ in., c. 1820. **£260-300** *DL*

Pseudo Meissen mark of underglaze blue crossed swords

A Meissen Augustus Rex two-handled tureen, painted in bright colours in the Kakiemon manner, blue AR monogram, minor rim chip and foot rim chips, 38 cm. wide, c. 1730. **£400-600** *C*

A Sèvres ecuelle, cover and stand, each gilt 'cailhouté bleu céleste' ground, stand enamelled in blue with outside decorator's interlaced 'L's enclosing 3 dots over 'R.C.', incised repairer's marks, 21.7 cm., c. 1760. **£400-500** *SS*

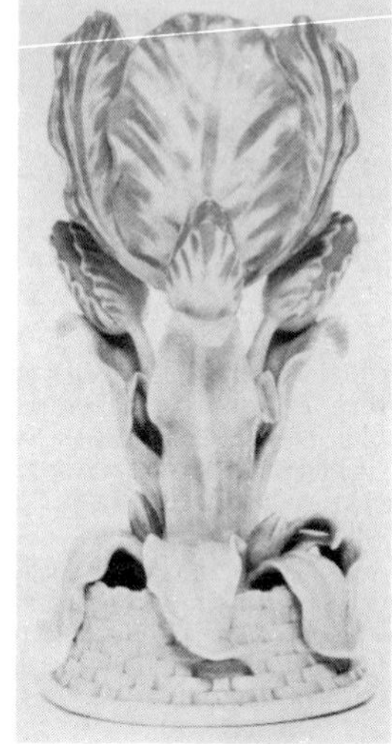
A pair of Belleek tulip vases, the pastel glazes with an iridescent sheen, printed dog and harp mark, one damaged, the other chipped, 32.3 cm., 1863-91. **£500-600** *S*

BELLEEK MARKS

BELLEEK
CO. FERMANAGH
impressed or relief, 1863-90

standard trade mark
(second version),
c.1891 to present

BELLEEK
FERMANAGH IRELAND

standard trade mark
(first version),
c.1863-91

BELLEEK

A Belleek polychrome vase, enriched in pink lustre and with gilding, the base enriched in pink and yellow lustres, black printed Belleek mark, one butterfly wing, one fish tail and the salamanders' tails chipped, 41 cm. high, c. 1880.
£600-800 *C*

A Chelsea tapering hexagonal vase painted in the Kakiemon palette in blue, iron-red, yellow and green the shoulder with turquoise scrolling foliage, the short neck with iron-red geometric designs, raised anchor mark, two minute rim chips to the top rim and a minute flake to the foot, about 23 cm. high, c. 1750.
£3,000-4,000 *C*

A Bow blue and white tapering oviform vase painted after a Chinese original, the shaped domed foot with Buddhistic emblems, small chip to rim, small firing crack to foot, 27 cm. high, 1755-58.
£2,200-£2,500 *C*

A pair of Coalbrookdale vases in Sèvres style, reserved on a bleu céleste ground, CBD marks in gilding, repaired, 11 in., 1851-61.
£400-500 *SC*

A pair of Bow vases and covers, decorated in Oriental style, in iron-red, underglaze blue and gilding, 8¾ in., marked 7 in underglaze blue, vases with 'scratch R', c. 1750, covers chipped, one vase with crack. **£1,500-2,000** *S*

A rare Chelsea-Derby garniture of a vase and two ewers, with gilt striped grounds, painted possibly by Richard Askew, all with oval panels of landscapes painted by Zachariah Boreman, gold anchor marks, one restored, 22 cm. vase and 23.5 cm. the ewers. **£1,100-£1,300** *P*

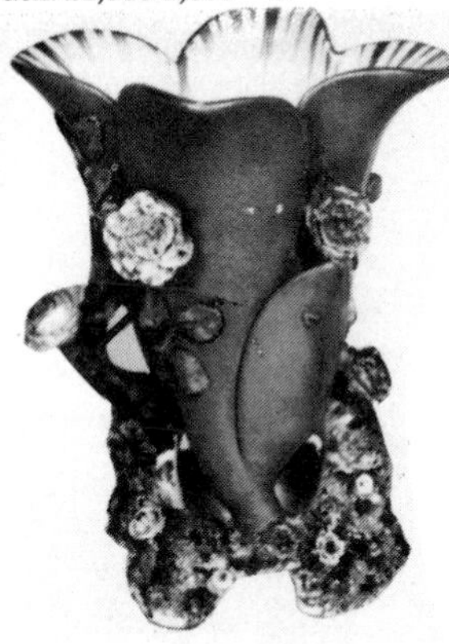

A pair of Coalbrookdale 'lily of the valley' vases, on green ground, picked out in naturalistic palette, CD marks in underglaze blue, some damage, 8¼ in., early 19th C. **£150-£200** *SC*

A fine pair of Chelsea claret ground vases, finely painted with Dutch interior scenes in the manner of Teniers, within panels enclosed by gilt floral and trellis borders, gold anchor marks, 6¼ in. **£800-900** *WHL*
The fine quality of the decoration, although probably not carried out at the factory may well turn out to be that of a member of the Duvivier family.

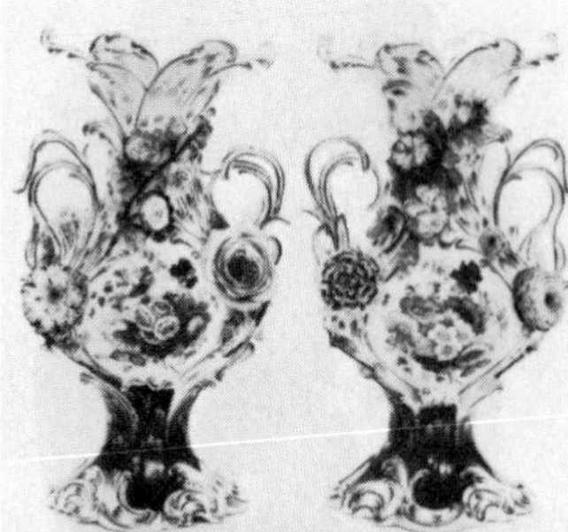

A pair of Coalport vases, painted with colourful sprays of summer flowers, the details gilt, minor chips, 10¼ in., c. 1835. **£500-600** *S*

A pair of Chinese style vases, each after a Cantonese original, picked out in burnished gilding and reserved on a black ground, perhaps Coalport, 12¼ in., 1830-40. **£300-350** *SC*

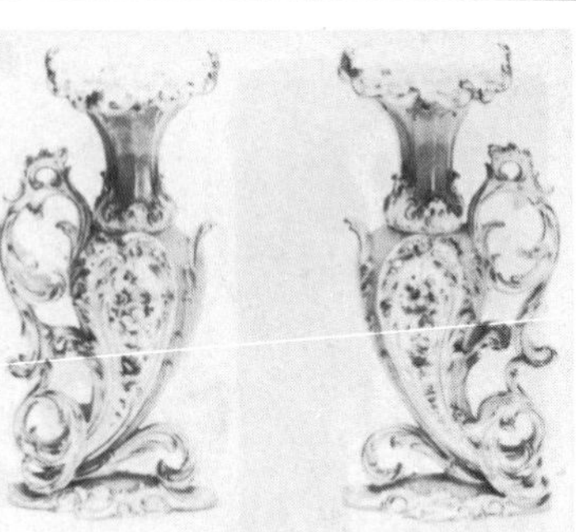

A pair of Coalport cornucopia vases, painted with flowers on a white and pale green ground embellished with gold, 25 cm., c. 1830-40. **£250-300** *Bea*

A pair of pink ground Coalport vases and covers reserved on a bright pink ground, ampersand marks in gilding, very slight repair, 9¼ in., 1861-75. **£250-400** *SC*

A pair of Coalport vases of Eastern inspiration, in bright colours and gilding, printed ampersand mark above pattern name 'Cashmere' in puce, 8¼ in., 1861-75. **£300-400** *SC*

A pair of commemorative Coalport vases and covers printed in underglaze blue, picked out in gilding and reserved on a blue ground, green printed marks, repaired, 17½ in., c. 1891. **£200-£300** *SC*

A garniture of Coalport vases painted with flowers and fantastic birds in a landscape by William Waterson within a gold cartouche on a deep blue ground, slight damage, late 19th C. **£250-350** *Bea*

Coalport (Rose & Co.)

- **factory was founded in the early 1790's by John Rose when he left Caughley**
- **Rose purchased the Caughley works in 1799 and ran them until he had them demolished in 1814**
- **produced hard-paste porcelain certainly after 1800, before then produced soapstone porcelain, this was quite similar to Caughley but does not have the yellow-brown translucency**
- **early wares heavy, with greyish appearance**
- **in this period quite similar to Newhall and Chamberlains**
- **in this period the highly decorated Japan wares have great quality as do some of the flower painted examples**
- **in around 1811 firm taken over by John Rose, William Clark and Charles Maddison**
- **in 1820 a new leadless glaze was invented and they also began to use Billingsley's frit paste**
- **in 1820 Rose also bought moulds from Nantgarw and Swansea and Billingsley came to work at Coalport**
- **best period for the Coalport factory began in 1820 when the factory produced a brilliantly white hard felspar porcelain, with a high level of translucency**
- **in terms of translucency and whiteness Coalport can be said to compete with Swansea and Nantgarw—although the factory never quite achieved the sheer brilliance of the Welsh factories and the potting is slightly heavier**
- **Coalport is often mistaken for Rockingham**
- **after 1820 CD, CD monogram, C.Dale, Coalbrookdale and Coalport were all marks used, before this date the marks tend to vary and much was unmarked**
- **in 1840's and 1850's Coalport perfected many fine ground colours: maroon, green and pink**
- **these often rivalled Sèvres especially in 1850's and 1860's**
- **Coalport also at this time produced some Chelsea copies, with fake marks—these are very rare**
- **the Coalport factory is still in existence today**

A garniture of three Coalport vases, 6¾ and 5¼ in. **£400-500** *LT*

A Coalport 'named view' vase painted on one side in autumnal palette with a named view of 'Hawthornden', reserved on a blue and gilt ground simulating enamel between yellow and gilt borders, green printed mark, 7¼ in., c. 1910. **£250-350** *SC*

A pair of Coalport vases with pierced covers, 3½ in., c. 1910. **£200-220** *NSN*

A pair of Coalport miniature vases, 4¼ in., c. 1910-15. **£95-120** *NSN*

A Bloor Derby garniture of vases reserved on a gros bleu ground, printed marks in iron-red, some staining, gilding rubbed, 6¾ and 8¼ in., 1820-30. **£550-600** *SC*

A Derby vase and cover, on deep blue ground with gilding, 5 in. wide, 1880. **£140-160** *NSN*

A pair of Derby Crown Porcelain Company vases and covers, each royal blue ground ovoid body decorated in shaded and tooled gilding, one knop repaired, printed initials mark, gilder's initials TB, 37.5 cm., date code for 1888. **£700-£900** *S*

The gilder's initials are probably those of Thomas Brown, recorded as a gilder who on occasions worked with Leroy for special plate productions.

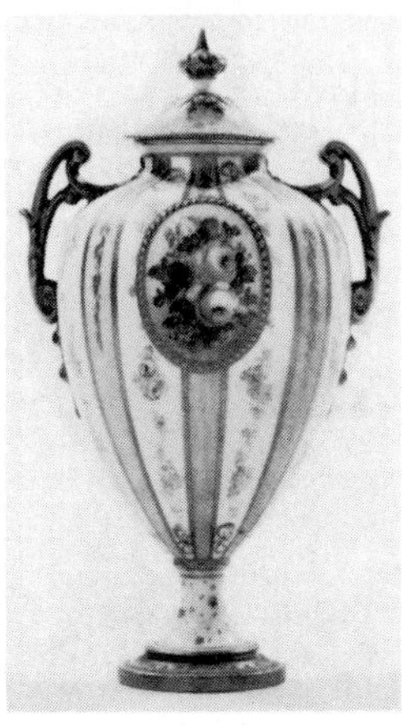

A Royal Crown Derby vase and cover painted by C. Gresley, signed, with pale-turquoise and gilt stripes between floral trails, knopped cover, printed mark, incised shape number 1505, hair crack in cover rim, 15 cm., date code for 1906. **£300-400** *S*

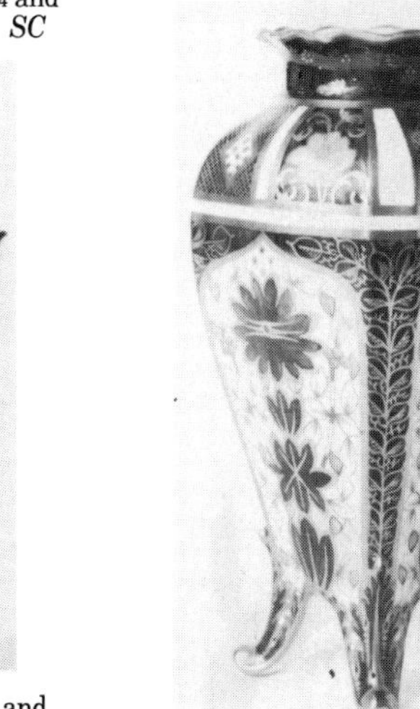

A Crown Derby vase, 6½ in., 1908. **£110-120** *NSN*

A Crown Derby vase, 5¼ in., 1914. **£110-120** *NSN*

A Derby vase and cover painted by A. F. Wood, 5¾ in., 1911. **£200-£250** *NSN*

A Derby vase painted by W. E. J. Dean, 4 in., 1917. **£170-190** *NSN*

A Derby vase and cover painted by A. Gregory, 5¾ in., 1913. **£450-£500** *NSN*

A Crown Derby spill vase, 6 in., 1920. **£120-140** *NSN*

A Royal Doulton vase painted by R. Holdcroft, signed, printed lion and circle mark, incised shape number 1216, impressed date code for 1926, 12 in. **£550-650** *S*

A specimen vase heavily gilt and decorated with rural scene of cattle in a stream, on a circular base by C. E. Hopkins, the base is slightly defective, ht. 32 in. **£1,700-1,900** *LT*

The vase is not marked but is almost certainly Royal Doulton.

A Royal Doulton vase painted by A. Eaton, signed, printed lion and crown mark, moulded shape number, impressed date code for 1915, 22 cm. **£400-500** *S*

A Höchst porcelain pot-pourri vase edged in blue and gilding, the creamy-white glaze falling short of the footrim, impressed 'NI' underglaze blue crowned wheel, 11 cm., 1760's. **£300-400** *SS*

A Lancastrian lustre vase designed by Walter Crane, decorated by William S. Mycock, impressed bee mark above date code for 1910, artist's monograms and year mark for 1910 of a running hare, impressed 2472, 10½ in. **£350-£400** *SC*

A pair of Dresden 'Schneeballen' vases and covers ground encrusted overall with blue-edged yellow-centred mayblossom, surmounted by parrots in flight, mock blue crossed swords and dot marks, several birds lack wing or tail feathers, 79 cm. high, c. 1860. **£1,300-1,500** *C*

A pair of Dresden vases and covers, the bright blue ground reserved with gilt scrollwork, 'AR' mark in blue, 32 cm., late 19th C. **£350-£400** *SS*

A pair of Longton Hall vases, outlined in turquoise and gold, painted with sprays of flowers and containing white may blossom, 17.2 cm. **£300-350** *L*

A Pilkington's Royal Lancastrian vase decorated by William S. Mycock, in silver/bronze lustre against a shaded crimson ground, bearing an inscription 'Cultores Veritatis Fraudis Inimici', impressed rosette mark, 2838, painted artist's monogram and dated 1921, 31.2 cm. **£200-250** *S*

A Lancastrian lustre vase decorated by William S. Mycock in reddish lustres, impressed marks, lustre monogram, including the date 1923, 7 in. **£300-350** *SC*

A pair of Meissen vases, in early 18th C. taste, painted in the manner of J. G. Herold, with figures on a quay, the ground gilt with borders and scrolls, crossed swords in underglaze blue, rim chip, 5 in. (13 cm.), mid 19th C. **£900-1,000** *S*

A pair of Meissen vases, each painted with naturalistically coloured sprays of summer flowers, crossed swords in underglaze blue, incised E116, 15¼ in. (38.6 cm.), late 19th C. **£600-750** *S*

A Meissen style vase and cover decorated possibly by Helena Wolfsohn, with a bright yellow ground, within gilt scroll borders, indistinct mark in underglaze blue, 19¾ in. (50.2 cm.), late 19th C. **£180-240** *SC*

A large Potschappel vase, cover and stand, cross and T in blue, cracks and chips, 102 cm., late 19th C. **£1,000-1,200** *S*

A large Minton 'new vase' and cover edged in gilt and turquoise enamel, decorated with vignettes of birds and views, 46.5 cm., c. 1838. **£450-500** *Bon*

A pair of Minton vases and covers, well painted, possibly by R. Pilsbury, reserved on a sky blue ground between burnished gilt borders, one cover and finials repaired, 14¾ in., 1860-70. **£600-£700** *SC*

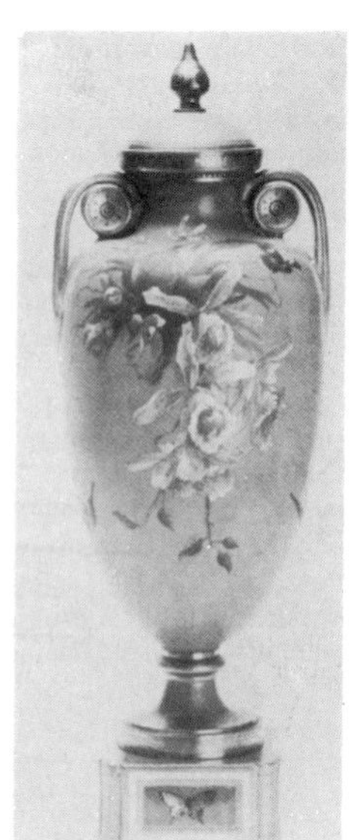

A Minton porcelain vase and cover, boldly decorated in thick enamel on a bright blue ground enhanced in gold, hair crack to pedestal foot, 59 cm., late 19th C. **£400-500** *Bea*

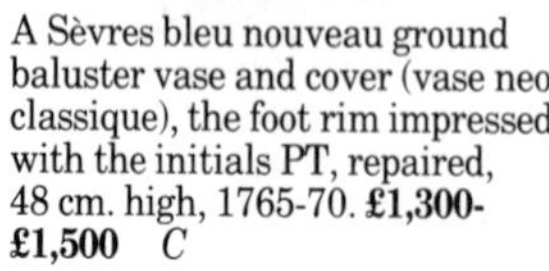

A Sèvres bleu nouveau ground baluster vase and cover (vase neo-classique), the foot rim impressed with the initials PT, repaired, 48 cm. high, 1765-70. **£1,300-£1,500** *C*

A pair of Sèvres-style vases and covers, the bodies with blue ground with gilt enrichment, some damage, 21 in. high, c. 1850-60. **£550-650** *NSF*

SÈVRES

- **factory moved to Sèvres in 1756 from Vincennes where production started, c. 1740**
- **in early days copied Meissen and influenced by Kakiemon**
- **in 1750's factory began producing vases in large quantities**
- **most sought after ground colour is the yellow (jaune jonquille)**
- **plaques for furniture became popular in 1760's**
- **factory also noted for clock-cases, small sets for tea, coffee and chocolate, and boxes**
- **managed to discover the secret of hard-paste porcelain in 1770**
- **'Jewelled porcelain' was introduced in 1773, used a technique of fusing enamels over gilt or silver foil**

A Rockingham miniature garniture on a ruby ground. **£1,500-2,000** *DWB*

A fine pair of Sarre-Guemines vases, painted in naturalistic enamel colours, signed 'L. Langlois', printed mark, late 19th C. **£400-450** *Bea*

A pair of 'Sèvres' jewelled vases, each painted with playful putti amongst clouds, gilt borders heightened with white, red and pale blue enamel studs, with gilt metal base and rim, minor chips, 12 in. (30.5 cm.), mid 19th C. **£700-£800** *S*

A pair of Sèvres pattern gilt metal mounted vases, decorated by Petit, the metal necks, fixed covers and spreading feet decorated in imitation of cloisonné, signed, 34 cm. high, last quarter of the 19th C. **£800-900** *C*

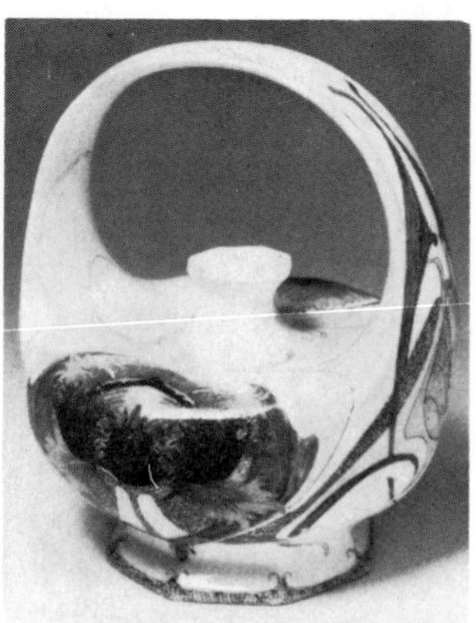

A Rozenburg 'eggshell' porcelain basket vase, of octagonal section painted by W. P. Hartgring in tones of yellow, brown and green against an ivory ground, printed crown and stork mark, Rozenburg den Haag, painted artist's monogram and flag year code for 1904, 15.5 cm. **£600-800** *Bon*

A pair of 'Sèvres' jewelled vases and covers, with moulded and gilt borders enriched with coloured enamel studs, some wear, one cover restored, 19 in. (48 cm.), mid 19th C. **£1,400-1,600** *S*

A pair of jewelled and ormolu mounted Sèvres-style vases and covers, with a deep blue ground moulded with gilt wreaths and arabesque borders between white and emerald coloured jewelling, set with ormolu double handles, interlaced 'L's' in blue, 48.5 cm., mid 19th C. **£1,800-2,200** *SS*

A fine metal mounted Sèvres-style vase and cover, with jewel beaded borders in ruby and opaque white enamel edged in gilding and reserved on a 'bleu celeste' ground, interlaced L's enclosing date letter A, painter's mark in blue enamel, some beading missing, 20¾ in. (52.7 cm.), late 19th C. **£900-£1,000** *SC*

A pair of 'Sèvres' gilt metal mounted vases each painted by Vautan, signed, painted interlaced L's, 20¼ in. (52.2 cm.), late 19th C. **£1,300-1,500** *S*

A pair of Sèvres gilt-bronze mounted vases and covers, painted by Armand, signed, painted interlaced L's, covers repaired, 47.5 cm., late 19th C. **£700-800** *S*

A 'Sèvres' vase and cover painted by H. Desprez, signed with a green ground painted pseudo Sèvres mark and title, 65.5 cm., late 19th C. **£850-950** *S*

A late 19th C. Sèvres-style vase, with figure painted panels and gilt decoration, 30 in. **£600-700** *PE*

The open-ended reference system
Miller's Antiques Price Guide builds up year by year to form the most comprehensive photo-reference system available. The first four volumes contain photographs of over 30,000 stock items!

A pair of 'Sèvres' gilt-bronze mounted vases and covers, each painted with a panel of Napoleon on horse back with his generals, within gilt leaves against a green ground, painted mark, one cover repaired, 23¼ in. (59 cm.), late 19th C. **£1,700-1,900** *S*

A large pair of Sèvres pattern ormolu mounted royal blue ground two-handled vases and covers, signed C. Hiccolier, 78 cm. high, c. 1900. **£1,200-1,500** *C*

A massive pair of Sèvres pattern armorial turquoise ground ormolu mounted two-handled vases and covers, mock interlaced L marks, covers restored, 104 cm. high, last quarter of 19th C. **£8,000-9,000** *C*

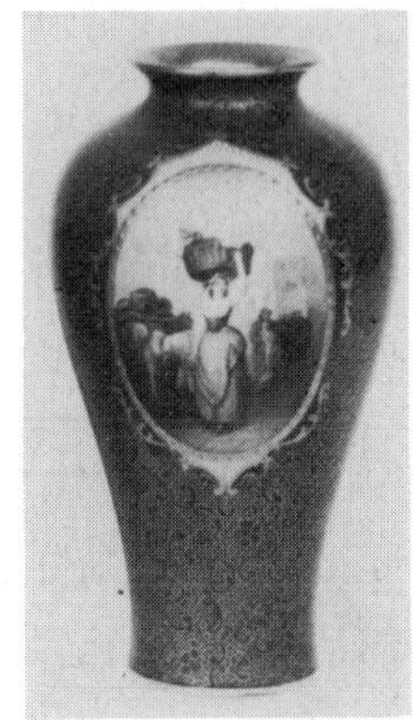

An interesting pair of Staffordshire 'Wilton' vases of meiping form, painted and signed by Leslie Johnson, titled beneath 'Hot spiced Gingerbread' and 'Strawberries', reserved on a gros bleu and printed gilt scroll ground, script marks in puce, printed marks in gilding, 8¾ in., 1924-34. **£200-250** *SC*

A fine pair of Vienna vases and covers painted by H. Stadler, profusely decorated in gold on a royal blue ground, printed mark for Franz Dorfl, one knop repaired, one cover slightly chipped but complete, 98 cm. **£5,000-6,000** *Bea*

A 'Vienna' vase and cover, painted and signed by H. Koller, with classical figures, against a gilt ground, shield in underglaze blue, printed title, knop repaired, 17½ in. (44.5 cm.), late 19th C. **£600-700** *S*

A pair of 'Vienna' vases and covers, each painted and signed by C. Heer, against a deep blue ground, shield in underglaze blue, one knop repaired, 11¼ in. (28.5 cm.), late 19th C. **£500-600** *S*

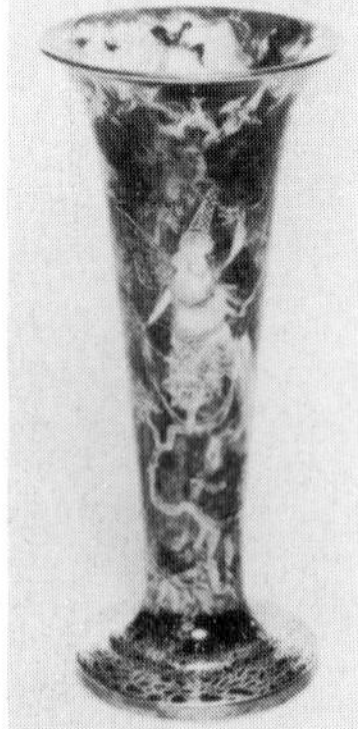

A Wedgwood fairyland lustre 'trumpet' vase, with the 'Butterfly Women' design, printed urn mark Z4968, 9½ in., 1920's. **£500-600** *S*

A pair of large 'Vienna' porcelain lidded vases, signed Ferd on bleu du roi ground with gilt roses, one damaged to rim, 18 in., 19th C. **£350-400** *WHL*

A pair of Worcester outside-decorated coral-red ground hexagonal vases and domed covers painted in the atelier of James Giles, one vase with repair to neck and shoulder, the other with small crack and chip to rim, one cover cracked, both with small chips, 29 cm. high, c. 1765. **£2,000-£2,500** *C*

Examples with blue scale grounds and similar bird painting are comparatively more common, other examples with a coral-red ground would appear to be unrecorded.

WORCESTER

It is, of course, vital to the study of porcelain to know the difference between hand painted and printed patterns. Easy and quick identification comes with constantly looking at comparative pieces. However a few points:

- **a printed pattern follows an etched or engraved copper plate**
- **a painted pattern is done by brush stroke and hence has a fluidity that is impossible with a print**
- **a brush is much less precise than an engraving — hence the hatch marks evident on a print**
- **brush work is most obvious where there is shading of colour**

A Worcester blue and white tapering hexagonal vase and domed cover, blue crossed swords and 6 mark, the cover repaired, 38.5 cm. high., c. 1760. **£800-900** *C*

A Chamberlain Worcester miniature vase, 2½ in. high, c. 1816. **£180-220** *NSN*

A good Wedgwood fairyland lustre vase printed in gilding and picked out in lustrous translucent glazes with 'Candlemas', printed Portland vase mark in gilding, Z5157 in puce, gilding very slightly rubbed, 7½ in., 1920's. **£600-700** *SC*

A superb Chamberlain's Worcester vase and cover of wine cooler shape, painted by Walter Chamberlain depicting the marriage of Dionysius and Ariadne, script marks in puce Chamberlain's Worcester, Manufacturers to their Royal Highnesses the Prince Regent and Duke of Cumberland, cover repaired, the lower body with hairline star crack, 46 cm. overall. **£3,000-4,000** *Bon*

A Flight Barr and Barr named view vase, painted with a view of 'Beauchief Abbey, Derbyshire', sepia script mark, one handle repaired, 6 in., 1813-40. **£300-350** *SC*

A Wedgwood fairyland lustre vase decorated with the 'Candlemas' design, printed urn mark, Z5157, gilding rubbed, 21.5 cm., 1920's. **£550-650** *S*

A Royal Worcester ivory ground basket vase, 5 in., 1880. **£65-75** *NSN*

A Royal Worcester spill holder, 7 in., c. 1870. **£110-130** *IHA*

A pair of Royal Worcester vases decorated in raised gilding, sepia and iron-red, green printed mark including date code for 1884, printed in purple 'Patent Metallic', impressed numerals, 11¼ in. **£400-£500** *SC*

A Royal Worcester vase modelled as a scantilly draped boy wearing a large hat, decorated in colours and enriched with gilding, impressed mark, 18 cm. high, c. 1880. **£150-£200** *C*

An unusual pair of Royal Worcester vases simulating cloisonné enamel, reserved on a bright blue ground, moulded marks, rubbed, 8½ in., late 19th C. **£300-350** *SC*

A Royal Worcester vase and cover, painted and monogrammed by Edward Raby, on a peach and ivory ground, purple printed mark with date code for 1892, finial repaired, 15¼ in. **£300-350** *SC*

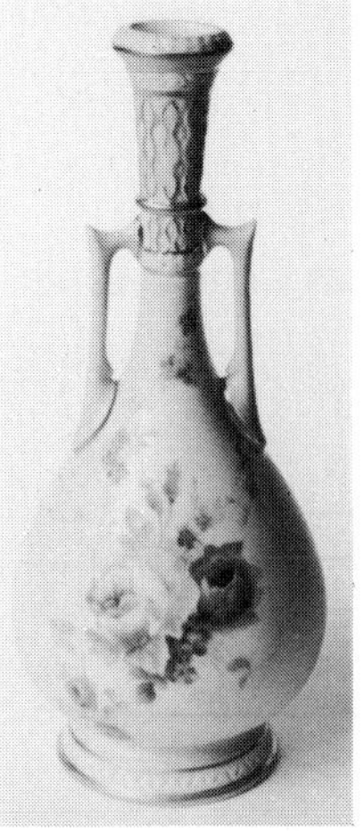

A Royal Worcester peach ground vase, 6½ in., 1896. **£75-95** *NSN*

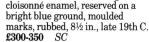

A pair of Royal Worcester vases in Japanese taste picked out in sepia, subdued colours and gilding, impressed marks, printed mark in puce with obscured date code, slight chip to one, 7¼ in., late 19th C. **£300-350** *SC*

A Royal Worcester peach ground vase, 3½ in., 1897. **£65-75** *NSN*

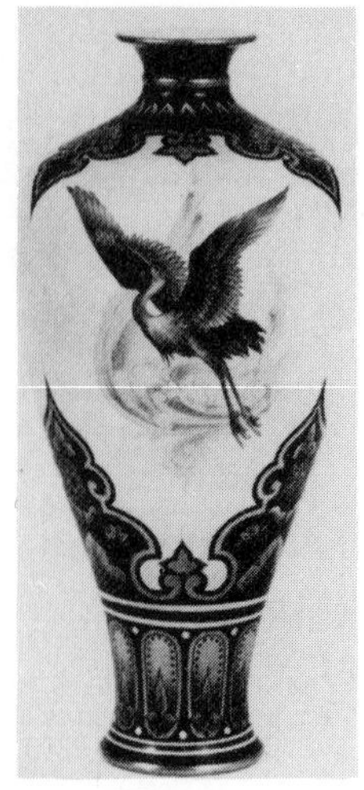
A Hadley's Worcester vase, printed and painted in sepia, within stylised stiff leaf and false gadroon borders picked out in dark colours, purple printed mark, 9 in., 1897-1900. **£100-150** *SC*

A Royal Worcester peach ground shell vase, 8¼ in., 1897. **£95-120** *NSN*

A pair of Royal Worcester vases and covers by Chivers, 12 in., 1902. **£700-800** *NSN*

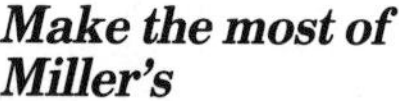
Make the most of Miller's

When buying or selling, it must always be remembered that prices can be greatly affected by the condition of any piece. Unless otherwise stated, all goods shown in Miller's are of good merchantable quality, and the valuations given reflect this fact.

A good and large Royal Worcester pierced vase in Eastern taste, well gilt, the details raised and tinted, against a shaded apricot ground, printed crowned circle mark, shape number 1199, Rd. No. 63498 and date code for 1899, 19¼ in. **£850-£950** *S*

A Hadley's Worcester vase and cover, painted with growing blue and yellow wild flowers, 12 in., 1900-02. **£250-300** *SC*

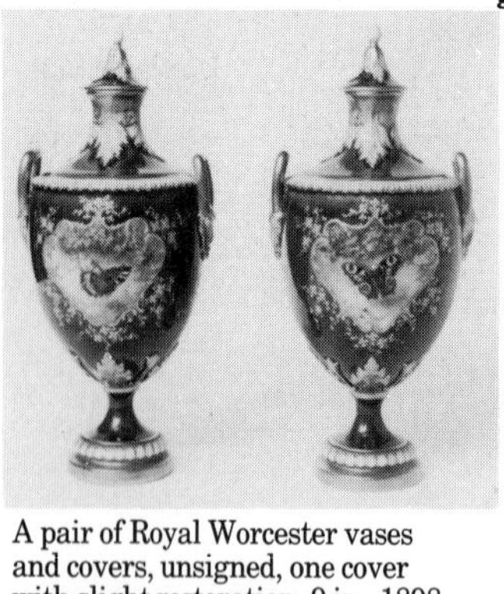
A pair of Royal Worcester vases and covers, unsigned, one cover with slight restoration, 9 in., 1898. **£800-850** *NSN*

This design is made more desirable by the unusual butterfly painting.

A Royal Worcester tomato-red ground two-handled vase, reserved and painted by Hawkins, signed, grey printed marks and pattern no. 2130 and date code for 1902, 25.5 cm. wide. **£500-600** *C*

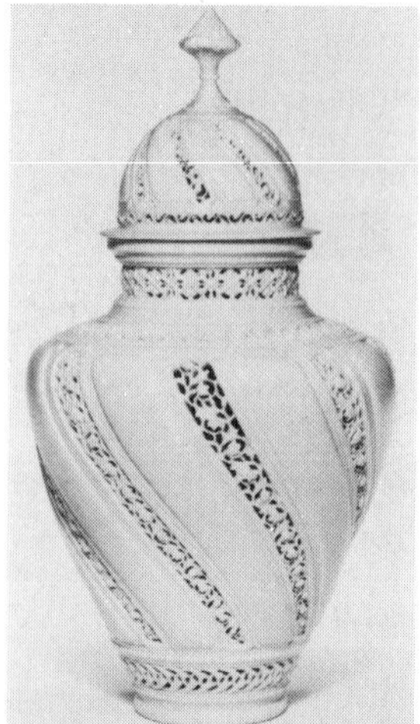
A good and rare Royal Worcester ivory ground reticulated vase and cover, in Persian taste, pierced in the manner of George Owen, printed crowned circle mark, shape number 988 and date code for 1892, 15¼ in. **£400-500** *S*

A Royal Worcester vase by George Owen finely pierced and coloured with jewelled zig-zag borders by Samuel Ranford, gilder's mark RS, 18 cm., date code for 1889. **£400-£500** *P*

A Royal Worcester reticulated vase by George Owen, 6½ in. high. **£2,100-2,500** *CDC*

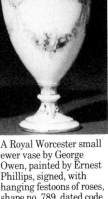

A Royal Worcester vase by George Owen, 6½ in. high. **£1,700-2,000** *McCMB*

The reticulated work of George Owen of the Royal Worcester factory during the late 19th C. and early 20th C. was by no means an innovation. Chinese potters utilised this technique in an even more intricate manner towards the end of the 16th C. It was called Ling Long or 'Devils Work'.

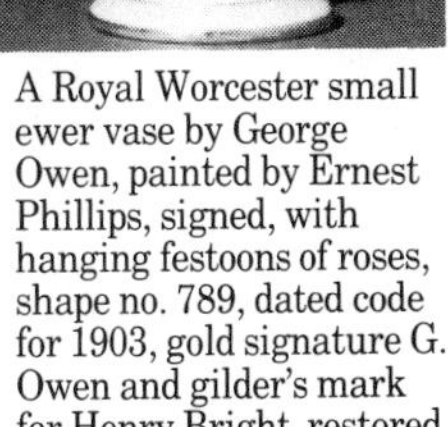

A Royal Worcester small ewer vase by George Owen, painted by Ernest Phillips, signed, with hanging festoons of roses, shape no. 789, dated code for 1903, gold signature G. Owen and gilder's mark for Henry Bright, restored, 18 cm. **£250-300** *P*

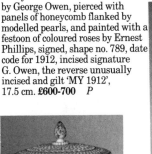

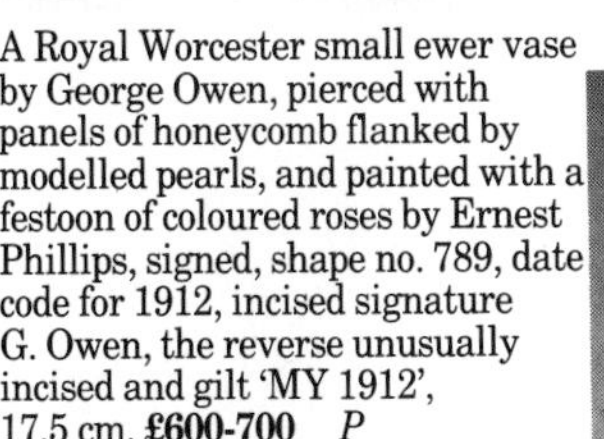

A Royal Worcester small ewer vase by George Owen, pierced with panels of honeycomb flanked by modelled pearls, and painted with a festoon of coloured roses by Ernest Phillips, signed, shape no. 789, date code for 1912, incised signature G. Owen, the reverse unusually incised and gilt 'MY 1912', 17.5 cm. **£600-700** *P*

A Royal Worcester reticulated slender oviform vase by George Owen, incised signature to the base, gilt marks and pattern no. 2256, date code for 1909, 31.5 cm. high. **£5,000-6,000** *C*

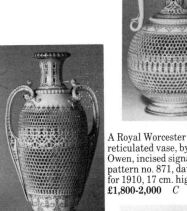

A Royal Worcester reticulated vase and cover by George Owen with gilt bird's head fixed ring handles, enriched with gilding, incised signature, gilt marks, pattern no. 2127, and date code for 1909, 13.5 cm. high. **£1,400-1,700** *C*

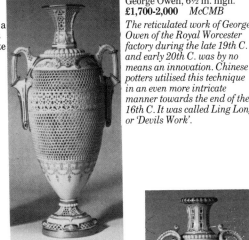

A Royal Worcester reticulated vase, by George Owen, incised signature, pattern no. 871, date code for 1910, 17 cm. high. **£1,800-2,000** *C*

A Royal Worcester reticulated vase, by George Owen, incised signature, gilt marks and date code for 1909, 22 cm. high. **£2,900-£3,200** *C*

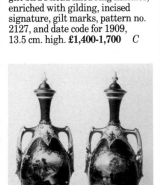

A superb Royal Worcester vase and cover by George Owen, applied with a leaf moulded rim and borders of modelled pearls, the piercing and borders with chased gold details, shape no. 2363, date code for 1918, incised signature G. Owen, 20.5 cm. **£3,000-4,000** *P*

A pair of Royal Worcester vases and covers, with landscapes by H. Davis, 12 in., 1905. **£1,200-£1,400** *NSN*

A large Royal Worcester urn shaped vase, sheep by Harry Davis, 1907. **£1,000-1,180** *NSN*

With cover **£1,500** *NSN*

A pair of Royal Worcester vases, painted by W. Hale, signed, details in raised enamels, against a shaded apricot ground, foot, handles and neck with gilt details, printed crowned circle mark, shape no. 2249, Rd. No. 397751 and date code for 1908, 8¾ in. **£600-700** *S*

A Royal Worcester peach ground helmet shape vase, 6 in., 1908. **£120-140** *NSN*

A large Royal Worcester vase painted by John Stinton, signed, with green, pink, bronzed and gilt details, minor chips, printed crowned circle mark, shape no. 1969, date code for 1908, 53.5 cm. **£1,200-1,600** *S*

A Royal Worcester vase and cover painted and gilt with a spider in its web among fruiting blackberry branches on a shaded ivory ground, printed mark in puce, 38 cm. **£250-£300** *L*

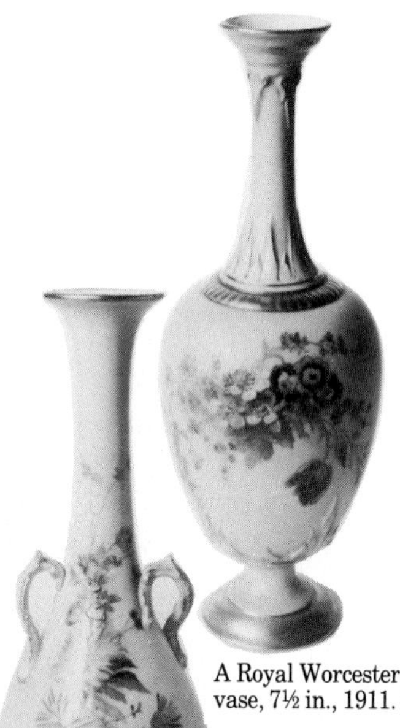

A Royal Worcester peach ground vase, 7½ in., 1911. **£75-95** *NSN*

A Royal Worcester peach ground vase, 7 in., 1909. **£75-85** *NSN*

A Royal Worcester vase supported on a high lobed foot, painted and signed by F. J. Bray, on a pale pink ground, purple printed mark in date code for 1911, 11¾ in. **£180-£220** *SC*

A pair of Royal Worcester peach ground bud vases, 3¼ in., 1912. **£110-130** *NSN*

A pair of Royal Worcester vases in warm enamel colours and gold, on an apricot ground, shape no. 302 H, 17 cm., date code for 1913. **£180-£240** *Bea*

A pair of Royal Worcester rose vases, 6 in., 1912. **£200-250** *NSN*

A good pair of Royal Worcester vases, each painted and signed by H. Davis, reserved on a ground of gilt seaweed fronds, pedestal bases, purple printed marks including date code for 1912, 8¾ in. **£400-£500** *SC*

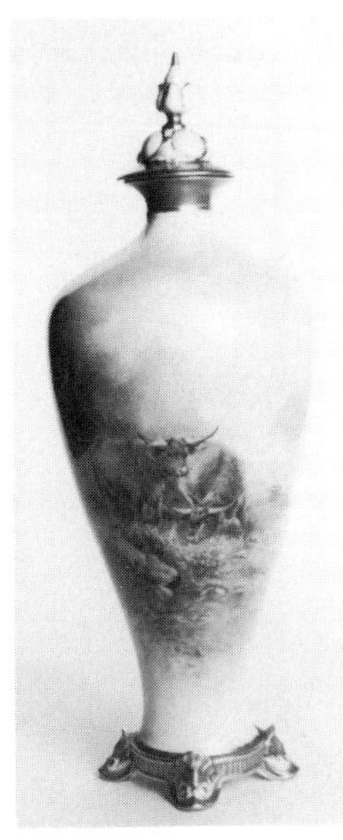

A Royal Worcester vase and cover painted by R. Sebright, signed, on a royal blue ground with gilt borders, printed crowned circle mark, stem and knop repaired, shape no. 2340 and date code for 1919, 36 cm. **£500-700** *S*

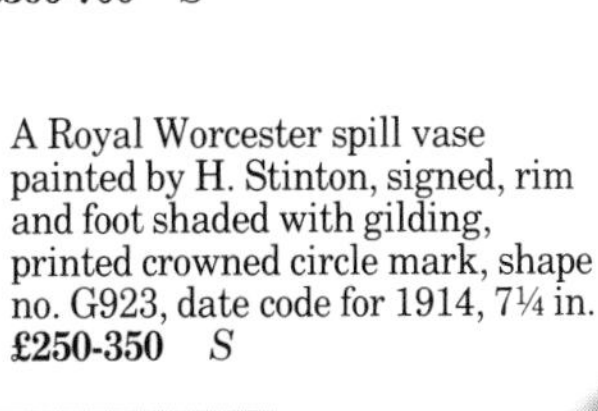

A Royal Worcester spill vase painted by H. Stinton, signed, rim and foot shaded with gilding, printed crowned circle mark, shape no. G923, date code for 1914, 7¼ in. **£250-350** *S*

A Royal Worcester vase and cover by J. Stinton, 12 in., 1919. **£500-£600** *NSN*

A Royal Worcester vase, deep pink ground, painted by Harry Davis, 12½ in., 1913. **£800-900** *NSN*

A Royal Worcester vase by John Stinton, 9½ in., 1914. **£400-450** *NSN*

A Royal Worcester vase painted by J. Stinton, signed, printed crowned circle mark, shape no. 2249, date code for 1920, 22.8 cm. **£500-600** *S*

A pair of Royal Worcester urn shaped vases and covers by Harry Davis in Corot style, 8½ in., 1919. **£1,200-1,400** *NSN*

A Royal Worcester pair of urn shaped vases by Harry Stinton, 1926. **£850-950** *NSN*

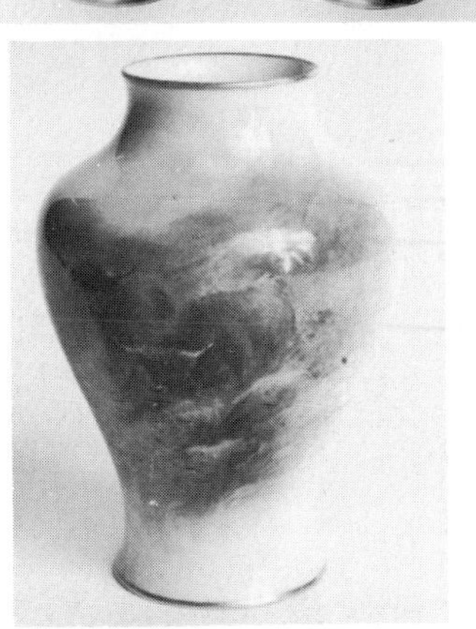

A Royal Worcester small vase by Harry Stinton, 4 in., 1920. **£200-£250** *NSN*

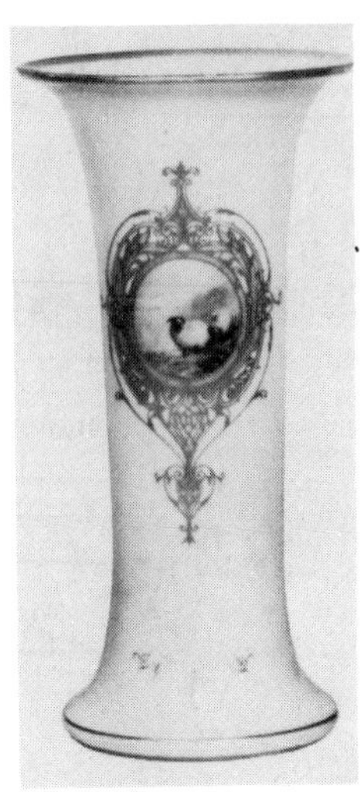

A pair of Royal Worcester vases painted and signed by Ernest Barker, picked out in green and pink, reserved on a pale ivory ground, green printed marks including date code for 1921, gilding rubbed, 9 in. **£300-350** *SC*

A Royal Worcester blue ground vase by Harry Davis in Corot style, 9 in., 1929. **£500-600** *NSN*

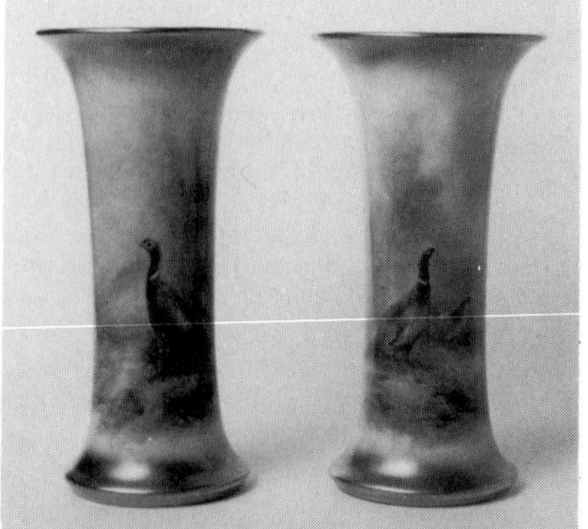

A pair of Royal Worcester spill vases with pheasants, by James Stinton, 7½ in., 1929. **£350-400** *NSN*

A Worcester blue scale ground tea caddy and cover, painted in the manner of James Giles, seal mark in underglaze blue, 16.3 cm., 1760's. **£500-600** *SS*

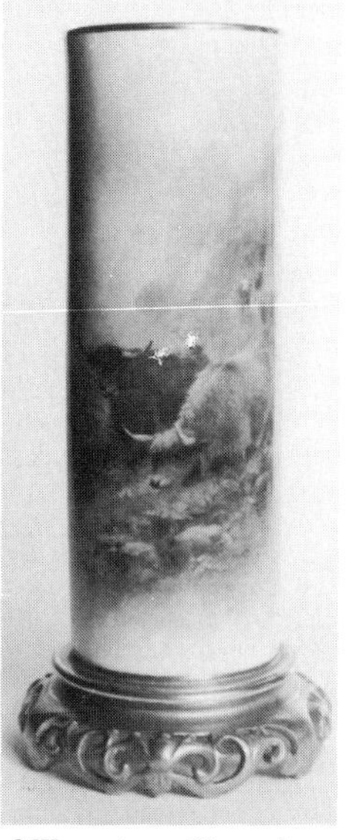

A Royal Worcester spill vase by Harry Stinton, 10 in., 1939. **£450-£550** *NSN*

A pair of Jacob Petit vases, 13 in. high, c. 1850. **£300-340** *IHA*

A pair of French porcelain vases with ormolu mounts, 20 in., c. 1860. **£300-350** *IHA*

A pair of French vases of rococo form, painted with a luxurious flower spray on one side, the reverse with classical ornaments, perhaps Jacob Petit, 15¾ in. (40 cm.), mid 19th C. **£300-400** *SC*

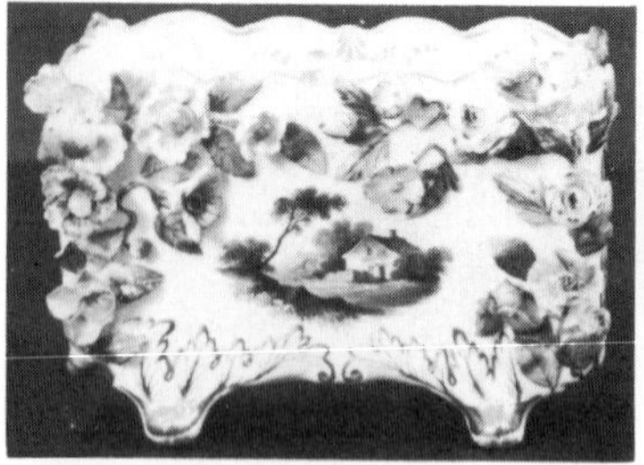

A pair of Rockingham green ground card holders with views of Surrey and Kent, 5 in. **£1,200-£1,500** *DWB*

A pair of Staffordshire porcelain spirit barrels with brass taps, 13 in. high, c. 1850. **£250-300** *BP*

A Crown Derby miniature coal scuttle, c. 1904. **£85-95** *NSN*

A Crown Derby miniature cauldron, c. 1908. **£75-85** *NSN*

A Grainger miniature watering can, 5 in., 1900. **£145-165** *NSN*

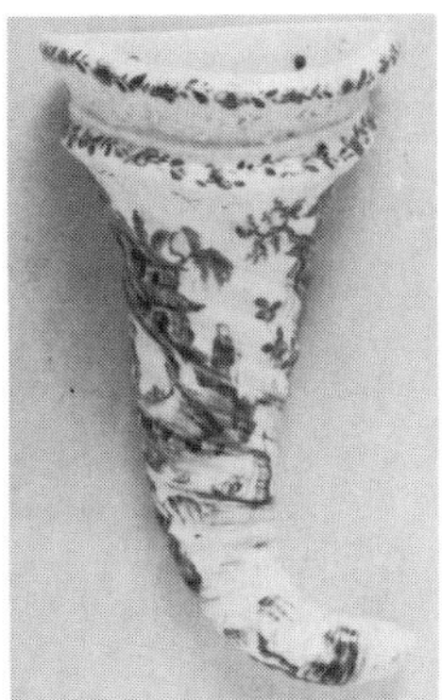

An extremely rare Worcester blue and white cornucopia painted in underglaze blue, moulded with flower heads and leaves below the rim, workman's mark in blue, 10 in., c. 1755. **£2,200-2,400** *S*

Compare with contemporary delftware cornucopiae in the pottery section. This pattern would appear to be unrecorded.

A Royal Worcester peach ground dressing table set, 10½ in. wide, 1917. **£140-160** *NSN*

A Chelsea asparagus etui or needlecase naturalistically modelled, gilt metal mount, 5¼ in., c. 1755. **£1,700-2,000** *S*

A rare German etui in the shape of a cauliflower florette, naturalistically painted, probably gold mounts, possibly Meissen, 12.7 cm., mid 18th C. **£650-750** *S*

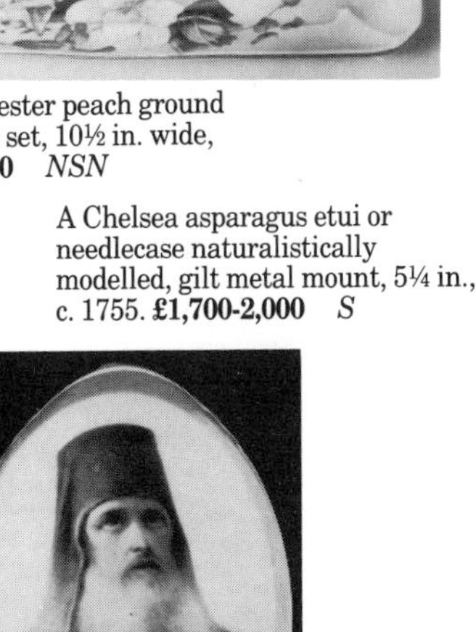

A porcelain Easter egg painted with a Saint, possibly St. Tikhov Zadonsky, signed N.L., the reverse gilt and decorated with sunrays and a star, 5 in. (13 cm.) high, c. 1900. **£350-400** *S*

An English porcelain pastille burner in the form of an antique oil lamp, decorated in iron-red, probably Spode or Coalport, gilding rubbed, 23 cm., c. 1810. **£180-240** *SS*

A Crown Derby cowbell, 4 in., 1909. **£100-110** *NSN*

A pair of Royal Worcester wine coolers, painted by H. Davis. **£1,900-2,400** *CDC*

A pair of Spode campana-shaped ice pails, covers and one liner, with blue borders gilt with foliage and iron-red flowerheads, script marks and pattern no. 2789, one cover and one handle restored, 34 cm. high, c. 1820. **£800-900** *C*

A Höchst porte-huilier, with spiral puce edged moulding, moulded with puce, turquoise and gilt rococo scrolls, with blue crowned wheel marks, the stand with moulded wheel mark in addition, and I.H. incised, one finial restored, the other restuck, the stand 24 cm. wide, c. 1765. **£2,000-2,300** *C*

A Royal Worcester snuffer, 'The Witch', unmarked', 3½ in. **£45-55** *NSN*

A Royal Worcester snuffer, 'The Nun', unmarked, 4 in. **£35-45** *NSN*

A pair of 'Derby' green ground campana shaped urns, some restoration. **£180-240** *DWB*

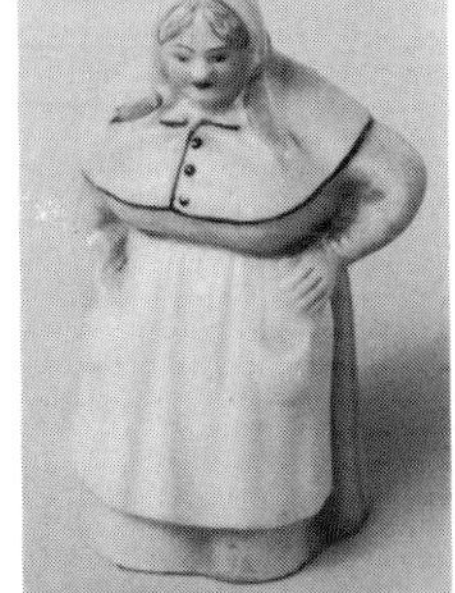

A Royal Worcester snuffer, 'The French Cook', 2½ in., 1917. **£85-£95** *NSN*

A Pilkington's Royal Lancastrian three-handled lustre glazed urn decorated by Gordon M. Forsyth and painted with classical Grecian figures on a shaded iron-red ground, artists lustre monogram impressed Bee's mark, dated 1913, England, repairs to 2 handles, 42.5 cm. high. **£700-900** *C*

A 'Girl in a Swing' seal, modelled as a boy colourfully dressed, holding in his hand a carnival mask, gold mount and ring with an agate seal engraved with Cupid and 'Unite', 3.6 cm., c. 1749-54. **£400-500** *P*

A Paris Veilleuse, the pierced stand painted with a wintry scen[e], the tea pot and cover gilt, gilding slightly rubbed, chip, 8½ in., (22 cm.), mid 19th C. **£200-300**

BIBLIOGRAPHY

Archer, M. and Morgan, B., *Fair as China Dishes.*
Atterbury, P. and Irvine, L., *The Doulton Story.*
Ball, A., *The Price Guide to Pot Lids and Other Underglaze Multicolour Prints on Ware.*
Barber, E. A., *The Pottery and Porcelain of The United States.*
Barret, R. C., *Bennington Pottery and Porcelain.*
Barrett, F. A. and Thorpe, A. L., *Derby Porcelain.*
Barrett, F. A., *Worcester Porcelain.*
Barrett, F. A., *Worcester Porcelain and Lund's Bristol.*
Battie, B. and Turner, M., *The Price Guide to 19th and 20th Century British Pottery.*
Berendsen, A., *Tiles, A General History.*
Bradley, H. G., *Ceramics of Derbyshire 1750-1975.*
Branyan, L. French, N. and Sandon, J., *Worcester Blue and White Porcelain 1751-1790.*
Brayshaw-Gilhespy, F., *Derby Porcelain.*
Charleston, R. J. and Towner, D., *English Ceramics 1580-1830.*
Charleston, R. J., *English Porcelain 1745-1850.*
Charleston, R. J., *World Ceramics.*
Crellin, J. K., *Medical Ceramics at The Wellcome Institute.*
Cushion, J., *Continental Porcelain.*
Dauterman, Carl C., *Sèvres.*
Degenhardt, R. K., *Belleek.*
Drey, *Apothecary Jars.*
Ducret, S., *German Porcelain and Faience.*
Eriksen, Svend, *Sèvres Porcelain.*
Exley, C. L., *The Pinxton China Factory.*
Freeman, G. and Gabszewicz, *Bow Porcelain.*
Frothingham, A. Wilson, *Lustre Ware of Spain.*
Garner, F. H. and Archer, M., *English Delftware.*
Garner, F. H., *Lambeth Earthenwares, ECC Transactions 1937.*
Gaunt, W. and Clayton Stamm, M. D. E., *William de Morgan.*
Godden, G. A., *An Illustrated Encyclopaedia of British Pottery and Porcelain.*
Godden, G. A., *British Pottery.*
Godden, G. A., *Caughley and Worcester Porcelains, 1775-1800.*
Godden, G. A., *Encyclopaedia of British Pottery & Porcelain Marks.*
Godden, G. A., *Godden's Guide to English Porcelain.*
Godden, G. A., *Lowestoft Porcelain.*
Godden, G. A., *Minton Pottery and Porcelain of The First Period.*
Godden, G. A., *The Illustrated Guide to Mason's Patent Ironstone China.*
Godden, G. A., *Victorian Porcelain.*
Gordon-Pugh, P. D., *Staffordshire Portrait Figures.*
Grant, M. H., *The Makers of Black Basaltes.*
Hackenbrock, Y., *Meissen and Other Continental Porcelain in the Irwin Untermeyer Collection.*
Haggar, R. G., *Mason Porcelain and Ironstone, 1796-1853.*
Haslam, M., *English Art Pottery 1865-1915.*
Hettes, K. and Rada, P., *Modern Ceramics.*
Holgate, D., *New Hall and Its Imitators.*
Honey, W. B., *Dresden China.*
Honey, W. B., *English Porcelain.*
Honey, W. B., *French Porcelain of the 18th Century.*
Honey, W. B., *German Porcelain.*
Honey, W. B., *Wedgwood ware.*
Hurlbutt, F., *Bow Porcelain.*
John, W. D., *Nantgarw Porcelain.*
John, W. D., *Swansea Porcelain.*
Jonge, C. H. de, *Dutch Tiles.*
King, W., *English Porcelain Figures of the 18th C.*
Lane, A., *English Porcelain Figures of The 18th Century.*
Lane, A., *French Faience.*
Lane, A., *Italian Porcelain.*
Liverani, G., *Five Centuries of Italian Majolica.*
Lloyd, T. E., *Victorian Art Pottery.*
Lockett, T. A., *Collecting Victorian Tiles.*
Lockett, T. A., *Davenport Pottery and Porcelain, 1794-1887.*
Mankowitz, W., *Wedgwood.*
Marshall, H. Rissik, *Coloured Worcester Porcelain of The First Period.*
Miller, J., *A Price Guide to Continental Porcelain.*
Miller, J., *A Price Guide to English Porcelain.*
Newman, H., *Veilleuses.*
Pine, N., *Goss China Arms, Decorations and Their Values.*
Pine, N., *The Price Guide to Crested China.*
Pine, N., *The Price Guide to Goss China.*
Poche, E., *Bohemian Porcelain.*
Poche, E., *Porcelain Marks of The World.*
Price, R. K., *Astbury, Whieldon and Ralph Wood, Figures and Toby Jugs.*
Ray, A., *English Delftware Tiles.*
Ray, A., *English Delftware Pottery in the Robert Hall Warren Collection.*
Ray, A., *'Liverpool Printed Tiles', in Transactions of the English Ceramic Circle Vol 9, part I 1973 pp 36-66.*
Reilly, R. and Savage, G., *The Dictionary of Wedgwood.*
Rice, D. G., *The Illustrated Guide to Rockingham Porcelain.*
Rollo, C., *Continental Porcelain.*
Ross, C., *Russian Porcelains.*
Ruckert, R., *Meissen Porcelain 1710-1810.*
Sandon, H., *Flight and Barr Worcester Porcelain 1783-1840.*
Sandon, H., *The Illustrated Guide to Worcester Porcelain.*
Sandon, H., *Royal Worcester Porcelain.*
Savage, G., *Eighteenth Century German Porcelain.*
Savage, G., *Porcelain through the Ages.*
Savage, G., *Seventeenth and Eighteenth Century French Porcelain.*
Schreiber *Collection Catalogue of Whieldon Wares.*
Severne Mackenna, F., *'Champions Bristol Porcelain'.*
Severne Mackenna, F., *'Chelsea Porcelain: The Triangle and Raised Anchor Wares'.*
Severne Mackenna, F., *Chelsea Porcelain: The Red Anchor Wares.*
Severne Mackenna, F., *Chelsea Porcelain: The Gold Anchor Period.*
Shinn, D. & C., *The Illustrated Guide to Victorian Parian China.*
Smith, A., *Liverpool Herculaneum Pottery.*
Smith, S., *Lowestoft Porcelain.*
Tapp, W. H., *Chinese Decoration Schemes on English Porcelains, Apollo, July 1973.*
Towner, D. C., *English Cream Coloured Earthenware.*
Towner, D. C., *Leeds Pottery.*
Twitchett, J., *Derby Porcelain.*
Twitchett, J. and Bailey, B., *Royal Crown Derby.*
Wakefield, H., *Victorian Pottery.*
Walton, P., *Creamware and other Pottery at Temple Newsam House, Leeds.*
Ward, R., *The Price Guide to the Models of W. H. Goss.*
Watney, B., *English Blue and White Porcelain of the 18th C.*
Watney, B., *Longton Hall Porcelain.*

School or College arms. Add **£3-5** *G&CC*

Peace 1919. Add **£10-15** *G&CC*

International League of Goss Collectors — See 'Price Guide to Goss China' for value of piece. *G&CC*

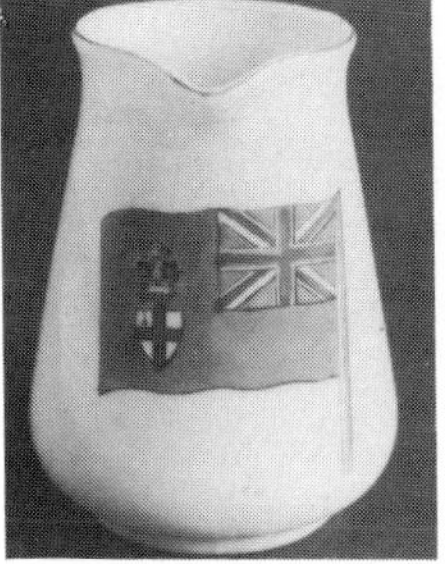
Flags and Burgees. Add **£5-15** *G&CC*

Verses. Add **£10-15** *G&CC*

GOSS DECORATIONS

Certain decorations add considerable value to Goss models. Some of the more important are listed below.

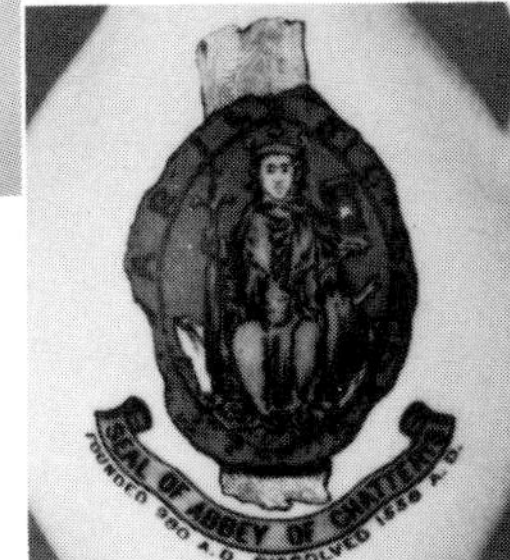
Abbeys and ecclesiastical. Add No Premium *G&CC*

Queen Victoria's Golden Jubilee 1887. Add **£30** *G&CC*

Crocuses. Add **£20** *G&CC*

Crystal Palace. Add **£10** *G&CC*

Regimental Arms. Add **£25-50** *G&CC*

Ye Trusty Servant. Add **£10-20** *G&CC*

Thistles. Add **£8-18** *G&CC*

The Primrose League. Add **£15** *G&CC*

Masonic. Add **£20-30** *G&CC*

Margaret Goss decorations. Value of whole piece **£60** *G&CC*

Boys Brigade. Add **£20** *G&CC*

George and Mary Coronation 1911. Add **£10-20** *G&CC*

Olympic Games. Add **£30-£40** *G&CC*

GOSS CHINA

The factory of William Henry Goss commenced the production of the finest parian ware in Stoke-upon-Trent around 1860. His son Adolphus introduced crested ware in the 1890's and collecting heraldic porcelain was popular until the outbreak of the Great War. The last piece was produced in 1935.

A range of Goss cottages was produced from 1893-1925 and these are very collectable.

Damage affects the value of Goss china a great deal and sub-standard pieces are worth ¼ to ½ of their perfect prices.

There are over 1,500 different shapes and over 7,000 decorations which appear on them. A page of decorations is shown in this section and the price given should be added on to the price of the piece to determine the true total value of any item. Only a representative selection can be shown here and readers are recommended to 'The Price Guide to Goss China' and 'Goss China, Arms Decorations, and Their Values' by Nicholas Pine (Milestone Publications, Horndean, Hants.) should they wish to study the subject further.

Goss animals. **£50-200** *G&CC*

SOME MODELS BY W. H. GOSS

Quadruple amphora. **£80** *G&CC*

Goss cottages, common varieties. **£50-130** *G&CC*

Wordsworth's Home, Cockermouth. **£200** *G&CC*

Monmouth masks. **£100-£250** *G&CC*

Orkney Craisie. **£18** *G&CC*

Manx Lobster trap. **£20** *G&CC*

Maple leaf. **£125** *G&CC*

Doll. **£250** *G&CC*

The complete range of League of Goss collectors models. **£30-300** *G&CC*

Cottage pottery mug. **£30** *G&CC*

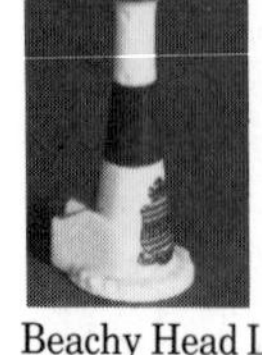

Beachy Head Lighthouse. **£30** *G&CC*

Winchester Warder's horn. **£250** *G&CC*

Yarmouth Jug. **£50** *G&CC*

Terra cotta vase. **£50** *G&CC*

The London Stone. **£100** *G&CC*

Lady Godiva on horseback. **£250** *G&CC*

Queen Charlotte's kettle. **£90** *G&CC*

John Knox's house, Edinburgh. **£300** *G&CC*

Bagware vase. **£10** *G&CC*

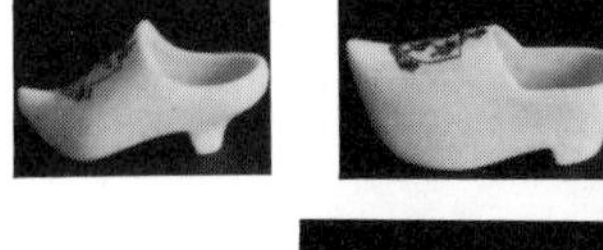
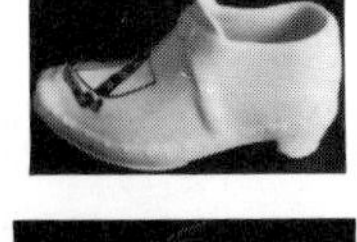

Six Goss shoes:
Dinant. **£15**
Dutch sabot. **£15**
Lancashire clog. **£25**
Norwegian shoe. **£18**
Queen Phillipa's riding shoe. **£70**
Boulogne shoe. **£18**
G&CC

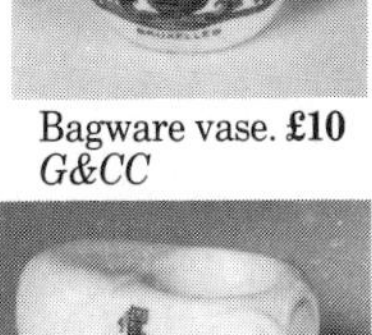
Capel Madoc stoup. **£30** *G&CC*

Cat & Fiddle Inn, Buxton. **£170** *G&CC*

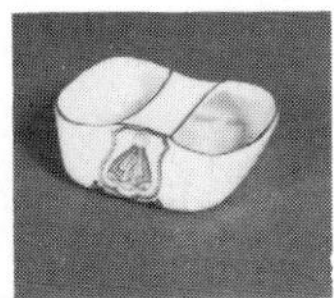
Welsh coracle. **£20** *G&CC*

Early and rare leaf jug. **£100** *G&CC*

Bass basket. **£10** *G&CC*

Burton beer barrel. **£8** *G&CC*

John Bunyan's cottage. **£700** *G&CC*

Blackgang Tower. **£25** *G&CC*

Cirencester Roman urn. **£80** *G&CC*

Rye cannon ball. **£35** *G&CC*

Sulgrave Manor. **£1,000** *G&CC*

Fenny Stratford Popper. **£10** *G&CC*

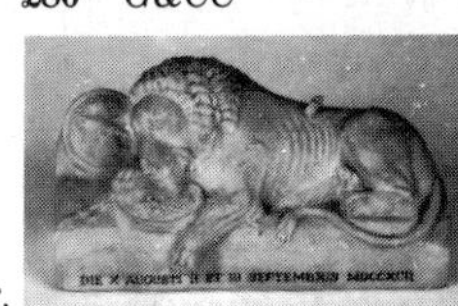
Lucerne Lion. **£200** *G&CC*

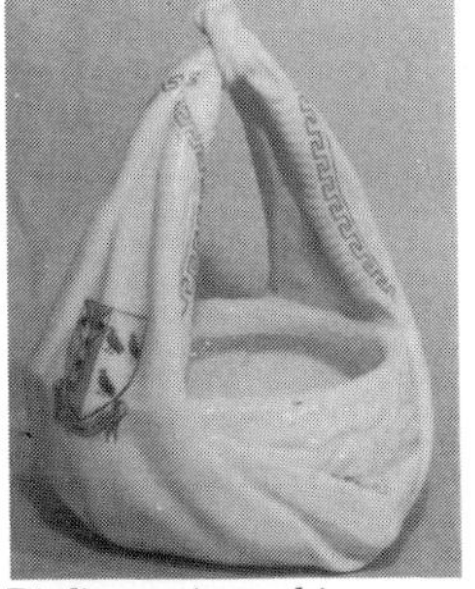
Bird's nest in napkin. **£150** *G&CC*

An early parian bread platter. **£50** *G&CC*

Miniatures. **£20-30** per item *G&CC*

Four lighthouses. **£20-£40** *G&CC*
Ramsey urn. **£5**
Blackpool Tower. **£28**
Stockport plaque stone. **£18** *G&CC*

Braunton Lighthouse. **£350** *G&CC*

A selection of smaller Goss models. **£4-6** *G&CC*

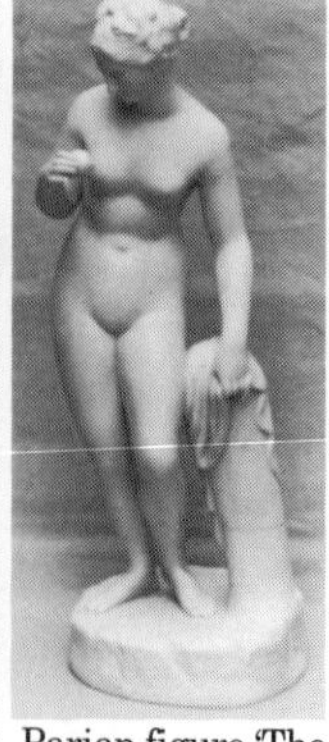

Parian figure 'The Bather'. **£400** *G&CC*

Goss buildings, stones and crosses. **£50-200** *G&CC*

CRESTED CHINA

Miscellaneous crested shapes. **£5-10** *G&CC*

Transport. **£10-50** *G&CC*

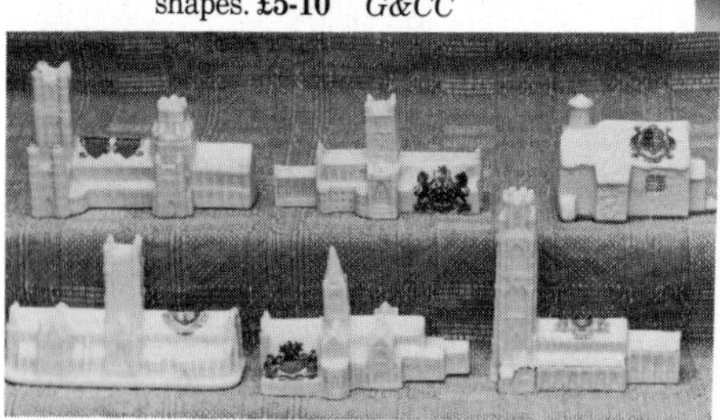

Cathedrals, churches and priories. **£20-35** *G&CC*

Transport. **£10-50** *G&CC*

CRESTED CHINA

Manufactured from around 1870-1935, some 200 factories produced over 6,000 different shapes which were sold bearing the coat-of-arms of the town in which they were sold.

Damage affects the price considerably and pieces with chips or cracks would only be worth ¼ to ½ the retail price.

All the manufacturers were in competition with the originators and market leaders W. H. Goss of Stoke-Upon-Trent. The most prolific producers were: Arcadian, Carlton, Willow, Shelley, Grafton and Savoy.

The most popular (and sought after pieces) are from the following themes: Military, Animals, Buildings, Figures and other unusual shapes. Small pots and domestic ware are only of nominal interest and value. Space only permits a small selection of pieces to be given here and readers are recommended to 'The Price Guide To Crested China' by Nicholas Pine should they wish to learn more. (Available from Milestone Publications, Horndean, Hants.)

Buildings. **£20-40** *G&CC*

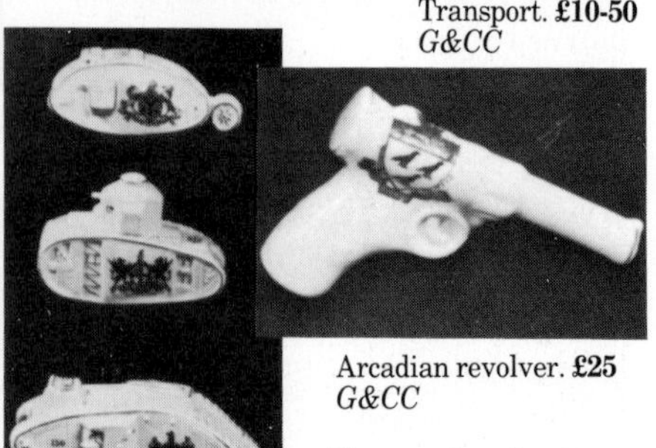

Arcadian revolver. **£25** *G&CC*

Three good tanks. **£25-£65** *G&CC*

Dogs. **£7-30** *G&CC*

Coloured buildings.
£30-60 *G&CC*

Figures and statues.
£10-20 *G&CC*

Birds, frogs and monkeys.
£7-20 *G&CC*

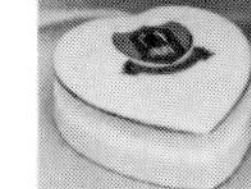

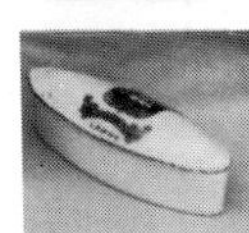

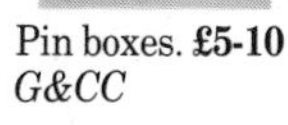

Pin boxes. **£5-10**
G&CC

Cats. **£7-20** *G&CC*

Seaside souvenirs.
£4-10 *G&CC*

Boozers' Delight! **£5-15**
G&CC

GREAT WAR HERALDIC CHINA

Carlton armoured car.
£60 *G&CC*

Folkestone War Memorial.
£50 *G&CC*

Carlton anti-aircraft motor. **£60** *G&CC*

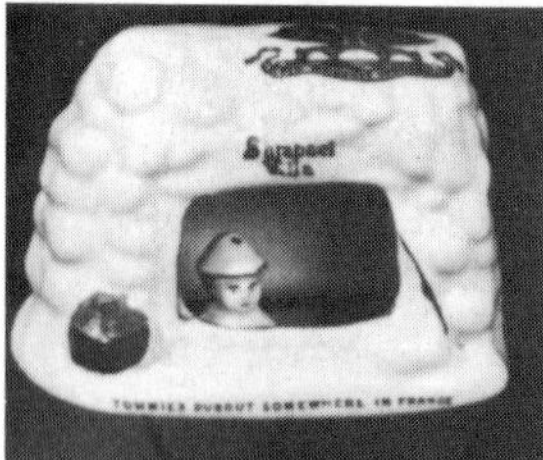

Carlton 'Shrapnel Villa'.
£25 *G&CC*

Shells and mines. **£10-£25** *G&CC*

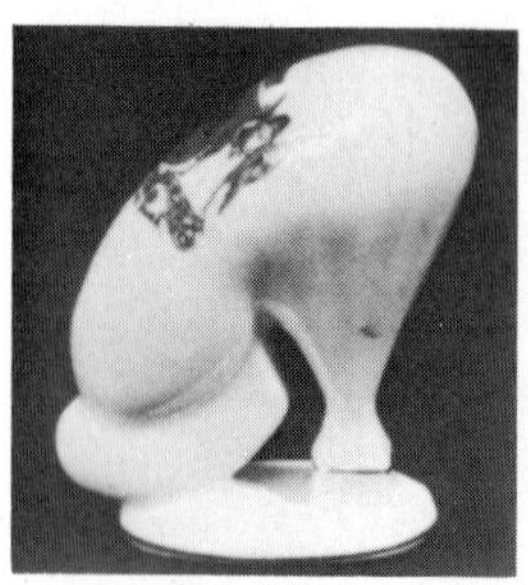

Arcadian observer sausage balloon. **£25** *G&CC*

Arcadian Red Cross van.
£15 *G&CC*

Cenotaph, **£4** and Cavell Memorial **£20** *G&CC*

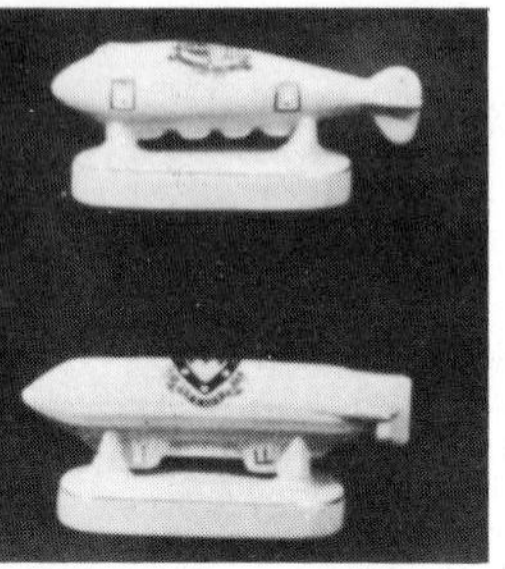

Two airships. **£15-20** *G&CC*

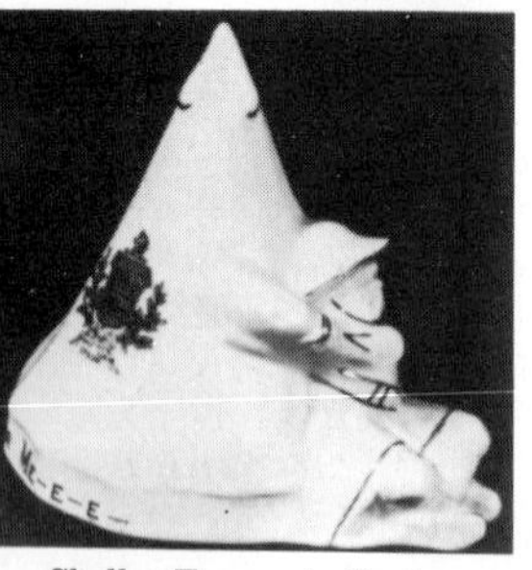

Shelley Tommy in Tent.
£50 *G&CC*

Carlton map of Blighty.
£25 *G&CC*

Carlton munitions worker. **£60** *G&CC*

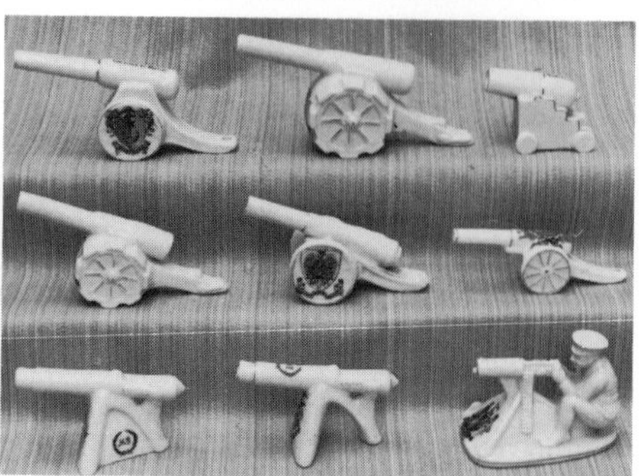

A selection of field guns, mortars and machine guns. **£10-25** *G&CC*

A selection of submarines and battleships. **£10-25** *G&CC*

Six monoplanes. **£30-55** *G&CC*

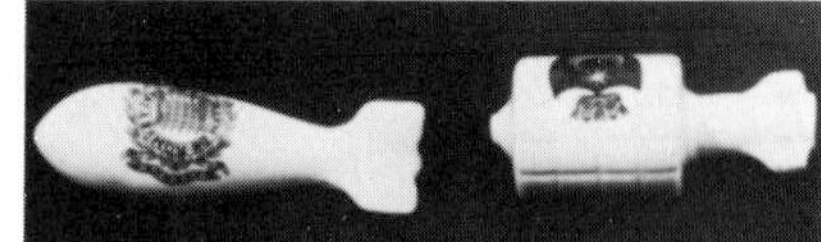

Aerial torpedoes. **£25** *G&CC*

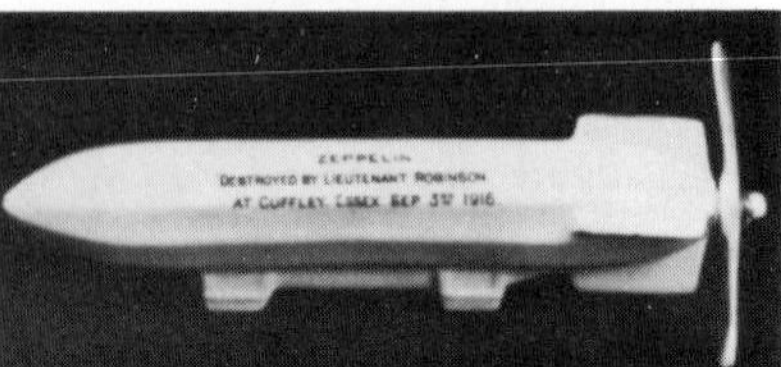

Savoy Zeppelin. **£90** *G&CC*

Caps and hats. **£10-20** *G&CC*

DIFFERENTIATING MING AND QING WARES

In order to distinguish Ming porcelain from the later Qing wares it is necessary to appreciate the technical rather than the decorative differences between the two. The Qing decorators frequently copied ancestral designs with great accuracy and at first sight it is sometimes difficult to attribute certain pieces.

A good example of this is the Doucai (contrasting colours) category. The originals were produced during the Ming reign of Chenghua (1465-87) and the copies were made in the reign of the Qing emperor Kangxi. Were it not for the characteristic smoky ivory appearance of the Ming glaze one might well be at a loss to differentiate early from late.

In the first place, with certain exceptions, Ming porcelain is more heavily glazed and the depth of glaze effects a bluish or greenish tint. The glaze is rarely evenly applied and if carefully examined one can detect runs and dribbles of excess glaze. Most Qing wares are covered in a glaze of uniform thickness. Particularly characteristic is the pure white appearance achieved by the Kangxi potters by only coating the vessel or dish in a thin and even wash. The reigns of Yongzheng and Qianlong did witness some pieces (non-export) which were deliberately covered in a thick glaze in order to emulate the early fifteenth century porcelains.

As far as potting is concerned there are more obvious idiosyncracies enabling easier identification.

For example, Ming vases if of sufficient size to warrant being made in two or more pieces are generally luted horizontally even on vessels which it would appear to be simpler to make in two vertical sections, Yongle and Xuande 'moon' or 'pilgrim' bottles are a case in point. Qing pilgrim bottles would invariably be made by joining two vertical halves.

The footrims on Ming wares are generally knife-pared and little effort made to remove the facets left by the blade. Most, if not all, Qing pieces are smoothed after the trimming. The feet on Ming dishes or bowls are for the most part higher than Qing examples. They are frequently undercut immediately indicating that they have been thrown by hand and not as many Qing pieces which have been moulded by a mechanical process utilising a profile cutter. A further point concerning the footrim on Ming wares — it will generally manifest a narrow orange zone abutting the edge of the glaze. This is due to the presence of iron in the body of the porcelain which appears to oxidise more strongly in the kiln in the area most closely in contact with the glaze.

This section is alphabetically arranged by object: bowl, box, censer, etc. In each group the wares are firstly divided into Chinese followed by Japanese and then ordered chronologically.

A green glazed buff pottery shallow bowl, with extensive silvery iridescence, foot chipped, 10.5 cm. diam., Tang Dynasty, fitted box.
£800-900 *C*

YINGQING

A type of porcelain produced during the Song and Yuan dynasties in various regions of central and southern China. The dominant characteristic being the pale blue/green translucent glaze; Yingqing translates as misty blue, the Chinese word Qing can mean either blue or green. Designs like Dingyao are either moulded or carved floral subjects.

A petal carved Yingqing bowl, carved with chrysanthemum petals, covered with a translucent pale blue glaze, an unglazed band round, 14.8 cm., Song Dynasty.
£350-400 *S*

A Jizhou tea bowl, the interior florettes in dark brown against a bluish-black ground, with feathery ochre mottling, the exterior with a 'tortoiseshell' glaze of dark brown splashed with ochre, stopping short of the base to reveal the coarse buff ware, 10.8 cm., Song Dynasty.
£400-500 *S*

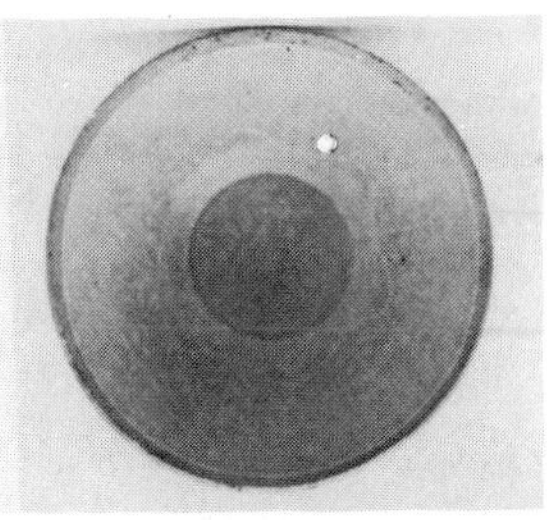

A moulded Yingqing bowl, the exterior plain, the interior decorated in impressed low relief within a band of key-fret below the unglazed rim, 2 lotus blooms in the centre, the glaze of attractive pale blue tone, 6 in. (15.3 cm.), Song Dynasty. **£1,000-1,200** *S*

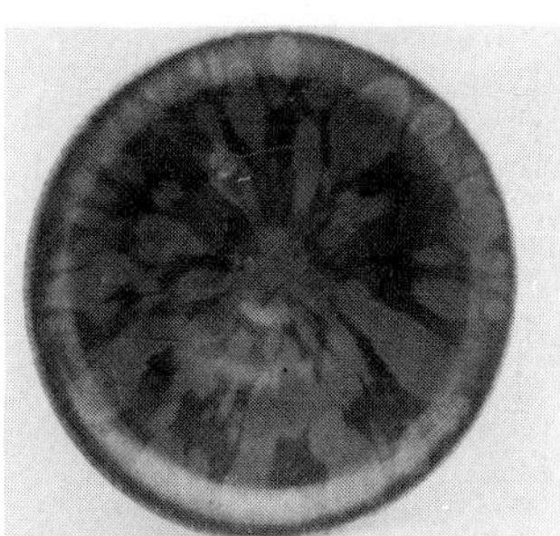

A splashed Henan bowl, the interior covered with a lustrous black glaze streaked with splashes draining towards the centre, the glaze on the exterior of uniform russet tone stopping short of the base to reveal the buff ware, 12 cm., Song Dynasty. **£1,000-£1,100** *S*

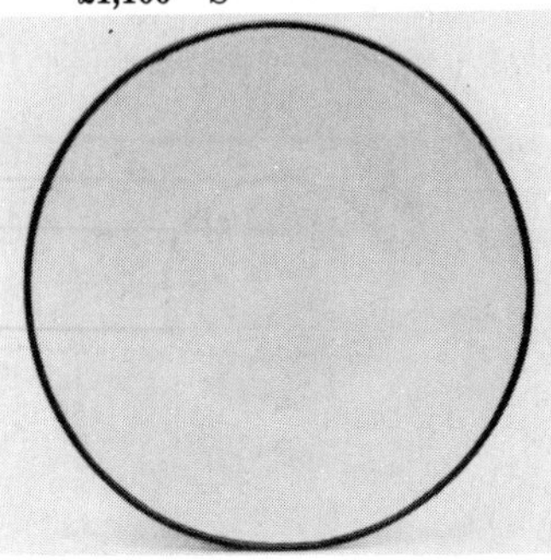

A carved Yingqing bowl, with a translucent light blue glaze, the base unglazed and burnt pale orange, the unglazed rim mounted in copper, 18.2 cm., Song Dynasty.
£1,500-1,800 *S*

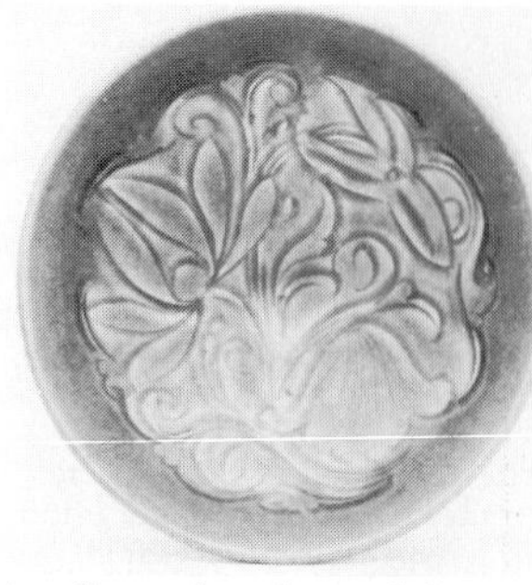

A well carved northern celadon bowl, incised on the interior with a medallion of lotus, the exterior encircled by a stepped band, the crackled glaze pooling on the edges of the design, footrim unglazed, 21.3 cm., Song Dynasty. **£2,000-£3,000** *S*

A well potted Junyao bowl covered both inside and out in a widely crackled glaze of milky lavender tone with some areas suffused with minute bubbles, falling slightly short of the base showing the orange-brown ware, fitted box, 5¾ in. (14.5 cm.), Song Dynasty. **£900-1,100** *S*

A celadon tapering cylindrical bowl carved under a translucent olive glaze, rim cracks, 9 cm. diam., Song Dynasty. **£500-800** *C*

A northern celadon bowl, the interior applied in slip, the exterior plain apart from an incised horizontal line beneath the rim, the bubble suffused glaze of soft olive green tone, 12.5 cm., Northern Song Dynasty. **£800-900** *S*

A good carved Longquan celadon bowl, with a meander of flowering tree-peony, on a delicately combed ground, the interior with a wave pattern, encircling an impressed floral medallion, the bright sea green glaze extending over the footrim and leaving an unglazed area in the centre burnt orange, 31.7 cm., early Ming Dynasty. **£4,500-5,000** *S*

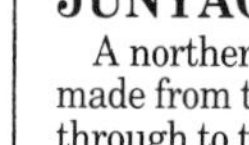

JUNYAO

A northern Chinese stoneware made from the Song Dynasty through to the Yuan and Ming periods. The coarse granular body is thickly applied with a blue glaze sometimes varying from lavender to deep purple. There are however a few examples of green Jun.

A Junyao bowl, of characteristic conical shape, minutely pitted, bubble suffused milky lavender blue glaze draining to a translucent tone, falling short of the base, 7¾ in. (19.7 cm.), Song Yuan Dynasty. **£1,500-2,000** *S*

DINGYAO

A northern Chinese type of porcelain produced during the Song and Yuan periods. The glaze is a rich ivory colour which appears either a pale green or brown where it has pooled. The decoration is mainly floral, either carved or moulded.

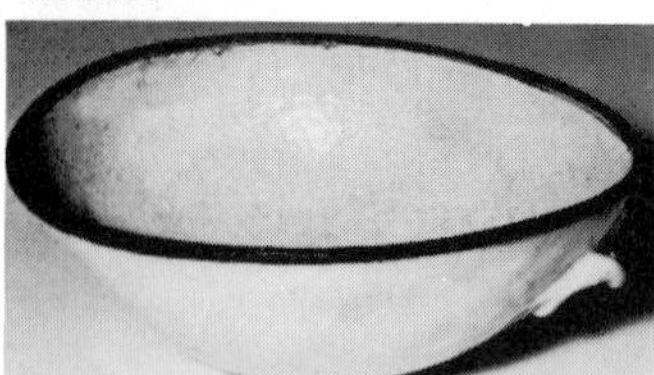

A Ding type semi-oviform bowl, the interior moulded with scrolling lotus below a band of key pattern under an ivory glaze, the rim bound in copper, short cracks, 17 cm. wide, Yuan/Ming Dynasty. **£600-700** *C*

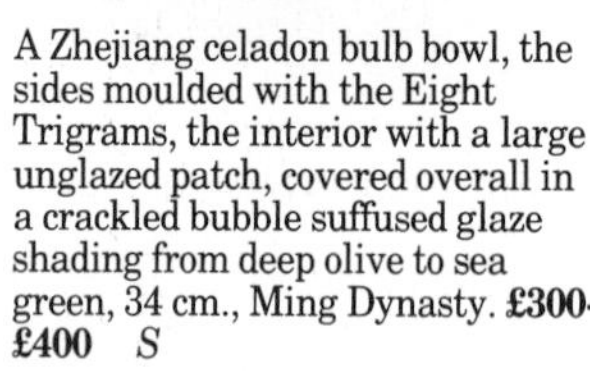

A Zhejiang celadon bulb bowl, the sides moulded with the Eight Trigrams, the interior with a large unglazed patch, covered overall in a crackled bubble suffused glaze shading from deep olive to sea green, 34 cm., Ming Dynasty. **£300-400** *S*

The Eight Trigrams are perhaps the most common motif on Ming bulb bowls.

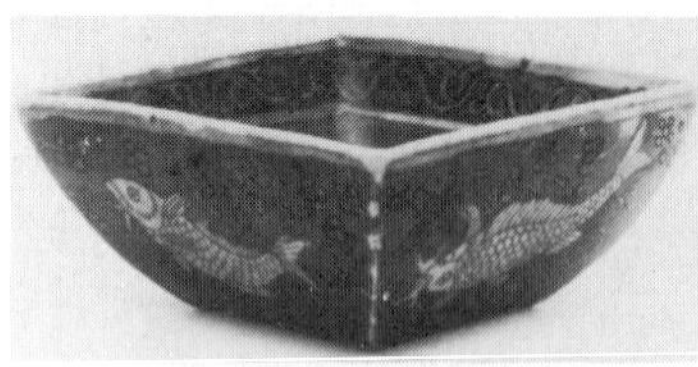

A rare Ming red ground bowl, the interior decorated with a fan-tailed carp in pale yellow and iron-red within a green border, the exterior decorated with a matching yellow carp, with an unglazed footrim, six character mark and period of Jiajing, 12 cm. **£3,000-4,000** *S*

A Ming blue and white bowl, 21.5 cm. diam., late 15th or 16th C. **£250-350** *C*

A blue and white warming bowl, decorated with 4 sprays of lingzhi fungus, the shallow inner bowl painted with a dignitary and his consort, the base pierced with a circular aperture, 12 cm., 16th C. **£300-350** *S*

An unusual punch bowl of large size, decorated in Japanese Imari style in underglaze blue, enamels, iron-red and gilding, with a silver mounted rim, lingzhi mark, Kangxi, 14½ in. (37 cm.). **£2,100-£2,500** *S*

A good 'famille verte' covered bowl, enamelled with blossoming trees, the spandrels with exotic butterflies with wings displayed on a seeded green ground, Kangxi, 8⅜ in. (21.2 cm.). **£1,500-1,700** *S*

A blue and white bowl, six character mark of Chenghua, Kangxi, 8¼ in. (21 cm.). **£350-£400** *S*

Retrospective marks are conventional on Kangxi wares, the most common being that of the Ming Emperor Chenghua.

An Arita bowl and cover, painted in inky shades of underglaze blue, internal chip to cover, 26 cm., late 17th/early 18th C. **£350-450** *SS*

A Chinese bowl in rich enamel colours reserved on an orange ground decorated with a design in black and gold, Qianlong, 26.3 cm. **£280-360** *Bea*

CHINESE PORCELAIN — VALUE POINTS

- **about 80% of the marks that appear on Chinese porcelain are retrospective**
- **if a piece bears a correct, as opposed to a retrospective, reign mark then its value compared to an unmarked but comparable specimen would probably be of the magnitude of 3 to 4 times more**
- **a piece of a known date but bearing the mark of an earlier reign would be adversely affected and could possibly fetch less than an unmarked piece of the same vintage**
- **as a rule condition will adversely affect a readily available type of ware more than a very rare or early type**
- **original covers or lids can raise the price considerably — especially if the vessel appears more complete with it. Hence a baluster vase, for example, would be less affected than a wine ewer**

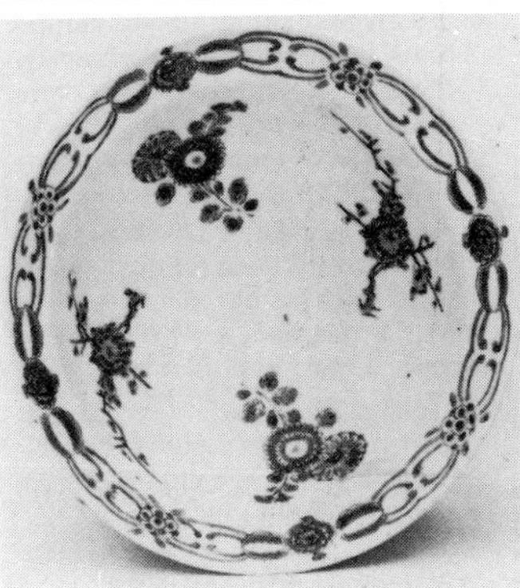

A Kakiemon bowl with everted rim, decorated in iron-red, enamels and gilding, the exterior with two floral sprays, 13.5 cm., late 17th/early 18th C. **£350-400** *S*

A 'famille rose' bowl, the interior painted with small floral spray, the exterior with floral sprays and 2 panels bearing Indian inscriptions, dated 1779, small areas of repainting, 9 in. (23 cm.) diam. **£300-400** *C*

A Kakiemon bowl of octagonal form with everted, brown-edged rim, decorated in iron-red, enamels and touches of gilding, the interior with a ho-o roundel, restored crack and chip, 19 cm., late 17th C. **£650-£750** *S*

Kakiemon is the name of a family of potters (the title being conferred by the overlord Nabeshima Katsushige). The first Kakiemon is reputed to have introduced the use of overglaze enamels into Japan in the late 1640's.

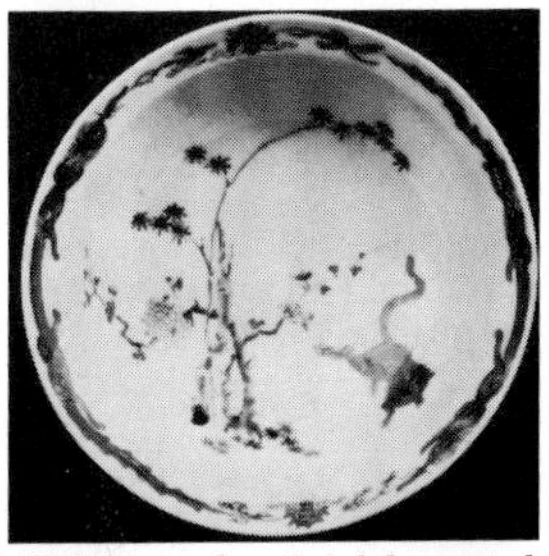

A Kakiemon deep bowl decorated in iron-red and coloured enamels, the exterior with cherry blossom above a chocolate brown band, 14.9 cm. diam., c. 1700. **£450-550** *C*

A 'famille rose' bowl on a pale claret coloured ground at the exterior, Yongzheng four character mark in a double square, chips restored, 12.5 cm. diam. **£300-£400** *C*

A pair of 'famille rose' basins, one broken, Qianlong, 33.5 cm. **£400-£500** *SS*

A Chinese blue and white fish bowl of large size, picked out in gilding, the body pencilled and washed in underglaze blue, wood stand, damaged rim, Qianlong, 25¼ in. diam. **£2,100-2,300** *SC*

A large Doucai basin, decorated with a frieze of ribbon tied musical stones hung with iron-red twin fish, sprays of aubergine and pale yellow lingzhi fungus, a florette studded collar of yellow trefoils on the incurved rim, wood stand, Qianlong, 34.6 cm. **£2,000-2,500** *S*

A rare Arita blue and white armorial shallow bowl and cover, painted with dragons and Buddhist objects, the interior with European coat-of-arms, fu-ki-cho-shun marks, 16.5 cm. diam., 18th C. **£350-400** *C*

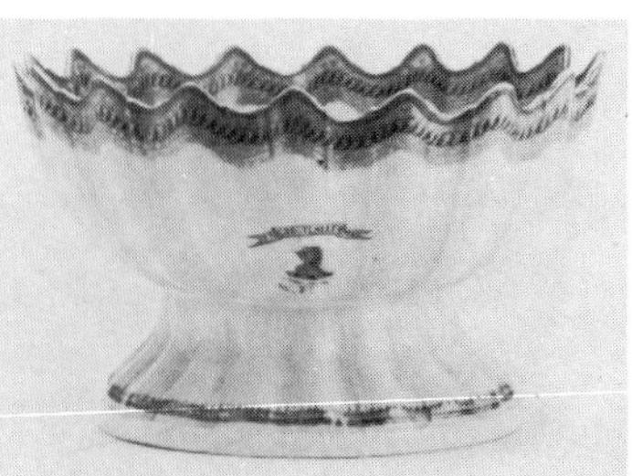

A Chinese armorial fluted bowl, painted inside and out with sprays of flowers in shades of orange and brown enamels and gold, Jiaqing, 27 cm. **£350-400** *Bea*

A pair of coral ground bowls, the interior plain, exterior with peonies and other plants in reserve, seal marks and period of Daoguang, 8¼ in. (20.9 cm.). **£400-500** *S*

TRANSITIONAL WARES

- **these wares are readily identifiable both by their form and by their style of decoration**
- **Forms: sleeve vases, oviform jars with domed lids, cylindrical brushpots and bottle vases are particularly common**
- **the cobalt used is a brilliant purplish blue, rarely misfired**
- **the ground colour is of a definite bluish tone, probably because the glaze is slightly thicker than that of the wares produced in the subsequent reigns of Kangxi and Yongzheng**
- **the decoration is executed in a rather formal academic style, often with scholars and sages with attendants in idyllic cloud-lapped mountain landscapes**
- **other characteristics include the horizontal 'contoured' clouds, banana plantain used to interrupt scenes, and the method of drawing grass by means of short 'V' shaped brush strokes**
- **in addition, borders are decorated with narrow bands of scrolling foliage, so lightly incised as to be almost invisible or secret (anhua)**
- **these pieces were rarely marked although they sometimes copied earlier Ming marks**

A double-handled bowl decorated in 'famille rose' enamels, the interior turquoise, seal mark and period of Daoguang, 5⅞ in. (14.9 cm.). **£200-300** *S*

A yellow ground 'famille rose' bowl, finely painted with gilt-edged medallions enclosing goats in landscapes interspersed by Precious Objects, a medallion in underglaze blue on the interior enclosing 3 further goats surrounded on the well by lingzhi and vine, seal mark and period of Daoguang, wood stand, 5⅞ in. (14.9 cm.). **£650-750** *S*

A well enamelled 'famille rose' fish bowl, Daoguang, 51 cm. diam., 37.5 cm. high. **£1,100-1,300** *SS*

A good 'Mandarin palette' bowl, on a gilt iron-red ground of 'Y' diapers and 'cailhouté' panels, 29 cm. **£750-£850** *SS*

A 'famille rose' shallow bowl, painted with 8 cranes, amongst pine, lingzhi and a peach tree, iron-red Daoguang six character seal mark and of the period, 17 cm. diam. **£300-400** *C*

A light blue ground 'famille rose' bowl, incised with feathery scrolls, the interior painted in underglaze blue, seal mark and period of Daoguang, 14.6 cm. **£800-950** *Bea*

A pink ground 'famille rose' bowl, the interior painted in underglaze blue, seal mark and period of Daoguang, 14.7 cm. **£1,000-1,200** *Bea*

A ruby ground 'famille rose' bowl, the exterior painted with four gilt edged medallions, the interior painted in underglaze blue, seal mark and period of Daoguang, 14.8 cm. **£1,400-1,600** *Bea*

A 19th C. Japanese crackleware fish bowl, 10 in. diam. **£100-120** *IHA*

A 19th C. Cantonese decorated bowl, 13 in. **£350-400** *JMW*

A pair of late 19th C. Imari decorated bowls in typical palette, 4½ in. high. **£200-250** *McCMB*

A pink ground 'famille rose' bowl, delicately painted on a milky pink enamel ground incised with overall feathery scrolls and multi-coloured stylised stems and blooms, the interior in underglaze blue with four sprays of flowers, and landscape, seal mark and period of Daoguang, 5⅞ in. (14.9 cm.). **£600-£700** *S*

An unusual 'famille rose' bowl, in pink and green, 18.5 cm., Guangxu. **£180-220** *S*

A 19th C. 'famille noir' bowl, 8½ in. diam. **£100-150** *TM*

VALUE POINTS FOR CHINESE PORCELAIN

- **condition — This is always an important factor when dealing with porcelain. Some collectors will only buy perfect pieces — this is particularly the case with Far Eastern buyers. They will pay high prices for excellent condition. This affects the price considerably as a very good piece with a hair line crack or small chip can reduce the value by up to two thirds.**
- **rarity — As with most aspects of antiques, rare items fetch substantially more than common counterparts. This is also important when thinking of damage, as damage to a common piece is much more likely to affect the price dramatically than a similar damage to a rare piece.**
- **imperial v. export — Most of the high prices for Chinese porcelain seem to come from the Hong Kong salerooms. The Far Eastern buyers tend to collect the pieces made by the Chinese potters for their own market rather than exportware. Hence prices are higher.**

A good and large 19th C. Imari bowl, decorated with formal designs in typical Japan colours, 16 in. diam., 7½ in. deep. **£500-£600** *PWC*

A late Ming blue and white 'Kraak porselein' pear-shaped bottle, 26 cm. high, c. 1600. **£900-1,000** *C*

A late Ming blue and white square bottle, the glaze in unusually glossy and unfritted condition, rim slightly chipped, 26 cm. high, early 17th C. **£800-900** *C*

A Fujisan earthenware bowl, 15.5 cm., gilt Fujisan, c. 1900. **£250-300** *S*

A painted Cizhou type bottle massively potted, covered in a white slip painted in brown, the further panels interspersed with blooms, 30.7 cm., Yuan/Ming Dynasty. **£900-1,000** *S*

A blue and white bottle, the spherical body decorated with dragon-tassels alternating with Precious Objects, 10⅝ in. (27 cm.), floral mark, Kangxi. **£500-600** *S*

A pair of Imari bottles decorated in underglaze blue, iron-red and gilding, one with a restored neck, 27 cm., late 17th C. **£1,000-1,200** *S*

A fine and large Arita apothecary's bottle of ovoid form with tapering neck and unglazed galleried rim, decorated in underglaze blue, 50.2 cm., late 17th C. **£2,000-£2,500** *S*

A 'famille rose' porcelain bottle, possibly depicting Queen Victoria at her coronation, the other side with a paddlesteamer, Daoguang four character mark and of the period. **£300-400** *C*

A blue and white pear-shaped bottle, painted in Mohammedan blue, the neck reduced and fitted with a bronze mouthrim, 23 cm., four character mark yong qing zhang jun (Eternal prosperity and enduring Spring), Jiaqing. **£800-£900** *SS*

An Imari sake bottle decorated in iron-red, green and black enamel and gilt with neck restored, 24.8 cm. high, early 18th C. **£200-£250** *C*

A Ming wucai rectangular box and cover, decorated in underglaze blue, iron-red and green and yellow enamels, with dragons amid scattered cloud scrolls, six character mark of Wanli within a double rectangle, and of the period, box, 14 in. long, 3⅞ in. high and 5⅛ in. wide (35.5 by 10 by 13 cm.). **£6,000-8,000** *S*

A Ming blue and white box and cover of compressed globular form, boldly painted in underglaze blue of characteristic violet tone, six character mark and period of Jiajing, 5 in. (12.8 cm.). **£4,000-£5,000** *S*

A Longquan celadon tripod censer moulded with a frieze of the eight Trigrams, covered with a glaze of pale sea-green tone, interior with three large spur marks and the footrim left unglazed, 17.2 cm., Yuan/early Ming Dynasty. **£700-£800** *S*

A rare Ming blue and white censer modelled in the form of a kylin, the pierced cover forming part of the animal's back, the whole painted with fur-markings and other details in tones of underglaze blue and flame motifs on the legs, 6¼ in. (16 cm.), Wanli. **£2,500-3,000** *S*

A blue and white censer of rectangular section, painted in tones of underglaze blue with confronting dragons chasing 'flaming pearls', 4½ in. (11.5 cm.), six character mark and period of Wanli, box. **£4,000-5,000** *S*

A rare blue-glazed pottery cup, covered inside and out in a translucent flecked glaze of deep blue colour, stopping in an uneven line short of the base to reveal the buff-coloured ware, 8 cm., Tang Dynasty. **£1,900-2,200** *S*

A Longquan celadon stem cup, the glaze falling short of the bevelled edge of the foot burnt to an orange tone in the firing, 12.5 cm., early Ming Dynasty, wood stand. **£600-£700** *S*

An ormolu-mounted Imari stem cup and cover with everted rim, decorated in underglaze blue, iron-red and gilding with a knop in the form of a seated puppy, the rims with rope-twisted ormolu mounts, the handles restored, 15.8 cm., late 17th/early 18th C., the mounts Scandinavian late 18th C. **£250-£300** *S*

Two wine beakers painted with iron-red dragons between clouds within borders of blue double lines, unencircled Xianfeng six character marks and of the period, 6 cm. diam., fitted box. **£650-750** *C*

A Changsha olive-green glazed ewer, with some degradation above the uncut foot, chipped, 19 cm. high, 10th C. **£450-550** *C*

A small Ming blue and white covered ewer, decorated on each side with a playful Buddhist lion, the foot encircled by a frieze of florettes and the domed cover with similar motifs, 12.3 cm., 16th C. **£400-500** *S*

A fine Kakiemon ewer of squat multi-lobed form, decorated in iron-red and blue and green enamel, the handle with scrolling foliage, 8.2 cm. high, late 17th C. **£1,800-£2,000** *S*

An unusual Arita blue and white ewer, painted with two medallions containing the letter S (syroop), and another similar, 18.1 cm. high, late 17th C. **£500-600** *C*

An Arita blue and white ewer of European form, handle glued, chipped spout, 36 cm., late 17th C. **£150-200** *SS*

A Han pottery horse's head, the dark grey pottery partly covered in a red coloured slip, Han Dynasty, 16 cm. **£600-700** *SS*

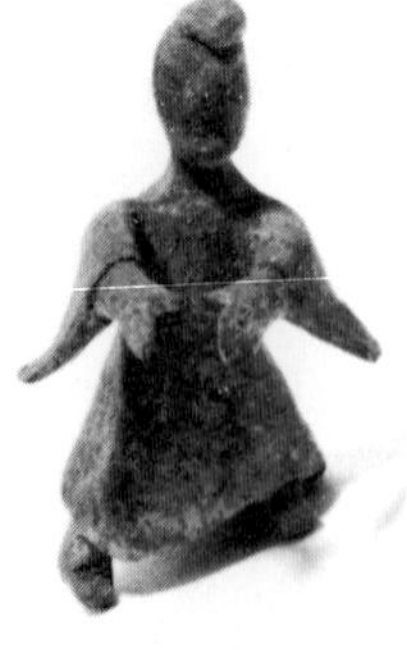

An unusual pair of unglazed grey pottery figures of dancers, the flat faces with primitively modelled features, extensive traces of earth encrustation, Han Dynasty, 15.1 and 13.7 cm. **£400-500** *S*

A green glazed pottery figure of a boar, a spiny ridge extending down the back, the green glaze degraded to mottled shades of turquoise and sage green with a faint iridescence overall, the exposed areas revealing the red pottery, Han Dynasty, 15.4 cm. **£350-450** *S*

A rare pair of biscuit chicken ewers and covers, the down and feathers incised, the comb and wattles aubergine, the wings and body yellow, green and aubergine, 5 in. (12.5 cm.) and 5¼ in. (13.5 cm.), Kangxi. **£1,500-2,000** *S*

A blue and white reticulated wine ewer, handle and rim cracked, 15.5 cm., Kangxi; and a later cover. **£90-120** *SS*

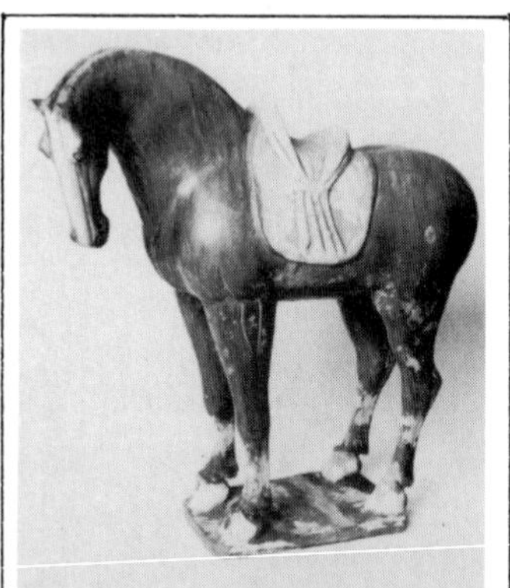

A good Chinese pottery tomb model of standing horse, the saddle and saddlecloth unglazed, the remainder with slightly streaked dark yellow glaze, socket for tail and groove for mane, base and legs with old restoration, Tang Dynasty, 21 in. high. **£13,000-£14,000** *WHL*

From the Eumorfopoulos Collection.

An unglazed grey pottery figure of a lady, 41 cm. high, Han Dynasty. **£2,500-3,500** *C*

A rare yellow-ground 'famille rose' ritual ewer, decorated overall with Buddhist emblems and stylised lotus flowers, the slender scroll spout springing from a vigorously modelled dragon's head, 7¾ in. (19.5 cm.), seal mark and period of Jiaqing. **£700-800** *S*

A rare grey pottery figure of a Shaman, the grey ware with traces of white slip on the face and with extensive earth encrustation overall, Han Dynasty, 24.1 cm. **£800-900** *S*

An unglazed red pottery figure of a standing groom, with white pigment remaining on his collar and black on his trousers and shoes, left arm restored, cap tip chipped, wood stand, Tang Dynasty, 29.5 cm. high. **£1,700-£1,900** *C*

A grey pottery figure of an attendant, the face with delicately modelled features, the body with extensive traces of red pigmentation, wood stand, Wei Dynasty, 29.3 cm. **£1,500-1,700** *S*

A straw glazed equestrienne figure, seated astride in a high waisted robe with long narrow sleeves concealing her hands, the face with delicately modelled features, Sui Dynasty, 23.8 cm. **£2,300-2,800** *S*

A rare straw glazed pottery equestrian figure, the degraded glaze showing traces of pigmentation, Tang Dynasty, 34.9 cm. **£3,000-4,000** *S*

A glazed pottery equestrian figure, the saddle splashed in green and amber glazes, the head unglazed, the animal applied predominantly with a straw coloured glaze mostly flaked away and showing traces of white slip and black and red pigmentation, Tang Dynasty, 36 cm. **£4,500-5,500** *S*

A spirited pottery figure of a prancing horse, originally painted, traces of other details in red and black pigments overall, Tang Dynasty, 17⅝ in. (44.7 cm.). **£11,000-13,000** *S*

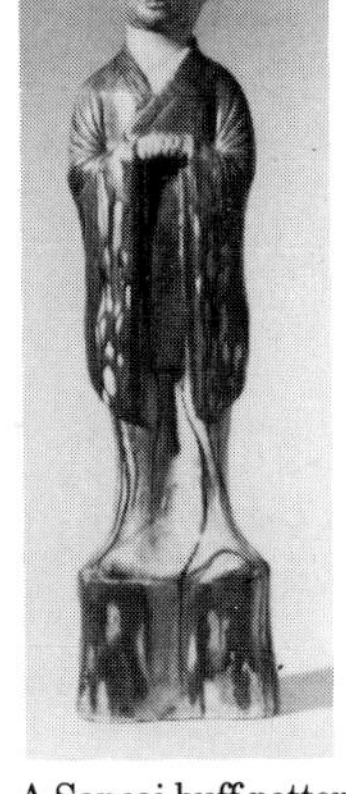

A Sancai buff pottery figure of an official, his face and butterfly-shaped hat unglazed, his simple robes glazed in ochre, green and straw colours, restored, Tang Dynasty, 70 cm. high. **£2,300-£2,600** *C*

A pair of unglazed pottery figures of attendants, traces of pigmentation, Tang Dynasty, 27 cm. **£450-550** *S*

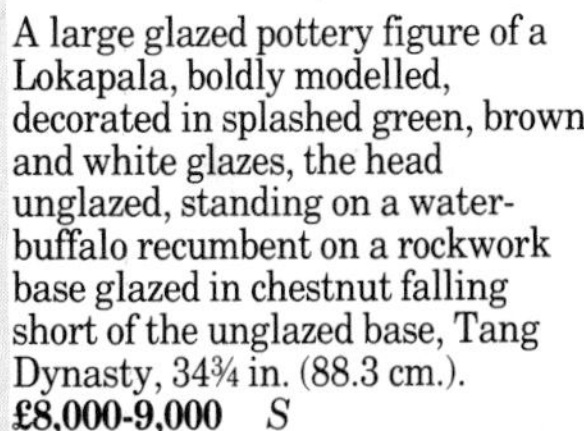

A large glazed pottery figure of a Lokapala, boldly modelled, decorated in splashed green, brown and white glazes, the head unglazed, standing on a water-buffalo recumbent on a rockwork base glazed in chestnut falling short of the unglazed base, Tang Dynasty, 34¾ in. (88.3 cm.). **£8,000-9,000** *S*

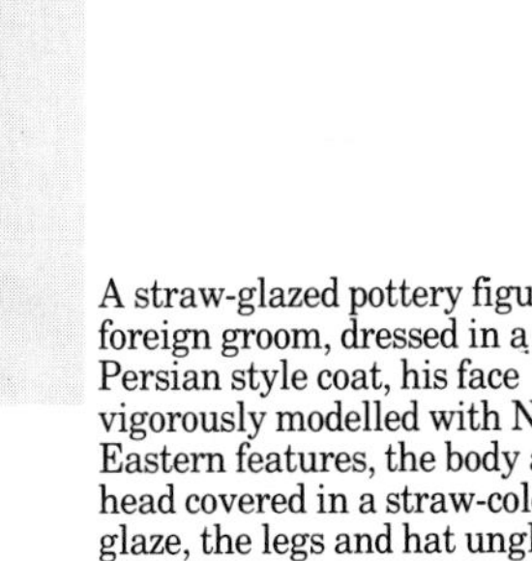

An unglazed red pottery figure of a foreign groom, the face with Middle Eastern features and the hair dressed in a roll, Tang Dynasty, 38.8 cm. **£900-1,100** *S*

An unglazed pottery figure of a warrior, the buff ware showing traces of pigmentation and gilding, Tang Dynasty, 58 cm. **£1,600-£1,900** *S*

A straw-glazed pottery figure of a foreign groom, dressed in a belted Persian style coat, his face vigorously modelled with Near Eastern features, the body and head covered in a straw-coloured glaze, the legs and hat unglazed, with traces of red pigment, Tang Dynasty, 17 in. (43 cm.). **£1,600-£1,800** *S*

A straw-glazed pottery figure of a Zebu ox, with large bulbous eyes and broad muzzle, the whole covered in a pale glaze, much having flaked off revealing a thin translucent layer beneath, Tang Dynasty, 10 in. (25.4 cm.). **£4,000-£6,000** *S*

An unglazed pottery figure of a foreign groom, traces of red pigmentation, Tang Dynasty, 41.7 cm. high. **£3,500-4,000** *S*

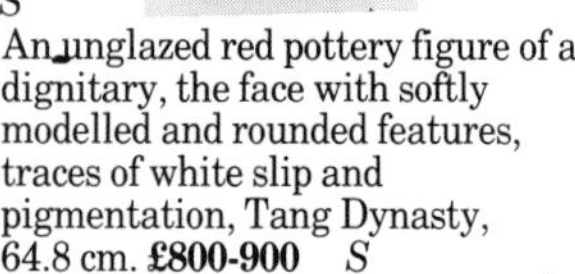

An unglazed red pottery figure of a dignitary, the face with softly modelled and rounded features, traces of white slip and pigmentation, Tang Dynasty, 64.8 cm. **£800-900** *S*

An unglazed pottery figure of a lady, the pinkish-buff ware with some earth adhering, Tang Dynasty, 25.3 cm. **£800-900** *S*

A straw-glazed pottery figure of a boar, recumbent, with small pointed tusks and bristly mane, covered in yellowish glaze stopping short of the base to show the buff ware, Tang Dynasty, 14.5 cm. **£800-900** *S*

A glazed tileworks equestrienne figure, modelled as Guanyin, astride a lion, the robes glazed in green, and diadem in yellow, wood stand, Ming Dynasty, 14½ in. (36.5 cm.) high. **£500-600** *S*

A Compagnie-des-Indes hound, with iron-red coat, with green collar and bell, Qianlong, 17.8 cm. **£1,200-1,400** *SS*

A pair of Chinese figures of boys, decorated in polychrome, slight glaze chips, Kangxi, 10½ in. **£400-£450** *SC*

A 'Blanc-de-Chine' figure of a dignitary, the glaze of ivory tone, 13⅛ in. (33.4 cm.), 18th C. **£550-£650** *S*

An export seated hound, the fur markings painted in iron-red and the relief-moulded blue collar suspending a gilt bell, restored, Qianlong, 25.5 cm. high. **£900-£1,200** *C*

A pair of 'famille rose' cranes with green beaks and pink crests, one with minor fritting and beak damaged, 33 cm. high, 18th/early 19th C. **£3,000-3,500** *C*

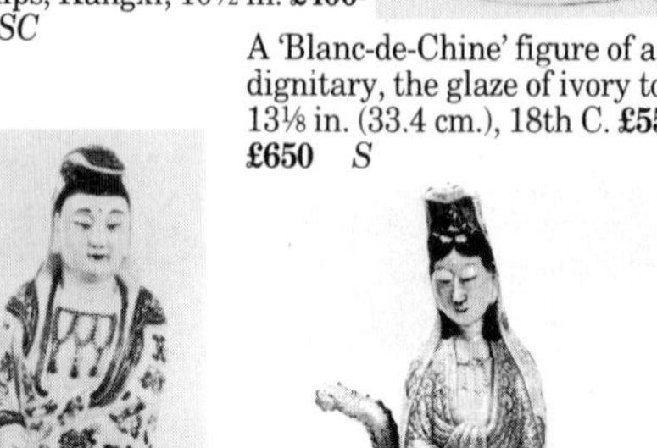

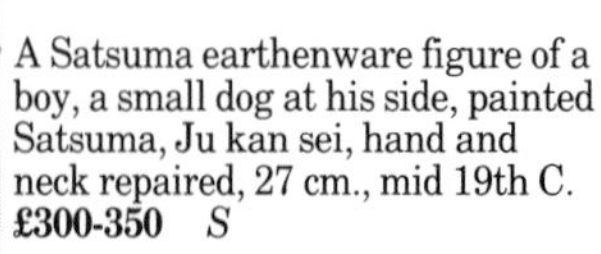

A Satsuma earthenware figure of a boy, a small dog at his side, painted Satsuma, Ju kan sei, hand and neck repaired, 27 cm., mid 19th C. **£300-350** *S*

A 'famille rose' figure of Guanyin, wearing long robes, enamelled in 'famille rose' palette, fire crack, Guangxu. **£180-240** *SC*

A Satsuma figure of Kwannon, with dragon, chipped horn and claw, 37 cm., late 19th C. **£280-£360** *SS*

Four 'famille rose' figures of Immortals, each in low flowing robes and colourfully decorated in enamel, impressed marks, late 19th or 20th C. **£400-500** *TM*

An unusual Doucai moon flask enamelled in colours, a leaping dragon on each of the slightly domed sides, encompassing an iron-red 'flaming pearl', the cylindrical neck encircled by a ruyi head band beneath the rim, a band of crested waves divided by jagged rocks encircling the unglazed base, Qianlong, 31.4 cm. **£4,000-5,000** *S*

An unusual small moulded northern celadon dish, the interior with a chrysanthemum spray medallion encircled by panels, beneath the rich olive glaze, unglazed base, Northern Song Dynasty, 9.3 cm. **£250-300** *S*

An early 15th C. Ming celadon dish, 13 in. diam. **£350-400** *BHA*

A large Kutani figure of a Bijin, her kimono painted on a graduated orange ground, repairs to firing crack on base, 56 cm., c. 1900. **£350-400** *S*

Locate the source

The source of each illustration in Miller's can be found by checking the code letters below each caption with the list of contributors on page 12.
In view of the undoubted differences in price structures from region to region, this information could be extremely valuable to everyone who buys and sells antiques.

A Lishui celadon dish, the interior carved with a crane in flight and foliage, with a finely crackled brownish olive glaze, Song Dynasty, 11¼ in. (28.5 cm.). **£400-£500** *S*

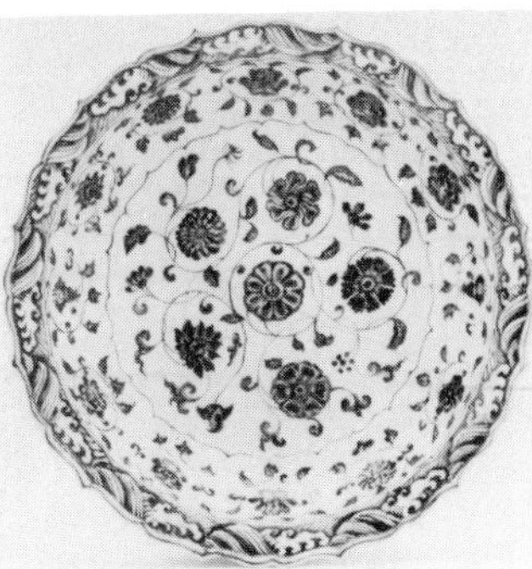

An early Ming blue and white dish, in dark washed tones of underglaze blue with pronounced 'heaped and piled' effect, the unglazed base and wedge-shaped footrim burnt to a speckled orange in the firing, Yongle, cracked, 33.9 cm. **£4,000-£5,000** *S*

A rare celadon moon flask decorated on either side with stylised lotus, later mounted in ormolu with ribboned foliate sprays pendant from the handles and a foliate scroll mount on the rim, seal mark and period of Yongzheng, 32.5 cm. overall. **£1,700-1,900** *S*

A Longquan celadon dish with 2 fish applied in relief beneath the sea-green glaze, Song Dynasty, 8¾ in. (22.2 cm.). **£700-800** *S*

A Longquan celadon dragon dish, the centre crisply moulded with a leaping scaly dragon and 'flaming pearl', encircled by freely carved wave pattern, covered overall with a rich sea-green glaze, leaving unglazed the wedge-shaped footrim, Yuan Dynasty, 37.7 cm. **£6,000-7,000** *S*

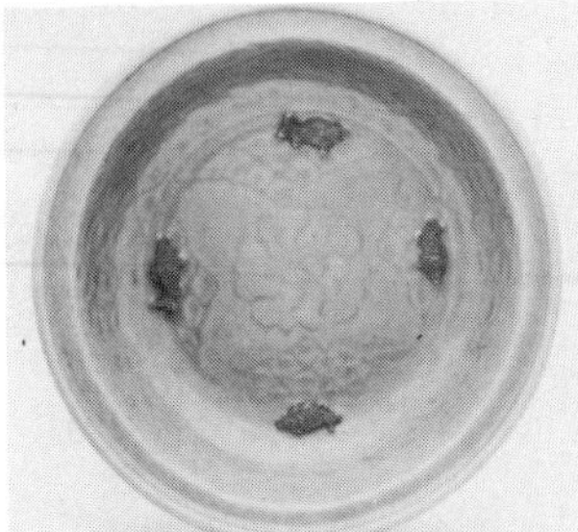

A rare biscuit-decorated Longquan celadon dish, the glaze in rich olive colour, an unglazed ring on the base burnt orange in the firing, Ming Dynasty, 28.7 cm. **£7,000-£8,000** *S*

A late Ming polychrome saucer-dish in yellow and green enamels and iron-red, encircled Chenghua six character mark, Tianqi/Chongzheng, frit chips, 15 cm. diam. **£350-400** *C*

An unusual small blue and white dish, the interior delicately painted in line and wash, a key-fret band round the rim, the underside with birds and 2 flowering branches, encircled by a frieze of emblems, six character mark of Xuande, Wanli, 12.4 cm. **£300-450** *S*

Compare the dish in the Percival David Foundation, Catalogue No. A699, illustrated by Macintosh, Chinese Blue and White Porcelain, pl. 43, with a river landscape within the same border, and of the same size.

A fine famille rose armorial dish for the Italian market, painted with an elaborate central coat-of-arms, coronet and feathery mantling in underglaze blue, green, yellow and iron-red enamels and gilt, the border with 4 bulls' heads divided by flower sprays and gilt-ground leafy arabesque vignettes (rim slightly chipped), c. 1740, 32.5 cm. diam. **£2,500-3,000** *C*

The arms are those of Marini
Cf. J. M. Beurdeley, op. cit. plate 156, page 185; and Ayres and Howard, op. cit., pp. 450-1, where they relate that there are at least six similarly painted services bearing these arms. There is a strong comparison to be drawn with the designs found on Italian maiolica and Southern French faience. The designs appear to be based on the elaborate architectural motifs of Jean Berain, and the arms were previously identified as those of Ataïde of Portugal.

A Kraak Porselein dish of saucer shape with a landscape panel on a blue-wash trellis pattern ground, Wanli, 8⅛ in. (20.6 cm.). **£300-£350** *S*

A Swatow blue and white dish, pseudo seal mark, 31 cm., early 17th C. **£200-400** *SS*

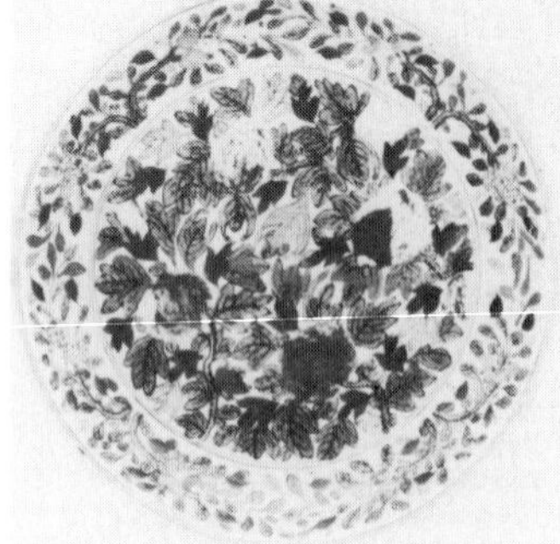

A rare Ming Wucai saucer dish of unusually large size, the centre with a double line medallion enclosing peony, in iron-red on green stalks, the underside with a well-drawn lotus meander, alternating tones, six character mark and period of Wanli, 15¼ in. (38.8 cm.). **£700-900** *S*

A rare pair of blue and white plaques, painted with a bird on a prunus bough, Wanli, 8¼ in. (20.9 cm.). **£400-500** *S*

A good Kraak Porselein dish painted in inky tones of blue, Wanli, 19½ in. (50 cm.). **£1,300-£1,500** *S*

A 'Kraak' dish of large size, painted in rich underglaze blue, chipped foot, slight glaze chips, Wanli, 19⅛ in. **£2,100-2,300** *SC*

Two rare Chinese blue and white dishes, each painted with a meeting of 2 Dutchmen doffing their hats, six character marks of Chenghua, Kangxi, approx. 15.5 cm. **£850-950** *SS*

A large 'famille verte' saucer dish, decorated in vivid enamels including an opaque bright yellow with a scene of a dignitary watching scholars, the rim encircled by a seeded green ground border with flowers and floral vignettes, Kangxi, 14⅛ in. (35.9 cm.). **£900-1,000** *S*

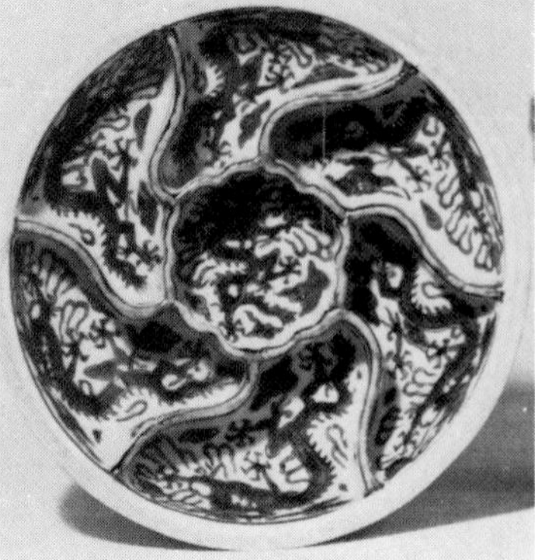

A Ming blue and white compartmented circular box base painted with dragons, the exterior similar, enriched with areas of iron-red, encircled Wanli six character mark and of the period, the red probably added later, minor interior cracks, 24 cm. diam. **£600-£700** *C*

A pair of blue and white dishes, each painted with cranes in flight amongst Buddhist emblems, six character marks qi shi bao ding zhi zhen (rare as the wonderful stone jade), and the precious tripod, Transitional, 6¼ in. (15.8 cm.). **£500-650** *S*

A 'famille verte' dish, the centre enamelled with a vase of peonies, flanked by smaller vessels, the rim encircled by a band of shaped panels, six character mark and period of Kangxi, 13 in. (33 cm.). **£600-700** *S*

A copper-red saucer dish, the minutely pitted glaze of dark pinkish red colour, draining both inside and out from the white edged rim, the gently domed base with a white glaze of faint bluish tone, six character mark and period of Kangxi, perspex stand, 18.2 cm. **£350-450** *S*

Two late Ming blue and white deep dishes, painted with a goose in flight, peony, lotus and lingzhi at the rim, fritted, Wanli, 18.5 cm. diam. **£650-750** *C*

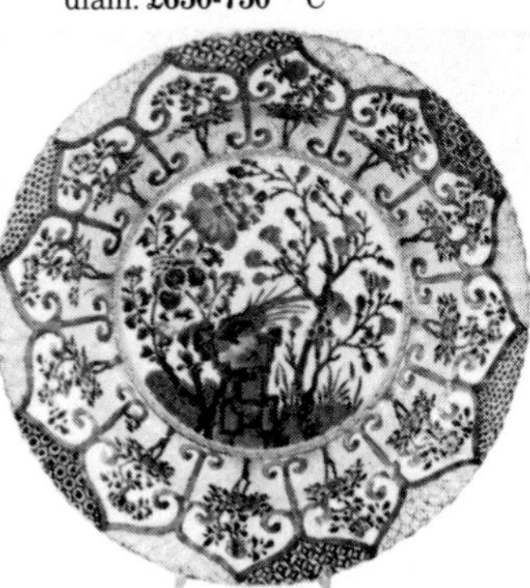

A pair of Chinese blue and white deep dishes, painted in bright underglaze blue, prunus marks, very slight glaze chips, Kangxi, 13¾ in. **£400-500** *SC*

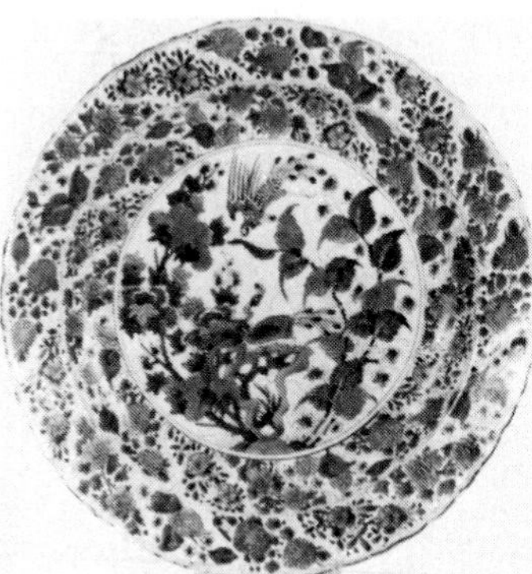

A Chinese blue and white dish, painted in rich underglaze blue, Aiyeh mark, Kangxi, rim chips, 14½ in. **£300-400** *SC*

A 'famille verte' dish, lingzhi mark, Kangxi, 14⅛ in. (36 cm.). **£450-£500** *S*

A pair of 'famille verte' plates, the scenes enclosed by a vignette-studded green brocade-diaper border, seal marks, Kangxi, 8⅝ in. (22 cm.). **£600-700** *S*

A Chinese armorial deep dish, painted with the coat-of-arms of the Skene family, with the motto 'Virtutis Regia Merces', Qianlong, 22.5 cm. **£400-450** *Bea*

An 18th C. Chinese blue and white plate, 11 in. diam. **£30-40** *IHA*

A Chinese export saucer dish, decorated with floral sprays in 'famille rose' enamels and gilt, Qianlong, 9¾ in. diam. **£80-120** *WW*

'FAMILLE VERTE'

A term coined by Jacquemart in the 19th Century to cover the overglaze enamel palette whose dominant colour is translucent green. The palette is a derivative of the Ming Wucai ('five colours'), and was fashionable from the second half of the 17th Century until the second quarter of the 18th Century.

A pair of 'famille verte' plates, each enamelled with the Eight Horses of Mu Wang, some damage, ding marks, Kangxi, 8½ in. (21.6 cm.). **£250-300** *S*

A large Imari plaque painted in enamel colours, underglaze blue and gold, 54 cm., 18th C. **£900-£1,000** *Bea*

A Chinese armorial plate charged with a variant of the arms of Saunders, 22.8 cm., 1740's. **£280-£360** *SS*

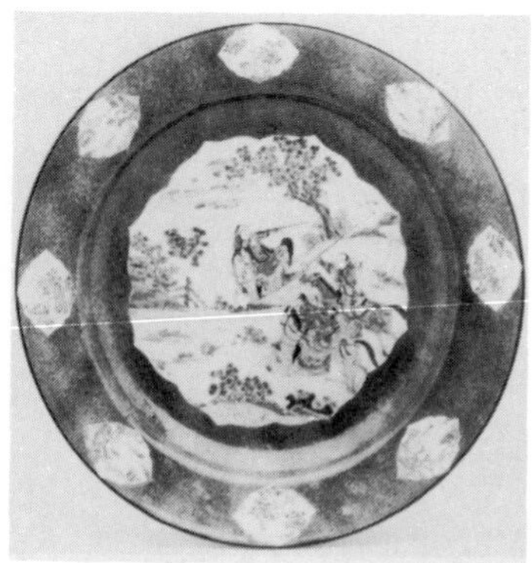
A powder blue ground 'famille verte' dish, on a 'bleu-souffle' ground, finely painted in gilding, the rim with 'famille verte' panels, hua mark, Kangxi, 16 in. (40.7 cm.). **£1,500-1,600** *S*

A good Shino Mukozuke dish of shallow rounded form with everted rim decorated in iron-red under a thick white glaze raised on 3 strap feet, kiln mark, 17.1 cm., 17th C. **£800-1,200** *S*

Mukozuke: A type of small dish used in the Tea Ceremony.

A pair of European-subject plates, each richly decorated in 'famille rose' enamels, all within a barbed medallion enclosed by green and black borders, the rim with vignettes reserved on a pink ground alternately pencilled with cell and wan diaper, early Qianlong, 9 in. (22.9 cm.). **£1,500-£1,700** *S*

'Famille rose' — a 19th Century French classification for a range of overglaze enamels which includes a rose-pink colour first used on Chinese porcelain from 1721. The rose or 'purple of Cassius' was first discovered by Andreas Cassius in Leyden in about 1650.

An octagonal meat dish, decorated in 'famille rose' enamels with European merchants standing on a river bank, within a scroll border in puce and iron-red, Qianlong, 45.5 cm. **£400-500** *L*

A blue and white saucer dish, the slightly recessed centre painted with a figure seated, playing a mandolin, the underside with 4 detached cloud scrolls, seal mark, Jiajing, 14.5 cm. **£250-300** *S*

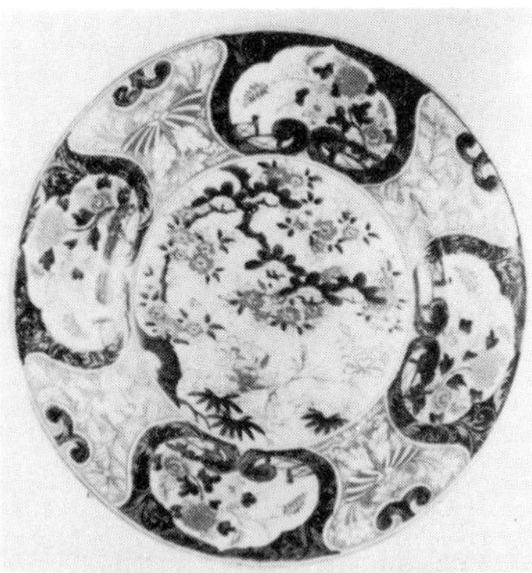

A very good and large Imari dish with wide everted rim, decorated in underglaze blue, iron-red and gilding, 56.2 cm., late 17th/early 18th C. **£1,200-1,400** *S*

An earthenware dish boldy enamelled with cranes in flight against a stylised moon, painted mark, 33 cm., c. 1860. **£300-350** *S*

A Chinese export tea and coffee service, 38 pieces, late 18th C. **£600-700** *DWB*

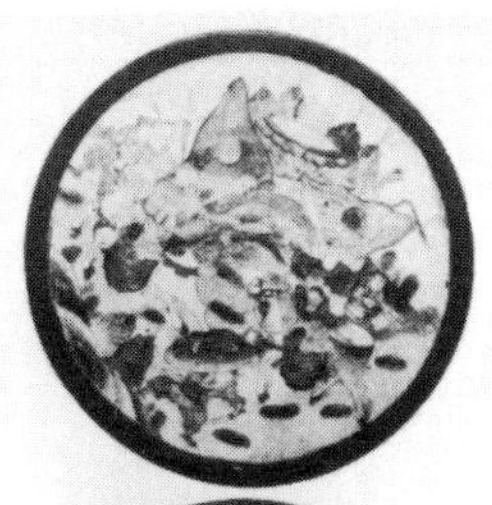

A pair of late 19th C. Japanese earthenware crackle glazed chargers decorated in mauve and green, 10½ in. diam. **£250-300** *TM*

A Kakiemon dish, painted in underglaze blue and coloured enamels, the reverse with a karakusa band, painted mark, 19.7 cm., 18th C. **£200-250** *S*

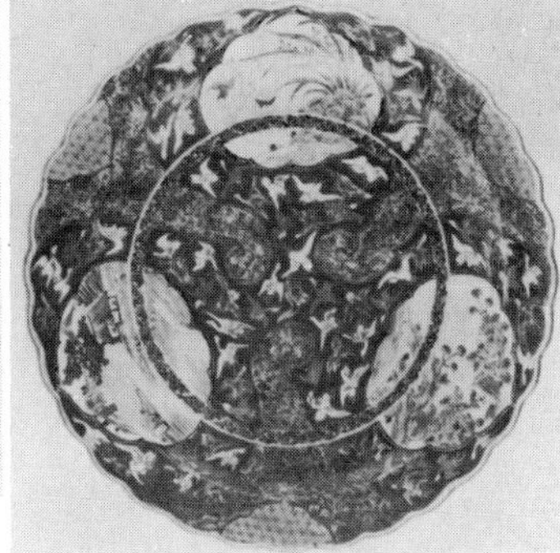

A pair of Arita plaques, each painted with 3 leaf-shaped panels, slight chip to one rim, 44.4 cm., late 19th C. **£350-450** *Bea*

A good large Imari saucer dish, painted with reserves, surrounded by small shaped panels, 24 in., late 19th C. **£450-550** *WHL*

An oval Canton dish, in typical bright enamel colours embellished with gold, 51.7 cm., mid 19th C. **£350-400** *Bea*

A large Japanese saucer dish painted with a mounted dignitary and attendants, within stylised foliate borders, 18 in., late 19th C. **£220-260** *WHL*

A pair of 'famille rose' dishes, Guangxu, 38 cm. **£300-400** *S*

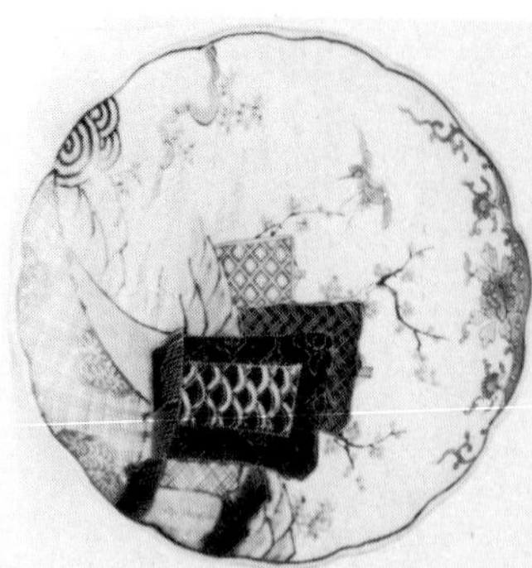

A set of 12 Imari dishes, 21.5 cm., late 19th C. **£200-250** *S*

A massive Arita blue and white dish painted with flowers, the reverse with butterflies, flowerheads and wave design, small rim chip, 93 cm. diam., late 19th C. **£1,500-1,700** *C*

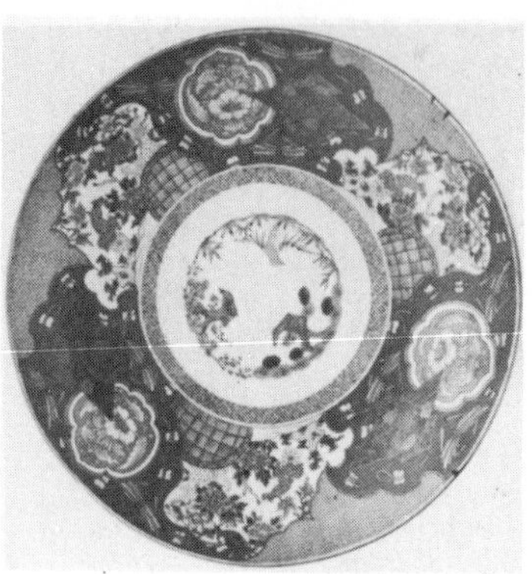

An Imari dish, the rim painted with asymmetrical panels of 'shishi' amongst flowering peonies, the exterior with stylised scrolling foliage, 53 cm. **£250-300** *L*

A Kinkozan earthenware dish painted and gilt with numerous figures, within a brocade border, gilt Kinkozan tsukuru, 16 cm., c. 1900. **£300-350** *S*

A Canton garden seat decorated in 'famille rose' palette, 47 cm., Daoguang. **£800-900** *S*

A pair of Cantonese porcelain studded tub shape terrace seats, typical decoration, one cracked, 19th C. **£900-1,100** *GSP*

A pair of 'famille rose' garden seats with pierced sides and top, moulded with studs and painted, 46 cm., late 19th C. **£1,050-1,250** *Bea*

A Satsuma koro and cover raised on four feet, decorated in iron-red, enamels and gilding, 11.3 cm., mid 19th C. **£400-500** *S*

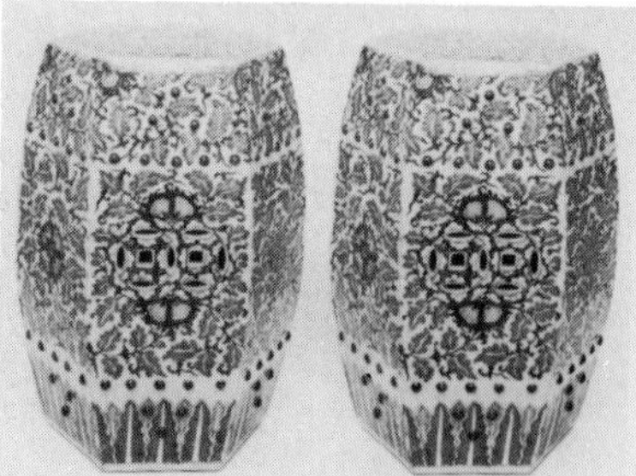

A pair of blue and white garden seats, studded and pierced, painted in underglaze blue with flowers amongst foliage, 19¾ in. (49 cm.), Guangxu. **£900-1,000** *S*

A Satsuma earthenware koro and cover, painted with numerous chrysanthemum, pierced metal cover, gilt Kinseido Hekizan sei and Satsuma mon, 27 cm., mid 19th C. **£800-900** *S*

A Longquan celadon jardiniere, the sides vigorously carved with a lotus meander covered overall with a sea-green glaze on the base, to reveal the stoneware burnt orange in the firing, metal liner, 17.4 cm. high by 25.4 cm. wide, Ming Dynasty. **£350-450** *S*

An unusual Kutani koro and cover, the base and interior burner painted with scrolls beneath a geometric border, two feet of burner damaged, 18 cm., c. 1880. **£500-600** *S*

A large Doucai jardiniere decorated on the exterior in characteristic palette of 'famille rose' enamels and underglaze blue, a multi-coloured band of lappets encircling the base and the rim, 13¼ in. (33.6 cm.), seal mark and period of Qianlong. **£4,300-5,000** *S*

A 19th C. Chinese 'famille verte' jardiniere, 9½ in. high, 10 in. diam. **£220-280** *TM*

A 'famille rose' jardiniere painted with 'shou' symbols on a yellow ground, 37 cm. diam., Guangxu. **£250-300** *S*

A 'Proto-Porcelain' jar, the lower part of the body deeply incised, the upper part of the body and the inside of the rim covered with a dark olive kiln gloss, the grey stoneware burnt to a rich brown colour where exposed, 21.2 cm., Han Dynasty. **£700-800** *S*

A fine Satsuma baluster-shaped koro and pierced domed cover with karashishi finial, the body brilliantly decorated in colours and gilt and moulded in relief, signed on the base Tokozan below a blue Shimazu mon, 30.3 cm. high, 19th C. **£1,100-1,300** *C*

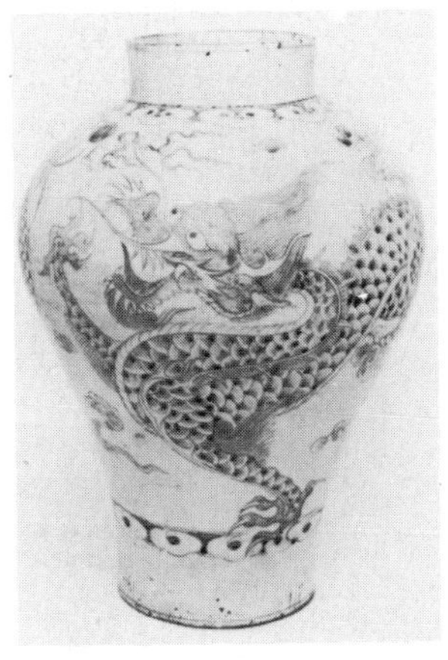

A Korean blue and white dragon jar painted with a dragon amidst stylised cloud scrolls chasing the 'flaming pearl', 45.2 cm., Yi Dynasty. **£9,000-11,000** *S*

Compare the jar from the Philadelphia Museum of Art included in the Asia Society Exhibition of the Art of the Korean Potter, 1968, catalogue no. 100, and another in the Cologne Museum für Ostasiatische Kunst, illustrated in Meisterwerke aus China, Korea und Japan, no. 98.

An unusual Yueyao funerary jar, the olive-green glaze continuing over the bevelled footrim, 26.8 cm., 10th C. **£3,000-£4,000** *S*

A Chinese Imari jardiniere, 14¾ in. (37.5 cm.) diam., Kangxi. **£1,400-£1,600** *S*

A 19th C. Chinese blue and white jardiniere, 10 in. high, 12 in. diam. **£200-250** *TM*

A pair of blue and white jardinieres each painted in underglaze blue, 45.5 cm. diam., 20th C. **£400-500** *S*

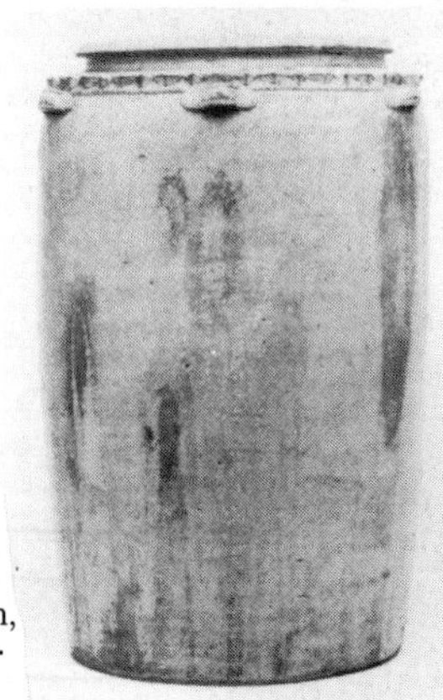

A Thanh-Hoa jar, set with a band of protruding lotus petals above a ring of lug handles, with a crackled ivory-tinted glaze stopping short of the base, 35.3 cm., 13/14th C. **£350-£400** *S*

Shorter jars with similar petal borders around the shoulders are illustrated in Sekai Toji Zenshu vol. 12, pl. III, and in Toji Taikei (New Heibonsha Series) no. 47, pl. 65 top.

A green-glazed pottery granary jar supported on tripod feet, each modelled as a bear standing on its hind legs, a wide tiled roof of conical form, the crackled glaze of rich green tone with areas of faint iridescence, applied over the soft red pottery, 23.5 cm., Han Dynasty. **£1,500-1,700** *S*

A green-glazed pottery jar and cover, base with three spur marks, the exterior applied with a rich green glaze degraded overall to an iridescence of silvery-sage green colour with small patches of turquoise and emerald, the interior unglazed to reveal the brick-red pottery, 13.2 cm., Han Dynasty. **£400-500** *S*

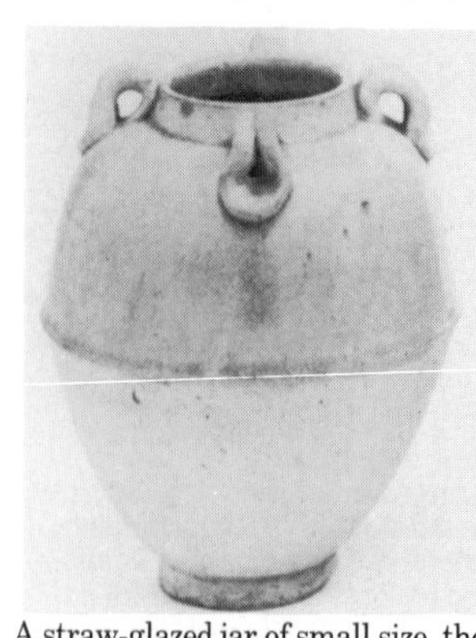

A straw-glazed jar of small size, the upper half of the body covered with a crackled straw glaze, continuing on the interior, 18.3 cm., Sui Dynasty. **£1,000-1,200** *S*

A rare glazed stoneware jar of small size, covered overall with a crackled olive-green glaze, falling well short of the foot on the exterior to reveal the buff ware, 15 cm., Sui Dynasty. **£2,500-2,700** *S*

A small green-glazed pottery jar with three handles and the stumps of a fourth, the uncut foot with three spur marks, some flaking, one handle polished, 7 cm. high, Tang Dynasty. **£300-400** *C*

A green-glazed pottery jar on a solid splayed base covered overall with a crackled green glaze falling well short of the foot to reveal the pinkish ware, the mouth with four wedge-shaped spur marks, 23.2 cm., Tang Dynasty. **£6,500-£7,500** *S*

A Yueyao jar covered in a glaze of characteristic greyish-olive tone, stopping in an even line short of the base to reveal the stoneware, 13.3 cm., late Six Dynasties. **£2,200-2,600** *S*

A straw-glazed stoneware Amphora, the finely crackled glaze of pale olive tint stopping short of the lower part of the body to reveal the greyish ware, 39.1 cm., Tang Dynasty. **£1,500-2,000** *S*

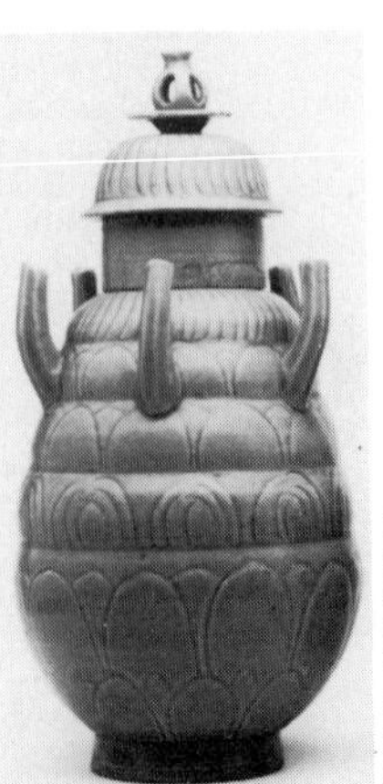

A Yueyao funerary jar and cover, carved on the sides with concentric stepped bands of overlapping petals, the domed cover carved with slender petals covered overall with a translucent olive-green glaze thinning on the foot to reveal the greyish ware, 32.8 cm., early Song Dynasty. **£4,000-4,500** *S*

A rare Henan brown-glazed Meiping, covered overall in a lustrous deep brown glaze, thinning around the neck and towards the base where it stops short to reveal the pale buff ware, 23.2 cm., Song Dynasty. **£1,800-£2,200** *S*

An unusual Longquan celadon jar and cover of small size, applied with a soft blue-green glaze, the base unglazed and burnt pale orange in the firing, 12.2 cm., Song Dynasty. **£300-400** *S*

A rare Cizhou type sgraffiato jar covered in a deep brown glaze thickly applied and falling short of the base, revealing the greyish-buff body to a petal border radiating from the base of the neck, 30.8 cm., Song Dynasty. **£2,000-3,000** *S*

An incised and painted Cizhou type jar, freely painted in brown with a broad peony meander, details boldly incised, all over a cream-coloured slip extending on to the interior and applied with a translucent glaze, stopping short of the base to reveal the buff ware, 15.8 cm., Ming Dynasty. **£600-£700** *S*

A pair of blue and white jars painted with floral meanders, rabbit marks, 8 and 7¾ in. (20.3 and 19.7 cm.), Wanli. **£650-750** *S*

A good carved celadon funerary jar and cover of Li Shui type, covered overall with a bubble-suffused glaze of rich olive-green tone stopping on the bevelled footrim to reveal the ware burnt reddish-orange in the firing, 29.6 cm., Northern Song Dynasty. **£3,000-£4,000** *S*

Li Shui is a type of southern celadon often confused with northern celadon probably because of the similarity of the olive glaze found on both wares.

A Ming blue and white jar, painted with elaborately strung beaded pendants with tassels, a petal border around the base and further formal borders on the shoulders and short straight neck, 7⅛ in. (18.1 cm.), six character mark of Xuande, Jiajing. **£500-600** *S*

A Chinese polychrome jar and cover, the baluster body painted in underglaze blue, overglaze greens, yellow, iron-red and black enamels, crack to body, rim repair, 47 cm., Transitional. **£800-900** *SS*

A painted Cizhou type jar, covered overall with a transparent glaze over the creamy slip, freely painted in ochre and brown with a bird in flight beside floral sprays, the base unglazed, 24.7 cm., Ming Dynasty. **£400-500** *S*

A rare blue and white jar painted in underglaze blue of vivid tone, 8 in. (20.3 cm.), six character mark and period of Jiajing. **£2,000-£3,000** *S*

A late Ming blue and white jar painted in soft tones of underglaze blue with an overall design of fruiting melon, neck encircled by a blue-ground key-fret border, 15.2 cm., Wanli. **£900-1,100** *S*

A polychrome jar, painted in enamels and underglaze blue, 11⅜ in. (28.7 cm.), Transitional. **£1,000-1,300** *S*

A Kirman blue and white kalian painted with birds and animals, the neck with lappet panels, small chips, hair cracks, stained, 6¼ in. (16 cm.) high, 17th C. **£250-300** *C*

A pair of blue and white jars and covers, painted in soft tones of underglaze blue, 6 in. (15.3 cm.), Transitional. **£850-950** *S*

An unusual polychrome jar and cover painted in enamels, 14¼ in. (36 cm.), Transitional. **£1,700-£1,900** *S*

A blue and white oviform jar, Kangxi, 23 cm. high, wood cover. **£550-600** *C*

A pair of Chinese blue and white jars and covers painted with figures playing go, 22¾ in., repaired, Kangxi. **£600-700** *SC*

A blue and white jar, painted with a continuous scene of a view across a lake, 9⅛ in. (23.2 cm.), Kangxi. **£150-250** *S*

A very rare 'famille verte' pitcher, decorated with the Eight Horses of Mu Wang in four panels between lightly moulded lappet and zig-zag borders, the neck with dragons on a bright iron-red ground within four linked panels, 8½ in. (20.6 cm.), Kangxi. **£400-500** *S*

A blue and white jar painted with a continuous scene of the Seven Sages in a Bamboo Grove, 7⅞ in. (19.8 cm.), Kangxi. **£400-500** *S*

A large 'famille verte' jar and cover, painted with a continuous lakeside scene, the shoulders encircled by a green key-fret band, the domed cover with a matching lakeside scene encircling the Buddhist lion knop in yellow and blue, 22¾ in. (57.6 cm.), Kangxi. **£600-800** *S*

A Japanese Arita jar, 6¾ in., c. 1700. **£140-160** *BHA*

Based on a Chinese Transitional jar, the rather schematic figures are probably copied from Dutch pottery or wooden prototypes sent to Japan for the Arita potters to copy, in the late 17th C.

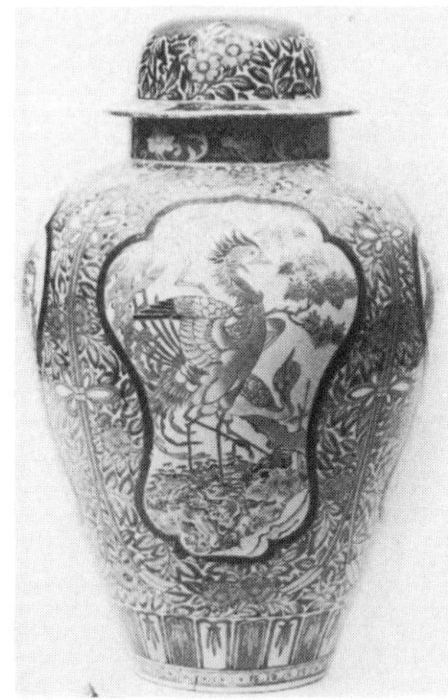
A large Imari jar and cover, painted in turquoise, yellow, green, aubergine, black, iron-red and gilding, lacking finial, hair cracks, 46 cm., early 18th C. **£600-700** *SS*

An Imari jar and cover, damaged neck, crackled glaze, 87 cm., early 18th C. **£350-450** *SS*

A large Arita oviform jar in underglaze blue, 38.8 cm. high, late 17th C. **£1,100-1,300** *C*

A large Satsuma jar and cover of rectangular form, painted with children, pierced cover painted with panels of flower scrolls, 29 cm., late 19th C. **£350-450** *Bea*

A green dragon jar and cover, pencilled in underglaze blue with two powerful dragons chasing 'flaming pearls' above a border of lotus petal panels round the base, the shoulders with the 'ba jixiang' decoration, all picked out in translucent green enamel of pale emerald colour, 20.2 cm., seal mark and period of Qianlong. **£3,000-£4,000** *S*

A chaire covered with a brown glaze with two translucent splashes, with brocade bag and later wood box, 7.9 cm., 18th/early 19th C. **£500-600** *S*

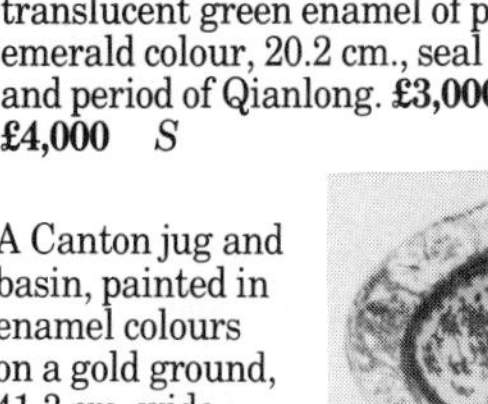

A Canton jug and basin, painted in enamel colours on a gold ground, 41.3 cm. wide, late 19th C. **£400-£500** *Bea*

A pair of iron-red jars and covers, 34 cm., Guangxu. **£220-300** *S*

A tea pot, Chienlung, 5 in. high. **£100-150** *IHA*

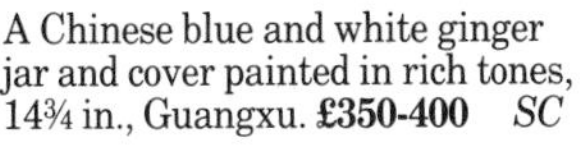

A Chinese blue and white ginger jar and cover painted in rich tones, 14¾ in., Guangxu. **£350-400** *SC*

A fine small Kakiemon oval tea pot and shallow domed cover with vertically ribbed sides, decorated in iron-red and coloured enamels, 14.7 cm. long, late 17th C. **£1,700-£2,000** *C*

A blue and white tureen, cover and stand, Qianlong, 14⅜ in. (36.5 cm.). **£500-600** *S*

A blue and white exportware urn, after a Marieberg original, painted in vivid cobalt showing traces of gilding, Qianlong, 11¾ in. (29.8 cm.). **£300-400** *S*

A pair of blue and white covered ecuelles painted in bright cobalt with scenes of pavilions set on the shores of a lake, Kangxi, 7½ in. (19.1 cm.). **£600-800** *S*

A Korean celadon vase, encircled by rudimentary knife-cut shallow grooves, the minutely crackled translucent glaze of brownish olive tone, Koryu Dynasty, 10½ in. (26.7 cm.). **£600-700** *S*

A pair of Chinese export urns and covers, potted in the European manner, in orange, green and blue enamels enhanced with gold, the matching cover with a pine cone knop, Qianlong/Jaiqing, one handle and one knop repaired, 33.5 cm. **£1,600-2,000** *Bea*

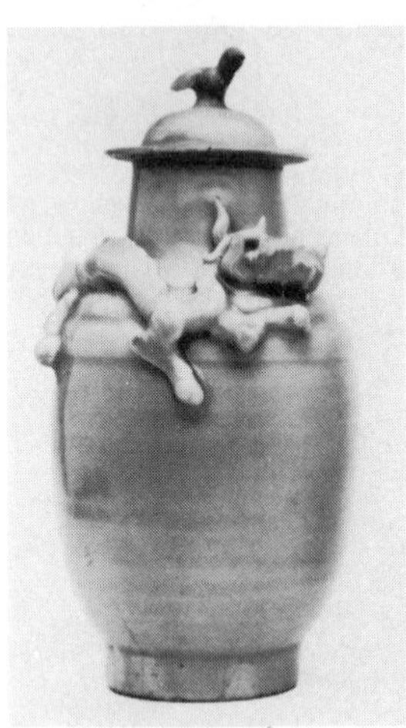

A pair of Longquan celadon funerary vases and covers, one vase applied in high relief with a dragon in pursuit of a 'flaming pearl', the other vase with a tiger, Song Dynasty, 23.2 and 23.5 cm. **£3,500-£4,500** *S*

A Yingqing funerary vase, with a freize of 9 free-standing figures beneath a dragon chasing a 'flaming pearl', light greenish grey translucent glaze pooling on the neck, Song/Yuan Dynasty, 13 in. (34.7 cm.). **£600-700** *S*

An extremely rare early Ming blue and white vase, the body well painted in cobalt, the reduced neck fitted with a gilt metal mount, 9 in. (23.2 cm. overall). **£6,000-7,000** *S*

It is most unusual to find ruyi-shaped panels filled with waves on a 'yuhuchun ping', although 2 are known with lotus petals, flowers and leaves floating on the waves.

An unusual Ming blue and white vase, painted in bright tones with geese in flight interspersed by flowering clumps of lotus, between scroll encircling the base and a flowering meander on the shoulders, two character mark sisheng (to meditate), Jiajing, 11½ in. (28.9 cm.). **£1,200-1,400** *S*

A finely painted Ming blue and white meiping, decorated with a continuous scene of dignitaries and boy attendants, the underglaze blue in purplish washed tones throughout, six character mark and period of Wanli, the mouth restored, 39 cm. **£7,000-9,000** *S*

A 'famille verte' rouleau vase, Kangxi, body crack, slight misfiring, 46.2 cm. **£280-360** *SS*

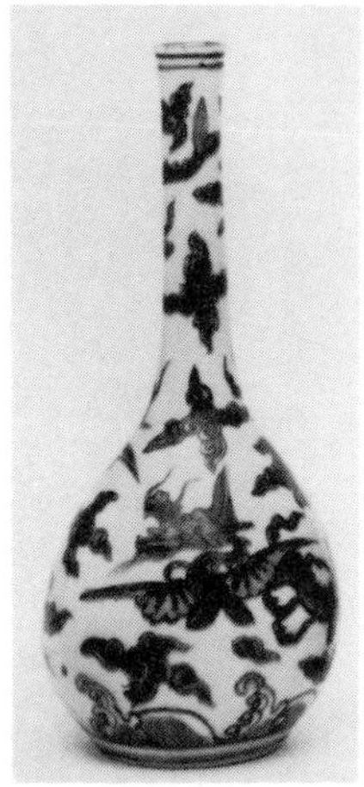

A good late Ming blue and white bottle vase, the underglaze blue of strong inky tone, Wanli, 11 in. (28 cm.). **£950-1,050** *S*

A blue and white vase, the underglaze blue of vivid tone, Transitional, 16¾ in. (42.5 cm.). **£400-600** *S*

The form of this vase is termed 'sleeve' or rollwagon. The latter term being derived from the Dutch 'rolwagen' used in China merchants inventories from about 1640.

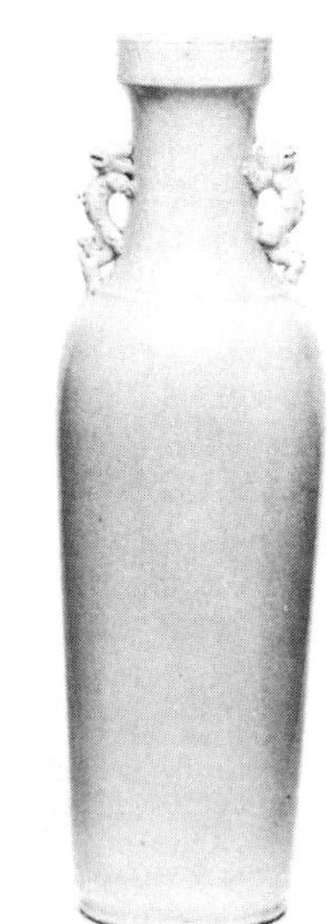

A Fujian vase, the minutely crackled glaze of creamy tone, 13½ in. (34 cm.), 17th C. **£500-£600** *S*

A blue and white vase, painted with sprays of peony, lotus and other flowers, with cloud scrolls interspersed with swastikas on the knop, and a band of pendant stiff leaves around the flared rim, Transitional, 14 in. (35.9 cm.). **£1,000-1,200** *S*

A pair of Kangxi blue and white circular tapered vases, with later gilding, Artemisia mark, 11½ in. high. **£300-350** *AG*

A Chinese blue and white rouleau vase, Kangxi, 44.5 cm. **£550-650** *SS*

Two blue and white baluster vases and tall domed covers, encircled leaf marks, Kangxi, both necks damaged, both about 35 cm. high. **£500-600** *C*

A blue and white bottle vase, Kangxi, chipped, 20 cm. **£220-£280** *SS*

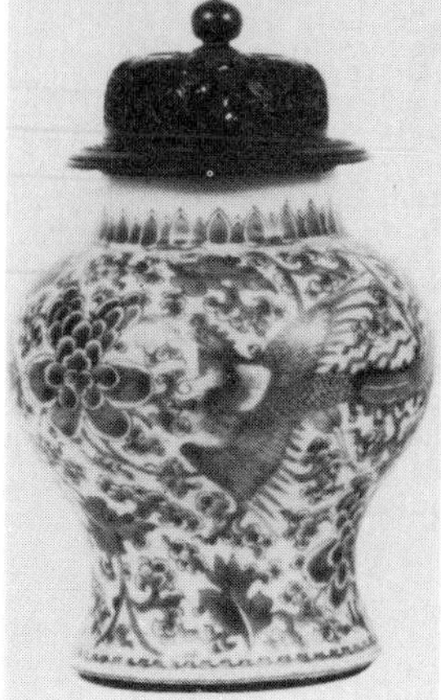

A pair of Chinese blue and white vases, Kangxi, one repaired at neck, 9¼ in. **£250-300** *SC*

A pair of Chinese porcelain beaker vases, painted in underglaze blue, Kangxi, one cracked and repaired at rim, 16½ in. high. **£800-1,200** *WHL*

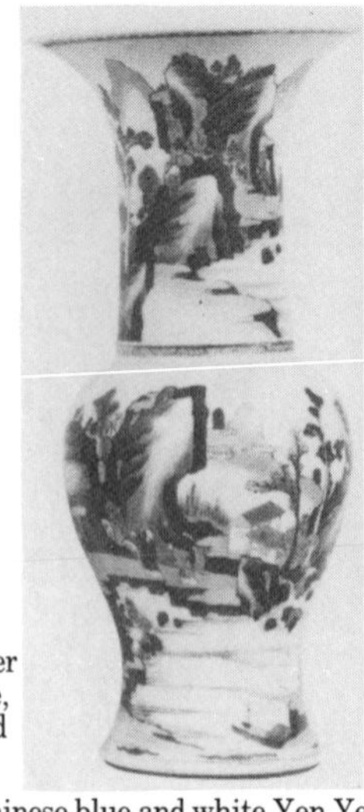

A Chinese blue and white Yen Yen vase, painted in rich tones of underglaze blue, Kangxi, 18½ in. **£650-750** *SC*

A Chinese blue and white bottle vase, Kangxi, 15 in. high. **£700-£800** *DWB*

A brightly painted blue and white Yen Yen vase, Kangxi, 18 in. (46 cm.) **£600-650** *S*

A Chinese blue and white vase painted in rich underglaze blue, six character Chenghua mark, Kangxi, slight chips to foot, 9½ in. **£150-200** *SC*

A blue and white Yen Yen vase, decorated with flowering prunus trees, reserved in white with pencilled details against a cracked ice ground washed in bright underglaze blue, Kangxi, 17¾ in. (45.2 cm.). **£600-700** *S*

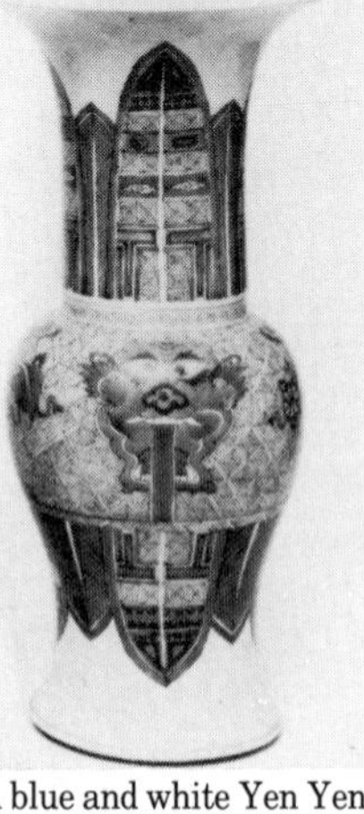

A blue and white Yen Yen vase, decorated in archaistic style with two animal masks divided by vertical bands with ruyi-head terminals, Kangxi, 18½ in. (46.5 cm.). **£350-450** *S*

A blue and white rouleau vase, the underglaze blue of vivid tone, Kangxi, 17¼ in. (43.7 cm.). **£900-£1,000** *S*

A blue and white flaring cylindrical brush pot, delicately painted in soft tones with a fisherman, unencircled Chenghua four character mark, Kangxi, 13 cm. high. **£900-1,000** *C*

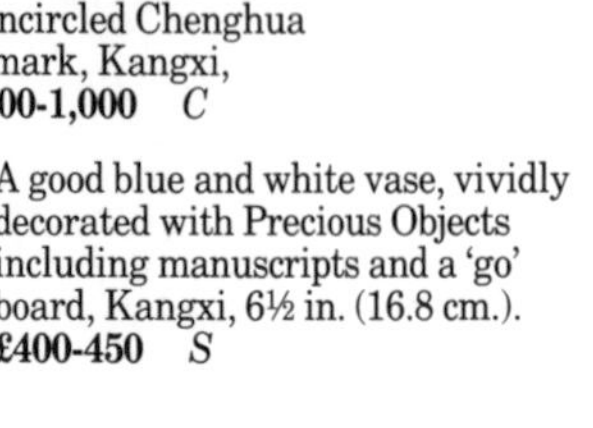

A good blue and white vase, vividly decorated with Precious Objects including manuscripts and a 'go' board, Kangxi, 6½ in. (16.8 cm.). **£400-450** *S*

A Chinese Imari baluster vase and cover, painted in underglaze blue and iron-red and gilt, finial chipped, late Kangxi/Yongzheng, 63 cm. high. **£1,100-1,300** *C*

A rare Arita garniture of three double gourd vases, painted in Delft style, one neck slightly reduced prior to firing, one subsequently reduced, chip, 37 to 43 cm., last quarter of the 17th C. **£500-600** *SS*

A good blue-glazed vase of 'cong' form, covered overall with a rich purplish glaze thinning slightly on the edges, seal mark and period of Qianlong, wood stand, 11½ in. (29.4 cm.). **£450-500** *SC*

A well potted copper-red glazed vase, thinly applied with a soft pinkish red glaze, deepening around the shoulders and neck, thinning around the base, rim, interior and base glazed in white, seal mark and period of Qianlong, 28.7 cm. **£1,500-1,700** *S*

A pair of Imari pot pourri vases and covers painted in typical palette, hair crack, wood knops, 30 cm., early 18th C. **£800-900** *SS*

JAPANESE ART PERIODS PREHISTORY AND PROTOHISTORY

c. 7,000 B.C. Jomon culture; first recorded pottery with simple design.
c. 300 B.C. Yayoi culture; bronzes and more sophisticated pottery.
1st to 4th C. A.D. Haniwa culture. Bronzes and distinctive red pottery.
A.D. 220; first influence from Korea.

ASUKA PERIOD — 552-645

HAHUKO PERIOD — 672-685

NARA PERIOD — 710-794

HEIAN PERIOD — 794-1185

KAMAKURA PERIOD — 1185-1333

MUROMACHI (AHIKAGA) PERIOD — 1338-1573

MOMOYAMA PERIOD — 1573-1615

1598: Immigrant Korean potters begin kilns at Kyushu, producing the first glazed pottery.

EDO (TOKUGAWA) PERIOD — 1615-1867

1616: First porcelain made by Ninsei (1596-1666)
1661-1673: Great age of porcelain; Arita, Nabeshima, Kutani and Kakiemon.
1716-1736: Popularity of lacquering and netsuke as art forms.

MEIJI PERIOD — (1868-1912)

Strong influence of Western cultures developing and growing. Japanese art appears to decline in many respects. Much trading with the West.

A flambé-glazed double gourd vase, covered inside and out with crimson purple glaze suffused with trickles of creamy pale blue, thinning to a crackled buff colour at the rim, wood stand, 34.8 cm., 18th C. **£600-700** *S*

A good blue-glazed vase, the mouth with brown-edged incurved rim, Qianlong, 16 in. (41 cm.). **£400-£500** *S*

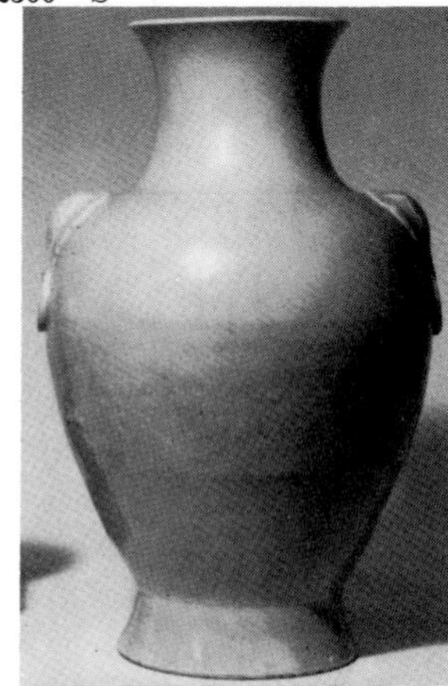

A pale celadon glazed baluster vase, Qianlong six character seal mark, 43.5 cm. high. **£350-400** *C*

A Guan-type vase of archaic 'hu' form, applied with a thick, widely crackled dove grey glaze of faint lavender tone, deepening in colour at the rim and extending on to the interior, the footrim treated with a dark brown wash, 16.4 cm., 18th C. **£800-900** *S*

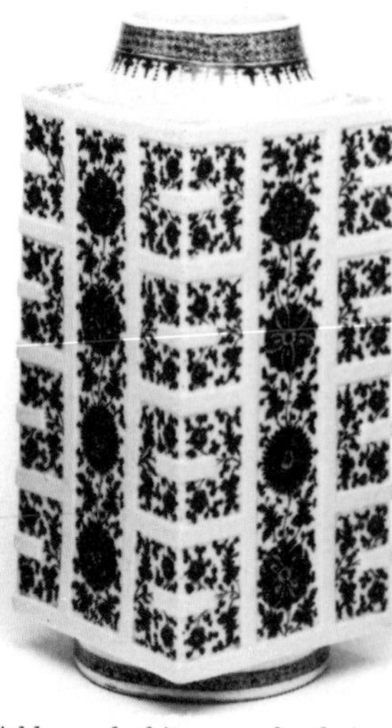

A blue and white vase of archaic 'cong' form, the incurved neck encircled by diaper and spearhead borders, 11¼ in. (28.7 cm.), 18th C. **£300-350** *S*

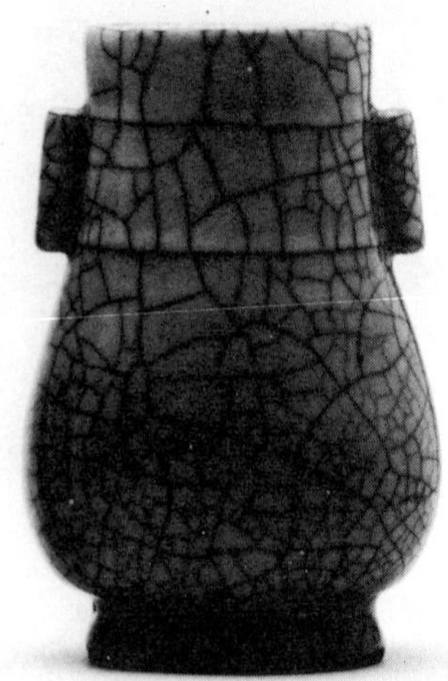

A Ge-type hu shaped vase, covered overall in a thick mushroom coloured glaze, irregularly veined with a broad black crackle, enclosing finer brown lines, the footrim washed in dark brown, 17.7 cm., 18th C. **£300-500** *S*

An exportware vase, decorated on the inner side with gold fish in iron-red, the exterior with deep blue glaze decorated in gilding, Qianlong, 14¾ in. (37.8 cm.). **£700-£800** *S*

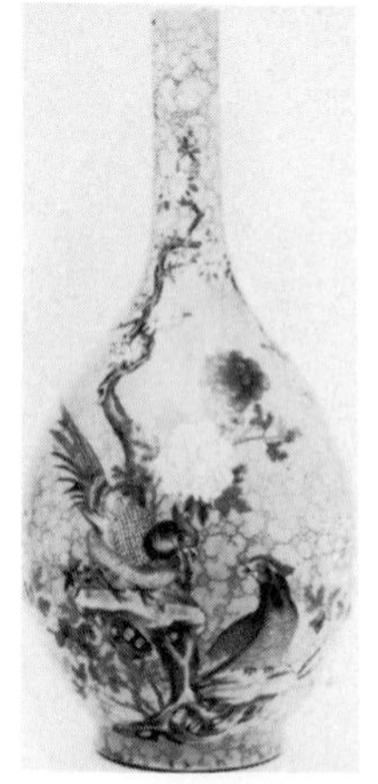

An unusual 'famille rose' vase of pear shape, enamelled on a turquoise enamel ground, with a pair of crested pheasants, seal mark of Qianlong in iron-red and of the period, wood stand, 21 in. (53.5 cm.). **£1,100-1,300** *S*

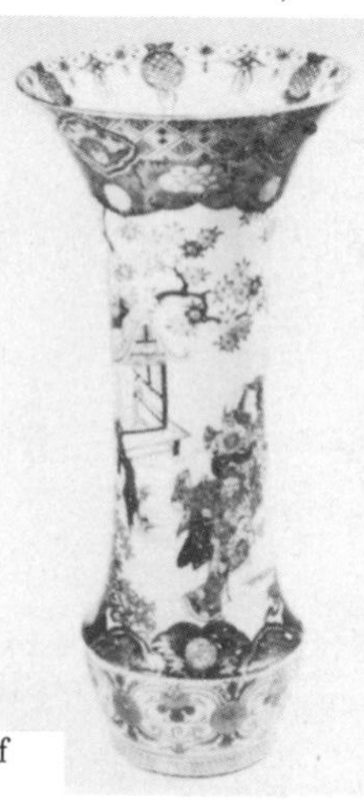

An Imari beaker vase, 31½ in. high, 18th C. **£600-650** *AG*

A pair of Canton double gourd vases, painted in 'famille rose' palette, Daoguang, 34 cm. **£650-£700** *S*

A Chinese 'famille rose' rouleau vase, decorated with panels of Precious Objects, monkeys, Buddhist lions at play, all on iron-red cell diaper ground, 60 cm., mid 19th C. **£400-500** *SS*

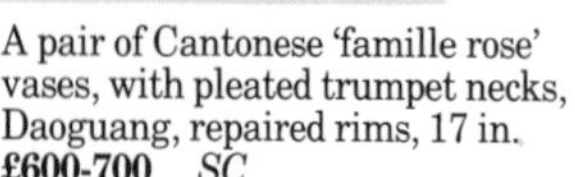

A pair of Cantonese 'famille rose' vases, with pleated trumpet necks, Daoguang, repaired rims, 17 in. **£600-700** *SC*

A 19th C. Chinese blue and white ovoid vase, with a carved hardwood stand, 12 in. high. **£550-650** *TM*

A pair of Canton vases with gilt metal mounts, with dragons and painted in bright enamel colours and gold, total height 42.5 cm., mid 19th C. **£350-450** *Bea*

An earthenware koro and cover, the body painted and gilt, 12 cm., mid 19th C. **£300-350** *S*

A pair of 19th C. 'famille rose' enamel vases, 25 in. high. **£850-£950** *TM*

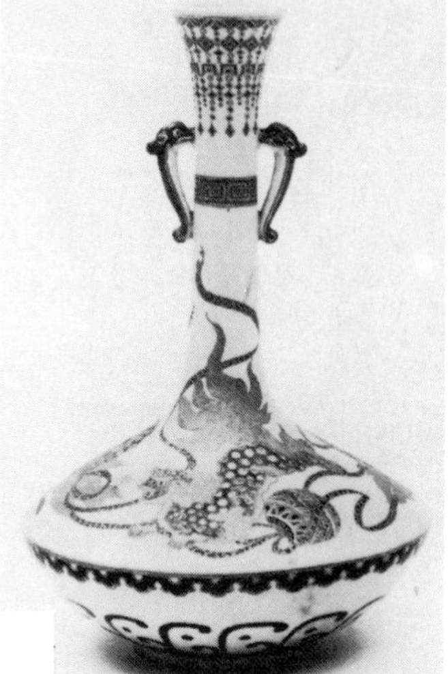

An earthenware vase, the discus body with a tall neck, painted and gilt with three 'shi-shi', signed, 30 cm., mid 19th C. **£400-450** *S*

A pair of 19th C. 'famille rose' enamel vases, 16½ in. high. **£800-£900** *TM*

A Satsuma earthenware vase of exaggerated shouldered form, well decorated with jardinieres filled with flowers, signed, gilding rubbed, 11½ in., c. 1850. **£450-£500** *SC*

A Japanese earthenware vase, finely painted in coloured enamels and gilding, overpainted with sprays of kiku, indistinct signature, slight staining, 7¼ in., c. 1850. **£300-350** *SC*

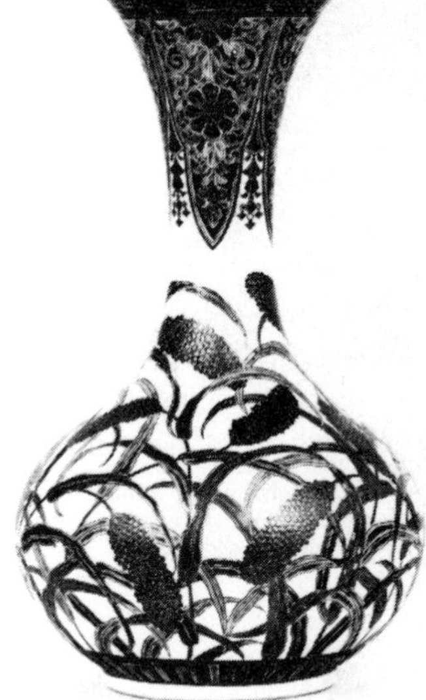

A Japanese earthenware vase, painted in bold colours and gilding with growing millet, signed, slight rubbing, 10¾ in., c. 1840-50. **£160-£200** *SC*

An Imari oviform vase and cover richly painted with female figures in blue cartouches, 27 in. high. **£600-650** *AG*

A Chinese large ovoid vase, decorated with a flowering prunus tree on a 'famille verte' ground, 23 in. high, 19th C. **£200-250** *GC*

A pair of 'famille verte' Yanyan vases, painted on rich apple green grounds, late Qing Dynasty, small foot chips, one neck repaired, wood stands, 45 cm. high. **£600-700** *C*

A large 19th C. Cantonese vase, 22 in. **£900-1,000** *PWC*

A pair of Satsuma vases each painted with an oval reserve, 15.5 cm., late 19th C. **£900-1,200** *Bea*

A pair of powder blue ground vases and covers, decorated in 'famille verte' palette in two gilt edged panels on a 'bleu soufflé' ground of bright mottled colour, 16 in. (40.7 cm.), 19th C. **£800-900** *S*

A pair of Satsuma vases, painted with dignitary or crowd scenes, 8.7 cm., late 19th C. **£500-600** *Bea*

A pair of Canton vases applied with dragons and Buddhist lions and painted in bright enamel colours on a flower scroll ground, one with hair crack, hard wood stands, 36 cm., late 19th C. **£350-400** *Bea*

A blue and white vase of 'hu' form, 53.5 cm., 19th C. **£250-350** *S*

An earthenware bottle vase, painted and gilt with a dignitary, 45 cm., c. 1880. **£700-800** *S*

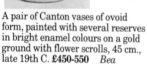

A pair of massive 19th C. Satsuma vases and cover. **£1,300-1,500** *McCMB*

A pair of Canton vases of ovoid form, painted with several reserves in bright enamel colours on a gold ground with flower scrolls, 45 cm., late 19th C. **£450-550** *Bea*

A Satsuma vase painted in colours and gilt, signed on both bases Dai Nihon Satsuma yaki Yuzan zo below a Shimazu mon, one handle repaired, 14.3 cm. high, 19th C. **£300-400** *C*

An Imari vase, the underglaze blue ground decorated with scrolling foliage and flowers, 62 cm., with wood stand 76 cm., late 19th C. **£750-850** *S*

(c.) A large pair of 19th C. Imari bottle vases, 25 in. **£750-850** *PWC*

(l. & r.) A pair of 19th C. Imari vases and covers, 25 in. **£600-£700** *PWC*

A pair of crackled glazed vases with lion's mask and ring handles, painted in 'famille rose' palette with continuous scenes of warriors, moulded four character marks, one chipped, 17¾ in., late 19th C. **£400-£500** *SC*

A Chinese blue and white vase and cover in Kangxi-style, painted in rich tones with orientals outside a pavilion, 16½ in., late 19th C. **£250-£300** *SC*

A Satsuma vase painted and gilt, signed on the base Tachibana Yoshinobu ga below a blue Shimazu mon, 18.5 cm., 19th C. **£450-500** *C*

A large vase painted in underglaze blue and yellow with numerous chrysanthemum, the stamens in low relief, painted Todai Kozan tsukuru, 52 cm., late 19th C. **£450-£550** *S*

A fine Kyoto globular vase painted in colours and gilt, signed on the base Kinkozan zo, 15.2 cm., late 19th C. **£350-400** *C*

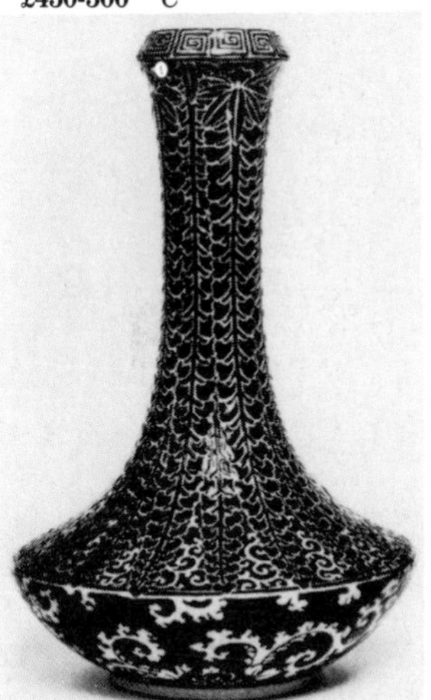

A Gyozan earthenware vase with a discus body and tall neck, enamelled Gyozan, 25 cm., c. 1870. **£150-200** *S*

A Satsuma vase with figures strolling beside a lake in a flower garden, reserved on a deep blue ground painted in gold, 30.3 cm., late 19th C. **£400-450** *Bea*

An earthenware vase and cover gilt and enamelled, gilt Takashi Yoshinobu, cover cracked, slight chip, wood stand, 37 cm., late 19th C. **£500-600** *S*

A Yoshiyei vase of ovoid form with elephant's head and ring handles, moulded in low relief painted in underglaze blue, on black lacquer and gilt trellis ground, signed, 18 in., c. 1900. **£400-500** *SC*

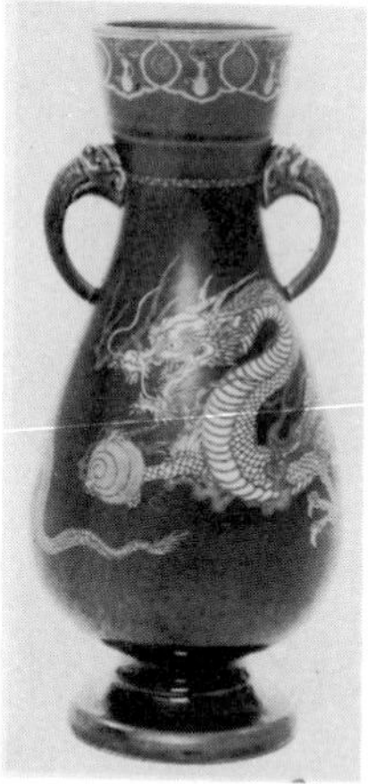

A Nakamura Boukei stoneware vase, with an olive green ground, impressed Nakamura Boukei and painted mark, 27 cm., c. 1900. **£200-300** *S*

A Seikozan earthenware vase, the neck gilt with vine leaves on a black ground, gilt Seikozan, 24 cm., c. 1900. **£350-400** *S*

A gilt decorated vase, the rich blue ground with a pattern of scattered mons, six character mark and period of Guangxu, 15 in (38.2 cm.). **£400-500** *S*

A Chinese blue ground vase decorated overall with lengthy inscriptions enclosing a pagoda, all in gilding between diaper borders, reserved on a rich blue glazed ground, wood stand, Guangxu, gilding rubbed, 21¼ in. **£500-600** *SC*

A pair of Cantonese 'famille rose' vases decorated with birds, insects and flowers, Guangxu, 14¼ in. **£400-500** *SC*

A 'famille rose' vase, painted mark of Qianlong, Guangxu, 49 cm. **£400-450** *S*

A 'famille rose' vase, Guangxu, rim restored, 91 cm. **£650-750** *S*

An earthenware vase well painted with panels of a young woman and child, the ground decorated in predominantly brown flambé glaze, gilt Kinkozan tsukuru, 23.5 cm., c. 1900. **£350-400** *S*

A Ninsei style Awata ware vase, seal of Ninsei in relief, 34 cm., c. 1900. **£280-360** *S*

A blue and white vase painted in various tones with stems of leafy bamboo, painted Fukagawa sei, 38 cm., c. 1900. **£220-300** *S*

A pair of blue and white vases and covers, 54 cm., 20th C. **£550-650** *S*

A pair of 'famille rose' vases, mark of Qianlong, 47 cm., early 20th C. **£250-300** *S*

A pair of blue and white vases, 92 cm., 20th C. **£700-800** *S*

A pair of turquoise ground 'famille rose' double gourd vases, mark of Qianlong, 29 cm., 20th C. **£250-£300** *S*

An unusual pair of Imari lanterns each with detachable roof, painted and gilt, 44 cm., late 19th C. **£500-£550** *S*

A polychrome vase decorated in underglaze blue and enamels, mark of Chenghua, modern, 23.5 cm. **£80-150** *S*

A Canton cache pot and cover painted with panels, 32 cm., Daoguang. **£450-500** *S*

A Longquan celadon shrine enclosing a biscuit figure of Guanyin, showing extensive traces of gilding, early Ming Dynasty, 24.7 cm. **£800-900** *S*

A set of 4 Chinese 'famille rose' plaques, Guangxu, 14½ by 10 in. **£300-400** *SC*

A green glazed pottery ladle under a glaze with extensive silvery iridescence, Han Dynasty, chipped, area of rim infilled, 18 cm. long. **£300-400** *C*

A pottery offering set comprising a shallow circular tray and 5 wine cups, the centre and underside of the tray unglazed, Tang Dynasty, tray 10 in. (25.5 cm.), cups 2 in. (5 cm.). **£1,600-2,000** *S*

A Cizhou pillow of bean shape, the top incised through the white slip, with a spray of flowering lotus on a ground of small circles, Song Dynasty, 34 cm. **£600-800** *S*

Chinese dynasties and marks

Earlier Dynasties

Shang Yin, c. 1532-1027 B.C.
Western Zhou (Chou) 1027-770 B.C.
Spring and Autumn Annals 770-480 B.C.
Warring States 484-221 B.C.
Qin (Ch'in) 221-206 B.C.
Western Han 206 B.C.-24 A.D.
Eastern Han 25-220
Three Kingdoms 221-265
Six Dynasties 265-589
Wei 386-557
Sui 589-617
Tang (T'ang) 618-906
Five Dynasties 907-960
Liao 907-1125
Sung 960-1280
Chin 1115-1260
Yüan 1280-1368

Ming Dynasty

洪武年製

Hongwu (Hung Wu)
1368-1398

永樂年製

Yongle (Yung Lo)
1403-1424

大明宣德年製

Xuande (Hsüan Tê)
1426-1435

大明成化年製

Chenghua (Ch'êng Hua)
1465-1487

大明弘治年製

Hongzhi
(Hung Chih)
1488-1505

大明正德年製

Zhengde
(Chêng Tê)
1506-1521

大明嘉靖年製

Jiajing
(Chia Ching)
1522-1566

大明隆慶年製

Longqing
(Lung Ching)
1567-1572

大明萬曆年製

Wanli (Wan Li)
1573-1620

大明天啟年製

Tianqi
(T'ien Chi)
1621-1627

崇禎年製

Chongzhen
(Ch'ung Chêng)
1628-1644

Qing (Ch'ing) Dynasty

大清順治年製

Shunzhi
(Shun Chih)
1644-1661

大清康熙年製

Kangxi (K'ang Hsi)
1662-1722

大清雍正年製

Yongzheng (Yung Chêng)
1723-1735

大清乾隆年製

Qianlong (Ch'ien Lung)
1736-1795

嘉慶年製

Jiaqing (Chia Ch'ing)
1796-1820

大清道光年製

Daoguang (Tao Kuang)
1821-1850

大清咸豐年製

Xianfeng (Hsien Fêng)
1851-1861

大清同治年製

Tongzhi (T'ung Chih)
1862-1874

大清光緒年製

Guangxu (Kuang Hsü)
1875-1908

大清宣統年製

Xuantong
(Hsüan T'ung)
1909-1911

洪憲年製

Hongxian
(Hung Hsien)
1916

GLOSSARY

blanc de Chine The fine white wares produced in Fujian province from the Song dynasty to the present day.

Chakra The Buddhist Wheel of the Law.

Cizhou A stoneware produced in Hopei and other provinces of China from the northern Song dynasty. It is decorated in dark brown slip on a cream ground. Later and perhaps less common designs were executed under green and turquoise translucent glazes. During the Song dynasty designs were painted in overglaze red and green enamels, the first known use of this technique on Chinese ware.

Dingyao A porcellaneous ware produced in the northern province of Hopei during the Song and Yuan periods. The glaze is of a warm ivory tone turning to a greenish or honey-brown colour where it has pooled.

Doucai Literally translated as 'clashing or contrasting colours'. The decoration utilised outlines executed in underglaze blue with details picked out in translucent overglaze enamels. Perhaps the most celebrated examples of this colour scheme are to be seen on the 'Chicken Cups' made during the reign of the Emperor Chenghua (1465-87).

'famille noire' A variant of 'famille verte' in which a black forms the ground colour.

'famille rose' A palette of overglaze enamels which appeared about 1720. The pink or rose colour from which the group gets its name is a derivation of gold and was originally discovered by Andreas Cassius of Leyden in about 1650. It was first used on German tin-glazed earthenware about 1680.

'famille verte' A palette utilised on porcelain from the 17th century onwards and was a development of Ming wucai, the dominant colour being a rich, if occasionally irregular, emerald green.

fuchi-beni An iron-red or brown oxide dressing usually applied to the rim of a bowl or dish, perhaps intended to prevent chipping.

flaming tortoise Like the stork (or crane) and the spotted deer, the tortoise is a familiar of the god of Longevity. The epithet 'flaming' in fact alludes to the accumulated growth of seaweed on the carapace of a turtle. To the Japanese a large accretion signifies great age and thus the symbolism.

fuku Happiness.

Ho ho The mythological phoenix, symbolic of the empress.

Ixing A red or brown coloured stoneware made in the southern province of Kiangsi from late Ming onwards and emulated by Dutch (Ary de Milde), German (Böttger) and English (Elers) potters from the 17th century.

Junyao A stoneware manufactured in northern China from the Song through to the Ming dynasty. It is generally heavily constructed and covered in a thick bluish glaze varying from pale lavender to a deep blue colour and sometimes has areas of purple achieved by the addition of copper to the glaze.

Kakiemon Perhaps the most celebrated Japanese porcelains named after the family of potters, the first of whom Sakaida Kakiemon allegedly introduced overglaze enamelling into Japan. The fully developed style of the last quarter of the 17th century is typified by the restrained and assymetrical decoration which leaves much of the surface bare emphasising the pure white ground.

kalasa A bottle which contains heavenly dew or ambrosia, the food of the immortals most commonly seen held by Guanyin, the goddess of Mercy.

karakusa A scrolling or undulating vine motif introduced from T'ang China.

kikumon A chrysanthemum flowerhead.

Kraak porselein Blue and white exportware porcelain of the late Ming period. The term 'kraak' or carrack is a type of Portuguese ship. A carrack, the Santa Catarina, was captured by the Dutch in 1603/4. The cargo included about 100,000 pieces of blue and white porcelain which caused a sensation in Amsterdam where it was subsequently sold for astronomical sums. The interest in this and similar captured vessels started the Dutch porcelain trade to western Europe.

linglong Fine and intricate openwork in the form of a geometric repeating pattern or trellis. Literally translates as 'Devil's work'.

lingzhih The sacred fungus (polyporus lucidus) symbolic of longevity.

mukozuke Usually a small bowl or dish used to serve the side dish which accompanies soup or rice in the Tea Ceremony meal. It sometimes takes the form of a natural object such as a fish or bird.

rollwagon A cylindrical vase surmounted by a constricted neck (see appendix).

ruyi A heart-shaped motif based upon the head of ruyi sceptre, a ceremonial object of Buddhist significance.

shishi A Buddhist guardian lion resembling a Pekinese dog.

shochikubai The Three Friends of Winter, pine, prunus and bamboo which not only represent different aspects of the character of an honourable individual but also symbolise the three great religions of the Far East, namely Buddhism, Confucianism and Daoism.

wucai Literally 'five colours', a palette of overglaze enamels which may include iron-red, green, yellow, black and aubergine generally used in conjunction with underglaze blue. The decoration is perhaps more boldly painted than the later more sophisticated 'famille verte' group.

Yingqing A porcelain manufactured during the Song and Yuan periods in Kiangsi and other areas of central and southern China. It is either moulded or carved under a pale greenish or bluish glaze.

Yueyao A grey bodied stoneware covered in a yellowish green or grey glaze produced in Jejian and other regions of China from about the 3rd century B.C. until the Song dynasty.

Opinions in the United Kingdom may vary as to whether or not the recession has bottomed out, but the fine furniture market is not waiting to find out. Prices of goods in the top and medium quality ranges are beginning to escalate; the former appreciably, the latter consistently, and when furniture in distressed condition finds a ready market, it can be taken as a signal that prices are poised for a dramatic rise.

This last happened during the 70's, when inflation-induced hysteria was said to be responsible, but inflation now is considerably lower than it was then, so why is the market showing such a distinct upturn?

The answer lies in international monetary markets, and it is surprising that leading analysts have not thought to follow the course of selected items of furniture in their reports, since these provide just as valid a barometer as coverage of movements in the City.

In real terms, of course, developments in world-wide transportation have also greatly facilitated the ease of international movement. So when the exchange rate favours the dollar, or socialist policies in France result in a marked momentum in the rate of inflation there, American and French buyers, for example, look on the English market as a favourable source of stock.

What saves the collector who has no intention of getting involved in considerations of international finance is the cyclical response of the antiques trade to external factors, which means that there are always troughs between the peaks.

During the recent trough, the market turned its attention to decorative items in the lower price brackets, and this theme is now being carried over into furniture.

A valid illustration concerns the way in which new areas of interest are constantly being opened up to combat price rises in established ones; the Edwardian revival of the Sheraton style being a case in point. With the return of improved purchasing power, however, interest in the revival has only served to stimulate renewed emphasis on the original with its delicacy of line and attractive use of exotic timbers such as satinwood, rosewood or kingwood.

Another reversal of an established trend is the interest the market in England has been taking in foreign furniture, not only French with which there has always been a reciprocal rapport, but Italian, German, Portuguese, Flemish (usually an incorrect term for a certain Northern European style) and the American and Oriental, which buyers from those areas would like to take back with them.

Is there any hope left then in the antique furniture market for serious collectors who may be unable to pay the price of a family car for a Sheraton rosewood sofa table crossbanded in satinwood, which is an item of almost universal appeal?

Yes, if they are prepared to risk taking the form out of the formbook and appreciate a 7 ft. sweep of the most beautiful mahogany imprisoned in a Victorian mahogany breakfront pedestal sideboard at £200-300. Incorporated in a severe décor, the overwhelming nature of its character would be reduced and it is impossible to duplicate that quality nowadays.

Alternatively, they should keep their eyes open for undiscovered treasures in garages, barns and attics, for appalling tales of neglect are still prevalent despite the attention antiques have been receiving from the media in recent years.

As the pundits have always advised, lifelong appeal must be the guiding principle that governs any purchase.

Buying for investment is as tricky as playing the Stock Market, but comparisons have shown that the peaks and troughs in the market usually level out so that antiques not only keep pace with inflation taken over a lifetime, but they also have the added advantage of providing continuous service as well.

A James I oak tester bed with leaf-carved, lunette and tongue-carved moulded cornice, the later tester panelled and decorated, the headboard with a pair of geometric marquetry arched and carved panels, restored, 6 ft. 10 in. high by 4 ft. 9½ in. wide by 6 ft. 10 in. long (208 by 146 by 208 cm.). **£3,600-£4,000** *S*

An interesting antique full tester bedstead with sunken arcaded panelled headboard, height 6 ft. 4 in. (193 cm.) by 4 ft. 10 in. (147 cm.) by 6 ft. 10 in. (208 cm.) overall, together with the woven wire spring, spring interior mattress and brown plush bedspread with metal thread floral design, possibly early 17th C. **£2,500-3,000** *JS*

A Jacobean-style 4-poster bed in bog oak with holly inlay, 85 in. high, c. 1930's. **£1,500-1,700** *CDE*

An English antique full tester oak bed, 4 ft. 6 in. wide. **£1,500-2,000** *PWC*

A fine George III painted 4-poster bed, the tester with a dome and each of the 3 sides moulded and arched and with a carved lambrequin edge surmounted by a swagged urn, on a simulated satinwood ground, approximately 9 ft. 4 in. high by 7 ft. 3 in. long by 7 ft. wide (284 by 221 by 213 cm.), with box spring and spring mattress, c. 1780. **£4,000-6,000** *S*

A very similar cornice design is illustrated in Hepplewhite's 'Cabinet Maker and Upholsterer's Guide' as recorded by J. Munro Bell, p. 249.

The Arms might be those of Morgan Vale of Bilby Hall, Nottinghamshire and his third wife, Catherine, daughter of John Brookes, whom he married on 9th May, 1780.

A George III-style mahogany framed 4-poster bed, the reeded baluster end posts carved with wheat ears and drapery, 82 in. high by 42 in. wide by 82 in. long. **£650-£700** *Bea*

A George III mahogany tester bed, with reeded and leaf-carved foot posts, cornice damaged, 6 ft. 6 in. long by 5 ft. 10 in. wide (198 by 178 cm.), c. 1775. **£3,000-3,500** *S*

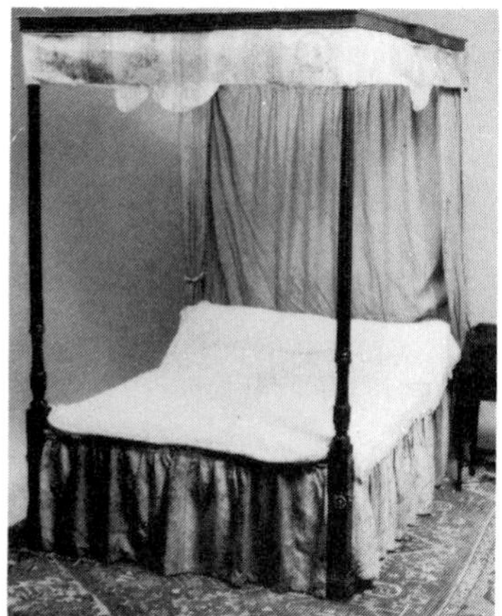

A Sheraton design mahogany 4-poster bed, double size, slender reeded pillar, canopy, fitted mattress. **£700-800** *LE*

A Regency green-painted 4-poster bed, 65 in. (155 cm.) wide. **£5,250-£6,000** *C*

A mid-Victorian carved mahogany 4-poster bed, 95 in. high. **£600-£700** *DSH*

A George III cream-painted 4-poster bed, 85½ in. (217 cm.) wide. **£8,000-9,000** *C*

A George III mahogany 4-poster bed of Hepplewhite design, with box spring and hair overlay mattress, 7 ft. 8 in. high by 4 ft. 6 in. wide (234 by 137 cm.), c. 1780. **£1,800-2,200** *SS*

A painted satinwood half-tester bed, with side rails and mattress, probably Austrian, 6 ft. 7½ in. high by 6 ft. 6 in. long by 4 ft. 6 in. wide (204 by 200 by 137 cm.), c. 1850. **£1,100-1,500** *S*

A 19th C. carved giltwood and canework double bedstead of French style, having deep box spring and flock mattress to fit, on squat scroll legs, 4 ft. 9 in. wide. **£350-400** *BHW*

A carved giltwood bed in Louis XV style, 162 cm. wide, early 20th C. **£1,000-1,200** *S*

An Empire burr-elm lit bateau, the sides inlaid with stylised floral cornucopia, 4 ft. high by 6 ft. 7½ in. long by 4 ft. 11 in. wide (102 by 201 by 150 cm.), c. 1815. **£4,500-5,000** *C*

An early 19th C. fruitwood cradle, 36 in. long. **£170-210** *FF*

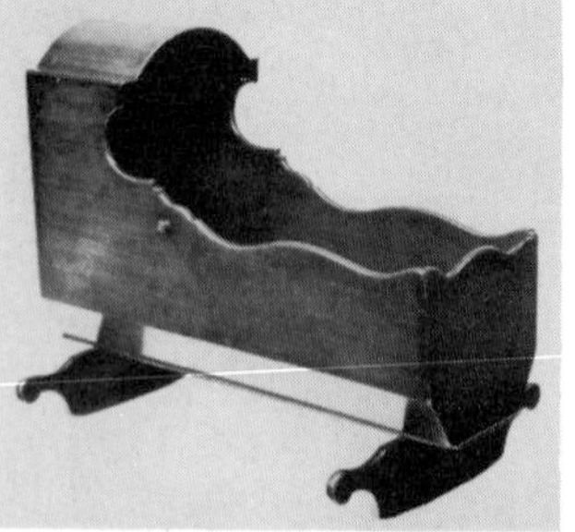

An early Georgian period red walnut child's cot, on scroll end rockers. **£750-850** *WW*

An early 19th C. oak framed cradle. **£250-300** *JMW*

A 17th C.-style panelled oak cradle, the body carved with lozenges and flowerheads, 30 in. high by 38 in. long. **£225-275** *S*

POINTS TO NOTE ON 'FAKES'

- **can't satisfactorily fake patination — but watch heavily applied wax polishes**
- **can't get modern brass to look like 18th C. brass — 18th C. brass had a higher copper content, which gives it a softer feel and a more subtle colour**
- **can't get realistic looking patches of discolouration round heads of nails and screws**
- **can't authentically fake herring-bone inlay — usually on fakes it is completely flat, which is an obvious giveaway, as after a period of time with changes in temperature and humidity the inlay lifts in places. This effect is extremely difficult for a restorer to perfect**

A child's Edwardian mahogany cot. **£200-250** *CoH*

A fine George III satinwood bonheur du jour, the shaped top centred by a Wedgwood plaque, inlaid at the front with boxwood shells on a green ground, the drawer with a leather-lined writing slide, ink and pen compartments, 3 ft. 11 in. high by 2 ft. 2 in. wide (119 by 66 cm.), c. 1795. **£4,000-£5,000** *S*

A George III satinwood bonheur du jour, inlaid with olivewood ovals, tambour cupboard doors inlaid with alternating amaranth stripes, 34 in. (86.5 cm.) wide. **£6,000-£7,000** *C*

A mahogany bonheur du jour, with tambour front, the hinged foldover top supported by 2 lopers, Dutch, restored, 42½ by 35 in. (108 by 89 cm.), early 19th C. **£350-450** *SC*

A Georgian mahogany bonheur du jour with shaped superstructure of shelf, writing flap with 2 lopers and frieze drawer below, most angles with boxwood lines, 26¾ in. **£1,000-£1,200** *GSP*

A satinwood bonheur du jour, fitted with cedar-lined drawers, the bowed base inlaid with lozenge-and-dot lines with a drawer with leather-lined slide mounted with Wedgwood-pattern medallions, 26 in. (66 cm.) wide. **£3,000-4,000** *C*

An early 19th C. rosewood bonheur du jour, with rosewood shelves and brass columns, the base with hinged writing flap above a frieze drawer and a concealed slide, on turned reeded legs, 3 ft. 11 in. high by 2 ft. 1¾ in. wide (190 by 65.5 cm.), c. 1810. **£600-700** *S*

A serpentine rosewood bonheur du jour, the projecting lower part with baize-lined slide and carved frieze drawer, 4 ft. 8 in. high by 3 ft. 11½ in. wide (143 by 121 cm.), c. 1850. **£550-650** *S*

A pair of painted satinwood side bonheur du jour on square tapering legs, painted with chains of flowers and with a pair of putti holding ribboned swags, 3 ft. 3½ in. high by 2 ft. 2½ in. wide (100 by 67 cm.), c. 1880. **£3,500-4,000** *S*

Make the most of Miller's

Every care has been taken to ensure the accuracy of descriptions and estimated valuations.
Where an attribution is made within inverted commas (e.g. 'Chippendale') or is followed by the word 'style' (e.g. early Georgian style) it is intended to convey that, in the opinion of the publishers, the piece concerned is a later – though probably still antique – reproduction of the style so designated.
Unless otherwise stated, any description which refers to 'a set' or 'a pair' includes a valuation for the entire set or the pair, even though the illustration may show only a single item.

A walnut and marquetry bonheur du jour in the French style, 4 ft. 1 in. high by 3 ft. 5 in. wide (125 by 104 cm.), mid 19th C. **£1,300-£1,500** *S*

A good quality Edwardian walnut veneer and rosewood crossbanded bonheur du jour, the whole strung with ebony and boxwood and having reed and ribbon loop handles and mahogany carcase, 3 ft. 6 in. wide. **£900-1,200** *AGr*

A Regency rosewood bonheur du jour in the manner of George Bullock, 37 in. (94 cm.) wide. **£3,000-4,000** *C*

A French-style ebonised and thuyawood ormolu decorated bonheur du jour, English, porcelain plaques probably Staffordshire, 4 ft. 8 in. high by 4 ft. wide (142 by 122 cm.), c. 1860. **£1,400-1,600** *SS*

A Louis XVI-style ebonised and amboyna-veneered bonheur du jour applied with Sèvres-style porcelain plaques and gilt brass mounts, 59 in. high by 53 in. wide, late 19th C. **£500-600** *Bea*

A mahogany library bookcase, the centre section with glazed doors enclosing adjustable shelves, the lower part with a fall-front, fitted interior above, 83½ by 93 in. (212 by 236 cm.), the pediment, glazed part and the 2 cupboards 20th C., the bureau late 18th C. **£600-800** *SC*

A Georgian mahogany breakfront bookcase, 108 in. wide by 96 in. high. **£4,500-5,000** *JF*

A pair of George III mahogany bookcases, 103 in. high. **£1,600-£1,800** *McCMB*

A fine George III mahogany breakfront library bookcase with pierced carved broken pediment, Gothic pattern glazed doors, enclosing a green velvet-lined interior, the base with 2 pairs of panelled doors applied, possibly at a later date, with interlaced foliate C scrolls, 98 in. wide by 107 in. high (248 by 271 cm.). **£11,000-£12,000** *C*

A 19th C. oak bookcase, reconstructed using earlier panels and carvings, 8 ft. 1 in. wide, 7 ft. 9 in. high. **£650-800** *WHL*

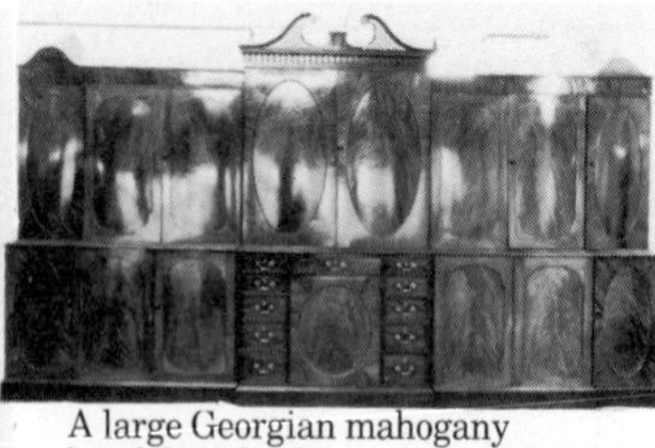

A large Georgian mahogany breakfront bookcase, in 3 sections, 15 ft. long, 94 in. high. **£3,000-£4,000** *DA*

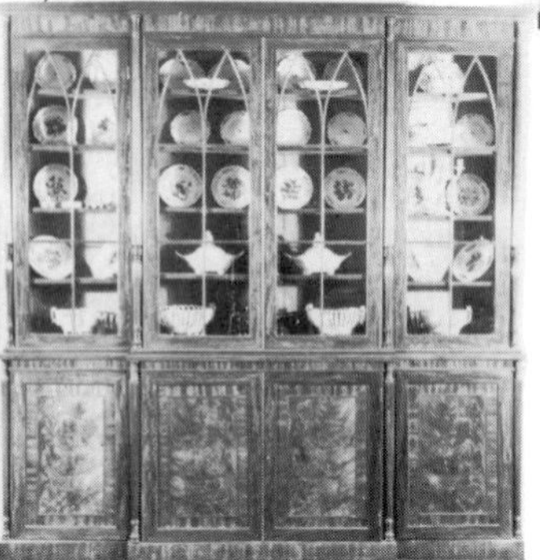

A Regency mahogany breakfront library bookcase with reeded cornice and turned and reeded columns at the corners and angles, 94 by 96 in. high. **£11,000-13,000** *DWB*

A George III mahogany breakfront library bookcase in the manner of Gillows, with hinged easel, 109 in. wide by 105½ in. high by 23 in. deep (277 by 268 by 59 cm.). **£5,500-6,000** *C*

BOOKCASES

- **the small bookcase really became fashionable with the demand for finer, smaller furniture during the Regency period**
- **these pieces tend to be in great demand and hence expensive mainly because of their small size and craftsmanship**
- **many are simple to reproduce and a large number of much later copies are around**
- **some look very similar to side cabinets and were often made to match**
- **dwarf bookcases no matter how modern are always in great demand and period examples tend to be expensive**

A George III period breakfront bookcase in mahogany, 120 in. wide by 16 in. deep by 90 in. high, c. 1800. **£3,750-4,400** *HAL*

A George III-style mahogany breakfront library bookcase on bracket feet, 92 in. high by 112 in. wide. **£1,200-1,400** *Bea*

A George III mahogany breakfront bookcase in 2 sections, under section enclosed by 4 panelled doors, with satinwood and rosewood bandings and diamond-shaped centres, 6 ft. 6 in. **£4,200-£4,800** *WSW*

A Regency mahogany library bookcase, lower part with 3 pairs of panelled cupboard doors enclosing shelves, 144 in. wide by 103 in. high (366 by 262 cm.). **£8,000-£10,000** *C*

A large Victorian mahogany bookcase. **£500-550** *CoH*

An Edwardian mahogany and inlaid library bookcase, 3 astragal glazed doors, inlaid interior shelves and breakfront base, 72 in. wide by 86 in. high. **£1,250-1,500** *DSH*

A Victorian breakfront bookcase, ebonised with gilt mounts and brass inlay, on plinth base, 72 in. wide. **£160-220** *DS*

A George III Adam painted satinwood breakfront bookcase cabinet decorated in the style of Kauffman, 59 in. wide by 100 in. high. **£2,700-3,000** *B*

A mid-Victorian figured walnut breakfront bookcase with moulded cornice and raised arch to the centre, 11 ft. 6 in. wide by 9 ft. 4 in. high. **£3,250-3,750** *M*

A large Victorian bookcase. **£450-£500** *CoH*

A pair of late George III mahogany library bookcases, 9 ft. high by 5 ft. 10 in. wide (274 by 178 cm.), early 19th C. **£1,500-2,000** *SC*

A South German walnut bureau cabinet, the base with sloping flap enclosing a fitted interior, on later block feet, 52½ in. wide by 80 in. high (133 by 203 cm.), mid 18th C. **£1,800-2,000** *C*

A mahogany breakfront bookcase with a plain moulded cornice and adjustable shelves, the lower part with 4 doors enclosing shelves and drawers, on plinth base, 102½ by 98½ in., (261 by 250 cm.), mid 19th C. **£1,800-2,200** *L*

A Victorian oak library bookcase on a plinth base, 90 in. high by 74 in. wide. **£350-400** *Bea*

BREAKFRONT BOOKCASES

- **originally bookshelves in libraries were fixtures**
- **freestanding bookcases were developed in the 17th C. and perfected in the 18th C.**
- **bookcases were made for the rich and have always been collectable**
- **again the smaller a bookcase is the more desirable it is; one should also always check height as many bookcases were made for higher ceilings than present room heights allow**
- **it is vital to remember the 18th C. love of proportion — if the groove for the first shelf is six inches from the bottom, the groove for the top shelf will be six inches from the top**
- **many breakfront bookcases started life as breakfront wardrobes**
- **tell-tale signs can be seen where about 8-10 inches have been cut off the depth**

A Queen Anne walnut bureau bookcase, 32 in. wide. **£19,000-£21,000** *HB*

A late George III mahogany bureau cabinet, the cylinder enclosing a sliding writing surface and fitted interior, 8 ft. 4 in. high by 4 ft. 3½ in. wide (261 by 131 cm.), early 19th C. **£2,500-3,000** *S*

A fine Queen Anne walnut and burr-walnut bureau cabinet, 39½ in. wide by 88 in. high by 22½ in. deep (100.5 by 223.5 by 57 cm.). **£22,000-24,000** *C*

Queen Anne bureau bookcase in finely figured walnut veneers, with fitted interior, the herringbone crossbanded fall including a bookrest concealing an interior with pigeonholes, shaped drawers and a well, brasswork, glass and feet early replacements, 38½ in. wide by 22½ in. deep by 81½ in. high, c. 1710. **£13,000-18,000** *HAL*

A Queen Anne walnut bureau cabinet, the upper part probably reduced, with 2 bevelled mirror-glazed cupboard doors enclosing shelves with 2 slides below, 41½ in. wide by 92 in. high by 23½ in. deep (105 by 234 by 60 cm.). **£5,000-£6,000** *C*

A Queen Anne walnut bureau cabinet, the sloping flap enclosing a fitted interior, 44 in. wide by 87 in. high by 23 in. deep (112 by 221 by 58 cm.). **£15,000-16,000** *C*

A Queen Anne walnut bureau cabinet with moulded double-domed cornice and 2 later-glazed cupboard doors enclosing a well-fitted interior, on later turned feet, 41 in. wide by 82 in. high by 23 in. deep (104 by 208 by 59 cm.). **£6,000-£8,000** *C*

A walnut bureau cabinet in Queen Anne style, with a mirrored door enclosing shelves above a candle stand and a fitted interior, 6 ft. 2 in. by 1 ft. 11½ in. by 1 ft. 4 in. (188 by 59 by 40.5 cm.), early 20th C., partly using early veneers. **£900-1,200** *S*

Mahogany bureau bookcases should have:—

- **good colour and patination**
- **domed or broken pediments**
- **good mouldings**
- **a good 'fitted' interior**
- **original feet and brasses**

A fine Queen Anne walnut bureau cabinet, the upper part with moulded double-domed cornice with later urn finials, with a well-fitted interior with pigeonholes, racks and 9 various sized drawers, on later turned feet, 42 in. wide by 92 in. high by 23¾ in. deep (107 by 234 by 60.5 cm.). **£33,000-35,000** *C*

A Queen Anne walnut bureau bookcase, the top with a later-fitted interior, 37½ in. wide (95 cm.). **£9,000-£10,000** *C*

A Queen Anne walnut bureau and associated bookcase, decorated with featherbanding, 6 ft. 8 in. high by 3 ft. wide (203 by 91.5 cm.), bureau c. 1710, bookcase made up from antique timber and veneers. **£2,500-3,000** *SS*

A George I walnut bureau cabinet, the cupboard doors enclosing shelves, pigeonholes and drawers, the base with well-figured crossbanded sloping flap outlined with herringbone bands enclosing a fitted interior, 41¼ in. wide by 83 in. high (105 by 211 cm.). **£6,000-8,000** *C*

A Queen Anne walnut bureau bookcase, with mirror doors enclosing shaped shelves and 3 small drawers, the fall revealing a stepped and fitted interior with inset, on later shaped bracket feet, restored, 7 ft. 10½ in. high by 3 ft. 3 in. wide (245 by 99 cm.), c. 1710. **£7,000-8,000** *SS*

An important George I walnut bureau cabinet by John Belchier, bearing the trade label of 'John Belchier at the Sun in St. Pauls Church Yard', 33 in. wide by 80 in. high (84 by 203 cm.). **£30,000-33,000** *C*

A fine walnut bureau cabinet, with a well fitted interior enclosing pigeonholes and 29 various-sized drawers surrounding a central cartouche-panelled door with architectural frame, 52 in. wide by 99 in. high by 23½ in. deep (132 by 251.5 by 60 cm.), early 18th C. **£10,000-12,000** *C*

The complex outline of the lower part points to a Germanic origin.

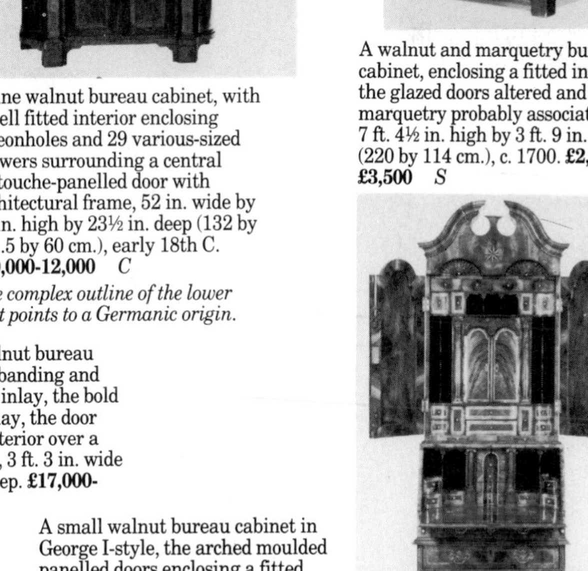

A walnut and marquetry bureau cabinet, enclosing a fitted interior, the glazed doors altered and marquetry probably associated, 7 ft. 4½ in. high by 3 ft. 9 in. wide (220 by 114 cm.), c. 1700. **£2,750-£3,500** *S*

A fine George II walnut bureau bookcase with crossbanding and double herringbone inlay, the bold cornice with star inlay, the door enclosing a fitted interior over a pair of candle slides, 3 ft. 3 in. wide by 8 ft. high, 2 ft. deep. **£17,000-£19,000** *MMB*

A small walnut bureau cabinet in George I-style, the arched moulded panelled doors enclosing a fitted interior, the base with fall front, featherbanded and enclosing a shaped fitted interior, 7 ft. high by 2 ft. 5 in. wide (240 by 74 cm.), early 20th C. **£2,700-3,000** *S*

An 18th C. Italian carved walnut and crossbanded bureau cabinet inlaid with lines, candle slides, flanked by Ionic pilasters, the lower part having a sloping fall with a foliate cartouche enclosing 6 short drawers, secret drawers and compartments, probably Veronese, 1.50 m. **£7,000-8,000** *P*

An early Georgian walnut bureau cabinet, with a sloping flap enclosing a fitted interior, 45½ in. (116 cm.) wide. **£4,200-£4,600** *C*

A good Italian figured walnut bureau cabinet, the lower part with a shaped crossbanded flap, enclosing drawers and pigeonholes, with interior restoration, 9 ft. 1 in. high by 4 ft. 1 in. wide (307 by 125 cm.), mid 18th C. **£13,500-£15,000** *S*

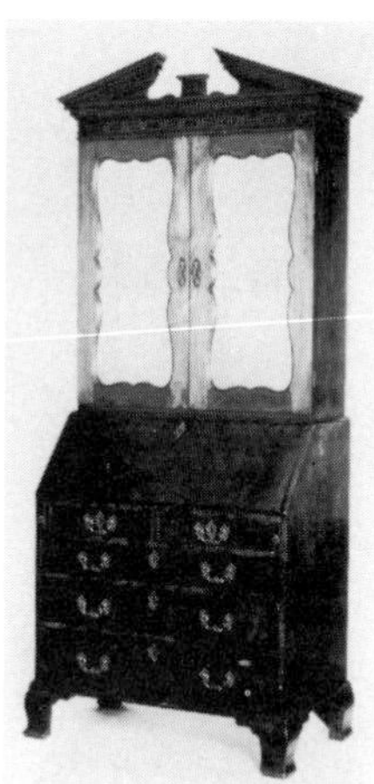

A George II mahogany bureau cabinet, the base with sloping flap enclosing a fitted interior, 38½ in. wide by 88 in. high (98 by 223.5 cm.). **£3,750-£4,500** *C*

An 18th C. South German walnut, crossbanded and parquetry bureau cabinet, with a later moulded arched cornice, enclosed by a pair of arched later glazed panel doors, on later slender cabriole legs, 1.13 m. **£2,700-3,000** *P*

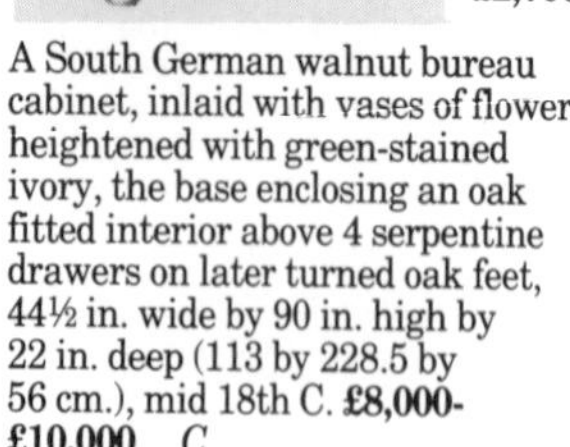

A South German walnut bureau cabinet, inlaid with vases of flowers heightened with green-stained ivory, the base enclosing an oak fitted interior above 4 serpentine drawers on later turned oak feet, 44½ in. wide by 90 in. high by 22 in. deep (113 by 228.5 by 56 cm.), mid 18th C. **£8,000-£10,000** *C*

A George II walnut and burr-walnut bureau cabinet, the base with sloping flap enclosing a fitted interior with pigeonholes, cedar-lined drawers and a well, on later ogee bracket feet, 43½ in. wide by 97½ in. high (110.5 by 248 cm.). **£6,000-7,000** *C*

A Dutch walnut bureau cabinet, with a fitted interior, 8 ft. 4½ in. high by 4 ft. 7 in. wide (256 by 140 cm.), mid 18th C. **£2,500- £3,000** *S*

A scarlet lacquer bureau cabinet, the base with sloping flap decorated in raised gilt with chinoiserie figures and buildings, with fitted interior including a well, 30 in. wide by 79½ in. high (76 by 202 cm.). **£7,000-8,000** *C*

A Venetian cream lacquered small bureau cabinet, the doors decorated with chinoiserie landscapes enclosing a green lacquered interior, the bombe base with sloping flap enclosing a fitted interior, 22½ in. (57 cm.) wide, 18th C. **£1,200-1,500** *C*

Factors that may indicate a piece as a 'marriage':—

a) Colour and quality of timber not matching
b) Different style of construction to top and bottom
c) Signs that the top has been altered in size or does not fit properly
d) Old screw holes where the top has been secured to the base not corresponding

A George III crossbanded mahogany-veneered fall front bureau bookcase, astragal glazed doors, the bureau fitted with drawers and pigeonholes. **£900-£1,200** *AGr*

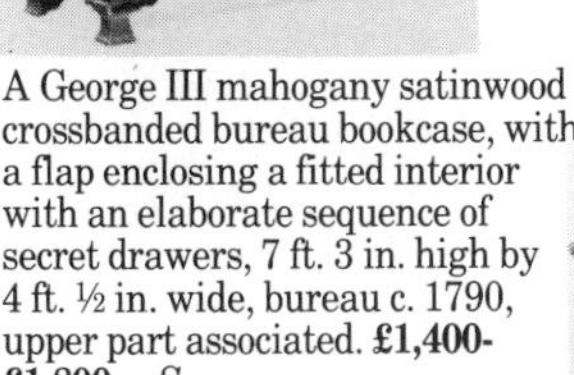
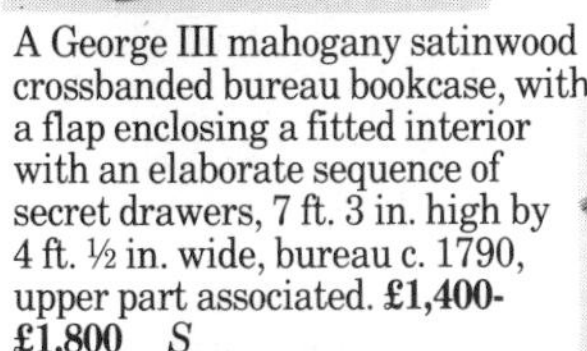

A George III mahogany satinwood crossbanded bureau bookcase, with a flap enclosing a fitted interior with an elaborate sequence of secret drawers, 7 ft. 3 in. high by 4 ft. ½ in. wide, bureau c. 1790, upper part associated. **£1,400-£1,800** *S*

A Dutch mahogany and marquetry bureau bookcase, the doors now glazed, above a pair of candle slides, the sloping front enclosing a fitted interior including a well, marquetry possibly later, 7 ft. high by 2 ft. 9½ in. wide (214 by 85 cm.), c. 1760. **£4,000-5,000** *S*

A fine mid-Georgian mahogany bureau cabinet with dentilled broken triangular pediment, the base with sloping flap enclosing a well-fitted interior with serpentine drawers framing a chamfered cupboard, 48 in. wide by 100 in. high (122 by 254 cm.). **£4,500-£5,500** *C*

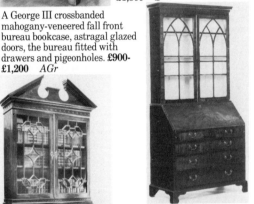

A George III mahogany bureau bookcase, the sloping front enclosing a fitted interior, 7 ft. 5 in. high by 3 ft. 8 in. wide (226 by 112 cm.), c. 1770. **£1,500-1,700** *S*

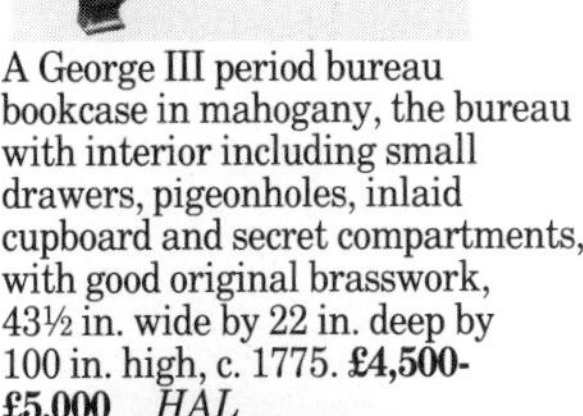

A George III period bureau bookcase in mahogany, the bureau with interior including small drawers, pigeonholes, inlaid cupboard and secret compartments, with good original brasswork, 43½ in. wide by 22 in. deep by 100 in. high, c. 1775. **£4,500-£5,000** *HAL*

A Georgian mahogany bureau bookcase, 41 in. **£1,050-1,250** *PWC*

A George III mahogany bureau bookcase, with a flap enclosing a fitted interior, 7 ft. 5 in. high by 3 ft. 3 in. wide (226 by 99 cm.), c. 1775. **£2,100-2,300** *S*

A 19th C. mahogany bureau bookcase, crossbanded and inlaid with satinwood, the fall front inlaid with an oval panel of an Adam urn, with fully fitted interior, 39 in. wide. **£800-1,000** *M*

An Edwardian bureau bookcase. **£1,800-2,000** *McCMB*

A late Georgian mahogany bureau bookcase, the bureau with a shaped fitted interior, fitted with ornate brass handles and escutcheons and on ogee bracket feet, 44 in. by 89 in. high (112 by 226 cm.). **£1,600-£1,800** *L*

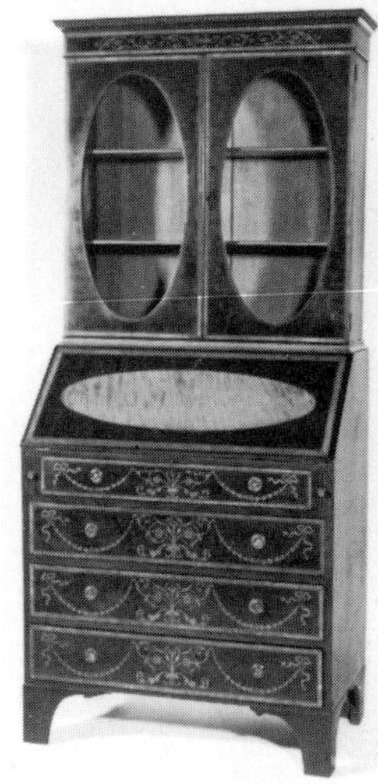

A small Edwardian inlaid mahogany bureau bookcase, the drawers and pediment with marquetry inlaid scrolls and garlands, 30 in. wide by 68 in. high. **£1,100-1,300** *SWO*

An inlaid Edwardian bureau bookcase crossbanded with satinwood, with astragal glazed doors. **£400-450** *HFM*

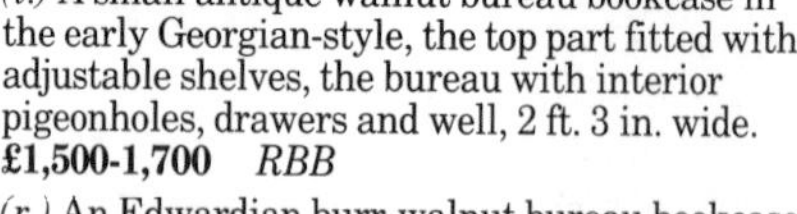

(l.) A small antique walnut bureau bookcase in the early Georgian-style, the top part fitted with adjustable shelves, the bureau with interior pigeonholes, drawers and well, 2 ft. 3 in. wide. **£1,500-1,700** *RBB*

(r.) An Edwardian burr-walnut bureau bookcase with fitted interior pigeonholes and drawers, adjustable shelves above, 2 ft. 3 in. wide. **£750-£1,000** *RBB*

An Edwardian Sheraton-style bureau bookcase. **£400-500** *JMW*

A mahogany bureau bookcase in George III-style, 6 ft. 8 in. high by 3 ft. 1 in. wide (203 by 94.5 cm.), c. 1930. **£600-800** *S*

No two editions alike!

Miller's is compiled from scratch each year. All new photographs and fresh information!

If you are unable to find the items you seek in this volume, they may have been included in earlier editions. These have now been reprinted to satisfy demand; details at the back of this book.

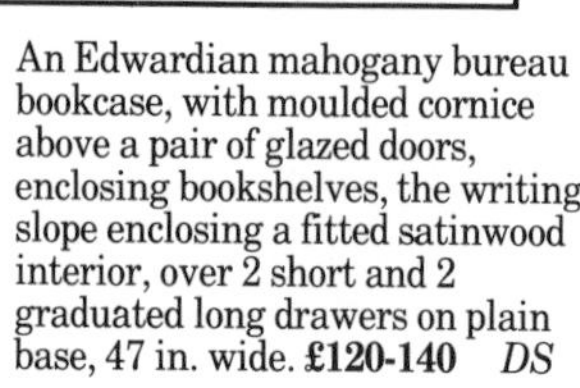

An Edwardian mahogany bureau bookcase, with moulded cornice above a pair of glazed doors, enclosing bookshelves, the writing slope enclosing a fitted satinwood interior, over 2 short and 2 graduated long drawers on plain base, 47 in. wide. **£120-140** *DS*

A William and Mary walnut bureau cabinet, the arched mirrored doors enclosing a later fitted interior and with a pair of candle slides, the flap enclosing a fitted interior above a well, on bun feet, mirror plates and feet replaced, 6 ft. 7½ in. high by 3 ft. 2½ in. wide (202.5 by 98.5 cm.), c. 1700. **£3,000-4,000** *S*

A George I walnut bureau cabinet, with bevelled mirror-glazed doors enclosing shelves and smaller drawers with 2 candle slides below, 7 ft. high by 3 ft. 6 in. wide (213 by 107 cm.), c. 1725. **£7,500-8,500** *S*

A North Italian walnut bureau cabinet, re-veneered, 7 ft. 10 in. high by 3 ft. 7 in. wide (239 by 109 cm.), c. 1760. **£3,300-3,500** *S*

A mahogany bureau bookcase, crossbanded in rosewood, c. 1900. **£800-900** *Wor*

A mid-Georgian mahogany bureau cabinet, the lower part with a sloping flap enclosing well-fitted interior with 8 shaped drawers and 8 pigeonholes surrounding a central architectural mirror-glazed cupboard, the interior with a parquetry floor above 4 steps inlaid with alternating fruitwood and mahogany squares above a slide and 4 graduated long drawers on ogee bracket feet, 45 in. wide (114 cm.). **£7,000-8,000** *C*

A George III mahogany bureau cabinet with moulded dentilled cornice, the sloping flap enclosing a fitted interior, 48½ in. wide (123 cm.). **£2,400-2,700** *C*

A mahogany bookcase, 47 in. wide, c. 1770. **£3,700-4,200** *CC*

A George III mahogany bookcase, 89 in. high, c. 1760. **£3,000-3,500** *CC*

An unusually small Sheraton-style inlaid mahogany bureau bookcase, 26 in. wide. **£400-500** *Fr*

A George III satinwood secretaire cabinet, with a fitted secretaire drawer mounted with grisaille enamel boss handles decorated with rustic scenes, 37½ in. wide by 83 in. high (96 by 211 cm.). **£5,000-£6,000** *C*

BACKS

- **always check the back of a piece of furniture, particularly a double height piece**
- **marriages are usually very evident from the back — as are pieces with made up bottoms or tops**
- **the edges of period timbers at the back will be black**
- **look out for pieces of replaced timber**
- **look out for disproportion**
- **don't necessarily reject a piece of furniture because it is a marriage — if you are being asked a price which reflects this**

A George III mahogany secretaire cabinet, a secretaire drawer enclosing a satinwood-veneered interior, 7 ft. 1 in. high by 3 ft. 6 in. wide (218 by 107 cm.), c. 1790. **£1,500-1,700** *S*

A George III secretaire cabinet with scrolled broken pediment inlaid with lunettes, the base with a secretaire drawer fitted with drawers and pigeonholes, 68 in. wide (173 cm.). **£2,250-2,500** *C*

A Regency rosewood narrow bookcase, the base with an ormolu-panelled frieze drawer, 29 in. (74 cm.) wide. **£2,500-2,800** *C*

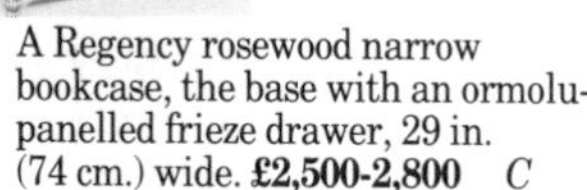

A George III mahogany and burr-yew secretaire cabinet, the base with a well-fitted secretaire drawer with pigeonholes, small drawers and a cupboard door inlaid with sycamore, 41½ in. wide by 100 in. high (105 by 254 cm.). **£5,000-£7,000** *C*

A rare George III Anglo-Indian ivory-inlaid hardwood cabinet, the whole elaborately inlaid with flowerheads and foliage, palm leaves and fruit trees, the upper part made up using decorative inlay cut from the rear of the top of the lower part, 5 ft. 10½ in. high by 4 ft. 3 in. wide (179 by 130 cm.), lower part c. 1770. **£17,000-£19,000** *S*

A 19th C. mahogany two-part bookcase, 44 in. **£500-600** *WHL*

A Georgian mahogany bookcase, 47 in. wide, c. 1810. **£700-800** *PH*

A 19th C. bookcase in figured mahogany, the base drawer with oak liners and brass swan neck handles, 44 in. **£250-300** *WHL*

A mahogany bookcase inlaid with urns, cornucopiae, anthemions and bellflower marquetry in harewood, satinwood bands and panels, 58 in., early 19th C. **£2,500-3,000** *CSK*

A 19th C. inlaid mahogany bookcase, 74 in. high. **£620-680** *HWO*

An Edwardian walnut bookcase, 45 in. wide. **£400-500** *Ph*

An 18th C. mahogany secretaire bookcase, profusely inlaid with urns, leaves and flowers, the secretaire is well fitted, standing on splay feet, 42 in. wide. **£2,000-£2,500** *LT*

A mahogany secretaire bookcase with fitted interior, 92 in. high by 42 in. wide, c. 1710. **£2,000-2,500** *NC*

A late Georgian mahogany secretaire bookcase, having fitted top drawer, decorated with ebony stringing, 3 ft. 8 in. wide, in poor condition. **£1,200-1,500** *WSW*

A Georgian mahogany secretaire bookcase, well fitted secretaire, 4 ft. 1 in. wide by 7 ft. 6 in. high. **£800-£1,000** *Fr*

An Edwardian 'Sheraton-style' inlaid mahogany bookcase, the drawers with inlaid shell pattern, 33 in. wide. **£900-1,000** *BW*

A late 18th C. mahogany secretaire bookcase with satinwood fitted interior, 45 in. wide. **£1,950-£2,100** *NC*

A George III mahogany secretaire cabinet, with false drawer fronts, enclosing a baize-lined slide with an easel and 4 hinged alphabetically-lettered flaps framing the recessed central kneehole cupboard, 45 in. wide by 89 in. high (114 by 227 cm.). **£4,000-4,500** *C*

A George III mahogany secretaire bookcase, 6 ft. 10 in. high, 3 ft. 3 in. wide (208 by 99 cm.), c. 1770. **£1,400-1,600** *SS*

A 'George III' mahogany secretaire bookcase, 2 astragal glazed doors with a fitted writing drawer, on ogee bracket feet, 42 in. **£750-850** *CSK*

A George III mahogany secretaire bookcase, the projecting lower part above a fitted secretaire drawer, 6 ft. 7½ in. high by 2 ft. 10¾ in. wide (202 by 87.5 cm.), c. 1790. **£2,750-3,250** *S*

A George III mahogany secretaire bookcase with kingwood crossbanding, 7 ft. 6 in. high by 3 ft. 10 in. wide (228 by 117 cm.), c. 1780, stringing and bandings later. **£1,500-£1,800** *S*

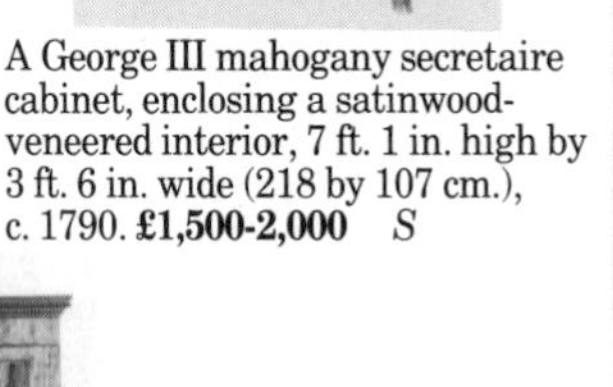

A George III mahogany secretaire cabinet, enclosing a satinwood-veneered interior, 7 ft. 1 in. high by 3 ft. 6 in. wide (218 by 107 cm.), c. 1790. **£1,500-2,000** *S*

A George III mahogany secretaire bookcase, the base with secretaire drawer above a pair of doors enclosing drawers, 9 ft. 2¾ in. high by 4 ft. 6 in. wide (281 by 137 cm.), c. 1780. **£1,200-1,600** *S*

A late George III mahogany secretaire bookcase, fitted with pigeonholes and short drawers, 91 in. high by 47 in. wide. **£1,000-£1,200** *Bea*

A George III mahogany secretaire bookcase, with stringing and set with satinwood panels, the base with a secretaire drawer veneered with 2 oval panels centred by a fan patera and enclosing an arrangement of drawers, 8 ft. 11½ in. high by 4 ft. 10 in. wide (273 by 149 cm.), c. 1790. **£1,700-£2,000** *S*

A George III mahogany secretaire bookcase, satinwood crossbanded, on bracket feet, 7 ft. 5½ in. high by 3 ft. 10½ in. wide (280 by 180 cm.), c. 1795. **£1,800-2,200** *S*

A late Georgian secretaire bookcase decorated with ebony stringings, 4 ft. wide. **£2,500-£3,000** *WSW*

An early Regency period secretaire bookcase, the shaped inlaid pediment mounted with brass finials, the secretaire with box-strung interior with pigeonholes concealed by a dummy pair of cockbeaded drawers, 42½ in. wide by 23 in. deep by 92 in. high, c. 1820. **£3,700-4,250** *HAL*

A good George III mahogany secretaire bookcase, the lower part with 2 long dummy drawers, opening to reveal a fitted interior with a baize writing surface and hinged book rest, flanked by pen and ink wells, with a sliding tray enclosing a well, flanked by alphabetically marked lidded compartments and secret drawers above a tambour filled kneehole cupboard, crossbanded throughout in satinwood, with later turned ebony pulls and turned feet, 92 by 52 in. (234 by 132 cm.), late 18th/early 19th C. **£1,800-2,400** *SC*

A George III mahogany secretaire bookcase, with hour-glass shaped glazing bars, the lower part with a fitted drawer with a 2 drawer dummy front, 89 by 45 in. (226 by 114 cm.), early 19th C. **£700-900** *SC*

A George IV mahogany secretaire bookcase, inlaid with stringing, the writing drawer with a baize inset, pigeonholes and rosewood veneered small drawers, on associated bun feet, 7 ft. 3 in. high by 3 ft. 7 in. wide (221 by 109 cm.), c. 1825. **£1,500-1,800** *SS*

A large Victorian mahogany secretaire bookcase, the secretaire drawer with a plain interior, 3 ft. 11 in. long by 7 ft. 6 in. high. **£400-£500** *DDM*

A George IV mahogany secretaire bookcase, on splayed bracket feet. **£700-800** *S*

A George IV mahogany secretaire bookcase, on bracket feet, 44½ in. **£550-650** *CSK*

A satinwood secretaire bookcase, inlaid with arrowhead parquetry, 6 ft. 4 in. by 2 ft. 3 in. (193 by 68 cm.), 1910-20. **£750-950** *S*

A mahogany secretaire bookcase with glazed doors, a deep secretaire drawer with fitted interior, above a pair of arched panel cupboard doors, 102 by 50 in. (259 by 127 cm.), mid 19th C. **£1,100-£1,300** *SC*

A George III mahogany dwarf bookcase, the adapted upper part with 2 narrow drawers framed by chequered lines, 18 in. wide (46 cm.). **£700-1,000** *C*

A Chippendale-style mahogany dwarf bookcase, on ogee bracket feet, 34½ in. **£1,250-1,400** *CSK*

A Regency mahogany dwarf bookcase, the raised stepped superstructure with 3 shelves 27 in. (68.5 cm.) wide. **£2,000-£2,200** *C*

A Regency period rosewood dwarf bookcase, 3 ft. 6 in. wide. **£250-£300** *AGr*

An early 18th C. Spanish chestnut open bookcase, restored, 30 in. wide. **£200-250** *HB*

Spanish chestnut strongly resembles oak and was used in construction work in Gothic and Renaissance times.

An Edwardian inlaid mahogany revolving bookcase, top 18 in. square. **£400-450** *IMC*

A mahogany bookshelf, 14 in. wide, c. 1820. **£500-550** *CC*

BUREAUX

Points to look for:—
- **Originality and condition**
- **Good colour and patination**
- **Good proportions**
- **Quality of construction**
- **Original handles and escutcheons**
- **Original feet**
- **Small size (3 ft. is about average)**
- **Stepped interior and a central cupboard**
- **Fitted 'well' with a slide**
- **Oak drawer linings**
- **Secret compartments**

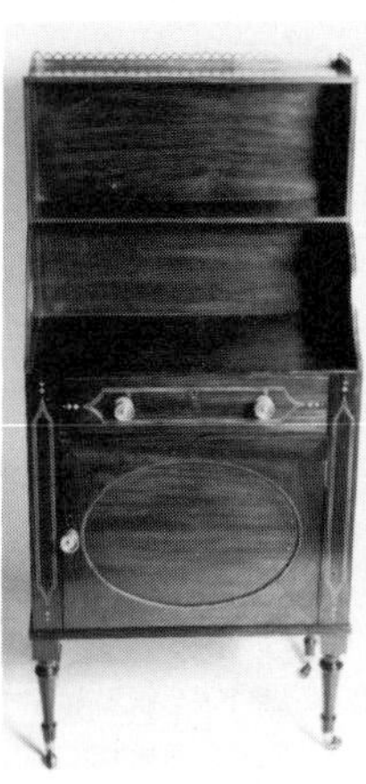

A mahogany open bookcase, 22 in., c. 1790. **£4,000-5,000** *HB*

A Queen Anne walnut bureau, box and ebony inlay. **£900-1,200** *CDC*

A William & Mary period bureau in figured walnut, with a herringbone crossbanded fall which incorporates a bookrest concealing a stepped interior with pigeonholes, drawers and a well above four herringbone crossbanded drawers and walnut feet, brass work and feet early but not original, 35¾ in. wide by 21 in. deep by 38 in. high, c. 1690. **£6,500-7,500** *HAL*

A Queen Anne-style walnut bureau, of small proportions, enclosing a fitted interior, 38 by 21 in. (97 by 54 cm.), 20th C. **£800-£1,000** *SC*

A fine Queen Anne walnut bureau, the sloping crossbanded flap inlaid with herringbone bands enclosing a fitted interior, the feet with restorations, 24 in. wide by 36½ in. high by 18 in. deep (61 by 93 by 46 cm.). **£6,000-7,000** *C*

A Queen Anne walnut bureau, enclosing a fitted interior with a well, 3 ft. 4 in. high by 3 ft. wide (101 by 91 cm.), c. 1710. **£3,100-£3,700** *S*

A Queen Anne walnut bureau inlaid with featherbanding, the fall revealing a stepped and fitted interior with well, on shaped bracket feet, restored, 3 ft. 3 in. high by 2 ft. 4¼ in. wide (99 by 72 cm.), c. 1710. **£1,500-1,800** *SS*

A George I walnut bureau on bracket feet, 3 ft. 5½ in. high by 3 ft. wide (105 by 91.5 cm.), c. 1720. **£2,500-3,000** *S*

A George I walnut bureau, the flap enclosing a fitted interior containing secret drawers, 3 ft. 3½ in. high by 3 ft. ¼ in. wide (100 by 92 cm.), c. 1725. **£3,000-3,500** *S*

An early 18th C. walnut bureau inlaid and banded with fall front, fitted pigeonholes, drawers and secret compartments, 36 in. wide. **£1,400-1,800** *HWO*

A George II oak bureau, country made, in poor condition, 3 ft. wide. **£500-600** *WSW*

A walnut-veneered bureau outlined with featherbanding, the crossbanded sloping flap enclosing drawers, pigeonholes and a well, 42 in. high by 39 in. wide. **£1,000-£1,200** *S*

A George I walnut-veneered bureau of low proportions with herringbone line inlay and crossbanded, the fall flap with engraved brass batswing escutcheon, the interior with central cupboard door, having brass hinges, escutcheon and a drawer inside, flanked by pilaster compartments, drawers and pigeonholes, 3 ft. 1 in. overall. **£3,600-4,000** *WW*

A Louis XV-style mahogany cylinder bureau with shaped top, the cylinder enclosing a fitted interior of pigeonholes and drawers, with pull-out writing slide, width 32 in. **£250-300** *DS*

A fine George II walnut bureau, crossbanded and inlaid with herringbone, the quartered fall flap opening to reveal a fitted interior with shaped drawers and secret compartments, over a sliding well, 3 ft. wide by 3 ft. 3 in. high by 1 ft. 8 in. deep. **£4,000-5,000** *MMB*

A George I oak bureau. **£1,200-£1,500** *DWB*

A George I walnut and herringbone banded bureau with stepped fittings and well enclosed by fall with four oyster curl panels, on bracket feet, 36 in. **£1,300-1,500** *DWB*

An early George II walnut bureau, crossbanded top inlaid with herringbone, with a fitted interior with a well, 3 ft. 5 in. high by 3 ft. 2 in. wide (104 by 96.5 cm.), c. 1725. **£2,000-2,400** *S*

A George II walnut bureau, brass handles, bracket feet. **£1,100-£1,300** *DWB*

A small George III period bureau in mahogany, the figured fall enclosing good interior above 4 drawers with replaced brasswork, 30 in. wide by 17½ in. deep by 40 in. high, c. 1780. **£1,400-1,800** *HAL*

BUREAUX

- **Bureaux were not made in this country until after the reign of Charles II**
- **this writing box on stand was initially produced in oak and then in walnut**
- **these were originally on turned or straight legs but cabriole legs became popular in the last decade of the 17th C.**
- **note the quality and proportion of the cabriole legs — good carving is another plus factor**
- **always more valuable if containing an *original* stepped interior and well**
- **also the more complex the interior — the more expensive**
- **from about 1680 most bureaux made from walnut, many with beautiful marquetry and inlay**
- **from about 1740 mahogany became the most favoured wood, although walnut was still used**
- **the 'key' size for a bureau is 3 ft. 2 in., as the width diminishes so the price increases dramatically**
- **original patination, colour and original brass handles are obviously important features for assessing any piece of furniture, but these are crucial when valuing bureaux and chests**

A mid 18th C. bureau in figured elmwood, the fall enclosing an interior with drawers, cupboard and pigeonholes, brasswork early but replaced, 34 in. wide by 18½ in. deep by 41½ in. high, c. 1750. **£3,450-4,000** *HAL*

An 18th C. mahogany slope front bureau, the front opening to reveal a well fitted interior with central cupboard and book type compartments, drawers and pigeonholes, with brass swing handles and escutcheons, 36 in. **£600-700** *WHL*

A mahogany bureau inlaid with a shell, foliage and chequered boxwood lines, 47 in., 19th C. **£800-£850** *CSK*

A walnut bureau with feather line inlay, the sloping flap with brass mounted outlines, with side carrying handles, 37 in., 18th C. **£1,000-1,200** *CSK*

A rare and unusual George III burr-walnut, tulipwood crossbanded and marquetry bureau, the top, sides and sloping fall decorated with ribband-tied laurel leaf garlands, enclosing a fitted interior with pigeonholes, drawer, central compartment and well with slide, on square tapered legs with paterae inlay, 82 cm. **£1,300-1,600** *P*

A late Georgian mahogany bureau of large size, the fall flap enclosing a fitted interior inlaid with chequered lines and oval floral panels, 48 in. **£650-700** *L*

A fine quality George III period bureau in mahogany, the figured surface above moulded fall enclosing interior with pigeonholes, drawers, secret drawers and fielded cupboard, brasswork early but replaced, 39¾ in. wide by 21½ in. deep by 42¾ in. high, c. 1800. **£1,300-1,750** *HAL*

A George III oak bureau, the fall front enclosing a fitted interior, restored, 42 by 36 in. (107 by 91 cm.), late 18th/early 19th C. **£500-600** *SC*

A George III mahogany slope front bureau, the interior fully fitted, 36½ in. **£500-600** *WHL*

A mahogany bureau with fitted interior and secret pillar drawers, 36 in. wide, c. 1780. **£1,400-1,600** *HB*

An 18th C. oak bureau, the fall flap enclosing a fitted interior with pigeonholes, drawers and a well, 2 ft. 11½ in. wide. **£500-600** *DDM*

A yew wood bureau, the fall front enclosing a fitted interior with a cupboard flanked by drawers and pigeonholes, reconstructed, 42 by 36 in. (107 by 92 cm.). **£500-600** *SC*

A mahogany slope front bureau with fitted interior, with brass handles and escutcheons. **£350-£400** *WHL*

A Georgian mahogany fall front bureau with 4 oak lined long drawers and secret drawer, standing on bracket feet, 3 ft. 2 in. wide. **£550-600** *DM*

A mid-Georgian mahogany bureau with a well-fitted serpentine interior with pigeonholes, 43 in. wide (104 cm.). **£1,200-1,500** *C*

A Dutch mahogany cylinder bureau, the leather-lined writing surface opening in conjunction with the cylinder flap, 3 ft. 8½ in. high by 3 ft. 7 in. wide (113 by 109 cm.), c. 1780. **£700-900** *S*

A Venetian walnut bureau enclosing drawers, 3 ft. 10 in. high by 4 ft. 2 in. wide (117 by 127 cm.), mid 18th C. **£4,500-5,500** *S*

An Anglo-Italian mahogany bureau decorated with floral marquetry, the rectangular fall flap enclosing a fitted interior, 35½ in. high. **£550-650** *AG*

An Indo-Dutch padouk bureau, the fitted interior enclosing a well above two short dummy drawers, on hairy paw feet, 4 ft. 4 in. wide (132 cm.), late 18th C. **£1,100-£1,200** *S*

An 18th C. Lombardy walnut, laburnum crossbanded and ivory marquetry bureau with ebonised mouldings, the whole decorated with engraved ivory, 1.07 m. **£4,200-4,600** *P*

A Dutch mahogany and marquetry cylinder bureau, the writing slide opening in conjunction with the cylinder, the whole later inlaid on a mahogany ground, 3 ft. 7 in. high by 3 ft. 7¼ in. wide (109 by 110 cm.), c. 1770, marquetry 19th C. **£2,800-3,400** *S*

An Italian walnut and floral marquetry bureau inlaid with flowering foliage, enclosing pigeonholes and drawers, 44½ in. wide (113 cm.), 18th C. **£3,250-£3,750** *C*

A mid 18th C. walnut and marquetry bureau of bombé form, the scrolled sloping front enclosing a fitted interior, 4 ft. 5 in. wide (135 cm.), c. 1755. **£3,600-4,600** *S*

A Dutch marquetry bureau, enclosing a fitted interior with a well, inlaid overall in floral marquetry on an oak ground, 3 ft. 7 in. high by 3 ft. 2 in. wide (109 by 97 cm.), c. 1750, marquetry 19th C. **£2,000-2,300** *S*

A finely carved antique oak bureau, the fall front richly decorated and carved with grotesque mask, etc., 38 in. wide. **£250-300** *BHW*

An 18th C. Dutch marquetry walnut bureau, profusely inlaid with flowers, vases of flowers, cherubs riding dolphins, the fall enclosing fine interior of cupboard, pigeonholes, 4 short drawers and 4 stepped drawers, well with secret compartment, 3 ft. 4 in. wide by 3 ft. 5½ in. high. **£2,500-3,000** *PFW*

An 18th C. Dutch marquetry bombé bureau on ball and claw feet having graduated fitted interior, 34 in. **£2,000-2,500** *JD*

A carved oak bureau, all carved in high relief with foliates and lion heads, the slope front enclosing a fitted interior, 38 in., 19th C. **£175-£225** *WHL*

A 19th C. ebonised escritoire inlaid in satinwood with leaf scrolls, the fall front revealing rosewood-veneered drawers and well, on cabriole legs with ormolu embellishments, 32 in. wide. **£450-£500** *M*

A rosewood and marquetry bureau de dame with a pair of glazed cupboards, flanking a central mirror, the fall front enclosing a fitted interior above a shaped frieze, inlaid and applied with gilt bronze mounts throughout, English, 55 by 32 in. (140 by 81 cm.), mid 19th C. **£1,000-1,200** *SC*

A mahogany and marquetry bureau on stand in the revived 'Queen Anne'-style, with key, 3 ft. 3 in. wide (99 cm.), c. 1900. **£500-£600** *S*

A 19th C. rosewood and floral marquetry bureau de dame, 26 in. wide. **£600-700** *JMW*

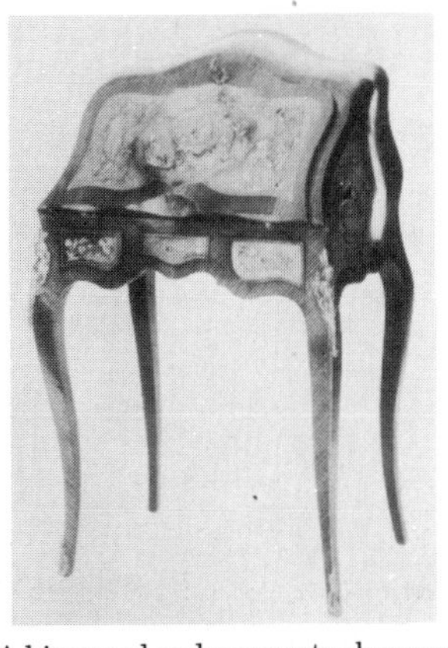

A kingwood and marquetry bureau de dame of bombé outline, inlaid with an armorial, strapwork and foliage, German, late 19th C. **£500-£600** *Bea*

A late 19th C. lady's mahogany and inlaid desk by James Shoolbred & Co., 26 in. wide. **£1,000-1,200** *PWC*

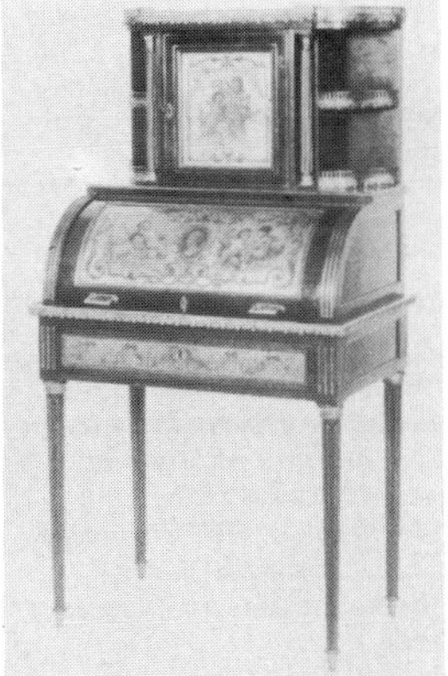

A lady's mahogany and Vernis Martin cylinder bureau applied with gilt brass mounts and painted with panels, the superstructure with a pink marble top, the cylinder front enclosing drawers and a writing slide, 54 in. high by 30 in. wide, French, 19th C. **£450-£550** *Bea*

A Louis XV kingwood and tulipwood crossbanded Bureau en Peinte, of slight bombé outline, veneered à quatre face, on cabriole legs terminating in sabots, 1 m. **£2,800-3,200** *P*

A Louis XV-style kingwood and floral marquetry bureau de dame with gilt metal gallery, bombé fall front with interior fitted with 3 drawers and well, 26 in. wide. **£600-700** *DSH*

A George III satinwood cylinder bureau, the tambour shutter with alternating rosewood slats inlaid with lines enclosing a fitted interior with pigeonholes, short drawers and a leather-lined slide, 36¼ in. wide by 26½ in. deep (92 by 67 cm.). **£3,000-3,500** *C*

A George III satinwood cylinder bureau, the tambour slide enclosing leather-lined surface, 32 in. (82 cm.) wide. **£2,300-2,500** *C*

A Louis XVI-style mahogany bureau de dame with brass geometric outlines, 25 in. **£500-£600** *CSK*

A lady's drum cylinder bureau, 20th C. **£500-550** *AGG*

An Empire ormolu-mounted mahogany bureau à cylindre with rectangular verde antico marble top with fully fitted interior, 49 in. (124 cm.) wide. **£1,500-2,000** *C*

An Empire mahogany bureau a cylindre with white marble top with pierced brass gallery, the roll top inlaid with lions and enclosing six small drawers, 50 in. wide. **£1,200-1,500** *CEd*

A mahogany cylinder bureau enclosing drawers, shelves and a baize-lined slide, Dutch or German, 4 ft. 2½ in. high by 4 ft. 8 in. wide (128 by 142 cm.), c. 1820 with later 19th C. satinwood inlay. **£2,000-£2,250** *S*

A Dutch marquetry cylinder bureau inlaid with walnut panels, swags, a roundel and a classical urn, 46½ in. high by 40 in. wide, late 18th/early 19th C. **£1,000-£1,200** *S*

A fine Louis XVI bureau à cylindre, the roll top with beaded brass border and enclosing a fitted interior, 60½ in. wide. **£3,500-£4,000** *CEd*

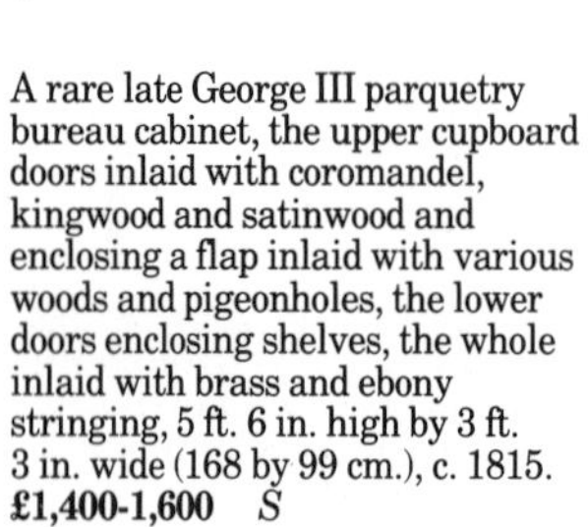
A rare late George III parquetry bureau cabinet, the upper cupboard doors inlaid with coromandel, kingwood and satinwood and enclosing a flap inlaid with various woods and pigeonholes, the lower doors enclosing shelves, the whole inlaid with brass and ebony stringing, 5 ft. 6 in. high by 3 ft. 3 in. wide (168 by 99 cm.), c. 1815. **£1,400-1,600** *S*

Make the most of Miller's
When buying or selling, it must always be remembered that prices can be greatly affected by the condition of any piece. Unless otherwise stated, all goods shown in Miller's are of good merchantable quality, and the valuations given reflect this fact. Pieces offered for sale in exceptionally fine condition or in poor condition may reasonably be expected to be priced considerably higher or lower respectively than the estimates given herein.

A 19th C. German mahogany cylinder-top bureau cabinet, sliding compartments and numerous small birds-eye maple drawers with cupboard and 2 drawers over, 43 in.
£700-900 *JD*

A 19th C. rosewood and kingwood bureau de dame of Louis XV design with floral marquetry inlays and ormolu decoration, 28 in. wide.
£650-750 *RBB*

A German walnut cabinet, the moulded cornice with a sliding frieze enclosing 3 secret drawers, a cupboard opening to reveal 20 painted and gilded drawers, the plinth base with later pad feet, probably Cologne, 41 in. wide by 69 in. high (119 by 179 cm.), 17th C. **£2,000-2,400** *C*

A William and Mary walnut and seaweed marquetry secretaire on chest, the fall flap inlaid with a roundel and spandrels enclosing a well-fitted interior with stained maplewood-veneered drawers bordered with ebony, on later turned feet, 48 in. wide (122 cm.).
£3,000-3,250 *C*

A William and Mary period cabinet on chest in finely figured walnut veneers on oak, with crossbanded herringbone inlaid doors concealing cabinet with crossbanded drawers, 46 in. wide by 71 in. high by 20 in. deep, c. 1690, exterior brasswork early but not original bun feet replaced.
£5,000-7,000 *HAL*

A William and Mary walnut chest-on-chest, on later bracket feet, 39 in. wide. **£3,200-3,600** *CEd*

A William and Mary escritoire with finely veneered kingwood fall front, fitted interior with cupboard, drawers, cubby holes and secret compartments, the drawers crossbanded in walnut, some damage, 43 in. **£3,500-4,000** *SWO*

A walnut and marquetry secretaire on chest, the crossbanded fall flap inlaid with compass-medallion framed by panels of seaweed marquetry and oyster lunettes, on later turned ebonised feet, probably Dutch or North German, 52½ in. wide (134 cm.), 17th C. **£3,000-£3,500** *C*

A William and Mary walnut escritoire, on bracket feet, 5 ft. 3 in. high by 3 ft. wide (160 by 91.5 cm.), c. 1695. **£1,650-1,800** *SS*

Miller's is a price GUIDE Not a price LIST.
The price ranges given reflect the average price a purchaser should pay for similar items. Condition, rarity of design or pattern, size, colour, provenance, restoration and many other factors must be taken into account when assessing values.

A Dutch walnut and marquetry cabinet on chest with shallow frieze, 7 ft. 1 in. high by 4 ft. 11½ in. wide (216 by 151 cm.), late 17th C., marquetry 19th C. **£2,500-£3,000** *S*

A Queen Anne walnut secretaire à abattant, the frieze fitted cushion drawer, the crossbanded and finely figured panel front opening to reveal a fully fitted interior, 39 in. wide. **£1,700-2,000** *WHL*

A William and Mary walnut-veneered cabinet on stand, with feather-banded drawers, now on bun feet, reduced in height, 4 ft. 5¾ in. high by 3 ft. 5¼ in. wide (136.5 by 105 cm.), c. 1700. **£1,000-£1,200** *S*

A Queen Anne burr-walnut cabinet on chest, the cavetto cornice with later top fitted with 2 crossbanded cupboard doors outlined with scorched bands, on later bracket feet, 44½ in. wide by 71 in. high (113 by 180 cm.). **£2,500-3,500** *C*

A small 18th C. oystershell walnut and satinwood enclosed cabinet on chest, 2 ft. 7 in. wide, 4 ft. 3 in. high. **£2,000-2,400** *RBB*

An early Georgian lacquered and walnut cabinet in 2 parts, the drawers veneered with well-figured walnut in chevron pattern borders, the exterior naively decorated at a later date with chinoiserie buildings and landscapes, 46 in. wide (117 cm.). **£800-1,200** *C*

A William and Mary black and gold lacquer cabinet, the cupboard doors mounted with shaped and engraved lockplates, on later turned feet, 39 in. wide (99 cm.). **£5,000-6,000** *C*

A late 17th/early 18th C. walnut escritoire, 3 ft. 9½ in. wide. **£1,000-£1,100** *GC*

A William and Mary design oyster walnut cabinet on chest, with satinwood crossbanding and stringing, 5 ft. 4½ in. high by 3 ft. 8 in. wide (164 by 112 cm.), c. 1850. **£3,000-3,250** *SS*

An early 19th C. continental ebony cabinet on stand, the interior with 18 small drawers surrounding a pair of small cupboard doors opening again to reveal a 'temple' interior with 2 sliding panels disclosing 8 small drawers and other secret drawers, with parquetry decoration in rosewood, ebony, walnut, stained and plain ivory, probably Spanish, 5 ft. 2 in. wide by 6 ft. 5 in. **£1,700-2,000** *EH*

A marquetry display cabinet in Dutch mid 18th C.-style, inlaid throughout with foliage on a walnut ground, modern, 216 by 175 cm. **£2,800-3,200** *S*

A French 18th C. oak cabinet, with a pair of copper wire mesh grille doors enclosing shelves, 61 in. wide by 20 in. deep by 7 ft. 6 in. high. **£1,250-1,500** *PWC*

A Dutch walnut display cabinet with domed cornice and canted wings, the base with 4 short drawers, the upturned vase-shaped supports with scroll stretchers, on bun feet, restored, 7 ft. 4 in. high by 5 ft. 7 in. wide (224 by 170 cm.), c. 1690. **£2,000-2,500** *SS*

A Dutch walnut display cabinet, 8 ft. 6 in. high by 6 ft. 2 in. wide (259 by 188 cm.), mid 18th C. **£2,200-2,500** *S*

A fine Victorian figured walnut and floral marquetry breakfront display cabinet, 76 in. wide by 90 in. high (193 by 229 cm.). **£5,000-6,000** *C*

A Louis XV-style pine display cabinet, 240 by 138 cm., early 19th C. **£1,900-2,100** *S*

A Victorian mahogany display cabinet, fine marquetry decoration in satinwood, 4 ft. 7 in. wide by 7 ft. 9 in. high. **£2,250-2,500** *RBB*

A walnut display cabinet, Dutch, 91 in. high by 55½ in. wide (231 by 141 cm.), 1900's. **£1,500-1,700** *S*

A Dutch walnut-veneered display cabinet with an arched moulded cornice, 82 in. high by 45 in. wide. **£1,100-1,300** *Bea*

Make the most of Miller's

Every care has been taken to ensure the accuracy of descriptions and estimated valuations. Where an attribution is made within inverted commas (e.g. 'Chippendale') or is followed by the word 'style' (e.g. early Georgian style) it is intended to convey that, in the opinion of the publishers, the piece concerned is a later — though probably still antique — reproduction of the style so designated. Unless otherwise stated, any description which refers to 'a set' or 'a pair' includes a valuation for the entire set or the pair, even though the illustration may show only a single item.

—GUIDE TO STYLES—

Dates	Monarch	Period	Woods
1603-1625	James I	Jacobean	
1625-1649	Charles I	Carolean	Oak period up to c. 1670
1649-1660	Commonwealth	Cromwellian	
1660-1685	Charles II	Restoration	
1685-1689	James II	Restoration	
1689-1694	William and Mary	William and Mary	
1694-1702	William III	William III	Walnut period 1670-1735
1702-1714	Anne	Queen Anne	
1714-1727	George I	Early Georgian	
1727-1760	George II	Early Georgian	Early mahogany period 1735-1770
1760-1811	George III	Late Georgian	
1812-1820	George III	Regency	Late mahogany period 1770-1810
1820-1830	George IV	Regency	
1830-1837	William IV	William IV	
1837-1901	Victoria	Victorian	
1901-1910	Edward VII	Edwardian	

A marquetry satinwood serpentine display cabinet, crossbanded in tulipwood and inlaid with swags, flowers and musical trophies, signed by and bearing the label of Edwards & Roberts, 7 ft. 3 in. high by 4 ft. 1 in. wide (221 by 124 cm.), 1890's. **£2,500-3,500** *S*

A Dutch walnut display cabinet, the bombé base with 2 short and 2 long drawers, 78 in. wide by 93 in. high (198 by 236 cm.). **£2,200-£2,400** *C*

A large mahogany and parcel-gilt display cabinet in the manner of William Kent, the base on square tapering legs headed by lion masks, 19th C. **£2,000-2,500**

A walnut display cabinet, the lower part with 2 shaped long drawers on 6 faceted baluster supports joined by flat wavy stretchers on turned feet, Dutch, 92 by 67 in. (234 by 170 cm.), late 18th C. but partly reconstructed and restored. **£1,400-£1,800** *SC*

A Dutch walnut display cabinet, enclosing 2 shelves covered in yellow silk, the bombé base with one long and two short drawers on hairy-paw and ball feet, 81 in. wide (206 cm.). **£2,500-3,000** *C*

A late 18th C. Dutch marquetry bombé cabinet on chest, 2 ft. 8 in. wide. **£4,000-5,000** *HB*

A 19th C. Dutch-style walnut-veneered display cabinet, 3 ft. wide. **£1,100-1,300** *WSW*

A walnut and Vernis Martin vitrine, on moulded cabriole supports, 71 by 37 in. (180 by 94 cm.), early 20th C. **£850-1,000** *SC*

A Maison Meynard kingwood cocktail cabinet in Transitional style, English locks, 155 by 76 cm., c. 1910. **£1,300-1,500** *S*

A Venetian painted vitrine, with serpentine-fronted shelves painted with polychrome flowers on a pale blue ground, decoration restored, 6 ft. 8½ in. high by 3 ft. 4 in. wide (205 by 101 cm.), mid 18th C. **£1,200-1,600** *S*

A French 19th C. mahogany and marquetry vitrine, 37 in. **£1,050-£1,250** *PWC*

A French 19th C. brass inlaid and mounted marquetry and mahogany vitrine, with moulded cornice, 35½ in. wide. **£650-750** *PWC*

A glass fronted walnut display cabinet, 69 in. high. **£770-800** *CDE*

A 19th C. French vitrine, embellished with ormolu acanthus scrolls and oak leaf garlands, with mirrored back and plate glass shelves, 104 in. high by 60 in. wide. **£1,800-2,000** *M*

An 18th C. mahogany china display cupboard with satinwood banding, shaped apron on carved cabriole legs and paw feet, 3 ft. 10 in. wide. **£900-1,100** *RBB*

A Victorian Cuban mahogany breakfront display cabinet. **£450-£500** *CGC*

An Edwardian mahogany breakfront display cabinet, on stand with square moulded legs and stretchers, 70 in. **£650-750** *CSK*

An Edwardian mahogany display cabinet, inlaid and chequer banded in satinwood all over, 37 in. wide. **£200-300** *DS*

An Edwardian mahogany and satinwood display cabinet by Marsh, Jones & Cribb Ltd., with glazed doors, the lower part with 3 frieze drawers above cupboard doors, 72 by 84½ in. high (183 by 215 cm.). **£1,500-1,800** *L*

The firm of Marsh and Jones of Leeds manufactured furniture in the 'Geometric Gothic' style in the 1860's and made furniture designed by Charles Bevan for Titus Salt Jnr., son of the millionaire industrialist and philanthropist, from 1865 to 1870. They changed their name in 1870 to Marsh, Jones and Cribb.

A George III-style mahogany bookcase on stand, with blind fret-carved frieze, astragal glazed doors and on square cabriole legs, 69 in. high by 40 in. wide. **£350-400** *Bea*

A tulipwood and parquetry breakfront 'meuble d'Appui' in Transitional-style, with a red and white veined marble top, 123 by 127 cm., c. 1880. **£950-1,100** *S*

An Edwardian inlaid mahogany display cabinet, 4 ft. wide. **£1,500-£1,700** *WSW*

A Georgian-style mahogany display cabinet with dentil moulded cornice above a central glazed door on a semi lunar shaped table, width 36 in. **£225-250** *DS*

A mahogany vitrine of serpentine outline, the marble top with three-quarter gilt-metal gallery with tasselled apron, 27 in. **£440-460** *CSK*

A walnut bow fronted display cabinet with a gadrooned cornice over a central door, raised on carved cabriole legs, width 48 in. **£350-400** *DS*

A mahogany serpentine display cabinet inlaid throughout with boxwood stringing, 5 ft. 9 in. by 4 ft. 2 in. (176 by 127 cm.), c. 1900. **£750-850** *S*

A late Victorian/Edwardian inlaid figured and crossbanded mahogany bow fronted double corner display cabinet. **£600-650** *EBB*

A Louis XV-style kingwood vitrine with serpentine top and sides with fitted glazed shelves, width 26 in. **£600-700** *DS*

A green painted and parcel gilt-oak display cabinet on stand, Low Countries, 7 ft. 2 in. high by 6 ft. 3 in. wide (218.5 by 191 cm.). **£2,200-2,800** *S*

A mahogany and marquetry display cabinet, inlaid throughout with ribbon tied foliage, 6 ft. 8 in. by 2 ft. 9 in. (204 by 84 cm.), c. 1900. **£950-1,050** *S*

A late Regency calamander and gilt-bronze mounted display cabinet on stand by Town & Emanuel, the back applied with the maker's label, later mirrored interior, 65 in. high by 40 in. wide. **£1,000-1,400** *Bea*

A pair of satinwood display cabinets with mahogany line and neo-classical marquetry inlay, with lined interior fitted shelves enclosed by glazed doors and canted sides, the bases with cupboards enclosed by panelled doors and sides, 3 ft. 10 in. **£1,800-2,000** *WW*

A fine 19th C. mahogany and crossbanded display cabinet, 24 in. wide by 18 in. deep by 51 in. high. **£400-£500** *WHL*

A pair of fine quality 19th C. French bijouterie cabinets lined in cerise velvet, parquetry-veneered in rosewood with box and ebony outline panels and gilt-metal stringing, 22 in. wide by 58 in. high by 15 in. deep. **£2,500-3,000** *WW*

By family tradition these cabinets are believed to have been purchased in the 1867 Paris Exhibition.

A Louis XVI-style kingwood-veneered and ormolu-mounted vitrine with a scagliola top, with an oval classical medallion, 58 in. high by 26 in. wide, late 19th/early 20th C. **£2,250-2,500** *Bea*

A late Victorian satinwood bowfront standing display cabinet painted in the style of Angelica Kauffmann, 31 in. **£1,400-1,600** *CSK*

An Edwardian inlaid rosewood corner cabinet, 34 in. wide by 82 in. high. **£550-650** *HWO*

A hardwood and bone side cabinet, blind fret carved and inlaid with paterae throughout, Egyptian, 99 by 51 in. (252 by 130 cm.) late 19th/early 20th C. **£1,000-1,200** *SC*

A 19th C. North European display cabinet. **£400-500** *HWO*

An exceptional Queen Anne period chest in black and gold raised lacquer work on a finely carved mid 17th C. giltwood stand. The back of the chest has been replaced and the rear legs of the stand have been strengthened, 45 in. wide by 22½ in. deep by 66 in. high. **£3,800-£4,500** *HAL*

A fine silver mounted ebony and tortoiseshell cabinet on stand with a hinged compartment above a pair of panelled doors, the richly fitted interior of drawers and cupboards applied with repousse silver swags on a red tortoiseshell ground, the cabinet 5 ft. 11 in. high by 3 ft. 10 in. wide, the base 4 ft. 7½ in. wide overall (181 by 117 by 141 cm.), c. 1660, the base regilt and with later upper framework. **£14,000-17,000** *S*

A late 17th C. lacquer cabinet on stand, the two door cabinet decorated with chinoiserie in gilt and red on a black ground, the interior fitted with an arrangement of drawers, 5 ft. 5¾ in. high by 3 ft. 9 in. wide (167 by 114 cm.), c. 1680. **£2,800-3,600** *S*

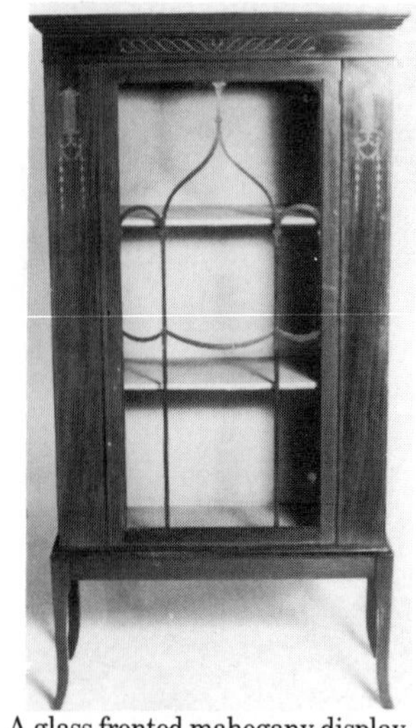

A glass fronted mahogany display cabinet with boxwood and ebony inlay, in need of restoration, 68 in. **£195-215** *CDE*

A good William and Mary japanned cabinet, the interior with ten drawers, on a contemporary carved giltwood stand, restored, 5 ft. 9 in. high by 3 ft. 6 in. wide (176 by 107 cm.), late 17th C. **£5,000-£6,000** *S*

A James II lacquered cabinet on stand, the cabinet painted to resemble tortoiseshell and gilded with chinoiserie, the interior with ten drawers, 45 by 63 in. (114 by 160 cm.). **£2,200-2,800** *L*

An ornate Edwardian French polished chiffonier/display cabinet, the whole amply embellished with applied, pierced and carved decoration, overall height 7 ft. **£300-400** *AGr*

A fine coromandel lacquer chest on stand, brightly coloured, the interior with an arrangement of 11 drawers, on a William and Mary giltwood stand, 4 ft. 6 in. high by 2 ft. 4 in. wide (137 by 71 cm.), cabinet late 17th C., stand c. 1700. **£4,500-5,500** *S*

A Charles II needlework cabinet on stand, the pair of doors worked in petit point and stumpwork, the interior fitted with an arrangement of ten burr yew-wood veneered drawers, the later giltwood stand carved with cherubs and foliage, 4 ft. 9 in. high by 3 ft. 2 in. wide overall (145 by 97 cm.). **£4,000-£5,000** *S*

A Goanese carved ebony cabinet on stand, 2 ft. 11½ in. high by 2 ft. 2½ in. wide (90 by 67 cm.), c. 1680, later engraved brass mounts, stand renewed. **£1,700-2,000** *S*

A 'Queen Anne' walnut cabinet on stand, width 39 in. **£400-450** *DS*

A William and Mary burr-yew cabinet, inlaid with herringbone bands, the later oak stand with spirally-turned legs joined by a double Y stretcher, 44¼ in. (112 cm.) wide. **£3,000-4,000** *C*

A Spanish brass inlaid, walnut and tortoiseshell table cabinet, the central cupboard enclosing 4 drawers, with brass carrying handles at the sides, on later bun feet, 4 ft. 2 in. high overall by 3 ft. 9½ in. wide (127 by 116 cm.), second half 17th C. **£1,200-1,500** *S*

A rare Spanish verre eglomise cabinet on stand, each drawer and the cupboard set with silver decorated mica panels within wave mouldings, 6 ft. 5 in. high by 4 ft. 8¼ in. (195.5 by 143 cm.), c. 1675. **£2,500-3,500** *S*

A Flemish carved oak cabinet on stand, the deeply fielded carved door flanked by a pair of fluted pilasters with Ionic capitals, 5 ft. 1½ in. high by 2 ft. 5½ in. wide (156 by 75 cm.), upper part late 17th C., lower part late 19th C. using 17th C. carving. **£750-850** *S*

Left:
A pair of lacquer cabinets on stands, each with doors enclosing an arrangement of drawers and with engraved gilt-brass escutcheon, strap hinges and mounts, decorated with chinoiserie, 4 ft. 2¼ in. high by 2 ft. 2¼ in. wide (127.5 by 66.5 cm.), c. 1790. **£1,450-£1,600** *S*

A George III satinwood and padouk wood collector's cabinet on stand, the doors enclosing an arrangement of drawers, later platform stretcher, 4 ft. 11¾ in. high by 2 ft. ½ in. wide (151 by 62 cm.), c. 1765. **£1,600-2,000** *S*

A German stained burr-elm cabinet on stand, the central cupboard enclosing a cupboard and drawers flanked by pietra dura panels, the base with a shallow secretaire drawer, 52½ in. (133 cm.) wide, early 18th C. **£6,000-8,000** *C*

A Goanese ebony cabinet on stand, profusely carved, with a pair of doors enclosing an arrangement of drawers, 4 ft. 5½ in. high by 2 ft. 8½ in. wide (136 by 82 cm.), late 17th C. **£3,000-3,500** *S*

A pair of ebony cabinets on stands, the frieze carved with equestrian military scenes, door with panel carved in the manner of Jean Maie of Blois, 36½ in. (93 cm.), wide, the carved panels 17th C., the cabinets mid 19th C. **£3,800-4,200** *C*

The military scenes possibly refer to episodes in the wars between Charles V, Holy Roman Emperor, and Francis I of France in the early 16th C. when the French allied with the Turks against the Empire.

An Italian walnut renaissance-style cabinet on stand, 4 ft. 7 in. high by 2 ft. 9 in. wide (140 by 84 cm.), 19th C. **£700-900** *S*

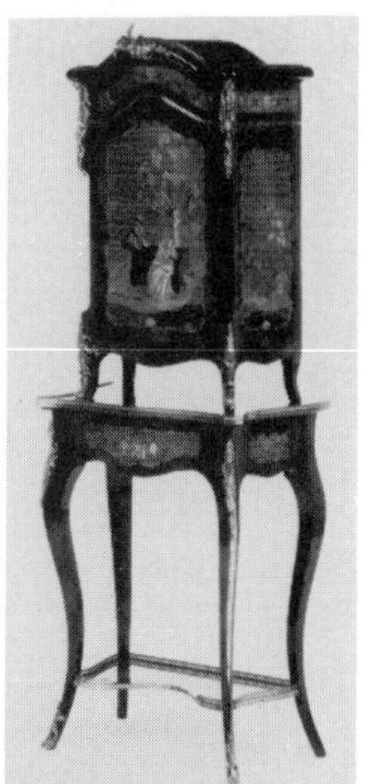

A kingwood and marquetry serpentine cabinet on stand inlaid throughout with panels of masks and foliage, possibly German, 175 by 67 cm., late 19th C. **£1,400-£1,600** *S*

A Chinese export black and gold lacquer cabinet on stand, with typical chinoiserie landscapes enclosing a well fitted interior on cabriole legged stand, 26 in. wide. **£1,600-1,800** *C*

An oak breakfront cabinet on stand set with Chinese bone and boxwood inlaid panels, undertier, 67 in. high by 80 in. wide. **£275-350** *Bea*

An unusual William IV rosewood-veneered writing cabinet, the pivoting panel which encloses numerous drawers and pigeonholes is 'locked' in conjunction with the slide and fitted frieze drawer below, 3 ft. 11½ in. high by 3 ft. 7 in. wide (121 by 109 cm.), c. 1830. **£1,000-£1,200** *S*

A good ebony-veneered marquetry cabinet on stand in Louis Quatorze revival style, inlaid overall with anthemion and foliage, the back formerly mirrored, 5 ft. 2 in. by 4 ft. 2½ in. by 1 ft. 9½ in. (157.5 by 129 by 54.5 cm.), c. 1840. **£2,000-£2,500** *S*

A mahogany breakfront cabinet on stand of Chinese Chippendale style, 43 in. wide by 89 in. high (109 by 226 cm.). **£3,250-£3,500** *C*

A walnut and tulipwood bow fronted small vitrine on stand, 123 by 77.5 cm., c. 1900. **£700-800** *S*

An Edwardian facsimile Chippendale design display cabinet. **£800-900** *Wor*

An ivory inlaid carved rosewood cabinet on stand with an elaborate superstructure on later cabriole legs, the whole carved with stylised floral decoration, animals and people in landscapes, 5 ft. 1 in. high by 2 ft. wide (155 by 61 cm.), late 19th C., stand 20th C. **£500-700** *S*

A Dutch mahogany secretaire à abattant, the frieze inlaid, the drawer flap and 3 lower drawers each crossbanded and outlined with a narrow diamond screen, 4 ft. 11 in. high by 3 ft. 2 in. wide (150 by 98 cm.), c. 1780. **£1,200-1,500** *S*

A Dutch mahogany secretaire à abattant with a pair of cupboard doors below enclosing shelves, 4 ft. 11 in. high by 3 ft. 2 in. wide (150 by 96.5 cm.), c. 1800. **£1,200-£1,500** *S*

A mahogany Chinese Chippendale style breakfront display cabinet with 2 pairs of glazed doors enclosing glass shelves, 88 in. high by 68 in. wide. **£2,700-3,000** *AG*

A William IV rosewood secretaire à abattant with one single cushion front drawer to the top, the writing flap enclosing a fitted interior of drawers and pigeonholes, 3 ft. 5 in. **£300-400** *DDM*

FRENCH FURNITURE PERIODS

1610-1643	**Louis XIII**
1643-1715	**Louis XIV**
1715-1723	**Regence**
1723-1774	**Louis XV**
1774-1793	**Louis XVI**
	DIRECTOIRE
1793-1795	**Revolution**
1795-1799	**Directoire**
1799-1804	**Consulate**
1804-1815	**Empire**
	RESTORATION
1815-1824	**Restoration**
1824-1830	**Charles X**
	LOUIS-PHILIPPE
1830-1848	**Louis-Philippe**
1848-1852	**2nd Republic**
1852-1870	**Napoleon III**
1871-1940	**3rd Republic**

A Dutch marquetry and mahogany secretaire à abattant, the fall front with ribbon-tied ropes and enclosing drawers and pigeonholes above doors with shaped panels, 4 ft. 6 in. high by 2 ft. 11 in. wide (137 by 89 cm.), c. 1800. **£950-£1,150** *S*

A satinwood secretaire à abattant in the Louis XVI-style with verde antico marble top, the oval inlaid fall flap enclosing a later fitted interior, 28 in. wide (71 cm.). **£1,400-1,600** *C*

A Louis XVI small mahogany secretaire à abattant with a white marble slab top, frieze drawer, the fall front enclosing small drawers, pigeonholes and a leather writing surface, triad mark to top, I over JL, 38½ in. wide by 16½ in. deep by 55½ in. high. **£1,300-1,500** *PWC*

A mahogany secretaire à abattant with an architectural superstructure and a flap enclosing a fitted architectural interior, Danish or North German, 7 ft. 5 in. high by 3 ft. 6 in. wide (226 by 107 cm.), c. 1830. **£1,500-1,800** *S*

A Scandinavian secretaire with a green marble top, the flap enclosing a fitted interior above 3 graduated long drawers, the whole inlaid with boxwood stringing, 4 ft. 5 in. high, 3 ft. 11 in. wide (135 by 119 cm.), c. 1800. **£800-1,000** *S*

An inlaid mahogany secretaire with fitted interior, 42 in. wide, c. 1770. **£900-1,000** *HB*

A pair of mahogany side cabinets, probably by Gillows, 32½ in. wide, c. 1810. **£4,000-4,500** *CC*

A Regency rosewood chiffonier with original brass inlay decoration and grilles. **£1,850-2,300** *RD*

A satinwood marquetry and lacquer secretaire à abattant, the fall front enclosing pigeonholes and 2 short drawers, the lower part with a single cupboard door, the back stamped Henri Janmart Ameublementen, Leibschestraat & Amsterdam, Dutch, 62 by 33 in. (158 by 84 cm.), c. 1900. **£700-800** *S*

A Sheraton satinwood and rosewood secretaire with tulipwood banding on 4 inlaid squared peg feet, 32 in. wide by 57 in. high. **£7,000-8,000** *GSP*

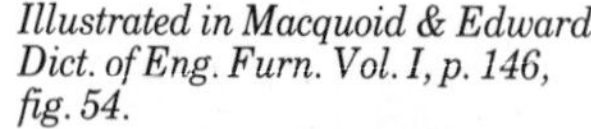

Illustrated in Macquoid & Edwards Dict. of Eng. Furn. Vol. I, p. 146, fig. 54.

A William IV mahogany chiffonier, 55½ in. high, c. 1820. **£600-750** *NC*

A late 17th C. oak chest, the frieze drawer applied with mouldings to simulate 2 drawers, inlaid in bone and ebony with star motifs, some restoration, 40½ in. high by 40 in. wide. **£600-750** *S*

A Regency rosewood chiffonier with mirror-backed open shelves, the lower part with 2 later glazed cupboard doors filled with lunette pattern gilt-brass mesh on plinth base, 59 in. wide (150 cm.). **£1,200-£1,500** *C*

A Regency rosewood chiffonier, 58 in. wide (147.5 cm.). **£1,200-£1,500** *C*

A fine early Victorian breakfront walnut credenza, fitted glazed side panels, the whole surmounted by a mirror ledge back in the revived Gothic style, 75 in. **£850-950** *LE*

A Victorian burr-walnut and ebonised chiffonier inlaid with amboyna bands, marquetry and geometric boxwood lines, 42 in. **£950-1,050** *CSK*

A Dutch mahogany secretaire cabinet, the superstructure with tambour shutters enclosing shelves, the drawer fitted with pigeonholes and short drawers, 58 in. high by 31½ in. wide. **£450-£550** *S*

A George III bow-fronted mahogany semi-circular side cabinet, with a crossbanded top above cupboard doors, enclosing a shelf, on square tapering legs, 2 ft. 8 in. high by 2 ft. 11½ in. wide (82 by 90 cm.), c. 1780. **£3,300-3,600** *S*

A late 18th C. French mahogany side cabinet with brass inlay, 32½ in. wide. **£1,600-1,800** *HB*

A Regency rosewood chiffonier, enclosing 2 shelves. **£160-200** *WHL*

A late Regency mahogany side cabinet, the panel doors filled with brass grilles and pleated silk panels, flanked by ring turned corners on turned supports, 36 by 39 in. (92 by 99 cm.), mid 19th C. **£350-450** *SC*

A late 19th C. oak dwarf side cabinet inset with 17th C. carved panels in high relief, 36 in., dated 1673. **£850-1,000** *CSK*

A George IV mahogany folio cabinet with beaded borders, the eared rectangular top above an inverted breakfront with long frieze drawer, 52½ in. **£600-700** *CSK*

A Hille cocktail cabinet, the mirror-lined interior elaborately fitted for glasses, alcohol dispensers and ice, 5 ft. 4 in. high by 4 ft. 8 in. wide (162 by 142 cm.), 1920's. **£1,400-1,600** *S*

A George III painted satin-birch breakfront side cabinet, with painted panels, on short square tapering legs, 3 ft. 1 in. high by 4 ft. 6 in. wide by 1 ft. 4 in. deep (94 by 137 by 41 cm.), c. 1790. **£3,750-£4,500** *S*

A North Italian ebony table cabinet, the centre with an architectural niche inset with a bronze figure of Adam, flanked by further architectural niches containing bronze figures of classical ladies, 40½ in. wide, 17th C. **£1,200-1,400** *CEd*

A Regency mahogany side cabinet, the top inlaid with anthemions, the frieze with a drawer above 3 cupboards, one enclosing drawers, 51 in. wide (129 cm.). **£1,500-£1,800** *C*

A George IV rosewood-veneered side cabinet, the mottled white marble top with dark grey veining, 3 ft. 2 in. high by 5 ft. wide (97 by 152 cm.), c. 1820. **£2,500-3,000** *S*

A porcelain-mounted kingwood side cabinet now with a moulded marble top, the doors applied with oval porcelain panels, the sides with a small porcelain panel painted with flowers, with 2 keys, 94.5 by 126 cm., c. 1860. **£1,500-£1,700** *S*

A Regency rosewood dwarf cabinet with Siena marble top, the cupboard doors filled with gilt-brass trellis backed by pleated silk, 68½ in. wide (174 cm.). **£1,900-£2,100** *C*

A 19th C. satinwood breakfront display cabinet, the frieze painted in the style of Angelica Kaufmann, 6 ft. 4 in. wide, 4 ft. 7½ in. high. **£2,400-2,800** *GC*

A William IV brass-inlaid rosewood side cabinet, of breakfront form, the side doors now glazed, 3 ft. high by 5 ft. 6 in. wide (91.5 by 168 cm.), c. 1830. **£3,250-£3,750** *S*

A marquetry side cabinet, of inverted breakfront form, inlaid with arabesque and walnut banding on ebony ground, the whole with gilt-metal bead mouldings, 3 ft. 10 in. high by 5 ft. 6 in. wide (117 by 168 cm.), c. 1870. **£600-800** *S*

An amboyna and ebony side cabinet, the cupboard door inlaid with marquetry, with mahogany lining and pine frame, 2 keys, 3 ft. 9¼ in. by 6 ft. 5 in. (114 by 199.5 cm.), 1860's. **£850-950** *S*

A mid 19th C. ebonised and buhl display cabinet, 3 ft. 2 in. **£550-£600** *WSW*

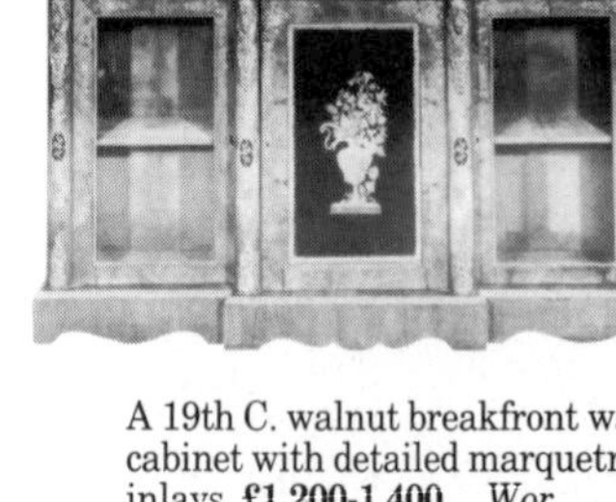

A 19th C. walnut breakfront wall cabinet with detailed marquetry inlays. **£1,200-1,400** *Wor*

A good ormolu-mounted ash library folio cabinet, with hinged rising book support, the projecting corners with rococo ormolu mounts, 2 ft. 8½ in. high by 4 ft. wide (83 by 122 cm.), c. 1840. **£3,300-3,500** *S*

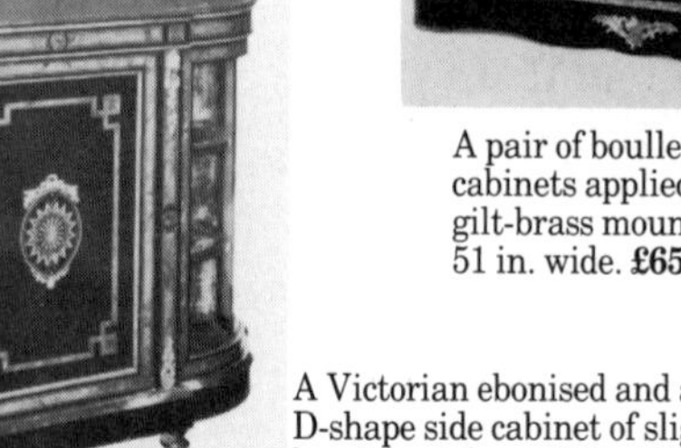

A pair of boulle and ebonised side cabinets applied throughout with gilt-brass mounts, 44½ in. high by 51 in. wide. **£650-750** *S*

A walnut display cabinet, 4 ft. 8 in. by 3 ft. 6½ in. (143 by 107 cm.), c. 1870. **£700-800** *S*

A Victorian ebonised and amboyna D-shape side cabinet of slight breakfront form, 59 in. (150 cm.). **£350-450** *L*

A Victorian credenza of inlaid walnut. **£850-1,000** *HWO*

CREDENZAS

- side cabinets are often known as credenzas
- a credenza normally implies the more ornate pieces, in the French or Italian taste
- some of these pieces display the over elaborate decoration and lack of craftsmanship which would decrease their desirability
- serpentine shaped front and sides is always a good feature

A mid 19th C. ebonised and boulle credenza, brass inlay missing. **£800-900** *WSW*

A mahogany and boulle serpentine side cabinet, 45 by 84 in. (114 by 214 cm.), c. 1870. **£1,100-1,400** *S*

A burr-walnut and 'Tunbridge ware' serpentine side cabinet, the door inlaid with a sycamore crossbanding and a geometric banding, the central panel with elaborate box foliage on a burr-walnut ground, 3 ft. 5½ in. by 5 ft. 11 in. (105 by 180.5 cm.). **£2,200-£2,500** *S*

A Regency cream-painted and parcel gilt dwarf cabinet with eared D-shaped breccia marble top, 47½ in. wide (121 cm.). **£1,500-£2,000** *C*

A Victorian boulle and ebonised credenza, with grotesque mask mounts and floral motifs, 74 in. wide. **£1,000-1,200** *AG*

A 19th C. French burr-walnut credenza. **£1,200-1,400** *DWB*

A burr-walnut side cabinet and mirror with moulded white marble top, 5 ft. 10 in. high overall by 5 ft. (178 by 152 cm.), c. 1855. **£600-£700** *S*

A walnut side cabinet, the cupboard applied with foliate fretwork on a damask ground flanked by velvet lined open shelves, formerly with a mirror back, 60 by 90½ in. (152.5 by 229.5 cm.), 1850's. **£350-450** *S*

A Victorian credenza with brass boulle inlay, with shaped centre cupboard and glazed side display cabinets. **£800-900** *PE*

An inlaid burr-walnut-veneered side cabinet of breakfront D-shape, the frieze inlaid with scrollwork with a pair of panelled scroll-inlaid doors flanked by ormolu-mounted reeded pilasters and a pair of curved glazed doors, 3 ft. 5 in. high by 5 ft. wide (104 by 153 cm.), c. 1860. **£1,000-1,200** *S*

A Regency mahogany breakfront side cabinet, with moulded top above a central drawer, flanked by a pair of dummy drawers, 58 in. wide. **£250-300** *DS*

An ormolu mounted burr-walnut and marquetry side cabinet, with curved glazed doors to the sides, 3 ft. 6½ in. high by 6 ft. wide (108 by 183 cm.), c. 1860. **£1,400-1,800** *S*

A pair of walnut side cabinets of inverted breakfront form, 3 ft 4 in. high by 4 ft. wide (102 by 122 cm.), c. 1860. **£1,700-1,900** *S*

A pair of 'Rococo Revival' painted and parcel-gilt wood and plaster serpentine side cabinets, each with a moulded Siena marble top, all in gilt on white, 3 ft. high by 3 ft. 7½ in. wide (91 by 111 cm.), c. 1840. **£1,100-1,200** *S*

An English walnut credenza with ormolu mounts, 44½ in. high, c. 1840. **£1,200-1,500** *BHA*

A mid-Victorian walnut chiffonier, the mirrored top with carved surround over a breakfront marble top, the base inlaid with boxwood marquetry, 4 ft. 6 in. wide. **£450-£500** *DS*

A 19th C. burr-walnut credenza with ormolu mounts, 74 in. wide by 16 in. deep. **£600-700** *NSF*

A walnut side cabinet with ormolu mounts and crossbanded in thuyawood, 3 ft. 8 in. high by 5 ft. 3 in. wide (112 by 161 cm.), mid 19th C. **£800-1,000** *S*

A burr-walnut side cabinet, with gilt-bronze mounts throughout, 43 by 72 by 20¼ in. (109 by 183 by 51.5 cm.), c. 1860. **£1,200-1,400** *S*

A walnut and ormolu mounted side cabinet, inlaid with marquetry and floral scrolls and set with 'Sèvres' panels, 3 ft. 9½ in. high by 6 ft. 8 in. wide (115.5 by 200 cm.), c. 1860. **£1,200-1,400** *S*

A late Regency mahogany dwarf display cabinet, the later glazed front framed by beaded volute, fitted with a door at each side, 38 in. wide (97 cm.). **£800-1,000** *C*

A pair of 19th C. French burr-walnut china cabinets with white marble tops. **£2,400-2,700** *DWB*

A French ebonised and boulle cabinet with rectangular black marble top and the cabinet with a single door inlaid with brass and foliate scrolls on a red tortoiseshell ground, 36 by 49 in., 19th C. **£600-£700** *L*

A walnut cabinet having a blind cupboard door with oval inset porcelain plaque, enclosing 3 shelves, with kingwood line inlay, 33 in. long by 16¼ in. wide by 42 in. high. **£550-650** *OL*

A dark mahogany side cabinet with brass handles, 42 in. high, c. 1880. **£170-200** *CDE*

A pair of Regency ormolu-mounted ebony, black lacquer and boulle pedestal cabinets of Louis XVI style, each with Sarancolin marble top, 25½ in. wide by 32 in. high (65 by 81 cm.). **£5,000-6,000** *C*

A good William IV pollard elm side cabinet, 6 ft. by 1 ft. 11½ in. (183 by 60 cm.), late 1830's. **£1,500-1,800** *S*

A small side cabinet, 26 in. wide. **£110-130** *CDE*

An inlaid walnut Victorian pier cabinet, 33 in. wide, c. 1890. **£300-£400** *Ph*

A Vernis Martin side cabinet with a serpentine single drawer above a bombé cupboard door enclosing shelves, 39½ by 33 in. (100 by 84 cm.), c. 1900. **£500-600** *S*

A 19th C. mahogany collector's cabinet with flap top enclosing a compartment and doors enclosing 6 drawers, 22 in. high. **£250-300** *HB*

An Hispano-Flemish ebonised cabinet, with an architectural arrangement of 7 short and 1 long drawer round a cupboard, veneered with engraved ivory flowers on a red tortoiseshell ground, on a George III black-japanned stand with pierced brackets and square legs, 2 ft. 6½ in. high by 2 ft. 2 in. wide (77 by 66 cm.), mid 17th C. **£900-1,100** *S*

A William IV rosewood combined workbox and collectors' cabinet, the sarcophagus-shaped lid revealing sewing accessories, 1 ft. 4½ in. wide (42 cm.), c. 1835. **£150-175** *SS*

Locate the source
The source of each illustration in Miller's can be found by checking the code letters below each caption with the list of contributors on page 12.
In view of the undoubted differences in price structures from region to region, this information could be extremely valuable to everyone who buys and sells antiques.

An early 18th C. German walnut-veneered table cabinet, with doors and sides crossbanded and inlaid in ebony with strapwork, maple-veneered interior, cupboard door inlaid with birds, 23½ in. high by 20 in. wide. **£750-850** *Bea*

A George III mahogany canterbury, 22 in. wide, c. 1800. **£600-700** *HB*

A George IV rosewood brass-inlaid canterbury with 4 compartments, 1 ft. 6 in. high by 1 ft. 7½ in. wide (46 by 49.5 cm.), c. 1820. **£900-£1,000** *S*

CANTERBURIES

- **name denotes a piece of movable equipment usually used for sheet music**
- **first music canterburies appeared c. 1800**
- **round tapered legs appeared in c. 1810**
- **the canterbury shows quite well the stylistic development of the 19th century — from the quite straight, slender severe to the bulbous and heavily carved later examples**
- **many Victorian examples with good carving fetch more than the earlier examples**
- **elegance is one of the major criteria in this small expensive piece of furniture**
- **note that some are made from the base of a whatnot or étagere but even more are modern reproductions**

A rosewood canterbury, 19 in. wide, c. 1840. **£350-400** *NP*

A walnut serpentine music canterbury, 38 in. high, c. 1850. **£450-500** *TA*

A good quality walnut and veneered whatnot/music cabinet, the double serpentine top above a cupboard door simulating 8 volumes of leather bound music, the whole decorated with boxwood stringing, 24 in. wide, 40½ in. high, 19th C. **£450-500** *WHL*

A 19th C. ebonised canterbury. **£80-120** *JMW*

A Victorian rosewood 3 compartment canterbury, 18 in. wide. **£300-350** *AGr*

A late George III mahogany canterbury, 21 by 20 in. (53 by 51 cm.), early 19th C. **£1,000-£1,200** *SC*

A burr-walnut whatnot magazine cabinet, 30 in. wide, c. 1850. **£420-£460** *CDE*

A burr-walnut canterbury, 25¼ in. wide (64 cm.), c. 1860. **£200-300** *S*

An unusual Edwardian period canterbury in satinwood having domed crossbanded lid concealing 4 racks, 19 in. wide by 13¼ in. deep by 27 in. high, c. 1900. **£740-850** *HAL*

A small oak and elm turner's chair, 28 in. high, mid 16th C. **£450-550** *RVA*

A good Gillows amboyna and porcelain music cabinet, stamped Gillow & Co. no. 2740, the cupboard below fitted with divisions, inlaid with diapers and harewood bandings throughout, 39 by 24 in. (99 by 51 cm.), late 19th C. **£800-900** *SC*

A fine ashwood bobbin-turned armchair with elaborately turned framed and railed seat, late 17th C. **£2,800-3,200** *S*

A fine James I oak panel back armchair with integral crest and toprail carved with leaves, scrolls and strapwork, with a panelled seat with deep corbelled moulding on pillar turned legs and plain stretchers, the back branded I.C., c. 1620, later finials. **£3,700-£4,000** *S*

An Elizabethan turned 'Great Chair' of highly elaborate form in ash and oak, late 16th C. **£1,200-£1,500** *S*

An oak wainscot chair with carved back panel, 44 in. high, mid 17th C. **£600-800** *RVA*

A Charles I oak armchair, c. 1630, feet with restoration. **£350-450** *S*

A very elaborate turner's chair in oak, ash and elm, 44 in. high, early 17th C. **£1,800-2,000** *RVA*

An oak armchair, back panel dated 1769, 41 in. high. **£400-500** *HB*

A joined oak elbow chair with a 2 panel back carved with a quatrefoil above lunettes, elm panel seat, late 17th C., probably Somerset. **£500-£600** *L*

A James I cupboard base panel back cacqueteuse armchair, attributed to the workshop of Humphrey Beckham, the outset angled arms on baluster-turned supports to a moulded panelled seat with later removable panel and interior cut out, the box base panelled within moulded uprights with a side opening door, c. 1620, Salisbury. **£2,000-2,500** *S*

ENGLISH CHAIRS

- **c. 1630 backs of chairs were like panelled sides from a coffer**
- **early 17th C. chairs very square and made of oak**
- **in Charles II period principal wood walnut — such chairs tend to break as walnut splits easily and is relatively soft**
- **chairs have carved top rails, often with a crown, the stretcher will then be similarly carved, the legs are either turned or plain and simple spirals — sometimes called barley sugar twists; the caning in the backs is usually rectangular — any chair with oval caning is highly desirable**
- **by the end of the 17th C. backs were covered in needlework, the cabriole leg made its appearance, now stretchers have subtle curves**
- **the beginning of the 18th C. — the Queen Anne spoon back chair — with upright shaped splat, plain cabriole front legs, pad feet**
- **George I — carved knees and ball-and-claw feet, solid splats were walnut or veneered, often in burr-walnut**
- **William Kent — introduced heavy carved mouldings — greatly influenced by Italian baroque**
- **from this time on chairs became lighter in design through the work mainly of Chippendale and Hepplewhite**
- **splats now pierced, legs square or tapered**
- **the square legs were also much cheaper than the cabriole legs, so they appealed to the large and growing middle class**
- **many of the designs came from France**
- **Hepplewhite, in particular, developed the chair with tapered legs, no stretchers and very plain splats**
- **during the 19th C. the taste was once again for heavier more substanital furniture**

A Charles I oak armchair, the rectangular panelled back carved with flat scrollwork and an arch, the down-curved arms and moulded seat on turned legs, c. 1630. **£700-800** *S*

A Charles I oak panel back armchair, the scroll and leaf-carved cresting above a panel of strapwork centred by a flowerhead, the panelled back chip-carved arched and centred by a leaf-carved panel within arched chip-carved moulded uprights with carved ear brackets, a later moulded panel seat and shaped seatrail, one arm patched, feet restored, c. 1640. **£3,000-£3,500** *S*

A fine James I panel back armchair, the arched toprail carved with the initials I M K within double scrolls and a fluted and stop-fluted fan half patera above a panel inlaid with an interlaced lozenge in bog oak and holly, c. 1620. **£7,000-£8,000** *S*

Illustrated by Victor Chinnery, op. cit., fig. 3:44, p. 251.

A Charles I oak side chair, the toprail with a dentilled and moulded cornice, the arch with a carved keystone, back feet replaced, c. 1640. **£500-600** *S*

(l.) A Victorian oak armchair with panelled back and padded leather drop-in seat. **£100-120** *Fr*

(r.) A Victorian carved dark oak hall chair. **£150-180** *Fr*

An oak wainscot chair, c. 1660. **£400-480** *LG*

A Charles II oak bobbin-turned armchair, the scrolling arms with ball-turned supports to a panelled seat with turned seatrail, legs and H-stretchers, c. 1675, the arms patched with signs of later upholstery, now removed. **£1,500-£2,000** *S*

A Commonwealth oak armchair covered in 17th C. Spanish woolwork, the shaped arms with turned supports and the turned legs with plain stretchers, c. 1650. **£1,350-1,450** *S*

A pair of North Italian carved walnut chairs inlaid with a geometric roundel, mid 17th C. **£1,300-1,500** *S*

Six fine 17th C. Flemish oak and elm dining chairs. **£1,100-1,300** *PWC*

A composed set of 4 oak and fruitwood bobbin and joint back stools, each with a leather panel padded back and seat, all late 17th C. with restorations. **£400-£450** *SC*

A set of 4 antique oak dining chairs with cane seats and backs, carving to back rail and seat frames, on barley twist legs and stretchers, 1 cane seat damaged. **£120-140** *BHW*

Seven very similar Cromwellian oak dining chairs. **£800-900** *DWB*

A good oak Yorkshire chair, original colour and patina, 41 in. high, c.1670. **£500-600** *RVA*

A harlequin set of 6 oak dining chairs, with later solid seats, all basically 17th C. with squab cushions. **£1,500-1,700** *C*

A set of 6 17th C. oak dining chairs. **£1,600-2,000** *BHA*

A good Charles II oak Derbyshire chair with carved back and conforming crossbar, c. 1670, with some restorations. **£500-600** *S*

A French oak nun's chair, c. 1700. **£200-250** *HB*

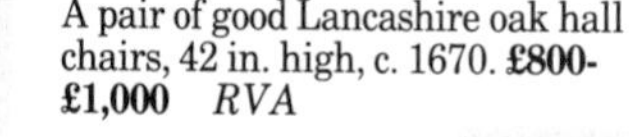

A pair of good Lancashire oak hall chairs, 42 in. high, c. 1670. **£800-£1,000** *RVA*

A good Lancashire oak dining chair, 44 in. high, c. 1680. **£400-£450** *RVA*

A William and Mary caned walnut armchair, with a scroll carved cresting, restored, c. 1690. **£300-£400** *S*

An important set of 9 James II oak dining chairs with moulded scrolled toprails centred by pierced interlaced leaves, on double bun feet, c. 1685. **£8,500-9,500** *S*

A French walnut armchair, 51 in. high, c. 1670. **£600-700** *RVA*

A pair of Charles II walnut side chairs, the toprail carved with putti supporting a crowned flowerhead, the caned panelled seat with leaf-carved seatrails, on double scroll front legs joined by a pierced stretcher, the leaf carved scrolled legs joined by twist-turned H-stretchers, possibly Flemish, c. 1680. **£1,600-2,000** *S*

A good William and Mary walnut armchair, the back with turned pillars with Corinthian capitals, a caned panel with arched top and base and leafy scroll cresting, c. 1690. **£900-1,200** *S*

A William and Mary period stained beechwood open arm elbow chair, with lightly carved shaped cresting rail, and a pair of matching standard chairs, some restoration to stretchers. **£500-600** *GC*

A set of 12 Flemish caned walnut chairs, crisply carved with leaves, restored, late 17th C. **£2,500-£3,500** *S*

A set of 7 Carolean style oak dining chairs including an armchair. **£650-750** *CSK*

A set of 5 Charles II-style beechwood dining chairs, including one armchair, caned back, caned seat on scroll supports joined by a Flemish rail, 52 in. (132 cm.) overall, 20th C. **£300-350** *SC*

A composite set of 8 18th C. ladderback dining chairs, comprising 6 singles and 2 carvers. **£800-900** *DDM*

A set of 4 early 18th C. country made chairs. **£400-500** *DWB*

A matched set of 6 single and 2 carver 18th C. ladderback dining chairs, with bobbin turned backs, rush seats, turned stretchers and legs ending in hoof feet. **£1,800-£2,000** *DDM*

A set of 8 elm and yew-wood Windsor armchairs, the solid seats on turned legs, early 19th C. **£4,500-5,000** *C*

(l.) An 18th C. ash and elm high back smokers bow/Windsor chair with pierced splats, shaped solid seat, turned legs and stretchers. **£200-250** *DDM*

(r.) An 18th C. ash and elm high back Windsor chair with pierced splat, turned supports and crinoline stretcher. **£200-250** *DDM*

A pair of Georgian yew-wood and elm chairs. **£575-625** *HWO*

WINDSOR CHAIRS

- **unknown before 1720's**
- **basically Georgian tavern and coffee house chairs**
- **earliest examples have comb backs, plainly turned splayed legs, no stretchers**
- **cabriole legs suggest a date between 1740-70**
- **hooped back introduced c. 1740**
- **wheel splat introduced c. 1790**
- **Gothic Windsors, recognised by the carving of their splats and their pointed-arch backs, made c. 1760-1800**
- **some better quality Windsors stained black or japanned black or green; these are more valuable in original condition — do not strip them**
- **most desirable wood is yew, followed by elm**
- **some mahogany Windsors were made for the gentry, these are always of good quality**
- **curved stretchers, carved and well proportioned backs add value**

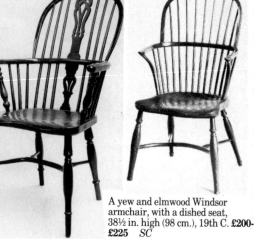

A yew and elmwood Windsor armchair, with a tall back and now reduced in height, 44 in. (120 cm.), early 19th C. **£250-300** *SC*

A set of 6 18th C. yew tree Windsors, Gothic-type back, crinoline stretcher. **£2,000-2,800** *SA*

A fine matched set of 6 yew-tree Windsor armchairs, 5 being low-backed, the sixth a high-back matching precisely in style, 4 chairs (one being the high-back) signed 'Whitworth Gamston' previously unrecorded. **£2,200-£2,400** *AS*

A yew and elmwood Windsor armchair, with a dished seat, 38½ in. high (98 cm.), 19th C. **£200-£225** *SC*

A pair of similar yew-wood and elm Windsor chairs, 19th C. **£400-450** *JMW*

An early 19th C. yew-wood and elm Windsor chair. **£350-400** *HB*

A matched set of 8 late 18th/early 19th C. ashwood spindle back dining chairs, on pad and ball feet. **£700-800** *S*

A yew-wood Windsor rocking chair with elm seat, c. 1790. **£300-500** *CDE*

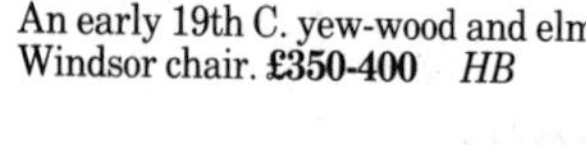

An early 19th C. yew child's high chair with shaped pierced splat and rail back, an elm seat, the turned yew legs with crinoline stretcher. **£650-750** *WW*

(l.) A 19th C. ash and elm high back Windsor chair, pierced splat, turned supports and stretchers. **£175-200** *DDM*

(c.) A 19th C. ash and elm low back Windsor chair of typical design with turned supports and stretchers. **£60-70** *DDM*

(r.) A 19th C. high back Windsor/ smokers bow chair with pierced splat, solid seat and stretchers. **£100-120** *DDM*

A 19th C. single yew-wood and elm Windsor chair. **£180-240** *JMW*

An elm armchair, reduced in height with rockers added. **£45-£55** *CDE*

An elm smokers bow, c. 1900. **£80-£90** *Ph*

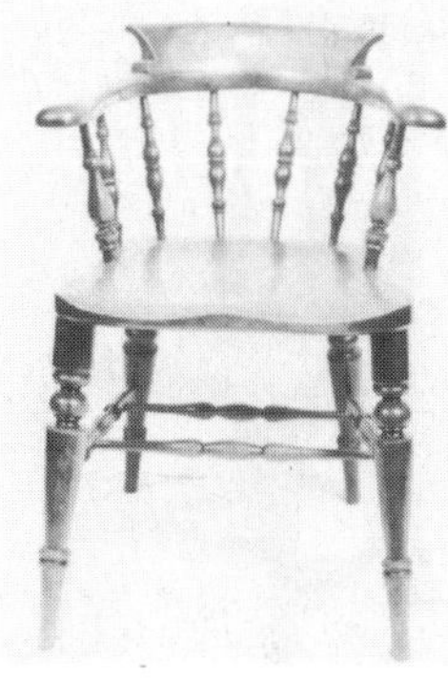
A Victorian elm and yew-wood smokers bow. **£180-220** *JMW*

A desk chair, c. 1900. **£100-120** *Ph*

A set of 6 20th C. elmwood kitchen chairs. **£100-150** *JMW*

An elm side chair, c. 1700. **£200-£250** *FF*

A pair of William and Mary-style walnut framed side chairs, the baluster legs joined by stretchers and terminating in braganza feet. **£300-350** *Bea*

A set of 6 Queen Anne walnut chairs with veneered vase-shaped splats and slip-in seats, the cabriole legs with H-shaped stretchers, c. 1710. **£6,000-7,000** *SS*

A set of 12 George I-style walnut and parcel gilt chairs, comprising 10 standards and 2 carvers, c. 1910. **£6,000-7,000** *SS*

A set of 12 George II-style mahogany dining chairs. **£4,200-£4,600** *DWB*

A set of 6 George II red walnut framed dining chairs, some damage, lacking 2 drop-in seats. **£1,800-£2,000** *S*

A pair of 18th C. Dutch walnut and marquetry chairs. **£850-950** *DWB*

A set of 6 George II-style mahogany dining chairs. **£300-£350** *DS*

A set of 3 George II solid walnut chairs, with restoration, c. 1755. **£700-1,000** *S*

A set of 4 early Georgian walnut dining chairs, each with a vase-shaped splat, on cabriole legs and pad feet. **£2,250-2,500** *CLG*

A set of 3 George I walnut side chairs, some of the legs spliced. **£3,250-3,500** *C*

A set of 4 early Georgian walnut dining chairs. **£5,000-6,000** *HB*

A pair of mid 18th C. mahogany chairs. **£1,200-1,300** *DWB*

A fine set of 14 Irish Chippendale-style dining chairs, having carved ribbon splats, on cabriole claw and ball supports and carved acanthus knees, comprising 12 single chairs and 2 carvers. **£2,200-2,500** *WSW*

A pair of George II mahogany dining chairs with carved yoke toprails, the drop-in seats covered in brown-ground petit point needlework, later blocks. **£2,500-£3,000** *C*

A set of 8 mahogany dining chairs in 18th C. revived Chippendale-style, including a pair of armchairs, possibly German, c. 1900. **£1,800-£2,000** *S*

A set of 8 George II-style mahogany framed dining chairs, including 2 armchairs, late 19th/early 20th C. **£1,800-2,200** *Bea*

A set of 8 George II-style mahogany framed dining chairs, including 2 armchairs, with carved and pierced 'Gothic' splats, early 20th C. **£2,200-2,600** *Bea*

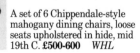

A set of 6 Chippendale-style mahogany dining chairs, loose seats upholstered in hide, mid 19th C. **£500-600** *WHL*

A matched set of 4 single and 2 carver Chippendale-style mahogany dining chairs, with carved acanthus and scroll backs, pierced vase splats, drop-in seats. **£1,000-1,200** *DDM*

A set of 12 George III mahogany dining chairs, with pierced Gothic-pattern splats carved with anthemions. **£5,500-6,500** *C*

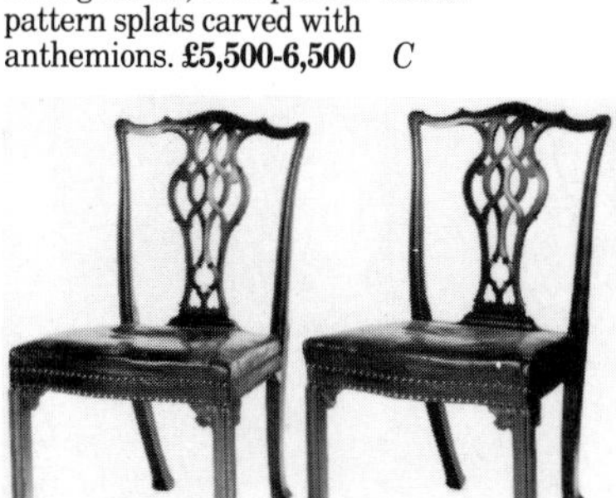

A set of 6 Chippendale-style mahogany single dining chairs, with pierced vase splats, on reeded and shaped legs. **£900-1,100** *DDM*

A single laburnum wood side chair, c. 1780. **£100-125** *FF*

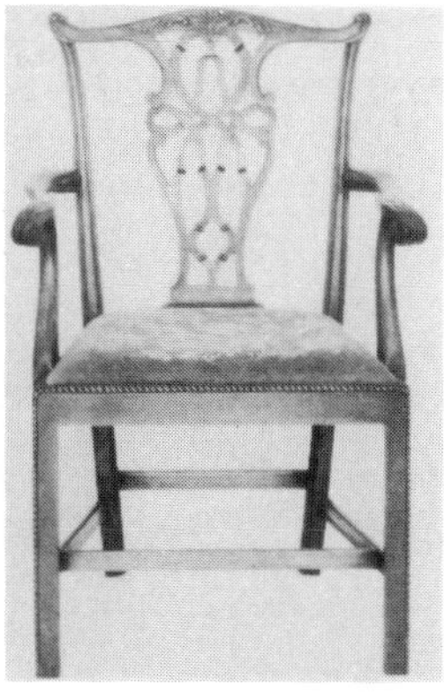

A set of 10 'Chippendale' mahogany dining chairs, the set including 4 elbow chairs, early 20th C. **£2,250-2,400** *N*

A set of 6 fine Chippendale period dining chairs in mahogany, the carved shaped splats above fretted rails and fluted legs, minor restoration, 21 in. wide by 18 in. deep by 37 in. high, c. 1775. **£2,500-£2,900** *HAL*

An English mahogany chair with drop-in seat and chamfered frame, 18th C. **£60-80** *WHL*

A set of 8 mahogany dining chairs including a pair of armchairs, c. 1900. **£3,000-4,000** *S*

A set of 6 early George III mahogany dining chairs, each with a serpentine toprail and chamfered legs, c. 1760. **£1,500-1,700** *S*

A set of 6 George III-style mahogany dining chairs, each with a shaped rail, interlaced splat, drop-in seat on square moulded supports, late 19th/early 20th C. **£800-1,000** *SC*

A set of 8 George III provincial mahogany dining chairs including a pair of armchairs, restored, c. 1770. **£1,600-2,000** *S*

A set of 16 George III-style mahogany dining chairs, including a pair of armchairs, late 19th C. **£2,600-3,000** *S*

A set of 8 George III-style mahogany framed dining chairs, including 2 armchairs, with pierced and carved ladderbacks, late 19th/early 20th C. **£1,100-1,300** *S*

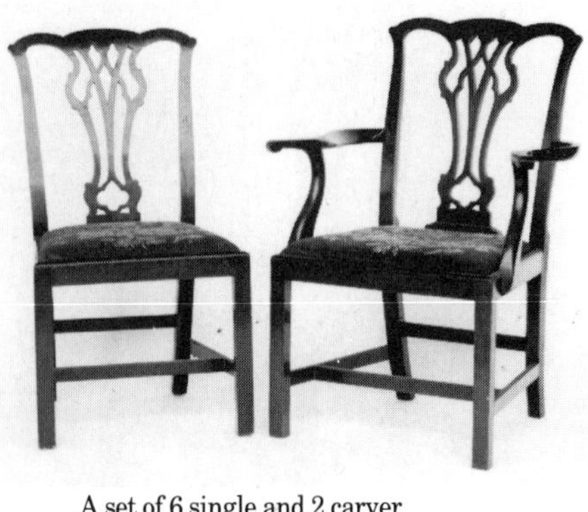

A set of 6 single and 2 carver Chippendale-style mahogany dining chairs. **£900-1,100** *DDM*

A 'Chippendale' armchair, c. 1770. **£300-350** *CDE*

A set of 12 mahogany dining chairs in George III-style including a pair of armchairs, c. 1900's. **£3,000-£3,500** *S*

A matched set of 8 19th C. mahogany ladderback dining chairs. **£1,300-1,500** *PB*

An elm and oak country chair of Chippendale-style, c. 1780. **£100-£150** *LG*

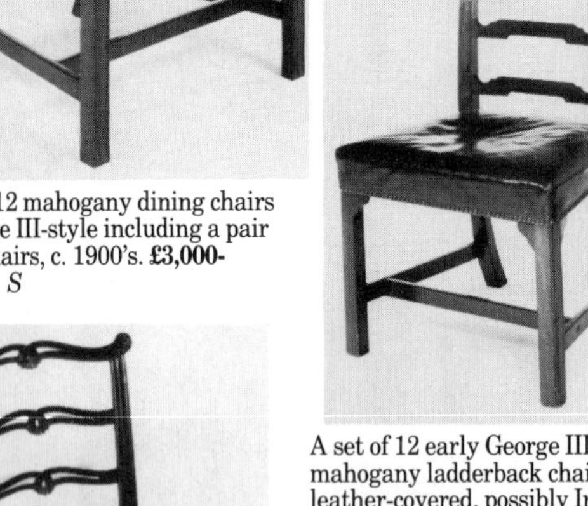

A set of 12 early George III mahogany ladderback chairs, leather-covered, possibly Irish, with restoration, c. 1770. **£4,750-£5,500** *S*

A set of 8 Hepplewhite-style dining chairs in Cuban mahogany, the carved fretted splats within arched rails above lift-out seats and fluted legs, 24½ in. wide by 18 in. deep by 38 in. high, c. 1850. **£1,800-2,300** *HAL*

A set of 6 George III Chippendale-style mahogany dining chairs upholstered in art silk brocade. **£500-600** *WHL*

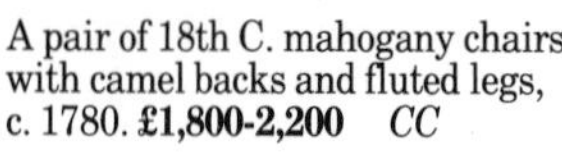

A pair of 18th C. mahogany chairs with camel backs and fluted legs, c. 1780. **£1,800-2,200** *CC*

A set of 6 Georgian mahogany dining chairs with camel backs, the lift-off seats on square underframes with stretchers, restored. **£600-£700** *L*

Three Hepplewhite period chairs, 2 singles and one carver. **£400-450** *WSW*

A set of 7 George III mahogany dining chairs including an open armchair, with arched shield-shaped backs and pierced splats carved with Prince of Wales plumes, and an open armchair en suite of later date. **£4,500-5,000** *C*

A chair of Hepplewhite design, 18th C. **£60-80** *WHL*

A set of 6 Hepplewhite-style dining chairs, including 2 armchairs, the shield backs with pierced and carved wheatears. **£400-500** *DS*

A set of 12 Victorian mahogany dining chairs in the Hepplewhite-style, bearing the trade label of 'Marsh, Jones, Cribb & Co 1899', inscribed with a craftsman's name. **£3,000-4,000** *C*

John Marsh and Edward Jones purchased the old established Leeds business of John Kendall in 1864 and opened a London showroom in Cavendish Square. Henry Cribb was taken into partnership in 1872. Towards the end of the century the firm was chiefly known for fine furniture in a variety of Georgian styles. A distinctive feature of the firm's trade label is that most known examples include the order number and a workman's name (probably the polisher).

A set of 6 George III-style mahogany dining chairs, each with a shield-shaped back, filled with 'Prince of Wales' feathers and drapery, late 19th C. **£800-1,000** *SC*

A set of 6 George III mahogany dining chairs including a pair of armchairs. **£1,100-1,300** *C*

A set of 8 George III mahogany dining chairs including a pair of armchairs, with shield-shaped backs, 3 with later blocks. **£3,000-£3,500** *C*

A set of 8 George III mahogany dining chairs including a pair of armchairs, carved with scrolls, paterae and a pagoda-like motif, c. 1780. **£4,500-5,000** *S*

A set of 6 Russian brass-inlaid mahogany chairs, with shield-shaped backs, c. 1815. **£2,000-£2,200** *S*

A set of 5 George III carved mahogany dining chairs after designs by Ince and Mayhew and contemporaries, the cartouche-shaped backs with re-entrant corners and pierced interlaced arched Gothic splats. **£3,600-£4,000** *P*

A set of 6 George III mahogany dining chairs, including a pair of armchairs. **£2,100-2,600** *C*

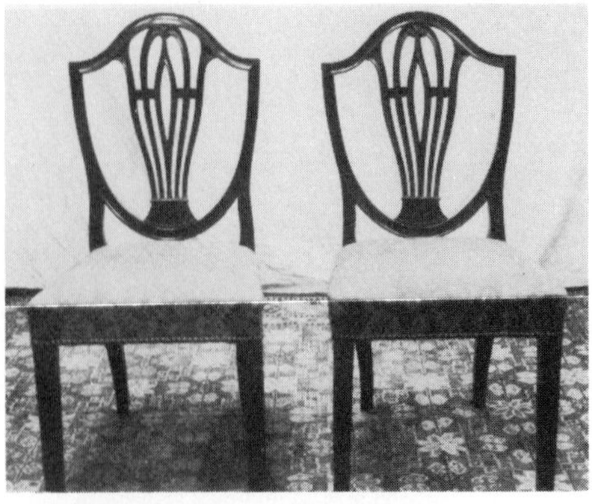

A set of 6 antique mahogany dining chairs of Hepplewhite design. **£400-£500** *WSH*

A set of 10 Adam-style mahogany dining chairs, including 2 armchairs, the medallion back decorated with bell flowers. **£1,200-£1,600** *DS*

A harlequin set of 5 late 18th C. mahogany dining chairs, 4 single and 1 carver. **£550-650** *JSm*

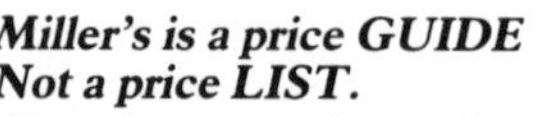

Miller's is a price GUIDE Not a price LIST.

The price ranges given reflect the average price a purchaser should pay for similar items. Condition, rarity of design or pattern, size, colour, provenance, restoration and many other factors must be taken into account when assessing values.

A set of 8 George III-style mahogany dining chairs, including a pair of armchairs, each with a wheatear moulded shield-shaped back, drop-in seat on square moulded supports and spade feet, 20th C. **£800-1,200** *SC*

A set of 6 George III-style mahogany framed dining chairs, including 2 armchairs, late 19th/early 20th C. **£700-800** *Bea*

A set of 8 Hepplewhite-style mahogany dining chairs including 2 armchairs, line inlaid overall. **£550-600** *DS*

A set of 8 reproduction Hepplewhite-style mahogany dining chairs. **£550-600** *CoH*

A set of 6 painted George III upright rail-back chairs. **£1,600-£1,800** *DWB*

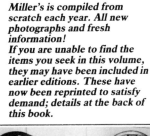

A set of 6 standard Victorian Hepplewhite-style dining chairs with shield-shaped open carved back. **£250-300** *BHW*

A set of 8 George III mahogany Hepplewhite dining chairs (6 plus 2 armchairs). **£4,000-5,000** *AGr*

A set of 3 Sheraton mahogany dining chairs with fluted backs, on moulded tapering supports, 19th C. **£90-120** *DS*

A set of 8 mahogany framed dining chairs including 2 armchairs, 7 chairs George III, 1 side chair later. **£2,500-3,000** *Bea*

A set of 6 George III Sheraton mahogany dining chairs, with reeded bar backs, drop-in seats and square tapered legs. **£550-650** *AGr*

A set of 8 early 19th C. mahogany dining chairs. **£3,200-3,500** *DWB*

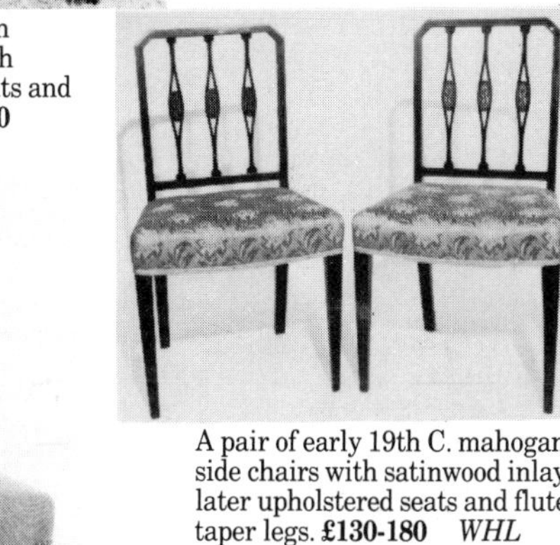
A pair of early 19th C. mahogany side chairs with satinwood inlays, later upholstered seats and fluted taper legs. **£130-180** *WHL*

A set of 9 George III mahogany dining chairs including an armchair, 8 with later blocks. **£2,500-3,500** *C*

A set of 6 George III mahogany dining chairs inlaid with holly and boxwood stringing, c. 1790. **£1,200-£1,400** *S*

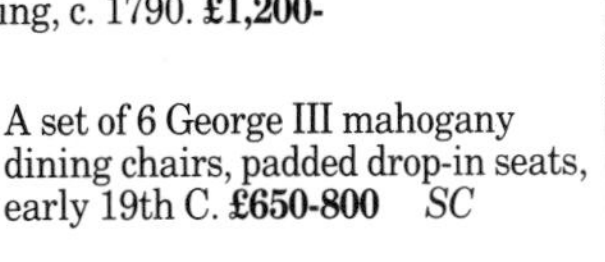
A set of 6 George III mahogany dining chairs, padded drop-in seats, early 19th C. **£650-800** *SC*

A set of 8 George III mahogany dining chairs, including an armchair, c. 1790. **£1,400-1,600** *S*

A set of 12 Dutch beechwood dining chairs, legs headed by paterae, distressed, c. 1790. **£850-1,050** *S*

A set of 9 painted satinwood dining chairs in George III-style, late 19th C. **£3,500-4,000** *S*

A set of 6 Sheraton-style Edwardian dining chairs, c. 1910. **£700-800** *Ph*

A late 18th C. mahogany armchair in the style of Sheraton, c. 1790. **£300-350** *CC*

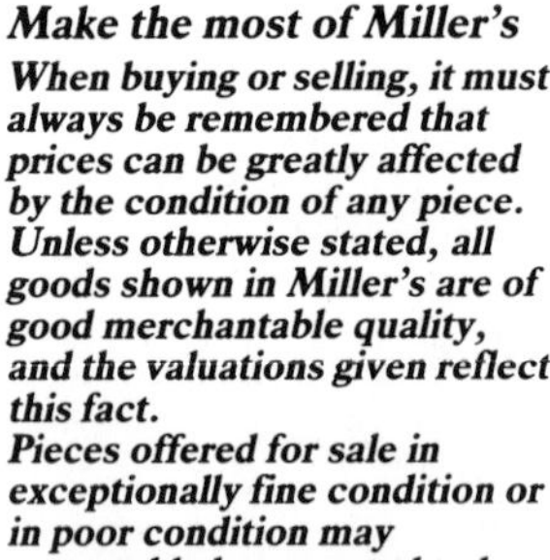

Make the most of Miller's

When buying or selling, it must always be remembered that prices can be greatly affected by the condition of any piece. Unless otherwise stated, all goods shown in Miller's are of good merchantable quality, and the valuations given reflect this fact.
Pieces offered for sale in exceptionally fine condition or in poor condition may reasonably be expected to be priced considerably higher or lower respectively than the estimates given herein.

A set of 8 Edwardian dining chairs, 2 arms, 6 singles. **£1,400-1,600** *Ph*

A set of 5 Regency brass-inlaid chairs including an armchair, the toprails and crossbars inset with bands and panels of cut-brass on ebony, c. 1810. **£550-650** *S*

A set of 6 Regency sabre leg dining chairs with rope work backs, brass inlay and drop-in seat. **£1,000-£1,200** *MMB*

A set of 8 Regency simulated rosewood chairs. **£1,100-1,300** *DWB*

A set of 8 Regency simulated rosewood dining chairs, including an armchair, the toprail inlaid with a panel of brass decoration, c. 1815. **£1,300-1,600** *S*

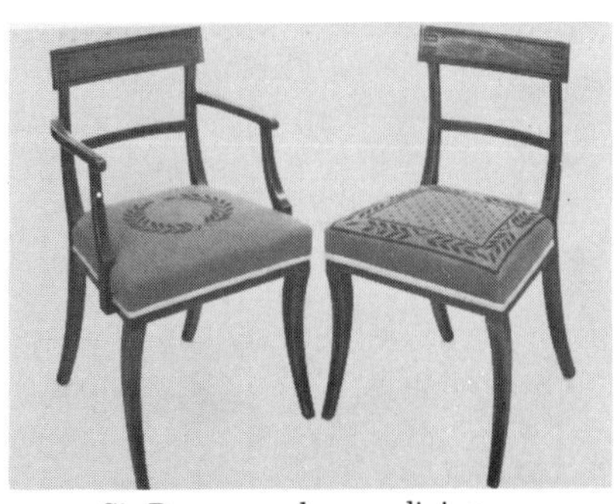

Six Regency mahogany dining chairs including 2 armchairs, one slightly different, all inlaid with ebony lines and panels and Greek key pattern, some seat strengthening. **£1,500-1,700** *L*

A set of 8 Regency simulated rosewood dining chairs, including a pair of armchairs, one bearing a label inscribed 'Linnell sale 1917'. **£2,800-3,200** *C*

A set of 8 Regency-style beechwood dining chairs with brass inlay, 2 arms, 6 singles. **£1,300-1,500** *RBB*

A set of 6 single and 2 elbow Regency mahogany dining chairs. **£3,000-3,200** *DWB*

A set of 5 Regency rosewood framed dining chairs inlaid with brass foliate motifs. **£550-700** *S*

A set of 6 English simulated rosewood single dining chairs with cane seats and brass inlay, c. 1815. **£2,250-2,550** *HB*

A set of 4 Regency mahogany dining chairs with curved solid cresting rails inlaid with ebony stringing and incised decorations. **£400-500** *L*

A set of 5 Regency simulated calamanderwood and parcel-gilt dining chairs in the manner of George Smith, including a pair of armchairs, covered in lime-green linen, 3 stamped M.P., 3 partly re-railed, and another en suite of later date. **£9,500-10,500** *C*

A set of 6 Regency mahogany dining chairs, the backs with broad toprails with reeded panels on either side of the brass inlaid centre section. **£700-800** *NSF*

A set of 6 (4 single, 2 elbow) Regency mahogany railback chairs with satinwood panels. **£1,650-£1,800** *DWB*

A set of 6 Regency brass inlaid simulated rosewood side chairs, with drop-in seats and sabre legs, c. 1810. **£800-1,000** *S*

A Regency mahogany armchair. **£250-320** *Ph*

A set of 4 Victorian mahogany dining chairs, c. 1850. **£400-500** *Ph*

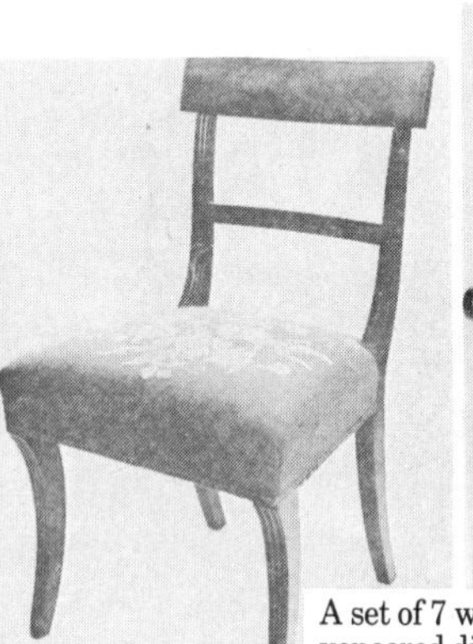
Six Regency mahogany dining chairs on reeded sabre legs with reeded uprights. **£1,000-1,200** *JSm*

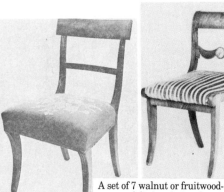

A set of 7 walnut or fruitwood-veneered dining chairs, drop-in seats on sabre supports, probably Scandinavian, early 19th C. **£800-£1,000** *SC*

A set of 6 Regency mahogany dining chairs, each with a drop-i seat, early 19th C. **£500-700** *S*

A set of 12 George III mahogany dining chairs, including a pair of armchairs, with seat rails, now obscured by Victorian leather upholstery, the 'X' design backs centred by paterae. **£5,000-6,000** *HyD*

A pair of painted Regency chairs. **£650-750** *DWB*

A set of 8 Regency oak dining chairs after a design by George Smith, including a pair of armchairs, in the Gothic-style, the block feet carved with rosettes, one with later blocks. **£1,300-1,500** *C*

The design of these chairs corresponds very closely to one of two designs for 'Parlor Chairs' first published by George Smith in 1807 and included as plate 37 in his Collection of Designs for Household Furniture of 1808. The treatment of the panelling on the legs has been simplified.

A set of 10 mahogany dining chairs, including 2 armchairs, each with a concave moulded rail, rattan panel back and seat, with a squab cushion, on ring turned supports, with restorations, early 19th C. **£1,000-1,200** *SC*

A set of 8 Regency period dining chairs in mahogany, having carved and reeded rails within reeded uprights above upholstered squabs on carved turned legs with crossing stretchers, carvers of later date, 21 in. wide by 22 in. deep by 33 in. high, c. 1820. **£2,800-3,500** *HAL*

A pair of Regency ebonised and gilded open armchairs, the oval horsehair-upholstered seats on tapering legs, one partly re-supported. **£4,500-5,000** *C*

A set of 4 Regency brown painted open armchairs, with pierced vertical splat backs inset with lozenges. **£500-600** *CEd*

A set of 8 Regency mahogany framed dining chairs including 2 armchairs, some damage. **£3,000-£3,500** *Bea*

A set of 12 early 19th C. mahogany rail back dining chairs, 10 single and 2 elbow chairs. **£3,600-4,000** *DWB*

A set of 6 Regency mahogany dining chairs. **£800-900** *DWB*

A set of 6 Regency period mahogany side chairs, the backs with rope twist horizontal rails and well-figured-veneered crest panels. **£1,700-1,900** *WW*

A set of 8 Regency mahogany dining chairs including a pair of armchairs, one partly re-railed. **£2,000-2,500** *C*

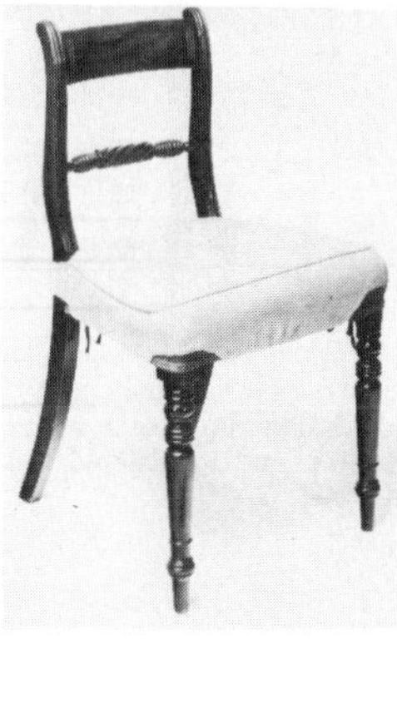

A set of 8 Regency dining chairs, including 2 armchairs. **£3,000-£3,500** *DS*

A set of 6 George III mahogany dining chairs, the stuffed seats on turned tapering legs, c. 1810. **£1,100-1,300** *S*

A pair of early 19th C. bar-back dining chairs. **£100-120** *JMW*

A set of 6 William IV mahogany dining chairs. **£750-850** *L*

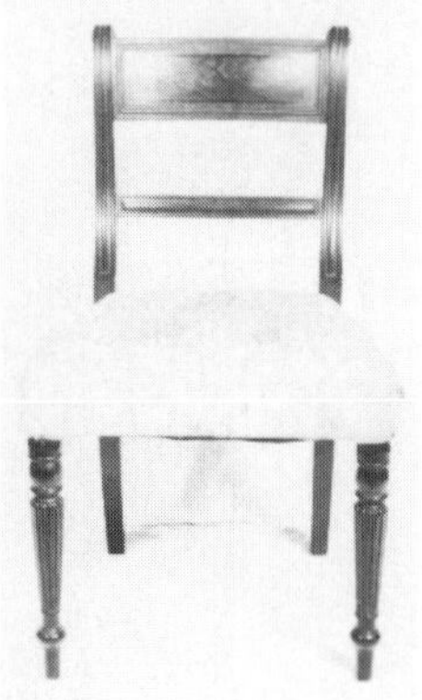
A set of 6 William IV mahogany bar-back dining chairs. **£1,100- 1,300** *JMW*

A set of 6 Regency green-painted dining chairs, the toprails with grisaille roundels, with caned seats. **£1,100-1,600** *C*

CHAIRS
'A rule of thumb'

When assessing the value of single or sets of medium quality chairs, the following rule will give you a rough guide. Remember on sets of rare or early chairs these ratios will increase.

A Pair: ***3 times single chair price***

Set of 4: ***6 to 7 times single chair price***

Set of 6: ***10 to 12 times single chair price***

Set of 8: ***15 plus times single chair price***

A set of 6 rosewood dining chairs, each with a scroll and shell moulded rail and caned seat with a gros point squab cushion, mid 19th C. **£700-900** *SC*

A rare set of 12 Regency beech simulated bamboo dining chairs. **£1,500-2,000** *RD*

A set of 12 late George IV mahogany dining chairs, with drop-in seats on gadrooned supports, mid 19th C. **£1,800-£2,000** *SC*

A set of 6 Victorian mahogany single dining chairs, each with hoop backs and upholstered seats. **£400-500** *DDM*

A set of 4 William IV dining chairs with tooled leather seats, all different designs. **£500-550** *CDE*

(l.) Four carved rosewood Regency dining chairs. **£350-400** *Fr*

(r.) A set of 6 Victorian Louis XIV-style walnut drawing room chairs. **£450-500** *Fr*

A set of 6 William IV mahogany dining chairs. **£900-1,100** *T*

A set of 6 early Victorian dining chairs, stylised scroll horizontal bars. **£425-475** *L*

One of a set of 12 mahogany dining chairs, c. 1840. **£2,200-2,750** *STR*

A set of 7 mahogany dining chairs with drop-in seats, William IV, early 19th C. **£1,000-1,200** *CDE*

A set of 8 William IV mahogany dining chairs including a pair of armchairs, the toprails carved above a scrolled moulded splat, c. 1830. **£2,000-2,200** *S*

A set of 8 George IV carved mahogany rail back chairs, with Trafalgar seats, on turned and reeded legs, comprising: 6 standards and 2 carvers, restored, c. 1825. **£1,200-1,500** *SS*

A set of 6 William IV rosewood chairs, with drop-in seats, c. 1835. **£700-800** *S*

A set of 8 William IV rosewood dining chairs. **£800-900** *PWC*

A pair of Victorian balloon back chairs. **£80-90** *CDE*

A set of 4 Victorian mahogany dining chairs, c. 1850. **£550-650** *Ph*

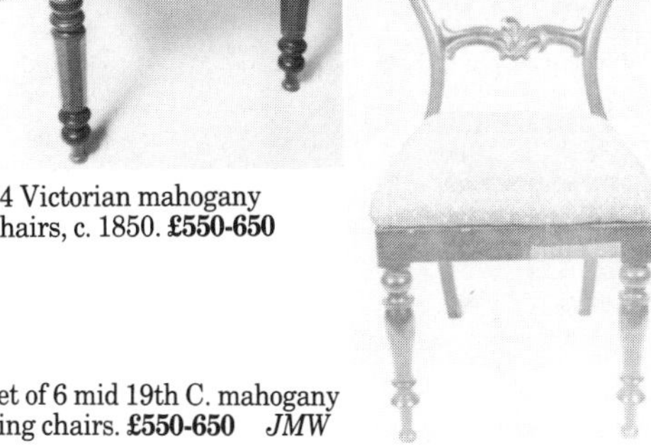

A set of 6 mid 19th C. mahogany dining chairs. **£550-650** *JMW*

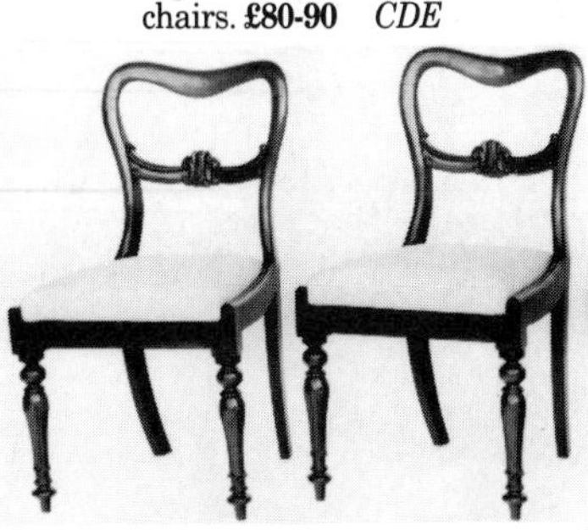

A set of 6 early 19th C. rosewood single dining chairs with shaped hooped backs on fluted front supports. **£650-800** *DDM*

A set of 6 mahogany dining chairs, c. 1850. **£550-650** *JMW*

A set of 8 Victorian mahogany dining chairs, the waisted hoop backs with pierced horizontal bars. **£800-850** *L*

A set of 6 Victorian balloon back chairs. **£480-540** *CDE*

A pair of walnut framed 19th C. dining chairs. **£80-100** *JMW*

A set of 4 Victorian mahogany hoop back single dining chairs, on turned supports. **£175-225** *DDM*

A set of 6 rosewood dining chairs, the moulded saddle-shaped backs with a C-scroll crossbar, c. 1845. **£1,000-1,200** *S*

A set of 6 William IV rosewood dining chairs, c. 1820. **£1,400-£1,600** *Ph*

A set of 5 Victorian mahogany balloon back single dining chairs with needlework drop-in seats on turned supports. **£325-350** *DDM*

A set of 6 Victorian mahogany dining chairs. **£600-700** *CDC*

A set of 3 mahogany dining chairs, c. 1850. **£135-155** *CDE*

A set of 4 chairs, c. 1880. **£300-£340** *CDE*

A set of 6 walnut parlour chairs, c. 1865. **£275-295** *CDE*

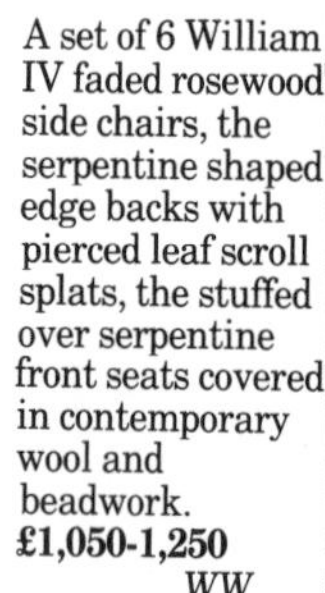
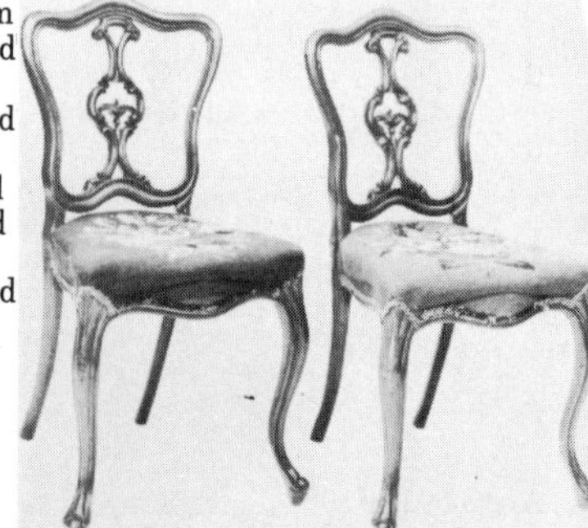
A set of 6 William IV faded rosewood side chairs, the serpentine shaped edge backs with pierced leaf scroll splats, the stuffed over serpentine front seats covered in contemporary wool and beadwork. **£1,050-1,250** *WW*

A set of 6 cabriole leg Victorian walnut frame salon/dining chairs. **£1,000-1,200** *LE*

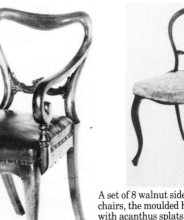

A set of 8 mahogany dining chairs, including 2 armchairs, mid 19th C. **£1,000-1,200** *SC*

A set of 8 walnut side or dining chairs, the moulded hoop backs with acanthus splats, stamped John Taylor & Son Manufacturers Edinburgh number 3003, c. 1850. **£1,000-1,200** *S*

A set of 6 Victorian mahogany dining chairs with balloon backs. **£700-800** *DS*

A set of 4 walnut side or dining chairs, with framework of interlaced leaves and flowerheads, c. 1845. **£600-800** *S*

A set of 6 Victorian dining chairs, c. 1840. **£900-1,000** *CDE*

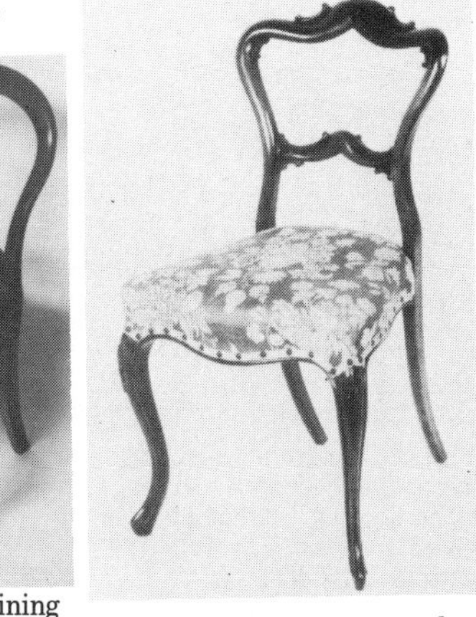

A set of 6 Victorian rosewood framed dining chairs on foliate-carved cabriole legs. **£650-750** *Bea*

A set of 6 Victorian mahogany framed dining chairs, on scroll carved cabriole legs with brass castors. **£700-850** *Bea*

A set of 8 Victorian dining chairs with upholstered backs and serpentine seats, on cabriole legs with pointed toes. **£900-1,100** *GR*

A walnut side chair, c. 1850. **£350-450** *S*

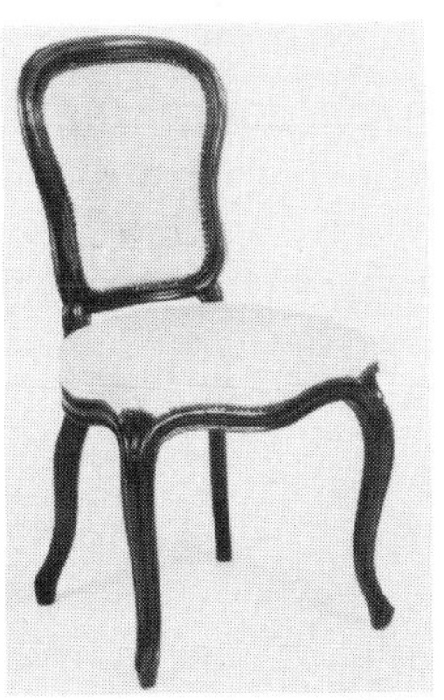

A set of 12 mahogany dining chairs in Louis XV-style, c. 1850. **£1,900-£2,100** *S*

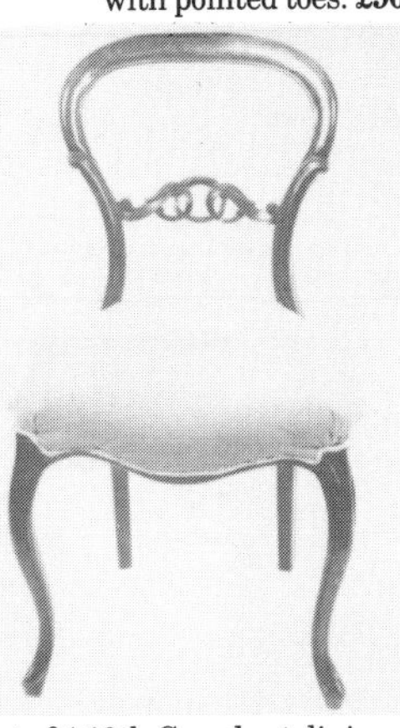

A set of 4 19th C. walnut dining chairs. **£500-550** *JMW*

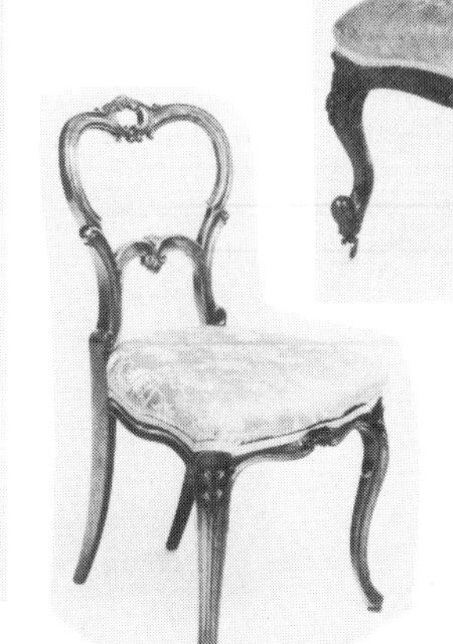

A set of 5 solid rosewood side or dining chairs stamped GILLOW, with stuffed serpentine seats and cabriole legs, c. 1850. **£600-700** *S*

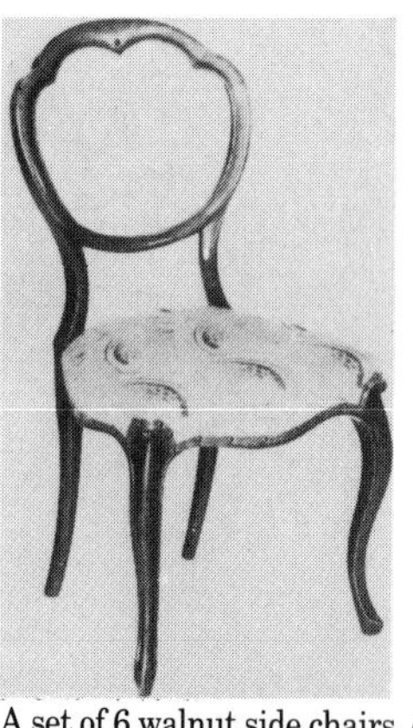
A set of 6 walnut side chairs, each with a moulded balloon-shaped back, padded serpentine seat, on moulded cabriole supports, mid 19th C. **£750-850** *SC*

A pair of walnut occasional chairs, c. 1850. **£115-135** *JMW*

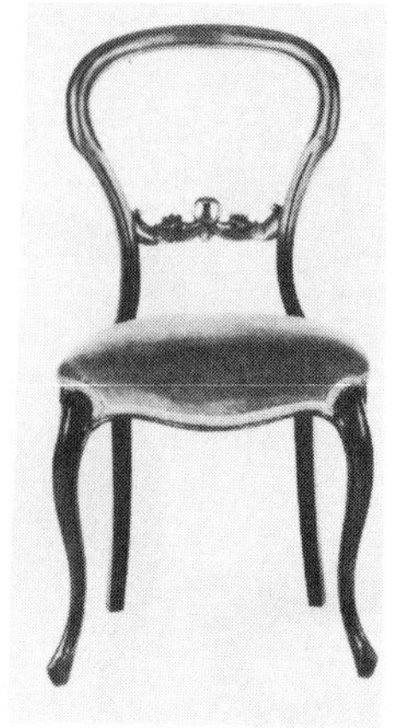
A set of 6 walnut balloon back side chairs, c. 1860. **£700-800** *S*

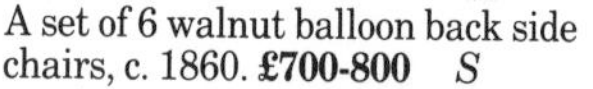
A set of 6 walnut dining room chairs, c. 1860. **£700-800** *S*

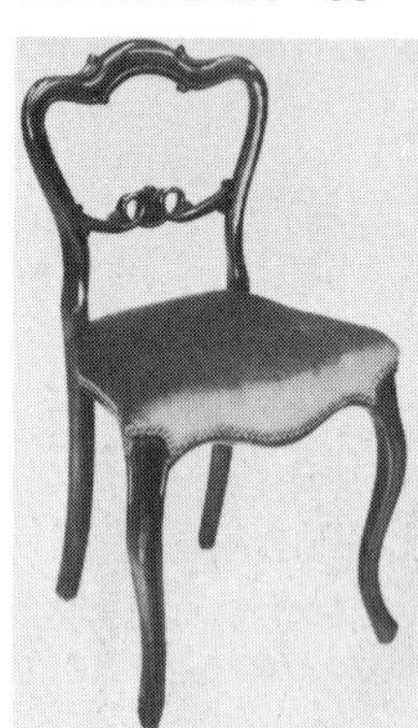
A set of 6 Victorian rosewood chairs, the shaped waisted backs with a stylised horizontal bar, the bowed front seats on cabriole supports. **£700-800** *L*

A set of 6 Victorian walnut chairs. **£850-1,000** *DWB*

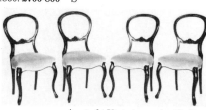

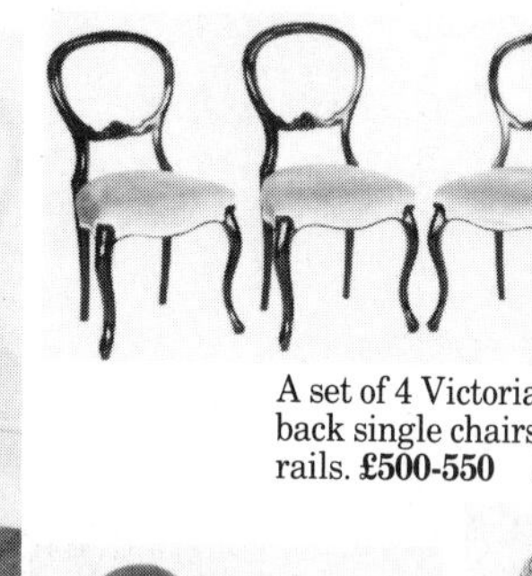
A set of 4 Victorian walnut balloon back single chairs with carved rails. **£500-550** *DDM*

A George II mahogany corner commode chair, c. 1740. **£600-800** *CC*

A Jennens & Bettridge salon chair with gilded and painted papier mâché back, makers stamp, mid 19th C. **£150-180** *WHL*

A rare set of 8 Hanghuali dining armchairs with solid splats set with mirror panels painted with birds, with solid seats, carved aprons and cabriole legs, late 19th C. **£2,000-£2,500** *S*

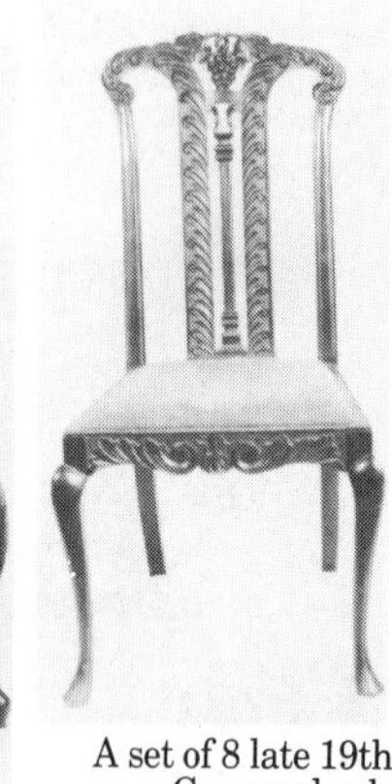
A set of 8 late 19th C. carved oak dining chairs. **£400-500** *JMW*

A George III oak corner armchair with a 'U' shaped back, mid 18th C. **£175-225** *SC*

A heavily carved corner chair, c. 1900. **£150-200** *JMW*

A set of 4 mahogany framed corner chairs, c. 1900. **£180-220** *JMW*

A George II walnut and fruitwood corner armchair, reduced pad feet, with restorations, mid 18th C. **£225-250** *SC*

A pair of late George I walnut child's chairs, c. 1720. **£1,800-£2,000** *S*

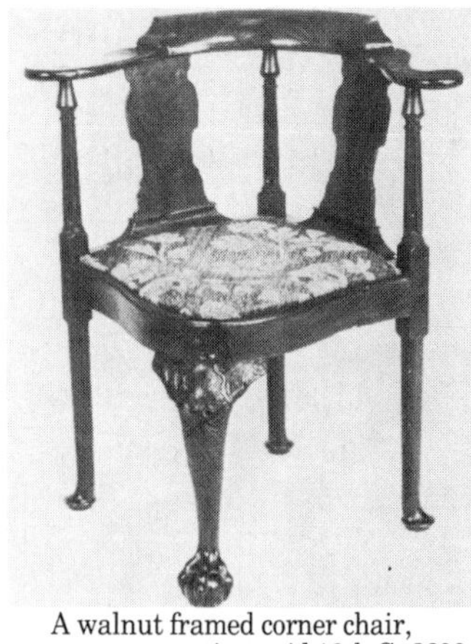

A walnut framed corner chair, some restoration, mid 18th C. **£600-£800** *Bea*

A Regency mahogany high chair converting to table and chair, c. 1815. **£125-225** *STR*

A very rare English oak misericord, 43 in. high, late 15th C. **£4,000-5,000** *RVA*

An early 19th C. child's high chair/feeding chair, with horseshoe shaped back. **£250-300** *GM*

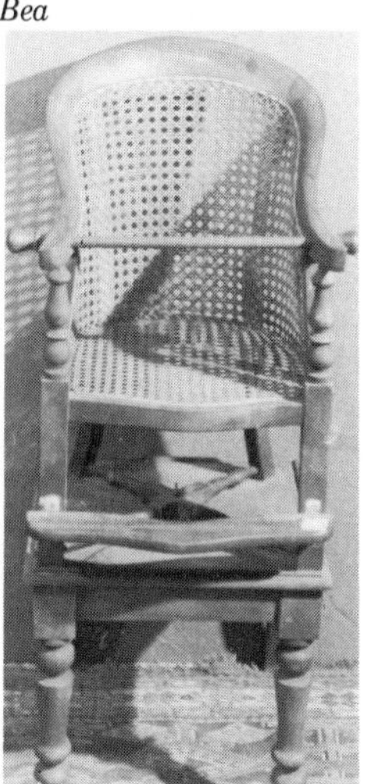

A pair of George II mahogany hall chairs, c. 1740. **£500-600** *CC*

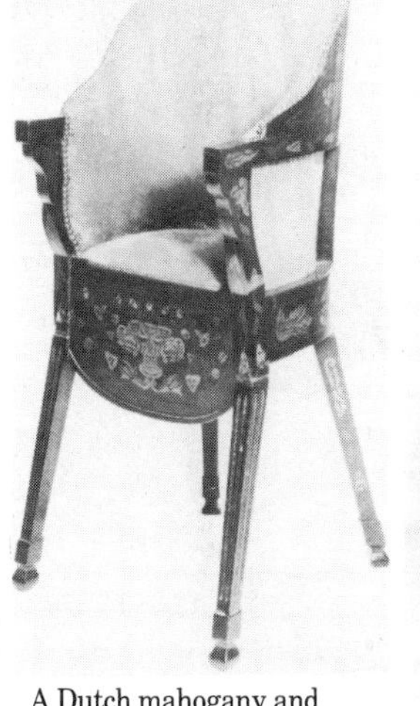

A Dutch mahogany and marquetry child's high chair, c. 1790, later marquetry. **£195-225** *S*

A set of 6 mahogany hall chairs, c. 1740. **£2,600-2,800** *HB*

A pair of walnut hall chairs, c. 1850. **£160-180** *CDE*

A North Italian marquetry prie-dieu with velvet-lined interiors, the moulded base below a lidded door with plain interior, the whole crossbanded in tulipwood, probably Piedmontese, 3 ft. high by 1 ft. 8 in. wide (92 by 51 cm.), c. 1760. **£2,000-2,500** *S*

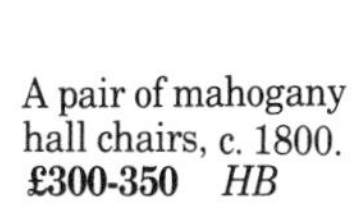

A pair of mahogany hall chairs, c. 1800. **£300-350** *HB*

A Victorian mahogany desk chair, c. 1880. **£90-100** *Ph*

A Victorian oak desk chair, c. 1900. **£120-150** *Ph*

A pair of Victorian oak hall chairs each with carved, scroll and shield backs, solid seats and cabriole front legs. **£90-110** *DDM*

A rosewood 'Gothic' side chair with a tall padded back and padded seat, mid 19th C. **£100-120** *SC*

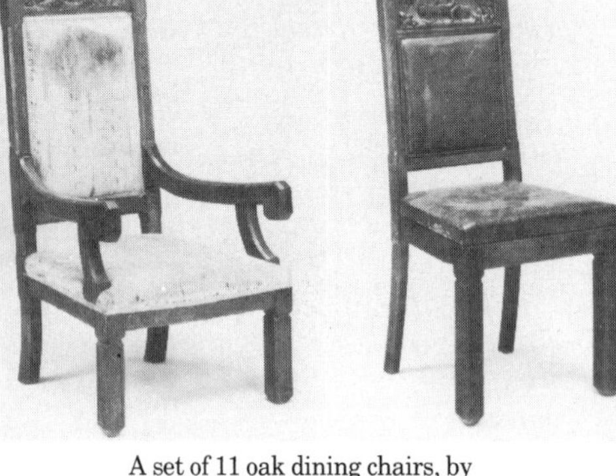

A set of 11 oak dining chairs, by Thomas Tweedy, including a pair of armchairs, the triangular crestings each with a carved panel telling the story of Robinson Crusoe, c. 1862. **£1,000-1,500** *S*

A set of 14 Victorian oak dining chairs including 2 armchairs by Gillows of Lancaster. **£3,250-£3,500** *C*

A set of 5 Edwardian dining chairs, including one armchair, with shaped inlaid backs, line inlaid overall. **£135-160** *DS*

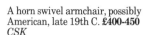

A pair of elm side chairs, the solid splats each carved with a squirrel amongst blossom, with padded seats, the seats covered in European material, 18th C. **£600-£800** *S*

A horn swivel armchair, possibly American, late 19th C. **£400-450** *CSK*

A set of 6 Regency Oriental-style chairs, 2 armchairs, 4 singles and settee in rosewood. **£1,400-1,600** *CDE*

A set of 5 George III mahogany dining chairs, 3 partly re-railed; another en suite of later date; and a pair of George III mahogany dining chairs, similar, re-railed, one with later additions to the legs. **£3,200-£3,600** *C*

A set of 11 mahogany dining chairs, each with a tan leather padded back, contained by a scale moulded frame, conforming seats on turned and fluted supports, mid 19th C. **£1,000-1,400** *SC*

A pair of George III painted framed Chippendale chairs. **£400-425** *HWO*

A set of 6 late 19th C. mahogany high back single dining chairs. **£200-250** *DDM*

A pair of giltwood chairs, c. 1750. **£250-300** *BP*

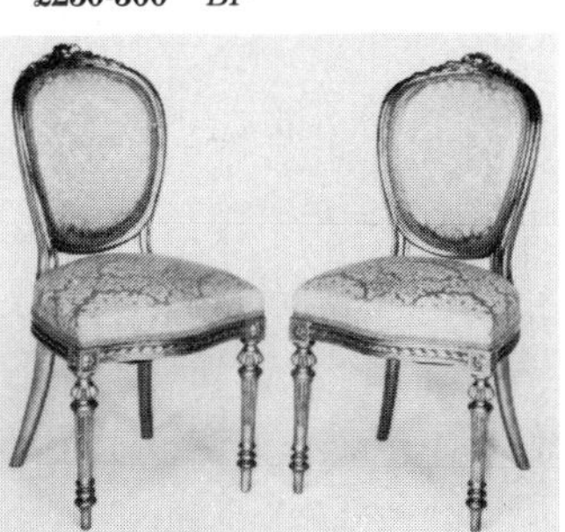

A set of 6 Louis XVI-style giltwood side chairs, c. 1880. **£800-1,000** *SI*

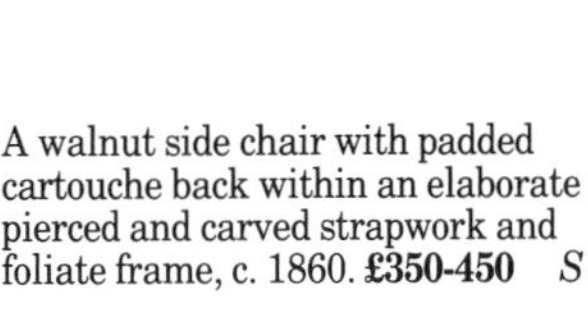

A walnut side chair with padded cartouche back within an elaborate pierced and carved strapwork and foliate frame, c. 1860. **£350-450** *S*

A set of 8 late 19th C. oak rush seat chairs, including 2 carvers. **£480-£540** *TA*

Twelve painted beech frame chairs including one armchair, each with open ladder shield shape backs, 18th/19th C. **£950-1,050** *L*

A Hepplewhite green hide covered mahogany armchair in the French style, c. 1780. **£900-1,200** *CC*

A set of 4 walnut and parcel-gilt library armchairs of mid-Georgian design. **£2,600-2,800** *C*

A pair of Charles II silvered walnut open armchairs, redecorated and re-railed. **£1,000-1,500** *C*

A Venetian walnut armchair, c. 1680. **£1,300-1,500** *S*

An Italian walnut open armchair covered in turkey-pattern foral gros- and petit-point needlework, later blocks, 17th C. **£500-600** *C*

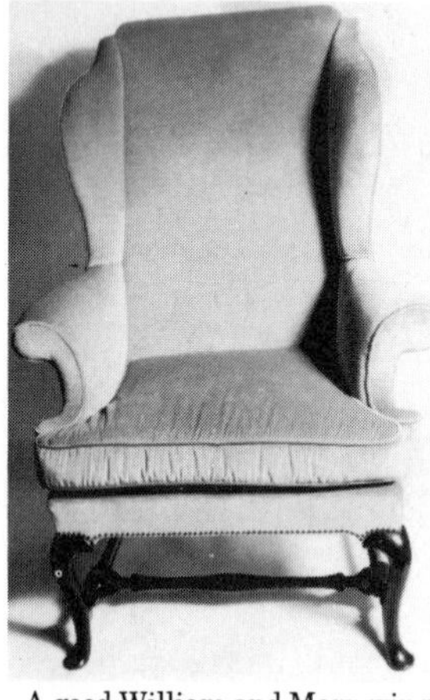

A good William and Mary wing chair. **£3,500-4,000** *HB*

An early 18th C. walnut framed wing arm easy chair, the upholstered seat, back and arms covered with faded green velour, on cabriole legs, restored. **£800-£1,000** *SS*

A fine William and Mary beechwood wing armchair, covered in 18th C. green damask, c. 1695. **£4,000-5,000** *S*

A Louis XIV walnut armchair, late 17th C. **£1,700-1,900** *S*

A Charles II armchair with straight padded arms, and a stuffed seat and squab cushion upholstered in 18th C. gros point needlework, c. 1680. **£1,500-£1,600** *S*

Two finely carved walnut William and Mary-style master open armchairs, both having extensively carved scroll arms and legs with shaped 'X' stretchers. **£500-550** *AGr*

A George I beechwood wing armchair, covered in multi-coloured flame-stitch needlework centred by a petit point armorial cartouche. **£2,200-2,500** *C*

A Queen Anne walnut wing armchair, c. 1700. **£800-1,000** *S*

A George II walnut library armchair, covered with contemporary yellow-ground gros and petit-point floral needlework. **£3,500-4,500** *C*

A George II mahogany library armchair, c. 1750. **£2,000-2,500** *S*

A beechwood armchair, the deep seatrail centred by a shell, possibly German, c. 1730. **£900-1,200** *S*

An early George III solid walnut open armchair, with padded seat, mid 18th C. **£225-275** *SC*

Miller's is a price GUIDE Not a price LIST.
The price ranges given reflect the average price a purchaser should pay for similar items. Condition, rarity of design or pattern, size, colour, provenance, restoration and many other factors must be taken into account when assessing values.

A George I period armchair in walnut, the shaped back carved in the form of eagles heads and scrollwork, the swept arms also terminating in eagles heads, the seat upholstered in old gros point, 30 in. wide by 20 in. deep by 40 in. high, c. 1720. **£1,500-1,900** *HAL*

A George II walnut armchair with velvet seat. **£200-230** *CDE*

A set of George III library steps. **£850-950** *T*

An early George III mahogany library armchair, mid 18th C. **£700-800** *SC*

A George III mahogany library armchair, restored, mid 18th C. **£800-1,000** *SC*

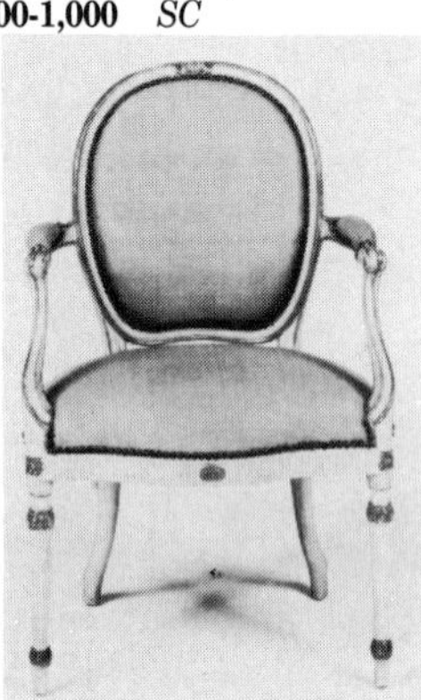
A pair of painted armchairs with fluted seatrails and fluted tapering legs, one c. 1775, the other a modern copy. **£800-1,000** *S*

An unusual Louis XVI grey painted invalid's chair by J. B. Lelarge, moved by cranks at the sides, on steel supported brass wheels, stamped I.B. Lelarge. **£1,200-1,500** *C*

A pair of giltwood fauteuils, one partly re-railed, Italian or Iberian, mid 18th C. **£2,000-2,200** *C*

A pair of George III mahogany framed open armchairs with lobed cresting rails. **£300-350** *Bea*

A set of 6 Dutch elmwood armchairs, c. 1780. **£3,500-3,750** *S*

A set of 4 George III mahogany library chairs on foliate carved cabriole legs and scroll toes. **£2,000-£2,500** *CEd*

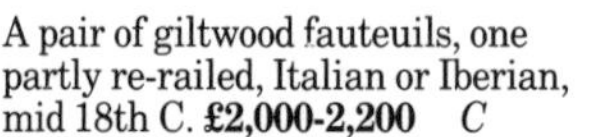

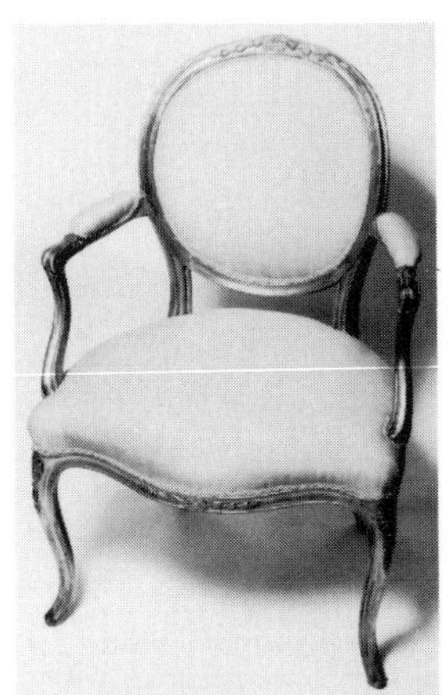
A pair of English giltwood chairs made in the French Louis XV style, c. 1780. **£2,200-2,600** *CC*

A mahogany Gainsborough armchair with lattice and flowerheaded blind fret, on chamfered legs with pierced wings, 18th C. **£1,500-1,800** *CSK*

A set of 3 George III painted armchairs, the bow front fluted seatrail on turned tapering fluted and leaf-carved legs headed by paterae, redecorated, c. 1770. **£2,000-2,500** *SI*

A set of 20 mahogany armchairs, in George III style, modern. **£2,500-£3,500** *S*

A pair of George III giltwood open armchairs, the moulded frames carved with bead-and-reel ornament and coned crestings. **£3,000-3,500** *C*

A George III giltwood open armchair. **£1,300-1,500** *C*

A pair of George III painted open armchairs. **£850-950** *DWB*

A George III mahogany framed elbow chair with padded seat and back, on square chamfered supports. **£300-350** *WSW*

A pair of giltwood armchairs in George III-style, c. 1880. **£800-£900** *S*

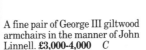

A set of 4 early George III mahogany library armchairs. **£2,200-2,500** *C*

A George III mahogany library armchair, covered in green velvet, and another en suite of later date. **£1,850-2,050** *C*

A fine pair of George III giltwood armchairs in the manner of John Linnell. **£3,000-4,000** *C*

The neo-classical idiom of these chairs is analogous with a drawing of a chair for an unknown client by John Linnell dating from the early 1770's. In particular the distinctive use of a ball finial clasped by leaves on the arms has been identified as a recurrent motif in Linnell's documented oeuvre; it is found for example on a suite of seat furniture supplied c. 1775-78 for Inveraray Castle as well as on the suite of lyre-back armchairs supplied to Robert Child for Osterley Park, c. 1768.

A George III mahogany armchair, with a tall 'U' shaped padded back, on square tapering supports and castors, late 18th C. **£400-500** *SC*

A George III mahogany upholstered armchair, c. 1765. **£4,000-5,000** *S*

A George III mahogany wing armchair, mid 18th C. **£700-800** *SC*

A pair of late George III mahogany bergeres, both now with replacement seats, on turned front supports and castors, early 19th C. **£2,000-2,200** *SC*

A pair of George III Hepplewhite painted armchairs, decorated with central urn motif and painted all over with swags and acanthus on a green ground with gilt borders. **£600-800** *AGr*

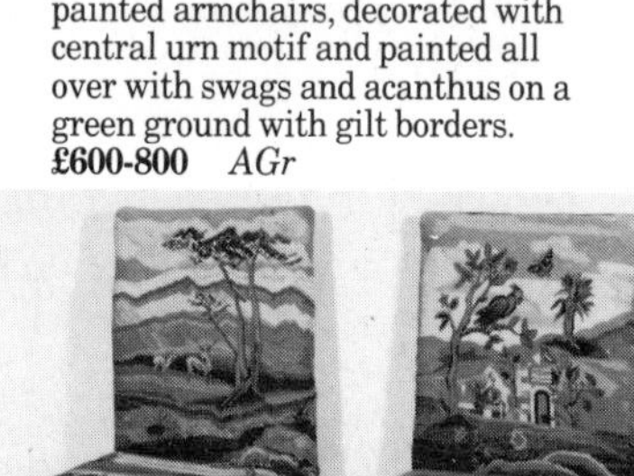

A Chippendale period open armchair. **£600-700** *DWB*

A pair of George III chairs with upholstered backs and seats. **£950-£1,100** *DWB*

A set of 7 late George III mahogany open armchairs, the toprails inlaid with plum pudding panels framed by boxwood lines, and 5 en suite of later date. **£3,000-3,500** *C*

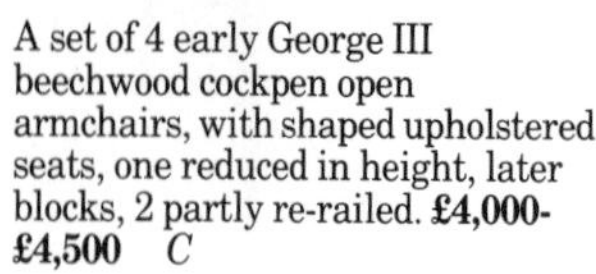

A set of 4 early George III beechwood cockpen open armchairs, with shaped upholstered seats, one reduced in height, later blocks, 2 partly re-railed. **£4,000-£4,500** *C*

A Georgian-style mahogany Gainsborough armchair. **£85-100** *DS*

A Georgian-style mahogany Gainsborough armchair. **£130-£160** *DS*

A mid 18th C. armchair in the Chippendale manner, c. 1760. **£1,250-1,500** *CC*

A set of 4 Louis XV giltwood bergeres, with scrolled toprails carved with foliage and rosettes. **£1,000-1,200** *CEd*

A Louis XVI painted bergere with moulded grey painted frame, c. 1780. **£1,900-2,100** *S*

An E. W. Pugin oak 'Granville' chair, the back-rail inlaid with ebony dots, stamped P.O.D.R. mark for 1870, 79 cm. **£1,400-1,600** *S*

This chair presumably takes its name from the Granville Hotel, Ramsgate, which Pugin worked on between 1869-70, although the same design appears in the 1881 catalogue of C. & R. Light. The P.O.D.R. mark is for October 17th, 1870.

A George III mahogany bergere armchair, with original leather cushions, c. 1800. **£400-500** *RD*

A pair of Louis XVI-style giltwood bergeres, c. 1860. **£750-950** *S*

A Régence tapestry covered oak fauteuil, carved with leafy scrolls, c. 1720, possibly Liège, tapestry late 17th C. **£2,000-2,500** *S*

A painted satinwood framed bergere chair, the frame painted with drapery and flowers, a tapestried seat, 19th C. **£450-500** *WHL*

A set of 6 Louis XV beechwood fauteuils. **£4,500-5,500** *C*

A Louis XV-style open armchair. **£360-400** *DWB*

A walnut and beechwood fauteuil with padded back and serpentine upholstered seat covered in gros point floral needlework, mid 18th C. **£2,400-2,600** *C*

A pair of Louis XV-style painted open armchairs. **£1,500-1,800** *DWB*

A Regency-style tub chair, c. 1900. **£90-110** *JMW*

A pair of Regency mahogany bergeres on reeded tapering legs headed by flowerhead bosses. **£3,500-3,750** *C*

A set of 6 Regency armchairs with black and gilt painted decoration. **£6,000-7,000** *MMB*

A set of 4 Louis XVI-style beechwood fauteuils. **£950-1,250** *S*

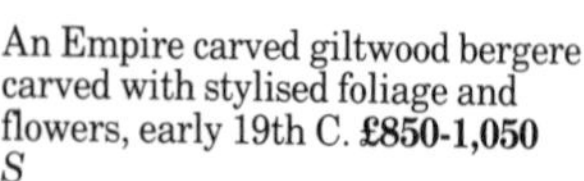
An Empire carved giltwood bergere carved with stylised foliage and flowers, early 19th C. **£850-1,050** *S*

A late 18th C. North Italian cream and gilt painted elbow chair. **£250-£300** *DWB*

A fine pair of Regency mahogany bergeres, with leather-covered loose cushions, early 19th C. **£5,500-6,000** *S*

A set of 4 giltwood fauteuils and a canapé en suite, 172 cm. wide, c. 1880. **£1,200-1,400** *S*

An 18th C. Italian silvered elbow chair. **£650-750** *DWB*

A Dutch barber's chair, the mahogany frame with swan neck handgrips, re-upholstered with removable seat and the rising mechanism partly removed, 38 in. high (99 cm.), early 19th C. **£500-£600** *L*

A pair of period-style open armchairs with maker's name Shoolbred & Co., Tottenham Court Road, London, on base, having satinwood crossbanding and ebony and boxwood stringing, c. 1900. **£300-350** *BHW*

An unusual 19th C. French porters chair. **£1,000-1,250** *RD*

A fine pair of late Regency period rosewood show frame tub shape armchairs with remains of upholstery, c. 1820. **£5,500-6,500** *WW*

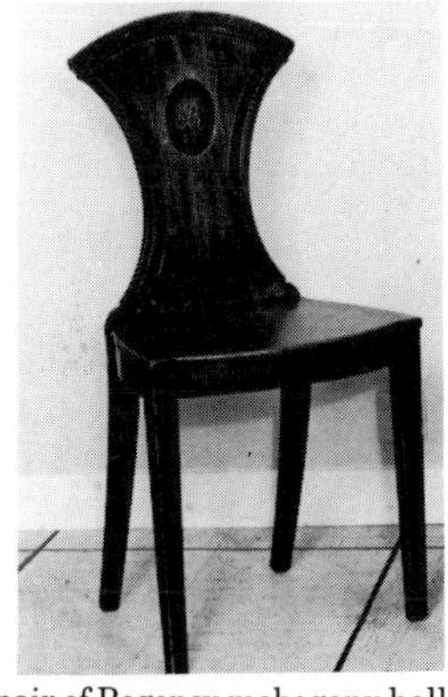
A pair of Regency mahogany hall chairs, the waisted backs with initial B in oval recess. **£300-350** *NSF*

A 19th C. framed nursing chair. **£150-180** *JMW*

A rare pair of Swedish mahogany armchairs, c. 1800. **£950-1,150** *HB*

A 'George II' gilt walnut library armchair, upholstered in machine-made gros point Cluny tapestry, c. 1900. **£750-850** *S*

A pair of late William IV mahogany armchairs, each with a cartouche moulded back, padded drop-in seat, mid 19th C. **£600-£700** *SC*

A pair of walnut framed open armchairs on cabriole legs with knurl feet, c. 1850. **£350-450** *CDE*

An early Victorian walnut frame spoon back gentleman's and lady's chair, on cabriole legs, together with 2 standard chairs en suite. **£1,000-1,200** *LE*

A mahogany captain's chair, c. 1830. **£130-150** *CDE*

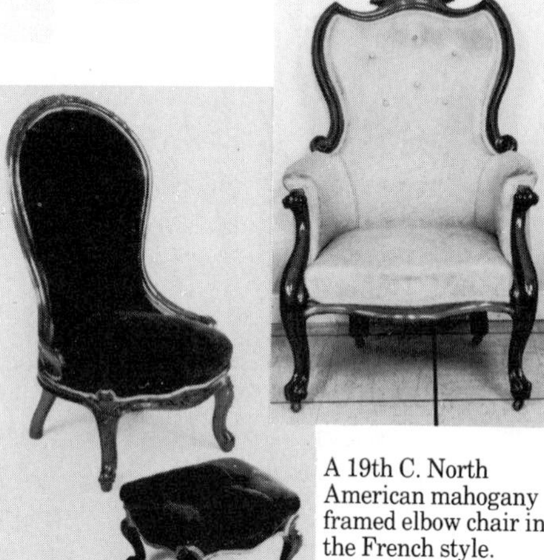

A Victorian walnut nursing chair and a similarly upholstered foot stool, the serpentine top on scrolling cabriole legs. **£250-275** *CSK*

A 19th C. North American mahogany framed elbow chair in the French style. **£350-400** *NSF*

A set of 4 giltwood Isobellino chairs, supported on Louis 'XIV' gadrooned legs joined by an 'X' stretcher, Spanish, c. 1860. **£750-£950** *S*

A Micmac quilled wood 'gossip' chair, with geometric panels of quillwork on birchbark on shaped seat, worn, 37 in. high (94 cm.), c. 1880. **£325-350** *C*

A good Charles II walnut open armchair, upholstered, 45 in. high, c. 1670. **£800-1,000** *RVA*

A fine William and Mary giltwood armchair, the arms with richly carved leafy handles and bold leaf-carved scroll supports, the slightly canted S-scroll legs swagged with chains of flowers and with square lower parts above almost diamond-shaped leaf-carved feet joined by flat leaf-carved H-shaped stretchers, re-railed and back legs replaced, c. 1690. **£2,000-3,000** *S*

A Victorian walnut spoon-back armchair and matching nursing chair, each with carved scroll and leaf decoration. **£650-750** *DDM*

A set of 10 19th C. oak 'William III' dining chairs, the set including 2 elbow chairs with lion-mask arm terminals, c. 1870. **£1,500-1,800** *N*

A pair of late Victorian inlaid wing armchairs with shaped cresting rails, raised on cabriole legs inlaid overall in bone and harewood. **£150-200** *DS*

A pair of late George II walnut and parcel gilt library armchairs, c. 1750. **£9,000-10,000** *S*

A set of Venetian 18th C.-style painted seat furniture. **£750-850** *DWB*

A small ladies' chair, c. 1870. **£135-£155** *CDE*

An armchair in the Oriental taste, c. 1890. **£65-85** *CDE*

A set of 7 George II mahogany hall chairs, c. 1740. **£2,000-2,500** *S*

A Victorian fruitwood desk chair, c. 1860. **£225-250** *Ph*

An Edwardian satinwood framed wing armchair, the back with stained and etched floral inlay above serpentine seat, upholstered in buttoned satin brocade. **£350-£450** *WHL*

A Victorian mahogany chair, c. 1870. **£250-275** *Ph*

A George I walnut armchair of generous proportions, with restoration, c. 1725. **£1,200-1,800** *S*

A harlequin set of 9 North Country mahogany open armchairs on square legs joined by stretchers, re-supported, minor variations. **£1,650-1,800** *C*

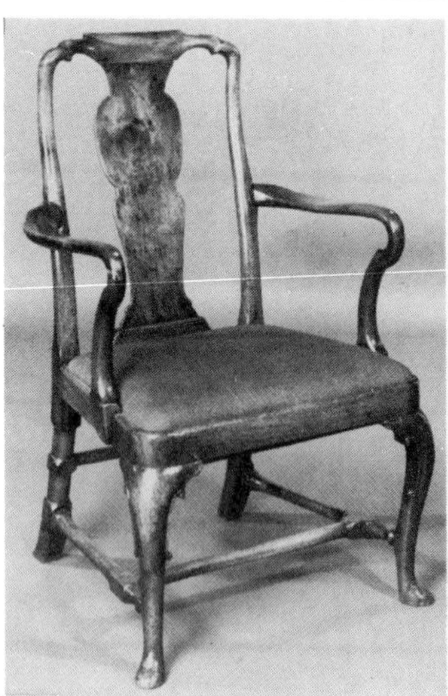
A Queen Anne walnut open armchair. **£4,000-5,000** *C*

A fine pair of George I red-japanned armchairs with pierced and carved leaf-scroll toprails, mainly in shades of gilt on a scarlet ground, painted decoration restored, c. 1720. **£8,500-9,500** *S*

A pair of George II fruitwood country made chairs with shaped splats. **£300-350** *DWB*

Make the most of Miller's
Every care has been taken to ensure the accuracy of descriptions and estimated valuations.
Where an attribution is made within inverted commas (e.g. 'Chippendale') or is followed by the word 'style' (e.g. early Georgian style) it is intended to convey that, in the opinion of the publishers, the piece concerned is a later – though probably still antique – reproduction of the style so designated.
Unless otherwise stated, any description which refers to 'a set' or 'a pair' includes a valuation for the entire set or the pair, even though the illustration may show only a single item.

A pair of 17th C.-style oak hall chairs, each ornately carved with fruiting vines and leaves with barley twist supports. **£160-190** *DDM*

A pair of walnut open armchairs covered in floral damask, basically mid 17th C. **£1,000-1,500** *C*

A set of 3 early 19th C. black and gold lacquer elbow chairs, with cross-frame backs, cane seats, on circular tapering legs, c. 1810. **£550-750** *SS*

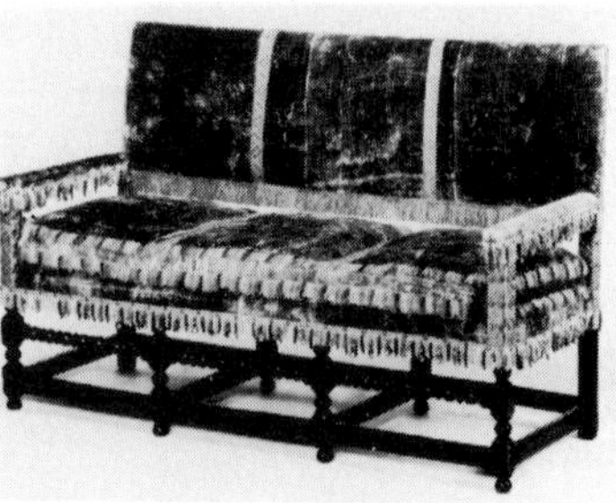
A Charles II oak settee on four front legs joined by a ball-turned stretcher bar above a squared stretcher, on ball feet, upholstered in green silk velvet with 17th C. wire tassel and fringe, frame reconstructed, 2 ft. 9½ in. high by 5 ft. 2 in. wide (85 by 157 cm.), c. 1670. **£2,000-2,500** *S*

A mid Georgian oak hall seat, with 4 fielded panel back, strung seat with a machine Turkey padded cushion, 73 in. (186 cm.), mid 18th C. **£250-300** *SC*

An early 18th C. fruitwood box settle with curved panelled back, lifting box seat, 66 in. wide. **£300-£350** *HWO*

An antique oak settle, c. 1800. **£200-250** *JMW*

A rococo carved elmwood settee, the triple chair-back with bent vase splats, each carved and pierced with a cartouche, probably Danish, with restoration, 5 ft. 3 in. wide (160 cm.), mid 18th C. **£1,500-£1,800** *S*

A 19th C. box seated hall settle. **£180-220** *JMW*

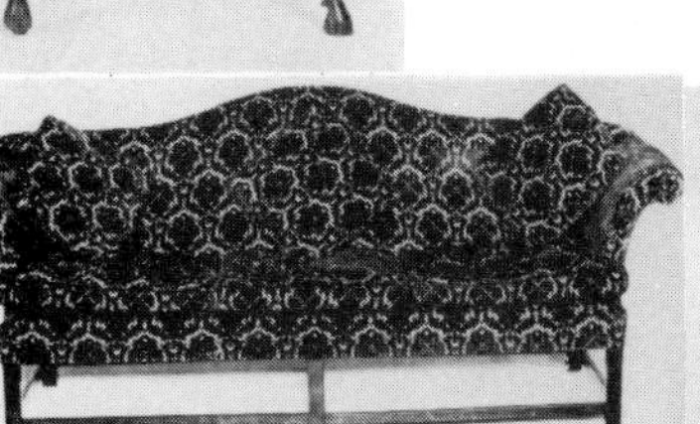

A George III mahogany sofa, with an arched padded back, scroll sides on square supports joined by a rail, 6 down-filled cushions, late 18th C. **£500-700** *SC*

A George II-style mahogany framed double chair back settee, with shell and leaf-carved cresting rails, 50 in. wide. **£900-1,100** *Bea*

A George II mahogany sofa with waved back, out-scrolled arms and serpentine seat, the broad frame crisply carved with foliate scrolls and ribbed cabochon cresting, 80 in. (214 cm.) wide. **£2,500-£3,500** *C*

A George III carved giltwood sofa, 5 ft. 11 in. wide (181 cm.), c. 1780. **£800-900** *S*

A George III carved giltwood sofa with fluted frame and padded arms, 6 ft. 8 in. wide (203 cm.), c. 1780. **£1,000-1,500** *S*

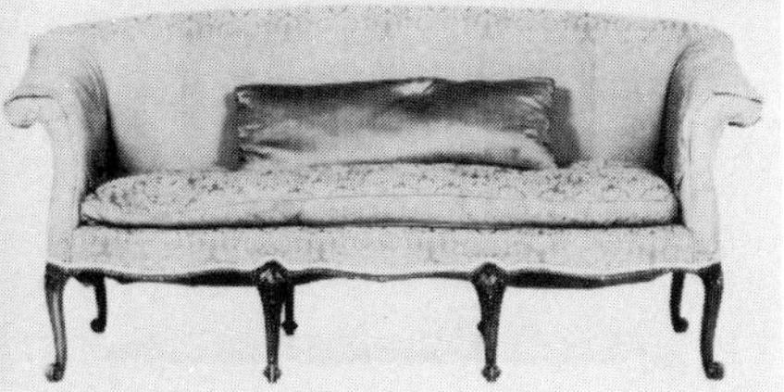

A mahogany settee in George III style, 6 ft. 9 in. wide (206 cm.), c. 1880. **£450-550** *S*

An 18th C. settee of Hepplewhite design, with serpentine back rail and seat later upholstered in cut velvet, much of the original painting and gilding remains, 64 in. **£750-850** *WHL*

An early Louis XV painted and parcel-gilt duchesse, c. 1725. **£1,800-2,200** *S*

A mahogany framed Regency sofa, 78 in. **£300-400** *WHL*

A small walnut sofa on cabriole legs with pad feet, 41 in. wide (104 cm.). **£1,000-1,200** *C*

A late Regency mahogany salon sofa, the bar back centred by a shell and flanked by scrolling and reeded rails on gondola shaped reeded frame, length 78 in. **£300-350** *DS*

An unusual Regency ebonised and gilded 3-seat settee, in the manner of Thomas Sheraton, with shaped toprail painted with oak leaves and foliage, 77 in. wide. **£1,000-1,200** *CEd*

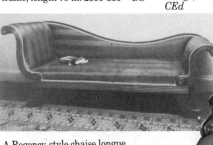

A Regency chaise longue. **£700-£800** *DWB*

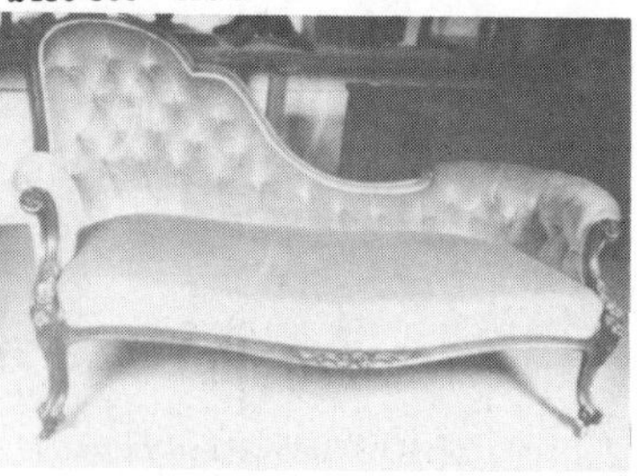

A Regency-style chaise longue. **£450-500** *AGG*

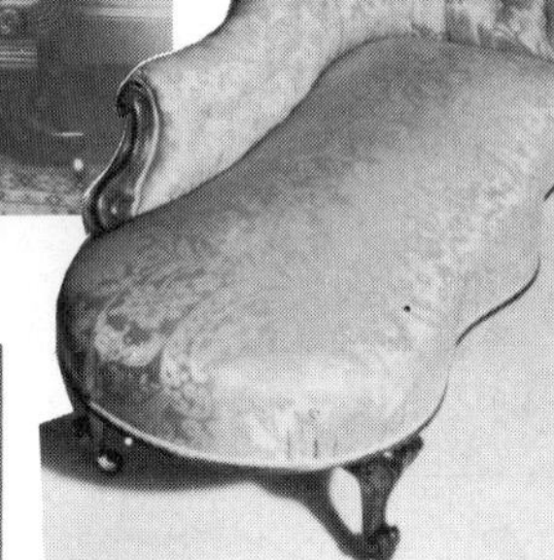

A Victorian walnut chaise. **£500-£600** *HB*

A Victorian walnut framed button upholstered settee. **£400-500** *JF*

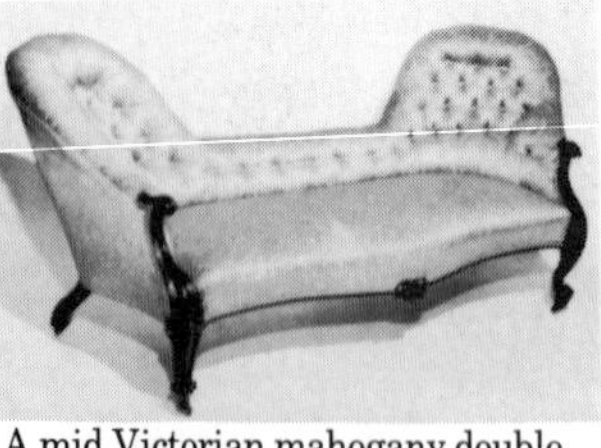

A mid 19th C. rosewood chaise longue. **£550-600** *JMW*

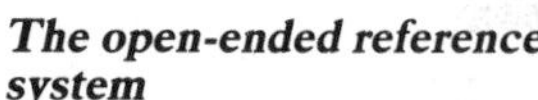

The open-ended reference system

Miller's Antiques Price Guide builds up year by year to form the most comprehensive photo-reference system available. The first four volumes contain photographs of over 30,000 stock items!

A Victorian rosewood sociable sofa on carved cabriole legs. **£1,250-£1,500** *GM*

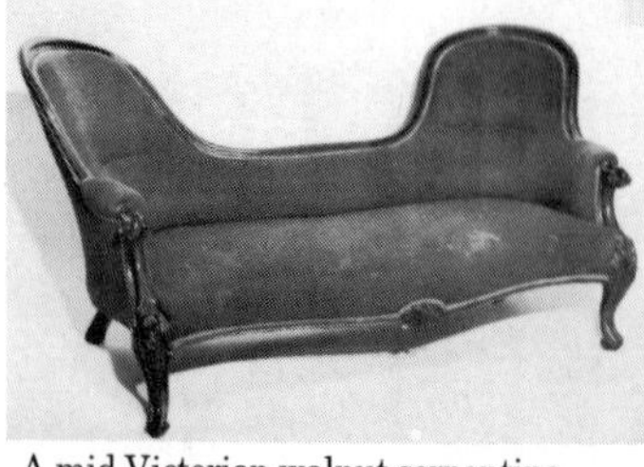

A mid Victorian mahogany double scroll end settee, upholstered in buttoned art silk damask, 7 ft. wide. **£250-300** *WHL*

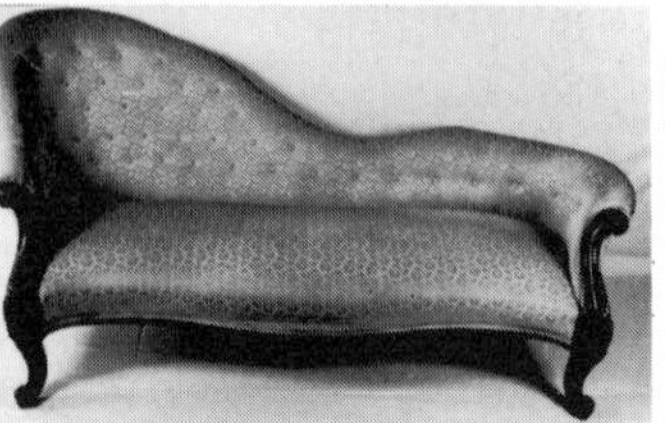

An early Victorian rosewood settee with shaped and padded back and serpentine seat raised on carved cabriole supports. **£400-450** *DS*

A Victorian settee, the button back with raised curved ends in figured velvet upholstery, the mahogany frame with scroll handgrips, 81 in. **£500-600** *L*

A mid Victorian walnut serpentine front settee with moulded frame, on carved scroll legs. **£450-500** *WHL*

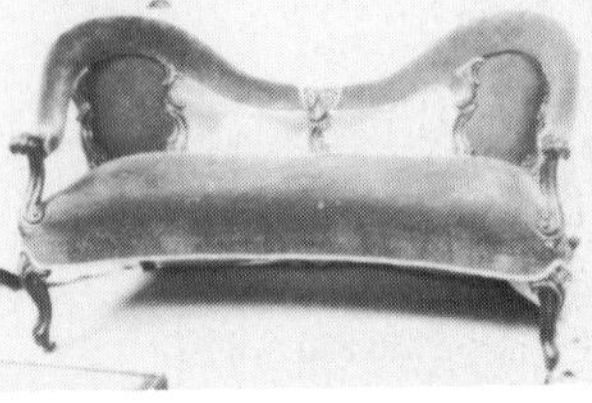

A mid Victorian walnut framed 2-seat settee. **£500-600** *JMW*

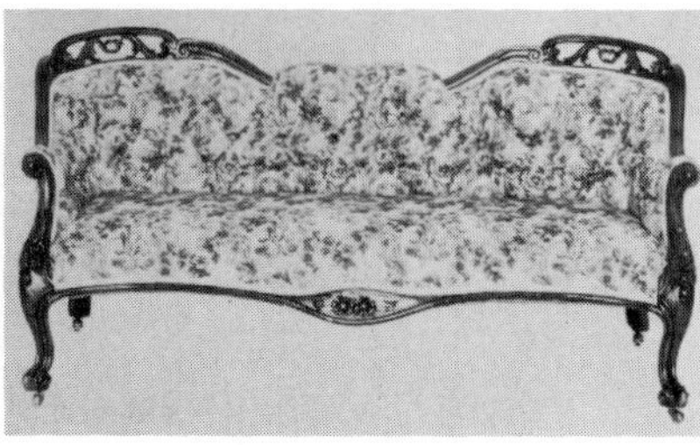

A Victorian walnut framed settee, 62 in. wide. **£750-900** *S*

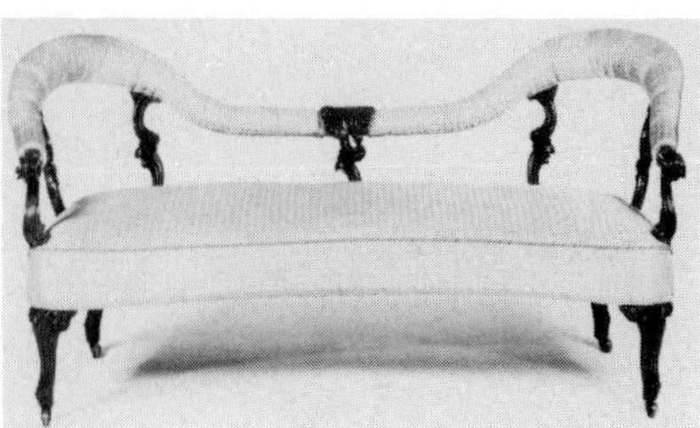

A sofa in carved oak and walnut, 5 ft. 4 in. long (163 cm.), c. 1860. **£425-475** *S*

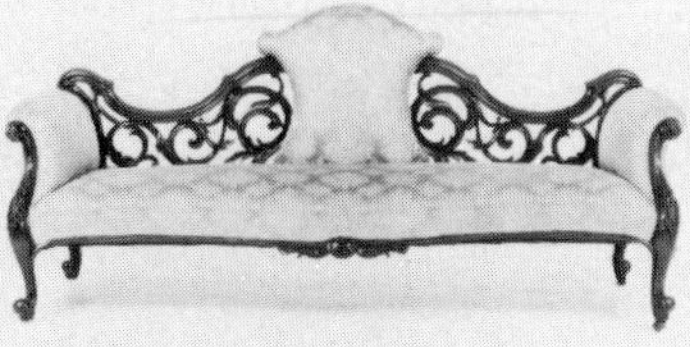

A walnut settee with sprung serpentine seat, 6 ft. 3 in. (190.5 cm.), 1850's. **£800-900** *S*

A pair of Gillow giltwood sofas in the French Louis XVI style, stamped Gillow, 5 ft. 4½ in. long (164 cm.), c. 1860. **£950-£1,000** *S*

A fine oak settee by Thomas Tweedy, carved with Man Friday and Crusoe, 7 ft. 7 in. wide (228 cm.), c. 1862. **£2,000-2,500** *S*

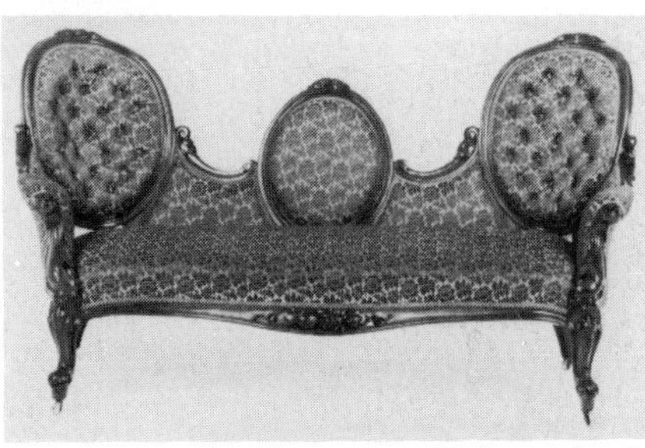

A walnut settee with 3 carved oval moulded backs, 5 ft. 10 in. wide (178 cm.), c. 1860. **£1,500-1,700** *S*

A Louis XV white painted and gilded canape covered in floral Aubusson tapestry, redecorated and restorations, possibly German, 72 in. wide (183 cm.). **£800-1,000** *C*

An Edwardian mahogany 2-seater settee, 42 in. wide, c. 1912. **£250-£300** *Ph*

A mid Victorian carved mahogany high back settee with showood frame and cabriole legs. **£325-£375** *Fr*

A Louis XVI-style carved giltwood canape, 4 ft. 10 in. wide (147 cm.), c. 1880. **£400-500** *SI*

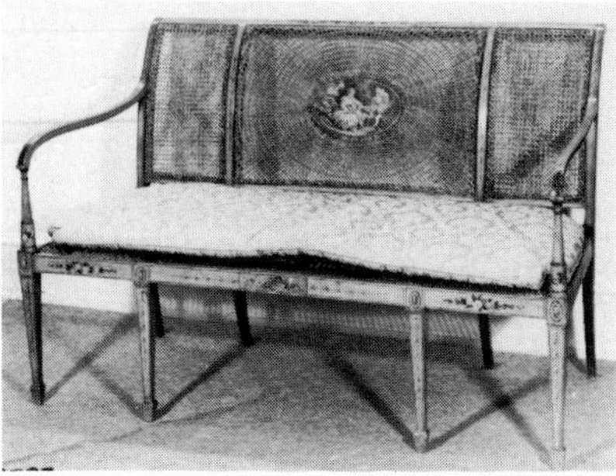

A late 19th C. satinwood settee, 58 in. **£700-800** *DWB*

A pair of George III window seats with slightly bowed fronts, on moulded taper legs with spade feet, 42 in. **£800-1,000** *DWB*

A pair of George III mahogany window seats. **£2,500-3,000** *DWB*

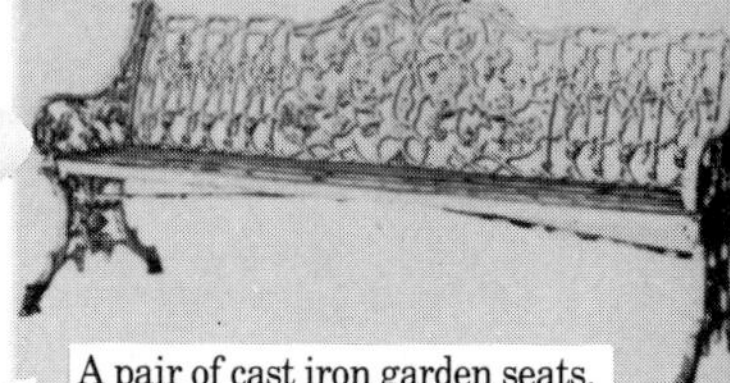

A pair of cast iron garden seats, each with an entwined vine cast back and arms, with a wooden slatted seat, 75 in. wide (191 cm.), mid 19th C. **£500-600** *SC*

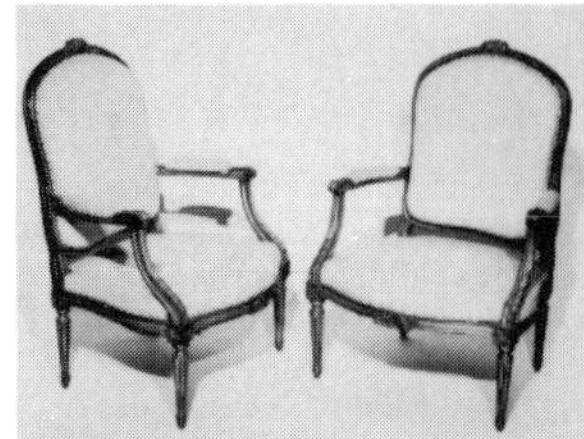

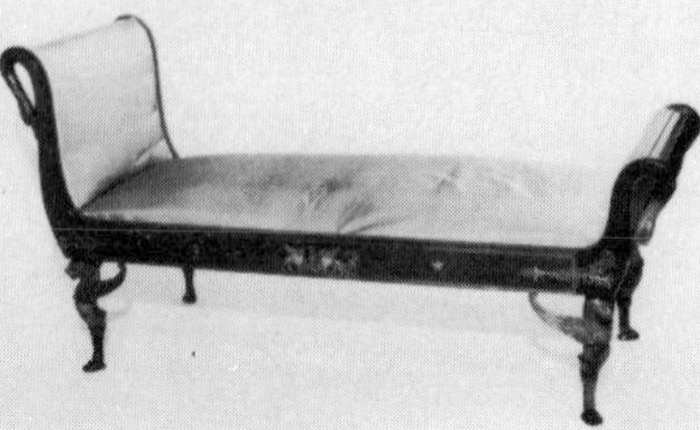

A French mahogany bateau lit with gilt mounts and gilt griffin legs, 69 in., 19th C. **£1,100-1,300** *WHL*

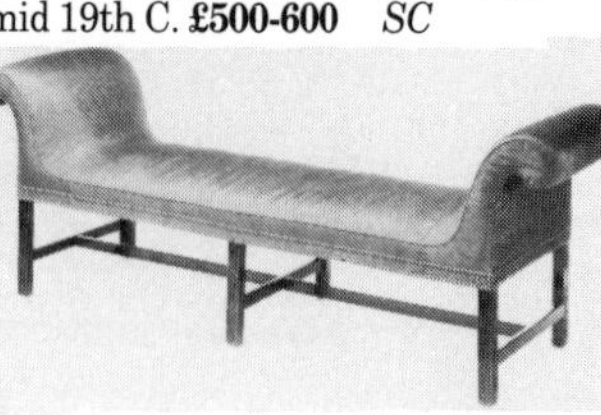

An early George III mahogany window seat covered in nailed brown moiré silk, the legs carved with blind fretwork, 80 in. wide (203 cm.). **£5,000-6,000** *C*

A fine 19th C. 4-piece French carved and gilded salon suite, the canape with moulded carved frame with floret and acanthus leaf and scroll decoration, together with 3 matching fauteuils. **£1,800-2,200** *WHL*

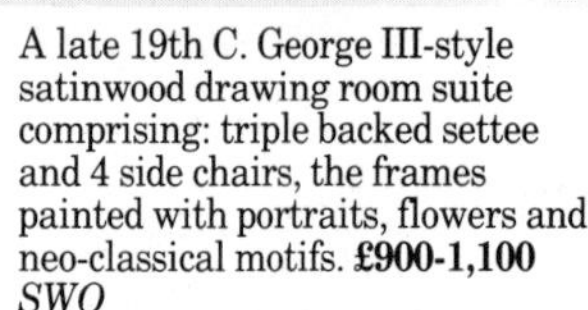

A late 19th C. George III-style satinwood drawing room suite comprising: triple backed settee and 4 side chairs, the frames painted with portraits, flowers and neo-classical motifs. **£900-1,100** *SWO*

A suite of walnut drawing room furniture, comprising an armchair, a low chair and a chaise longue, c. 1860. **£1,000-1,200** *S*

A 7-piece Victorian suite comprising a couch, 2 armchairs and 4 side chairs, carved mahogany frames with patterned moquette upholstery. **£300-400** *JHR*

A suite of walnut seat furniture comprising a sofa, a side chair and an armchair, c. 1860. **£1,000-£1,200** *S*

A late Victorian inlaid walnut 9-piece drawing room suite comprising: a 3-seater buttoned settee, lady's and gent's easy chairs and 6 single chairs. **£1,600-1,800** *BW*

Miller's is a price GUIDE Not a price LIST.

The price ranges given reflect the average price a purchaser should pay for similar items. Condition, rarity of design or pattern, size, colour, provenance, restoration and many other factors must be taken into account when assessing values.

A mahogany and rosewood drawing room suite comprising: 3 side chairs and 2 low chairs, a pair of bergeres and a settee, all inlaid with beechwood and ivory cornucopiae, the settee 4 ft. 2 in. wide (127 cm.), c. 1890. **£750-850** *S*

A painted and cane satinwood bergere suite, comprising a pair of bergeres and a double chair-back settee, painted throughout with flowers, c. 1900. **£700-800** *S*

An inlaid rosewood drawing room suite comprising: a tall backed armchair, a lower backed armchair, a set of 4 chairs, a pair of lower chairs and a settee, with ivory and satinwood floral inlay, the settee 5 ft. wide (153 cm.), c. 1890. **£1,200-1,400** *S*

A 'Liberty's' 3-piece lounge suite, lacquered in the Chinese style, original black and silver figure decorated damask. **£1,250-1,500** *A*

A mahogany framed bergere 3-piece suite with fawn floral pattern loose cushions. **£500-600** *DA*

An Edwardian drawing room suite comprising: 2-seat sofa, 2 arm and 2 standard chairs, in finely carved mahogany frame. **£400-500** *BHW*

A blue japanned suite comprising a pair of bergeres and a sofa, the frames decorated in the Chinese style on a bright blue ground, 1920's. **£500-600** *S*

A Hille japanned satinwood bergere suite in the Chippendale style, comprising a pair of bergeres and a sofa, sofa 6 ft. 4 in. wide (193 cm.), 1920's. **£1,800-2,000** *S*

A small English Gothic coffer, 25 in. wide by 12 in. high, early 16th C. **£1,100-1,300** *RVA*

A late Gothic oak boarded chest, the moulded front stiles curved on the inner edge to form an arch, with iron hinges, lockplate and hasp, top marked, 2 ft. 4½ in. high by 4 ft. 5 in. wide (72 by 134 cm.), early 16th C. **£400-500** *S*

A Henry VIII oak 6-plank chest with hinged top, the front deeply carved with simple Gothic tracery panels and chevron panels, ironwork replaced, 1 ft. 11½ in. high by 4 ft. 11 in. wide (60 by 150 cm.), c. 1520. **£1,000-1,200** *S*

A Henry VIII oak chest, the 4-panel front well carved with linenfold, each end with 2 plain panels, 2 ft. 3½ in. high by 4 ft. 4 in. wide (70 by 132 cm.), c. 1540. **£700-900** *S*

A French Henri II carved walnut coffer, with loop handles, Bourgogne or Lyonnais, 2 ft. 5½ in. high by 5 ft. long (75 by 152 cm.), late 16th C. **£2,000-2,250** *S*

COFFERS

- **13th C. chests hollowed out of tree trunks, clamped with iron, pin-hinged**
- **14th C. still hollowed from tree trunks but strap-hinged**
- **carved and panelled fronts appear at the end of the 14th C.**
- **in Tudor times the plank coffer and framed front popular — linenfold more developed-tracery decoration lost popularity early on**
- **Elizabethan coffers — same design but much finer inlay and carving, particularly Nonsuch inlay**
- **Jacobean saw the introduction of the drawer under the coffer — the mule chest — and by the end of the 16th C. drawers become popular and the days of the plain coffer numbered**
- **through the Cromwellian and Restoration periods coffers still made in oak — although chests in walnut were becoming more popular. By the William and Mary period coffers were becoming a rarity**

A late Gothic oak boarded chest, the 2-plank top with cleats, the front elaborately chip-carved with moulded arches containing double Gothic arches divided by radiating moulded ribs, with traces of original gesso and polychrome decoration, the ends continuing to form the shaped feet, top possibly restored, 2 ft. 2½ in. high by 4 ft. 6½ in. wide (67.5 by 138 cm.), c. 1540. **£900-1,100** *S*

A late mediaeval 6-plank oak chest, the front with interlaced foliate arches, and the end-boards pierced to form feet, the feet re-shaped, 1 ft. 11 in. high by 4 ft. 2 in. wide (59 by 127 cm.), mid 16th C. **£800-900** *S*

A German ironbound walnut chest, 46 in. long, late 16th C. **£1,500-£1,700** *RVA*

A 16th C. Italian carved walnut cassonne, minor restoration, 69 in. **£700-800** *WHL*

An English ironbound oak church coffer, 56 in. wide, early 16th C. **£1,500-1,750** *RVA*

A Queen Anne oak corn chest, the front with a wainscot panel and carved with the initials DH and AH and the date 1706, 3 ft. 6¾ in. high by 7 ft. 5¼ in. wide (108 by 226 cm.). **£800-1,000** *S*

Reputedly from Rufford Hall, Lancashire.

A joined oak chest of large size the front carved with Gothic tracery with roundels, the wide stiles similarly carved and the side panels with Gothic tracery, with some alterations, 74 in., 16th C. **£4,000-4,250** *L*

A fine Nuremburg iron chest, the steel lockplate elaborately pierced and finely engraved, the interior with a small fitted chest with an elaborate foliage false escutcheon, 2 ft. 4 in. high by 3 ft. 5 in. wide by 2 ft. 4 in. deep (71 by 104 by 71 cm.), mid 17th C. **£3,500-4,000** *S*

A good Elizabethan oak coffer with original hinges and iron lock, 55 in. wide, late 16th C. **£1,800-2,000** *RVA*

A Spanish walnut chest of large size, with original iron lock and later oak top and with restorations, 63 by 33 in. (160 by 84 cm.). **£300-£350** *L*

A good Anglo-German chest of Nonsuch type, inlaid with various woods, 48 in. wide, late 16th C. **£1,600-1,800** *RVA*

An oak chest with simple panelled top, 2 ft. 1 in. high by 3 ft. 11 in. wide (64 by 120 cm.), early 17th C. **£500-600** *S*

An oak coffer of small proportions having carved front and side panels, plank top, 31½ in. **£500-£550** *LE*

An Elizabethan oak cupboard with lid enclosing a shallow compartment above cupboard doors carved with figures of kings, 2 ft. 3½ in. high by 4 ft. 10 in. wide (69 by 147 cm.), reduced in height and now with a lifting top, c. 1600. **£1,500-2,500** *S*

A small oak plank coffer, the top carved with interlaced and lunette designs, initialled T.I., 21 by 36 in. (53 by 92 cm.), mid 17th C. **£250-£300** *SC*

A fine ealry 17th C. oak 3-panel coffer, floral inlaid with bog oak and holly and dated M.Y. 1636, 4 ft. wide. **£425-475** *AGr*

A fine Charles II oak and fruitwood chest on later turned feet, 44 in. (112 cm.) wide. **£1,200-1,400** *C*

An oak coffer with a triple panelled front with stylised scrolling decoration, 46 in., 17th C. **£225-£250** *CSK*

An alto adige cedarwood chest, decorated on the inside with 2 panels, centred by an armorial cartouche, on bun feet, lid restored, 2 ft. 6¾ in. high by 6 ft. 4¼ in. wide (83 by 193.5 cm.), 17th C., later feet. **£700-900** *S*

A fine 17th C. Jacobean oak coffer, 52 in. wide. **£800-900** *B*

An unusual pine coffer bound with elaborate repousse silver mounts on a later stand, 2 ft. 10 in. high by 2 ft. wide (86 by 61 cm.), late 17th C. **£350-450** *S*

An oak commode, 21 in. wide, c. 1690. **£150-190** *LG*

An 18th C. elm blanket chest, 3 ft. 6 in. wide. **£120-150** *JMW*

A rare Charles II dated oak long coffer, the 6-panelled top rising above a finely carved frieze with the owner's name, John Tolson, and dated 1683, 7 ft. 2 in. long. **£1,000-1,200** *B*

A Georgian dower chest, veneered with pollard-oak and with crossbanded and ebonised mouldings, with a lift-up top and 2 drawers, 41½ by 29 in. high (105 by 74 cm.). **£700-800** *L*

An 18th C. oak coffer, 57 in. wide. **£360-400** *HWO*

A Jacobean oak chest, the top section fitted with 2 long drawers and the base fronted by 2 panelled cupboards enclosing 3 long drawers, 4 ft. 3 in. high by 4 ft. 2 in. wide (130 by 127 cm.), c. 1660. **£450-500** *SS*

A 17th C. oak chest, 3 ft. **£450-£500** *WSW*

An 18th C. oak coffer with triple panelled top and a carved and inlaid front, 3 ft. 8 in. **£175-225** *DDM*

CHESTS — COFFER TYPE

- **By the 13th century coffers with hinges were in use**
- **By the 16th century these chests fall into two main categories — boarded and joined**
- **They were made originally for storage, usually for linen and clothing**
- **The majority of coffers on the market today date from the 17th and early 18th century, although much earlier examples can sometimes be found**
- **carved and inlaid decoration used up to mid 1650's**
- **chests with drawers were introduced in the second half of the 17th C.**
- **after this many other forms of decoration were used on the more special coffers including ivory, mother-of-pearl, box and holly (this followed the prevailing fashion for decorating the more popular chests with drawers in them).**
- **Many early plain coffers were embellished with carving in the Victorian era, and to the inexperienced eye, the rather rigid quality of later carving can be difficult to differentiate from the bolder and freer contemporary carving**

POINTS TO LOOK FOR:—

a) **Originality and good condition**
b) **Colour and patination**
c) **High quality carving and inlaid decoration**
d) **Quality of joinery and lack of splits in the panels**
e) **Original iron fittings — ring hinges etc.**

A reconstructed oak hutch on stand, 39½ in. wide. **£350-400** *McMB*

A brass mounted kingwood coffre fort of Louis XIV design, enclosing a recessed interior and a fall flap revealing 3 drawers, 19½ in. wide. **£600-650** *CEd*

A George III travelling trunk, leather-covered and decorated with brass-headed studs, bearing the initials GR, dated 1774, the interior lined with a print with the 'Victory over the French by Field Marshal Wellington, June 21st, 1813', 3 ft. 3½ in. wide (100 cm.), late 18th C. **£400-600** *S*

A carved walnut cassone on stand of inverted breakfront form, with a pair of cupboards each carved with a grotesque mask, 54 in. high by 95 in. wide (137 by 211 cm.), Florence, c. 1880. **£1,300-1,500** *S*

A lacquered chest on stand in the George II style, painted with Chinese warriors and travellers, 3 ft. 3½ in. by 4 ft. (100 by 122 cm.), c. 1900. **£250-300** *S*

A George III oak mule chest, a 4-drawer dummy front and 2 real drawers on stump feet, 33½ by 56 in. (85 by 142 cm.), mid 18th C., later handles. **£250-300** *SC*

An antique oak sectional chest, 3 ft. 2 in. wide by 1 ft. 10 in. deep by 38 in. high. **£280-360** *DA*

A George III oak mule chest, 6 dummy drawers and 3 real drawers, flanked by quadrant corners, crossbanded throughout in mahogany, 34½ by 63 in. (87 by 160 cm.), late 18th C. **£500-600** *SC*

A William and Mary small oyster walnut chest decorated with holly banding, later bun feet, 2 ft. 4 in. high by 2 ft. 8 in. wide (71 by 81 cm.), c. 1690. **£1,750-2,000** *SS*

A William and Mary oyster-veneered walnut chest, the top inlaid with concentric roundels, 37¼ in. wide (95 cm.). **£7,000-£8,000** *C*

A Queen Anne walnut chest with crossbanded and quartered top inlaid with herringbone bands, on later bracket feet, 30½ in. wide (77.5 cm.). **£1,500-2,000** *C*

A small William and Mary kingwood oyster chest of drawers, the top inlaid in oysters in circles and geometric patterns, with similar sides crossbanded in rosewood, restored, 31½ in. wide by 31 in. high. **£1,100-1,300** *B*

A Queen Anne walnut chest with crossbanded top bordered with a herringbone band below an oak slide on bracket feet, 32 in. wide (81 cm.). **£2,400-2,600** *C*

A Queen Anne walnut chest with crossbanded and quartered top, with half-herringbone banding and replacement bracket feet, 39¼ in. wide. **£500-550** *DSH*

A George I walnut bachelor's chest with hinged top, 2 shallow drawers and 3 graduated long drawers, on bracket feet, 2 ft. 5 in. high by 2 ft. 6 in. wide (74 by 76 cm.), c. 1725, feet replaced. **£3,000-5,000** *S*

A George I-style walnut veneered bachelor's chest, 35 in. high by 31 in. wide, reconstructed from early 18th C. pieces. **£600-800** *Bea*

A walnut and burr-elm bachelor's chest with crossbanded rectangular folding top, 59 in. (150 cm.). **£2,300-£2,500** *C*

A George II mahogany bachelor's chest with folding top, 29½ in. wide (75 cm.). **£2,200-2,500** *C*

A George II mahogany bachelor's chest, the hinged top supported by lopers, on bracket feet, restored, 2 ft. 6¼ in. high by 2 ft. 5½ in. wide (77 by 75 cm.), c. 1750. **£1,750-£2,000** *S*

An oak chest of 4 long drawers, the top with moulded edge on bun feet, 38 by 37 in. (97 by 94 cm.), early 18th C. but carved throughout with bands later. **£350-400** *SC*

A late 17th C. oyster laburnum chest, 37½ in. **£2,600-3,000** *DWB*

A mid Georgian mahogany small chest of drawers, the top with re-entrant corners and brushing slide, with brass escutcheons and handles, 31 in. **£600-700** *GSP*

A fine quality George III period chest in mahogany, the figured moulded surface above 5 moulded drawers with original brasswork throughout, 36 in. wide by 19½ in. deep by 34 in. high, c. 1790. **£700-£850** *HAL*

A mahogany chest of drawers, 37½ in., c. 1770. **£650-700** *NC*

BEADING

- **18th C. beading was all done out of the one piece of wood – hence the grain always runs true**
- **with Victorian and Edwardian beading, the beads were glued on**

A George III chest with 2 short and 3 long graduated drawers on ogee bracket feet, 32 by 31 in. (81 by 79 cm.), late 18th C. **£500-600** *SC*

A walnut oyster-veneered chest with wide boxwood crossbandings and a moulded top above 2 short and 3 long drawers, on bracket feet, 37 in. (94 cm.), 18th C. **£2,200-£2,500** *L*

A George III mahogany chest of drawers with original oval brass drop handles, baize lined brushing slide and inlaid boxwood edges on bracket feet, 33 in. **£500-550** *GSP*

PHELPS
Limited
ESTABLISHED 1870

A Dutch marquetry chest of drawers, the shaped top quartered-veneered in walnut with a central diamond shaped panel, 4 short and 2 long drawers, 34 in. (87 cm.), late 18th/early 19th C. **£1,000-1,200** *L*

A camphorwood military secretaire chest with a fitted secretaire drawer, inlaid throughout with an ebony moulding, 4 ft. 2½ in. by 4 ft. (128 by 122 cm.), c. 1850. **£1,000-1,200** *S*

An unusual George III mahogany travelling chest fitted with brass carrying handles and raised on bracket feet, 3 ft. 8½ in. high by 3 ft. wide (113 by 91.5 cm.), c. 1810. **£1,200-1,500** *SS*

An early George III mahogany serpentine chest, 43 in. wide (109 cm.). **£4,500-5,000** *C*

A George III mahogany serpentine chest, the eared top crossbanded with tulipwood, the upper drawer formerly fitted, 39 in. wide (99 cm.). **£2,000-2,500** *C*

A George III mahogany serpentine chest, drawers mounted with silvered brass handles, 44 in. wide (112 cm.). **£2,500-3,000** *C*

A George III mahogany serpentine front commode, the top and canted corners inlaid with stringing, with later handles. **£1,600-1,800** *SWO*

A George III tulipwood serpentine commode with fitted top drawer, with later silvered handles, 40½ in. wide (103 cm.). **£1,800-2,200** *C*

A George III mahogany serpentine commode with moulded top and 4 graduated drawers, on shaped bracket feet, 2 ft. 8 in. high by 3 ft. 3 in. wide (81 by 99 cm.), c. 1765. **£2,200-2,400** *S*

A George III mahogany serpentine chest, the moulded edge top above 4 long graduated drawers, the top drawer divided, having original brass swan neck handles and escutcheons, 3 ft. 10 in. **£1,800-£2,000** *WW*

An early George III serpentine mahogany chest with blind fret decoration, 3 ft. 2 in. high by 4 ft. 4 in. wide (96 by 132 cm.), c. 1760. **£1,200-1,500** *S*

A George III small mahogany chest inlaid with chevron stringing, 2 ft. 7 in. high by 2 ft. 6¼ in. wide (79 by 77 cm.), c. 1790. **£425-475** *SS*

A George III mahogany serpentine chest, the top drawer formerly fitted, the border inlaid with simulated fluting and paterae, 39 in. wide (99 cm.). **£1,500-£2,000** *C*

A George III mahogany serpentine chest with later brass rosette handles, 32 in. high by 44 in. wide by 23 in. deep. **£900-1,000** *PB*

A George III mahogany bow-front chest, decorated with coromandel crossbanding and satinwood stringing, 2 ft. 10 in. high by 3 ft. 11 in. wide (86.5 by 120 cm.), c. 1800. **£1,000-1,200** *SS*

A bow-fronted mahogany chest of drawers with boxwood and ebony stringing, restored, 46 in. wide, c. 1870. **£150-175** *CDE*

A Hepplewhite mahogany bow-fronted chest of drawers, 37 in. wide, c. 1780. **£900-1,100** *Ph*

A George III mahogany bow-front chest of 4 long drawers applied with moulded pilasters, 39½ by 41 in. (100 by 104 cm.), early 19th C. **£250-300** *SC*

A George III mahogany serpentine chest in the French taste, crossbanded in rosewood, the top inlaid with boxwood and ebonised stringing, 1.09 m. **£2,000-2,250** *P*

A mahogany bow-front chest of drawers with later top, 47½ in. wide, late 19th C. **£150-180** *CDE*

A George III mahogany bow-fronted chest by Gillows, stamped Gillows, Lancaster, 46¼ in. (117.5 cm.). **£750-850** *C*

A George III mahogany bow-fronted chest, 39½ in. **£1,600-1,800** *DWB*

A George III satinwood bow-fronted chest, the frieze inlaid with rosewood key-pattern lines, 42 in. wide (107 cm.). **£1,750-2,000** *C*

A late Georgian bow-front chest of drawers with cockbeaded edges, brass handles on shaped apron base, 40 in. wide. **£120-140** *DS*

A late 18th C. Flemish walnut commode of tapered serpentine shape with fine ormolu handles, 4 ft. wide. **£3,000-4,000** *HB*

An early 19th C. mahogany chest with slight bow front, 42 in. **£150-£175** *A*

A walnut library folio chest, the rectangular top inset with a leather panel, 2 ft. 6½ in. high by 4 ft. 7 in. wide (77 by 140 cm.), late 19th C. **£1,800-2,000** *S*

An 18th C. Dutch walnut and oak bombé chest, 33 in. high, 33 in. wide by 21½ in. deep. **£800-900** *PB*

A Regence provincial commode, veneered in burr-elm, possibly Grenoble, 2 ft. 8 in. high by 4 ft. 4 in. wide (82 by 132 cm.), c. 1720. **£4,500-5,000** *S*

CHESTS OF DRAWERS — GUIDE TO DATING

- **early 17th C. drawers were nailed together**
- **up to c. 1660 drawers had bearers attached to the side which ran in deep grooves on the side**
- **after c. 1670 bottom runners, usually made of oak, appeared**
- **no 18th C. drawer completely fitted the space between front and back — a space left for ventilation**
- **good quality drawers tend to have sides of oak, with rounded top edges**
- **the idea of veneering on flat surfaces came to England with the foreign influences of the Restoration**
- **c. 1680-90 walnut came to be used more and more along with the bracket foot**
- **in the mahogany period from c. 1740, the square shape gave way to the bow front, serpentine, etc.**
- **up to 1770 grain in bottom boards of drawers tended to run front to back, from 1770 the grain tended to run from side to side**
- **18th C. cabinet makers made the bottom boards from 2 or 3 pieces of the same wood; the Victorians used one piece which was usually screwed**
- **satinwood appeared in chests c. 1780-90**
- **corner mouldings were a Sheraton innovation, hence give a date of after 1799**
- **if a chest has three short drawers one would suspect that it started life as the top of a tallboy**

A rare late Louis XIV green japanned commode, the bowed front painted and with gilt-bronze handles, 3 ft. 6½ in. wide (98 cm.), early 18th C. **£6,000-7,000** *S*

A Regence provincial walnut commode, the drawers mounted with bronze lockplates and handles, 50 in. wide by 32½ in. high by 25¾ in. deep (127 by 82.5 by 65 cm.). **£4,500-5,000** *C*

An 18th C. Dutch walnut and marquetry bombé chest. **£3,200-£3,500** *DWB*

A Dutch mahogany and floral marquetry bombé chest, with neo-classical giltmetal handles and lockplates, 36½ in. wide (93 cm.). **£3,200-3,600** *C*

A mid 18th C. Dutch walnut and marquetry chest, the top inlaid with marquetry flowers, birds and an urn, top distressed, 2 ft. 8½ in. high by 2 ft. 11 in. wide (82 by 90 cm.), c. 1765. **£2,500-3,000** *SI*

A Lombard marquetry commode of inverted angled serpentine form, veneered in walnut with ebonised panels and mouldings, the top inlaid with birds and flowers, top drawer formerly fitted as a secretaire, 3 ft. ½ in. high by 4 ft. 7½ in. wide (93 by 141 cm.), c. 1700. **£3,500-4,000** *S*

An early Louis XV kingwood crossbanded and brass mounted commode of bowed outline, 1.08 m. **£2,100-2,300** *P*

A French provincial walnut commode with later moulded serpentine top, 45 in. wide (114.5 cm.), mid 18th C. **£2,600-£3,000** *C*

A Louis XV kingwood and tulipwood parquetry commode, stamped Macret, with gilt-bronze mounts and mottled rust and grey marble top, 2 ft. 9 in. high by 3 ft. 2½ in. wide (84 by 98 cm.), mid 18th C. **£2,500-3,000** *S*

A Louis XV kingwood parquetry commode, indistinctly stamped, with a mottled pink and grey marble top, extensively restored, 2 ft. 10½ in. by 3 ft. 9 in. (87 by 114 cm.), c. 1750. **£4,500-5,000** *S*

An early Louis XV kingwood and tulipwood bombé commode with serpentine breccia marble top, 53½ in. wide (136 cm.). **£2,500-£3,500** *C*

CARVING

- **if original should always be proud of the piece**
- **flat or incised carving would have been added later and virtually always detracts from the value of a piece**
- **Victorian carving is almost always quite flat as they had become more sparing with timber**

An important Louis XIV ormolu mounted boulle commode, the top inlaid in contre-partie marquetry of brass in a scarlet tortoiseshell background in Berainesque design, 120 cm. wide by 65 cm. deep by 82 cm. high, c. 1700. **£32,000-£35,000** *B*

A Louis XV kingwood parquetry commode, stamped Fromageau JME with a grey mottled marble top, 2 ft. 10½ in. high by 4 ft. 2½ in. wide (88 by 128 cm.), mid 18th C. **£3,500-4,000** *S*
Jean-Baptiste Fromageau, received Master 1755.

A pair of North Italian commodes, parquetry-veneered in mahogany and oak, on chevron-veneered legs, 2 ft. 6½ in. high by 2 ft. 10 in. wide (77.5 by 86.5 cm.). **£2,500-2,800** *S*

A Louis XV/XVI Transitional marquetry breakfront commode with a brèche d'alep marble top, inlaid with marquetry panels, 4 ft. 2 in. wide (127 cm.), c. 1775. **£3,000-3,500** *S*

A mahogany bombé commode with neo-classical giltmetal handles, lockplates and cameo medallion angles, Swedish or Dutch, 41½ in. wide (105.5 cm.), late 18th C. **£1,750-2,000** *C*

An 18th C. South German walnut crossbanded and parquetry commode of arc en arbelette outline, inlaid with boxwood lines and ogee shaped geometric panels with cube and trellis inlay, 1.22 m. **£2,800-3,200** *P*

An 18th C. French provincial walnut bow-front commode having patterned inlay and figured walnut panels with original brass furniture. **£350-450** *Fr*

An Italian walnut serpentine commode with crossbanded top and 3 long drawers on moulded cabriole feet, 48¼ in. wide (123 cm.), 18th C. **£1,800-2,200** *C*

A Dutch bombé mahogany commode, finely inlaid, partly with ivory, depicting boar and stag hunting scene, 53 in. wide. **£2,600-£3,000** *DA*

A South German walnut serpentine chest inlaid with geometric designs, 47½ in. wide (121 cm.), mid 18th C. **£2,500-£3,500** *C*

A Louis XVI-style Transitional tulipwood commode inlaid with marquetry and harewood bands and applied with gilt-metal mounts, 59½ in. **£650-700** *CSK*

An 18th C. Dutch walnut serpentine front chest of drawers having marquetry inlay and crossbanding, 4 ft. 2 in. wide by 3 ft. 1 in. high. **£2,750-3,000** *Fr*

A Louis XVI tulipwood and mahogany crossbanded rectangular commode of slight broken outline, inlaid with boxwood lines and applied with gilt-metal mounts, 79 cm. **£800-1,000** *P*

A South German walnut commode with crossbanded serpentine top inlaid with interlaced strapwork, with panels of stained burr-maple, 48½ in. wide by 33½ high by 25 in. deep (123 by 85 by 63.5 cm.), mid 18th C. **£7,000-8,000** *C*

A late 18th C. South German crossbanded and line inlaid walnut serpentine front commode chest, damaged, 4 ft. 7 in. wide. **£800-£1,000** *GC*

A marble-topped parquetry commode of Transitional form, with moulded marble top, the front with chevron stripes in tulipwood and kingwood, 2 ft. 10 in. high by 4 ft. 2 in. wide (87 by 128 cm.), c. 1770. **£2,500-2,800** *S*

A George III marquetry commode, the serpentine satinwood top inlaid with a spray of flowers in a partridgewood oval and crossbanded in mahogany, 2 ft. 8½ in. high by 3 ft. 7¾ in. (82 by 111 cm.), c. 1775. **£2,500-3,000** *S*

A George III mahogany serpentine commode, the upper drawer with a divided and lidded interior below a baize-lined slide, 35 in. wide (89 cm.). **£3,000-4,000** *C*

A late 18th C. Dutch parquetry commode of breakfront form, the grey mottled marble top above parquetry-veneered drawers and a dummy drawer rosewood-veneered and outlined with boxwood stringing, feet replaced, top broken, 2 ft. 11½ in. high by 2 ft. 10 in. wide (90 by 86 cm.), c. 1775. **£800-£1,000** *SI*

A painted satinwood commode in George III style, painted throughout with musical trophies, cherubs and swags of ribbon-tied flowers, 3 ft. by 4 ft. 6 in. (92 by 137 cm.), c. 1900. **£1,200-1,400** *S*

A George III satinwood commode, 3 ft. ½ in. high by 4 ft. 3 in. wide (92 by 129 cm.), c. 1790, feet c. 1820. **£3,000-4,000** *S*

Reputed to have come from Brighton Pavilion.

An antique Italian walnut commode with moulded decoration to the rim and figure decoration to the corners, 61 in. wide. **£900-£1,000** *NSF*

A Franco-Flemish kingwood and marquetry commode of Transitional design with breccia marble top, 40½ in. wide (103 cm.). **£1,300-1,500** *C*

A serpentine fronted commode with 2 doors enclosing 3 drawers, on cabriole legs, 42 in. (107 cm.). **£250-£300** *L*

A late 18th C. Italian commode, in rosewood, the quarter-veneered top centred by a cartouche of flowers and floral sprays within geometric border and subsidiary stringing, the sides similarly inlaid over quarter-veneered bordered squares, set on square tapered marquetry inlaid feet, now with additional supports, 124 cm. wide by 89 cm. high. **£1,100-1,300** *OT*

An unusual George III mahogany chest, with square tapering fluted legs, 2 ft. 5 in. high by 2 ft. 5½ in. wide (74 by 75 cm.), c. 1790. **£1,000- 1,200** *SS*

A marquetry commode in Transitional style with a marble top, 97 by 135 cm., c. 1900. **£600-£800** *S*

A North Italian walnut commode, with chequered crossbanding and quarter-veneered top, 3 ft. 1½ in. high by 3 ft. 10 in. wide (95 by 117 cm.), c. 1790. **£1,000-1,200** *SS*

A French Directoire mahogany commode with a white marble top, having brass mounts, with brass ring handles and escutcheons, oak lined, the fluted corner pilasters to turned tapering feet, panelled sides, 4 ft. 3 in. **£1,800-2,200** *WW*

A South German walnut commode, with 2 drawers, on fluted and moulded square tapering supports, 32 by 29½ in. (81 by 75 cm.), late 18th C. **£1,000-1,200** *SC*

A North Italian miniature parquetry commode in kingwood within purple-heart banding, the top with green-stained Greek key border, 11 in. high by 1 ft. 3 in. wide (28 by 37.5 cm.), late 18th C. **£400-500** *S*

A sycamore and marquetry commode, crossbanded with tulipwood, doors inlaid with urns and a central ribbon-tied swag, each enclosing 2 drawers on square tapering legs, the feet inlaid with acanthus, 45 in. wide (114 cm.). **£1,600-1,800** *C*

An Empire elm commode with a Ste. Anne marble top, with a door panelled to resemble 2 short and 2 long drawers enclosing drawers and strong box drawers, German or Belgian, 3 ft. 2 in. high by 4 ft. 1 in. wide (96 by 125 cm.), early 19th C. **£700-900** *S*

Two 18th C. South German crossbanded walnut and line inlaid bow-front commode chests of small proportions, 2 ft. 1 in. and 1 ft. 11 in. wide, one with pieces of veneer missing. **£1,000-1,200** *GC*

A North Italian marquetry commode in the Maggiolini-style, inlaid with foliage, the frieze with a long drawer above 2 drawers sans traverse, 48½ in. wide (123 cm.), late 18th C. **£3,500-4,000** *C*

A George III satinwood commode with shaped top inlaid with central lunette and bordered in rosewood, 42½ in. wide (108 cm.). **£8,500-£9,500** *C*

An early 19th C. French walnut commode with marble top, raised on moulded pad feet. **£450-550** *AGr*

A fruitwood and parquetry commode with serpentine breccia marble top and 2 drawers inlaid sans traverse with trellis-and-rosette pattern parquetry, Dutch, 32 in. wide (81 cm.), late 18th C. **£1,600-1,800** *C*

A Milanese marquetry straight front commode with crossbanded and inlaid decoration, 4 ft. wide, 1 ft. 11 in. deep. **£5,000-6,000** *MMB*

A kingwood marquetry commode in Transitional style, inlaid throughout with flowerhead trellis and foliage, Swedish, 84.5 by 122 cm., mid 20th C. **£500-700** *S*

A pair of Sicilian tulipwood-veneered serpentine commodes, quarter-veneered quarter-banded wood, 2 ft. 10½ in. high by 2 ft. wide (88 by 61 cm.). **£800-1,200** *S*

A Dutch mahogany chest with shaped crossbanded top above a baize-lined slide, 2 ft. 6 in. high by 3 ft. wide (76 by 91.5 cm.), c. 1755, legs probably later. **£1,200-1,400** *S*

An Edwardian mahogany music cabinet of 6 drawers with fall fronts, on squat cabriole legs, some damage, 21 in. wide. **£130-160** *BHW*

A Danish walnut and parcel-gilt bombé commode with marble top above 4 drawers, 29 in. wide (74 cm.), mid 18th C. **£3,000-£3,500** *C*

A 17th C. Flemish oak 2-part chest, fitted with original brass handles and locks, some missing, 41 in. wide by 50½ in. high. **£350-400** *WHL*

A Louis XV-style burr-walnut commode. **£500-600** *CDC*

A rare Louis XV petite commode of kingwood and tulipwood, 16½ in. wide, c. 1755. **£2,500-3,000** *HB*

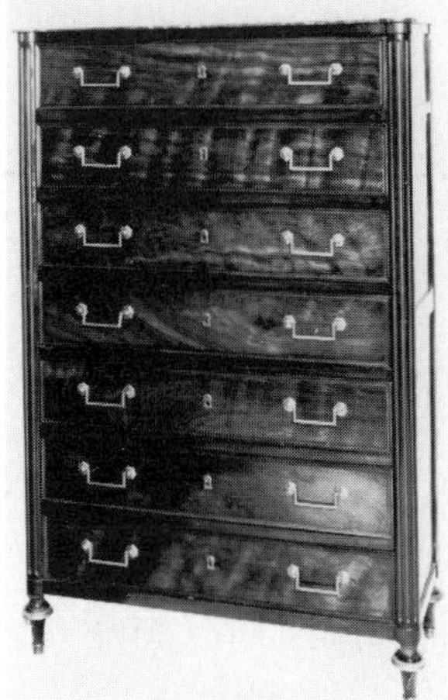

A Louis XVI mahogany semainier, with a mottled brown marble slab to the top, 37½ in. wide by 16¼ in. deep by 58 in. high. **£1,400-1,600** *PWC*

A George III Irish mahogany tall chest, 5 ft. 5½ in. high by 2 ft. 10½ in. wide (166 by 87 cm.), c. 1770. **£700-800** *SI*

A lady's walnut and porcelain mounted secretaire commode in the Louis XV manner, applied throughout with gilt brass foliate mounts and Sèvres-style plaques, French, 32 in. high by 28 in. wide, late 19th C. **£650-700** *Bea*

An 18th C. Continental walnut chest of 2 drawers. **£500-600** *WSW*

An early George III mahogany secretaire, the lower part with a fitted secretaire drawer enclosing pigeonholes and short drawers, 27 in. wide by 57¾ in. high (69 by 147 cm.). **£6,000-6,500** *C*

An early George III mahogany secretaire chest, the fall-front panelled as 2 long drawers, with 3 further long drawers below, 5 ft. 9 in. high by 3 ft. 4 in. wide (175 by 101 cm.), c. 1760. **£1,500-1,800** *S*

A George III period tall chest in mahogany having figured moulded surface above 7 cockbeaded drawers with replaced brasswork, 37 in. wide by 18 in. deep by 48 in. high, c. 1800. **£650-800** *HAL*

A 19th C. marquetry tallboy of 6 drawers with brass ring handles flanked by pilasters, 38 in. **£800-£900** *JD*

Points to look for:—

- ***Original condition***
- ***Colour and patination***
- ***Original feet***
- ***Original handles and escutcheons***
- ***Quality of mouldings and other decoration***

For 18th century chests the following additional points apply:—

- ***Small size (34 in. or under)***
- ***Quality of timber used***
- ***Fitted brushing slide***
- ***Oak linings to the drawers***

A Dutch mahogany chest, decorated with inlaid floral bands and boxwood stringing, marquetry panels to the sides, 39½ by 57½ in. high, early 19th C. **£750-850** *AG*

A Dutch marquetry tall chest inlaid with scroll and foliate designs on a mahogany ground, on high bracket feet, 37 by 59 in. (94 by 150 cm.) high, 19th C. **£700-£800** *L*

An unusual Wellington chest in fine walnut veneers, the figured surface with carved edge and 7 lockable drawers with original brasswork, 26½ in. wide by 19½ in. deep by 42 in. high, c. 1850. **£1,500-£2,000** *HAL*

A mahogany and marquetry secretaire chest, with a frieze drawer above 5 further drawers, one with a fitted interior, Dutch, 62 by 40 in. (158 by 102 cm.), early 19th C., the marquetry slightly later. **£1,400-1,800** *SC*

An early 19th C. French flame mahogany-veneered secretaire a abattant, the top inset marble above a frieze drawer, the burr-maple fitted interior enclosed by a fall flap inset leather and having false drawer fronts, oak lined, the plinth base on shaped block feet, 31½ in. **£550-650** *WW*

A 19th C. Continental mahogany chest, 41 in. wide by 66 in. high. **£400-450** *HWO*

A satinwood Wellington chest by James Winter, stamped J.W., 101 Wardour Street, Soho, London, inlaid with ebony stringing, 3 ft. 9½ in. by 1 ft. 9¼ in. (115.5 by 54 cm.), c. 1870. **£550-650** *S*

A Charles II oak chest on stand, applied with geometric mouldings, the stand with a single long drawer, now on bracket feet, 44 by 38 in. (112 by 97 cm.), mid 17th C. **£600-800** *SC*

A Flemish kingwood-veneered and seaweed marquetry chest on stand, the low stand with a drawer veneered en suite, on later ebonised feet, top re-veneered, possibly originally taller, 3 ft. 3 in. high by 3 ft. 4 in. wide (99 by 102 cm.), c. 1690. **£1,500-2,000** *S*

A fine 17th C. Flemish ebony and scarlet tortoiseshell cabinet on a later stand with a rosewood-veneered top, the front and sides decorated with geometric panels of red tortoiseshell with surrounds inlaid with cornucopiae and flowering foliate scroll stems in scagliola, framed and divided by mother-of-pearl speckled borders and ivory lines, 1.39 m. **£4,500-£5,000** *P*

A Queen Anne walnut chest on stand with herringbone banding, on later turned feet, the base with restorations, 40½ in. wide (103 cm.). **£1,400-1,800** *C*

An oak chest on stand, 63 in. high, c. 1690. **£2,800-3,200** *CC*

A William and Mary walnut crossbanded chest on stand, decorated with crossbanded roundels and satinwood stringing, on later bun feet, 3 ft. 11½ in. high by 3 ft. 3 in. wide (121 by 99 cm.), c. 1690. **£1,000-1,100** *SS*

A William and Mary walnut chest on stand, on later turned legs, base later, restored, 5 ft. 2 in. high by 3 ft. 4¼ in. wide (157 by 103 cm.). **£900-1,200** *S*

A 19th C. William and Mary-style japanned chest, 38 in. **£1,300-£1,500** *SWO*

A solid walnut chest on stand, the upper part with a boletchon moulded frieze drawer, the lower part with 3 short and 1 long drawer, on cabriole supports, 63 by 42 in. (160 by 107 cm.), mid 18th C. **£500-600** *SC*

A Queen Anne yew-wood and marquetry chest on stand on Georgian walnut cabriole legs and pad feet, the legs with restorations, 47 in. wide (104 cm.). **£1,700-£2,000** *C*

PATINATION

- **means layers of polish, dirt, dust, grease, etc. which have accumulated over the years — really the whole depth of surface of a piece of antique timber**
- **the patination on different woods varies considerably but the same piece of wood will basically colour to the same extent (always allowing for bleaching by sunlight, etc.)**
- **walnut furniture often had an oil varnish applied to give it a good base to take the wax polish — this has led to the lovely mellow patina which is virtually impossible to fake**
- **dirt and grease from handling are important guides (especially under drawer handles, on chair arms, etc.) — these areas should have a darker colour — if they don't beware!**
- **pieces which have carving or crevices, dirt will have accumulated, giving dark patches**
- **colour and patination are probably the most important factors when valuing a piece of furniture**
- **by repolishing a piece of furniture and removing evidence of patination, a dealer can conceal replacement or conversion**

A mahogany chest on stand, possibly American, 43 by 77 in. high (109 by 195 cm.), basically 18th C. with later underpart. **£2,750-3,000** *L*

A Queen Anne walnut chest on stand, inlaid with banding, on associated cabriole supports, 5 ft. 5 in. high by 3 ft. 3 in. wide (165 by 99 cm.), c. 1710. **£600-700** *SS*

A George I walnut-veneered chest on stand with a moulded cornice, the stand with a short drawer flanked by square drawers, handles and one back leg replaced, 5 ft. 9½ in. high by 3 ft. 5 in. wide (174 by 104 cm.), c. 1725. **£1,200-1,500** *S*

An 18th C. walnut-veneered chest on stand with banded drawer fronts, on later cabriole legs, 38 in. wide by 63 in. high. **£1,100-1,300** *NSF*

A pollard oak-veneered small chest on stand with a crossbanded top, 34½ in. high by 32 in. wide. **£450-£550** *Bea*

A rare Queen Anne walnut small chest, the crossbanded top divided longitudinally and opening to form a baize-lined surface, one drawer fitted with compartments for writing implements, 2 ft. 8½ in. high by 1 ft. 8½ in. wide (82 by 52 cm.), c. 1700. **£3,000-4,000** *S*

A Danish serpentine fronted walnut chest on stand with crossbanded top and four crossbanded burrwood drawers divided by fluted brass fillets and spots, restored, 4 ft. 3½ in. high by 4 ft. 1½ in. wide (131 by 126 cm.), c. 1740, later stand. **£1,700-1,900** *S*

A George I figured walnut, crossbanded and herringbone inlaid secretaire-tallboy, fitted with interior drawers and pigeonholes, 42½ in. wide. **£3,000-4,000** *NSF*

A George I walnut and burr-walnut tallboy, the lower part with a secretaire drawer enclosing a fitted interior of pigeonholes and 4 short drawers, trade label 'Daniel Wild, Cabinet Maker, St. Paul's churchyard, near Wattling Street, London', 41½ in. wide (106 cm.). **£5,500-6,000** *C*

A good George I walnut tallboy, 5 ft. 11 in. high by 3 ft. 6½ in. wide (180 by 108 cm.), c. 1720. **£5,500-£6,000** *S*

A William and Mary oak and walnut chest on chest, with featherbanding, later shaped bracket feet, restored, 5 ft. 4½ in. high by 3 ft. 4 in. wide (164 by 102 cm.), c. 1700. **£1,000-£1,100** *SS*

A fine George I period chest on chest in figured walnut veneers on oak, the moulded pediment above 8 cock-beaded herringbone inlaid crossbanded drawers with early replaced brasswork, 38 in. wide by 20½ in. deep by 69 in. high, c. 1720. **£3,300-3,750** *HAL*

An early George I walnut tallboy in 2 parts, 5 ft. 8½ in. high by 3 ft. 6 in. wide (174 by 107 cm.), c. 1730. **£2,400-2,600** *S*

An early Georgian period walnut-veneered tallboy chest with herringbone line inlay, the flared cornice above 3 short and 3 long oak-lined drawers, the base with a slide with brass ring handles, all with brass swan neck handles, on bracket feet, 3 ft. 4 in. **£2,600-£3,000** *WW*

An early 18th C. walnut chest on chest, the lower part fitted escritoire, 3 ft. 8 in. wide by 6 ft. high. **£3,750-4,500** *RBB*

A George II period chest on chest in figured walnut veneer, the moulded cornice above crossbanded cock-beaded drawers with good quality replaced brasswork all on shaped bracket feet, 40 in. wide by 20½ in. deep by 69¼ in. high, c. 1730. **£3,000-3,750** *HAL*

A George I walnut tallboy in 2 parts with 3 short and 6 graduated long drawers, 5 ft. 10 in. by 3 ft. 8 in. wide (176 by 112 cm.), c. 1725. **£1,800-2,200** *S*

An 18th C. walnut, crossbanded and herringbone inlaid secretaire-tallboy, the canted corners with reeded ornamentation, the secretaire drawer with fitted interior of smaller drawers beside the central cupboard, 44½ in. wide by 75 in. high. **£1,700-2,000** *NSF*

The open-ended reference system
Miller's Antiques Price Guide builds up year by year to form the most comprehensive photo-reference system available. The first four volumes contain photographs of over 30,000 stock items!

A George III mahogany chest on chest, with key pattern cornice and fluted frieze, 6 ft. 5 in. high by 3 ft. 9 in. wide (196 by 114 cm.), c. 1770. **£800-1,000** *SS*

A George II walnut-veneered tallboy/secretaire with pine sides, drawers oak-lined, with fitted secretaire drawer, 3 ft. 3 in. **£900-£1,100** *WSW*

A George III oak tallboy, of fine colour with moulded cornice, crossbanded drawers on ogee bracket feet, 40 in. wide. **£900-£1,000** *CEd*

A George III mahogany tallboy, the stepped pediment with inlaid dentil cornice and roundel decoration, the top with blind fret side panels, the whole with replacement pierced brass handles and escutcheons, 3 ft. 6 in. wide by 6 ft. 4 in. high. **£550-£650** *DDM*

A George III mahogany tallboy with dentil and blind fret cornice, 41 in. **£550-650** *GSP*

An 18th C. mahogany chest of drawers, the fitted escritoire with pendant frieze, 3 ft. 6 in. **£800-£1,000** *RBB*

A George III mahogany tallboy with broken scrolled cresting pierced with fretwork interrupted by fluted urns, the lower drawer fitted as a secretaire, on ogee bracket feet, 49 in. (124.5 cm.). **£4,500-5,000** *C*

A George III figured mahogany tallboy chest with brass handles, surmounted by moulded and dentil cornice, on splayed feet, 3 ft. 9 in. wide by 6 ft. 1 in. high. **£550-600** *WHL*

A George III mahogany tallboy secretaire, the lower part with a fitted secretaire drawer, on bracket feet, 42 by 79 in. (107 by 201 cm.). **£1,200-1,400** *L*

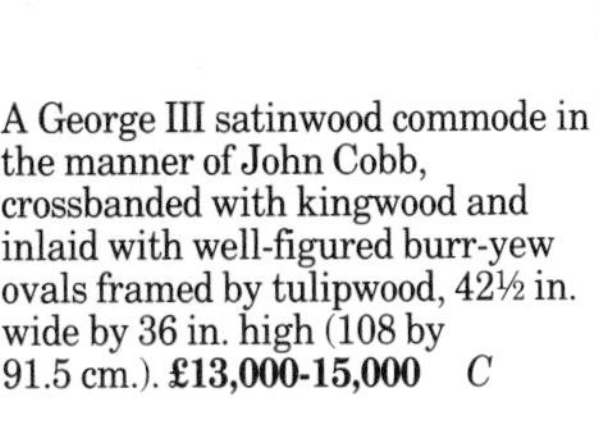

A George III satinwood commode in the manner of John Cobb, crossbanded with kingwood and inlaid with well-figured burr-yew ovals framed by tulipwood, 42½ in. wide by 36 in. high (108 by 91.5 cm.). **£13,000-15,000** *C*

A Victorian mahogany escritoire, the fall flap revealing nest of inlaid drawers and pull-out slide, 41 in. wide. **£600-700** *DA*

A George IV mahogany crossbanded and satinwood inlaid bow front commode, the top with feather motif roundel, chequer stringing and bowed back, scroll frieze with a drawer, the interior with compartments, rising mirror and 3 long drawers, some inlay later, 3 ft. high by 4 ft. wide (91.5 by 122 cm.), c. 1825. **£400-500** *SS*

A mahogany step-commode, 30 in. long, c. 1820. **£130-160** *CDE*

A German bombé commode with scagliola marble top, veneered in rosewood with panels of mahogany with rosewood flowers, having chiselled gilt brass rococo mounts with escutcheons, panelled back to the oak carcase, 4 ft. 5 in. **£2,400-£2,600** *WW*

A mahogany serpentine 3-step commode, 20 in. wide, c. 1865. **£150-170** *CDE*

A Georgian mahogany tray-top commode. **£200-250** *JMW*

A Georgian washstand with fold over top, cupboard, drawer and rising mirror, unconverted. **£240-£270** *Wor*

A Victorian mahogany night commode, the hinged back shelf and box base raised on short turned reeded legs. **£130-160** *DA*

An 18th C. Dutch painted corner cupboard, 35¾ in. high. **£500-550** *T*

A Dutch painted bow fronted hanging corner cupboard, c. 1740. **£1,100-1,250** *NC*

A Queen Anne oyster-veneered walnut hanging corner cupboard, 27 in. wide by 48½ in. high (68.5 by 123 cm.). **£2,000-2,500** *C*

A mahogany hanging corner display cabinet, 41¼ in., c. 1780. **£575-650** *NC*

A good quality George III hanging bow-front corner cabinet in mahogany, the moulded cornice above crossbanded doors flanked by fluted pilasters, the brasswork being original, 28½ in. wide by 19½ in. deep by 40 in. high, c. 1790. **£450-650** *HAL*

A hanging corner display cabinet, 43 in. high, c. 1790. **£195-215** *CDE*

(l.) A Georgian oak corner cupboard with fielded panelled door, with original brass fittings. **£140-180** *Fr*

(r.) An antique walnut corner cabinet with burr-walnut panelled door. **£160-200** *Fr*

A mahogany hanging corner cupboard, 43 in. high, c. 1770. **£700-800** *HB*

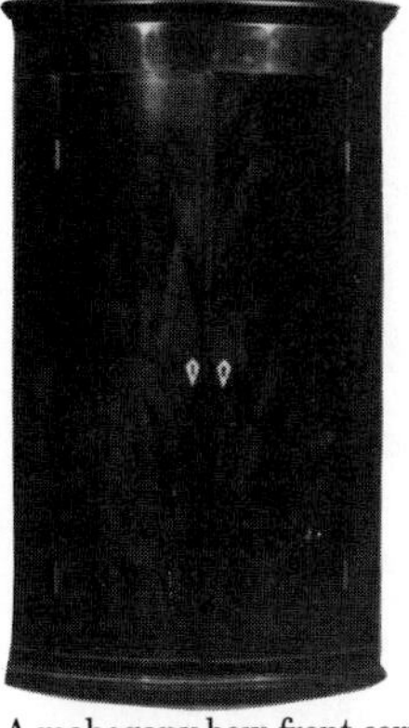

A mahogany bow-front corner cupboard with moulded cornice, ivory escutcheons, enclosing 3 shelves, 46 in. high. **£350-400** *OL*

A late 18th C. mahogany full height corner cupboard with moulded arched top, fluted pilasters, shaped door with 8 moulded and fielded panels on moulded plinth, 84 in. high by 41 in. wide. **£800-£1,000** *DSH*

An early George III mahogany standing corner cupboard, doors enclosing shaped shelves and drawers, 94 in. high by 45 in. wide. **£1,000-£1,100** *Bea*

A George I crossbanded mahogany bow-fronted standing corner cupboard, 2 doors with fitted shelves, behind, 2 half drawers with 2 doors below with fitted shelves, raised on bracket feet and having original brass butterfly hinges and escutcheons, 3 ft. wide by 7½ ft. high. **£1,200-1,500** *AGr*

Use the Index!

Because certain items might fit easily into any of a number of categories, the quickest and surest method of locating any entry is by reference to the index at the back of the book. This has been fully cross-referenced for absolute simplicity.

An 18th C. Scandinavian painted pine standing corner cupboard, 69 in. **£450-500** *DWB*

A mahogany Sheraton period double corner cupboard, 47 in. wide, c. 1780. **£1,700-2,000** *HB*

A 19th C. corner cupboard, 28 in. high. **£100-120** *JMW*

An 18th C. oak corner cupboard, the top with 2 panelled doors enclosing 3 shaped shelves, over 2 further smaller cupboard doors enclosing one shelf, 3 ft. 8 in. wide by 7 ft. high. **£600-£700** *DDM*

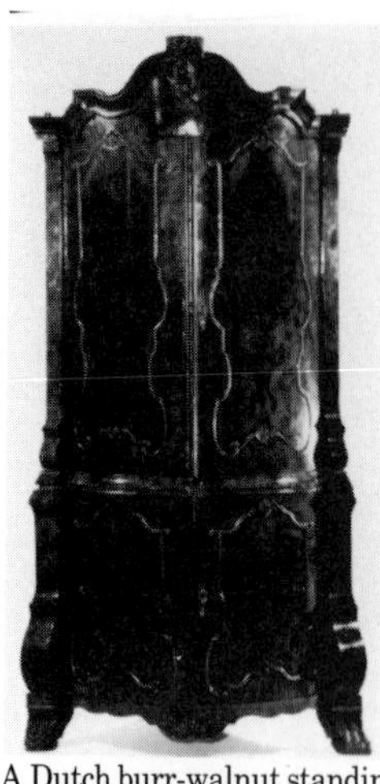

A Dutch burr-walnut standing corner cupboard, the arched moulded cornice centred by a shell plaque, 45 in. wide by 91½ in. high (114 by 232 cm.). **£2,700-2,900** *C*

A cupboard of simple form, with a pair of doors and ringed columnar front legs, 3 ft. 7 in. high by 4 ft. 3 in. wide (109 by 129 cm.), c. 1630. **£1,800-2,200** *S*

A rare Flemish linenfold cupboard with 3 doors, 55 in. wide by 40 in. high, early 16th C. **£3,500-4,500** *RVA*

A George III mahogany standing corner cupboard, with barrel back and arched top, the base with a pair of fielded panel doors enclosing a shelf, 8 ft. 5 in. high by 4 ft. 11 in. wide (289 by 150 cm.), c. 1765. **£2,500-3,000** *S*

A James I oak buffet, 46 in. wide by 45 in. high, early 17th C. **£2,300-£2,600** *RVA*

A Charles I oak hutch, slim flanking side panels, on simple pillar-turned legs with plain stretchers, 2 ft. 8 in. high by 2 ft. 9 in. wide (81 by 84 cm.), c. 1630. **£1,200-1,500** *S*

A fine South German walnut, ash and oak buffet, the central section with arched panelled back, 2 panels painted with coats-of-arms and 2 inlaid with arabesques, possibly Swabian, 79 in. wide (200 cm.), late 16th C. **£6,000-8,000** *C*

A Charles I oak court cupboard, the nulled frieze containing a drawer, formerly but not originally with a central shelf, 3 ft. 5 in. high by 3 ft. ½ in. wide (114 by 92 cm.), c. 1635. **£1,100-1,500** *S*

A fine late 17th C. Bruges oak buffetkast, carved with scenes after Memling, the Bruges artist, and flanked and centred by twisted fruitwood columns, the centre rail inscribed with the date Anno 1696, 57 in. high by 68 in. wide by 27 in. deep. **£2,200-2,400** *B*

A good Charles I oak and marquetry press cupboard, the upper section with a leaf-carved frieze inlaid with a marquetry vase of flowers and within a carved moulding divided by chequered banding and flanked by carved bulbous supports, 5 ft. 1¼ in. high by 6 ft. 9½ in. wide (155.5 by 270 cm.), c. 1640, possibly reduced in width. **£4,000-5,000** *S*

This piece was probably made in the Halifax area of Yorkshire. See Victor Chinnery, op. cit. pages 468-72.

A French provincial walnut bread cupboard carved with foliage and flowerheaded tendrils in low relief, 32½ in., 18th C. **£800-900** *CSK*

A James I press cupboard with moulded cornice and fluted frieze, all inlaid with ebonised endless knot motifs, cornice with restoration, some decoration on the front later, 5 ft. 2 in. high by 5 ft. 3 in. wide (158 by 160 cm.), c. 1620. **£1,300-1,800** *S*

An early 17th C. Flemish inlaid oak press cupboard, the upper part with simple inlay in ash and bog oak, the cupboard doors with simple flat carving and the sides with fielded diamond and rectangular panels, minor restorations, 5 ft. 4 in. high by 4 ft. 3 in. wide (162 by 129 cm.), c. 1620. **£6,500-7,500** *S*

An Elizabethan-style carved oak cupboard in 2 parts, upper section made-up and including antique timber, the base c. 1650 with later carving and replaced top, 6 ft. 9½ in. high by 5 ft. 11 in. wide (207 by 180 cm.). **£900-1,000** *SS*

An oak tridarn, 52½ in. wide (133 cm.), 17th C. **£2,000-2,500** *C*

A Welsh oak duodarn, the base fitted with 3 drawers above 2 panelled cupboard doors, on block feet, 57 in. wide, early 18th C. **£800-1,200** *CEd*

A late 17th C. carved oak court cupboard with carved frieze on turned supports, carved and panelled upper doors and moulded panelled lower door, 51 in. wide by 56 in. high. **£1,300-1,500** *DSH*

A William III oak tridarn, the arched panel bearing the initials T.H. and the date 1701, flanked by fielded panelled doors, the base with 2 frieze drawers and 2 further doors, on stile feet, 80 in. high by 54 in. wide. **£800-1,000** *S*

CARVING

- **if original should always be proud of the piece**
- **flat or incised carving would have been added later and virtually always detracts from the value of a piece**
- **Victorian carving is almost always quite flat as they had become more sparing with timber**

An oak court cupboard, 52 in. wide, c. 1670. **£1,200-1,800** *FF*

A Charles II oak court cupboard, 6 ft. high by 4 ft. 3 in. wide (183 by 135 cm.), c. 1680. **£800-1,000** *SS*

A Charles II oak Yorkshire court cupboard with original carving and inlays, 75 in. high by 55 in. wide, dated 1681. **£3,500-3,750** *RVA*

A 17th C. court cupboard with carved decoration to doors and friezes, 61 in. **£500-600** *A*

A 17th C. dated Westmorland oak court cupboard, the carved frieze with stylised decoration flanking the initials I.S.M. and the date 1699, 60 in. wide by 4 ft. 6 in. high. **£800-900** *B*

A 17th C. Dutch carved oak cupboard with scale pattern pediment, 66 in. overall by 78 in. high. **£2,600-3,400** *GSP*

A Flemish oak and ebony cupboard, 5 ft. 11¾ in. high by 4 ft. 7 in. wide (182.5 by 125 cm.), mid 17th C. **£3,500-4,000** *S*

An Edwardian oak court cupboard, 46 in. wide. **£200-250** *Ph*

A fine 19th C. Flemish cupboard, with exceptionally fine carving in 17th C. style, 53 in. wide by 78 in. high. **£2,500-3,000** *RD*

An oak court cupboard, doors with carved panels depicting the Flight into Egypt and the Nativity divided by a carving of the Madonna and Child dated 1641, 61 in. wide (155 cm.), 19th C., the carved panels Flemish 17th C. **£3,000-£3,500** *C*

A Flemish rosewood armoire, centred by carved ribbon-tied flowers and leaves, the base with a long drawer divided into two ebony panels, 6 ft. 5 in. high by 5 ft. 9½ in. wide (195 by 176 cm.), mid 17th C. **£1,500-2,000** *S*

A North German walnut armoire carved overall, 75½ in. wide by 79 in. high (192 by 201 cm.), partly 17th C. **£3,250-3,750** *C*

An early Louis XV provincial walnut armoire on carved feet, 5 ft. 1 in. by 4 ft. 8½ in. (155 by 143.5 cm.), c. 1725, possibly Liege, top section later. **£2,000-2,200** *S*

A fine Anglo-Dutch black-japanned cupboard, 7 ft. 5 in. high by 5 ft. 4 in. wide by 1 ft. 7 in. (266 by 163 by 49.5 cm.), c. 1720. **£12,000-£13,000** *S*

A Swedish walnut armoire inlaid with strapwork and roundels, 7 ft. 9 in. high by 5 ft. 11 in. wide (136 by 180 cm.), early 18th C., on later bun feet. **£2,500-3,000** *S*

A kingwood-veneered armoire, the moulded cornice centred by carved and brass moulded key block, above a pair of shaped moulded and quarter-veneered panelled doors with rococo brass mounts and flanked by ebonised columns with brass capitals, 6 ft. 7½ in. high by 5 ft. 6 in. wide (202 by 171 cm.), mid 18th C. **£2,500-3,000** *S*

A Dutch walnut and marquetry-veneered armoire, the shaped pediment with applied scroll acanthus leaf and floral central motif carving, 68 in. wide by 95 in. high by 24 in. deep, 18th C. **£3,500-£4,000** *WHL*

A Dutch oak and marquetry press, the panelled doors enclosing shelves and drawers, 7 ft. 6 in. high by 5 ft. 7 in. wide (290 by 170 cm.), c. 1780, marquetry later. **£2,500-£3,500** *S*

An antique oak court cupboard in 2 stages with moulded cornice, the frieze and stiles carved floral and bearing the date 1770, on later bun feet, 5 ft. 6¼ in. (168 cm.). **£1,600-£1,800** *JS*

A Commonwealth oak clothes press of wainscot panelled construction with moulded frames and plain panels, the front incorporating 2 cupboard doors with butterfly hinges and 5-panel base, 5 ft. 5¾ in. high by 6 ft. ½ in. wide (167 by 184 cm.), c. 1650. **£800-1,200** *S*

A Dutch walnut and marquetry armoire, inlaid with flowers, foliage and designs throughout, 76 by 74 in. (193 by 188 cm.), reconstructed in the 19th C., incorporating 18th C. doors and some other pieces. **£1,200-1,400** *SC*

An old Italian carved wood and parcel gilt vestment cupboard, 74 in. wide. **£800-900** *PWC*

A late 18th C. French oak armoire, 52 in. wide. **£450-550** *HB*

An imposing German Gothic walnut credence cupboard, the sides with blind fret carved Gothic panels, decorated with roundels with original polychrome decoration and chequered inlay, 64 in. wide by 55 in. high. **£1,700-£1,900** *B*

A George II oak hanging cupboard with shaped raised fielded panels, 4 ft. 6 in. **£600-700** *JSm*

A Welsh oak hanging cupboard of 3 doors, original colour and patina, c. 1670. **£2,000-2,300** *RVA*

A Chippendale fiddle back mahogany linen press with later decoration of satinwood banding and oval marquetry panels, the architectural cornice with central fluted urn, with an interior fitted slide, enclosed by a pair of inlaid doors with contemporary rococo and moulded outline with ornate brass handles, on ogee bracket feet, 4 ft. 1 in. **£1,500-1,700** *WW*

An 18th C. French provincial oak armoire, with fitted shelves and drawers enclosed by a pair of relief carved, fielded panel doors with shaped tops, original engraved brass escutcheons and turned brass hinges, 5 ft. 2 in. wide by 6 ft. 10 in. high by 21 in. deep. **£1,100-1,400** *WW*

An early 19th C. oak cupboard, probably Continental, 46 in. **£700-£800** *HB*

A French walnut armoire, 40 in. wide by 69 in. high, early 17th C. **£1,000-1,200** *RVA*

A fine Georgian mahogany press cupboard with inlaid oval panel doors, with ivory escutcheons, 54 in. wide. **£600-700** *DA*

An early Victorian figured mahogany linen press. **£350-£400** *JMW*

A George III Sheraton mahogany linen press having swan neck cornice, oval panelled and crossbanded doors, 7 ft. 6 in. high by 4 ft. wide. **£650-750** *AGr*

A finely figured mahogany gentleman's wardrobe with crossbanded oval panels and edges to doors and drawers, minus trays, 4 ft. 6 in. **£600-700** *JSm*

A fine Anglo-Indian ivory inlaid clothes press, fitted with 2 shaped panelled and fielded doors enclosing slides and inlaid with branches of bamboo in exotic flowerhead borders, Vizagapatam, 54½ in. wide (138.5 cm.). **£25,000-£30,000** *C*

A Georgian mahogany gentleman's wardrobe, with trays, dentil and dropped cove cornice, pierced brass handles, standing on bracket feet, 4 ft. **£900-1,000** *JSm*

A Regency mahogany linen press inlaid with satinwood ovals, with gilt brass handles and shaped bracket feet, 52 in. wide. **£400-£450** *DS*

An Edwardian satinwood bedroom suite with boxwood and ebony stringing and quarter-veneered comprising: wardrobe with central bow-front and inlaid ovals 80 in., dressing table with triptych mirror 51 in., washstand with glass back 48 in., bedside cupboard 17 in., bedstead with similarly veneered head and footboard 54 in., towel rail, together with a similar satinwood box commode. **£1,000-£1,200** *HyD*

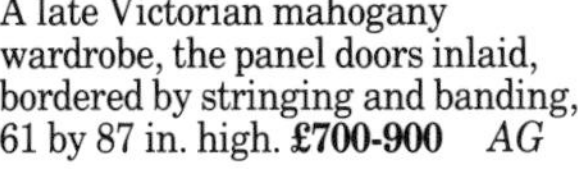

A late Victorian mahogany wardrobe, the panel doors inlaid, bordered by stringing and banding, 61 by 87 in. high. **£700-900** *AG*

A fine 19th C. mahogany breakfront wardrobe, the centre section with flame figured, panelled, crossbanded and gadrooned doors enlcosing sliding trays, plinth base, 7 ft. 6 in. wide. **£1,000-1,200** *PWC*

A George III mahogany and satinwood cupboard with holly and ebony inlaid arcaded frieze, 42¾ in. wide. **£450-500** *DSH*

A Gothic-style oak aumbry, the hinged front carved and pierced with arches and a roundel, 41½ by 35 in. wide, 20th C. **£200-250** *S*

An early oak spice cupboard, 14 in. high. **£160-200** *HB*

An early 19th C. French Provincial oak buffet, 44 in. wide. **£800-900** *HB*

A George IV-style bedside cabinet in mahogany, the galleried surface above bow-front with inlaid door, mounted on 4 legs, 14 in. wide by 14 in. deep by 29 in. high, c. 1860. **£280-330** *HAL*

A walnut harlequin Davenport with jack-in-the-box drawers and pigeonholes, 2 ft. 11 in. high by 1 ft. 10 in. wide (89 by 56 cm.), c. 1840. **£1,100-1,300** *S*

A rare and unusual William IV rosewood Davenport, the sliding upper part with a hinged writing surface enclosing a fitted interior, 2 ft. 10 in. high by 1 ft. 7¾ in. wide (86.5 by 50 cm.), c. 1830. **£2,000-£2,500** *S*

A George IV small Davenport in pale mahogany, with sliding galleried top, hinged leather-lined slope and pen drawer, 2 ft. 8 in. high by 1 ft. 3 in. wide (81 by 38 cm.), c. 1820. **£1,600-1,800** *S*

A walnut harlequin Davenport, the rising stationery compartment working in conjunction with the writing slope, walnut lined, pine carcase, 1 ft. 10½ in. wide (57 cm.), c. 1860. **£700-800** *S*

Make the most of Miller's

When buying or selling, it must always be remembered that prices can be greatly affected by the condition of any piece. Unless otherwise stated, all goods shown in Miller's are of good merchantable quality, and the valuations given reflect this fact. Pieces offered for sale in exceptionally fine condition or in poor condition may reasonably be expected to be priced considerably higher or lower respectively than the estimates given herein.

Unless otherwise stated, any description which refers to 'a set' or 'a pair' includes a valuation for the entire set or the pair, even though the illustration may show only a single item.

A pale walnut and satinwood-lined Davenport, pen tray at side, on spiral legs and bun feet. **£620-£680** *Wor*

A small walnut Davenport, 33 in. high, c. 1850. **£550-600** *CDE*

A Victorian rosewood Davenport. **£400-450** *McMB*

A small walnut crossbanded Davenport, interior of pen box missing, 32 in. high, c. 1850. **£450-£500** *CDE*

A mid 19th C. walnut Davenport desk, 22 in. wide. **£600-680** *LS*

A Victorian walnut Davenport of traditional design with satinwood crossbanding and inlay, 22 in. wide. **£475-550** *DS*

A Victorian walnut Davenport with decorative marquetry panels. **£450-500** *Fr*

A good 19th C. walnut Davenport, base with elaborate scroll and pierced carved decoration. **£400-£500** *WHL*

A fine Victorian walnut piano front Davenport with pierced gallery, spring-assisted concealed stationery rack, 4 real and 4 dummy drawers to the sides, the lift-up front enclosing a sliding writing surface with pen trays and ink well, 1 ft. 10½ in. wide and deep. **£1,100-1,300** *DDM*

DAVENPORTS

- **The name derives from Gillow's cost book where an illustration of this piece of furniture appeared for the first time. Beside the illustration was written 'Captain Davenport — a desk'.**
- **first examples date from the late 1790's**
- **they were extremely popular during the Regency and well into Victoria's reign**
- **there are two quite distinct types of davenport — the quite severe Regency as opposed to the more generous and often highly carved Victorian**
- **they are bought by a quite different market — at the moment the walnut well carved Victorian can be said to be selling much better than the earlier Regency**
- **points to look out for: burr-walnut, satinwood, secret drawers or complex interior arrangement, good quality carving and cabriole legs, galleried top**
- **unless stated all davenports in this section are fitted with 4 real opposed by 4 dummy drawers.**

A Victorian burr-walnut piano top Davenport, the top front enclosing a pull-out slide with rising writing slope and a pull-out pen and ink tray with button beyond activating the pop-up top with decorative fretted letter compartments, 22 in. wide by 37 in. high. **£1,100-1,300** *B*

A Victorian walnut piano top Davenport with drop front compartment enclosing pigeonholes and drawers, fitted centre drawer and side cupboard. **£1,100-1,300** *JH*

A Victorian burr-walnut Davenport with a rising stationery compartment, sliding leather-lined writing surface, a pair of panel doors to the sides enclosing cupboards and drawers, 27½ in. wide. **£950-1,050** *AG*

An eclipse patent marquetry harlequin writing desk, inlaid with foliage on a rosewood ground, the hinges stamped, The Eclipse Brand's Patent No. 7524, 3 ft. 1 in. by 3 ft. 2 in. (94 by 96 cm.), c. 1910. **£1,100-1,300** *S*

A figured walnut Davenport with column front supports and a door on the right enclosing 4 drawers, 3 ft. 4 in. high by 1 ft. 10 in. wide (102 by 56 cm.), c. 1870. **£575-625** *S*

A late Victorian rosewood and floral painted cylinder top Davenport, the interior with lined writing slide and 2 short drawers, 3 ft. 3 in. high by 1 ft. 6½ in. wide (99 by 47 cm.), c. 1880. **£650-750** *SS*

A faded walnut writing desk with fitted interior, 39 in. high, c. 1875. **£110-130** *CDE*

A Queen Anne walnut kneehole desk with quartered crossbanded top, on later bracket feet, 32 in. wide (81 cm.). **£3,000-4,000** *C*

A Victorian ebonised Davenport with piano top, pull-out writing slide, a raised stationery compartment with secret catch release. **£350-450** *M*

A Queen Anne walnut kneehole desk with crossbanded rounded rectangular top, 30½ in. wide (77 cm.). **£3,500-4,000** *C*

A fine quality Queen Anne period kneehole writing desk in walnut veneers, the figured quartered crossbanded herringbone inlaid surface with moulded edge, the cupboard with secret slide, 32 in. wide by 18 in. deep by 30 in. high, c. 1710, original throughout. **£3,750-4,400** *HAL*

An early Georgian walnut kneehole dressing table, the drawer fronts having herringbone banding fitted, 1 long drawer and small drawer with cupid's bow apron, 2 ft. 9 in. **£800-900** *RBB*

A George I walnut kneehole writing table, 2 ft. 7 in. high by 2 ft. 7 in. wide (79 by 79 cm.), c. 1725, top and bracket feet replaced. **£1,000-1,500** *S*

KNEEHOLE DESKS

- **kneehole desk is like a pedestal but with a recessed cupboard in between the pedestals**
- **it was most likely an 'upstairs' piece — hence being used as a dressing table/desk**
- **they were first made c. 1710 in walnut**
- **most then had 3 drawers across the top and 3 down each pedestal**
- **this piece of furniture has suffered from demand and there are many fakes and gross alterations**
- **many are made from chests of drawers (check the sides of the small drawers and if the desk has been made from a chest of drawers they will have a new side)**
- **it is unusual to have a brushing slide in a kneehole desk — this *could* point to a conversion.**

An early Georgian walnut kneehole desk with moulded quartered and crossbanded top on partly replaced bracket feet, 34½ in. wide (88 cm.). **£1,600-£1,800** *C*

A George I period writing desk in walnut, the figured quartered book-matched herringbone crossbanded moulded surface above crossbanded inlaid drawers with original brasswork surrounding a hinged cupboard and secret drawer, 31 in. wide by 18 in. deep by 31½ in. high, c.1720. **£3,600-£4,100** *HAL*

A mid Georgian mahogany kneehole desk with moulded top, a slide and a recessed kneehole cupboard, 45 in. wide (114 cm.). **£900-1,200** *C*

A George I walnut kneehole writing desk, 2 ft. 6½ in. high by 2 ft. 8 in. wide (77 by 81.5 cm.), c. 1720. **£2,500-3,000** *S*

An Edwardian inlaid mahogany kidney-shaped kneehole writing desk, 48 in. **£1,700-1,900** *SWO*

A kneehole desk of traditional design, 30½ in. wide by 18½ in., mid 18th C. **£800-900** *WHL*

A George III mahogany desk with a frieze drawer and a recessed cupboard, flanked on either side by 3 drawers, on bracket feet, 29½ by 30 in. (75 by 76 cm.), late 18th C. **£800-1,000** *SC*

A George III period kneehole desk in mahogany, the crossbanded moulded figured surface above 7 graduated cockbeaded drawers enclosing a cupboard, mounted on shaped bracket feet, the good quality brasswork being of later date, 34 in. wide by 21 in. deep by 30 in. high, c. 1790. **£1,800-2,400** *HAL*

A George III mahogany kneehole desk, the central cupboard flanked by banks of 3 drawers, on shaped bracket feet, 2 ft. 8 in. high by 2 ft. 10 in. wide (81 by 86.5 cm.), c. 1765. **£800-1,000** *S*

A yew-wood-veneered kneehole writing table, the kneehole with recessed cupboard and shallow drawer, 2 ft. 8 in. high by 2 ft. 9 in. wide (81 by 84 cm.). **£2,500-3,000** *S*

A George III-style mahogany kneehole desk with satinwood crossbanding, boxwood and ebony stringing, 30½ in. high by 34 in. wide, late 19th/early 20th C. **£450-£500** *Bea*

A Louis XIV boulle bureau mazarin in brass and red tortoiseshell, the top with a Berainesque design, drawers re-lined, distressed, 2 ft. 7½ in. high by 3 ft. 6½ in. wide (79 by 108 cm.), c. 1680. **£8,000-9,000** *S*

A George III mahogany double-sided kneehole desk with leather-lined top, 2 ft. 8 in. high by 4 ft. 1 in. wide (81 by 124 cm.), c. 1780. **£2,200-2,500** *S*

A North Italian walnut kneehole desk with 3 frieze drawers and a leather-lined slide above 2 cupboards on later turned feet, 59 in. wide (150 cm.), early 18th C. **£3,500-4,000** *C*

A late 18th C. figured mahogany partners desk, 54 by 42 in. **£3,750-£4,250** *RD*

An early George III-style mahogany partners desk of continuous serpentine outline, 30 by 59 by 31 in. (76 by 150 by 79 cm.), 20th C. **£3,500-4,000** *SC*

A George III-style mahogany pedestal partners desk, the top 55 by 37½ in. **£1,700-1,900** *T*

A late Georgian mahogany pedestal partners desk, the front with 2 frieze drawers and 3 drawers either side, the reverse with 2 frieze drawers and 2 cupboards, 56 by 37¾ by 30¾ in. high (143 by 96 by 78 cm.). **£2,200-£2,500** *L*

A late Georgian mahogany pedestal desk with the unusual arrangement of a frieze drawer either end, in need of some repair. **£5,000-5,500** *L*

A Georgian mahogany partners desk, 77 in. wide (196 cm.). **£6,000-£7,000** *C*

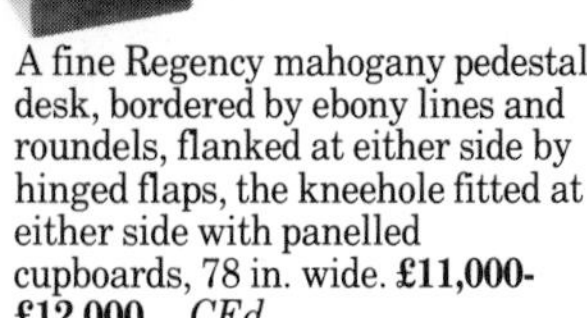

A fine Regency mahogany pedestal desk, bordered by ebony lines and roundels, flanked at either side by hinged flaps, the kneehole fitted at either side with panelled cupboards, 78 in. wide. **£11,000-£12,000** *CEd*

A 19th C. mahogany twin pedestal partners desk, fitted drawers, insert leather top, plinth base, 60 in. **£1,500-1,700** *LE*

A Victorian satin birch pedestal desk, in need of restoration. **£750-£850** *WSW*

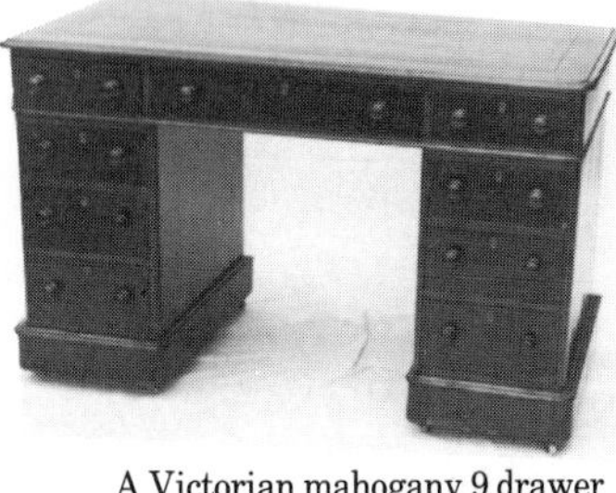

A Victorian mahogany 9 drawer pedestal desk with turned knob handles. **£350-400** *Fr*

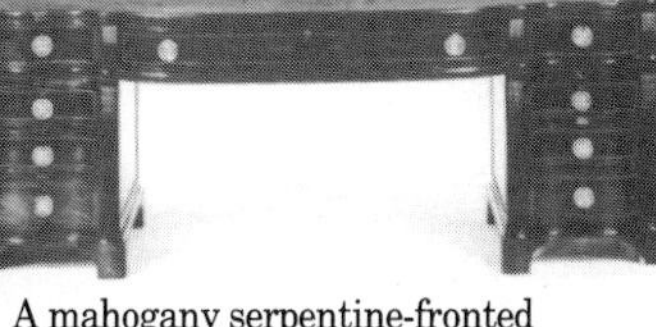

A mahogany serpentine-fronted pedestal desk with a 3-quarter gallery and a tooled leather top, 2 ft. 6 in. by 6 ft. 9 in. (76 by 207.5 cm.), c. 1870. **£1,500-2,000** *S*

A good quality 19th C. partners desk in mahogany, the embossed claret hide writing surface above drawers and cupboards with brass pulls on plinths with castors, 60 in. wide by 41½ in. deep by 29 in. high, c. 1880. **£2,500-3,500** *HAL*

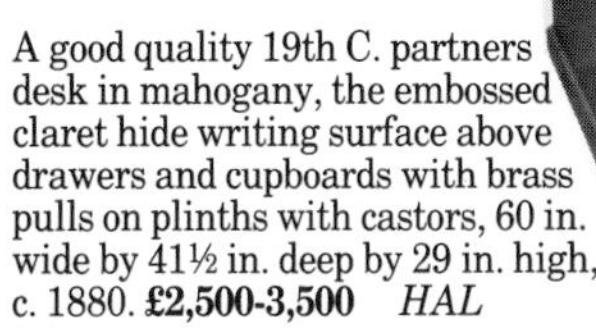

A George III-style partners desk, drawers and panelled cupboards concealing further drawers, the ends with replaced astragal mouldings, hide and brass replaced, 59 in. wide by 35 in. deep by 30½ in. high, c. 1850. **£1,750-£2,300** *HAL*

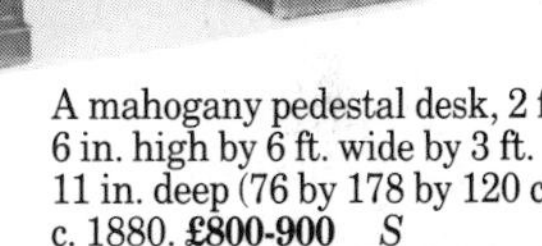

A mahogany pedestal desk, 2 ft. 6 in. high by 6 ft. wide by 3 ft. 11 in. deep (76 by 178 by 120 cm.), c. 1880. **£800-900** *S*

A mahogany partners desk, 2 ft. 7½ in. high by 5 ft. wide (80 by 152.5 cm.), c. 1840. **£4,500-5,500** *S*

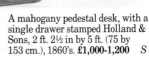

A mahogany pedestal desk, with a single drawer stamped Holland & Sons, 2 ft. 2½ in by 5 ft. (75 by 153 cm.), 1860's. **£1,000-1,200** *S*

A small Victorian mahogany pedestal desk, the top inset with green tooled leather, 3 ft. 10 in. wide. **£250-300** *DS*

A late 19th C. mahogany pedestal desk, 60 by 36 in. **£450-550** *JMW*

A Victorian mahogany pedestal desk. **£500-600** *WSW*

An inlaid satinwood-veneered pedestal desk, the well-figured top with a crossbanding of kingwood and an inset moulded brass border, on 8 ormolu-mounted feet, 2 ft. 6 in. high by 5 ft. long (76 by 153 cm.), c. 1910. **£2,000-2,400** *S*

A satinwood and marquetry desk, with a kidney-shaped top and inlaid throughout with scrolling foliage and flowers, 29 by 53 in. (74 by 135 cm.), early 20th C. **£1,500-£1,700** *SC*

An Edwardian mahogany kidney-shaped writing desk, the moulded top with worn leather inset, inlaid throughout with acanthus leaves and flowers, 29½ in. high by 52 in. wide by 28 in. deep. **£2,200-2,400** *PB*

A Victorian mahogany pedestal desk, 53 in. wide. **£500-600** *DA*

A Regency mahogany Carlton House desk, the hinged leather-lined writing flap surrounded by 4 drawers and flanked at the sides by 2 further small drawers, fitted with 3 drawers in the frieze, on turned tapering legs, 58 in. wide. **£9,000-£10,000** *CEd*

A satinwood Carlton House writing table inlaid with mahogany bands, musical instruments and foliate arabesques, labelled Druce & Company, 53 in. **£6,000-7,000** *CSK*

An Edwardian carved mahogany twin pedestal writing desk, on carved supports. **£350-400** *EBB*

A late Regency mahogany library desk, with paw feet flanking pierced giltmetal trellis-work panels lined with yellow silk on plinth base, 84 in. (213 cm.), **£9,000-10,000** *C*

A mahogany satinwood and marquetry Carlton House writing table, inlaid with Adam-style marquetry of neo-classical motifs, 3 ft. 1½ in. high by 4 ft. 6 in. wide (95 by 137 cm.), slightly reduced in height, late 19th C. **£2,500-3,000** *S*

A mahogany writing desk, the leather-lined surface with a bow-fronted drawer above the kneehole, 3 ft. 8¾ in. wide (113.5 cm.), c. 1910. **£400-500** *S*

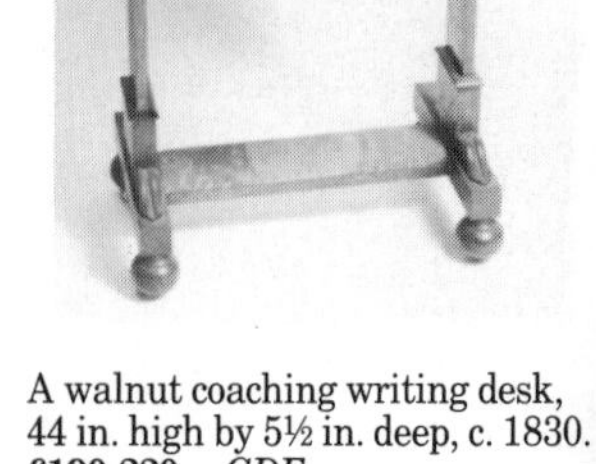

A walnut coaching writing desk, 44 in. high by 5½ in. deep, c. 1830. **£190-220** *CDE*

A Louis Philippe walnut kneehole roll-top desk, on cabriole legs with claw and ball feet with C-scrolled headings, 52 in. **£1,000-1,200** *CSK*

A Wooton Desk Co. mahogany kneehole desk, bearing the label 'Wooton Desk Co., 45 Gordon St., Glasgow patented May 1st 1875', 2 ft. 7 in. high by 4 ft. 1½ in. wide (79 by 126 cm.), c. 1875. **£1,000-£1,100** *S*

A large 19th C. mahogany cylinder front pedestal writing desk, with pull-out writing surface, 5 ft. wide. **£550-650** *DDM*

A pollard oak and walnut library desk, with an inset writing surface, frieze fitted with drawers on either side, 32 by 48 by 60 in. (81 by 122 by 153 cm.), mid 19th C. **£1,200-£1,400** *SC*

A carved oak pedestal desk with 6 upper drawers and letter compartments, leather top, Belgian reproduction. **£650-700** *HFM*

A Victorian inlaid mahogany writing desk, stamped James Shoolbred & Co., in a drawer. **£700-£800** *WSW*

A Victorian walnut 'Dickens' desk, 60 in. wide, c. 1900. **£800-900** *Ph*

A George III mahogany draughtsman's kneehole table, with double-hinged top, possibly Scottish, handles replaced, 4 ft. wide (125 cm.), c. 1780. **£1,350-£1,550** *S*

A Commonwealth oak dresser with split baluster and mitred mouldings, 2 ft. 9 in. high by 6 ft. 9 in. wide (84 by 206 cm.), c. 1660. **£1,800-2,000** *S*

A mid 17th C. oak dresser with 3 geometric panelled drawers, complete with later plate rack, 7 ft. long. **£2,250-2,500** *AGr*

A mid Georgian mahogany architect's desk, the top hinged on a ratchet frame, fitted with 2 candle slides, with restorations, 31½ by 39 by 24 in. (78 by 99 by 61 cm.), mid 18th C. **£1,400-1,800** *SC*

A late 17th C. oak low dresser, 34 in. high by 66 in. wide. **£1,500-£1,800** *S*

A low oak dresser with a moulded top and 3 drawers with projecting geometric mouldings, with restorations, 76 by 29½ in. (193 by 75 cm.) high. **£950-1,150** *L*

Locate the source

The source of each illustration in Miller's can be found by checking the code letters below each caption with the list of contributors on page 12.
In view of the undoubted differences in price structures from region to region, this information could be extremely valuable to everyone who buys and sells antiques.

A George II oak low dresser, with restorations, 72 in. (183 cm.). **£2,500-3,000** *L*

An early 18th C. oak dresser base with 3 crossbanded frieze drawers, 31½ in. high by 78 in. wide. **£1,400-£1,600** *S*

A low oak cupboard dresser with a central cupboard flanked on either side with 3 drawers with burr-oak crossbandings, 80½ by 36 in. (204 by 91 cm.), basically 18th C. **£800-£1,000** *L*

An 18th C. oak dresser base, 69 in. wide. **£1,000-1,200** *McCMB*

A George III period mule chest in oak, the figured lifting moulded surface crossbanded in mahogany, 65 in. wide by 22½ in. deep by 39 in. high, c. 1770. **£880-1,050** *HAL*

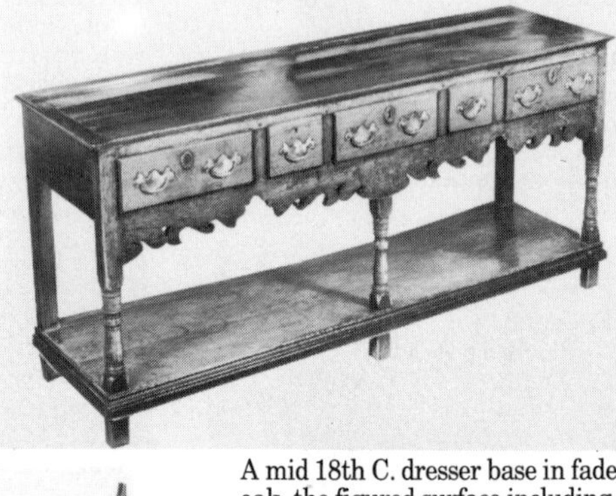
A mid 18th C. dresser base in faded oak, the figured surface including a plate-stay, the 5 drawers with moulded fronts and good quality replaced brasswork, 66 in. wide by 19 in. deep by 31 in. high, c. 1760. **£2,000-2,400** *HAL*

Miller's is a price GUIDE Not a price LIST.

The price ranges given reflect the average price a purchaser should pay for similar items. Condition, rarity of design or pattern, size, colour, provenance, restoration and many other factors must be taken into account when assessing values.

A late 17th C. oak dresser, brass drop handles and escutcheons and 3 turned front legs, 76 in. wide by 71 in. high. **£1,200-1,400** *DSH*

An 18th C. Dutch oak dresser, 5 ft. 4 in. **£420-£500** *DDM*

A Charles II-style oak and elm dresser, all applied with geometric mouldings on twist turned supports, reconstructed using some earlier pieces of timber, 85 by 72 in. (216 by 183 cm.). **£450-550** *SC*

A George I oak dresser, fitted 3 crossbanded frieze drawers, on cabriole legs, 7 ft. 4 in. high by 6 ft. 2 in. wide (224 by 189 cm.), c. 1720. **£1,500-1,700** *SS*

An early 18th C. oak Welsh dresser. **£1,350-1,500** *LS*

An early 18th C. oak dresser, with double arched apron, 4 ft. 9 in. **£1,700-1,900** *WSW*

An oak dresser, 4 ft. 2 in. wide by 1 ft. 4 in. deep by 75 in. high. **£600-£700** *DA*

An early 18th C. oak Welsh dresser, the base with 3 crossbanded frieze drawers inlaid with boxwood lines, a shaped apron below and on cabriole legs with pointed pad feet, 75 in. wide. **£2,000-2,200** *Bea*

An oak Welsh dresser with pan stand base and plate rack, 67 in. wide by 73 in. high. **£1,500-2,000** *DA*

An 18th C. oak dresser. **£1,600-£1,800** *HWO*

A large 18th C. oak dresser, 5 ft. 9 in. wide by 6 ft. 9 in. high. **£1,400-£1,600** *MMB*

A George III oak dresser, 5 ft. 10 in. **£1,200-1,500** *WSW*

An 18th C. dresser in oak of good patina, the rack with fretted cornice above 3 shelves with plate stays, the base with drawers and panelled cupboards decorated by original brass pulls and ivory escutcheons, 62 in. wide by 19 in. deep by 80 in. high. **£2,000-2,850** *HAL*

An 18th C. oak dresser. **£1,200-£1,400** *HWO*

An oak Welsh dresser, the base enclosed by 2 cupboards and 2 drawers, below a panelled plate rack back, 50 in. wide, c. 1720. **£2,500-3,000** *KHD*

A walnut dresser, the waved serpentined pediment shelves carved with acanthus C-scrolls and musical instruments, 42 in. **£700-£800** *CSK*

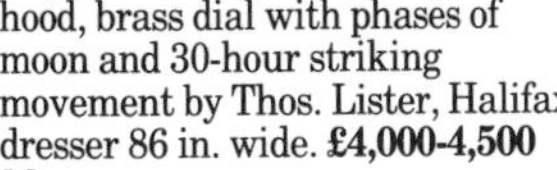

A rare 18th C. oak clock/dresser and rack, the open rack with centre longcase clock, having a square hood, brass dial with phases of moon and 30-hour striking movement by Thos. Lister, Halifax, dresser 86 in. wide. **£4,000-4,500** *M*

An 18th C. oak Welsh dresser, 6 ft. 8 in. high by 5 ft. long by 1 ft. 9 in. wide. **£1,400-1,600** *DDM*

An 18th C. oak dresser, 85 in. long. **£750-950** *McCMB*

A late 18th C. oak dresser, 6 ft. 9 in., with set of 6 ft. open plate shelves. **£800-900** the two *AGG*

A George III oak dresser, on bracket feet, 83 by 72 in. (211 by 183 cm.), early 19th C. **£1,750-£2,000** *SC*

A George III oak dresser, 6 ft. 9 in. high by 4 ft. 10 in. wide (206 by 147 cm.), c. 1760, top possibly later. **£600-700** *S*

A mid 18th C. oak dresser with a moulded cornice and 3 open shelves, 3 frieze drawers, a shaped apron and on turned legs joined by an undershelf, 72 in. high by 56 in. wide. **£900-1,000** *S*

An early 19th C. oak dresser, with shaped apron carved with fan motifs and on square legs, 82 in. high by 51 in. wide. **£600-800** *S*

A George III mahogany dumb waiter, the triple graduating tiers on a fluted turned column, with pointed pad feet, 41 in. **£450-500** *CSK*

DUMB WAITERS

- there is some controversy about when dumb waiters made an appearance
- they were certainly produced in the 1720's but are rare until the 1750's
- defined by Sheraton (Cabinet Dictionary 1803) as 'a useful piece of furniture, to serve in some respects the place of a waiter, whence it is so named'
- 18th C. dumb waiters *generally* consist of three tiers
- made usually from mahogany
- in Chippendale period supports often carved with foliage, acanthus leaves, broken scrolls, etc.
- Robert Adam's neo-classical style radically changed the design
- the pillars now tended to become plainly cylindrical with turned collars at top and bottom
- the late 18th C. and early 19th C. saw the introduction of pierced galleries often made of brass
- during the Regency period some dumb waiters made from rosewood
- marriages are around so beware
  - — differing turning on three trays
  - — two-tier examples (they can be right but are often 'naughty').

An early George III mahogany 3-tier dumb waiter, 3 ft. 7 in. high by 2 ft. ½ in. maximum diameter (109 by 62.5 cm.), c. 1765. **£1,200-£1,400** *S*

A pair of mahogany 3-tier dumb waiters of George III-style with graduated revolving shelves, one bearing the trade label of C. Mellier & Co., 48, 49 & 50 Margaret St., Cavendish Sq., 26 in. wide (66 cm.). **£4,000-4,500** *C*

C. Mellier & Co. started trading c. 1860 at 2 Frith Street and continued in business until 1931.

A late 18th C. mahogany dumb waiter with folding shelves, 34 in high, c. 1790. **£1,200-1,400** *CC*

A George III mahogany dumb waiter, the revolving tiers with dish mouldings, 3 ft. 9 in. high (114 cm.), c. 1770. **£400-500** *SS*

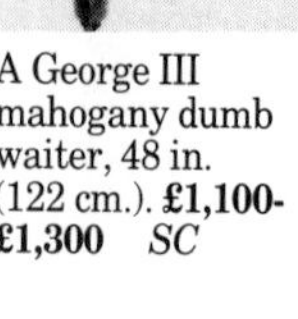
A George III mahogany dumb waiter, 48 in. (122 cm.). **£1,100-£1,300** *SC*

A mahogany dumb waiter on gunbarrel stem, 41 in., c. 1770-80. **£1,100-1,300** *HB*

A mahogany Chippendale period table top dumb waiter, 24 in. diam. **£400-500** *HB*

A 3-tier mahogany dumb waiter, 42 in. high, c. 1800. **£400-500** *STR*

A fine pair of late George II library globes by Benjamin Martin, one terrestrial and one celestial, restored, 2 ft. 11 in. high by 1 ft. 11 in. diam. (89 by 58 cm.), dated 1757. **£3,000-4,000** *S*

A pair of Regency globes, the terrestrial inscribed 'manufactured by T.M. Bardin 16, Salisbury Square London with Corrections & Additions to 1821', the celestial inscribed 'made by T.M. Bardin', the terrestrial with a glazed compass, 36 in. high (91.5 cm.). **£3,500-4,000** *C*

A pair of table globes, the terrestrial globe by T. M. Bardin correct to 1817, the turned beechwood stands with baluster supports, stand restored, 1 ft. 6 in. high by 1 ft. 5 in. diam. (46 by 43 cm.), early 19th C. **£1,800-£2,200** *S*

A large Italian terrestrial globe on stand, 3 ft. 3 in. high by 3 ft. wide (99 by 92 cm.), late 18th C., the date on the globe is apparently 1799, but restored. **£2,000-2,200** *S*

An early 19th C. celestial globe by Newton, 14½ in. high, c. 1820. **£350-450** *CC*

An early 19th C. terrestrial globe. **£950-1,050** *HWO*

A pair of early 19th C. terrestrial and celestial table globes, by Newton Sons & Berry, dated 1839. **£1,200-1,400** *S*

An Indo Persian cast brass Islamic celestial sphere, the surface bored for the poles of the equator and ecliptic, 76 mm. diam., probably 18th C. **£1,500-2,000** *C*

A George III terrestrial table globe, dedicated to the Rt. Hon. Sir Joseph Banks Bart., K.B.B., President of the Royal Society, containing all the latest discoveries to the year 1799 by Captain Cook, 1 ft. 11 in. diam. (58 cm.). **£950-£1,200** *S*

A celestial globe by Marlby, Bishopsgate St., on a mahogany frame and concave stretcher, dated 1852, 3 ft. 7 in. (109 cm.). **£700-£900** *S*

A pair of Charles Smith & Sons 18 in. terrestrial and celestial globes, each sphere applied with coloured gores and supported by brass meridian engraved with circle of degrees, on turned and carved rosewood stand, centred by magnetic compass with printed rose, English, 44 in. (111 cm.). high, c. 1840. **£7,000-9,000** *S*

A pair of Newton's library globes, the terrestrial globe with corrections to 1857 and the celestial globe with corrections to 1866, each bearing a silver plaque engraved Presented by Br^{O} R. Kearns, W.M. to Chine Lodge 1884, 25 January 1894, distressed, 3 ft. 4 in. high by 1 ft. 10 in. diam. (101 by 56 cm.). **£2,600-2,800** *S*

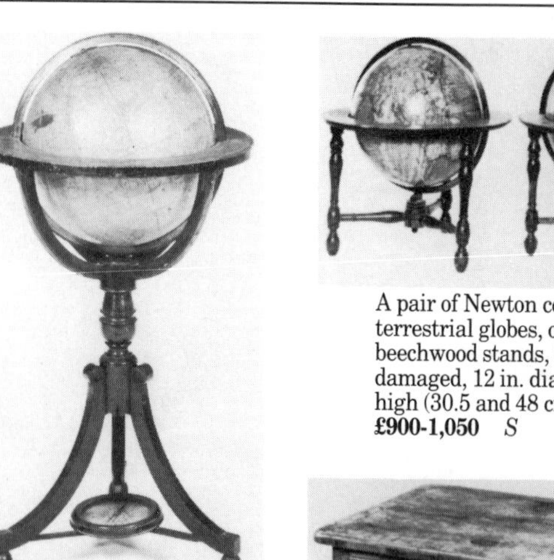

A pair of Newton celestial and terrestrial globes, on turned beechwood stands, terrestrial globe damaged, 12 in. diam. by 19 in. high (30.5 and 48 cm.), dated 1841. **£900-1,050** *S*

A George I walnut lowboy, the moulded crossbanded top with boxwood and ebony stringing, 2 ft. 2 in. high by 2 ft. 3½ in. wide (66 by 70 cm.), c. 1720. **£1,900-2,100** *S*

Use the Index!

Because certain items might fit easily into any of a number of categories, the quickest and surest method of locating any entry is by reference to the index at the back of the book.

A Queen Anne walnut lowboy, the legs with restorations and replacements, 28½ in. wide by 27½ in. high (72 by 70 cm.). **£4,000-£5,000** *C*

An 18th C. Queen Anne-style oak lowboy, 31 by 20 in. **£850-950** *JMW*

A yew-wood lowboy, 30½ in. wide, c. 1780. **£320-350** *CDE*

An early 18th C. oak lowboy, 29 in. wide. **£900-1,000** *HB*

An 18th C. oak lowboy, 2 ft. 8 in. wide. **£250-300** *DDM*

An oak lowboy with a moulded top, fitted with 3 crossbanded drawers above a waved apron and on 4 cabriole legs with pad feet, 35 in. (89 cm.), 18th C. **£300-350** *L*

An early/mid 18th C. oak and mahogany crossbanded lowboy. **£420-500** *LS*

A Charles II giltwood overmantel, with later rectangular plate on moulded frame carved with ribbons and flowerheads within a border of pierced and scrolling acanthus foliage surmounted by winged putti, C-scrolls and feathers, 51½ by 54 in. **£7,000-8,000** *CEd*

A walnut mirror with rectangular bevelled plate, the angles with a ducal monogram lacking easel support, Flemish or N. German, 15 by 17¼ in. (38 by 45 cm.), 17th C. **£550-650** *C*

A Louis XIV giltwood looking glass, the sanded frame with semi-circular pilasters with gesso strapwork and leafy clasps, possibly Aix-en-Provence, 6 ft. 7 in. high by 3 ft. 7½ in. wide (201 by 110 cm.), c. 1700. **£2,500-3,000** *S*

MIRRORS

- **mirrors of burnished metal were known in Tudor times**
- **glass mirrors more common from the Restoration on**
- **the Duke of Buckingham is often thought of as the innovator of glass mirrors. This was certainly the period for veneered surrounds, in walnut, olive and laburnum**
- **by the end of the 17th C. mirrors to stand on surfaces appeared**
- **by Queen Anne mirrors more common as glass less expensive — the frames became more elaborate — walnut veneer was glued to oak or pine frame**
- **early Georgian saw the development of the architectural influence on design — this was the period of the Classical revival**
- **early 18th C. was influenced by rococo designs**
- **after this the Chinese influence is apparent**
- **this was followed and embellished by the scrolling outlines of Chippendale — broken pediments became popular**
- **Adam reacted against the Chippendale style by concentrating on the classical influence — some purely gilt mirrors produced**
- **c. 1780 cheval mirrors became more general — this period dominated by the designs of Hepplewhite. His designs are characterised as somewhere between Chippendale and Sheraton, with a less formal design than Adam**

A Queen Anne walnut mirror, the base with 2 scrolled candle-branches with turned nozzles and drip-pans, 24½ by 18 in. (62 by 46 cm.). **£1,850-2,050** *C*

A pair of early George II wall mirrors, each engraved with a swag, contained by a dark blue coloured glass frame, 27½ by 15½ in. (70 by 42 cm.), early 18th C. **£500-600** *SC*

A William and Mary walnut and seaweed marquetry mirror with later bevelled plate in cushion frame edged with scorched borders and inlaid with panels of arabesque foliage, lacking cresting, 39 by 30½ in. (99 by 77 cm.). **£4,000-£4,500** *C*

A Carolean walnut and marquetry inlaid cushion frame rectangular hanging mirror, decorated with birds, flowers and foliate scrolls, 40½ by 34½ in. overall. **£1,600-£1,800** *GC*

A pair of Flemish ebonised mirrors with bevelled plates in mirrored surrounds, with ripple moulded borders, the frames mounted with foliate repoussé copper panels and angles, 65 by 40½ in. (165 by 103 cm.), 17th C. and later. **£4,000-£4,500** *C*

A Queen Anne giltwood pier glass, frame carved with strapwork, acanthus foliage and flowerheads centred by a putto mask and flanked by eagles' heads, 55 by 26 in. **£1,400-1,800** *CEd*

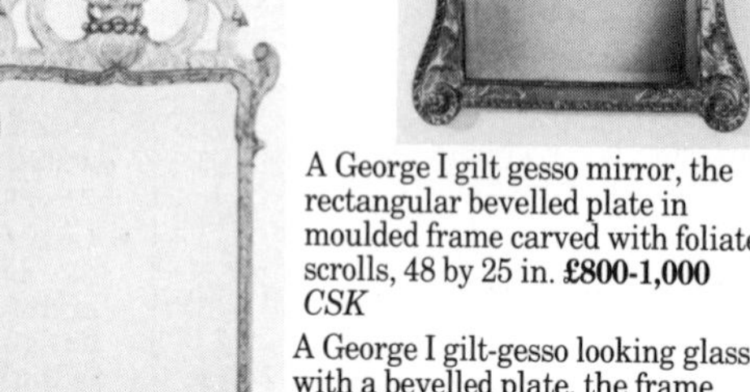

A Queen Anne walnut and parcel-gilt overmantel with triple bevelled plate, the central later, fitted with 2 associated brass candle-branches, 20¼ by 58¼ in. (51.5 by 148 cm.). **£5,000-6,000** *C*

A George I gilt gesso mirror, the rectangular bevelled plate in moulded frame carved with foliate scrolls, 48 by 25 in. **£800-1,000** *CSK*

A George I gilt-gesso looking glass with a bevelled plate, the frame with pierced scroll cornice and scallopshell apron decorated with leaf scrolls and husks, 3 ft. 11½ in. high by 2 ft. 2½ wide (120 by 67 cm.), c. 1720. **£1,200-1,600** *S*

A George I Irish wall mirror, the shaped cresting centred by a shell supported by birds, scrolls and acanthus leaves and carved with moon faces, all in gilt on a black ground, 3 ft. 11½ in. high by 2 ft. 3½ in. wide (120 by 70 cm.), c. 1725. **£1,400-1,600** *SI*

Bearing the trade label of Thomas Moyler, 25 Suffolk Street, Dublin.

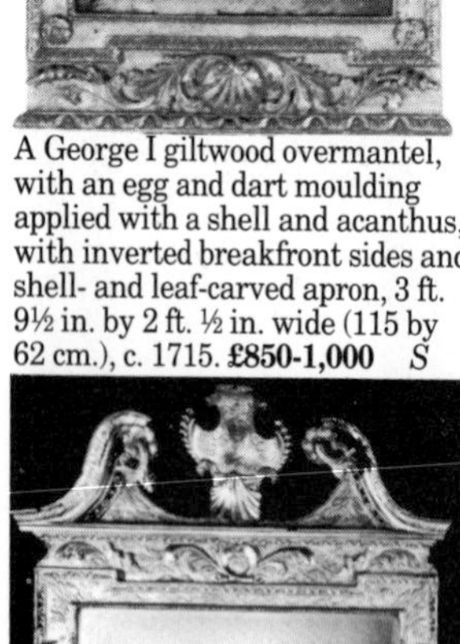

A George I giltwood overmantel, with an egg and dart moulding applied with a shell and acanthus, with inverted breakfront sides and shell- and leaf-carved apron, 3 ft. 9½ in. by 2 ft. ½ in. wide (115 by 62 cm.), c. 1715. **£850-1,000** *S*

A George I gilt-gesso pier glass, with arched divided bevelled plate, 70 by 30 in. (178 by 76 cm.). **£1,400-£1,600** *C*

A gilt-gesso mirror with divided bevelled plate in narrow foliate slip with faceted mirrored outer border, the frame moulded with strapwork, the base centred by a shell with 2 brackets for candle-branches, 59 by 30½ in. (150 by 77.5 cm.). **£2,500-3,000** *C*

An engraved glass and gilt-bronze looking glass, the bevelled plate within canted etched border glasses outlined in bead-moulding, probably Venetian, mirror plate replaced, 4 ft. 4 in. high by 2 ft. 5 in. wide (132 by 74 cm.), c. 1720. **£2,400-2,800** *S*

A George II giltwood mirror with rectangular bevelled plate, the eared frame moulded with foliage edged with bead-and-reel ornament, regilded, 65 by 38 in. (165 by 97 cm.). **£2,000-3,000** *C*

A rare and interesting Chinese mirror painting depicting 3 figures in a landscape with Windsor Castle in the background, within an elaborate C-scroll and husk swagged frame surmounted by swords, quivers and arrows, 4 ft. 2 in. high by 3 ft. 8½ in. wide (127 by 113 cm.), mirror painting early 18th C., frame c. 1760. **£10,000-£13,000** *S*

The iconography is presumed to represent the Act of Union, taken from a contemporary print.

A George II giltwood mirror with bevelled rectangular plate, 57½ by 28½ in. (146 by 67 cm.). **£2,200-£2,600** *C*

A George II mahogany mirror, the rectangular bevelled plate with an egg-and-dart frame below a swan neck cresting centred by a floral cartouche, 5 ft. by 2 ft. 6½ in. (157 by 77 cm.), c. 1740. **£4,500-5,500** *S*

A George II carved giltwood pier glass, the bevelled plate contained within a sanded frame with flowers and leaves at the corners, possibly Irish, 7 ft. 1 in. high by 3 ft. 3½ in. wide (216 by 100 cm.), c. 1740. **£3,500-4,000** *S*

A George II walnut and parcel-gilt pier glass, with bevelled plate in eared and scrolled frame, the broken scrolled cresting centred by a cabochon cartouche, 57 by 29 in. (145 by 74 cm.). **£3,750-£4,000** *C*

A George II gilt-gesso pier glass with bevelled plate in adapted sanded frame bordered with flowerheads, 65½ by 34 in. (166 by 86 cm.). **£7,000-8,000** *C*

A mid Georgian giltwood mirror with oval plate in broad scalloped frame, the base centred by a ram's mask, the pierced shell cresting with a satyr mask, 58½ by 38 in. (149 by 96.5 cm.). **£5,000-£7,000** *C*

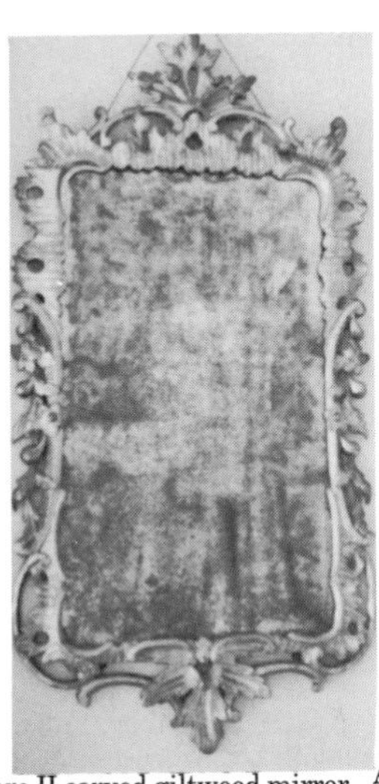
A George II carved giltwood mirror, with original Vauxhall glass, 43 by 23 in. **£950-1,050** *HWO*

A George II period pier glass in carved giltwood, the scrolling pediment flanking a cartouche above carved shellwork and scrolling egg-and-dart moulding framing a later plate, 53 in. high by 28 in. wide, c. 1740. **£1,400-1,800** *HAL*

A pair of giltwood mirrors with oval plates in moulded frames surrounded by naturalistic bulrushes with crossed asymmetric crestings, 49½ by 27½ in. (126 by 70 cm.). **£4,000-6,000** *C*

A George II carved giltwood wall mirror, within a pierced frame carved with flowers and scrolls flanked by turbaned female masks with grotesque mask apron, cresting missing, 4 ft. 2 in. high by 3 ft. 1 in. wide (127 by 95 cm.), c. 1750. **£2,750-3,000** *S*

A pair of giltwood wall mirrors in George II style, 3 ft. 2½ in. by 2 ft. 3 in. (98 by 68.5 cm.), early 20th C. **£500-600** *S*

A late George II mahogany and parcel gilt wall mirror, the fret pierced cresting centred by a shell, shaped and moulded ears and apron, 43 in. overall (109 cm.), mid 18th C. **£550-700** *SC*

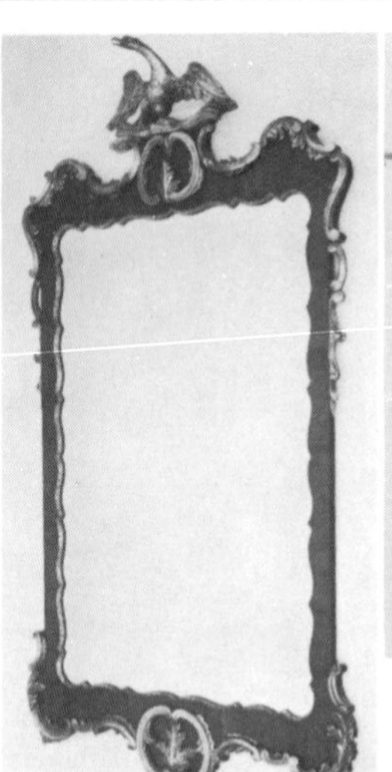
A mahogany and gilt wall mirror in the mid Georgian style, contained in mahogany frame applied with C scrolls, leafage and eagle surmount, 30 by 56 in. (76 by 142 cm.) **£325-375** *L*

A George II-style walnut pier glass, overall height 72 in. **£1,200- 1,500** *McCMB*

A rare carved giltwood looking glass, with a frame of small engraved mirror-glass plates all within carved giltwood borders, Austria or Bohemia, 3 ft. 3 in. high by 2 ft. 2 in. wide (99 by 66 cm.), c. 1740. **£2,000-2,200** *S*

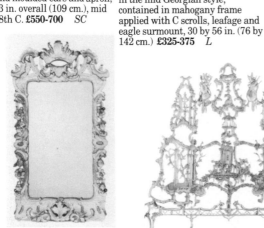

A George II giltwood wall mirror, 3 ft. 10 in. high by 2 ft. 2½ in. wide (117 by 67 cm.), c. 1755. **£600-800** *S*

An important mid 18th C. English giltwood rococo overmantel mirror, the lower part with 3 plates divided and enclosed by scrollwork and the upper part composed of many plates framed by scrollwork, rocks, branches and pillars, the triple-mirrored cresting centred by a seated sheep and divided by 2 well carved musical trophies, 8 ft. 10 in. high by 8 ft. 2 in. wide (270 by 249 cm.), c. 1760. **£14,000-18,000** *S*

A late 19th C. Florentine mosaic wall mirror, 39 by 32 in. overall. **£400-500** *PWC*

Locate the source
The source of each illustration in Miller's can be found by checking the code letters below each caption with the list of contributors on page 12.
In view of the undoubted differences in price structures from region to region, this information could be extremely valuable to everyone who buys and sells antiques.

An early George III carved giltwood mirror, with plate contained in a border of smaller plates with leaf-scroll frame, 4 ft. 9 in. high (145 cm.), c. 1760. **£1,600-1,900** *S*

A mahogany framed mirror, 46 in. high, c. 1760. **£1,000-1,250** *CC*

An early George III carved giltwood looking glass, with shaped plate, 3 ft. 3 in. high by 2 ft. 3 in. wide (99 by 68 cm.), c. 1760. **£600-£800** *S*

A mahogany fretwork framed mirror, 28 in. high, c. 1750. **£200-£250** *NC*

A George III giltwood mirror, the frame pierced and carved with S and C-scrolls, the cartouche cresting surmounted by flowerheads and wreaths, 47 by 25½ in. (119.5 by 65 cm.). **£1,500-£2,000** *C*

A George II giltwood mirror, the frame outlined with shells and bead-and-reel ornament, the broken cresting centred by a foliate cartouche, 52 by 27 in. (132 by 58.5 cm.). **£1,750-2,250** *C*

A George III giltwood mirror with mirrored borders divided by a band of ribbon twist and overlaid with anthemions and flowerheads, 60 by 43 in. (153 by 109 cm.). **£1,600-£1,800** *C*

A pair of George III carved giltwood girandoles, each with a ho-ho bird standing on a C-scroll cresting above an arched bevelled plate, with an arcaded apron below hung with acanthus leaves, C-scrolls and rocailles and with a pair of floral candle-arms, 4 ft. high by 2 ft. 2 in. wide (122 by 66 cm.), c. 1760. **£5,500-6,000** *S*

An Irish George III giltwood mirror attributed to William and John Booker, the tablet frieze with pierced C-scrolls and foliage between detached Corinthian column angles, lacking base, 74½ by 46 in. (189 by 117 cm.). **£3,500-£4,500** *C*

John and Francis Booker took over their father's Essex Bridge business after his death in 1750. They appear in Peter Wilson's Dublin Directory for 1761-62 as 'glass grinders' and 'sellers'.

A George III giltwood and composition mirror, with vase and wheatear cresting suspending bell-flowers, 56¾ by 23½ in. (144 by 60 cm.). **£1,200-1,500** *C*

A George III-style overmantel, within a giltwood frame pierced and carved with C-scrolls and foliage, surmounted by a pagoda and flanked by 2 eagles, 31 in. high by 48 in. wide, mid 19th C. **£450-£600** *S*

A pair of 18th C. repoussé brass mirrors, Flemish, 33 in. high. **£1,500-2,000** *CC*

A pair of giltwood framed mirrors, 26 in. **£900-1,100** *NC*

A Georgian-style giltwood mirror, broken arched pediment with ropework surrounding the plates and carved giltwood apron, 52 in. wide. **£160-200** *DS*

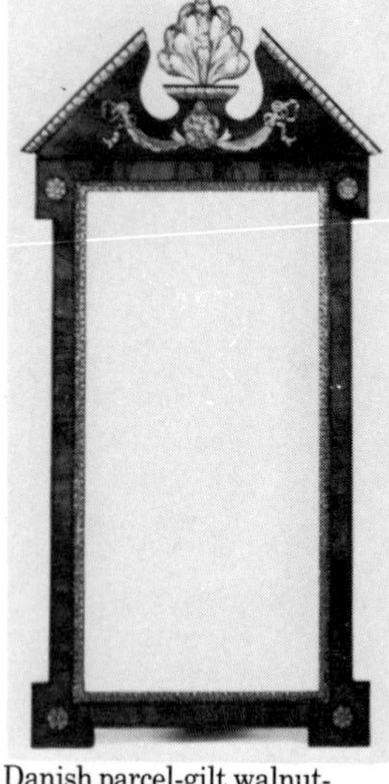

A Danish parcel-gilt walnut-veneered wall mirror, with inner bead and petal mouldings and outset corners, the broken triangular pediment centred by an anthemion, plate replaced, some decoration added, 4 ft. 10 in. high by 2 ft. 5 in. wide (147 by 74 cm.), c. 1765. **£600-800** *S*

A Chippendale period carved giltwood rococo frame wall mirror, the original plate with moulded column pilaster open scroll surround, the sides with trailing fruit and flowers, 28½ in. by 4 ft. **£2,500-2,700** *WW*

A George III carved giltwood wall mirror, decorated with basket of flowers, shells and scrolls, 53 by 24 in. **£450-500** *GM*

An important Chippendale giltwood pier glass, the 2 section plate surrounded by heavy pierced rococo scrolls, entwined flowers, 6 ft. by 3 ft. **£1,200-1,400** *DS*

An antique carved giltwood mirror in Chinese Chippendale taste, 4 later plates, 69 in. high. **£700-£800** *GSP*

A large pair of giltwood and gesso convex girandoles, each with an ebonised slip contained by a moulded frame applied with balls beneath a tall cresting surmounted by an eagle, with cut glass drips and drops, fitted for electricity, 70 by 47 in. (118 by 120 cm.), early 19th C. **£4,000-5,000** *SC*

An unusual small Regency convex girandole, candle arms with cut glass drips, 27½ in. overall (70 cm.), early 19th C. **£200-225** *SC*

A fine quality pair of 18th C. French hanging mirrors with finely carved giltwood and decorated frames surrounding early but not original plates, 31 in. wide by 48 in. high, c. 1800. **£1,800-2,400** *HAL*

A mahogany fret cut framed mirror, 24 in. high, c. 1800. **£140-£150** *FF*

A Regency giltwood convex girandole surmounted by a sea dragon perched on rocks, 4 candle arms, 4 ft. 2 in. high by 3 ft. 2 in. wide (127 by 97 cm.), c. 1820. **£700-£750** *S*

A giltwood wall mirror, possibly German, 57 by 44 in. (145 by 112 cm.), c. 1840. **£850-950** *S*

A naturalistically carved and painted wood framed mirror, repainted, 5 ft. 9 in. by 5 ft. 1 in. (175 by 155 cm.), late 19th C. **£400-£500** *S*

A carved mahogany 19th C. convex wall mirror. **£300-350** *JMW*

A Regency giltwood circular convex mirror, the plate with ebonised slip surrounded by ropework and with 2 candle holders, 25 in. diam. **£120-£140** *DS*

An English lacquered toilet mirror, 31 in. high, c. 1700. **£600-700** *HB*

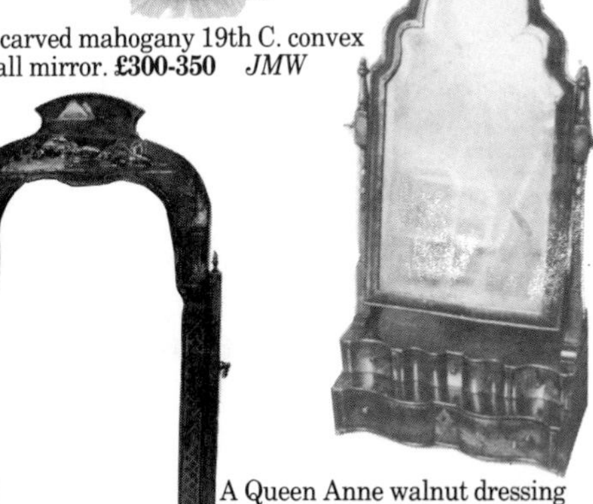
A Queen Anne walnut dressing table mirror, fitted with serpentine fronted drawers. **£800-1,000** *RD*

An early 18th C. red lacquered toilet mirror with 3 drawers, 28 in. high, c. 1710. **£400-500** *CC*

A green and gold lacquer toilet mirror decorated with chinoiserie figures between turned supports, the bureau base with sloping flap enclosing short drawers and a cupboard door, 18½ in. wide (47 cm.). **£450-550** *C*

A Queen Anne red-japanned toilet mirror, the lower part enclosing drawers and pigeonholes above a drawer, decorated in gilt with chinoiseries, foot replaced, top section later, 1 ft. 6 in. wide (46 cm.), c. 1700. **£600-800** *S*

A George I walnut toilet mirror with a tall swing plate on standard supports, the base fitted with 4 ogee moulded drawers, with restorations, 33 by 20 in. (84 by 51 cm.), early 18th C. **£450-550** *SC*

A Queen Anne green-japanned toilet mirror with an arrangement of drawers, the whole decorated with figures and birds in landscapes, extensively restored, 2 ft. 11½ in. high by 1 ft. 2½ in. wide (90 by 39 cm.), c. 1710. **£600-£700** *S*

A George III mahogany and tulipwood banded dressing table mirror, on chevron banded supports, base fitted with 2 drawers, 32 by 28 in. (81 by 71 cm.), late 18th/early 19th C. **£120-160** *SC*

A George III mahogany toilet mirror, with a rectangular swing plate above 3 serpentine drawers, all inlaid with chequer stringing, restored, the plate associated, 21 by 17 in. (54 by 43 cm.), 18th C. **£100-120** *SC*

A green-japanned toilet glass, the lower part with a fitted interior above a drawer containing compartments and boxes, the whole decorated in gilt, probably North Italian, early 18th C. **£350-450** *S*

A George III mahogany and satinwood inlaid oval framed toilet mirror, 1 ft. 4 in. wide (41 cm.), c. 1800. **£200-220** *SS*

A 'Sheraton' serpentine box mirror, 23½ in. high. **£350-400** *HB*

A mahogany serpentine front box toilet mirror, 30 in., c. 1780. **£300-£350** *HB*

A George III mahogany toilet mirror, 15 in. wide, c. 1800. **£150-£200** *IHA*

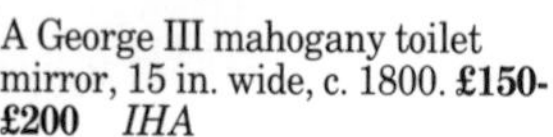

A beech framed toilet mirror, 28½ in. high. **£45-75** *W*

A George III mahogany and parcel gilt framed toilet mirror, 28 in. high, c. 1800. **£330-380** *HB*

A large mahogany framed dressing table mirror with lidded compartment in base, 37 in., c. 1850. **£145-165** *CDE*

An early 19th C. Brazilian rosewood toilet mirror, 21 in. **£110-£130** *FD*

A Victorian mahogany toilet mirror with 3 drawers, 29½ in., c. 1870. **£120-130** *Ph*

A Victorian mahogany toilet mirror, c. 1880. **£60-70** *Ph*

A Victorian mahogany toilet mirror, 30 in., c. 1890. **£60-70** *Ph*

A German mahogany framed mirror, 54 in. **£110-140** *CDE*

A cheval mirror with mahogany frame, 63 in. high, c. 1830. **£200-£250** *CDE*

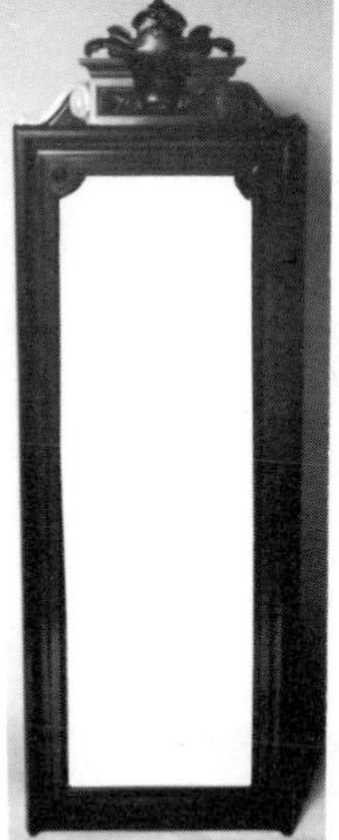

A German mahogany ebonised mirror, 68 in., c. 1860. **£180-£220** *CDE*

A mahogany framed dressing table mirror, 37 in. high, c. 1850. **£55-£65** *CDE*

A 'Strawberry Hill Gothic'-style cheval glass, 63 in., c. 1875. **£400-£450** *CDE*

A Regency mahogany cheval mirror on square supports and reeded arched splayed legs, lacking candle branches, 30 in. wide. **£350- 450** *CEd*

A mahogany framed overmantel, 47 in. high, c. 1880. **£60-70** *CDE*

An oak dressing mirror and stand, 60 in. high. **£40-50** *CDE*

A Louis XV carved giltwood firescreen, with a rising panel covered on one side with a Beauvais tapestry panel after Jacques Neilson, woven on a scarlet damask ground, 3 ft. ½ in. high by 1 ft. 11½ in. wide (93 by 60 cm.), c. 1755. **£1,200-1,600** *S*

A pair of mahogany pole screens, with original Adam design painted on silk, 55½ in. high, c. 1790. **£1,000-1,250** *CC*

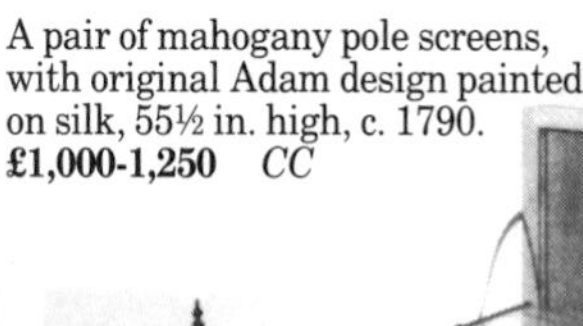

A 'Chippendale' mahogany folding screen with fretted frieze, 45 in., c. 1760. **£475-525** *CC*

A pair of George III giltwood firescreens with rectangular painted silk panels, 21 in. wide. **£400-500** *CEd*

A pair of late 18th C. embossed plaster and painted bird pictures in the manner of Samuel Dixon of Dublin, 20 in. high, c. 1790. **£600-700** *CC*

A mahogany pole screen with inlaid tripod base and woven silk picture, 61 in. high, c. 1820. **£135-£165** *NP*

A Sheraton-style satinwood screen stand inlaid with yew-wood oval and boxwood lines, 41½ in. **£225-£250** *CSK*

A Regency period pole screen with finely carved base and brass mounts, 15 in. wide by 47 in. high, c. 1820. **£775-875** *HAL*

A Dutch painted polychrome leather 6 leaf screen decorated in imitation of Chinese coromandel lacquer, the leather panels 18th C. now backed on to canvas, each leaf 21½ in. wide by 93 in. high (55 by 236 cm.). **£3,250-3,750** *C*

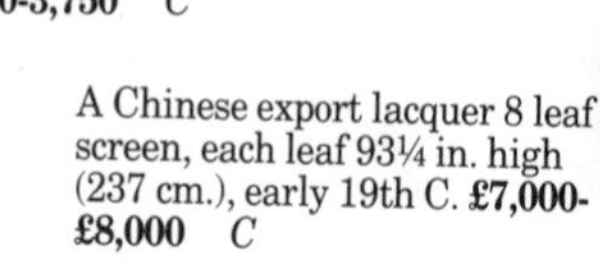

A Chinese export lacquer 8 leaf screen, each leaf 93¼ in. high (237 cm.), early 19th C. **£7,000-£8,000** *C*

A fine Chinese export black and gold lacquer 6 leaf screen decorated each side in raised gilt in two tones mounted with gilt brass hinges, each leaf 21½ in. wide by 87 in. high (55 by 221 cm.), late 18th/ early 19th C. **£5,000-5,500** *C*

A 19th C. leather 6 leaf screen painted in Chinese style, each leaf 22 by 96 in. **£4,000-4,500** *DWB*

A Sheraton period mahogany serpentine front sideboard, the line inlaid top with a brass curtain rail, the front banded in satinwood and harewood with boxwood lines, replacement brass handle, on line inlaid square tapering legs, 6 ft. **£3,000-3,500** *WW*

A George III mahogany sweep front sideboard with kingwood crossbandings, boxwood and ebony stringing and fan spandrels, 60 in. (152 cm.). **£1,250-1,400** *L*

A Canton screen with four sections, porcelain plaques painted in enamel colours, 63 in. wide by 54 in. high (160 by 137 cm.). **£500-£650** *Bea*

A pair of mid 19th C. Aubusson Portiers, with decoration of pale pink and blue with red on a cream ground, 286.5 by 112 cm., framed. **£800-900** *S*

A George III-style mahogany bowfront sideboard inlaid with quadrant medallions, boxwood and ebony stringing, 34 in. high by 48½ in. wide, late 19th C. **£800-£1,000** *S*

A George III mahogany sideboard, the fluted stiles carved with paterae and raised on turned fluted tapering legs, 2 ft. 11 in. high by 6 ft. 5 in. wide (89 by 196 cm.), c. 1785. **£1,600-1,800** *S*

A Chinese export black and gold lacquer 8 leaf screen with arched crestings, the other side decorated with exotic birds in fruiting foliage, 176 in. wide extended, by 83½ in. high (447 by 212 cm.), early 19th C. **£4,400-4,700** *C*

A Victorian giltwood firescreen in the manner of A. W. N. Pugin, embroidered in relief with an eagle amongst flowers, 32 in. wide (81 cm.). **£1,800-2,000** *C*

A George III mahogany serpentine sideboard, 37½ in high by 77½ wide. **£700-800** *S*

A Sheraton-style small bowfront sideboard veneered in plumbago and fiddle back mahogany with line inlay and satinwood banding, the front with a central drawer and serpentine frieze with shell inlaid panels, the bottle drawer and glass cupboard door with inlaid circles, brass lion mask ring handles, 4 ft. 3 in., late 19th C. **£900-1,000** *WW*

A mahogany serpentine front sideboard, 2 ft. 8 in. high, c. 1790-1810. **£2,600-2,800** *HB*

A George III mahogany semi-circular sideboard on tapering square legs with spade feet, 37 in. high by 72 in. wide. **£1,500-1,700** *S*

A George III mahogany bowfront sideboard inlaid with satinwood bands and chequered boxwood lines, on later moulded sabre legs, 71½ in. **£1,100-1,200** *CSK*

A George III mahogany bowfront sideboard, 36½ in. high by 55 in. wide. **£700-800** *Bea*

A George III faded mahogany sideboard, 42 in. wide (107 cm.). **£1,900-2,400** *C*

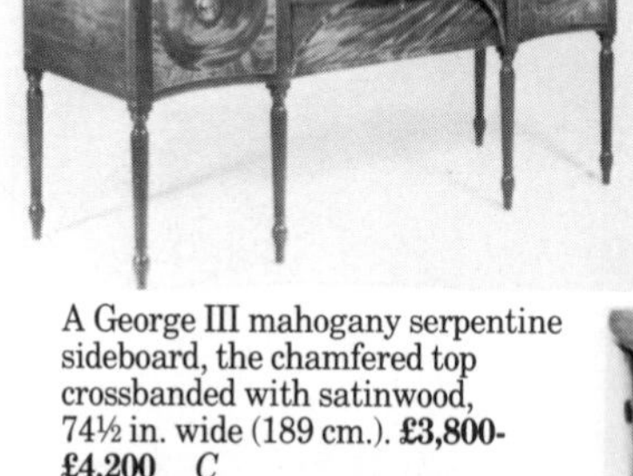

A George III mahogany serpentine sideboard, the chamfered top crossbanded with satinwood, 74½ in. wide (189 cm.). **£3,800-£4,200** *C*

A George III mahogany sideboard, the crossbanded serpentine top inlaid with boxwood lines, restorations, 62 in. wide (157.5 cm.). **£2,500-3,500** *C*

A good George III demi lune sideboard, the top segmentally veneered and crossbanded, 37 by 72 in. (94 by 183 cm.), late 18th C. **£1,600-2,000** *SC*

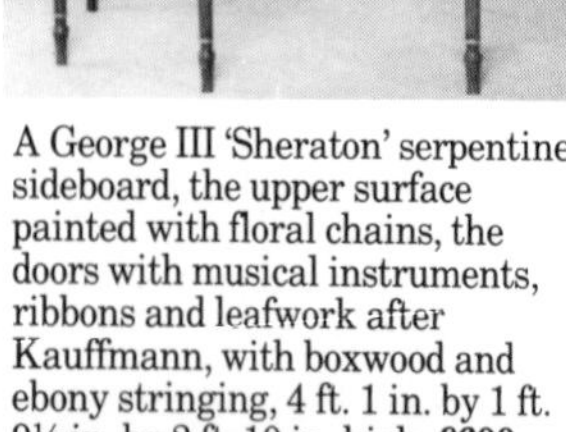

A George III 'Sheraton' serpentine sideboard, the upper surface painted with floral chains, the doors with musical instruments, ribbons and leafwork after Kauffmann, with boxwood and ebony stringing, 4 ft. 1 in. by 1 ft. 9½ in. by 2 ft. 10 in. high. **£600-£700** *AGr*

A George III mahogany serpentine sideboard, satinwood and tulipwood banded and boxwood and ebony line inlaid some alterations, 72 by 28 in. deep. **£2,250-2,500** *DWB*

A George III mahogany pedestal sideboard with bowed front centre section and frieze drawer set with the original leaf-cast brass handles, the right pedestal enclosing an arrangement of graduated drawers, the left pedestal containing a deep cellaret drawer and another, 4 ft. 2 in. high by 4 ft. 1½ in. wide (127 by 125 cm.), c. 1825. **£675-750** *S*

A George III mahogany serpentine sideboard of small size, the top crossbanded and outlined with stringing and the front fitted with 2 deep drawers flanking a central drawer, 60 by 24 in. deep by 36 in. high (152 by 61 by 91 cm.). **£3,500-£4,500** *L*

A George III mahogany serpentine sideboard on tapering legs, 67 in. wide (171 cm.). **£2,600-2,800** *C*

A George III mahogany serpentine sideboard with arched centre flanked by cellaret drawers crossbanded with tulipwood and bordered with stained pollard oak, 72 in. wide (183 cm.). **£1,750-£2,000** *C*

A George III mahogany bowfront sideboard, crossbanded in satinwood, 78 in. wide. **£700-800** *CEd*

A George III mahogany small sideboard with well-figured bowed top crossbanded with rosewood, 47¼ in. wide (120 cm.). **£3,600-£4,000** *C*

A late Georgian mahogany pedestal sideboard, applied with drapes, beaded and acanthus mouldings, 61 in. **£500-550** *CSK*

A Georgian mahogany sideboard having cellaret, linen drawer and cutlery drawer, inlaid with satinwood stringing. **£650-850** *HFM*

A late George III mahogany and satinwood banded and boxwood line inlaid serpentine sideboard on taper legs with spade feet, 78 by 34½ in. deep. **£1,500-1,800** *DWB*

A Sheraton satinwood banded mahogany serpentine sideboard with centre drawer and 2 deep drawers, 54 in. **£2,500-3,000** *GSP*

A Sheraton-style mahogany breakfront sideboard with crossbanded satinwood top, on square tapering supports with spade feet, 60 in. wide, 19th C. **£300-350** *DS*

A Regency mahogany sideboard inlaid with ebony line decoration, the recess with a pair of smaller cupboard doors enclosing a bottle rack, 2 ft. 7½ in. high by 7 ft. 11½ in. wide (80 by 242 cm.), c. 1815. **£750-850** *SI*

A Regency mahogany and crossbanded bowfronted sideboard, 43½ in. **£1,500-2,000** *DWB*

A Sheraton period breakfront mahogany sideboard, the reeded top satinwood banded and inlaid, 6 ft. **£1,500-1,700** *WW*

A Dutch mahogany buffet, the crossbanded top lifting to reveal 2 shelves with a slide on either side, tambour cupboard, 2 ft. 11½ in. high by 3 ft. 1 in. closed (90 by 94 cm.), c. 1790. **£1,350-1,500** *S*

A Dutch mahogany buffet with a lift-out pewter basin and cistern framed by folding shelves, 47 in. wide (119.5 cm.), late 18th C. **£2,200-2,500** *C*

A marquetry and satinwood side cabinet, in the manner of Thomas Chippendale, manufactured by Edwards & Roberts, the domed top with rosewood crossbanding enclosing a yew interior, 39½ by 60½ in. (100 by 154 cm.), 1880's, stamped Edwards and Roberts. **£1,200-1,400** *S*

An excellent quality Regency period sideboard in mahogany, the galleried surface above shaped cockbeaded drawers, the lion's mask brass work being early but replaced, 64 in. wide by 25½ in. deep by 36½ in. high, c. 1830. **£1,000-1,500** *HAL*

An early Victorian mahogany chiffonier, cushion drawer over a pair of arched Gothic crossbanded doors, 3 ft. 9 in. wide. **£140-180** *DS*

A good Victorian serpentine mahogany chiffonier with a pair of panel cupboard doors flanked by a pair of arch panel doors enclosing cutlery drawers and cellaret on a conforming base, 61 in. wide. **£225-£275** *DS*

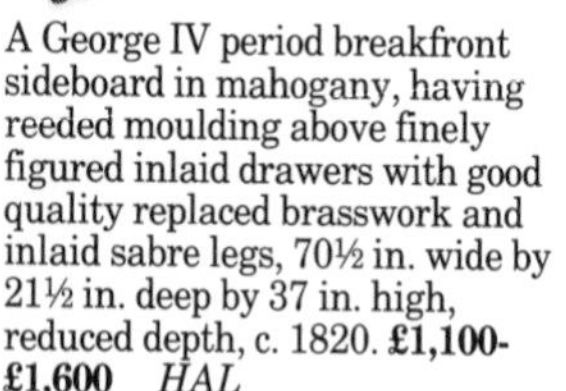

A George IV period breakfront sideboard in mahogany, having reeded moulding above finely figured inlaid drawers with good quality replaced brasswork and inlaid sabre legs, 70½ in. wide by 21½ in. deep by 37 in. high, reduced depth, c. 1820. **£1,100-£1,600** *HAL*

A late 19th C. large mahogany sideboard. **£450-550** *PWC*

A good pedestal sideboard with two serpentine drawers, flanked on either side by a massive pedestal boldly carved, with a bowfront cupboard, 47 by 109 in. (120 by 277 cm.), early 20th C. **£1,000-£1,200** *SC*

A painted satinwood and parcel-gilt dining room side table, the top with a central oval medallion of flowers, 3 ft. 1 in. high by 4 ft. 6 in. wide (94 by 137 cm.), late 19th C. **£800-900** *S*

A Victorian breakfront sideboard with deeply carved back, 7 ft. **£800-£900** *AGG*

A good ivory inlaid coromandel side or writing cabinet, the lower part with a slim centre drawer fitted with a writing surface, the whole inlaid with 'Renaissance' motifs, 4 ft. 6 in. by 3 ft. 11 in. (145 by 120 cm.), c. 1870. **£1,500-1,700** *S*

A large oak and parquetry sideboard, the lower part with a geometrically inlaid top above 3 marble slides and drawers, and cupboard doors enclosing sliding shelves, 6 ft. 8 in. by 7 ft. 1½ in. (204 by 217 cm.), 1850's. **£500-£600** *S*

An unusual 19th C. Continental carved oak buffet sideboard. **£1,000-1,200** *CGC*

A fine satinwood side cabinet with an inlaid frieze and biscuit panels, 7 ft. 3½ in. high by 5 ft. 10 in. wide (223 by 178 cm.), c. 1880. **£1,000-£1,500** *S*

An Edwardian walnut chiffonier, 36 in. wide, c. 1910. **£300-400** *Ph*

An Edwardian mahogany mirror backed sideboard, 73 in. wide, c. 1910. **£375-450** *Ph*

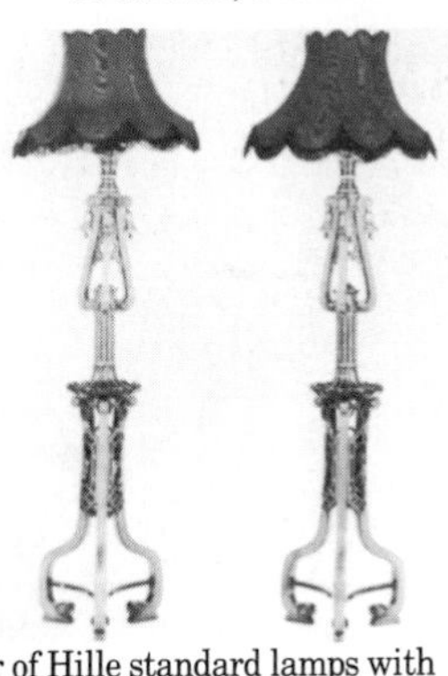
A pair of Hille standard lamps with triple scroll upper parts hanging with bells above an inverted panache, 5 ft. 4 in. high (162 cm.). **£700-800** *S*

A pair of 'Chippendale revival' carved giltwood torchères, 4 ft. 8 in. high (142 cm.), c. 1840. **£800-900** *S*

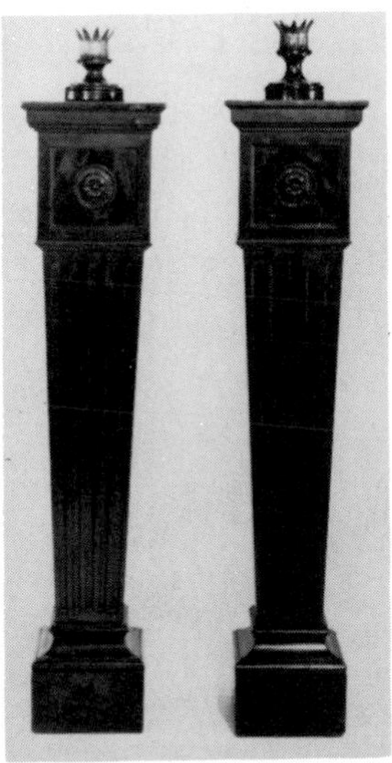
A pair of George III mahogany pedestals, each with an adapted ormolu nozzle fitted for electricity, 56 in. high (142 cm.), excluding fittings. **£1,600-2,000** *C*

A pair of William and Mary walnut and oak torchères, one probably with later top, 37¼ in. high by 9¾ in. wide (94.5 by 25 cm.). **£2,000-2,500** *C*

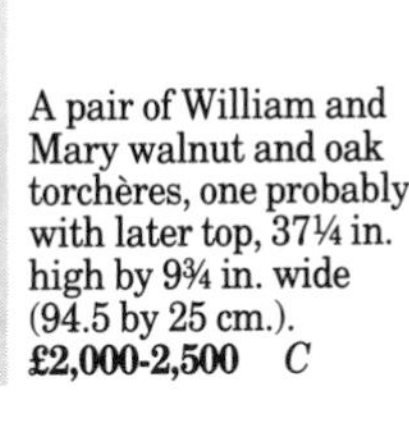
A pair of George II-style walnut and parcel gilt lamp standards, fitted for electricity and with shades, 75 in. high. **£800-900** *Bea*

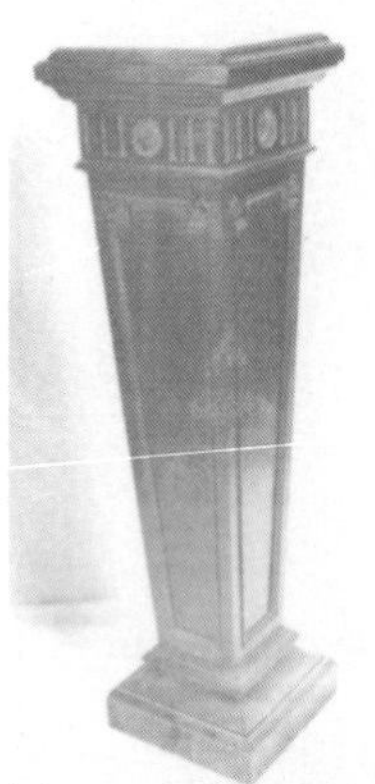

A late 19th C. mahogany stand, 4 ft. high. **£110-150** *JMW*

A pair of chinoiserie stands painted and gilt with chinoiserie on a black ground, 4 ft. 5 in. by 2 ft. 1 in. by 1 ft. 9 in. (135 by 63.5 by 53.5 cm.), 1900-20. **£450-550** *S*

A pair of gilt gesso torchères in George I style, 3 ft. 1¾ in. high (96 cm.), made up c. 1900. **£2,000-£2,300** *S*

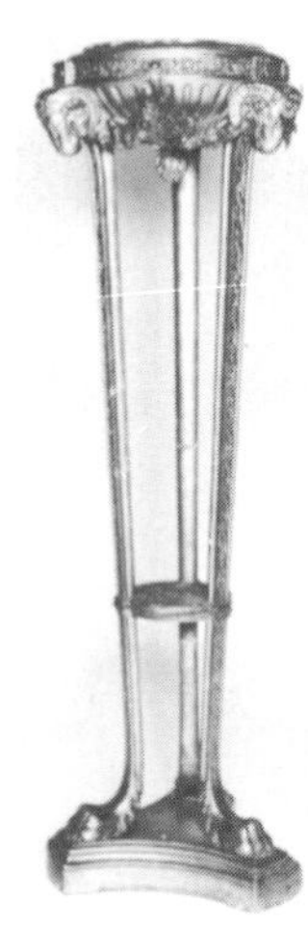

A fine George III giltwood torchère, with moulded circular top on 3 moulded supports carved with foliage, 55 in. high. **£1,000-1,200** *CEd*

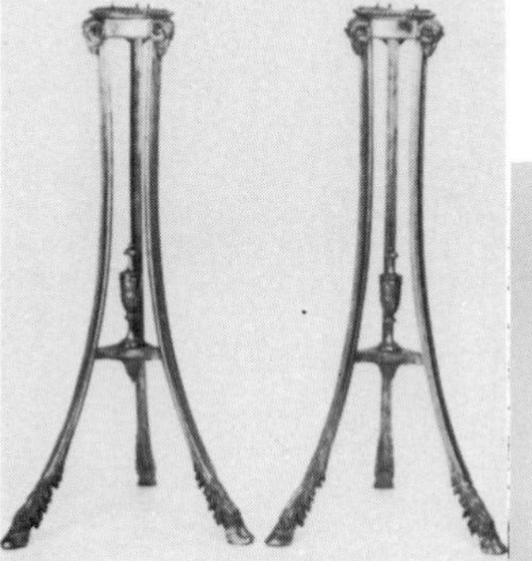

A pair of George III carved giltwood torchères, 4 ft. 7 in. high (140 cm.), c. 1770. **£1,600-1,800** *S*

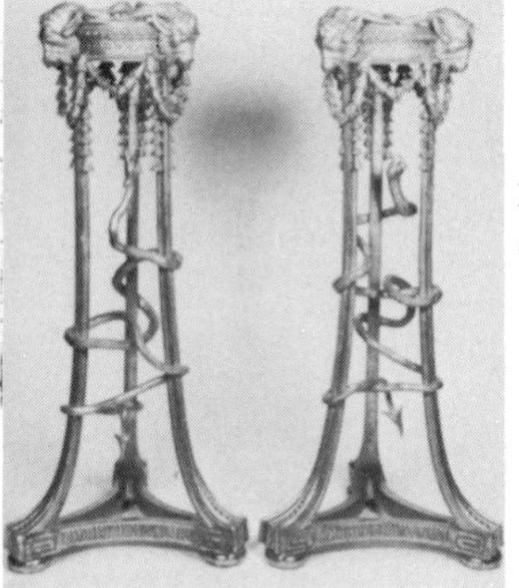

A fine pair of George III giltwood tripod torchères, 56 in. high (142 cm.). **£7,000-8,000** *C*

A painted and giltwood torchère with white marble top, 52 in. high, c. 1800. **£330-380** *HB*

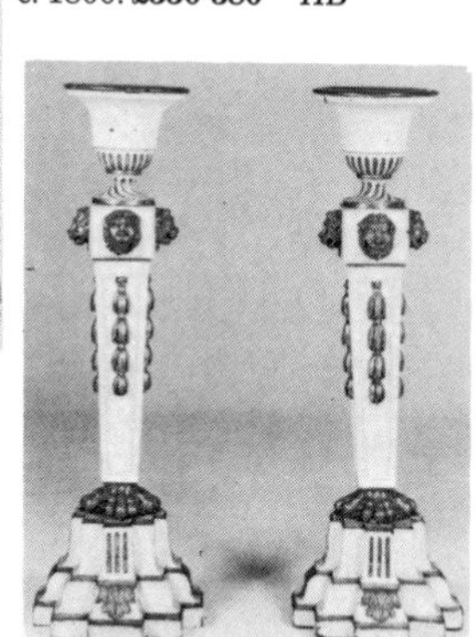

A pair of white painted and gilt torchères, 4 ft. 6 in. high (147 cm.), repainted and gilded, c. 1900. **£500-£600** *S*

A pair of walnut pedestals, the coffered moulded circular tops in foliate lunette borders above winged cabochoned friezes, each 46½ in. high, 19th C. **£500-550** *CSK*

An unusual pair of mahogany and satinwood crossbanded pedestal display cabinets, 4 ft. high by 1 ft. 3 in. wide (122 by 38 cm.), c. 1900. **£500-600** *S*

A mid 19th C. carved wood jardiniere stand with inset marble top, 37 in. **£240-260** *CDE*

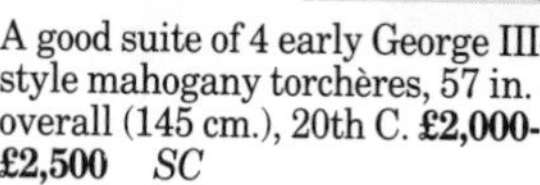

A good suite of 4 early George III-style mahogany torchères, 57 in. overall (145 cm.), 20th C. **£2,000-£2,500** *SC*

The torchères were probably made for the drawing room at Papplewick Hall.

A pair of early George III faux bois and parcel gilt vase stands with galleried platforms, possibly Irish, 1 ft. ½ in. high (32 cm.), c. 1765. **£350-450** *S*

A Continental mahogany jardiniere, 31 in. high, c. 1800. **£850-950** *HB*

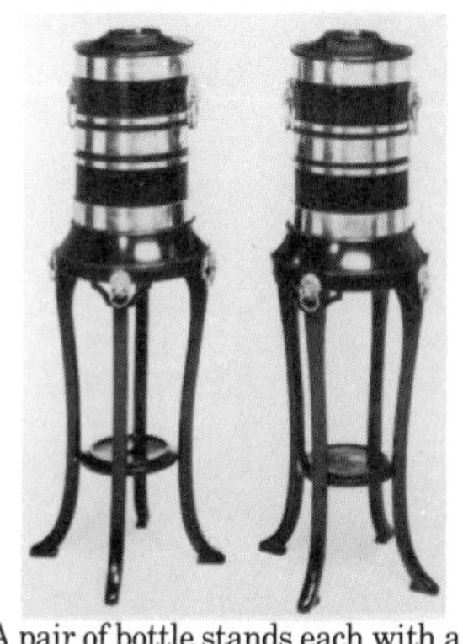

A pair of bottle stands each with a brass-bound urn and cover with lion head and ring handles, 37 in. (94 cm.), late 19th C. **£500-600** *S*

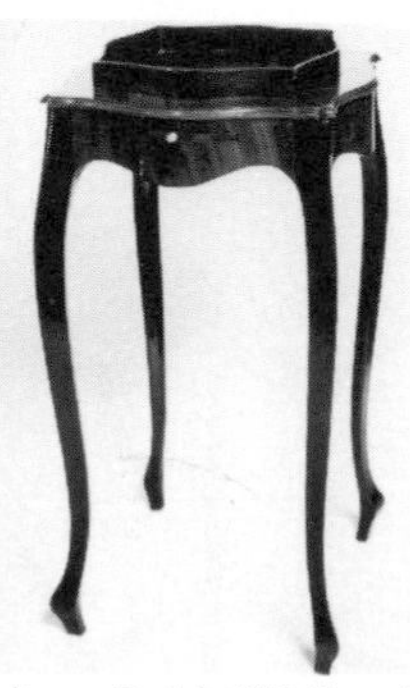

A rare Dutch 18th C. mahogany kettle stand, 26 in. high. **£600-£700** *HB*

A mahogany folio rack, adjustable through an acute angle, 3 ft. 5 in. high by 2 ft. 2 in. wide (104 by 66 cm.), c. 1840. **£500-600** *S*

A mahogany torchère, 40 in., c. 1760. **£450-500** *CDE*

A good rosewood and satinwood double sided folio stand, the top with locked flaps, with fitted box plinth, 7 ft. 4 in. high by 4 ft. 3 in. wide (147 by 129 cm.), c. 1840. **£800-1,000** *S*

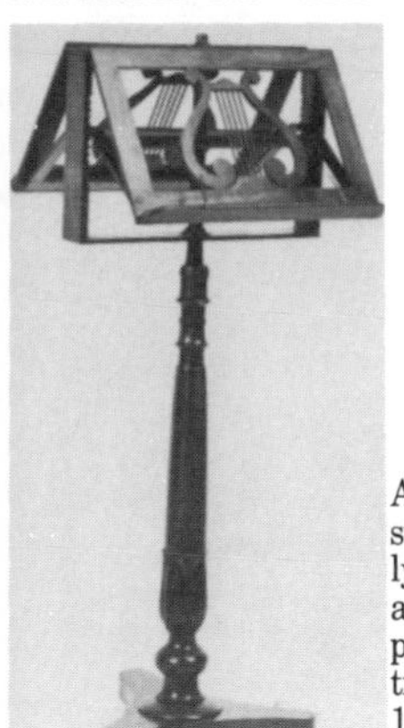

A George IV mahogany duet music stand, the twin folio racks with lyre-shaped splats and ratchet adjustments, the telescopic turned pillar with a lotus leaf carving, the triform base on ceramic castors, 1 ft. 5½ in. wide (44.5 cm.), c. 1825. **£450-550** *SS*

A Regency mahogany reading table, on turned baluster support and 3-cornered base, 23 in. wide. **£400-450** *CEd*

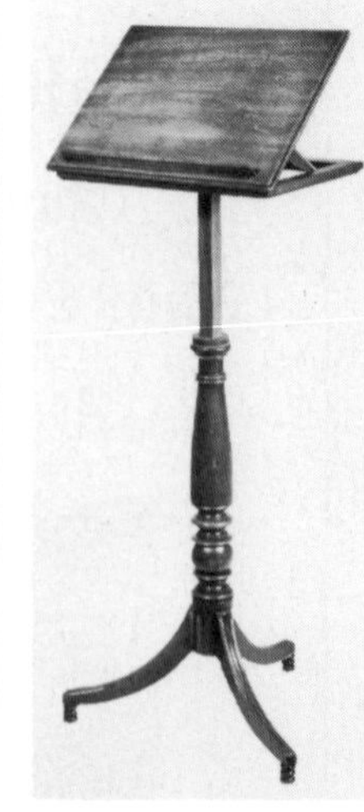

A George III period music or reading stand in mahogany with folding adjustable surface, 18 in. wide by 13½ in. deep by 41 in. high, c. 1780. **£575-650** *HAL*

A small circular mahogany plant stand, 14½ in. diam., c. 1810. **£350- 400** *CC*

A Bavarian pinewood bear hall stand, 208 cm., c. 1880. **£900-£1,000** *S*

A Coalbrookdale cast iron hall stand, stamped indistinctly Coalbrookdale No. 19, 6 ft. 5 in. (199.5 cm.), c. 1860. **£400-500** *S*

A pair of 19th C. kingwood kidney- shaped etagères, having pierced brass gallery to the top tier. **£600-700** *WSW*

A small etagère, 43 in. high, c. 1880. **£240-260** *CDE*

A Dutch rosewood and ebonised box on stand, the box inlaid overall both inside and outside in geometric patterns, 17 by 29 in. high (43 by 74 cm.). **£375-425** *L*

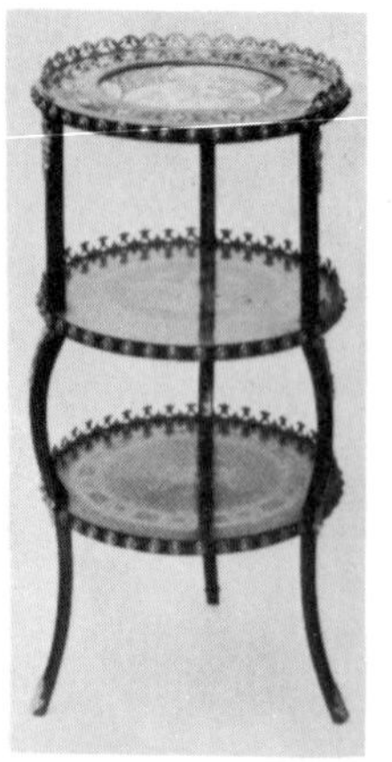

A pair of Louis XVI-style kingwood-veneered etagères applied with gilt brass mounts, each with a circular top set with a Cantonese dish within a border inlaid with strapwork, Cantonese dishes damaged, 32½ in. high by 15½ in. diam., late 19th C. **£375-£425** *Bea*

STOOLS

- **until the middle of the 17th C. stools were virtually the only form of seat for one person**
- **many 17th C. 'joint' or 'joyned' stools have been reproduced**
- **look for good patination, colour and carving on oak examples. Yew-wood examples with good turning are highly desirable**
- **by the end of the 17th C. the chair was taking over and the oak stool became less popular, walnut stealing the show from about 1670**
- **stools now tend to follow the style of chairs of the period, they also tend to be upholstered**
- **many Queen Anne stools have stretchers**
- **these have usually disappeared by George I**
- **when mahogany was introduced from 1730-40, stools became simpler, the cabriole leg being replaced with the straight leg, often with stretchers**
- **mid 18th C. the 'drop-in' seat became fashionable**

A good Charles II oak stool, 22 in. high, c. 1670. **£400-500** *RVA*

A pair of Charles II back stools, c. 1675. **£1,000-1,100** *S*

A 17th C. upholstered oak stool, 22 in. high. **£500-600** *HB*

An early 18th C. turned oak joint stool, 18 in. wide. **£600-700** *HB*

An oak stool table with oval top and a frieze drawer on splayed baluster legs joined by stretchers, 23½ in. wide (60 cm.), 17th C. **£1,250-1,500** *C*

A George I walnut stool with drop-in gros point needlework top, 1 ft. 9¼ in. (54 cm.), c. 1725. **£1,200-£1,400** *S*

A Queen Anne walnut stool, 22½ in. wide (57 cm.). **£2,500-£3,000** *C*

A pair of walnut stools with lambrequin seat rails, 19 in. wide (48 cm.). **£3,000-3,250** *C*

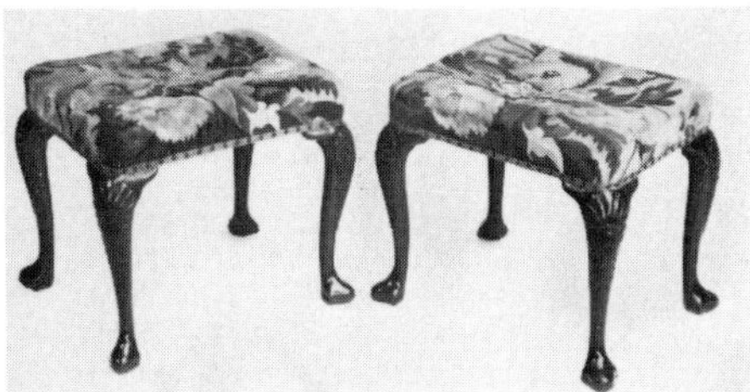

A pair of George I walnut stools with upholstered seats covered in verdure tapestry, 22 in. wide (56 cm.). **£5,000-6,000** *C*

A fine pair of walnut stools covered in early 18th C. petit-point needlework, 16 in. diam. (41 cm.). **£5,000-6,000** *C*

A pair of George II red-walnut framed stools, shaped underframes and on shell carved cabriole legs with claw and ball feet, 17 in. high by 22 in. wide. **£3,000-3,200** *Bea*

An Irish George II red-walnut stool on cabriole legs headed by shells and hoof feet, 20 in. wide (51 cm.). **£1,100-1,300** *C*

An oak stool with Victorian stump beadwork, 15 in. square, c. 1790. **£80-95** *BP*

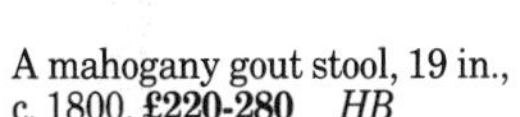

A mahogany gout stool, 19 in., c. 1800. **£220-280** *HB*

A walnut stool, 23 in. wide, c. 1840. **£250-300** *CDE*

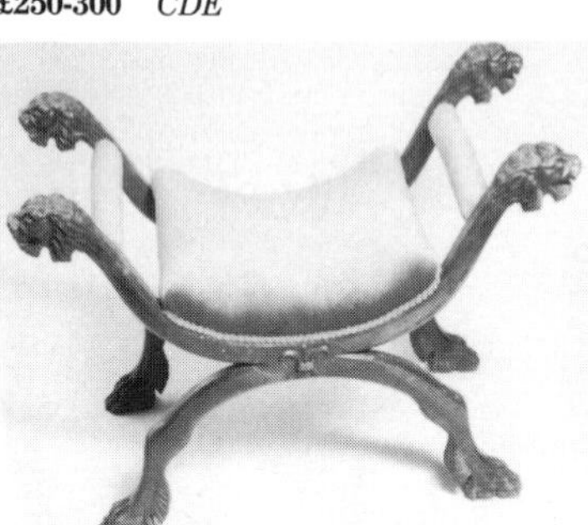

A walnut stool, 32 in. wide, c. 1850. **£190-240** *NP*

A mahogany framed stool with ball and claw feet, old legs, c. 1740, new frame 1920's, 24½ in. wide. **£85-£95** *CDE*

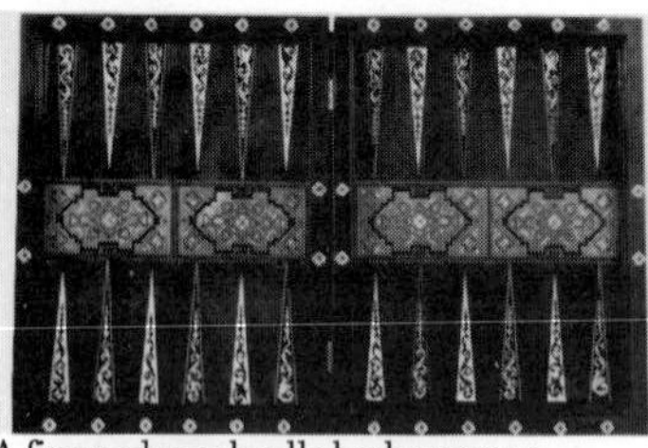

A fine and rare boulle backgammon table with hinged box top, the interior inlaid in ebony, ivory and kingwood, with boulle panels, opening on to 2 gateleg supports and with a drawer in the frieze, the 6 square tapering legs with carved giltwood collars and bases, joined by moulded stretchers and on bun feet, the whole inlaid with strapwork and foliage in brass pewter and tortoiseshell, 2 ft. 5 in. by 1 ft. 11 in. wide (74 by 54 cm.), late 17th/early 18th C. **£23,000-27,000** *S*

Stylistically this piece would appear to be Flemish in origin though, by the latter part of the 17th C., Antwerp craftsmen had infiltrated into many other European capitals, including Munich and Vienna, where their work was much admired and imitated.

An extending walnut piano stool, height (down) 22 in., c. 1860. **£100-£135** *NP*

A velvet covered sarcophagus stool, 20 in. square, c. 1865. **£75-85** *CDE*

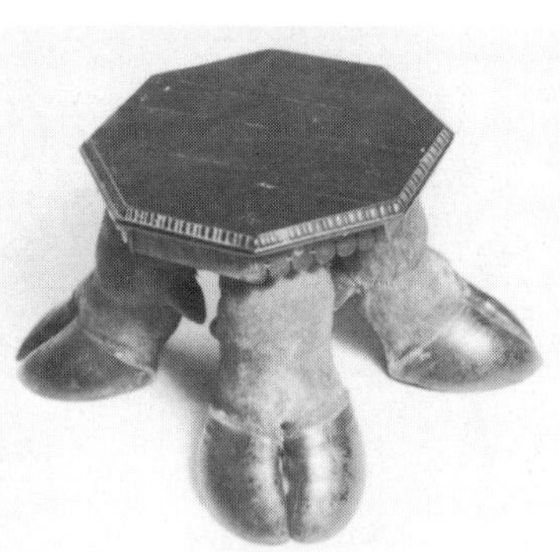
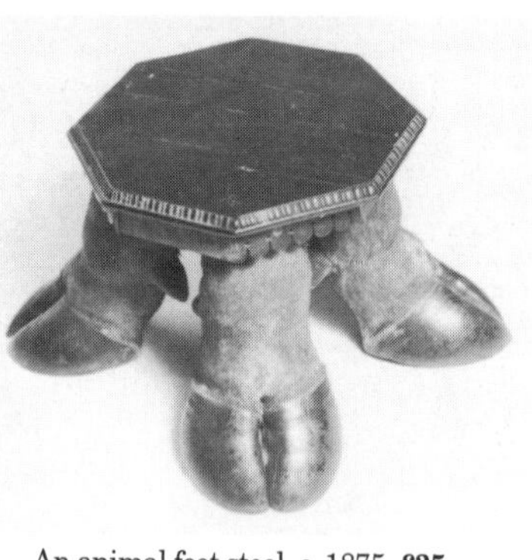

An animal foot stool, c. 1875. **£35-£50** *NP*

A walnut games table, the crossbanded folding top inlaid with fruitwood lines centred by a compass medallion, the well-figured interior with a well lined with marble paper, flanked by slides, 33 in. wide (84 cm.), late 17th C. **£1,800-2,400** *C*

A 19th C. Indian silvered wood stool, 18 in. square. **£350-400** *HB*

A pair of beadwork and giltwood stools, 10 in., c. 1860. **£120-130** *BP*

A brass adjustable harp stool, c. 1920. **£140-160** *IHA*

A beech music stool stained to simulate mahogany, c. 1910. **£75-£85** *TA*

A fruitwood games table with rectangular folding top outlined with amaranth lines on tapering baluster supports and later turned feet, 32½ in. wide (82.5 cm.), late 17th C. **£3,000-3,400** *C*

A George I red-walnut concertina action card table, the interior with counter wells, 2 ft. 5 in. high by 2 ft. 10½ in. wide (74 by 88 cm.), c. 1725. **£700-800** *S*

A George II solid walnut games table, the fold-over top with outset corners enclosing a baize-lined interior, with dishes for counters, 29½ by 34 in. (75 by 87 cm.), mid 18th C. **£500-600** *SC*

A Queen Anne walnut card table, the top with counterwells and candle recesses, the frieze with partly replaced concertina action, restorations, 33 in. wide (84 cm.). **£9,000-10,000** *C*

A George II red-walnut triple-top games table, the cabriole legs carved at the knees with shells and terminating in claw and ball feet, 29½ in. high by 32 in. wide. **£1,500-£1,700** *S*

A George II walnut card and games table, the hinged top inlaid with strapwork marquetry, the interior set with candle-stands and counter wells, above a hinged surface inlaid with a chess and backgammon board, restored, 2 ft. 6 in. high by 2 ft. 11½ in. wide (76 by 90 cm.), c. 1730. **£3,000-3,500** *S*

An early Georgian mahogany card table, the interior with counter wells, 38½ in. wide (82.5 cm.). **£2,500-3,000** *C*

A rosewood-veneered combined card and games table of George I design, with a baize-lined interior with candle-stands and counter wells and below a burr-maple veneered chess and backgammon board, possibly Anglo-Indian, 34½ in. wide (88 cm.), late 18th C. **£1,500-2,000** *C*

A Queen Anne red-walnut half-round tea table, 2 ft. 6 in. high by 2 ft. 8 in. wide (76 by 81.5 cm.), c. 1710. **£1,050-1,250** *S*

A rare pair of George II Irish mahogany concertina action card tables, 2 ft. 5½ in. high by 2 ft. 11½ in. wide (75 by 90 cm.), c. 1755. **£10,000-13,000** *SI*

A George III mahogany card table, the rectangular fold-over top lined with green baize, with concertina action, 2 ft. 5 in. high by 2 ft. 10 in. wide (74 by 86 cm.), c. 1770. **£550-750** *S*

A George II mahogany triple-top games and writing table, the polished interior inlaid for chess and backgammon and with a hinged bookrest enclosing a well, 2 ft. 6½ in. high by 2 ft. 9 in. wide (77 by 84 cm.), c. 1740. **£1,100-£1,200** *S*

A 19th C. Continental mahogany card table with fold-over top, fitted drawer and having floral marquetry inlay, 2 ft. 4 in. **£1,200-£1,400** *RBB*

A late George II mahogany card table, the serpentine baize-lined top with leaf-carved border, 2 ft. 5 in. high by 3 ft. wide (74 by 92 cm.), c. 1760. **£1,200-1,400** *S*

A George III mahogany triple top games table, 2 ft. 5½ in. high by 2 ft. 10¼ in. wide (75 by 87 cm.), c. 1765. **£1,000-1,300** *S*

An early George III mahogany card table with ribbon and rosette ornament above a frieze carved with blind fretwork, with a concertina action, 35½ in. wide (90 cm.), **£800-1,000** *C*

A George III mahogany card table, the rectangular top with serpentine front crossbanded and inlaid with boxwood and ebony lines, 2 ft. 5 in. high by 2 ft. 10 in. wide (74 by 86 cm.). **£650-750** *S*

A George III satinwood card table, the serpentine top inlaid with a demi-lunette crossbanded with rosewood, 35½ in. wide (90 cm.). **£1,150-1,300** *C*

A pair of George III period card tables in mahogany, having crossbanded inlaid figured surfaces concealing replaced baize above box strung aprons mounted on turned legs, 36 in. wide by 18 in. deep by 29 in. high, c. 1800. **£1,900- 2,500** *HAL*

(l.) An 18th C. mahogany silver table, 30½ in. wide. **£450-500** *PWC*

(r.) A Chippendale period mahogany fold-over top card tabl 36 in. wide. **£350-400** *PWC*

A George III satinwood card table, the 'D'-shaped fold-over top with kingwood crossbanding, boxwood and ebony stringing. **£1,300-£1,400** *Bea*

A George III 'Hepplewhite' bowfronted folding card table with brass beading, boxwood and ebony stringing, central gilt metal patera, 3 ft. wide by 1 ft. 6 in. deep. **£900-£1,100** *AGr*

A George III mahogany games table on slender square tapering supports and block feet, restored, 28½ by 38 in. (72 by 97 cm.), late 18th C. **£500-600** *SC*

A George III rosewood card table, crossbanded in satinwood, 2 ft. 5 in. high by 2 ft. 10½ in. wide (74 by 90 cm.), c. 1795. **£1,750-2,000** *S*

An unusual George III Ango-Indian teakwood games table of Pembroke table form, the sliding panel enclosing a backgammon well and reversing to form a chessboard, 2 ft. 4 in. high by 3 ft. 5½ in. wide (72 by 105 cm.), late 18th C. **£1,400-1,600** *S*

A 19th C. mahogany 'D' form fold top card table with boxwood stringing. **£200-250** *WHL*

A George III mahogany and marquetry demi-lune games table, the top finely inlaid with a harewood, boxwood and kingwood demi-lune, contained by broad satinwood banding, 29½ by 39 in. (75 by 99 cm.), late 18th C. but restored in the 19th C. **£400-500** *SC*

A George III marquetry card table, the top inlaid with a fan medallion and with crossbanding of flowers and laurel divided by lilies, 3 ft. 2 in. wide (96.5 cm.), c. 1785. **£1,500-1,800** *S*

A George III mahogany tea or games table, the demi-lune top crossbanded in ebony, 29 by 38½ in. (74 by 98 cm.), late 18th C. **£900-1,000** *SC*

METRIC CONVERSION TABLE

¼ in.	**= 0.64 cm.**
½ in.	**= 1.27 cm.**
1 in.	**= 2.54 cm.**
2 in.	**= 5.08 cm.**
3 in.	**= 7.62 cm.**
4 in.	**= 10.16 cm.**
5 in.	**= 12.70 cm.**
6 in.	**= 15.24 cm.**
7 in.	**= 17.78 cm.**
8 in.	**= 20.32 cm.**
9 in.	**= 22.86 cm.**
10 in.	**= 25.40 cm.**
11 in.	**= 27.94 cm.**
1 ft.	**= 30.48 cm.**
1 ft. 6 in.	**= 45.75 cm.**
2 ft.	**= 60.96 cm.**
2 ft. 6 in.	**= 76.20 cm.**
3 ft.	**= 91.44 cm.**
4 ft.	**= 1.22 m.**
5 ft.	**= 1.52 m.**
6 ft.	**= 1.83 m.**
7 ft. 6 in.	**= 2.29 m.**
9 ft.	**= 2.74 m.**

An 18th C. circular folding top card table of satinwood, 31 in. diam. **£1,100-1,400** *CC*

A pair of early 19th C. North Italian marquetry card tables, with cut corners, crossbanded in tulipwood and inlaid with panels of military trophies on rosewood grounds in shaded sycamore, the hinged baize-lined tops with foliate scroll borders, 96 cm. **£6,000-£7,000** *P*

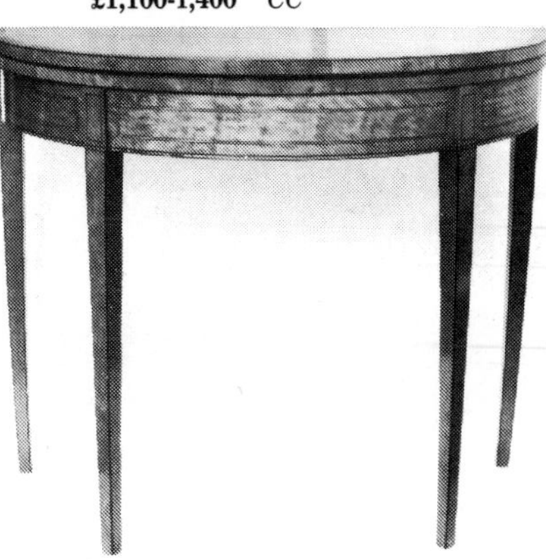

A George III satinwood and kingwood banded demi-lune card table, the top inlaid with boxwood and ebony line and kingwood edging, 36 in. wide. **£1,000-£1,200** *B*

A fine pair of George III satinwood card tables with baize-lined tops crossbanded with rosewood with moulded ebonised borders, 40½ in. wide by 28½ in. high by 18 in. deep (103 by 72.5 by 46 cm.). **£11,000-£13,000** *C*

A George III Irish mahogany card table, the interior baize lined, some veneers missing, top loose, 2 ft. 4 in. high by 3 ft. 4 in. wide (71 by 102 cm.), c. 1780. **£1,500-1,800** *SI*

A pair of mid 19th C. French faded rosewood-veneered serpentine swivel top card tables, the interiors with baize, the shaped friezes on solid rosewood cabriole legs (1 with scroll toes, 1 with toes cut off), 36½ in. **£650-750** *WW*

A mahogany gaming table with baize interior and counter wells, 36 in., 19th C. **£200-250** *WHL*

A late 19th C. French boulle card table, the frieze decorated with grotesque mask and applied banding, flanked by caryatids, 35 in. wide. **£1,200-1,400** *AG*

A mid 18th C. Dutch mahogany and marquetry card table, the top inlaid with floral marquetry birds, insects and an urn, top split, 2 ft. 4 in. high by 2 ft. 11½ in. wide (71 by 90 cm.), c. 1750. **£1,000-1,300** *SI*

A George III mahogany card table with serpentine baize-lined top crossbanded with tulipwood and inlaid with chequered lines, 38 in. wide (96.5 cm.). **£1,800-2,200** *C*

A Dutch marquetry serpentine card table, 31½ in., 19th C. **£700-£800** *CSK*

A well figured walnut marquetry serpentine games table, the top inlaid in ivory and ebony with a chess board flanked by flowers, 2 ft. 5 in. high by 3 ft. 1½ in. wide (74 by 95 cm.), c. 1850. **£700-800** *S*

An early George III mahogany games table with chamfered crossbanded serpentine triple flap top, 36 in. wide (91.5 cm.). **£2,000-£2,250** *C*

A Louis XV-style rosewood and marquetry card table, applied with gilt brass mounts, 30 in. high by 35 in. wide, mid 19th C. **£475-525** *Bea*

A walnut card table, the top crossbanded in kingwood and inlaid with a reserve of flowers, 2 ft. 6 in. by 2 ft. 10 in. (76 by 87 cm.), c. 1880. **£1,000-1,200** *S*

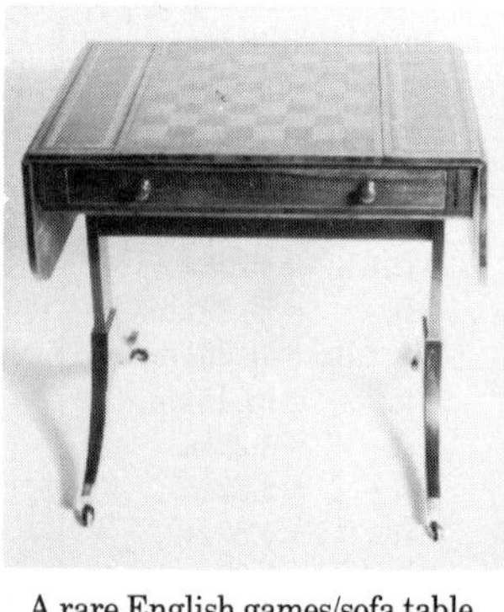
A rare English games/sofa table with leather inlaid backgammon in well, c. 1785. **£3,500-4,000** *HB*

A good Regency mahogany card table, inlaid with ebony stringing, the frieze with ebony bead border, on a turned pillar with platform and four sabre supports carved with acanthus at the knees, 36 in. (91 cm.). **£325-375** *L*

A crossbanded and inlaid rosewood card table, 36 in. wide, c. 1810. **£700-800** *HB*

A Regency rosewood card table with chamfered corners, on 4 scroll supports and scroll legs, 2 ft. 4½ in. by 2 ft. 11½ in. wide (72 by 90 cm.), c. 1820. **£1,400-1,600** *S*

A Regency rosewood and satinwood card table, the baize-lined top inlaid with a wide scroll banding, 2 ft. 5 in. high by 3 ft. wide (73 by 91 cm.), c. 1820. **£1,650-1,800** *S*

A pair of Regency mahogany card tables with rounded rectangular felt-lined tops crossbanded with rosewood, 36 in. wide (91.5 cm.). **£2,000-3,000** *C*

A good pair of Regency mahogany card tables with 'D' shaped crossbanded baize-lined and swivelling tops, 36 in. **£3,300-£3,500** *GSP*

A Regency mahogany-veneered shaped folding-top card table with carved apron, 35½ in. **£250-300** *WHL*

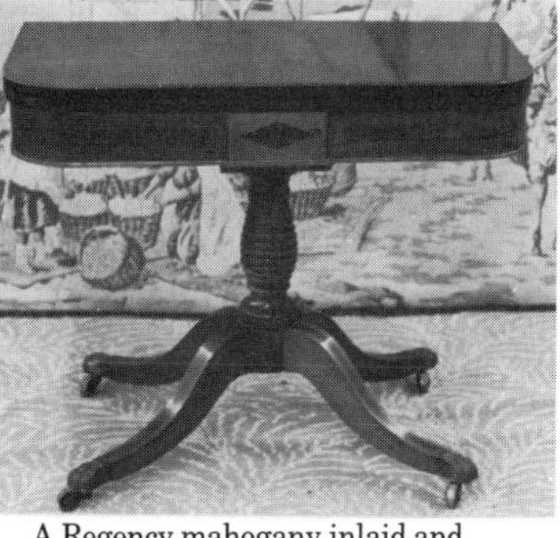

A Regency mahogany inlaid and crossbanded swing-top card table, brass mounted on reeded column and quadruple splayed pod with brass paw feet, 35½ in. wide by 29½ in. **£375-400** *GM*

A rosewood card table, the rectangular swivelling top with rounded corners and a baize-lined interior, 3 ft. wide (92 cm.), 1830's. **£200-300** *S*

A pair of William IV rosewood card tables on turned faceted moulded columns with concave platform and turned feet, 36 in. **£700-750** *CSK*

A fine pair of Regency amboyna card tables with baize-lined folding tops bordered with broad rosewood bands, 36 in. wide (91.5 cm.). **£6,000-7,000** *C*

A Dutch East Indies satinwood card table with crossbanded top, 41¾ in. wide (106 cm.), c. 1830. **£700-800** *S*

A mahogany side table, 46 in. wide, c. 1830. **£220-250** *CDE*

A 19th C. rosewood fold-over card table. **£250-300** *JMW*

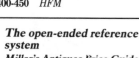

A walnut serpentine fold-over card table with baize inset, Victorian. **£400-450** *HFM*

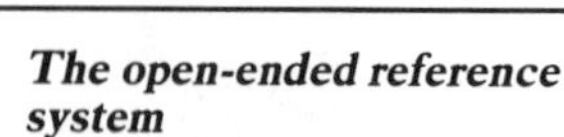

The open-ended reference system

Miller's Antiques Price Guide builds up year by year to form the most comprehensive photo-reference system available. The first four volumes contain photographs of over 30,000 stock items!

A mahogany folding-top card table, 34 in., c. 1900. **£350-400** *Ph*

A figured walnut and veneered fold top card table, the 'D' shaped top swivelling to reveal a games compartment and apron with finely carved scroll work, 36 by 18 in. folded. **£350-400** *WHL*

A burr-walnut serpentine card table with a baize-lined interior, 2 ft. 11½ in. wide (90 cm.), c. 1860. **£450-550** *S*

An early 19th C. satinwood and inlaid pedestal games table, 20 by 17 in. **£600-700** *JMW*

A late 19th C. rosewood card table with ivory inlay and gilding, the folding surface revealing a blue baize lining with leather tooled border. **£1,500-2,000** *PSH*

This piece was in pristine condition which is reflected in the price.

An early 19th C. mahogany fold-over card table, 36 in. **£180-240** *JMW*

An early Victorian rosewood card table with fold-over swivel top on a tapering octagonal pillar and the concave sided base with carved scroll feet, 36 in. (91 cm.). **£200-£250** *L*

A small Victorian inlaid walnut folding card table with a circular baize-lined interior, on carved pedestal, on 4 splay carved feet with castors, 36 in. wide. **£300-£325** *BHW*

A Victorian walnut card table inlaid with line marquetry, raised on columned carved end standards and cabriole legs joined by a stretcher, length 36 in. **£180-200** *DS*

A rosewood card table, the top crossbanded with kingwood and purpleheart enclosing a baize-lined interior, 30 by 36 in. (76 by 91.5 cm.), c. 1910. **£400-500** *S*

A baize-lined folding-top card table, 56 in. wide, c. 1875. **£280-340** *CDE*

A late Victorian/Edwardian inlaid rosewood two-tier card table, having envelope folding top, 22 in. **£400-500** *WSW*

A George III inlaid mahogany work table with conch shell inlay, with boxwood and ebony stringing, 16½ in. square. **£500-550** *WSW*

A mahogany envelope top card table with marquetry inlays and boxwood stringing, 23½ in. **£385-£465** *CDE*

A George III period needlework table in mahogany, the figured ebony inlaid crossbanded surface above single drawer and sliding pleated bag, textiles replaced, 20 in. wide by 13¾ in. deep by 30 in. high, c. 1800. **£825-925** *HAL*

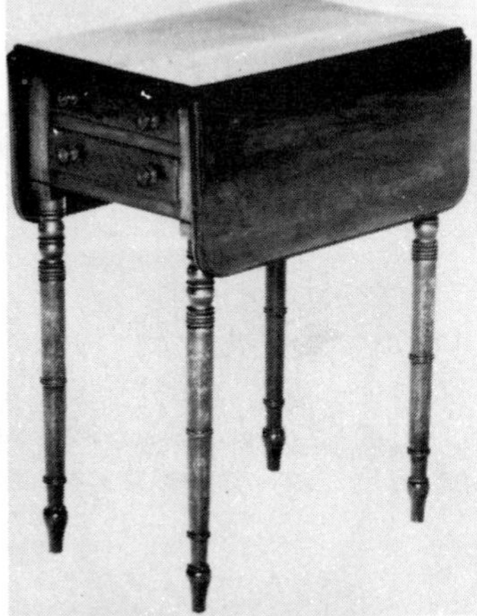
A late George III mahogany work table, mid 19th C. **£250-300** *SC*

A George III octagonal satinwood work table, the top centred by a print, the edge banded in stained holly and inlaid with star filled ribbon, 2 ft. 4½ in. by 1 ft. 3 in. wide (72.5 by 39 cm.), c. 1795. **£2,000-2,250** *S*

A small mahogany side table, 19½ in. wide, c. 1840. **£250-280** *LG*

A Sheraton period needlework table, the figured inlaid and strung lifting surface above bag in later pleated satin supported on 4 slim legs with brass feet and castors, 18 in. wide by 14 in. deep by 30 in. high, c. 1800. **£750-900** *HAL*

A late Georgian mahogany work table with 2 drawers at one end and a sliding work bag, on turned and ringed supports and inlaid with stringing, 20 in. (51 cm.). **£475-550** *L*

A Regency mahogany work table inlaid with boxwood lines, the lid enclosing a fitted compartment, 18½ in. **£420-480** *CSK*

A Regency rosewood sewing table with 2 drawers opposing 2 dummy drawers, brass inlay, 18 in. wide, c. 1820. **£450-550** *STR*

A Louis XV-style kingwood and marquetry work table inlaid throughout with panels of flowers and scrolling foliage, 28½ in. high by 23½ in. wide, mid 19th C. **£575-£650** *Bea*

A sewing table with top in rosewood, with mahogany crossbanding and satinwood stringing, late 18th/early 19th C. **£300-350** *KHD*

A Regency tulipwood work table with a cedar-lined drawer on pierced lyre-shaped trestle ends, 18 in. wide (46 cm.). **£950-1,100** *C*

A Regency ebony inlaid mahogany writing and sewing table, the top with gadrooned border, pull-out pigskin covered sewing well below, 2 ft. 5 in. high by 2 ft. 2 in. wide (74 by 66 cm.), early 19th C. **£1,250-£1,400** *S*

An early 19th C. rosewood games/work table, work basket missing, 1 ft. 9 in. **£225-275** *DDM*

A Regency rosewood work table with quarter-beaded mouldings, having 1 drawer, square cone-shaped pedestal with carved shell motifs, 19 by 17 in. **£600-700** *WSW*

A rosewood work table, 23 in. wide, c. 1820. **£400-450** *BP*

A Regency rosewood sewing table with fitted interior, 18 in. wide, c. 1820. **£400-500** *STR*

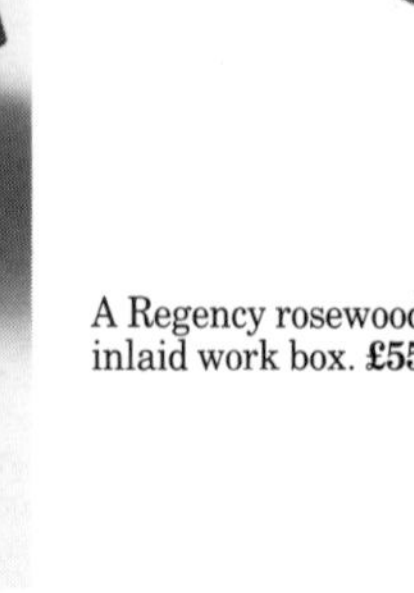

A Regency rosewood and brass inlaid work box. **£550-650** *JMW*

A fine burr-walnut and mahogany work table, of globe form, with hinged roll top enclosing a fitted interior, centred by a giltwood serpent, 38 in. high, early 19th C. **£4,000-5,000** *CEd*

A good parquetry work table, the top enclosing a fitted interior with a sliding tray above a pull-out pleated silk wool bag, veneered throughout with geometrics and Van Dykes, 29 by 19 in. (74 by 49 cm.), mid 19th C. **£500-600** *SC*

A William IV rosewood games table applied with beaded borders, the crossbanded lid enclosing baccarat and chess boards, 22 in. **£400-500** *CSK*

A mahogany work table, 24½ in. wide, c. 1860. **£360-400** *CDE*

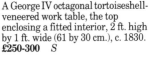

A Victorian mahogany sewing box with satinwood fitted interior, 21½ in. wide, c. 1850. **£320-365** *NP*

A Victorian walnut work table. **£285-325** *FD*

A George IV octagonal tortoiseshell-veneered work table, the top enclosing a fitted interior, 2 ft. high by 1 ft. wide (61 by 30 cm.), c. 1830. **£250-300** *S*

A 19th C. satin birch sewing table, the interior with covered compartments, 31.5 cm. wide by 58.5 cm. high. **£600-£700** *P*

An ebonised work table, the panelled frieze with a drawer lined in ash above a deep U-shaped drawer, the legs with ivory fluting, 2 ft. 4 in. high by 2 ft. 2 in. wide (71 by 66 cm.), c. 1870. **£500-600** *S*

A papier mâché work box inlaid with mother-of-pearl, 30 in. high, c. 1860. **£380-450** *NP*

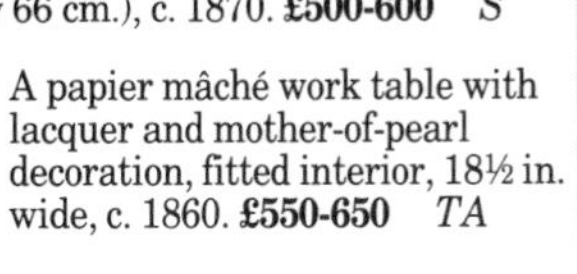

A papier mâché work table with lacquer and mother-of-pearl decoration, fitted interior, 18½ in. wide, c. 1860. **£550-650** *TA*

A rosewood games table with a chess board and a backgammon and cribbage board above a drawer, 20 in., 19th C. **£300-350** *CSK*

A 19th C. black lacquered and chinoiserie decorated work box, for restoration. **£180-220** *JMW*

An inlaid walnut games table, complete with Chinese ivory chess set, 23 in. wide, c. 1830. Complete **£420-460** Table only **£320-360** *TA*

A burr-walnut games and work table, the interior for chess, backgammon and cribbage, drawer and compartments above a work bag, 2 ft. 5 in. high by 2 ft. wide (74 by 61 cm.), c. 1850. **£475-525** *S*

A fernwork work table, 22½ in. wide, c. 1920's. **£300-350** *CDE*

A late 19th C. mahogany work box. **£70-90** *JMW*

A rare George III mahogany games table, the sides with pull-out candle slides, 2 ft. 6 in. high by 1 ft. 8 in. wide (76 by 51 cm.), c. 1770. **£3,000-£4,000** *S*

A 19th C. circular parquetry games table, the top inset with a chequer board and diced yew-wood, rosewood and other exotic wood parquetry, 24 in. diam. **£300-350** *DS*

A hexagonal rosewood games table, crossbanded in satinwood with brass inlay, 18 in. wide, c. 1810. **£600-700** *HB*

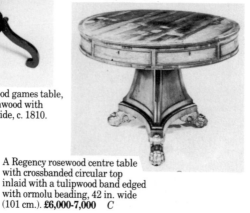

A Regency rosewood centre table with crossbanded circular top inlaid with a tulipwood band edged with ormolu beading, 42 in. wide (101 cm.). **£6,000-7,000** *C*

A Regency rosewood centre table with tip-up top, 49 in. wide (124.5 cm.). **£1,500-2,000** *C*

A rare mahogany expanding circular table, the gilt-tooled leather top with 8 frieze drawers each pulling out to support a 6¼ in. segment fitting into the tongued and grooved rim of the table, 5 ft. diam. (152 cm.), 6 ft. diam. (183 cm.) fully extended, c. 1840. **£1,500-1,700** *S*

Similar tables were patented by Jupe.

A rosewood centre table, the circular top with a moulded border, 2 ft. 4 in. high by 4 ft. 4 in. diam. (71 by 132 cm.), c. 1840. **£800-£1,000** *S*

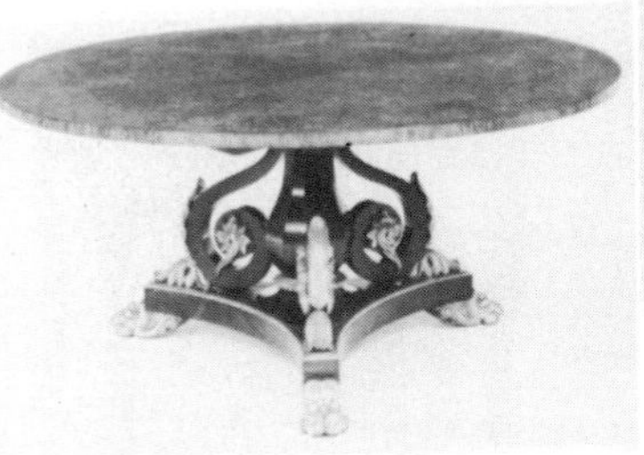

A good early Victorian circular hinged dining table, the top in well figured pollard oak with 2 broad bandings, 2 ft. 4 in. high by 5 ft. 1½ in. diam. (71 by 156 cm.), c. 1840. **£3,500-4,000** *S*

A William IV mahogany drum table, 39 in. diam., c. 1830. **£450-£500** *CDE*

A good George IV rosewood centre or breakfast table, the circular hinged top inlaid with a band of flowers and leaves in pale wood, 2 ft. 6 in. high by 3 ft. 11½ in. diam. (77 by 121 cm.), c. 1830. **£1,500-£1,800** *S*

An early Victorian rosewood tip-up breakfast table. **£550-600** *DWB*

A fine 19th C. oak octagonal dining table, the moulded top segmented and inlaid with parquetry, centred by a star inlaid in various stained and natural woods, 2 ft. 5½ in. high by 5 ft. wide (75 by 152 cm.). **£2,500-3,000** *S*

Reputedly purchased at the Great Exhibition, London, 1851.

A late 19th C. oak centre table, 2 ft. 6 in. high by 4 ft. 1 in. wide (76 by 124 cm.), c. 1850. **£450-550** *SI*

An Anglo-Indian padoukwood centre table, with a leaf-carved border, 2 ft. 4 in. high by 5 ft. 1 in. diam. (71 by 155 cm.), c. 1835. **£800-1,000** *S*

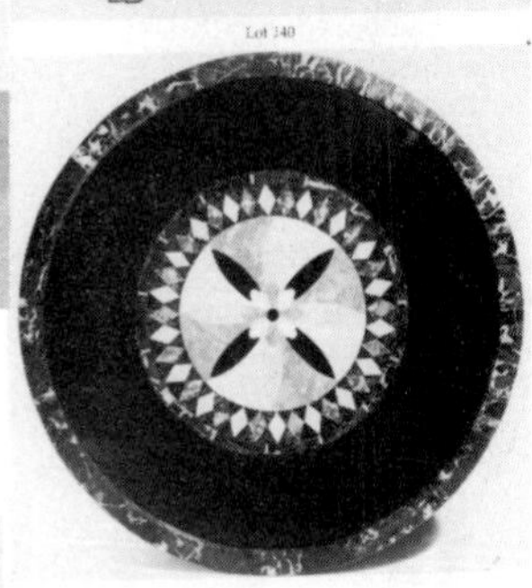

A rare specimen marble and slate low centre table, the 32 in. diameter dished top inlaid with a variety of parquetry marbles about a central patera, English, possibly Torquay, 20½ in. (52 cm.) overall, mid 19th C. **£1,600-2,000** *SC*

A walnut and pietra dura centre table, the 28 in. white marble top inlaid with butterflies in a central roundel contained by radiating bands of specimen marbles, possibly Torquay, 32 in. overall (81 cm.), mid 19th C. **£500-600** *SC*

A Louis XVI-style marquetry and ebonised centre table, profusely inlaid with musical trophies and scrolling foliage, 29½ in. high by 52 in. wide, mid/late 19th C. **£700-£800** *Bea*

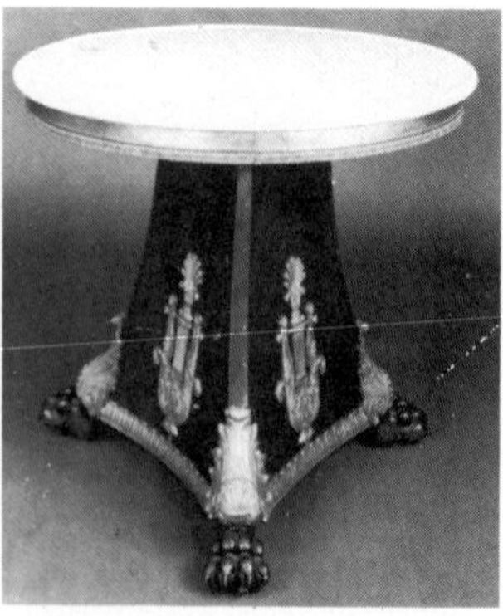

A bronze and ormolu centre table with Carrara marble top, 34½ in. diam. (88 cm.), early 19th C. **£4,000-4,500** *C*

A walnut centre table in well-figured wood, the top crossbanded in tulipwood, 2 ft. 5½ in. high by 4 ft. 8 in. wide (75 by 147 cm.), c. 1860. **£900-1,100** *S*

A parquetry centre table in satinwood, maple, rosewood, kingwood, tulipwood, yew-wood and walnut, 2 ft. 6 in. high by 4 ft. 1½ in. long (76 by 126 cm.), c. 1850. **£700-800** *S*

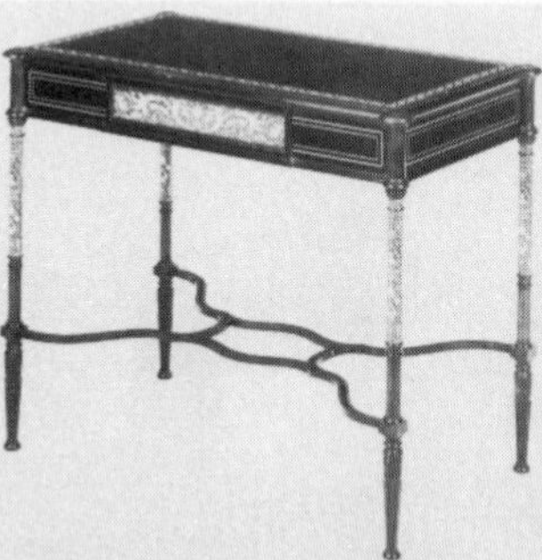

An ivory-inlaid rosewood centre table in the style of Collinson and Lock, the upper section of each leg with inlaid ivory in neo-Mannerist style, 2 ft. 5½ in. high by 2 ft. 11½ in. wide (74 by 90 cm.), c. 1880. **£850-950** *S*

A good coromandel, marquetry and bone-inlaid centre table, 2 ft. 4¾ in. by 3 ft. 9 in. by 2 ft. (73 by 114 by 61 cm.), c. 1870. **£1,200-1,500** *S*

No two editions alike!
Miller's is compiled from scratch each year. All new photographs and fresh information!
If you are unable to find the items you seek in this volume, they may have been included in earlier editions. These have now been reprinted to satisfy demand; details at the back of this book.

A late Victorian mahogany centre table inlaid with foliate and harewood trails, 35½ in. **£500-£600** *CSK*

A Queen Anne walnut centre table with moulded crossbanded top bordered with herringbone bands, possibly later, 32 in. wide (81 cm.). **£3,000-4,000** *C*

A walnut and parcel-gilt centre table with moulded crossbanded rectangular top, 22 in. wide (86 cm.). **£3,000-4,000** *C*

A small mahogany occasional table in Chippendale style with figured surface, fretted brackets and square taper legs with spade feet, c. 1870. **£255-330** *HAL*

An early 18th C. German marquetry centre table, the finely decorated marquetry top in roundels with stars and shapes in oysterwood, kingwood, boxwood inlay, 48 in. wide, restored. **£1,200-£1,400** *B*

An unusual Swedish mahogany centre table on platform base, 2 ft. 6½ in. square (77 cm.), c. 1820. **£1,200-1,600** *S*

A George III coromandel and satinwood crossbanded oval occasional table, the frieze with simulated drawers and leaf scroll inlay, 3 ft. wide (91.5 cm.), c. 1790. **£1,100-1,300** *SS*

A good South German walnut marquetry serpentine centre table, the moulded top in quarter-veneered wood and with a giant foliate panel, legs restored, 2 ft. 6½ in. high by 3 ft. 5½ in. long (77 by 106 cm.), mid 18th C. **£7,000-£8,000** *S*

A marquetry serpentine centre table with a flower-inlaid drawer, 2 ft. 4 in. high by 2 ft. 8 in. wide (71 by 81 cm.), c. 1850. **£600-700** *S*

A good serpentine parquetry centre table, the moulded quarter-veneered tulipwood top with a central panel of diamond cube parquetry, with a drawer, 2 ft. 5 in. high by 3 ft. 5 in. wide (74 by 104 cm.), c. 1850. **£750-850** *S*

A large Victorian walnut circular dining table raised on carved legs with grotesque telamons and paw terminals, carved centre column, 59 in. diam. **£700-800** *AG*

A gilt gesso centre table, in Queen Anne style, with fleur de peche marble top, 2 ft. 3 in. high by 2 ft. 2 in. wide (68.5 by 66 cm.), c. 1900. **£800-900** *S*

A George III mahogany and crossbanded oval breakfast table, 45½ by 58 in. **£2,200-2,800** *DWB*

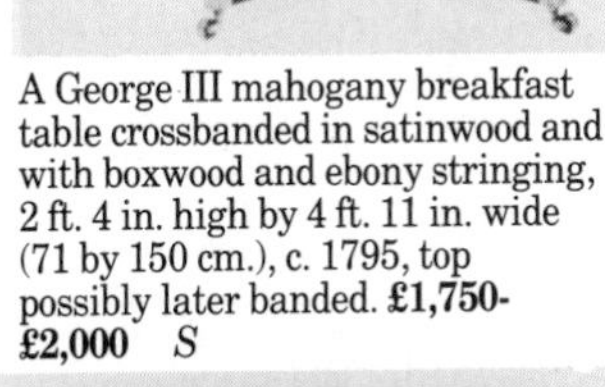

A George III mahogany breakfast table crossbanded in satinwood and with boxwood and ebony stringing, 2 ft. 4 in. high by 4 ft. 11 in. wide (71 by 150 cm.), c. 1795, top possibly later banded. **£1,750-£2,000** *S*

A Regency mahogany dining table, the rosewood crossbanded tilt top on turned column and down-curved legs, 48 in. diam. **£600-700** *CSK*

A Regency circular dining table, 2 ft. 4½ in. high by 5 ft. diam. (72 by 152 cm.), c. 1815. **£2,200-2,500** *S*

A Regency rosewood breakfast table, the circular top with moulded ormolu border on spreading polygonal stem, 51½ in. diam. (131 cm.). **£1,600-1,800** *C*

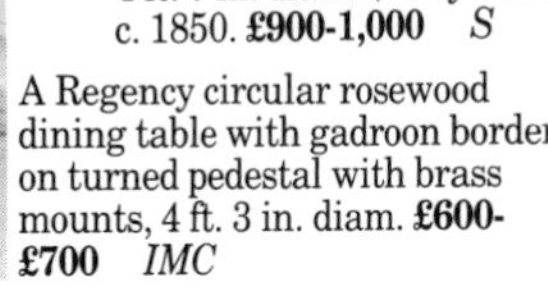

A good rosewood circular table, the hinged top with a rounded edge and moulded frieze, 2 ft. 5 in. high by 4 ft. 7 in. diam. (74 by 140 cm.), c. 1850. **£900-1,000** *S*

A Regency circular rosewood dining table with gadroon border on turned pedestal with brass mounts, 4 ft. 3 in. diam. **£600-£700** *IMC*

An early 19th C. rosewood tip-up dining table. **£740-800** *DWB*

REGENCY FURNITURE

- really an expression of the neo-classical taste which was evident all over Europe
- based on the French styles developed in the Consulate (1799-1804) and Empire (1804-15) periods
- one of the greatest English exponents was Thomas Hope
- mainly used mahogany and rosewood
- the decoration was based on many classical forms, Roman, Egyptian, Greek and Etruscan — often all used on one piece
- rosewood was often French polished and, when in short supply, was often simulated by painting on beech
- often noted for good brass inlay
- Regency furniture has not had an altogether happy time over the last year — with prices remaining relatively static if not falling back. This is probably something to do with the lack of Continental and American buyers but also the neo-classical as a style is quite dependent on fashion trends

A Regency mahogany breakfast table, crossbanded and with ebony line inlay. **£750-850** *DWB*

An early Victorian burr-walnut supper table, on carved centre column and scrolling tripod base, 52 in. diam. **£450-550** *DS*

A mahogany pull top extension dining table, 44 in. diam., c. 1830. **£300-350** *CDE*

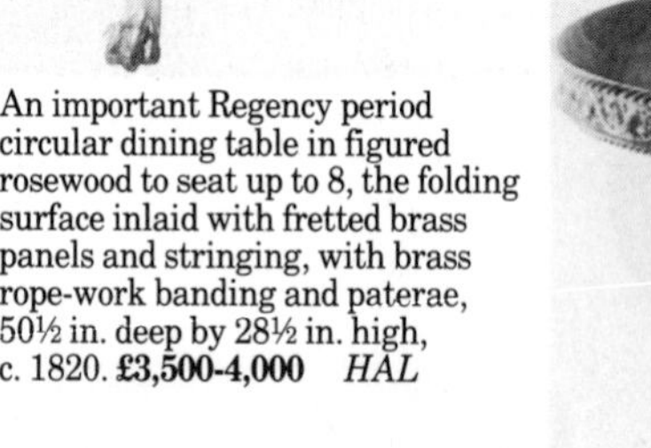

An important Regency period circular dining table in figured rosewood to seat up to 8, the folding surface inlaid with fretted brass panels and stringing, with brass rope-work banding and paterae, 50½ in. deep by 28½ in. high, c. 1820. **£3,500-4,000** *HAL*

A mid Victorian loo table, the mahogany circular top inlaid with roses, 51½ in. **£300-350** *WHL*

An Anglo-Indian rosewood breakfast table, the circular tilt-top with a gadrooned and foliate scrolled frieze, 49 in., early 19th C. **£800-900** *CSK*

A William IV mahogany pedestal library table, the later octagonal tilt-top on a faceted reeded tapering column, 62 in. **£550-625** *CSK*

A fine mid Victorian mahogany patent extending dining table by Jupe, the circular top revolving to incorporate 8 leaves on a bulbous moulded column, concave platform and paw feet, 66 in. diam. closed, 82 in. diam. half extended, 98 in. diam. fully extended, with mahogany leaf rack enclosed by a panelled door, 25 in. **£35,000-£40,000** *CSK*

A figured walnut oval top standard table. **£300-350** *JHR*

A burr-walnut breakfast table, the quarter-veneered tip-top on a fluted jewelled column, stamped John Taylor & Son Manufacturers Edinburgh number 3443, 4 ft. 4 in. diam. (132 cm.), c. 1850. **£1,200-£1,400** *S*

A Victorian loo table, quarter-veneered in burr-walnut, 46 by 34 in., c. 1860. **£200-300** *STR*

A walnut breakfast table with lobed oval tip-top, 4 ft. 11 in. wide (150 cm.), 1850's. **£750-850** *S*

A mid Victorian oval walnut inlaid loo table, 47 in. wide. **£550-650** *IMC*

A Victorian walnut dining table inlaid with marquetry, ebonised and boxwood lines, 49 in. **£450-£500** *CSK*

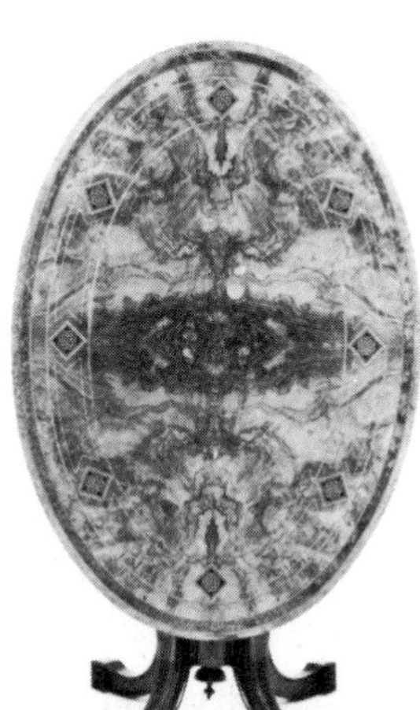

A walnut and Tunbridge ware table, the oval top quarter-veneered in well figured wood and inlaid with floral mosaic within a burr-chestnut border, 2 ft. 4½ in. by 4 ft. (72 by 122 cm.), c. 1865. **£400-£500** *S*

A walnut breakfast table, the oval top with a moulded border, on turned supports and downswept quadruple moulded feet, 28 by 54 in. (71 by 137 cm.), end 19th C. **£500-600** *SC*

A Victorian walnut oval salon table with tilting plain figured top and chamfered edge, 3 ft. 2 in. **£350-£400** *DDM*

A George III mahogany rectangular breakfast table, 4 ft. 6 in. by 3 ft. 2 in. **£350-400** *WHL*

A George III period breakfast table in mahogany, the figured inlaid crossbanded folding surface above turned pedestal supported on 4 swept reeded legs with original brass feet and castors, 48 in. wide by 46½ in. deep by 28½ in. high, c. 1800. **£1,900-2,500** *HAL*

A Regency faded mahogany and rosewood banded breakfast table, 40 by 50 in. **£1,700-2,000** *DWB*

A Regency rosewood breakfast table, the top with broad crossbanded edge, 4 ft. 9¼ in. by 3 ft. 8½ in. (145.5 by 113 cm.), c. 1810. **£1,200-1,800** *S*

A small George IV breakfast table in mahogany, having faded figured crossbanded folding surface above turned pedestal on 4 swept reeded legs with brass feet and castors, c. 1810. **£1,200-1,500** *HAL*

A Regency mahogany breakfast table, the crossbanded top on a turned pillar and 4 down-swept supports ending in brass paw feet and castors, 60 by 44 in. (152 by 112 cm.). **£900-1,000** *L*

A Regency mahogany rectangular breakfast table, the tilt-top with rosewood banding, supported on a part wrythen fluted stem, the legs each with inlaid stringing and brass castors, 4 ft. 3½ in. **£1,400-£1,600** *DDM*

A large 3 pedestal expanding mahogany dining table with 2 'D' ends inlaid with a rosewood border and a crossbanded edge, with 5 extra leaves, 183 in. long overall by 57 in. wide (465 by 145 cm.), c. 1850. **£4,000-5,000** *S*

A Regency mahogany breakfast table, the rosewood banded rectangular tilt-top with rounded ends, 50 in. **£550-600** *CSK*

A George III mahogany breakfast table with crossbanded top bordered with rosewood, 55½ in. wide (141 cm.). **£1,300-1,500** *C*

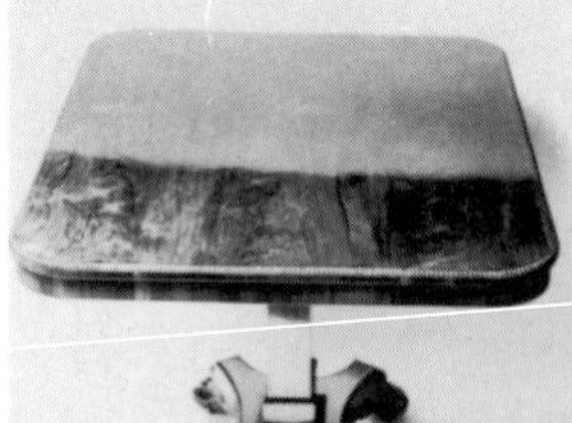

A Regency rosewood breakfast table, 36 by 30 in., c. 1815. **£550-£675** *STR*

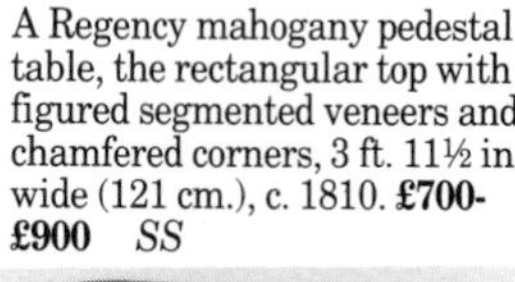

A Regency mahogany pedestal table, the rectangular top with figured segmented veneers and chamfered corners, 3 ft. 11½ in. wide (121 cm.), c. 1810. **£700-£900** *SS*

A George III rosewood breakfast table with tip-up top inlaid with a boxwood line, 44 in. wide (112 cm.). **£3,000-4,000** *C*

A George III mahogany breakfast table on a ring turned stem and 4 moulded downswept supports, the supports now strengthened with blocks, 29½ by 67 by 47 in. (75 by 170 by 120 cm.), late 18th C. **£500-£600** *SC*

A long George III-style mahogany pedestal dining table with 2 additional leaves, 10 ft. 8 in. extended length, 48 in. wide. **£1,000-1,200** *DS*

A George III mahogany 2 pillar dining table, the top with 2 half-round sections, each pivoting on a columnar stem, 28 by 74 by 66 in. (71 by 188 by 168 cm.), end 18th C. **£900-1,200** *SC*

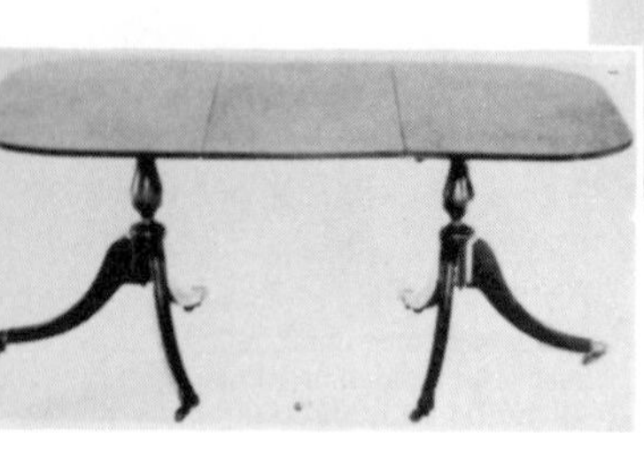

A George III-style mahogany 2 pillar dining table, 29½ by 88 in. (75 by 220 cm.), including 2 leaves, 20th C. **£550-700** *SC*

A mahogany dining table in the George III style, with 2 extra leaves, 3 ft. 8 in. wide by 8 ft. 11 in. fully extended (112 by 271 cm.), early 20th C. **£1,000-1,200** *S*

A mahogany 2 pedestal dining table in late George III style, 3 ft. 11 in. by 7 ft. 7 in. fully extended (119.5 by 251.5 cm.), the pedestals mid 20th C., the top Victorian but with alterations. **£2,000-2,200** *S*

A William IV mahogany 3 pedestal dining table, the top with rounded corners, 4 ft. 2 in. wide by 12 ft. 10 in. long (127 by 391 cm.), c. 1830. **£5,000-5,500** *S*

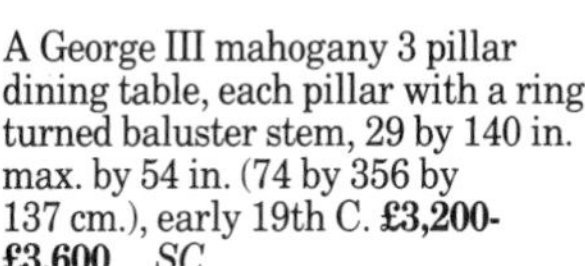

A George III mahogany 3 pillar dining table, each pillar with a ring turned baluster stem, 29 by 140 in. max. by 54 in. (74 by 356 by 137 cm.), early 19th C. **£3,200-£3,600** *SC*

A 2 pillar mahogany dining table with 2 large 'D' shape ends with 2 extra leaves now supported by wooden rods fixed on brackets, 53 by 131 in. extended (134 by 332 cm.), mid 19th C. with alterations. **£1,100-1,300** *L*

A Regency mahogany dining table with well-figured top, 49 by 90 in. (125 by 229 cm.) including an extra leaf. **£7,000-8,000** *C*

. late Georgian 3 pillar mahogany dining table with 2 extra leaves, the top with reeded edge, slight repairs, the leaves probably later, 41.5 by 142 in. (105 by 361 cm.) extended. **£4,500-5,500** *L*

A George III Irish mahogany 4 pedestal dining table, 2 ft. 4 in. high by 13 ft. 1½ in. wide (71 by 400 cm.), showing 3 of the 4 pedestals, c. 1795. **£9,000-11,000** *SI*

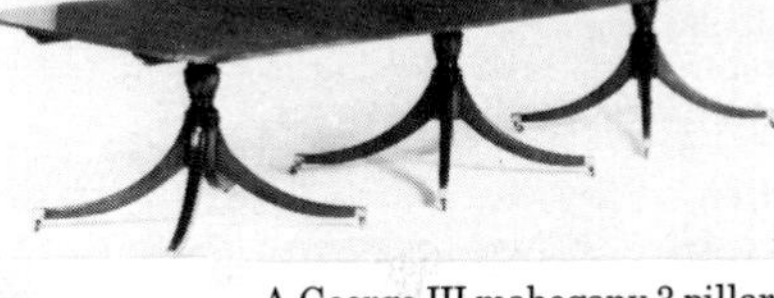

A George III mahogany 3 pillar dining table, 2 ft. 3¾ in. high by 10 ft. 2 in. fully extended (70.5 by 310 cm.), c. 1800, table bearers replaced. **£8,000-10,000** *S*

A George III mahogany dining table in 3 sections including 2 'D' ends, and a matching centre section, with 2 flaps supported on a double gateleg, 28 by 104 in. extended by 50 in. (71 by 264 by 127 cm.), late 18th C. **£800-1,000** *SC*

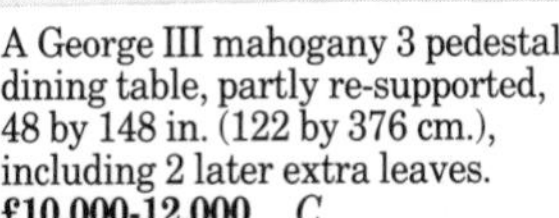

A George III mahogany 3 pedestal dining table, partly re-supported, 48 by 148 in. (122 by 376 cm.), including 2 later extra leaves. **£10,000-12,000** *C*

An early 19th C. mahogany 'D' end dining table, 28½ in. high by 41 in. wide by 104 in. long. **£1,150-£1,250** *Bea*

A George III period dining table in mahogany to seat up to 12, the figured boxwood-strung surface above shaped apron supported on slim square taper legs with spade feet, with restorations, 115 in. wide by 41½ in. deep by 28¼ in. high, c. 1790. **£2,400-3,000** *HAL*

A mahogany 'D' shape dining table with 2 ends and centre leaf inlaid with stringing and on 8 square tapering supports with block feet, 48 by 72 in. (122 by 183 cm.) extended. **£400-500** *L*

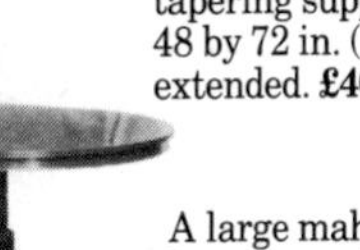

A large mahogany dining table in late George III style, 18 by 4 ft. (548 by 122 cm.) fully extended, modern. **£3,000-4,000** *S*

A George II-style mahogany dining table, the rounded rectangular top with gadrooned edge on cabriole legs, with extra leaf, extended 6 ft. by 3 ft. 6 in. **£225-275** *DS*

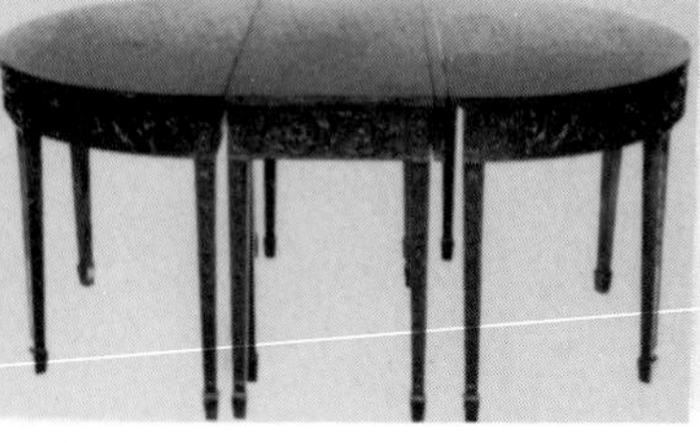

A George III-style mahogany dining table in 3 sections, the ends of demi-lune outline, 30 by 48 by 137 in. (76 by 122 by 300 cm.), including 3 leaves, 20th C. **£1,000-£1,200** *SC*

A mahogany dining table with 5 extra leaves, 2 ft. 4 in. by 10 ft. 8¾ in. by 4 ft. 10 in. (71 by 326 by 147 cm.), c. 1850. **£1,300-1,500** *S*

A circular mahogany extending dining table raised on 5 square tapering supports, extending by the insertion of 3 additional leaves, closed 60 in. diam., 96 in. extended, 19th C. **£550-600** *L*

A good Regency mahogany dining table with rounded rectangular top, the end with panelled veneer extending on a scissors underframe, folding to become a side table, size extended 92 by 48 in. **£2,300-£2,700** *DS*

Possibly by Gillows of Lancaster.

A Victorian mahogany extending dining table, 2 ft. 4 in. high by 7 ft. 8 in. long (71 by 234 cm.). **£450-550** *S*

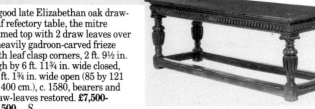

A good late Elizabethan oak draw-leaf refectory table, the mitre framed top with 2 draw leaves over a heavily gadroon-carved frieze with leaf clasp corners, 2 ft. 9½ in. high by 6 ft. 11¾ in. wide closed, 13 ft. 1¾ in. wide open (85 by 121 by 400 cm.), c. 1580, bearers and draw-leaves restored. **£7,500-£8,500** *S*

A Georgian mahogany fall flap dining table, 54 by 47¼ in. **£200-£250** *NSF*

A fine Elizabethan oak refectory table, the rectangular 2 plank top with cleated ends and sides, formerly a draw-leaf table, some restoration, 2 ft. 9¼ in. high by 8 ft. 2½ in. long (84.5 by 250 cm.), c. 1600. **£4,500-5,500** *S*

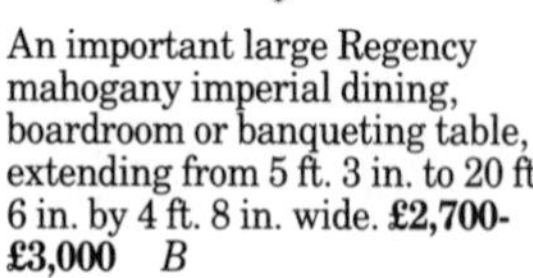

An important large Regency mahogany imperial dining, boardroom or banqueting table, extending from 5 ft. 3 in. to 20 ft. 6 in. by 4 ft. 8 in. wide. **£2,700-£3,000** *B*

An oak draw-leaf dining table, banded top on fluted bulbous baluster legs, extending to 103 in., part 17th C. **£650-750** *CSK*

A Flemish oak draw-leaf table, on bulbous baluster legs joined by flat stretchers, 2 ft. 7½ in. high by 8 ft. 2½ in. long by 2 ft. 6 in. wide (80 by 250 by 76 cm.), mid 17th C. **£3,000-£3,300** *S*

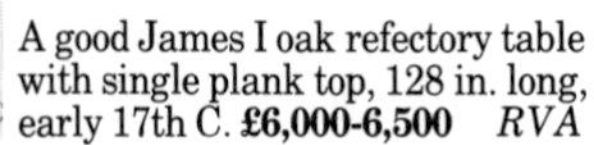

A good James I oak refectory table with single plank top, 128 in. long, early 17th C. **£6,000-6,500** *RVA*

An oak refectory table, 2 ft. 7 in. high by 8 ft. 4 in. long (79 by 254 cm.), re-constructed from earlier fragments. **£2,000-2,200** *S*

A Dutch 17th C.-style oak centre table applied with C-scrolls, the rectangular top with a long frieze drawer, on bulbous turned column supports, 63 in. **£450-500** *CSK*

A Queen Anne oak refectory table, the 2 plank top with a mitred border, frieze with the incised date 1719, 2 legs replaced and drawer deficient, 107.75 in. (273 cm.) long. **£1,900-2,300** *L*

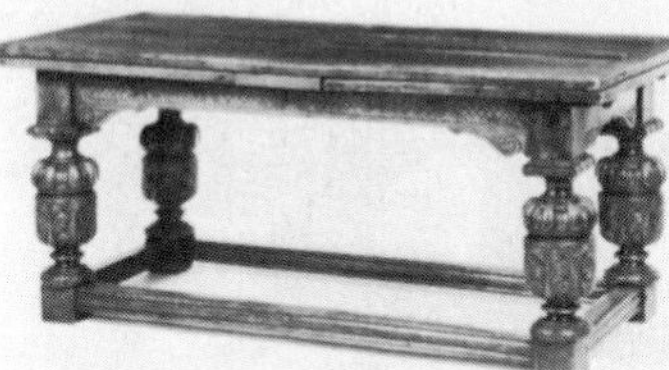

An oak draw-leaf table in Elizabethan style, the frieze with geometric inlay, 2 ft. 9½ in. wide by 6 ft. long by 11 ft. 2 in. fully extended (85 by 183 by 340.5 cm.), c. 1920. **£800-1,000** *S*

An oak refectory dining table of early 17th C. origin. **£3,000-£3,500** *LS*

A Charles II oak rectangular double action gateleg table, with a drawer, 4 ft. 8½ in. (144 cm.) wide, c. 1680. **£1,500-2,000** *S*

A Charles II oak gateleg table, the ball-turned and squared section legs each with 2 horizontal bobbin-turned crossbars with 3 bobbin-turned pearwood spindles, 2 ft. 5 in. high by 4 ft. 3 in. wide (74 by 129 cm.), c. 1675. **£2,600-3,200** *S*

A William and Mary oak double gateleg writing table, 2 ft. 5 in. high by 2 ft. 6 in. wide (73 by 76 cm.), c. 1690. **£1,100-1,400** *S*

A Charles II red walnut oval gateleg table, the spiral twist supports united by stretchers, 3 ft. 5 in. (104 cm.) wide, c. 1680. **£900-£1,100** *S*

An antique heavy oak oval gateleg dining table with bobbin turned legs, twin gates at each side, opening to 79 by 59 in. **£900-1,100** *DA*

An oak gateleg table with oval twin-flap top and a frieze drawer, 42¼ in. (107 cm.) wide open, 17th C. **£450-550** *C*

A late 17th C. small occasional table in oak, the figured faded folding surface above single drawer and turned gatelegs, 35½ in. wide by 30½ in. deep by 28 in. high, c. 1690, drawer pull later. **£500-£750** *HAL*

A 17th C. rare oak single flap gateleg side table, 52 in. long. **£600-700** *HB*

A William and Mary oak gateleg table, fitted with a drawer, 28 by 59 by 48 in. (71 by 150 by 122 cm.), late 17th/early 18th C. **£400-450** *SC*

A late 17th C. oak gateleg table, with a drawer, on ring turned supports and stretchers, 29 by 48 by 68 in. (71 by 122 by 173 cm.) extended. **£400-500** *SC*

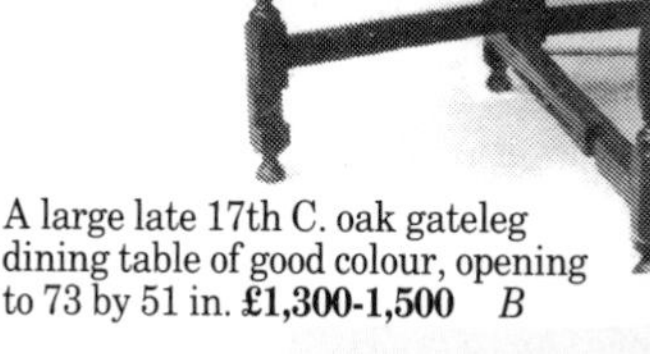

A large late 17th C. oak gateleg dining table of good colour, opening to 73 by 51 in. **£1,300-1,500** *B*

A William and Mary oak gateleg table, the oval top with a moulded edge, on baluster and reel turned supports, with restorations, 29 by 56 by 63 in. (74 by 142 by 160 cm.) extended, late 17th/early 18th C. **£1,000-1,200** *SC*

A late 17th C. oak oval gateleg dining table. **£1,450-1,600** *LS*

A Charles II oak gateleg dining table, the oval top on baluster turned supports joined by rails, 28 by 42 by 54 in. (71 by 107 by 137 cm.), third quarter 17th C. **£500-600** *SC*

An 18th C. oak Irish wake table with plain half-oval leaves, supported on turned legs with plain stretchers and gate action, 5 ft. 3½ in. wide by 5 ft. 10½ in. extended by 2 ft. 4 in. high. **£1,000-£1,300** *DDM*

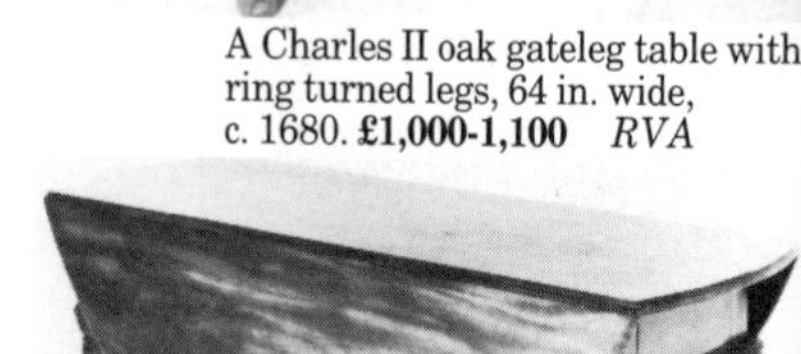

A Charles II oak gateleg table with ring turned legs, 64 in. wide, c. 1680. **£1,000-1,100** *RVA*

An early 18th C. oak gateleg circular table, 52 in. diam. **£500-£600** *DA*

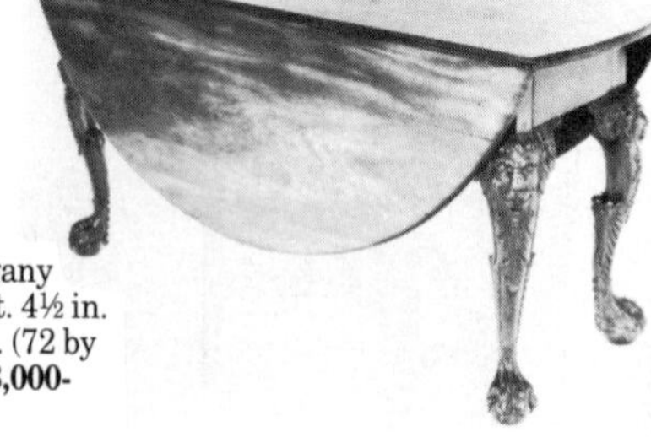

A good George II mahogany gateleg dining table, 2 ft. 4½ in. high by 5 ft. 11 in. diam. (72 by 150 cm.), mid 18th C. **£3,000-£4,000** *S*

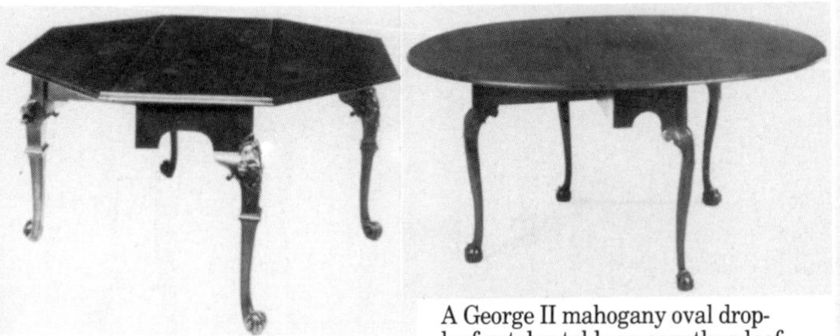

A mid Georgian mahogany gateleg dining table, 56½ in. (142 cm.) wide, open. **£5,000-6,000** *C*

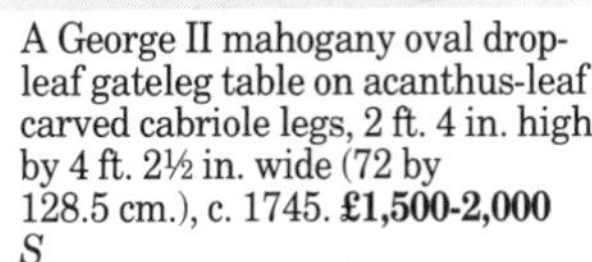

A George II mahogany oval drop-leaf gateleg table on acanthus-leaf carved cabriole legs, 2 ft. 4 in. high by 4 ft. 2½ in. wide (72 by 128.5 cm.), c. 1745. **£1,500-2,000** *S*

A mahogany gateleg dining table, 42 in. **£600-700** *CSK*

An early Georgian period oak oval twin flap dining table, 3 ft. 7½ in. by 3 ft. 11 in. **£550-650** *WW*

A George II walnut gateleg dining table, the circular top with a moulded border, with restorations, the top French polished, 28½ by 57 in. (72 by 145 cm.) diam., mid 18th C. **£800-1,000** *SC*

A mahogany drop-leaf table, 52 in. open, c. 1860. **£110-130** *CDE*

A mahogany Sutherland table, 57 in. extended, c. 1865. **£150-£200** *CDE*

WALNUT

- **the walnut period is generally accepted as running from c. 1670-1740, when mahogany took over as the major wood used**
- **walnut had many advantages: beautiful colour, suitable for veneer work, the burr and curl were particularly desirable, easy to carve**
- **it was, however, prone to worm**
- **cabinet makers replaced joiners as supreme craftsmen**
- **London became furniture making centre**
- **the first time one was able to distinguish between town and country pieces**
- **country chests were lined in pine**
- **Charles II reign heralded return of exiled aristocracy plus continental fashions in furniture**

Plus factors with walnut:—

- **patination and colour**
- **good choice of veneers**
- **with chests — a quartered top**
- **herringbone inlay**
- **crossbanding**
- **stringing**
- **marquetry**

A Victorian mahogany Sutherland table, 49 in. fully open, c. 1880. **£300-350** *Ph*

A mahogany drop-leaf table, 49 in. wide, open, c. 1770. **£1,300-1,500** *HB*

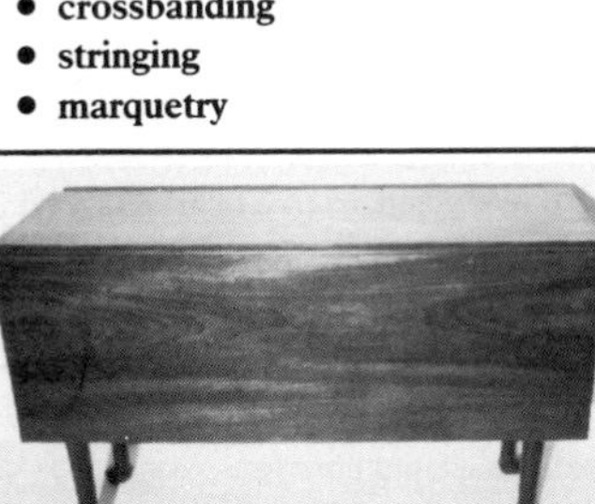

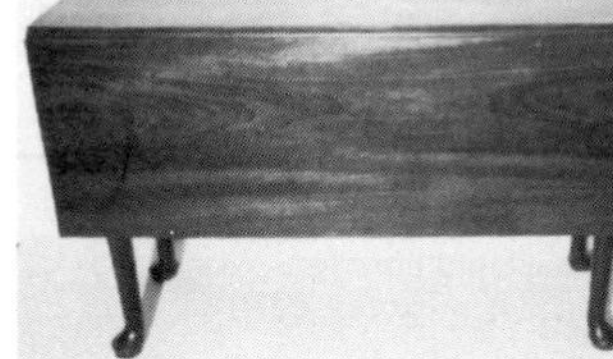

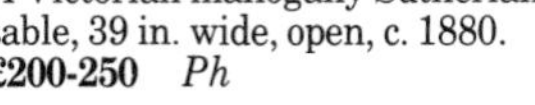

A Victorian mahogany Sutherland table, 39 in. wide, open, c. 1880. **£200-250** *Ph*

A George III Chippendale period mahogany supper table, 44 by 45 in. extended. **£175-200** *DS*

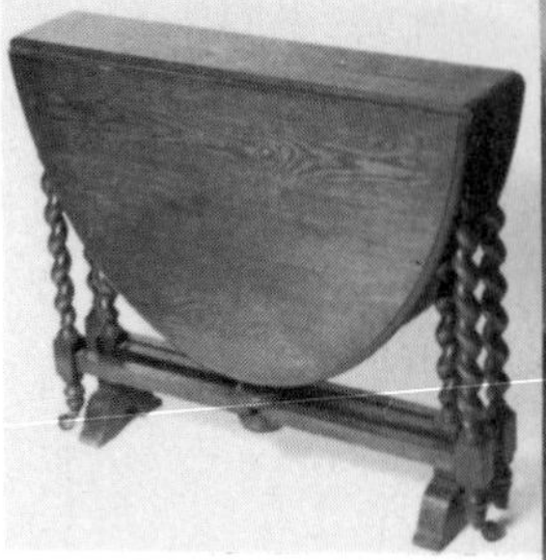

An oak gateleg Sutherland table, 36 in. wide, c. 1920's. **£50-70** *CDE*

A George III satinwood Pembroke table, painted at a later date with a central oval of summer fruit with a frieze drawer on square tapering legs decorated with pendant bellflowers, 36½ in. (93 cm.) wide, open. **£2,400-2,600** *C*

A fine George III satinwood occasional Pembroke table in the French manner, the oval top on moulded cabriole legs carved with ribbon-tied husks, 2 ft. 6 in. high by 3 ft. ¾ in. wide open (76 by 93.5 cm.), c. 1785. **£10,000-£12,000** *S*

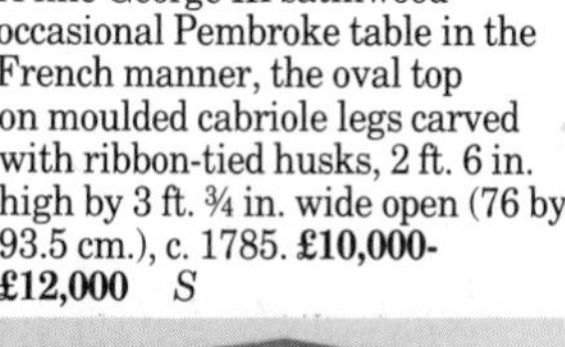

An excellent quality George III-style mahogany and satinwood inlaid Pembroke table, the oval hinged top with a central satinwood panel from which radiate fan lines to a lunette border, the frieze fitted with a husk inlaid drawer, stamped T. Willson, 45 in. wide by 33 in. deep by 28½ in. high. **£1,750-2,250** *HAL*

A rare George III satinwood harlequin Pembroke table to a design by Thomas Sheraton, crossbanded in amaranth, the interior with two rising cases of drawers, one with a long drawer fitted as a dressing table with a central toilet glass, bottles and lidded compartments, the other with small drawers and pigeonholes, the harlequin mechanism operated by the pull-out supports for the leaves, 2 ft. 4½ in. high by 2 ft. 6½ in. deep, c. 1795. **£14,000-16,000** *S*

Provenance: The 1st Earl Macartney, 1737-1806, Ambassador to St. Petersburg from 1764-67. The design for this piece is in The Cabinet-Maker and Upholsterers Drawing Book by Thomas Sheraton, 1793, pages 417-430, plate 56.

A George III satinwood Pembroke table, 2 ft. 4 in. high by 3 ft. 4 in. open (71 by 102 cm.). **£2,750-£3,000** *S*

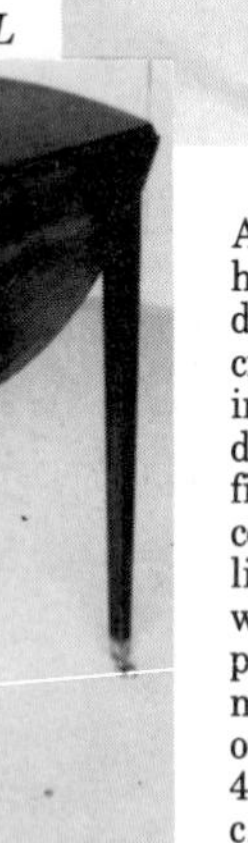

A George III Sheraton oval mahogany Pembroke table, crossbanded in kingwood with ebony and boxwood stringing, 2 ft. 7 in. long by 3 ft. 1 in. when extended. **£950-1,050** *AGr*

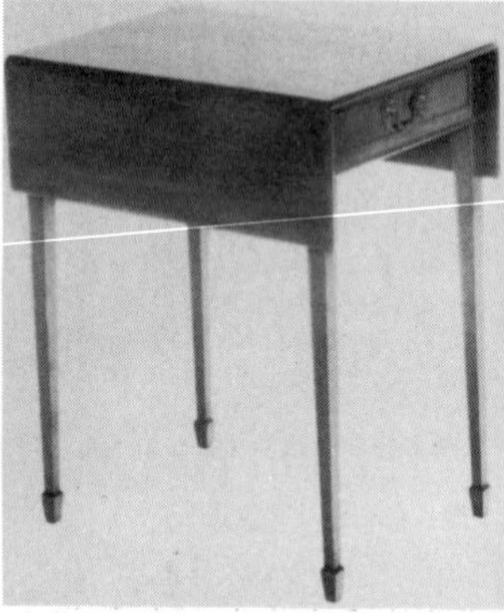

A George III mahogany Pembroke table of small proportions, 29 by 24 by 33 in. (74 by 61 by 84 cm.), late 18th C. **£800-1,000** *SC*

A George III burr yew-wood and satinwood Pembroke table, the top with a moulded edge crossbanded in tulipwood and centred by an oval medallion, 85 by 71 cm. extended. **£1,300-1,500** *P*

A Georgian mahogany Pembroke table, the frieze with one drawer crossbanded and inlaid with panels of satinwood and burr yew-wood, restored, 30 in. (76 cm.). **£250-£300** *L*

A George III small mahogany rectangular Pembroke table, the slender square legs with an 'X' shaped stretcher, 2 ft. 3 in. (69 cm.) wide, c. 1770. **£475-525** *SS*

A good Regency mahogany pedestal Pembroke table, 38 in. wide. **£600-650** *PWC*

A George III mahogany Pembroke table with chamfered moulded legs with pierced brackets, 2 ft. 3¾ in. high by 1 ft. 11 in. wide (70 by 58 cm.), c. 1765. **£550-700** *S*

A Sheraton-style mahogany Pembroke table, 50 in. extended, 20th C. **£280-340** *JMW*

An early George III mahogany Pembroke table with waved twin-flap top (probably reduced) and 2 drawers in the bowed frieze, one formerly fitted, 30½ in. (71 cm.) wide. **£2,000-3,000** *C*

A Georgian mahogany Pembroke table, 45 in. wide, c. 1800. **£225-£250** *Ph*

A 19th C. satinwood Pembroke table, with tulipwood banding and boxwood and ebony line inlay, in late 18th C. style, 42½ by 34 in. **£6,000-7,000** *DWB*

A Regency Pembroke table, concave-sided platform and scrolled quadripartite feet, 43 in. (109 cm.) wide. **£1,200-1,400** *C*

A mahogany Pembroke table, 28½ by 20½ by 25 in. (72 by 52 by 64 cm.) extended, mid 19th C. **£250-300** *SC*

A Dutch satinwood Pembroke table, inlaid with leafy branches on a rosewood ground, with a drawer in the frieze, 2 ft. 4½ in. high by 2 ft. 11 in. wide (72 by 89 cm.), late 18th C. **£800-1,000** *S*

A Georgian mahogany Pembroke table with plain top, reeded edge, 3 ft. wide. **£200-250** *DDM*

A Regency pillar Pembroke table in faded mahogany by Duncan Fyfe, 48 in. open. **£580-640** *CDE*

A 19th C. walnut crossbanded and inlaid Pembroke table. **£1,500-£1,700** *JMW*

A Regency rosewood and crossbanded sofa table with beaded mouldings, the frieze with 2 real and 2 dummy drawers, stamped 'Wilkinson, Ludgate Hill, 7839', 3 ft. ½ in. (93 cm.) wide when closed, c. 1810. **£1,200-1,500** *SS*

A Regency mahogany sofa table, 62 in. (157.5 cm.) open. **£1,200-1,600** *C*

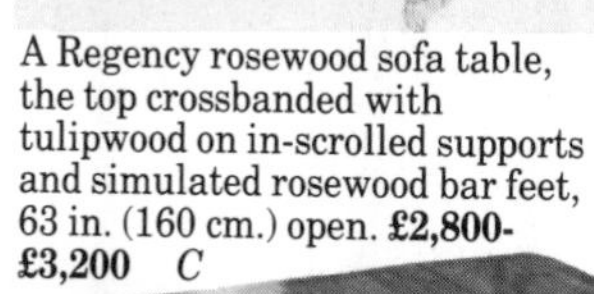

A Regency rosewood sofa table, the top crossbanded with tulipwood on in-scrolled supports and simulated rosewood bar feet, 63 in. (160 cm.) open. **£2,800-£3,200** *C*

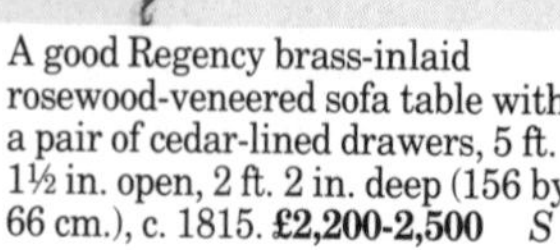

A good Regency brass-inlaid rosewood-veneered sofa table with a pair of cedar-lined drawers, 5 ft. 1½ in. open, 2 ft. 2 in. deep (156 by 66 cm.), c. 1815. **£2,200-2,500** *S*

A 19th C. mahogany and ebony inlaid Pembroke writing table, one drawer with writing slope and compartment, 33 in. wide. **£350-£400** *NSF*

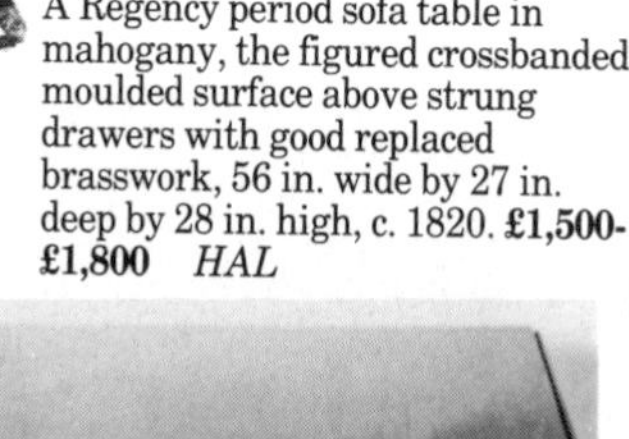

A Regency period sofa table in mahogany, the figured crossbanded moulded surface above strung drawers with good replaced brasswork, 56 in. wide by 27 in. deep by 28 in. high, c. 1820. **£1,500-£1,800** *HAL*

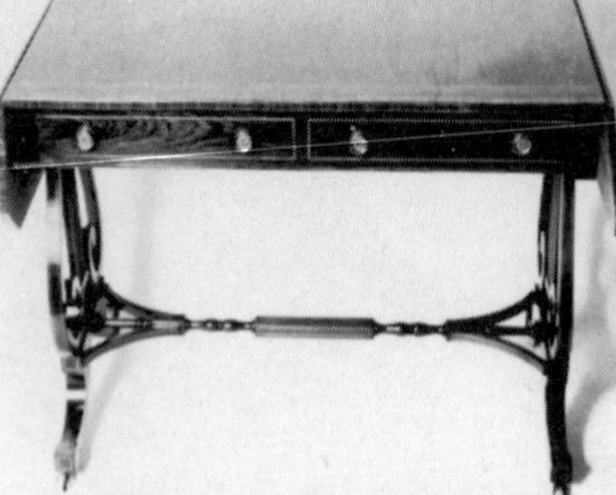

A pair of Regency rosewood sofa tables, crossbanded in coconut palm, 57 in. extended, c. 1820. **£18,000-22,000** *CC*

A Regency calamanderwood and rosewood small sofa table, with a later turned stretcher, possibly Anglo-Indian, 40 in. (101.5 cm.) wide. **£550-750** *C*

A Regency mahogany sofa table, outlined with boxwood stringing, 28 in. high by 57 in. wide. **£800-£1,000** *Bea*

A small 19th C. mahogany sofa table, the plain top with reeded edge, real and dummy drawers to the frieze on 2 plain supports each ending in reeded curving legs and brass cap castors, 1 ft. 9 in. wide by 2 ft. 2 in. long by 3 ft. 11 in. extended. **£200-225** *DDM*

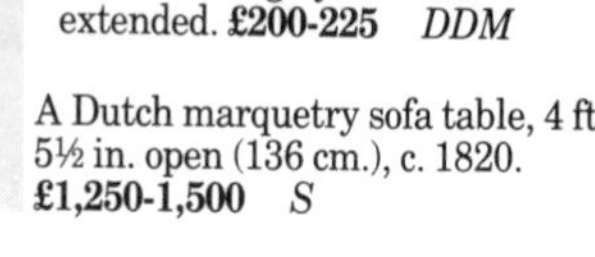

A Dutch marquetry sofa table, 4 ft. 5½ in. open (136 cm.), c. 1820. **£1,250-1,500** *S*

A George IV rosewood sofa table, inlaid with brass lines and applied with beaded mouldings, hipped splayed legs with brass caps and castors, 28 in. high by 59 in. wide. **£1,000-1,200** *Bea*

A mahogany sofa/library table with 3 drawers, 44 in. closed, c. 1815-35. **£1,600-1,800** *HB*

A Regency mahogany sofa table with rounded twin-flap top bordered with a wide band of satinwood, 67 in. (170 cm.) wide. **£5,000-5,500** *C*

A Regency rosewood sofa table, the top crossbanded with satinwood, 60¼ in. (153 cm.) open. **£3,000-£3,500** *C*

An early 19th C. walnut and mahogany crossbanded sofa table. **£600-650** *LS*

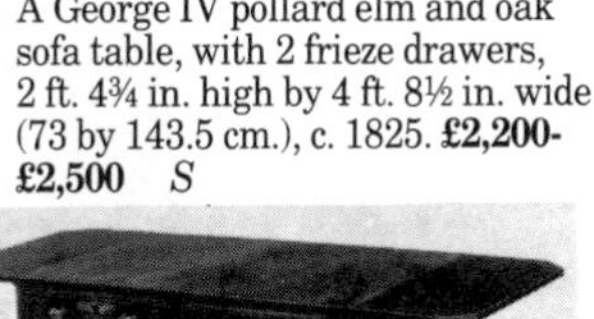
A George IV pollard elm and oak sofa table, with 2 frieze drawers, 2 ft. 4¾ in. high by 4 ft. 8½ in. wide (73 by 143.5 cm.), c. 1825. **£2,200-£2,500** *S*

A Regency mahogany sofa table, on 4 turned supports with hipped splayed legs, brass paw caps and castors, 29 in. high by 54 in. wide. **£750-900** *S*

A fine Sheraton period rosewood-veneered sofa table banded in satinwood and line inlaid, the top with satinwood edge and side flaps, with hinged ink and pen narrow drawers, having brass knob handles, the trestle ends with splay feet, on brass sabots and castors, 3 ft. 2 in. **£3,300-3,600** *WW*

A Regency rosewood sofa table with coromandel and satinwood banding, 4 ft. 10 in. extended. **£1,500-2,000** *WW*

A Regency rosewood and cut brass inlaid sofa table, with one real and one dummy drawer, splayed legs ending in brass paw finials and castors, 3 ft. ½ in. (93 cm.) wide when closed, c. 1815. **£850-1,000** *SS*

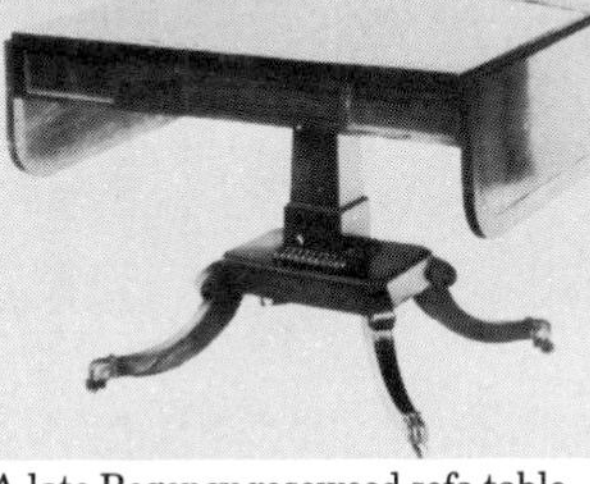
A fine Regency pollard elm sofa table, the frieze with 2 panelled drawers edged with ebonised bead-and-reel, 69 in. (175 cm.) wide, open. **£2,800-3,500** *C*

A late Regency rosewood sofa table, inlaid in cut brass with a band of foliate motifs, 29 in. high by 60 in. wide. **£1,100-1,300** *Bea*

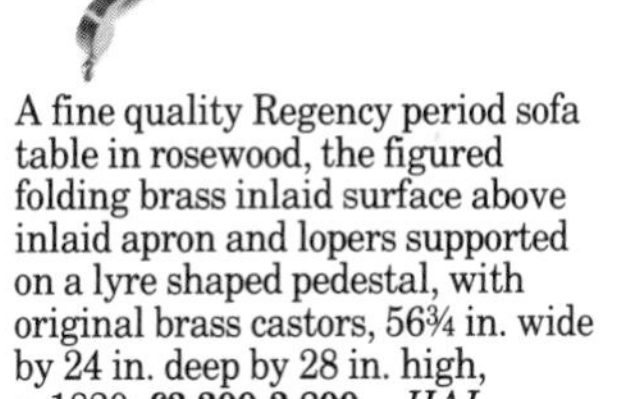
A fine quality Regency period sofa table in rosewood, the figured folding brass inlaid surface above inlaid apron and lopers supported on a lyre shaped pedestal, with original brass castors, 56¾ in. wide by 24 in. deep by 28 in. high, c. 1820. **£3,300-3,800** *HAL*

A Regency mahogany and rosewood banded sofa table with 2 real and 2 dummy drawers, the quadruple ringed pillars on reeded splayed legs, 3 ft. 6½ in. (108 cm.) wide when closed, c. 1815. **£900-£1,000** *SS*

An early 19th C. rosewood sofa table on turned pedestal and rosewood platform base, with satinwood crossbanding and ormolu bordering. **£1,250-1,500** *Wor*

A late Regency mahogany sofa table, the top with a broad satinwood banding above 2 real and 2 dummy drawers on a platform, 29 by 50 in. (74 by 127 cm.) extended by 28 in. (71 cm.), early 19th C. **£600-800** *SC*

An early Victorian rosewood sofa table, 28½ in. high by 59 in. wide. **£700-800** *S*

SOFA TABLES

- **an elegant feminine writing table, usually with two shallow drawers**
- **genuine ones are rarer than it might appear**
- **either had two vertical supports or a central pillar**
- **many fine examples made in mahogany with satinwood or rosewood stringing and crossbanding**
- **rosewood examples can be of exceptional quality**
- **examples with stretchers tend to be later**
- **lyre end supports, particularly with a brass strip, are likely to increase value**
- **many sofa tables have been made from old cheval mirrors**
- **if the stretcher rail is turned and has a square block in the centre — it could be from a converted cheval mirror**
- **many good sofa tables have been carved with Egyptian heads in the manner of Thomas Hope**
- **long drawers are undesirable but many have been cut down**

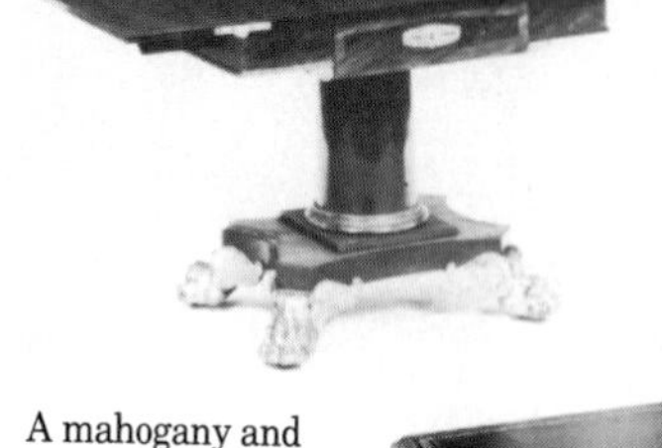

A mahogany and parcel-gilt sofa table with square flaps, Swedish, 2 ft. 6½ in. high by 4 ft. 11 in. wide (77.5 by 150 cm.), 1840's. **£500-600** *S*

An unusual pair of Regency small writing tables each with embossed hide writing surface above single cockbeaded drawer with original brasswork, 27 in. wide by 19 in. deep by 29 in. high, c. 1830. **£1,600-£2,250** *HAL*

A late Georgian small mahogany writing table, the top with a small hinged panel rising to reveal pen and ink wells with one drawer, 29 in. (73 cm.). **£700-800** *L*

A rare mid 18th C. Dutch lady's writing table in fine quality marquetry having inlaid surface above single drawer containing compartments for quills and ink wells, 22 in. wide by 25½ in. deep by 24½ in. high, c. 1780. **£700-£1,100** *HAL*

A George III satinwood writing table, the top crossbanded with rosewood, square tapering legs inlaid with lines and headed by paterae, 39½ in. wide by 23 in. deep (100 by 58.5 cm.). **£6,000-6,500** *C*

A George III ladies' harewood and boxwood line inlaid writing table, top split. **£700-800** *DWB*

A George III bowfront writing table, with ebony lines and oak linings and brass oval handles, line inlaid in ebony to the front and sides, on brass bucket castors, 41 in. wide. **£450-500** *DS*

An early George III padoukwood writing table, the top crossbanded with satinwood, the frieze with a hinged flap enclosing 10 various-sized short drawers, 59¼ in. (151 cm.) open. **£1,500-2,000** *C*

A late George III mahogany writing table, the square leather-lined top with 2 drawers each side and false drawers, 42 in. square (107 cm.). **£1,600-1,800** *C*

A Louis XVI-style mahogany centre writing table inlaid with satinwood and partridge wood panels with boxwood vine borders, 27 in. **£1,500-1,800** *CSK*

A George III mahogany-veneered library table, the top with squared protruding corners, line inlaid and banded in satinwood, the frieze inlaid satinwood key pattern and fitted with an oak lined drawer, on rococo carved paterae cabriole legs, 35 in. **£1,000-1,200** *WW*

A Chippendale-style writing table in mahogany, the embossed hide surface above 6 drawers with good quality brass work and fluted legs, 66 in. wide by 39½ in. deep by 30¼ in. high, c. 1880. **£1,750-£2,400** *HAL*

A George III mahogany writing table crossbanded with satinwood, fitted with 3 frieze drawers on moulded square tapering legs, 59 in. wide (150 cm.). **£3,500-£4,000** *C*

A Regency mahogany writing table fitted with 3 frieze drawers each side on ring turned fluted tapering legs, 60 in. wide (152 cm.). **£4,000-£4,250** *C*

A Regency rosewood writing table bordered with a brass line on turned tapering legs, stamped S. Jamar, 56½ in. wide (144 cm.). **£2,200-2,400** *C*

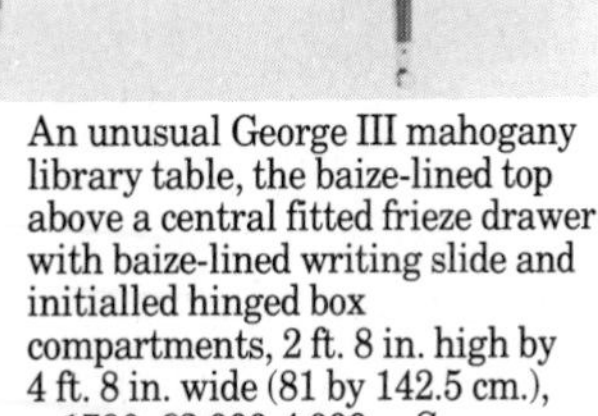

An unusual George III mahogany library table, the baize-lined top above a central fitted frieze drawer with baize-lined writing slide and initialled hinged box compartments, 2 ft. 8 in. high by 4 ft. 8 in. wide (81 by 142.5 cm.), c. 1790. **£3,000-4,000** *S*

A late Georgian mahogany kneehole writing table inlaid with boxwood lines, 42 in. **£650-750** *CSK*

An unusual Lombard oval marquetry writing table, 2 ft. 7½ in. high by 3 ft. 10 in. wide (80 by 117 cm.), c. 1785. **£1,200-1,400** *S*

A double-sided mahogany writing table in George II style, the rectangular top in 3 panels, the centre veneered in diamonds and flanked by oval veneered panels, 2 ft. 7½ in. high by 4 ft. 8 in. wide (80 by 142.5 cm.), c. 1900. **£800-£900** *S*

A Regency mahogany writing table with well figured top crossbanded with calamanderwood, the frieze drawers partly lined with cedar, 42½ in. wide (108 cm.). **£6,500-£7,000** *C*

A Regency rosewood and brass line inlaid library table, fitted with 3 frieze drawers to one side, the reverse with false drawers, brass mounted border, 48 by 32 in. **£10,000-12,000** *DWB*

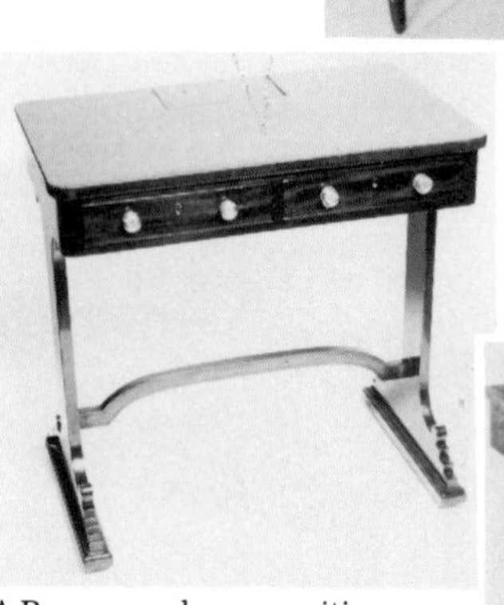

A Regency mahogany writing table, 30 in. wide. **£750-850** *HB*

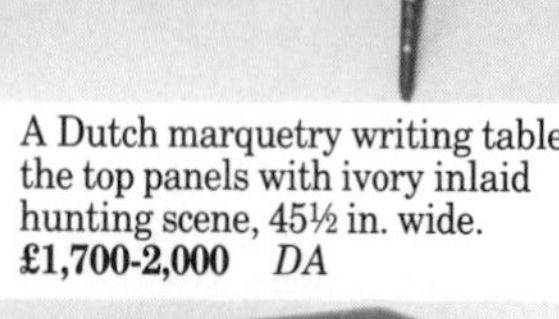

A Dutch marquetry writing table, the top panels with ivory inlaid hunting scene, 45½ in. wide. **£1,700-2,000** *DA*

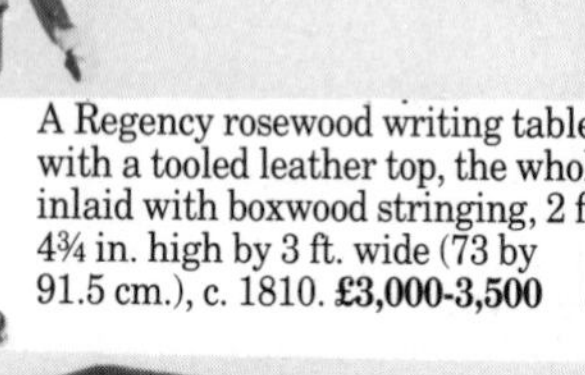

A Regency rosewood writing table with a tooled leather top, the whole inlaid with boxwood stringing, 2 ft. 4¾ in. high by 3 ft. wide (73 by 91.5 cm.), c. 1810. **£3,000-3,500** *S*

A George III mahogany writing table with leather-lined top, edged with boxwood lines, possibly adapted, 36¼ in. wide (92 cm.). **£3,500-4,000** *C*

A Regency mahogany writing table crossbanded with rosewood, with 4 cedar-lined drawers, 47 in. wide (120 cm.). **£3,000-3,250** *C*

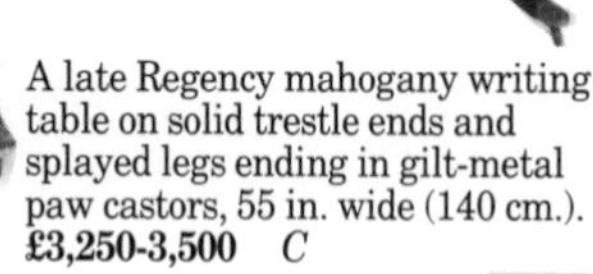

A late Regency mahogany writing table on solid trestle ends and splayed legs ending in gilt-metal paw castors, 55 in. wide (140 cm.). **£3,250-3,500** *C*

A Regency rosewood writing table in the manner of John Mclean, the panelled frieze fitted with 3 drawers and false drawers on trestle ends, 48 in. wide (122 cm.). **£14,000-16,000** *C*

A Regency partridgewood writing table. **£4,500-5,000** *DWB*

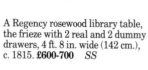

A Regency rosewood library table, the frieze with 2 real and 2 dummy drawers, 4 ft. 8 in. wide (142 cm.), c. 1815. **£600-700** *SS*

A pair of early Victorian walnut library tables, the well figured tops with moulded edges having front frieze drawers, cedar lined, 4 ft. 5 in. **£800-900** *WW*

A William IV rosewood library table, the top with leaf-carved moulded edge, the frieze with 2 bead-moulded drawers, 2 ft. 4½ in. high by 4 ft. 4 in. wide (72.5 by 132 cm.), c. 1835. **£1,700-2,000** *S*

A William IV rosewood library table on carved lion paw feet, 2 ft. 4 in. high by 4 ft. 11 in. wide (71 by 150 cm.), c. 1835. **£800-900** *S*

An early Victorian mahogany library table, with 2 drawers in the frieze faced with leafy bosses, repolished, 2 ft. 5 in. high by 4 ft. 4 in. wide (74 by 132 cm.), c. 1840. **£650-750** *S*

A mid 19th C. walnut writing table, 42 in. long. **£300-350** *McCMB*

A Victorian walnut writing table, inlaid with floral marquetry, 48 in. **£800-850** *CSK*

A Louis XV-style bureau plat in finely figured satinwood and kingwood veneers, the faded green embossed writing surface set within an inlaid border, the ormolu banding, mounts and sabots being of the finest quality, 32½ in. wide by 19½ in. deep by 28 in. high, c. 1850. **£2,300-2,750** *HAL*

A fine Dutch marquetry bureau plat, the top inlaid with ivory figures of mythology, on cabriole legs and with plate glass top, 50 in. wide. **£1,700-2,000** *DA*

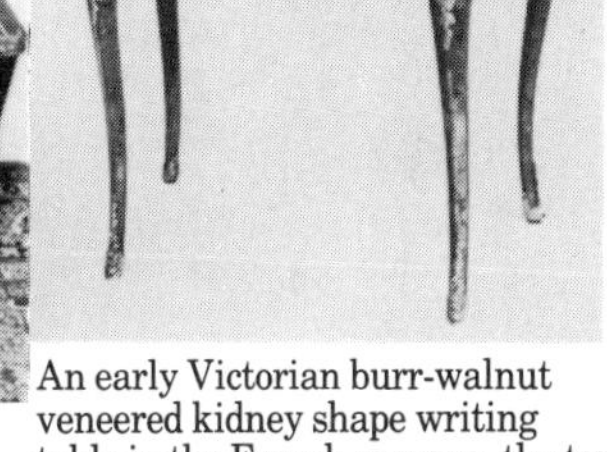

An early Victorian burr-walnut veneered kidney shape writing table in the French manner, the top inset with maroon gilt tooled leather, banded in harewood, having cast gilt brass rococo mounts to the cabriole legs, 3 ft. 9 in. **£1,100-1,300** *WW*

A walnut-veneered ormolu-mounted bureau plat, a real and 2 dummy drawers, 2 ft. 4½ in. high by 3 ft. 11¼ in. wide (72.5 by 120.5 cm.), c. 1860. **£1,000-1,200** *S*

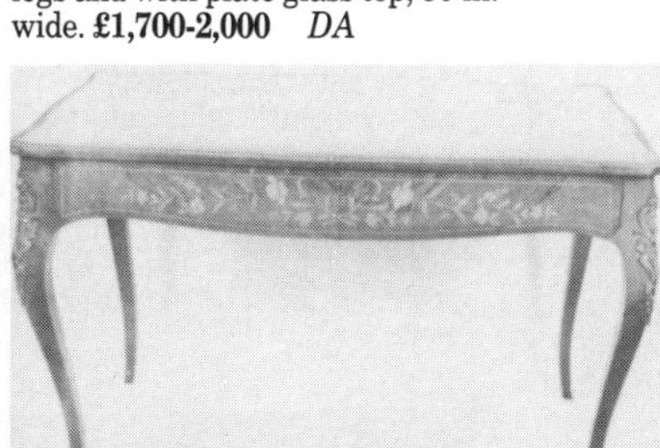

A 19th C. kingwood and floral marquetry writing desk. **£1,000-£1,200** *JMW*

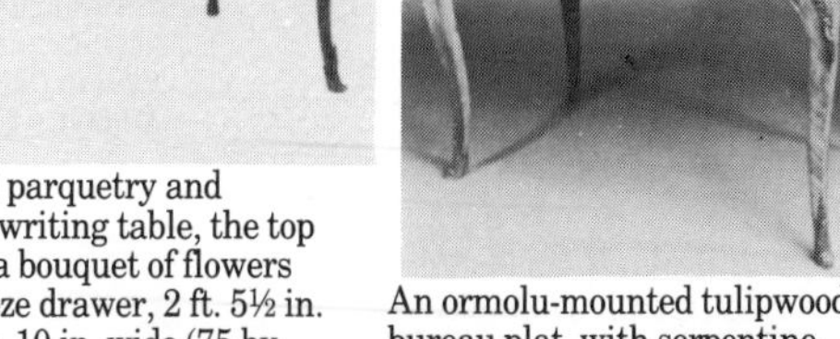

A rosewood parquetry and marquetry writing table, the top centred by a bouquet of flowers above a frieze drawer, 2 ft. 5½ in. high by 3 ft. 10 in. wide (75 by 120 cm.), c. 1880. **£950-1,050** *S*

An ormolu-mounted tulipwood bureau plat, with serpentine leather-lined top, 50 in. (127 cm.) wide, mid 19th C. **£2,000-2,500** *C*

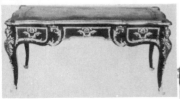

A Louis XV-style bureau plat applied throughout with gilt brass foliate mounts and caryatids, on cabriole legs, modern, 31 in. high by 37 in. deep by 70 in. wide. **£1,000-1,100** *Bea*

A George III mahogany library table with baize-lined top, inscribed in pencil on a drawer 'Earl Balcarres, Lord Lindsay Elected Member for Wigan 1820', 109½ in. wide by 55 in. deep by 33½ in. high (278 by 140 by 85 cm.). **£6,000-£7,000** *C*

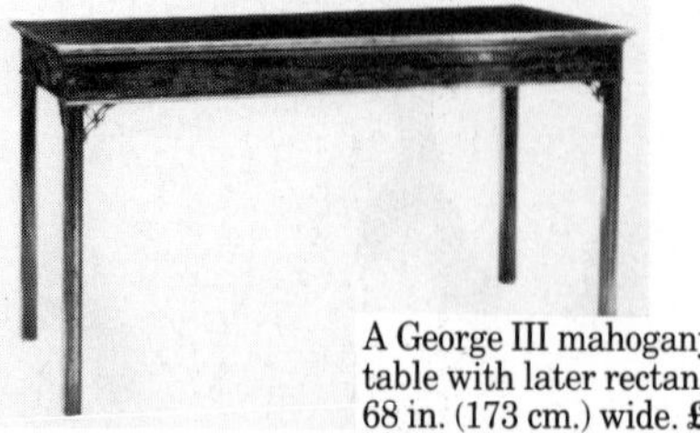
A George III mahogany serving table with later rectangular top, 68 in. (173 cm.) wide. **£1,000-£1,200** *C*

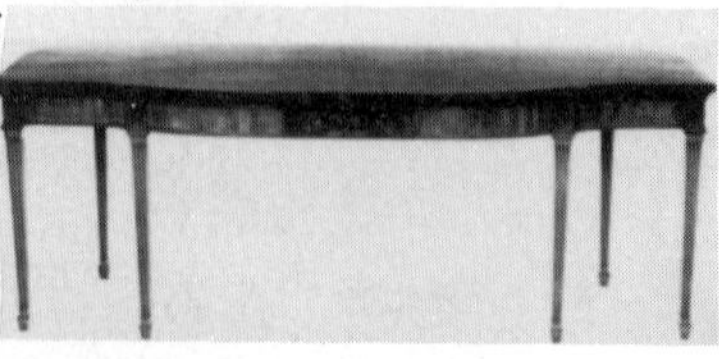
A George III serving table crossbanded with curved sides and semi-elliptical front, 36 by 100 by 35½ in. (92 by 254 by 90 cm.), mid 18th C. **£3,500-4,000** *SC*

A fine pair of George III mahogany serving tables, the tops veneered with segments, 3 ft. high by 5 ft. 6 in. wide (91.5 by 168 cm.), c. 1755. **£8,500-9,500** *S*

A George III mahogany serving table, the fluted frieze punctuated by oval paterae and on tapering fluted square legs, 35 in. high by 36 in. deep by 84 in. wide. **£700-£800** *Bea*

A fine pair of marble-topped giltwood centre tables, one top veneered in panels of mottled dar red and white marble, the other i mottled dark red and orange-yellc 2 ft. 10 in. high by 4 ft. wide (86 b 122 cm.), 19th C. **£10,000-12,000** *S*

A pair of Adam-style mahogany pier tables with crossbanded tops of everted outline, 36 by 70 in. (92 by 188 cm.), 20th C. **£1,800-2,200** *SC*

A fine pair of early George II walnut side tables with inset Sicilian jasper-veneered tops, 62¾ in. (160 cm.) wide. **£8,000-£9,000** *C*

A good oval mahogany serving table of George III design, 36 by 87 by 33½ in. (92 by 221 by 85 cm.), 20th C. **£1,200-1,400** *SC*

A George II Irish walnut side table, probably Cork, 2 ft. 7 in. high by 4 ft. 2 in. wide (79 by 127 cm.), c. 1740. **£600-700** *S*

A George III satinwood side table, the D-shaped top veneered with satinwood segments and centred b a semi-circular mahogany panel, possibly Irish, 2 ft. 6 in. high by 3 ft. wide (76 by 91 cm.), c. 1790. **£1,800-2,000** *SI*

A good George III harewood-veneered and marquetry pier table of semi-circular outline, the kingwood and rosewood crossbanded top inlaid in fruitwood and satinwood, foliate bands, 36 in. high by 42½ in. wide. **£900-1,100** *S*

A George III satinwood and marquetry side table inlaid with a demi-patera framed by green-stained bell-flowers and foliate scrolls, 60 in. (152.5 cm.) wide. **£3,000-4,000** *C*

A George II Irish mahogany tray top centre table, 2 ft. 3 in. high by 2 ft. 5 in. wide (69 by 74 cm.), c. 1755. **£1,400-1,600** *SI*

An Irish mid Georgian walnut side table with black marble top, on cabriole legs, reduced, 48 in. (122 cm.) wide. **£2,200-2,400** *C*

A hardwood side table with marble slip above a pierced and carved frieze with scrolls and foliage, 2 ft. 8¾ in. high by 4 ft. wide (83 by 122 cm.), c. 1830. **£600-800** *S*

A pair of George I walnut side tables with Flemish ebony and kingwood parquetry tops with bone and ebony borders, 2 ft. 4 in. high by 2 ft. 4½ in. wide (71 by 72.5 cm.), c. 1735. **£3,500-4,400** *S*

The English base may have been especially made to take the slightly earlier Flemish tops.

A George III mahogany side table with well-figured serpentine top inlaid with boxwood lines, possibly adapted, 39¼ in. (100 cm.) wide. **£700-800** *C*

A fine pair of George III console tables, the D-shaped tops rosewood veneered and crossbanded in satinwood, c. 1800. **£6,000-7,000** *SI*

A Dutch walnut and veneered side table, the top crossbanded and inlaid with marquetry flowers and foliage, centred by a marquetry panel, on bun feet, restored, 2 ft. 5¾ in. high by 3 ft. 8½ in. wide (75.5 by 113 cm.), mid 19th C. **£1,600-1,800** *S*

A Dutch walnut marquetry side table, the top with a crossbanded and moulded edge, the whole with later inlay of summer flowers and foliage, 2 ft. 5½ in. high by 2 ft. 7 in. (75 by 79 cm.), c. 1750. **£2,600-£3,000** *S*

A Regency rosewood side table in the Louis XVI style, 24 in. (61 cm.) wide. **£1,500-1,750** *C*

A Louis XVI-style rosewood side table applied throughout with gilt brass foliate mounts, 28 in. high by 30 in. wide, late 19th C. **£700-850** *S*

An Italian giltwood side table, the later top inset with a panel of red velvet with a broad gadrooned border, 57½ in. (145 cm.) wide, late 17th C. **£1,000-1,200** *C*

A good pair of German painted and parcel-gilt console tables, each with a shaped slate top painted to simulate marble, 3 ft. 2½ in. high by 4 ft. 7 in. wide (98 by 140 cm.), mid 18th C. **£3,500-4,500** *S*

A Louis XVI bois citronnier and parquetry console desserte with eared D-shaped Carrara marble top, 41½ in. wide by 39 in. high (105 by 99 cm.). **£7,000-9,000** *C*

A Queen Anne walnut and burr-walnut tea table with concertina action, 32 in. wide by 29 in. high by 15¾ in. deep (81 by 74 by 40 cm.). **£6,000-7,000** *C*

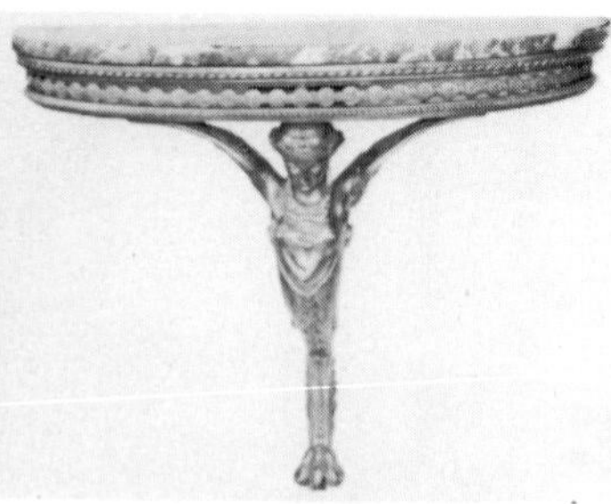
A good 18th C. semi-elliptical giltwood and gesso console table, 41 in. wide. **£360-400** *PWC*

A pair of late Louis XVI giltwood console tables with Carrara marble tops, 30¼ in. (77 cm.) wide. **£750-£1,000** *C*

A pair of Victorian oak pier tables by Gillows of Lancaster, each with green marble top, lion monopodia supports and solid panelled back on plinth base, 72 in. (183 cm.) wide. **£5,000-5,500** *C*

A mid Georgian red-walnut tea table, restorations, 32½ in. (82.5 cm.) wide. **£2,000-3,000** *C*

A North Italian polychrome painted and gilded side table with inset grey and white mottled marble top and later back edge with fluted border, 37 in. (94 cm.) wide, mid 18th C. **£800-1,000** *C*

A Regency rosewood and parcel-gilt console table in the manner of George Smith, 58 in. (147 cm.) wide. **£1,750-2,000** *C*

A mid 19th C. rosewood side table with marble top, 60 in. wide by 20 in. deep. **£350-400** *NSF*

Use the Index!

Because certain items might fit easily into any of a number of categories, the quickest and surest method of locating any entry is by reference to the index at the back of the book. This has been fully cross-referenced for absolute simplicity.

A George I red-walnut half round tea table, 30 in. **£1,800-2,000** *WW*

A Georgian mahogany fold-over tea table with polished interior, standing on pad feet. **£300-350** *HFM*

A George II Irish mahogany tea table, 2 ft. 5 in. high by 2 ft. 10 in. wide (74 by 86 cm.), c. 1755. **£1,200-£1,500** *SI*

A late George II mahogany silver table, with Gothic-pierced frieze with 3 columns forming each leg, originally with a stretcher and gallery, 2 ft. 5 in. high by 2 ft. 9 in. wide (74 by 84 cm.), c. 1760. **£1,200-£1,500** *S*

A Chippendale-style mahogany silver table, decorated with blind fret, with finialled arched cross stretchers, 30½ in. **£700-800** *CSK*

A fold over top supper table with inlaid batswing oval raised on 4 fluted taper legs, 36 in., 18th C. **£200-250** *WHL*

A good George III D-shaped inlaid crossbanded and figured mahogany fold-over tea table, 36½ in. **£600-£650** *EBB*

An 18th C. mahogany serpentine front tea table on moulded square tapered legs. **£550-600** *JSm*

A good George III mahogany fold-over top tea table, 37½ by 34 in. open and 17 in. closed. **£450-500** *KHD*

A late Regency mahogany fold-over swivel top, bowfronted games/tea table, raised on 2 scroll supports, 3 ft. 3 in. when open. **£450-500** *AGr*

An Irish Regency mahogany folding tea table, the top crossbanded in rosewood and inlaid with a brass line, 2 ft. 5½ in. high by 3 ft. wide (75 by 91 cm.), c. 1815. **£600-700** *SI*

A rosewood tea or games table with rectangular swivelling top, 37½ in. wide (95 cm.), c. 1830. **£300-400** *S*

A rosewood tea table by T. & G. Seddon, London, 36 in. wide, c. 1830. **£650-700** *LG*

A good Regency mahogany tea table with turned feet and brass castors, 28 in. high by 36 in. wide. **£380-440** *Bea*

A pair of Regency mahogany tea tables bordered with ebonised lines on twin lyre supports, 36 in. (91.5 cm.). **£2,400-2,600** *C*

A rare small Regency mahogany single drop leaf tea table with candle slide, the legs having carved paw feet. **£275-325** *Fr*

A pair of William IV mahogany tea tables raised on square pillar supports with carved knops, raised on quatre-form bases with scrolling feet, 36 in. wide. **£800-900** *AG*

A Victorian shaped mahogany folding-top tea table, 36 in. **£300-£400** *JD*

A fine George III mahogany library table with revolving leather-lined top, fitted with small drawers divided by cupboard doors with false drawer fronts, 45½ in. (116 cm.) diam. **£6,000-7,000** *C*

A George III satinwood drum table with revolving circular leather-lined top crossbanded with rosewood, 25¼ in. (65.5 cm.) diam. **£2,400-2,800** *C*

A George III mahogany drum table with inset leather top, the frieze with 4 drawers and 4 dummy drawers, 42½ in. diam. by 30 in. high (108 by 76 cm.). **£1,500-£1,800** *L*

A George III-style mahogany drum top library table, the lower part fitted with a cupboard door, on cast bronze claw feet, 50 in. diam., late 19th C. **£1,000-1,400** *SC*

A Regency-style satinwood library table. **£500-600** *CDC*

A Regency mahogany drum top library table, the top inset with gilt-tooled red leather, with alternate real and dummy drawers, 2 ft. 5½ in. high by 3 ft. 6 in. diam. (75 by 107 cm.), early 19th C. **£1,200-1,400** *S*

A Regency rosewood drum top table, with alternate real and dummy drawers, 2 ft. 7 in. (79 cm.) diam., c. 1815. **£650-700** *SS*

A 19th C. mahogany drum table, the circular top with reeded rim, fitted with drawers and imitation drawer fronts below, 53½ in. diam. **£1,100-1,300** *NSF*

A good early 19th C. circular mahogany drum top library table, 48 in. **£1,400-1,600** *PWC*

A George III satinwood dressing table, the hinged divided top inlaid with stringing and containing a fitted interior with an adjustable mirror, lidded boxes and compartments, later handles, 2 ft. 11 in. high by 2 ft. 2 in. wide (89 by 66 cm.), c. 1780. **£5,000-6,000** *S*

A George III walnut dressing table, double flap enclosing a divided interior, including a later mirror, 27½ in. wide. **£500-600** *CEd*

A Sheraton mahogany and rosewood crossbanded combined dressing table and washstand, 3 ft. high by 1 ft. 10 in. wide (91.5 by 51 cm.), c. 1790. **£450-600** *SS*

A George III mahogany washing table, with the original brass washing bowl and 4 canisters with an adjustable concealed mirror, 3 ft. high by 1 ft. 10 in. wide (91.5 by 56 cm.), c. 1795. **£600-700** *S*

A George III mahogany dressing table, 2 ft. 8 in. high by 2 ft. 3 in. wide (81 by 69 cm.), c. 1790. **£350-£450** *S*

A mahogany crossbanded dressing table having a lift up centre section with adjustable mirror, 2 side flaps enclosing fitted compartments with 1 real and 5 dummy drawers to front, length 28 in., width 18½ in. **£500-600** *OL*

An 18th C. kingwood dressing table, with fully fitted interior, legs with blind fretwork decoration, 25 in. square, c. 1775. **£1,750-£2,250** *RD*

An 18th C. kingswood dressing table, with fully fitted interior, legs with blind fretwork decoration, 25 in. square, c. 1775. **£1,750-£2,250** *RD*

It is unusual to find this in kingwood — it is much more common in mahogany.

A George III mahogany toilet table, with an adjustable mirror, the front with a deep drawer with holes for a basin, 2 ft. 9½ in. high by 3 ft. wide (85 by 91 cm.), c. 1790. **£1,200-£1,500** *S*

A George III mahogany toilet table, the folding top enclosing fitted compartments and a rectangular easel plate above a frieze slide, 26½ in. **£850-950** *CSK*

A William IV mahogany dressing table, 53½ in. wide. **£350-400** *CEd*

A kingwood and marquetry small dressing table, 72.5 by 61 cm., 1860's. **£900-1,000** *S*

A mahogany bowfront dressing table, 37 in. wide, c. 1800. **£1,200-£1,500** *HB*

A Regency mahogany dressing table attributed to Gillows of Lancaster, 42 in. (107 cm.) wide. **£1,600-1,800** *C*

cf. a dressing table of the same model, one of five supplied by Gillows in 1811 to Richard Gascoigne for Parlington Hall, Yorkshire. The earliest sketch of this popular Gillows model occurs in 1806 in the firm's Estimate Book for 1803-15.

A painted satinwood dressing chest, probably Austrian, 5 ft. 1 in. high by 2 ft. 11 in. wide (155 by 89 cm.), c. 1850. **£550-650** *S*

A George III marquetry inlaid gentleman's washstand, the hinged top opening to reveal interior fitted with mirror and folding shelves above central well with liner, inlaid with shell and floral marquetry with boxwood and ebony stringing, fitted brass handles, 47 in. **£700-800** *WHL*

A walnut dressing table, 5 ft. 7 in. by 4 ft. 5½ in. (170 by 137 cm.), c. 1860. **£800-1,000** *S*

A rosewood and parquetry dressing table, the serpentine top inlaid with cube pattern, with mirror-lined interior, 72.5 by 58.5 cm., c. 1870. **£600-700** *S*

Miller's is a price GUIDE Not a price LIST.

The price ranges given reflect the average price a purchaser should pay for similar items. Condition, rarity of design or pattern, size, colour, provenance, restoration and many other factors must be taken into account when assessing values.

When buying or selling, it must always be remembered that prices can be greatly affected by the condition of any piece. Unless otherwise stated, all goods shown in Miller's are of good merchantable quality, and the valuations given reflect this fact.

Pieces offered for sale in exceptionally fine condition or in poor condition may reasonably be expected to be priced considerably higher or lower respectively than the estimates given herein.

A walnut and parcel-gilt dressing table, 2 ft. 6 in. by 4 ft. 9 in. by 2 ft. 1¾ in. (76 by 145 by 65.5 cm.), mid 1870's, walnut lined, formerly with a fixed mirror, now with a wall mirror with inset strapwork corners, the cresting with a vacant cartouche below an earl's coronet, 3 ft. 3 in. by 2 ft. 1 in. (99 by 63.5 cm.), mid 1870's. **£400-500** *S*

According to tradition this desk and mirror were formerly in the possession of Lord Cardigan.

An Edwardian period dressing table in satinwood, the oval mirror supported by a scrolling brass gallery above shaped inlaid compartments, 60 in. wide by 26 in. deep by 73½ in. high. **£2,000-£2,500** *HAL*

The quality and condition of this piece is exceptional.

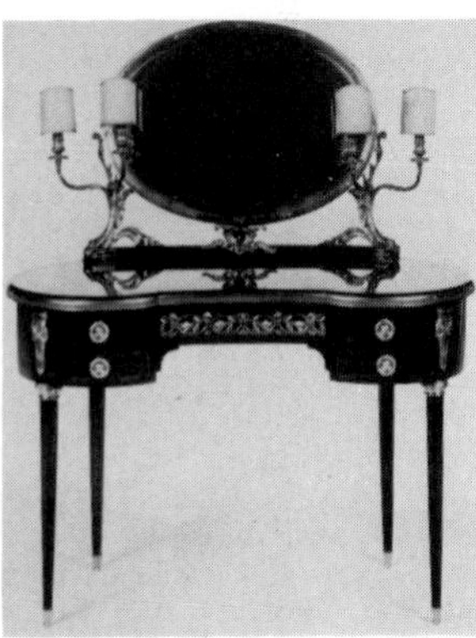

A kingwood and gilt-bronze dressing table, bearing a label Mercier Freres, 100 Faubourg St. Antoine, Paris, with key and plate glass top, 136 by 113 cm., c. 1910. **£2,000-3,000** *S*

A George II mahogany syllabub table, carving later, restored, 2 ft. 3½ in. high by 3 ft. diam. (70 by 91 cm.), c. 1755. **£400-500** *S*

A Chippendale-style carved mahogany supper table, the dished tilt-top with wheat-ear motifs, 2 ft. 8 in. (81 cm.) diam., c. 1880. **£400-£500** *SS*

A mahogany tripod table, the well-figured swivelling top with spindle gallery, 30½ in. (77.5 cm.) wide. **£1,700-2,000** *C*

A fine George II mahogany tripod table, with gallery supported by turned spindles, on a birdcage support, fluted and acanthus-carved stem and three splayed legs with scroll toes, 26½ in. high by 18 in. diam. **£3,000-3,500** *Bea*

A George II mahogany tripod table, top associated, 2 ft. 4½ in. high by 1 ft. 11 in. diam. (72.5 by 58.5 cm.), c. 1750. **£700-1,000** *S*

An early George III mahogany tripod table, the tip-up top with spindle gallery, 30 in. (76 cm.) diam. **£1,750-2,000** *C*

A fine George II carved mahogany small tripod stand, the circular fluted stem with leafy knop and the leaf-carved cabriole legs with claw and ball feet, 1 ft. 8½ in. diam. (52 by 32 cm.), c. 1750. **£8,000-£9,000** *S*

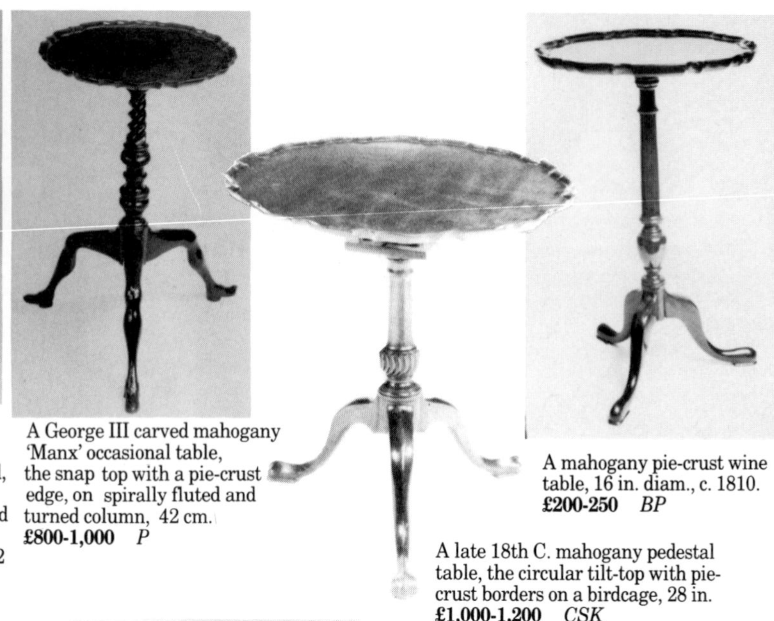

A George III carved mahogany 'Manx' occasional table, the snap top with a pie-crust edge, on spirally fluted and turned column, 42 cm. **£800-1,000** *P*

A mahogany pie-crust wine table, 16 in. diam., c. 1810. **£200-250** *BP*

A late 18th C. mahogany pedestal table, the circular tilt-top with pie-crust borders on a birdcage, 28 in. **£1,000-1,200** *CSK*

A mid Georgian mahogany tripod table, 23 in. (58.5 cm.) wide. **£1,100-1,500** *C*

A George III mahogany tripod table with tip-up pie-crust top, 19 in. (48 cm.) wide. **£3,800-4,200** *C*

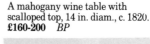

A mahogany tip top wine table, some damage, 17 in., c. 1830. **£135-£155** *NP*

A mahogany wine table with scalloped top, 14 in. diam., c. 1820. **£160-200** *BP*

A mid/late 18th C. burr-walnut circular tip-up tripod table. **£370-£400** *LS*

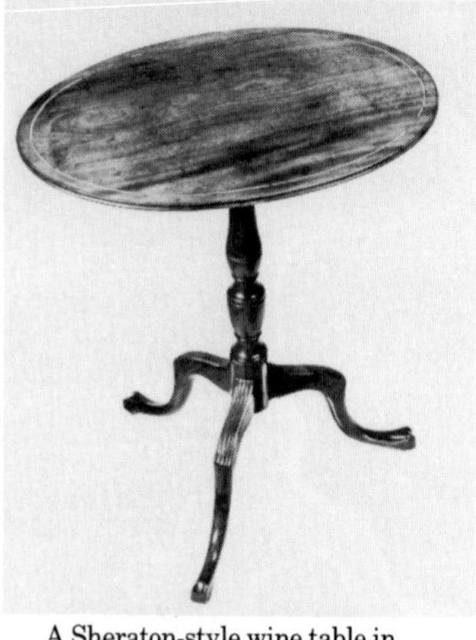

A Sheraton-style wine table in mahogany with figured folding inlaid surface above turned stem mounted on reeded shaped legs, 22 by 16 by 25 in. high, c. 1840. **£275-£330** *HAL*

A mahogany tripod table with birdcage fitment, 21½ in. diam., c. 1740. **£750-950** *CC*

A Georgian mahogany birdcage table, 27 in. diam., c. 1790. **£250-£300** *Ph*

An early 19th C. French kingwood tilt top occasional table or screen table, 29 in. high. **£350-400** *GM*

A George III oak pedestal table, the tripod base carved with quatrefoil on scrolled supports headed by masks, 30 in. (76 cm.) wide. **£300-£500** *C*

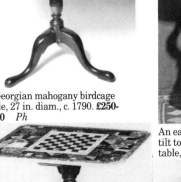

A walnut and pietra dura tripod table, the marble top inlaid with a chess board contained by a broad band of geometric specimen marbles, English, possibly Torquay, 28½ by 30 by 21½ in. (72 by 76 by 55 cm.), late 19th C. **£350-£450** *SC*

A Tunbridge ware octagonal table with Berlin woolwork border, c. 1875. **£500-600** *SA*

A pedestal table with brown and grey variegated marble top, 21 in. diam., c. 1830. **£175-200** *CDE*

An unusual George III rosewood tripod stand, on a ringed baluster above a cluster column support, probably Colonial, 2 ft. 5 in. high by 1 ft. 1 in. wide (74 by 33 cm.), late 18th/early 19th C. **£300-400** *S*

An 18th C. mahogany octagonal top table with birdcage fitting, 33 in. wide, c. 1760. **£2,500-2,900** *CC*

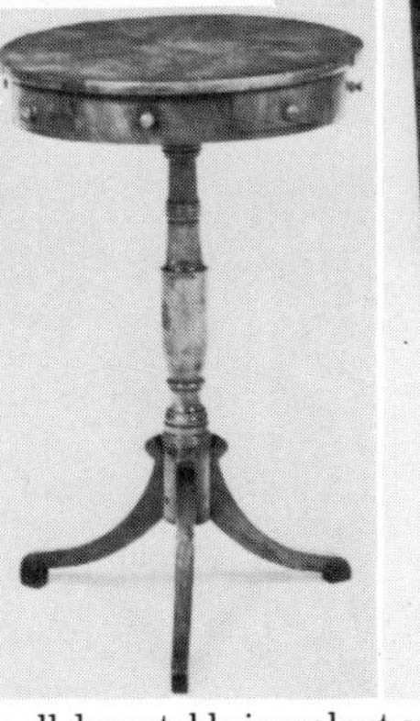

A small drum table in walnut and fruitwood, the veneered top inlaid with a Maltese cross, possibly American, 2 ft. 3 in. high by 1 ft. 6 in. diam. (68.5 by 46 cm.), c. 1780. **£500-600** *S*

A mahogany tip-top table, 17½ in. wide. **£75-85** *CDE*

A George III mahogany tripod table with an octagonal tip-up top, birdcage support, fluted stem and on 3 acanthus-carved splayed legs, carving possibly later, 26 in. high by 25 in. wide. **£800-1,000** *S*

A George III Manx mahogany table. **£350-400** *DWB*

A mahogany occasional table, 23 in. square, c. 1800. **£200-250** *Ph*

A mahogany pedestal table, 16½ in. wide, c. 1820. **£200-250** *HB*

A William IV rosewood occasional table, the circular marble top with coloured pietra dura border, 19½ in. diam. **£350-400** *M*

An unusual pair of carved giltwood centre tables, on melusine feet, 2 ft. 4 in. high by 2 ft. 3 in. wide (71 by 69 cm.), the tops early 18th C., the bases c. 1840. **£1,500-1,800** *S*

A pedestal table veneered with a cube parquetry of walnut, rosewood, mahogany and other woods, 2 ft. 3 in. high, c. 1835. **£700-800** *S*

An Italian black limestone centre table inlaid with specimen marbles and semi-precious stones, 30½ in. (77.5 cm.) wide, mid 19th C. **£1,800-2,400** *C*

A late 18th C. mahogany adjustable reading table, 20 in. wide, c. 1790. **£500-650** *CC*

A walnut occasional table with burr-walnut top, 24 in. diam., c. 1860. **£240-280** *CDE*

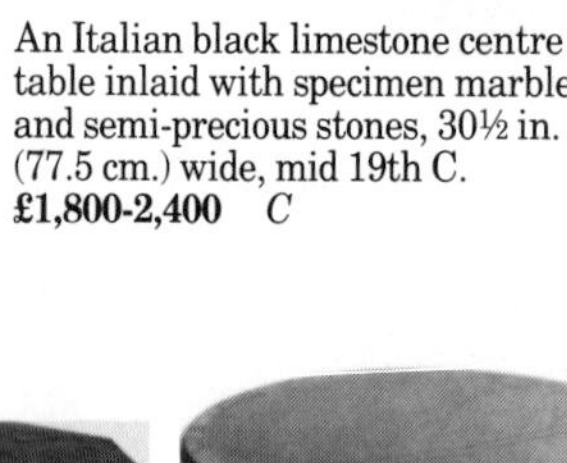

An occasional table with marquetry panel, 23½ in. diam., c. 1860. **£240-280** *CDE*

A Dutch satinwood table, quarter-veneered and centred by a lacquer roundel within double crossbandir and line inlay, 2 ft. 8¼ in. high by 2 ft. 6¾ in. diam. (71.5 by 68 cm.), c. 1795. **£1,200-1,400** *S*

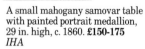

A Victorian rosewood occasional table, 18½ in. diam. **£85-95** *CDE*

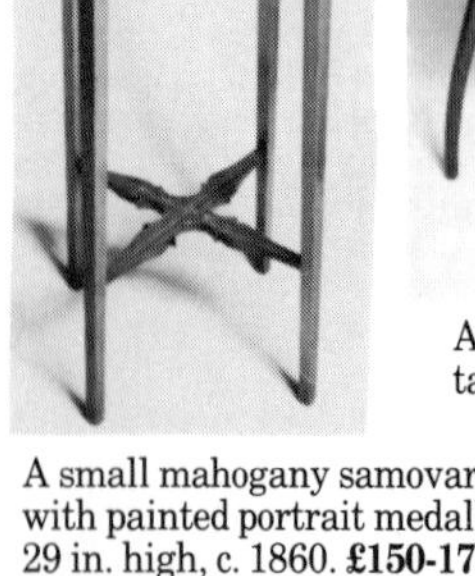

A small mahogany samovar table with painted portrait medallion, 29 in. high, c. 1860. **£150-175** *IHA*

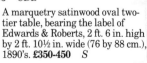

A marquetry satinwood oval two-tier table, bearing the label of Edwards & Roberts, 2 ft. 6 in. high by 2 ft. 10½ in. wide (76 by 88 cm.), 1890's. **£350-450** *S*

A good mahogany and marquetry tray top centre table with an oval bevel plate glazed tray contained by a pierced gallery with cast handles, all inlaid with roundels and ribbon entwined garria, stamped R 1774, possibly Gillows, 36½ by 29 in (93 by 74 cm.), late 19th C. **£500-600** *SC*

A parquetry gueridon in the Louis XV style inlaid with yew and fitted with a drawer in the shaped frieze, 16½ in. (42 cm.) wide. **£650-800** *C*

A mahogany occasional table with boxwood stringing, 15 in. diam., c. 1910. **£75-85** *TA*

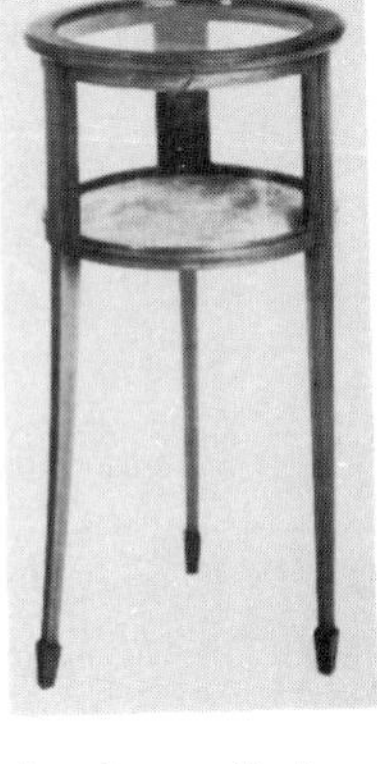

A mahogany display table, 35 by 19 in. (89 by 48 cm.), 1890's. **£350-400** *S*

A kingwood and marquetry occasional table, 31 by 19 in. (79 by 49 cm.), c. 1880. **£1,400-£1,600** *S*

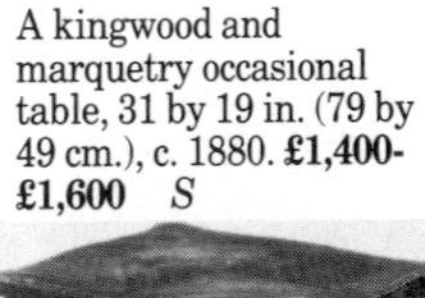

A French occasional table with rouge marble top, c. 1790. **£350-£400** *BP*

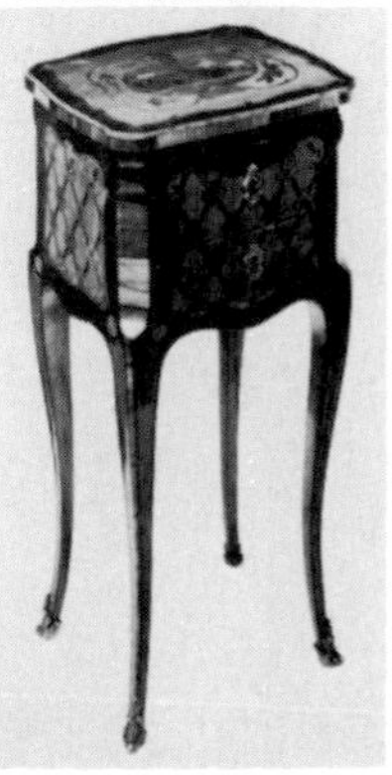

An amaranth, tulipwood and marquetry table en chiffoniere with inlaid serpentine top, stamped J.F. Oeben J.M.E., 12¼ in. (31 cm.) wide. **£1,350-1,450** *C*

A Louis XV marquetry table, the oval top inlaid with a pastoral scene, 2 ft. 4 in. high by 2 ft. 1 in. wide (71 by 63 cm.), c. 1760. **£4,500-£5,000** *S*

A gilt-bronze mounted kingwood table ambulante with a concave frieze drawer, with key, 29 in. high by 18 in. wide (74 by 46 cm.), c. 1900. **£1,000-£1,200** *S*

A tulipwood occasional table, the serpentine top quarter-veneered and crossbanded above a side door applied throughout with borders of gilt-bronze cast with leaves, 27½ by 16½ in. (70 by 42 cm.), c. 1880. **£700-800** *S*

A Louis XVI marquetry table en chiffoniere on square tapering feet, inlaid with sprays of flowers, stamped Topino, 2 ft. 3 in. high by 1 ft. ½ in. wide (69 by 32 cm.), c. 1780. **£1,800-2,000** *S*

A Louis XV kingwood and marquetry table en chiffoniere, 17 in. wide. **£1,800-2,000** *PWC*

A tulipwood and marquetry occasional table in the French taste with ormolu-bordered eared serpentine top inlaid with a basket of flowers on a sycamore ground, 21 in. (53 cm.) wide. **£1,000-1,200** *C*

A rosewood and satinwood vide poche, inlaid with a diamond and polka dot trellis, 71 by 73 cm., c. 1860-80. **£1,700-1,900** *S*
Possibly made in England by Donald Ross of Ealing.

A good Louis XV-style kingwood tulipwood and marquetry vide poche, the shaped top inlaid within a metal bound border, fitted frieze drawer, bearing a Waring and Gillow ivorene plaque and stamped no. 1443, 29 by 26 in. (74 by 66 cm.), late 19th/early 20th C. **£750-850** *SC*

A good Louis XV tulipwood and kingwood table en chiffoniere, 16 in. wide. **£1,650-1,850** *PWC*

A mahogany occasional table, 35 in. long, c. 1920's. **£155-175** *CDE*

A French display table, with various coloured woods, c. 1840. **£1,600-1,800** *SA*

A japanned tray top table in George II style with a moulded drawer in the frieze, painted with chinoiserie throughout, 2 ft. 3½ in. by 2 ft. 11 in. (70 by 89 cm.), c. 1920. **£700-800** *S*

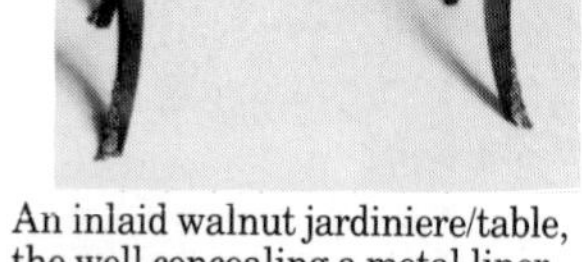

An inlaid walnut jardiniere/table, the well concealing a metal liner, 24 in. wide, c. 1870. **£370-410** *TA*

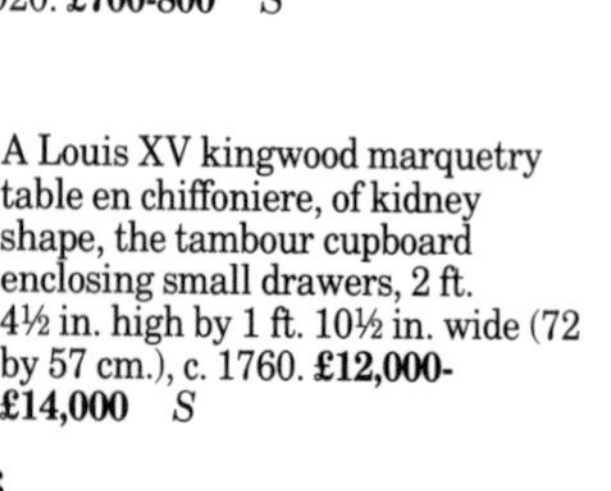

A Louis XV kingwood marquetry table en chiffoniere, of kidney shape, the tambour cupboard enclosing small drawers, 2 ft. 4½ in. high by 1 ft. 10½ in. wide (72 by 57 cm.), c. 1760. **£12,000-£14,000** *S*

An Edwardian mahogany bijouterie table, the top with all over shaped and glazed panels on turned slender legs, 2 ft. wide. **£200-225** *DDM*

A mid Georgian mahogany occasional table, the top inlaid with ebonised and boxwood chequered lines, 28 in. (71 cm.) wide. **£750-£950** *C*

A pair of Regency mahogany occasional tables with bowed tops, each with a frieze drawer inlaid with boxwood lines, 27 in. (68.5 cm.) wide. **£4,600-5,000** *C*

A gilt-metal and mahogany 2-tier table, 23 in. high, c. 1840. **£350-£400** *CC*

An Edwardian mahogany occasional table with rectangular double-flap top with Art Nouveau-style inlaid flower decoration, 42 in. wide. **£300-350** *DSH*

A gilt-bronze circular centre table, with pink marble top, 81 by 53 cm., 1870's. **£500-£600** *S*

A Louis XVI tulipwood table signed P. Defriche, 2 drawers in the frieze, one with a secret drawer below, altered, the maker's mark is on the back of the left-hand drawer, 2 ft. 3 in. high by 2 ft. 1½ in. wide (69 by 65 cm.), c. 1780. **£2,000-£2,500** *S*

Pierre Defriche, received Master 1766.

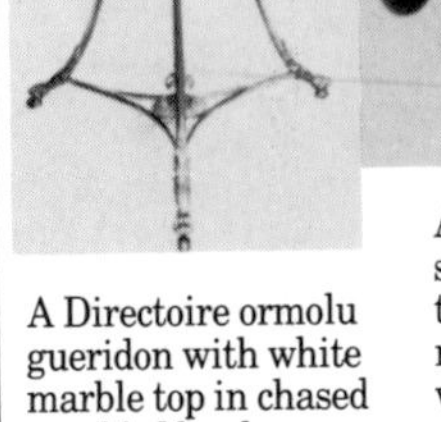
A Directoire ormolu gueridon with white marble top in chased moulded border, 19¼ in. (48.9 cm.) wide. **£1,700-2,000** *C*

An 18th C. Dutch walnut and seaweed marquetry side table in the William and Mary taste, the rectangular top radially veneered with a symmetrical design composed of oyster veneers and panels of foliate scroll stems, having a moulded acacia border and containing a similarly inlaid frieze drawer, 85 cm. **£900-1,000** *P*

A satinwood occasional table, painted with a musical trophy and swags of flowers, 2 ft. 3¾ in. by 2 ft. 3¼ in. (70.5 by 69.5 cm.), c. 1890. **£550-650** *S*

A George III rosewood occasional table in the French taste, the tray top with a hinged flap, 26½ in. (67 cm.) wide. **£1,500-1,800** *C*

A mahogany occasional table, 21 in. square, c. 1910. **£30-40** *Ph*

A Georgian crossbanded and inlaid rosewood occasional table, the top drawer fitted with writing slope and pen tray, 20½ by 16½ in. **£650-£750** *BW*

A rare George III mahogany triangular 'spider leg' table, 2 ft. 5½ in. high by 1 ft. 11 in. wide (74 by 55 cm.), c. 1755. **£450-500** *S*

A George III mahogany 'spider leg table, width open 31 in., c. 1760. **£1,200-1,300** *HB*

A mahogany gateleg spider table, the top on spindled columns and splayed down curved legs with cross stretchers, 26½ in., 19th C. **£400-500** *CSK*

A set of George III satinwood quartetto tables, inlaid with kingwood, 2 ft. 5½ in. high by 1 ft. 6½ in. wide (75 by 47 cm.), c. 1800. **£5,000-6,000** *S*

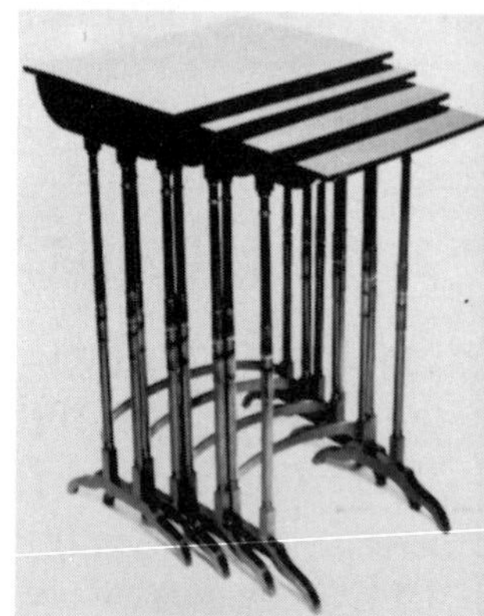
A set of George III rosewood quartetto tables, 19 in. wide, c. 1800. **£1,600-1,700** *HB*

A mahogany trio of tables, 20 in., c. 1820. **£275-325** *BP*

A nest of Regency rosewood tables with beaded and crossbanded tops, 20 in. wide, c. 1820. **£1,400-£1,700** *CC*

A Victorian papier mâché and ebonised nest of 4 tables, with shaped papier mâché tops, all on turned frames and splayed feet, 24 to 15 in. **£1,700-1,900** *CSK*

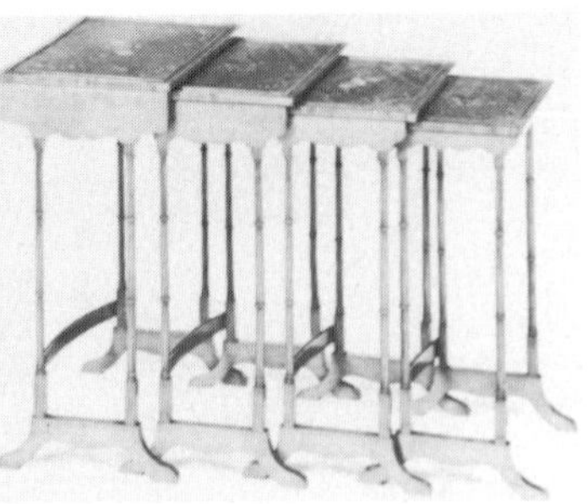
A nest of 4 satinwood side tables, each quarter-veneered and painted with swags of flowers, the largest 2 ft. 4 in. by 1 ft. 8 in. (71 by 50.5 cm.), c. 1900. **£1,100-1,300** *S*

A late Victorian mahogany butler's tray table, 31 in. long. **£75-80** *CDE*

A Spanish oak table with single plank top, fitted with 3 frieze drawers with geometric incised mouldings, 58 by 24 in. (147 by 61 cm.). **£600-700** *L*

An oak cricket table, 30 in. diam., c. 1820. **£95-125** *W*

An unusual Charles II oak cricket table, the 12-sided top mounted on a star-shaped underframe, 2 ft. 3½ in. high by 2 ft. 6 in. wide (70 by 76 cm.), c. 1670. **£950-1,050** *S*

An oak cricket table, 21 in. wide, c. 1780. **£150-200** *LG*

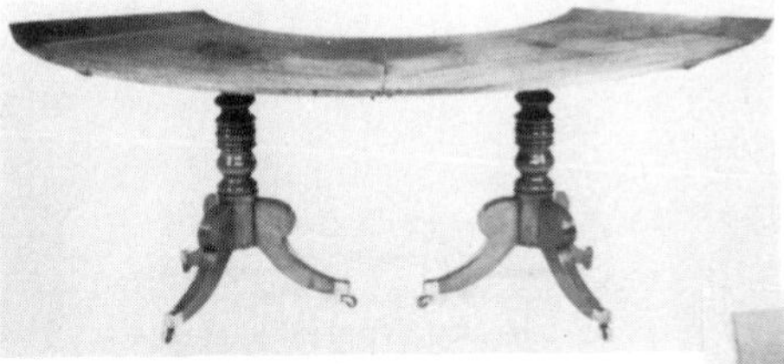

A Regency mahogany wine table, 93 in. wide (236 cm.), unextended. **£1,200-1,500** *C*

An unusual Georgian mahogany estate office table, 49½ by 36½ in. **£550-650** *PWC*

A mahogany butler's tray table, 31 in. wide, c. 1830. **£270-300** *NP*

A George III satinwood and marquetry screen table, crossbanded in mahogany and with fretwork inlaid spandrels and a rosewood crossbanding, 2 ft. 7½ in. high by 1 ft. 6 in. wide (80 by 46 cm.), c. 1770. **£4,000-5,000** *S*

An unusual Swiss table, with a rectangular hinged beechwood top above a panelled frieze with waved mouldings and marquetry panels, 2 ft. 8½ in. high by 3 ft. 6¾ in. wide (82.5 by 109 cm.), mid 17th C. **£2,000-2,200** *S*

A Pontypool metal tray table with modern stand, 28 in. wide, c. 1770. **£700-900** *CC*

A late 17th C. Dutch oak folding table, 2 ft. 5 in. high by 3 ft. 2 in. wide (74 by 97 cm.). **£1,000-1,200** *S*

A George III mahogany architect's table, the top surface rising upon double ratchets above a pull-out split leg front, 40 in. wide. **£1,000-£1,200** *B*

A Victorian walnut-veneered writing table, stamped Maple & Co., and crossbanded in tulipwood with gilt-bronze mounts, the frieze drawer inset with a porcelain plaque, 3 ft. 3 in. high by 3 ft. 5½ in. wide (100 by 106 cm.), mid 19th C. **£1,400-1,700** *S*

A walnut reading stand/table, fully adjustable, c. 1860. **£500-600** *TP*

A fine George III rosewood and satinwood architect's table, the rising easel top inlaid and crossbanded with mahogany, the frieze inlaid with ribbon-tied bead swags with a slide each side and a drawer enclosing a divided interior with baize-lined easel slide, 36 in. wide (91.5 cm.). **£10,000-12,000** *C*

A walnut writing table, the serpentine lower part with a single long drawer, on cabriole legs with gilt-bronze mounts at the knees, 3 ft. 8 in. high (112 cm.), c. 1870. **£1,000-1,200** *S*

A George III mahogany corner table with square ends and concave centre with rosewood crossbandings, 48 by 68 in. (122 by 173 cm.) diagonally. **£550-600** *L*

A George III mahogany architect's table with a fitted deep drawer with various compartments, on square chamfered legs, stamped Gibbside, 42 in. wide. **£800-1,000** *CEd*

A George III mahogany architect's table, the leather-lined top on a double ratchet support above a drawer incorporating the front section of the legs, the moulded legs with concealed columns on castors, 2 ft. 8½ in. high by 3 ft. 3 in. wide (82 by 99 cm.), c. 1765. **£1,700-£2,000** *S*

A lady's Victorian inlaid rosewood writing table, having 2 stationery drawers and 3 small bevelled mirrors over, with brass gallery, 2 ft. 11 in. **£280-340** *WSW*

A good late Victorian inlaid satinwood occasional table, inlaid with ribbon-tied husk swags, urns and foliage, 29 in. high by 24 in. diam. **£300-400** *Bea*

A Queen Anne gilt-gesso side table, the shaped frieze with trellis pattern panels, restorations, 33 in. wide (84 cm.). **£3,250-3,750** *C*

An American walnut side table on ring turned legs joined by stretchers, 2 ft. 5½ in. high by 3 ft. 8½ in. wide (75 by 113 cm.), early 18th C. with restorations. **£700-£800** *S*

A side table with grey marble top, 36 in. **£220-250** *CDE*

A good pair of mahogany side tables, in the manner of William Kent, each with a finely gadrooned and Greek key fret moulded frieze, and 2 bead and scroll foliage moulded front supports joined by a platform, 36 by 64 by 18½ in. (92 by 163 by 47 cm.), early 20th C. **£800-1,000** *SC*

An Edwardian marquetry treasure table. **£600-700** *HWO*

An oak side table, 29 in. wide, c. 1700. **£150-200** *LG*

An occasional table, 30 in. open. **£110-130** *CDE*

A small Charles I oak side table with 2 drawers, the top associated, 2 ft. 4 in. high by 2 ft. 4 in. wide (71 by 71 cm.), c. 1640. **£1,300-1,500** *S*

A George III mahogany bow-fronted dressing table with ebony stringing, 2 ft. 5 in. wide. **£575-£650** *AGr*

An early Victorian mahogany dressing table, maker's label l.h. drawer — 'T. & G. Seddon', 3 ft. 6 in. wide. **£100-125** *AGr*

A Regency mahogany side table with folding rectangular top, 36½ in. wide (93 cm.). **£500-700** *C*

A Maple & Co. walnut-veneered 5-piece bedroom suite comprising a wardrobe with foliate-carved frieze, 85 in. high by 80 in. wide, a dressing table with triple glass mirror, on cabriole legs, 31 in. high by 45 in. wide, a similar dressing table, a single bedstead and bedside cupboard. **£600-700** *Bea*

A William and Mary oak and walnut side table, the 2 plank top with end cleats above a walnut-veneered frieze drawer, 2 ft. 3¾ in. high by 2 ft. 11¼ in. wide (70 by 90 cm.), c. 1695. **£1,900-2,200** *S*

A pair of walnut-veneered centre tables, tops inlaid with a broad band of floral marquetry, 28½ in. high by 40½ in. wide, late 19th C. **£1,100-1,300** *S*

An early Victorian rosewood centre table raised on solid trestle end supports joined by a turned stretcher, 40 in. (102 cm.). **£250-£300** *L*

A rosewood and boulle centre table, the crossbanded top with border inlaid in brass and pewter, centred by a copper oval, 41 in. wide (104 cm.), 17th C., Flemish or German. **£2,750-3,500** *C*

A fine coromandel wood teapoy with boxwood inlay, fitted with original caddies and mixing bowls, 16 in. wide, c. 1800. **£2,500-2,800** *CC*

A yew-wood teapoy, 21 in. wide, c. 1810. **£1,000-1,250** *CDE*

A William IV rosewood teapoy, the interior fitted with 4 hinged lidded compartments and 2 glass mixing bowls (not original), 2 ft. 6 in. high by 1 ft. 5¼ in. wide (76 by 44 cm.), c. 1835. **£400-500** *S*

An early 19th C. oval papier mâché tray on later stand, 33 in. wide. **£350-500** *RD*

The early trays have raised edge.

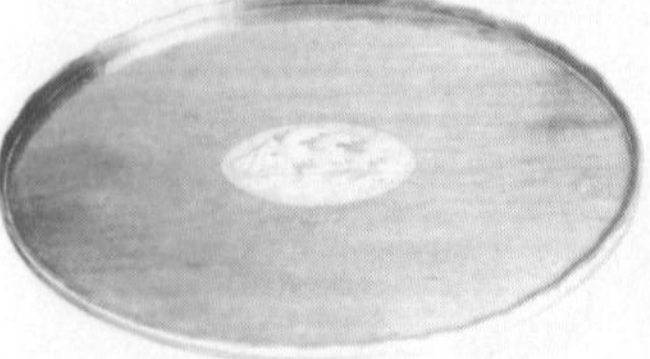

A mahogany tray, 28 in. **£100-£150** *HB*

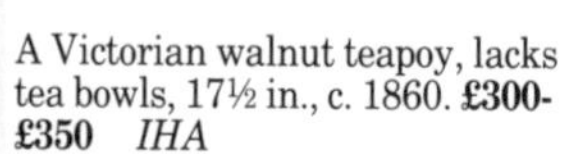

A Victorian walnut teapoy, lacks tea bowls, 17½ in., c. 1860. **£300-£350** *IHA*

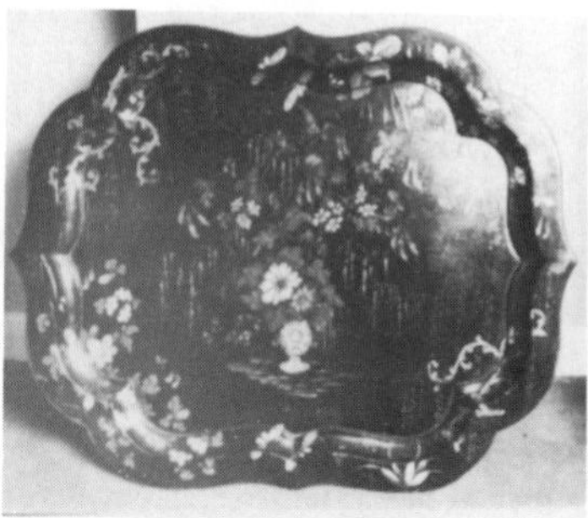

A black papier mâché tray, 32 in. wide, c. 1840. **£175-225** *RD*

A Victorian papier mâché tray with gilt scalloped border, the reverse inscribed Southan Hall and branded B. Walton & Co. Warranted — 19½ in. **£350-400** *CSK*

A graduated set of 4 early Victorian papier mâché rectangular trays, gilt with flower sprays and insects on maroon ground, 30¼, 26½, 16¾ and 15 in. **£1,800-2,000** *CSK*

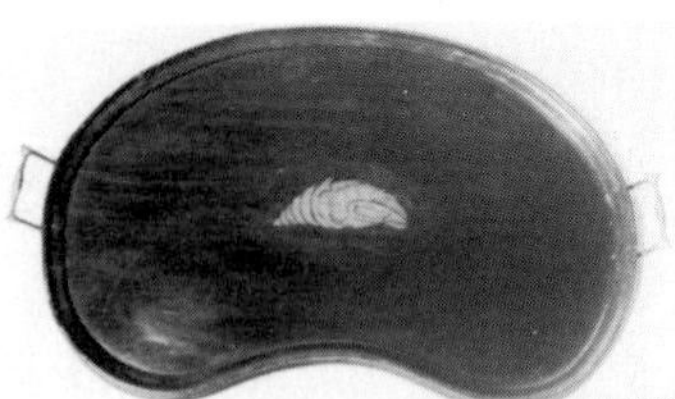

An Edwardian inlaid mahogany tray. **£60-80** *FF*

A faded mahogany washstand, 30 in., c. 1780. **£190-240** *CDE*

A small mahogany washstand, cut down to 26 in. **£180-220** *HB*

A mid 18th C. mahogany washstand, 30 in. high. **£350-400** *CC*

A George III bowfront corner washstand with double flap-over top. **£500-600** *WSW*

A pair of George III mahogany corner washstands with frieze drawers and stretcher bases, 27 in. wide. **£600-700** *GM*

A Regency black and gold lacquer whatnot, 18 in. wide (46 cm.). **£1,000-1,200** *C*

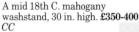

A pair of early 19th C. rosewood whatnots, 31 in. high. **£900-1,000** *HB*

A mahogany washstand, 32 in., c. 1820. **£250-300** *HB*

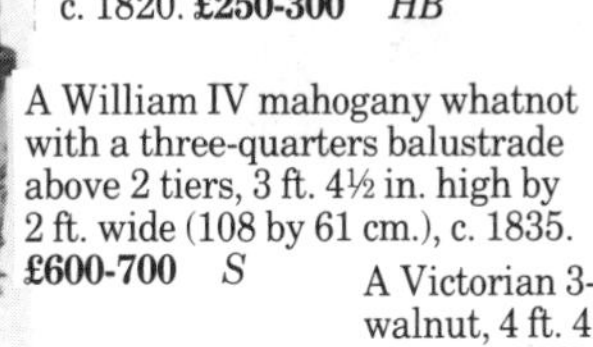

A William IV mahogany whatnot with a three-quarters balustrade above 2 tiers, 3 ft. 4½ in. high by 2 ft. wide (108 by 61 cm.), c. 1835. **£600-700** *S*

A Victorian 3-shelf whatnot in walnut, 4 ft. 4 in. wide. **£500-£600** *JMW*

A Victorian satinwood and mahogany crossbanded canterbury whatnot with gilt-metal mounts and gallery, drawer stamped A J Owen & Co., New Bond Street. **£1,400-1,600** *CSK*

A pair of 19th C. small brass and leather covered whatnots, 16 in. wide. **£350-400** *CC*

A Victorian teak whatnot, 45 in. high, c. 1890. **£150-200** *Ph*

A Victorian walnut 4-tier whatnot with pierced gallery over serpentine shaped stages and baluster supports, 22 in. wide. **£225-275** *DS*

An Edwardian ebonised whatnot, 33 in. wide, c. 1910. **£175-200** *Ph*

A Victorian walnut whatnot/ cabinet, 24 in. wide, c. 1880. **£275-£325** *Ph*

A George III mahogany oval wine cooler, 22½ in. wide by 20 in. high, c. 1770. **£1,000-1,400** *RD*

A mahogany Chippendale period wine cooler, 28 in. wide. **£1,300-£1,500** *HB*

A mahogany brass oval jardiniere, mounted with pierced handles on cabriole legs and claw and ball feet, zinc liner, 27 in. wide. **£500-550** *CEd*

A George III mahogany brass-bound wine cooler, 18½ in. diam. (47 cm.). **£1,500-1,800** *C*

A George III open cellaret of brass bound oval form, carried on plain splayed rectangular legs, brass lion handles, 25 in. **£2,000-2,250** *LE*

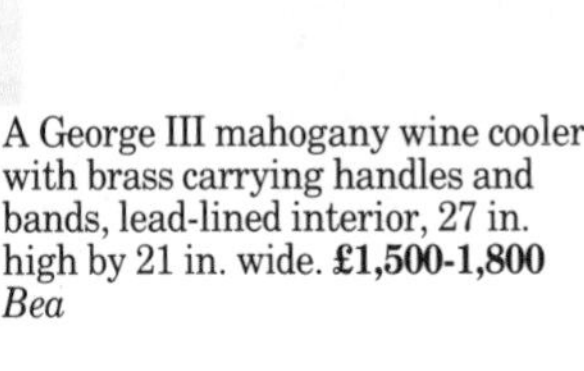

A George III mahogany wine cooler with brass carrying handles and bands, lead-lined interior, 27 in. high by 21 in. wide. **£1,500-1,800** *Bea*

A George III mahogany hexagonal brass bound cellaret with carrying handles on the sides, 2 ft. 4 in. high by 1 ft. 6 in. wide (72 by 46 cm.), c. 1765. **£1,100-1,300** *S*

A George III mahogany and brass bound cellaret, lead lining and drainage plug, 28 in. high. **£1,500-1,600** *LE*

A George III octagonal mahogany cellaret, 2 ft. 3 in. by 1 ft. 5 in. (69 by 43 cm.), c. 1790. **£400-500** *S*

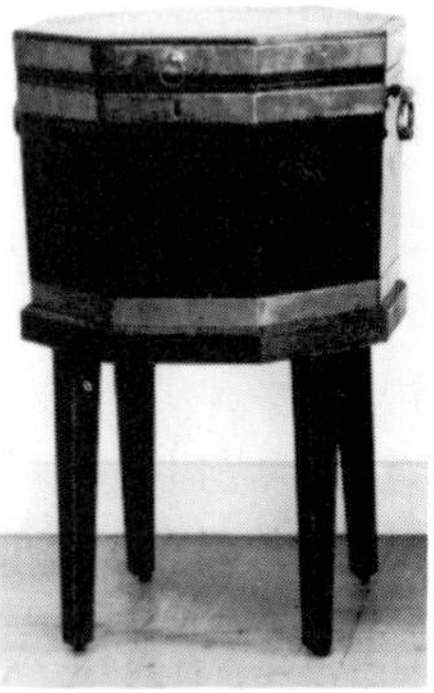

An 18th C. mahogany octagonal brass bound wine cooler with brass carrying handles and shell inlay to the lid. **£700-800** *RBB*

A carved mahogany wine cooler in George III style, late 19th/early 20th C. **£1,450-1,650** *S*

A late Georgian mahogany cellaret inlaid with boxwood lines, the arched tambour panel lid above 2 doors on bracket feet, 21 in. **£500-£550** *CSK*

A Regency mahogany shaped bow-fronted cellaret crossbanded in kingwood, boxwood and ebony stringing and brass beading, having later zinc lining, 2 ft. 4 in. wide by 1 ft. 6 in. deep by 1 ft. 8 in. high. **£2,250-2,500** *AGr*

An oblong 'Sheraton' mahogany cellaret inlaid with boxwood lines and having brass carrying handles. **£550-650** *JSm*

A Regency mahogany sarcophagus-shaped cellaret, 25 in. wide (63.5 cm.). **£1,100-1,500** *C*

An English mahogany wine cooler with dummy drawers, 21 in. high, c. 1800. **£650-700** *HB*

A fine quality Regency period cellaret in faded mahogany, the lifting surface above shaped compartment with exposed dovetailing, the lions mask brass carriers and fretted feet being original, 18½ in. wide by 18 in. deep by 17½ in. high, c. 1820. **£400-£460** *HAL*

A French Empire mahogany sarcophagus wine cooler, with laurel swags, ram masks and brass lion mask and ring handles, 26 in. **£600-700** *GSP*

A pair of George III mahogany plate pails, the coopered brass bound bodies with brass loop handles, one distressed, 1 ft. 5½ in. high (44 cm.), c. 1770. **£500-600** *SI*

An oval wine cooler with brass binding and classical design handles, the stand carved with scallops and scrollwork, 2 ft. **£400-£500** *RBB*

A mahogany wine cooler of sarcophagus form, the interior fitted with 5 foil lined compartments, each having a slightly domed cover, c. 1825. **£350-£400** *KHD*

An 18th C. brass-bound oak bucket with original red painted interior, 13½ in. diam. **£200-250** *CC*

A George III mahogany peat bucket of coopered construction with 2 brass bands and a brass ring handle, 1 ft. 2 in. high (36 cm.). **£300-400** *SI*

A mid Georgian brass-bound mahogany plate bucket, 15 in. diam. (38 cm.); and a mid Georgian mahogany brass-bound peat bucket, 15 in. diam. (38 cm.). **£1,750-2,250** *C*

A brass-bound oak bucket, 12 in. diam., c. 1830. **£60-65** *MPA*

A Georgian mahogany plate bucket, brass bound with swing handle and brass liner, 15 in. tall by 14 in. diam. **£650-700** *M*

An extremely important pair of George III mahogany and brass-bound ribbed buckets, 17 in. high. **£2,500-3,000** *GM*

A late 18th C. brass-bound mahogany oval bucket, 14½ in. wide, c. 1780. **£350-400** *CC*

A mid Georgian brass-bound mahogany oval bottle carrier, 15½ in. wide (39 cm.). **£1,500-£1,800** *C*

An early 19th C. plate bucket. **£400-450** *HWO*

An early Victorian leather bucket with copper rim, 9½ in. diam. **£55-£60** *NP*

A miniature Dutch walnut and marquetry bureau cabinet inlaid throughout with vases of flowers and floral sprays, the piano front enclosing short drawers, the panel below enclosing 4 long drawers and on claw feet, 37 in. high by 21 in. wide. **£900-1,000** *Bea*

A late Victorian small chest of drawers with porcelain handles, 9 in. high. **£55-60** *HA*

A mahogany apprentice piece chest of drawers with brushing slide, 17 in. high, c. 1820. **£200-250** *BP*

A mahogany commode apprentice piece with ivory escutcheon, 11 in., c. 1800. **£100-125** *LG*

A Dutch kettle warmer, satinwood ground within a partridgewood banding, the interior with brass liner, 1 ft. 9½ in. high by 11¼ in. wide (55 by 28 cm.), c. 1795. **£950-£1,100** *S*

A walnut and marquetry linen press with 5 drawers on bun feet, one replaced, inlaid throughout, Dutch, 75 by 33 in. (191 by 84 cm.), late 18th C. **£1,250-1,500** *SC*

A Louis XVI-style set of oak 3-tier bed steps on cabriole supports, 23 in. **£750-850** *CSK*

Regency mahogany library steps with graduated treads, 104 in. high by 23 in. wide (264 by 58.5 cm.). **£3,250-3,750** *C*

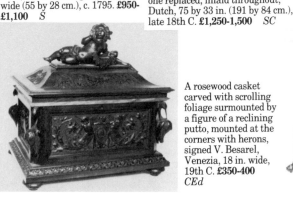

A rosewood casket carved with scrolling foliage surmounted by a figure of a reclining putto, mounted at the corners with herons, signed V. Besarel, Venezia, 18 in. wide, 19th C. **£350-400** *CEd*

A fine set of Regency mahogany library steps, 7 ft. 11 in. high (241 cm.), c. 1810. **£5,000-6,000** *S*

A good Waring and Gillow 'Louis XVI'-style bedroom suite comprising 6 pieces, all parcel gilt and painted in Wedgwood blue and variously bearing Waring and Gillow plaques; and a pair of very similar side chairs, each with a squab cushion, 20th C. **£750-900** *SC*

A Scandinavian pine spinning wheel in working condition, 37 in. high, c. 1840. **£125-175** *W*

An elm spinning wheel, 36 in. high, c. 1880. **£70-90** *BP*

A carved oak Victorian gong, 35 in. high, c. 1860. **£100-125** *NP*

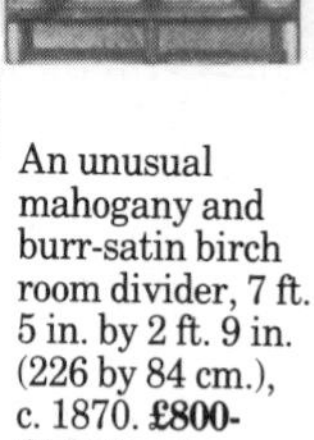

An unusual mahogany and burr-satin birch room divider, 7 ft. 5 in. by 2 ft. 9 in. (226 by 84 cm.), c. 1870. **£800-£1,000** *S*

This unusual piece of panelling was originally part of Queen Victoria's state room from HRH Yacht Osborne.

An English oak door frame surrounded by linenfold panels, and the upright posts of the panelled frame decorated with pilasters and Gothic tracery, overall 10 ft. 2 in. high by 7 ft. 2 in. wide (300 by 210 cm.), c. 1500. **£3,750-4,000** *S*

A pair of giltwood corner shelves, 135 by 71 cm., end 19th C. **£700-£800** *S*

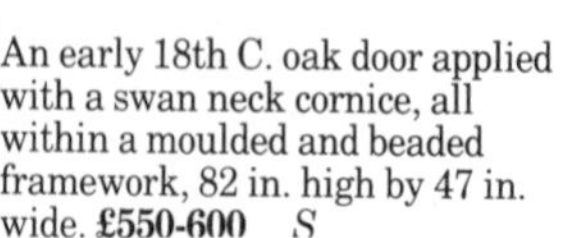

A late 19th C. Gothic-style oak pulpit with 4 steps leading to hexagonal stand with Gothic arch, pillar and quatrefoil decoration, 85 in. high. **£450-500** *DSH*

A rare pinewood prison door, inside reinforced with iron straps, the outside entirely covered with iron sheets, small grille with separate iron door in the arch, doorknockers on either side, 175 by 95 cm., 16th C. **£5,200-5,500** *SZ*

An early 18th C. oak door applied with a swan neck cornice, all within a moulded and beaded framework, 82 in. high by 47 in. wide. **£550-600** *S*

A George III period mantelpiece in pinewood, the carved shelf mould above frieze decorated by carved urns, paterae and fluted panels supported on jambs with carved astragal moulding, 65½ in. wide by 6 in. deep by 56 in. high, c. 1790, minor restorations. **£1,200-1,800** *HAL*

A fine George II painted pine fireplace, 5 ft. 5 in. high by 6 ft. 11 in. wide (165 by 211 cm.), c. 1740. **£4,000-5,000** *S*

An oak fire surround with inverted breakfront carved moulded cornice 7 ft. 3 in. wide (218 by 221 cm.), the opening 4 ft. 4½ in. high by 4 ft. ½ in. wide (133 by 123 cm.), constructed in the 19th C. using 16th and 17th C. components. **£1,800-2,200** *S*

Make the most of Miller's

When buying or selling, it must always be remembered that prices can be greatly affected by the condition of any piece. Unless otherwise stated, all goods shown in Miller's are of good merchantable quality, and the valuations given reflect this fact.
Pieces offered for sale in exceptionally fine condition or in poor condition may reasonably be expected to be priced considerably higher or lower respectively than the estimates given herein.

A fine Italian carriage body, the leather top outlined with large and small brass headed studs, the back painted with a coat of arms, the interior upholstered and covered in red velvet damask, 5 ft. 8 in. high by 5 ft. 3½ in. wide (173 by 161 cm.), c. 1750. **£5,500-6,500** *S*

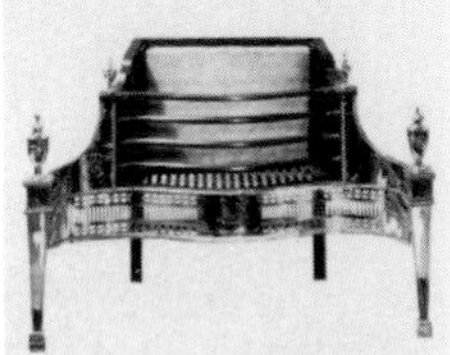

A good George III period firegrate with serpentine steel front above pierced fretted beaded chased brass apron mounted on elegant square section tapering chased legs with finials and spade feet, 36 in. wide by 17 in. deep by 22½ in. high, c. 1800, firebrick and back legs renewed. **£800-1,000** *HAL*

A pine bed (head only shown) with original sides and slats, 4 ft. 6 in. wide, c. 1840. **£200-250** *AL*

A Scandinavian pine extending bed in 3 sections, opens to 6 ft. long, c. 1800. **£145-200** *W*

An 18th C. Irish bookcase, 6 ft. 6 in. by 4 ft. 6 in. by 1 ft. 6 in. **£550-£650** *Ad*

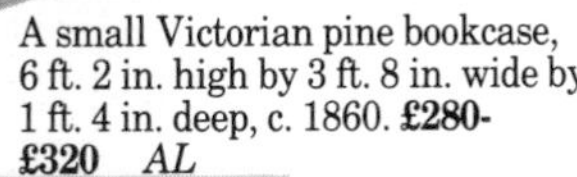

A small Victorian pine bookcase, 6 ft. 2 in. high by 3 ft. 8 in. wide by 1 ft. 4 in. deep, c. 1860. **£280-£320** *AL*

A pair of Victorian pine hall chairs, c. 1850. **£100-120** *AL*

An elm and beech kitchen chair. **£20-25** *WHA*

A Tiverton chair, beech with elm seat, with contemporary tin repairs. **£60-70** *AL*

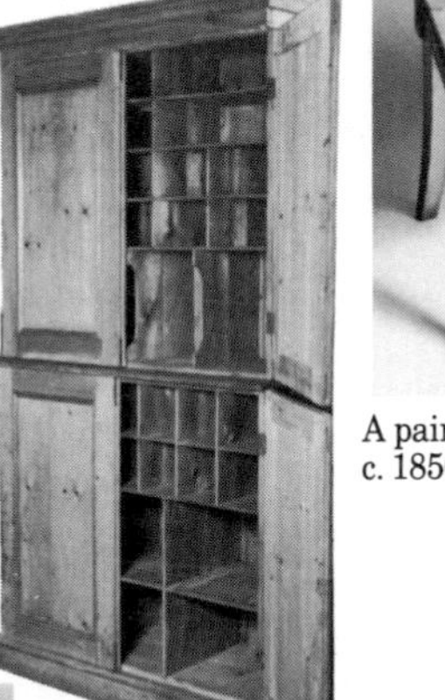

A Georgian pine filing cabinet, 7 ft. ½ in. tall by 4 ft. 6 in. wide, c. 1750. **£300-350** *AL*

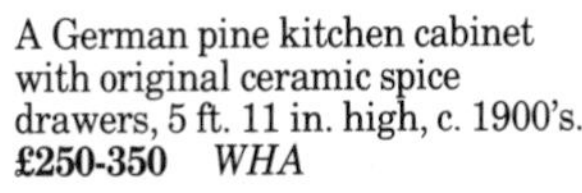

A German pine kitchen cabinet with original ceramic spice drawers, 5 ft. 11 in. high, c. 1900's. **£250-350** *WHA*

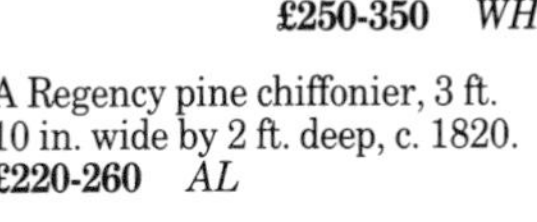

A Regency pine chiffonier, 3 ft. 10 in. wide by 2 ft. deep, c. 1820. **£220-260** *AL*

An elm and beech kitchen chair. **£20-25** *WHA*

A set of 3 pine chairs, c. 1850. **£90-£120** *W*

A 19th C. beech bar back carver. **£35-45** *PM*

A set of 4 beech kitchen chairs with cut down legs. **£85-100** *PM*

A barrel backed pine settle, 6 ft. wide, c. 1840. **£325-375** *AL*

An elm stool, 21 in. high, c. 1880. **£18-25** *W*

A pine stool, 18 in. diam., 12 in. high, c. 1860. **£30-40** *AL*

A 19th C. pine stool. **£18-22** *AH*

A pine dome top Scandinavian coffer, all original iron, c. 1800. **£145-200** *W*

A small pine chest, with original ironwork, 2 ft. wide, c. 1850. **£45-£65** *W*

A dome pine child's box with original ironwork, 18½ in. long, c. 1860. **£30-38** *MPA*

A 19th C. pine chest, 3 ft. 2 in. **£60-£70** *WHA*

An early pine chest of drawers with original knobs and wooden escutcheons, 3 ft. wide, c. 1780. **£120-140** *AL*

A rare South German or Swiss pine painted coffer, 4 ft. 8 in. wide, mid 17th C. **£2,500-3,000** *RVA*

An early pine chest, some damage to mouldings, 3 ft. 10 in. wide, c. 1750. **£130-160** *AL*

A German painted pine chest, 3 ft. 9 in., c. 1852. **£75-100** *WHA*

A pine chest with well concealed secret drawers, 2 ft. 11 in. wide, c. 1860. **£45-60** *Far*

A 19th C. mule chest with rising top and 2 drawers under, 2 ft. 4 in. wide by 4 ft. 5 in. long by 2 ft. 8 in. tall. **£295-340** *PM*

An unusual pine chest, divided top, original locks, 4 ft. wide, c. 1820. **£220-260** *AL*

A domed painted pine German chest, 2 ft. 7 in. wide, c. 1860. **£55-£75** *WHA*

A German painted pine dome top chest, 4 ft. 2 in., dated 1829. **£175-£200** *WHA*

A pine mule chest with wooden hinges to lid, 3 ft. 3 in. wide, c. 1790. **£95-150** *W*

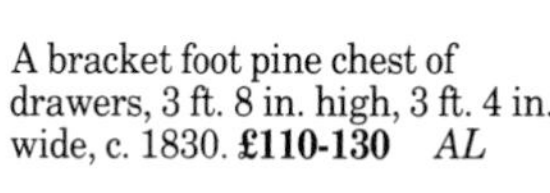

A bracket foot pine chest of drawers, 3 ft. 8 in. high, 3 ft. 4 in. wide, c. 1830. **£110-130** *AL*

A Regency pine chest of drawers with original handles, 2 ft. 9 in. wide, 3 ft. 4 in. high, c. 1835. **£160-£180** *AL*

A pine chest of drawers, 2 ft. 9 in. wide, c. 1860. **£95-125** *W*

A mid Victorian chest of drawers with pot space, 2 ft. 10 in. wide, c. 1860. **£125-175** *W*

A pine chest of drawers, 3 ft. 2 in. wide, c. 1890. **£95-150** *W*

A small pine commode, black china handles, 2 ft. 2 in. wide, c. 1860. **£90-100** *AL*

A Victorian pine splashback chest, 3 ft. 3 in. wide, c. 1840. **£130-160** *W*

A pine flour barrel made to resemble a chest of drawers, 2 ft. 2 in. wide by 2 ft. 6 in. high, c. 1850. **£70-80** *AL*

A pine flight of drawers with original handles, 2 ft. 8 in. by 9 in. by 10 in., c. 1850. **£65-75** *AL*

A Victorian pine chest of drawers with shaped back and scrolled ends, 2 ft. 7 in. wide by 1 ft. 4 in. deep by 2 ft. 10 in. high. **£95-110** *AH*

A tall pine chest of drawers o turned feet, original brass escutcheons, 3 ft. 1 in. wide, c. 1840. **£100-160** *W*

A low pine chest of drawers, 3 5 in. wide, c. 1860. **£85-125** *W*

A pine chest of drawers, 2 ft. 8 in wide. **£75-110** *WHA*

A small pine chest of drawers, 1 ft 6 in. wide, c. 1880. **£38-42** *AL*

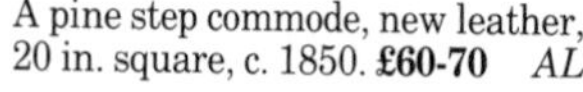

A pine step commode, new leather, 20 in. square, c. 1850. **£60-70** *AL*

A pine commode, 2 ft. 1 in. wide.
£75-100 *WHA*

A Scandinavian commode with original fittings, lift-up top, 20 in. wide, c. 1890. **£60-80** *W*

An astragal glazed, barrel-backed pine corner cupboard, 6 ft. 8 in. high, c. 1840. **£400-500** *AL*

A pine press table with splay legs, 20 in. square, c. 1850. **£70-80** *AL*

A Scandinavian pine commode table, 18 in. wide, c. 1890. **£55-75** *W*

A Scandinavian commode, 19½ in. wide, c. 1890. **£55-65** *W*

A pine proving cupboard, tin lined, 3 ft. 4 in. wide by 3 ft. 8 in. high, c. 1840. **£100-130** *AL*

A pine proving cupboard, back missing, 3 ft. 10 in. wide, c. 1840. **£110-130** *AL*

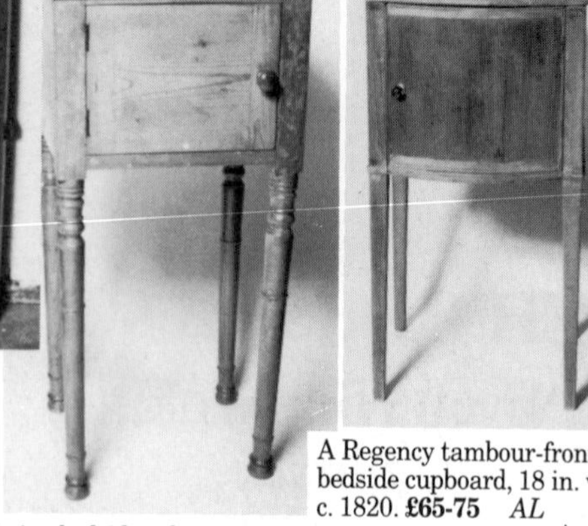
A Regency tambour-fronted bedside cupboard, 18 in. wide, c. 1820. **£65-75** *AL*

A pine bedside cabinet, 15 in. square, 2 ft. 6 in. high, c. 1860. **£55-£65** *AL*

A pine corner cupboard, with barrel back and shaped shelves, 6 ft. 7 in. high, c. 1840. **£575-650** *Ad*

A mid 19th C. pine desk/cupboard, 2 ft. 10 in. wide. **£110-150** *WHA*

A pine cupboard, 3 ft. 3½ in. wide. **£90-120** *WHA*

A pine pot cupboard, 2 ft. 6½ in. high, c. 1900. **£45-55** *W*

A pine pot cupboard, 15½ in. wide, c. 1850. **£60-80** *W*

An Irish glazed cupboard, 6 ft. 5 in. high, c. 1820. **£400-500** *Ad*

An Irish pine food cupboard with knife drawer, 6 ft. 4½ in. high, c. 1820. **£700-800** *W*

An 18th C. Irish food cupboard, 6 ft. 6 in. by 5 ft. 6 in. by 1 ft. 6 in. **£595-£650** *Ad*

A pine food cupboard, 4 ft. 2 in. wide. **£175-225** *Far*

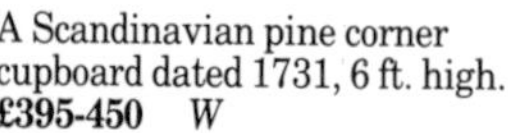
A Scandinavian pine corner cupboard dated 1731, 6 ft. high. **£395-450** *W*

Use the Index!
Because certain items might fit easily into any of a number of categories, the quickest and surest method of locating any entry is by reference to the index at the back of the book. This has been fully cross-referenced for absolute simplicity.

An Irish pine dresser in 2 sections, 6 ft. 8 in. high by 4 ft. wide, c. 1840. **£420-460** *AL*

An Irish dresser, new handles, 4 ft. wide, c. 1840. **£300-380** *AL*

An 18th C. Irish food cupboard, 6 ft. 7 in. by 5 ft. 3 in. by 1 ft. 6 in. **£595-£650** *Ad*

A French pine dresser, 6 ft. 2 in. wide, c. 1900. **£500-700** *Ad*

A pine 'chicken coop' dresser, with later top, 4 ft. 9 in. wide, c. 1850. **£1,500-1,800** *Ad*

An Austrian pot cupboard, 3 ft. by 1 ft. 6 in. by 2 ft. 8 in. high, 19th C. **£125-150** *Ad*

A late Victorian Cornish dresser, 6 ft. 6 in. high, c. 1870. **£300-375** *Ad*

A pine dresser with leaded glass, 5 ft. 8 in. wide, c. 1890. **£275-350** *W*

A large Lincolnshire pine dresser, 5 ft., c. 1880. **£475-550** *W*

A pine breakfront dresser, 4 ft. 8 in. wide. **£350-400** *Far*

A mid Victorian dresser, 7 ft. by 6 ft. 4 in. by 1 ft. 7 in. **£850-925** *Ad*

A pine glazed dresser, 4 ft. 4 in. wide, c. 1860. **£550-590** *Far*

An 18th C. Irish dresser, 6 ft. 8 in. by 4 ft. 8 in. by 1 ft. 5 in. **£525-£570** *Ad*

An 18th C. Irish dresser, 6 ft. 6 in. by 4 ft. 6 in. by 1 ft. 6 in. **£450-£495** *Ad*

A Victorian pine pedestal desk, 2 ft. deep by 4 ft. wide. **£275-325** *PM*

A Victorian pine desk, new leather top, 4 ft. 1 in. wide. **£250-300** *Far*

A Victorian pitch pine schoolteacher's desk with rising lid and cupboard below. **£95-115** *PM*

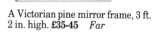

A Victorian pine mirror frame, 3 ft. 2 in. high. **£35-45** *Far*

A Victorian pine desk, hinged top, the doors hiding 2 sets of sliding trays, 4 ft. wide. **£180-220** *AL*

A pine pedestal desk, new leather and handles, 4 ft. 6 in. wide, c. 1860. **£400-480** *AL*

A pine-framed mirror, 2 ft. 10 in. wide, c. 1830. **£90-125** *Far*

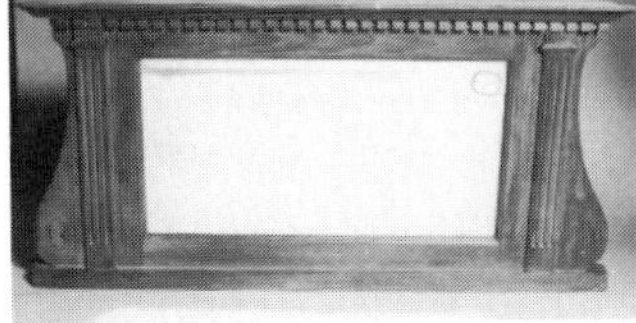
A Victorian pine overmantel mirror, 3 ft. 4 in. wide. **£30-40** *Far*

A pine-framed wallhanging mirror, 5 ft. high, c. 1890. **£75-100** *W*

A Victorian pine mirror frame, 18 in. wide. **£20-30** *Far*

A pine framed mirror in Regency style, 2 ft. 8 in. tall by 1 ft. 9 in. wide. **£85-110** *PM*

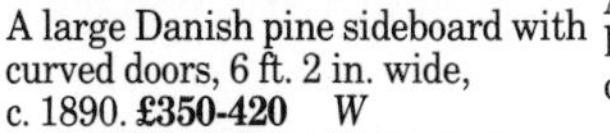
A large Danish pine sideboard with curved doors, 6 ft. 2 in. wide, c. 1890. **£350-420** *W*

A Regency pine side table, 'bamboo' legs, original handles, 3 ft. wide, c. 1820. **£70-85** *AL*

A Victorian pine chiffonier, 5 ft. 4 in. wide. **£325-375** *Ad*

A pine cricket table, 2 ft. 6 in. diam., c. 1810. **£90-100** *AL*

A Victorian pine table, 4 ft. long open, 3 ft. 7 in. wide, c. 1880. **£80-£100** *Far*

A pine side table, 2 ft. 11 in. wide, c. 1840. **£60-70** *AL*

A pine octagonal wine table, 17½ in. wide, c. 1900. **£65-95** *W*

A mid Victorian pine side table with original handles, 3 ft. 6 in. wide. **£70-100** *W*

A small Scandinavian pine drop leaf table, 3 ft. 1 in. diam., c. 1900. **£60-75** *W*

A pine side table, 2 ft. 11½ in. wide, c. 1890. **£50-70** *Far*

A 19th C. pine table, 2 ft. 11 in. diam. **£70-100** *WHA*

A Victorian pine table, 2 ft. 6 in. wide, c. 1880. **£60-70** *Far*

A pine side table, 3 ft. 3 in. **£100-£150** *WHA*

A Victorian pine side table, 3 ft. 6 in. wide, c. 1860. **£60-70** *Far*

A late Victorian pine table, 2 ft. 11 in. deep. **£65-75** *Far*

A Victorian pine drop-leaf kitchen table with one drawer, 3 ft. 6 in. wide by 1 ft. 9 in. closed and 3 ft. 3 in. extended. **£55-75** *AH*

A pine drop leaf table, 3 ft. 9 in. extended, c. 1880. **£65-85** *Far*

A Victorian pine lyre-ended library table, 3 ft. wide by 1 ft. 9 in. deep by 2 ft. 8 in. high. **£140-160** *AH*

A Victorian pine dressing table with bevelled mirror, 3 ft. wide by 1 ft. 6 in. deep by 4 ft. 10 in. high. **£65-85** *AH*

A pine dressing table, 2 ft. 6 in. wide, c. 1870. **£65-85** *W*

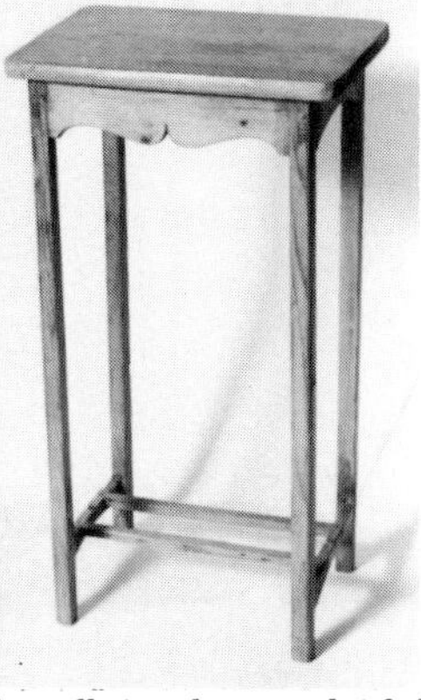

A small pine plant stand, 1 ft. by 1 ft. 2 in. by 3 ft., c. 1840. **£28-32** *AL*

A pine washstand with base drawer, 1 ft. 11 in. wide, c. 1860. **£60-90** *W*

A pine washstand, 2 ft. 7 in. wide, c. 1900. **£55-70** *Ad*

A pine washstand, 2 ft. 7 in. wide, c. 1890. **£55-75** *W*

A pine washstand, 2 ft. 11 in. wide, c. 1850. **£120-145** *W*

A marble topped washstand, 3 ft. wide. **£90-150** *WHA*

A Victorian pine washstand, 3 ft. 1 in. wide by 1 ft. 9 in. deep by 3 ft. high. **£85-105** *AH*

A pine washstand, 2 ft. 7 in. wide, c. 1870. **£55-65** *W*

A Swedish pine washstand/side cabinet, 2 ft. 8½ in. wide, c. 1890. **£160-185** *Far*

A Victorian pine washstand with tiled and shaped back, 3 ft. wide by 1 ft. 6 in. deep by 3 ft. 5 in. high. **£55-65** *AH*

An unusual pine washstand, 2 ft. 11 in. wide by 3 ft. 2 in. high, c. 1820. **£70-80** *AL*

A pine washstand, 2 ft. 4 in. wide c. 1860. **£55-60** *AL*

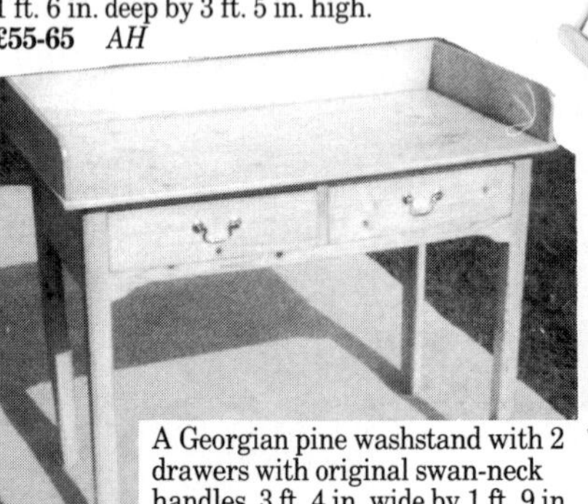

A Georgian pine washstand with 2 drawers with original swan-neck handles, 3 ft. 4 in. wide by 1 ft. 9 in. deep by 2 ft. 9 in. high. **£175-195** *AH*

One of a pair of pine washstands, 3 ft. wide, c. 1825. **£160-190** pair *AL*

A 19th C. pine wardrobe, 6 ft. 10 in. tall by 2 ft. 8 in. wide. **£215-245** *PM*

A Regency pine washstand, 3 ft. 9 in. high by 2 ft. 2 in. deep, c. 1840. **£100-130** *AL*

An Irish press, 4 ft. 10 in. wide, c. 1790. **£650-750** *Ad*

A Victorian pine wardrobe in 8 sections, original mirror, 1 ft. 8 in. deep by 4 ft. 10 in. wide by 6 ft. 6 in. high, c. 1860. **£420-460** *AL*

A 19th C. Austrian armoire, 6 ft. 8 in. by 4 ft. 9 in. by 1 ft. 8 in. **£520-£580** *Ad*

A 19th C. German armoire, 6 ft. 8 in. by 4 ft. 11 in. by 1 ft. 10 in. **£450-495** *Ad*

A pine wardrobe, original brass handles, 6 ft. 1 in. high, c. 1920. **£80-125** *W*

An Austrian armoire, 3 ft. 3 in. wide, c. 1840. **£325-375** *Ad*

A 19th C. Scandinavian cupboard with shelves, 3 ft. 9½ in. wide. **£250-300** *Ad*

A 19th C. German armoire, 7 ft. high by 6 ft. wide by 2 ft. deep. **£950-1,100** *Ad*

A Danish pine breakdown wardrobe, all original fittings, 6 ft. 5 in. high, c. 1870. **£300-375** *W*

An architectural breakfront wardrobe with shelves and drawers, 7 ft. 11 in. wide, c. 1900. **£750-1,000** *Ad*

A German painted pine armoire, dated 1881. **£400-500** *WHA*

A small Victorian pine linen press with shelves, 3 ft. 4 in. wide by 5 ft. 10 in. high. **£320-360** *AL*

A pine linen press with slides, in 2 sections, 5 ft. wide, c. 1860. **£380-£420** *AL*

A pine escritoire, 3 ft. 1 in. wide, c. 1890. **£395-450** *W*

A Georgian pine bachelor's wardrobe/press. **£230-280** *DM*

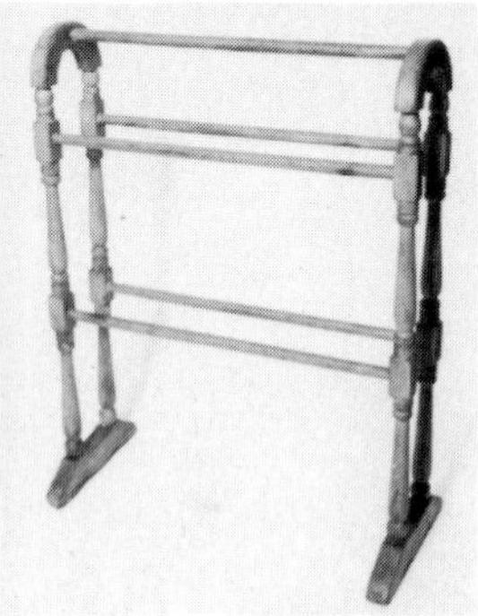

A pine towel rail, 3 ft. wide, c. 1880. **£25-35** *W*

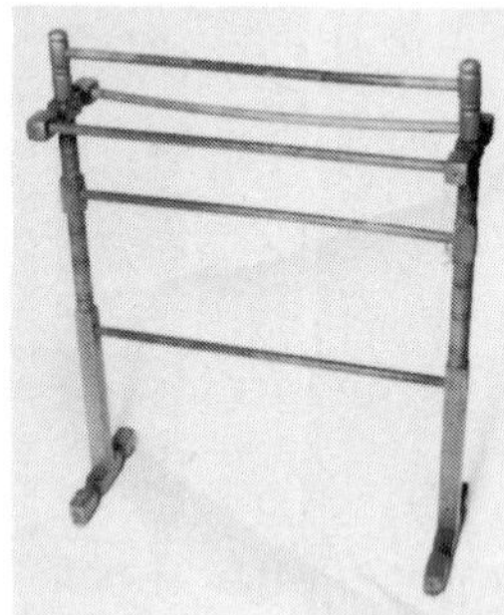
A pine towel rail, c. 1900. **£18-25** *W*

A Victorian pine screen, 5 ft. 10 in. high. **£38-42** *AL*

An elm wheelbarrow with a wrought-iron wheel, 5 ft. long, c. 1860. **£90-110** *AL*

A set of pine shelves, 3 ft. high by 2 ft. 6 in. wide, c. 1870. **£60-70** *AL*

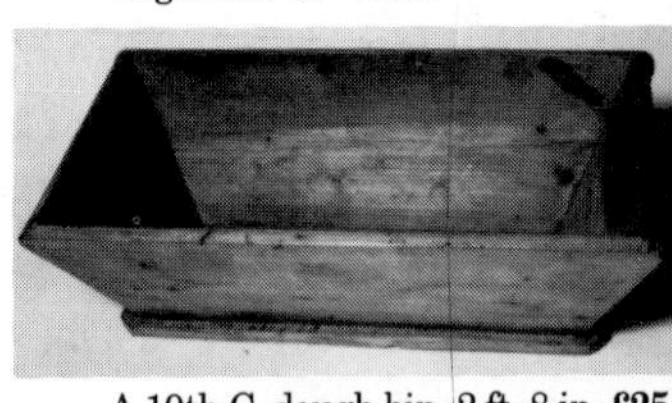
A 19th C. dough bin, 2 ft. 8 in. **£25-£35** *WHA*

A small German painted pine box, 2 ft. ½ in., c. 1850's. **£55-75** *WHA*

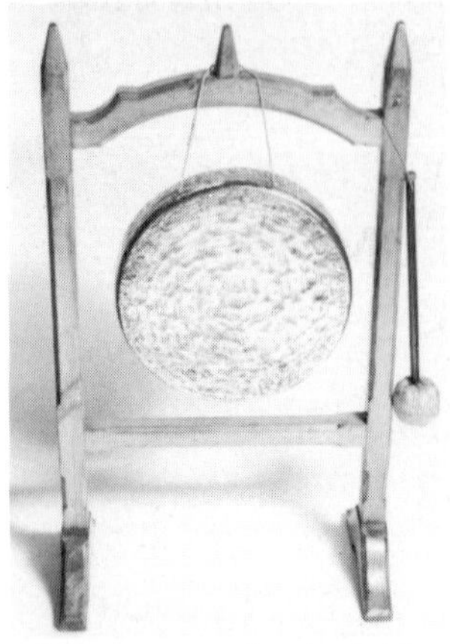
A brass gong on pine stand, 4 ft. high, c. 1860. **£72-78** *AL*

A 19th C. pine dough bin, 2 ft. 10 in. wide. **£170-200** *FF*

A German pine shoe cleaning box, 1 ft. 10 in. **£35-65** *WHA*

CLOCKS

Where, during 1982, many clock dealers were reporting falling sales and such depressed prices that some were forced into closure, there has subsequently been a dramatic turnaround.

The key to the upturn in trade has been good quality. Overseas and domestic buyers alike are happily paying from 10 up to 40% more than they were a year ago, particularly for certain longcase and wall clocks in good, authentic condition. Of the former, mahogany cased, white dial London clocks predating 1815 are in particular demand — perhaps because so many original dials were swapped for brass dials in response to past popular demand. Broad clocks and those exceeding 8 ft. in height, however, are still depressed and, it would seem, are likely to remain so, with prices estimated to have fallen by around 10% over the year.

The scarcity of good Vienna wall clocks dated at between 1800 and 1830 has doubtless been a factor in their 40% price increase — a rise shared with slim, elegant German regulators from c. 1860-75.

Small, inlaid balloon clocks are becoming increasingly collectable, enjoying particular favour among members of the medical and legal professions.

Specialist clocks of all kinds are improving rapidly provided they are of good quality and in authentic condition. Those most heavily tipped for the year ahead are named mahogany bracket clocks and skeleton clocks having 5- or 6-spoke wheel work. But beware of faked-up reproductions.

An early 18th C. walnut and marquetry longcase clock, the 12 in. square brass dial with subsidiary seconds dial, false ringed and engraved calendar aperture, signed 'John Allaway, London', the later 8 day 4 pillar movement rack striking on a bell, 88 in. high (224 cm.), some damage and restoration to case. **£800-900** *SS*

A walnut longcase clock by Peter D'Argent, London, the 12 in. arched brass dial with seconds subsidiary and calendar aperture, the arch with strike/silent subsidiary, the twin train 8-day movement with anchor escapement, 8 ft. 3 in. (2.52 m.) high, 18th C. **£1,300-1,500** *P*

A mahogany longcase clock with quarter striking on 4 tubular bells and 1 blued steel gong, signed Jay R. Attenborough & Co. Ltd., 142 & 144 Oxford Street, 8 ft. 11 in. (241 cm.), c. 1890. **£1,200-1,400** *S*

A mahogany longcase clock, with brass dial, the boss in the arch inscribed Tempus Fugit, the movement with anchor escapement and rack striking on a bell, the dial plate cast S. Baker, with 2 weights and a pendulum, 89 in. overall (226 cm.), early 19th C. **£600-700** *SC*

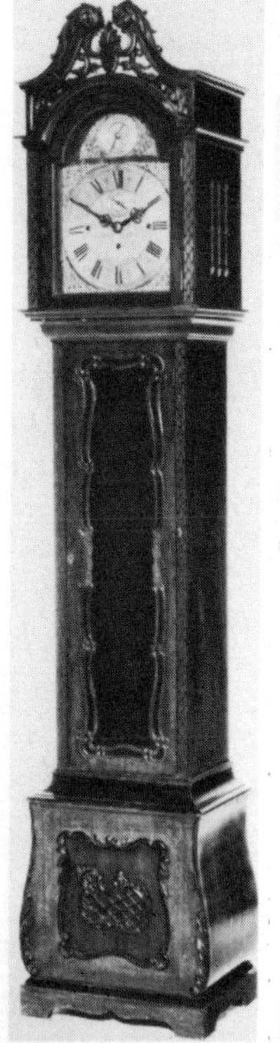

An Edwardian mahogany longcase clock, the 13 in. brass dial signed J.W. Benson, London, 96 in. (244 cm.), late 19th/early 20th C. **£1,700-2,000** *SC*

An ormolu-mounted longcase clock, the 13¾ in. square dial signed J.W. Benson, 25 Old Bond St., London, the 3 train movement with 3 massive brass cased weights striking on 8 bells and 8 gongs, anchor escapement, with pendulum, door key and winder, 7 ft. 11 in. high (241.5 cm.). **£3,000-£4,000** *S*

A walnut longcase clock by Edward Bird, London, 1710, the 8 day 6 pillar movement with latched plates, and inside countwheel, the 10 in. square brass dial with silvered chapter ring and with later scroll cresting, some restoration, 6 ft. 7½ in. **£3,500-4,000** *L*

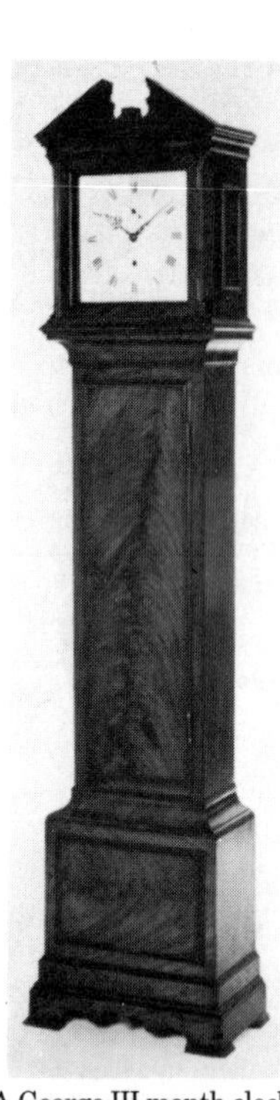

A George III month clock by John Billings, London, having 9¾ in. silvered dial, the single train movement with anchor escapement, 5 turned pillars, 75½ in. **£3,500-£4,500** *S*

An early 18th C. walnut longcase clock by Richard Bockett, the sides with fretwork panels, the case inlaid with ribbon tied chequered lines, paterae and stringing, 8 ft. 2 in. high (249 cm.), c. 1715, later inlaid. **£1,300-1,500** *S*

An oak and mahogany longcase clock, the 14 in. enamel dial signed Brentnal, Mold, the movement with anchor escapement, rack striking on a bell, the case with a swan neck pediment, with 2 weights, a pendulum and a winder, 88 in. (224 cm.), mid 19th C. **£400-£500** *SC*

A late 18th C. oak longcase clock, the 8-day rack striking movement with seconds ring and date aperture, by John Buckingham, Plymouth Dock, 6 ft. 9 in. high. **£850-950** *IAT*

An 18th C. walnut and seaweed marquetry longcase clock by Nathaniel & Thomas Chamberlaine, London, brass dial, signed, having crown and putti spandrels, calendar aperture and seconds subsidiary, the twin train 8-day 5-pillar movement with anchor escapement and inside countwheel strike, 7 ft. 1½ in. high (2.17 m.). **£1,850-2,150** *P*

A mahogany longcase clock signed J.B. Brindley, Newcastle-under-Lyme, the movement with anchor escapement and rack striking on a bell, with 2 weights and a pendulum, a winder and an odd mahogany plinth, 90 in. (229 cm.), mid 19th C. **£300-400** *SC*

A mid Georgian solid walnut 8-day chiming longcase clock by John Brown, Kilmarnock, the case inlaid with boxwood and ebony, parquetry bird, 3 sunbursts and stringing, with engraved arched 12 in. dial, silvered chapter ring, second hand and month calendar, chiming on 7 (6 + 1) bells on the hours and quarters, 7 ft. high. **£750-850** *AGr*

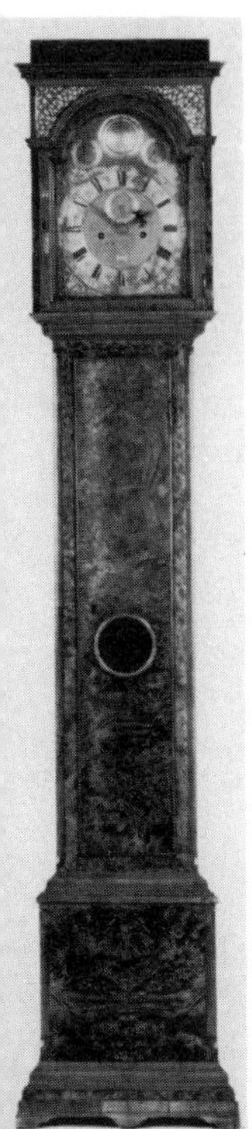

An unusual walnut quarter-repeating longcase clock, the 12 in. dial with a plaque in the leaf-engraved arch signed Claudius Du Chesne Londini between Sonne/Silence and pendulum adjustment dials, the 5-pillar movement with pull quarter repeat on 6 bells, 7 ft. 9 in. high (236 cm.). **£3,200-3,500** *S*

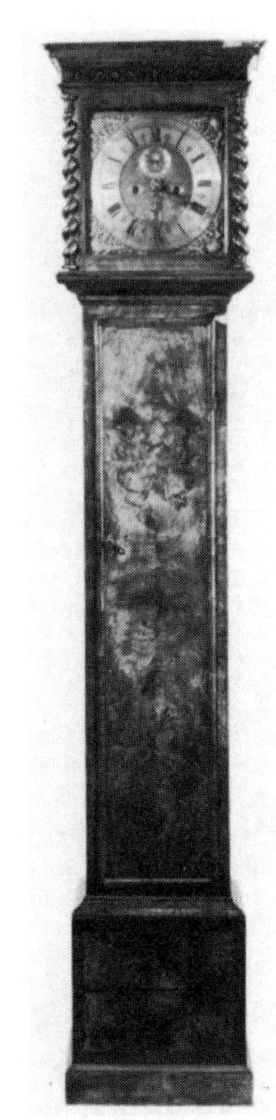

A late 17th C. walnut longcase clock by Sam Clay, Gainsborough, the 12 in. (30 cm.) brass dial with calendar aperture and seconds subsidiary, the twin train movement with anchor escapement and inside countwheel strike, 7 ft. 1½ in. (2.17 m.). **£2,300-3,000** *P*

A walnut regulator longcase clock by Dent, London, the 9½ in. (24 cm.) silvered dial with seconds subsidiary, signed, the twin train movement with deadbeat escapement with jewelled pallets, fine adjustment to the crutch, the pendulum suspended from the backboard, 6 ft. high (1.83 cm.). **£1,800-2,300** *P*

An 18th C. oak longcase clock with satinwood inlay, brass face with second hand and date recorder, Edward Cooper, London, c. 1790. **£650-850** *GR*

A mahogany longcase regulator, the case with painted decoration, the silvered regulator dial signed Croft London, deadbeat escapement (lacking pallets on the arbor and pendulum), 5 ft. 11 in. high (182 cm.). **£1,700-2,000** *C*

A mahogany longcase clock, dial signed Wm. Dobbie, Falkirk, 85 in. (216 cm.), early 19th C. **£600-700** *S*

A Georgian mahogany and inlaid longcase clock, the 17 in. (43 cm.) circular white painted dial inscribed P. Donegan, Dublin, the twin train movement with semi-deadbeat anchor escapement, 7 ft. 8 in. high (2.33 m.). **£450-600** *P*

A George III mahogany longcase clock, signed Andrews, Dover, bell lacking, 8 ft. 4 in. high (254 cm.). **£1,300-1,800** *S*

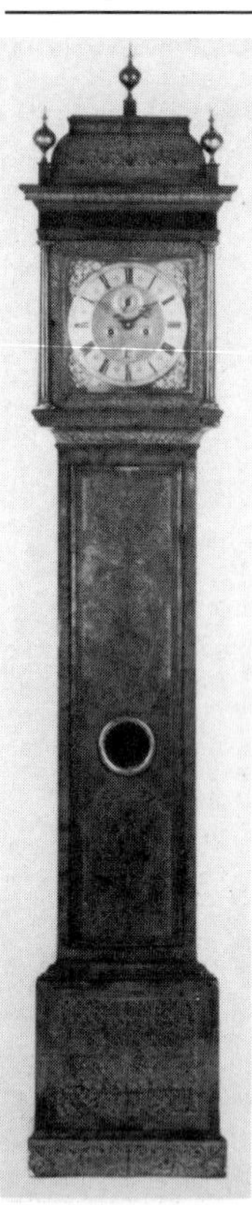

An arabesque marquetry 30-day longcase clock, the dial signed John Ebsworth Londini Fecit, the movement with 6 ringed pillars, bolt and shutter maintaining power and outside countwheel, the going train with 5 wheels and the striking with 4, 8 ft. high (244 cm.). **£3,800-4,500** *S*

John Ebsworth, a good maker, was free of the Clockmakers' Company in 1665 and Master from 1697 to 1703.

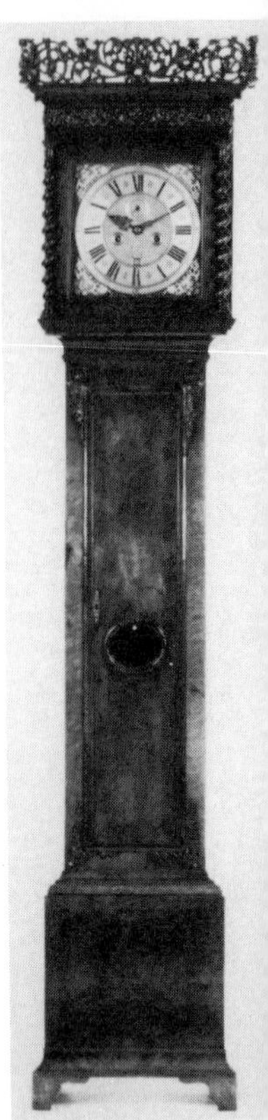

A walnut month longcase clock signed Fromanteel and Clarke, Dutch striking and deadbeat escapement, the case veneered in wood of faded colour, 7 ft. 10 in. high (239 cm.). **£2,000-3,000** *S*

The Fromanteels were a large family of Dutch Clockmakers who worked in England. They made the first pendulum clocks in 1658.

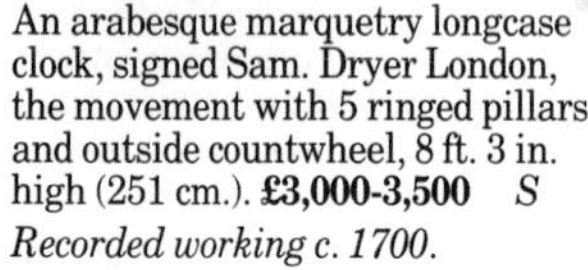

An arabesque marquetry longcase clock, signed Sam. Dryer London, the movement with 5 ringed pillars and outside countwheel, 8 ft. 3 in. high (251 cm.). **£3,000-3,500** *S*

Recorded working c. 1700.

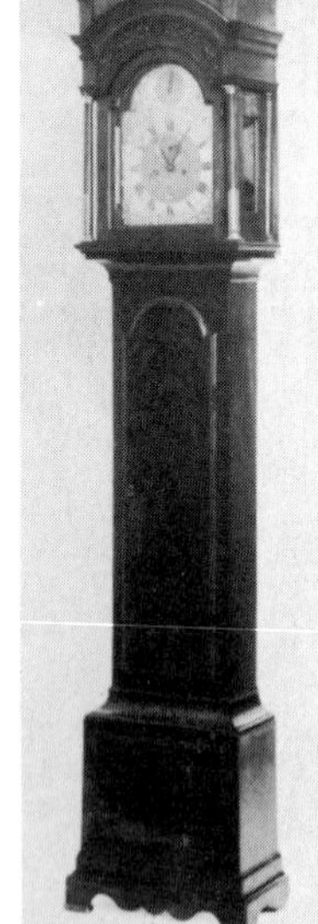

A George III 8-day longcase clock by John Ellicott with 12 in. brass dial, silvered chapter ring, seconds dial, calendar aperture and strike/silent dial in the arch, the movement with deadbeat escapement striking on one bell, 108 in. **£1,700-2,000** *Bea*

A fine William III walnut and marquetry longcase clock, signed Chris Gould Londini Fecit, the movement with 5 ringed pillars, bolt-and-shutter maintaining power, anchor escapement and external countwheel strike, 7 ft. 2 in. (219 cm.) high. **£7,000-8,000** *C*

A floral marquetry longcase clock, the dial signed Fra Gregg Russel Street Covent Garden with 5 ringed pillars and inside countwheel, the waist door inlaid on an ebony ground, the sides veneered in richly figured walnut, 7 ft. high (213 cm.). **£3,000-4,000** *S*

Francis Gregg is recorded working in Russell Street in 1711, and in St. James's from 1714 to 1729.

An 18th C. oak longcase clock, the 11 in. brass dial engraved Jn. Gullock, Rochford, single hand, 30 hr., birdcage movement, 6 ft. 10 in. high. **£550-650** *IAT*

A George III mahogany musical and automaton longcase clock, the painted dial signed Wil^{m} Guy Rye, the arch with inset scene of figures, the automaton of a fiddler, drummer and dancers, the curtain falling after the tune, 3-train anchor movement with rack of 12 bells and hammers, in disrepair, 7 ft. 10 in. high (234 cm.). **£3,500-£4,000** *C*

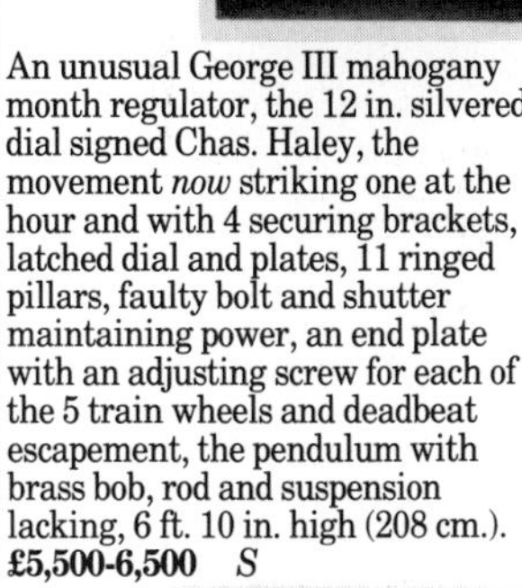

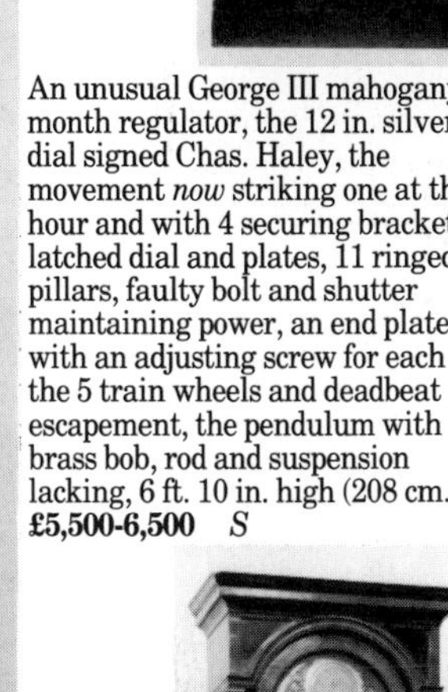

An unusual George III mahogany month regulator, the 12 in. silvered dial signed Chas. Haley, the movement *now* striking one at the hour and with 4 securing brackets, latched dial and plates, 11 ringed pillars, faulty bolt and shutter maintaining power, an end plate with an adjusting screw for each of the 5 train wheels and deadbeat escapement, the pendulum with brass bob, rod and suspension lacking, 6 ft. 10 in. high (208 cm.). **£5,500-6,500** *S*

An Ewardian 8-day longcase clock by R. H. Halford and Sons, London, the 15½ in. brass dial with seconds dial, strike/silent, chime/silent and Whittington/Westminster dials, the 3 train movement chiming and striking on 8 tubular bells, pendulum incomplete, 111 in. **£2,200-2,500** *Bea*

A mahogany longcase clock, the 2 train movement with striking on a single gong, subsidiary seconds and calendar aperture, signed Hamilton & Inches Edinburgh, 2 weights, 1 case key, 1 key, 1 pendulum, 85 in. high (216 cm.), c. 1900. **£700-800** *S*

An early 18th C. mahogany longcase clock, the brass dial engraved Jms. Hendrie, Wigton, the 8-day movement with inside countwheel, 6 ft. 9 in. high. **£875-£925** *IAT*

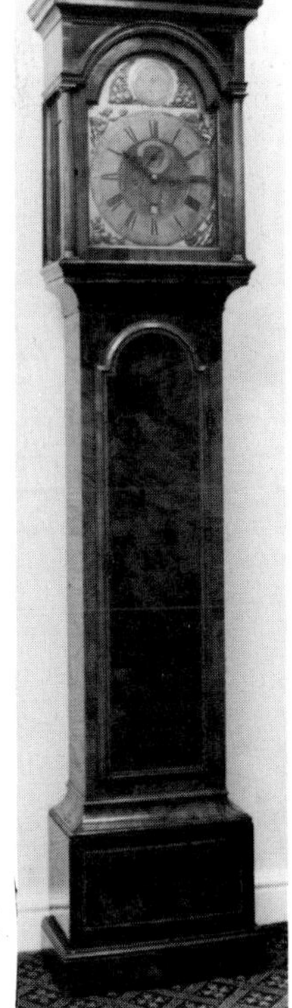

A Georgian longcase clock in a figured walnut case with square hood, brass dial plate with 8-day movement by John Hitchin, London. **£1,300-1,500** *M*

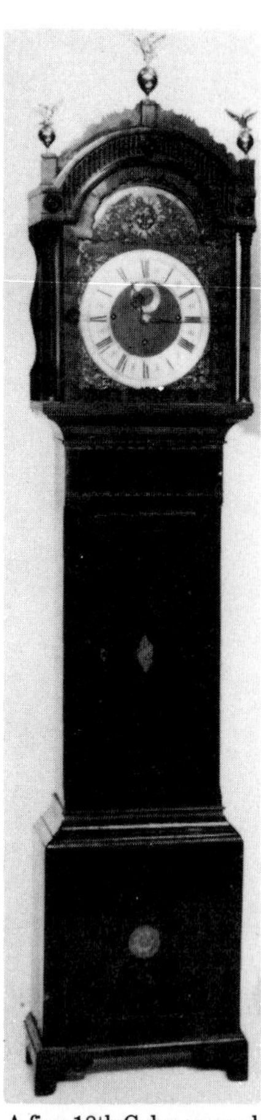

A fine 18th C. longcase clock by Ben Holburt of Bath, the 8-day movement with brass face, the movement fitted with 8 bell musical chimes and hour bell striking quarters and hours, 90 in. high. **£900-1,200** *WHL*

A walnut 'Renaissance' longcase clock, the 12 in. lacquered dial inscribed James Jay, 142 & 144 Oxford Street, W., the cleaned movement with anchor escapement and rack striking on a bell, the waist door carved with strapwork and masks on scroll feet, including 2 weights and a pendulum, 105 in. (267 cm.), mid 19th C. **£1,000-£1,200** *SC*

An oak longcase clock, the 12 in. dial signed D. Kellock, the movement with rack striking, 9 ft. 2 in. high (279 cm.). **£1,200-1,400** *S*

A walnut and marquetry longcase clock by Joseph Knibb, c. 1670. **£20,000-£23,000** *TP*

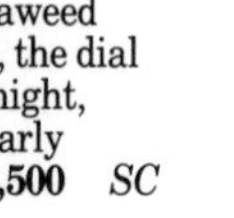

A longcase clock by Thomas Lister, Luddenden, with 8-day movement, 88 in. **£1,800-2,200** *DSH*

A walnut and seaweed marquetry clock, the dial signed Henry Knight, London, 77 in., early 20th C. **£2,000-2,500** *SC*

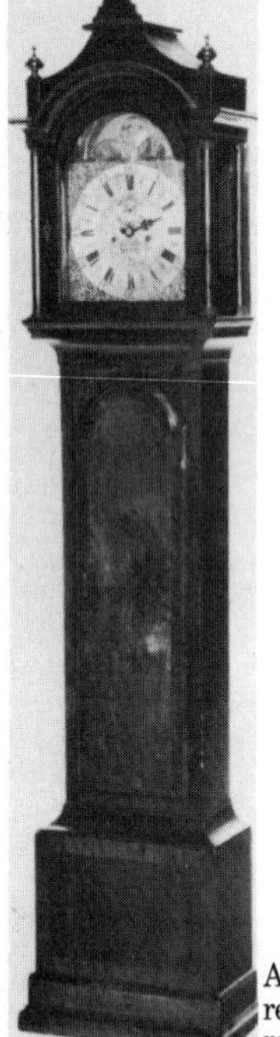

A George III mahogany longcase clock, the dial inscribed Robert Lawson, Leigh, 92½ in. **£1,800-£2,000** *SC*

A Victorian mahogany longcase regulator, engraved silvered regulator dial signed John Lecomber Liverpool 117, jewelled deadbeat escapement of the high count train with individual end caps and indirect drive, 8 ft. 6 in. (258 cm.) high. **£2,700-3,000** *C*

HINTS TO DATING LONGCASE CLOCKS

DIALS		
8 in. square	to c. 1669	Carolean
10 in. square	from c. 1665-1695	
11 in. square	from 1690-1700	
12 in. square	from c. 1700	from Queen Anne
14 in. square	from c. 1740	from early Georgian
Broken-arch dial	from c. 1715	from early Georgian
Round dial	from c. 1760	from early Georgian
Silvered dial	from c. 1760	from early Georgian
Painted dial	from c. 1760	from early Georgian
Hour hand only	to c. 1680	
Minute hand introduced	c. 1663	
Second hand	from 1675	post-Restoration
Matching hands	from c. 1775	George III or later

CASE FINISH		
Ebony veneer	up to c. 1725	Carolean to early Georgian
Walnut veneer	from c. 1670 to c. 1770	Carolean to mid-Georgian
Lacquer	from c. 1700 to c. 1755	Queen Anne to mid-Georgian
Mahogany	from 1730	from early Georgian
Softwood	from c. 1760	from mid-Georgian
Mahogany inlay	from c. 1795	from mid-Georgian
Marquetry	from c. 1680 to c. 1760	from Carolean to mid-Georgian
Oak	always	

An oak and mahogany 8-day longcase clock by Lowe, Gloucester, rack striking showing date and seconds hand, 7 ft. high, c. 1820. **£450-500** *IAT*

A mahogany longcase clock, the 8-day movement with deadbeat escapement and rack striking, the 13 in. painted dial signed MacKinlay, Edinburgh, 6 ft. 4½ in. **£750-850** *L*

Peter MacKinlay, Edinburgh, 1836.

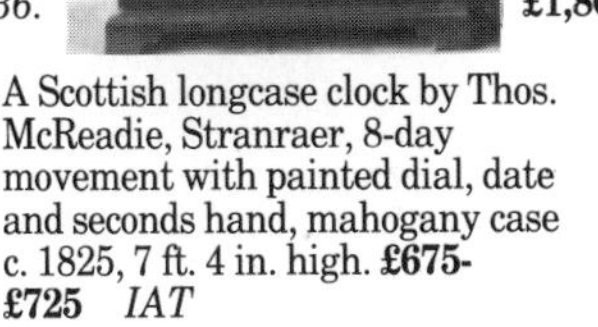

A Scottish longcase clock by Thos. McReadie, Stranraer, 8-day movement with painted dial, date and seconds hand, mahogany case c. 1825, 7 ft. 4 in. high. **£675-£725** *IAT*

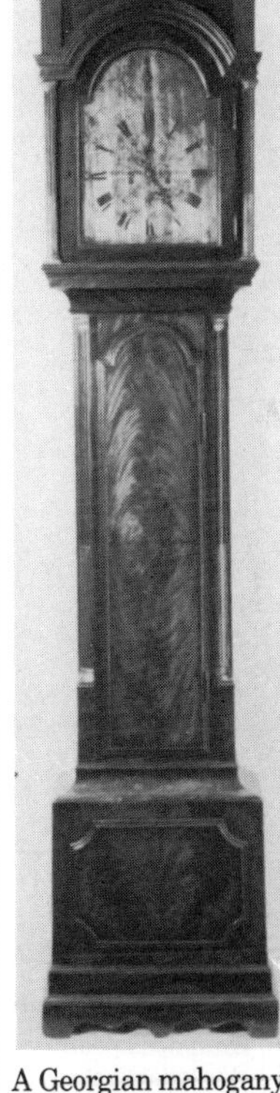

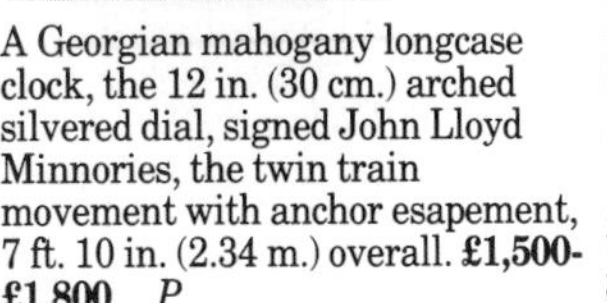

A Georgian mahogany longcase clock, the 12 in. (30 cm.) arched silvered dial, signed John Lloyd Minnories, the twin train movement with anchor esapement, 7 ft. 10 in. (2.34 m.) overall. **£1,500-£1,800** *P*

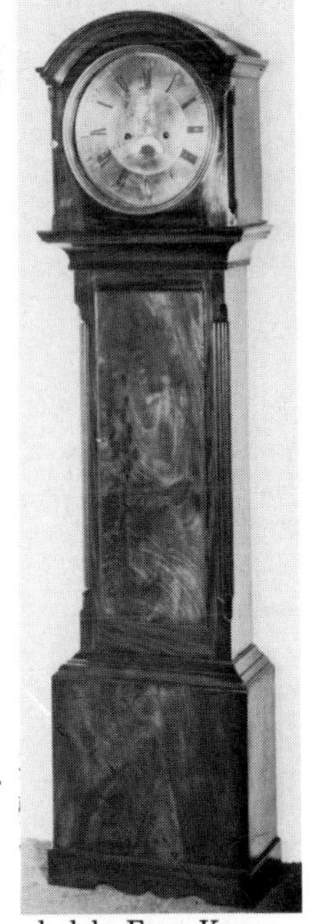

A longcase clock by Fran. Kerr Monaghan, with 8-day movement, chased brass dial in mahogany case, 72 in. high. **£600-700** *DSH*

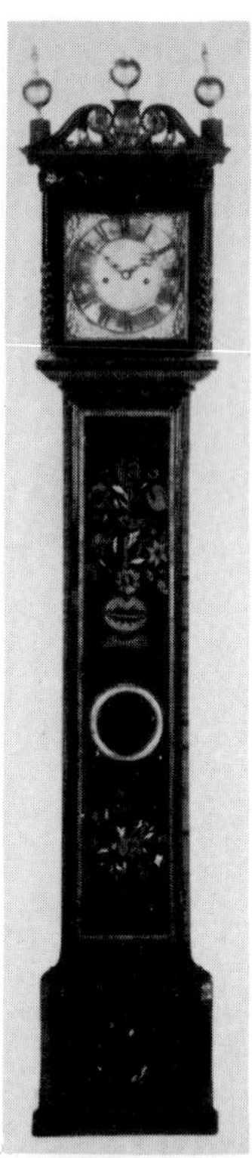

A George I walnut longcase clock by William Newman of Cork, with brass face, the door inlaid with marquetry and chequered decoration, 7 ft. 4½ in. high (225 cm.). **£1,500-2,000** *SI*

A small olivewood marquetry longcase clock, the 10½ in. dial signed S. Moore Tewksbury, the later movement with gong striking, in an oyster-veneered case with a rectangular hood and a bull's eye, partly inlaid in green-stained bone, the sides crossbanded in straight grained wood, 6 ft. 4 in. high (193 cm.) excluding carved cresting and gilt finials, case c. 1690. **£7,000-8,000** *S*

A mahogany quarter chiming longcase clock, the 12 in. brass dial signed B.S. Morse, Watford, Cambridge/Westminster, strike/silent and chime/silent, the 3 train movement with anchor escapement and chiming the quarters on a carillon of bells, 10 ft. 1 in. (2.88 m.) high. **£1,600-1,800** *P*

A longcase clock, brass and steel dial inscribed with Old Father Time and Tempus Rerum Imperator, mahogany case crossbanded and inlaid. William Newman, Norwich. **£1,100-1,300** *GR*

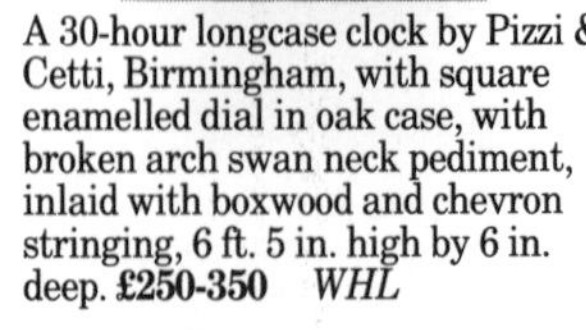

A 30-hour longcase clock by Pizzi & Cetti, Birmingham, with square enamelled dial in oak case, with broken arch swan neck pediment, inlaid with boxwood and chevron stringing, 6 ft. 5 in. high by 6 in. deep. **£250-350** *WHL*

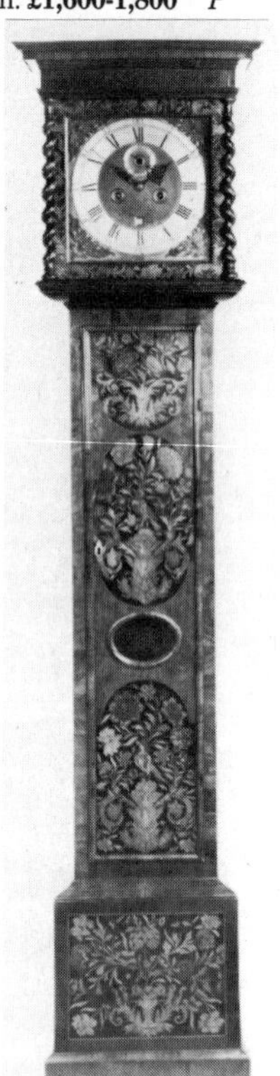

An oak and mahogany longcase clock, the 12 in. brass dial signed Parkinson, Lancaster 1767, the restored movement with anchor escapement, 92 in. (234 cm.), late 18th C. **£600-700** *SC*

A walnut and marquetry longcase clock, the dial signed Henry Perry London, the movement with 4 ringed pillars, anchor escapement and internal countwheel strike, 6 ft. 7 in. high. **£3,500-4,000** *C*

An oak Gothic revival longcase clock by Parkinson and Frodsham, with 3 train gut fusee movement, 86 in. (219 cm.), c. 1850. **£1,100-£1,400** *S*

A 19th C. mahogany longcase clock with circular silvered dial, 8-day movement striking on a bell, maker James Plumbly 16 New Cavendish Street, London, in excellent order. **£800-900** *M*

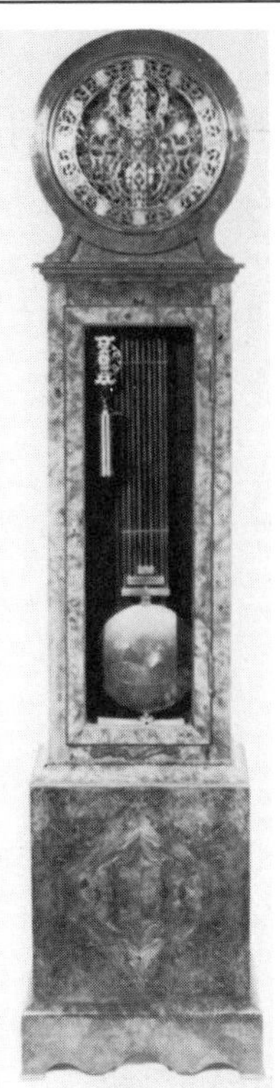
A rare skeletonised regulator, movement with scroll cut back plate, the high count train with lantern pinions, 5 ft. 11½ in. high. **£2,400-3,000** *C*

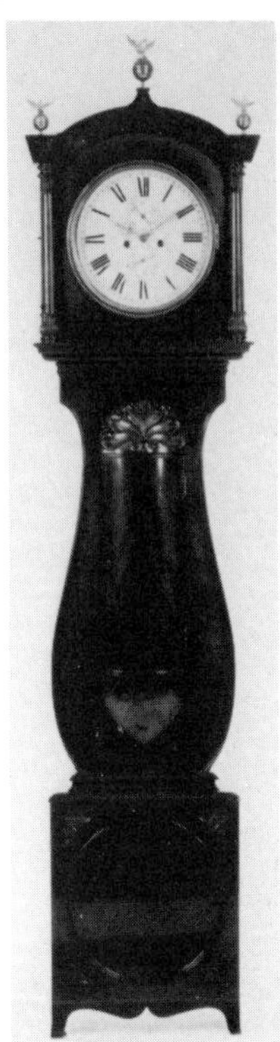
A William IV longcase clock, the dial signed David Robertson, Perth, with 2 weights and pendulum, 85 in. (216 cm.), c. 1835. **£500-£600** *S*

A mahogany longcase clock, the dial signed Edward Samm, Linton, 7 ft. 8 in. high. **£950-1,050** *S*

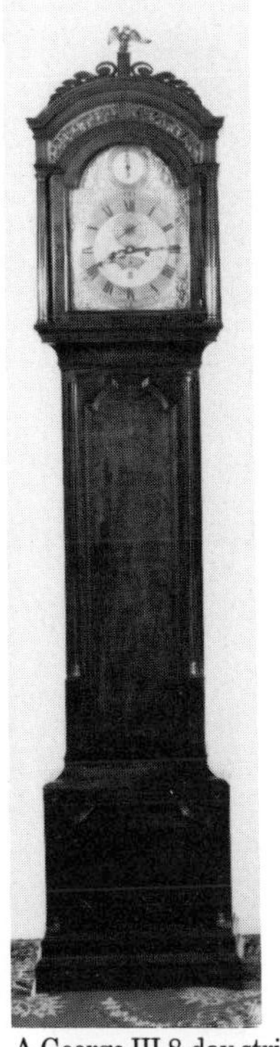
A George III 8-day striking longcase clock, with arched brass dial and having strike and silent, date and second indicators, by Thomas Strange, Kingston, in a fine-quality Chippendale-style mahogany case. **£2,000-3,000** *WSW*

A mahogany and marquetry longcase clock, signed Daniel Quare fecit London, 8 ft. 3 in. **£1,700-£1,900** *S*

A fine early Georgian green lacquer longcase clock, the case with chinoiserie decoration, the brass dial signed William Tomlinson London, the movement with anchor escapement and rack strike, 9 ft. high (275 cm.). **£2,700-£3,000** *C*

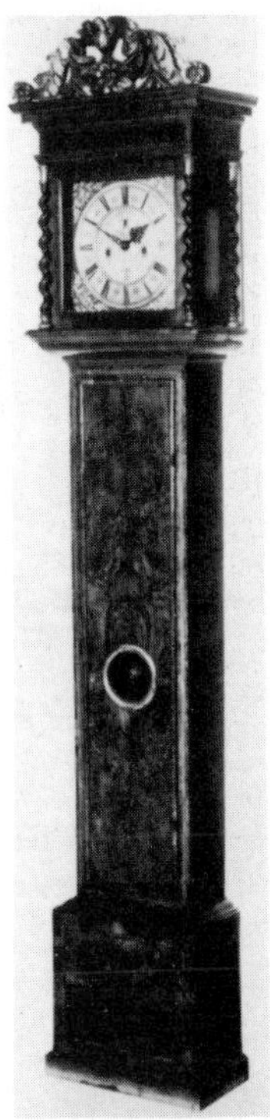
A walnut longcase clock, the dial signed J. Windmill, London, 5 ringed pillar movement with anchor escapement, 88 in., early 18th C., the case restored. **£6,000-7,000** *SC*

A Scottish mahogany regulator, the 12 in. dial signed Marshall Wishaw, the movement with pillars secured by nuts at each end, maintaining power, high count train of 4 wheels and deadbeat escapement with pallet adjustment, the pendulum with wood rod, beat adjustment and roller suspension from the backboard, 7 ft. 1 in. high (216 cm.). **£1,400-1,800** *S*

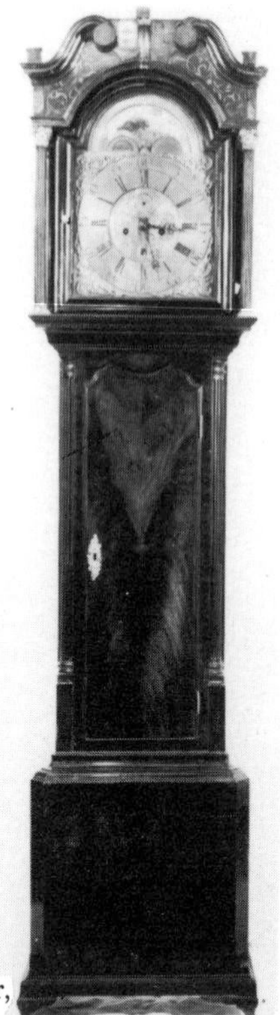

A George III mahogany longcase clock, 7 ft. 8 in. high. **£1,100-1,400** *CDC*

An early 18th C. walnut and seaweed marquetry inlaid longcase clock, the dial signed Tho Pare Londini Fecit, 7 ft. 6½ in. **£6,500-7,500** *P*

A George III oak longcase clock, the painted arched dial bearing the Brown's coat-of-arms and motto Floreat Magestas, 6 ft. 9½ in. high (207 cm.). **£750-850** *S*

Left
A mahogany longcase clock, 14 in. enamel dial, the movement with anchor escapement and rack striking on a bell, the case with swan neck pediment, inlaid throughout with boxwood lines and designs, 90 in. (225 cm.), early 19th C. **£500-£600** *S C*

Left
(l.) An 18th C. walnut and mahogany longcase clock, the plain case with crossbanded decoration, the brass face inscribed Rich'd Kenyon, with pierced spandrels, silvered chapter ring, date aperture and seconds dial, 8-day movement, 7 ft. 3 in. **£500-600** *DDM*

(r.) A late 18th C. oak longcase clock, the case with mahogany banding, the brass face inscribed Higginbotham, Macclesfield, with pierced spandrels and seconds hand, 8-day movement, 6 ft. 8 in. **£350-400** *DDM*

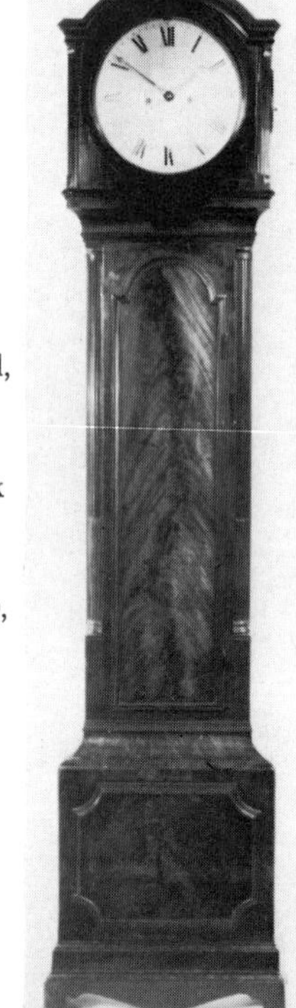

A mahogany longcase clock, circular silvered dial, false-plate movement with rack strike and anchor escapement, early 19th C., 6 ft. 10 in. high (208 cm.). **£1,100-£1,500** *C*

An inlaid mahogany musical longcase clock, with 14 in. painted dial, the music including Blue Bells of Scotland and God Save the Queen, the 3 train movement with 14 bells and hammers activated by a pin-drum, 7 ft. 10 in. high (239 cm.), early 19th C. **£1,400-£2,000** *S*

Left
A William IV mahogany longcase clock, 7 ft. 11 in. (237 cm.), c. 1840. **£550-650** *S*

(l.) A 19th C. oak longcase clock, the hood with brass mounts, the case with mahogany crossbanding, the painted dial inscribed Jas. Foxton, Sutton Ashfield; 30 hour movement with date aperture, 6 ft. 11 in. **£350-400** *DDM*
(l.c.) An early 19th C. oak longcase clock with mahogany and walnut banding, the painted dial inscribed N. Radcliffe, Elland, 30 hour movement, seconds and date dials, 7 ft. 10 in. **£200-250** *DDM*
(r.c.) A 19th C. oak longcase clock, fluted case and crossbanded door, the painted dial inscribed Jno Coates, Horncastle, with 30 hour movement and date dial, 7 ft. high. **£250-300** *DDM*
(r.) A late 18th/early 19th C. oak longcase clock with crossbanded and inlaid case, the painted dial inscribed Rich'd Herring, Newark, 8-day movement with moon phase, seconds and date dials, 7 ft. high. **£400-450** *DDM*

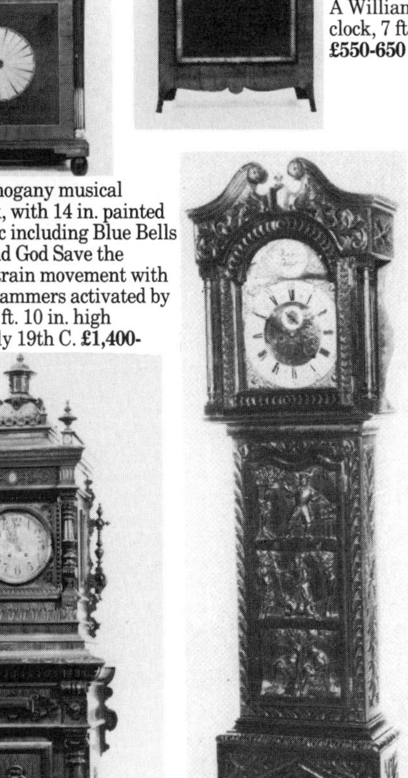

An oak longcase clock, signed Tempus Fugit, with anchor escapement and rack striking on a bell, the waist door carved with mediaeval 'hunting scenes' with a pendulum, 2 weights and a winder, 90 in. (229 cm.), mid 19th C. **£650-£750** *SC*

A small mahogany skeletonised regulator, now with rectangular base, silver skeletonised chapter-ring, blued moon hands with centre seconds hand, double 4 legged gravity escapement, 5 ft. 5 in. high (165 cm.), 19th C. **£1,800-2,200** *C*

A Victorian walnut musical pedestal clock, 8-day striking, 6 ft. 7 in. high. **£1,200-1,400** *CDC*

A late Victorian chiming longcase clock, the 3 train movement with Whittington and Westminster chimes on tubular gongs, inscribed 'Goldsmiths and Silversmiths Co., 112 Regent St., London', 89 in. high. **£1,000-1,200** *S*

A good boulle longcase clock; the dial with enamel numerals, the whole inlaid with cut-brass foliage on a red tortoiseshell ground with scenes from the Commedia dell' Arte, 91 in. (236 cm.), c. 1875. **£2,000-£3,000** *S*

A mahogany longcase clock, the 3 train movement with quarter striking on 8 rod gongs, 7 ft. 1 in. high (213 cm.), c. 1880. **£1,000-1,200** *S*

A mahogany longcase clock, the 3 train movement with quarter striking on 8 tubular bells, with 3 brass weights and 1 key, 7 ft. 11 in. (242 cm.), c. 1900. **£1,800-2,000** *S*

A mahogany and marquetry longcase clock with quarter striking on 7 tubular bells, the dial with arabic numerals, subsidiary seconds and subsidiary strike/silent, chime/silent and Whittington/ Westminster chimes, 9 ft. 9 in. high (267 cm.), c. 1910. **£2,000-2,500** *S*

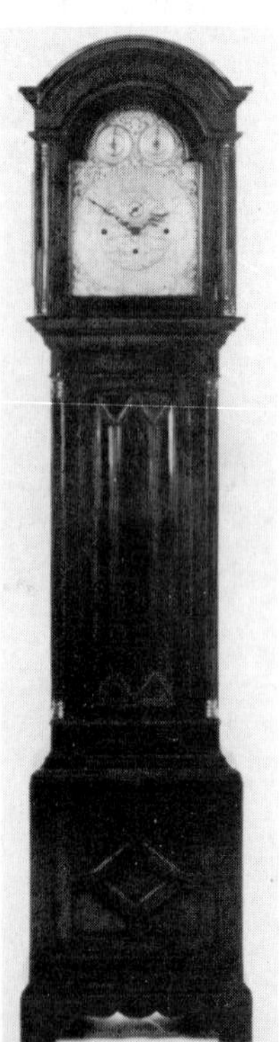

A stained beechwood longcase clock with quarter striking on 8 rod gongs, with pendulum and weights, c. 1910. **£1,000-1,200** *S*

A mahogany and walnut miniature longcase clock with French drum movement, 17¾ in. high, c. 1900. **£200-240** *TP*

An oak longcase clock, the 3 train movement with striking on 8 bells and 3 gongs, the dial with roman numerals, signed Maple & Co., London, with 3 weights, 2 keys and pendulum, 8 ft. 9½ in. (273 cm.), c. 1910. **£1,700-2,000** *S*

An Edwardian mahogany and marquetry chiming longcase clock, the brass dial with age and face of moon in arch, the 3 train movement with deadbeat escapement and chiming on 9 tubular bells, 107½ in. high. **£300-£350** *CSK*

HINTS TO DATING BRACKET CLOCKS

DIALS

Square dial	to c. 1770	pre-George III
Broken arch dial	from c. 1720	George I or later
Round/painted/silvered	from c. 1760	George III or later

CASE FINISH

Ebony veneer	from c. 1660 to c. 1850	Carolean to mid-Victorian
Walnut	from c. 1670 to c. 1795	Carolean to mid-Georgian
Marquetry	from c. 1680 to c. 1740	Carolean to early Georgian
Rosewood	from c. 1790	from mid-Georgian
Lacquered	from c. 1700 to c. 1760	Queen Anne to early Georgian
Mahogany	from c. 1730	from early Georgian

A small early George III ebonised bracket clock, the 5 in. dial signed Willm. Allam London, the 5 pillar movement with verge escapement and lenticular bob, in a bell top case with cone finials and gilt-metal frets above the unusual ogee arch, 14 in. high (35.5 cm.). **£3,500-£4,000** *S*

An early Regency mahogany bracket clock, with slower/faster dial signed Barraud, Cornhill, London, the twin chain and fusee movement with anchor escapement striking on a bell, 16½ in. high. **£400-500** *CSK*

Probably Paul Phillip, a member of the Livery Makers Company, 1796, Master of the Clockmaker's Company 1810-11, died 1820. Partner with W. Howell and G. Jamison for making Mudge's timekeepers.

A late Stuart ebonised striking bracket clock, pull quarter repeat on 3 quarter bells, verge escapement and well executed scroll engraved backplate with the partially obliterated signature Mansell Bennett Londini Fecit, 13½ in. high (34 cm.). **£3,500-£4,000** *C*

A mahogany bracket clock by John & Robert Barker, 17 Aldgate High St., no. 1791, the movement with twin chain fusee and anchor escapement, the silvered dial engraved with foliate spandrels, with key and pendulum, 12½ in. high (32 cm.), c. 1840. **£450-550** *S*

An ebonised quarter repeating bracket timepiece, 7 in. dial signed Jno Blundell Greenwich, the movement with pull quarter repeat on 2 bells, and verge escapement with bob pendulum, 14½ in. high (37 cm.). **£1,200-1,500** *S*

A good ebony bracket clock by Thomas Boxell, Brighton, with twin chain fusee and striking on a single gong, with key, 15½ in. (39.5 cm.), c. 1840. **£450-550** *S*

A painted and gilt bronze and cut glass bracket clock, probably originally for the Turkish market, inscribed Maximilian Borrell, London, the repeating movement with baluster pillars, shouldered plates, striking on a bell, 30 in. (76 cm.), early 19th C. **£900-£1,100** *SC*

A good mahogany quarter chiming bracket clock no. 12180 by Brockbank Atkins & Moore, London, with winder, 20½ in. (52 cm.), 1880's. **£1,500-2,000** *S*

A mahogany bracket clock, the 8 in. diam. dial inscribed Clare, Manchester, the movement with anchor escapement, pull quarter repeat, striking on an overhead bell, 19½ in. (50 cm.), early 19th C. **£450-550** *SC*

An early 19th C. mahogany quarter chiming and musical bracket clock by George Brinkman, London, the 4 train fusee movement with anchor escapement, chiming the quarters on 8 bells and playing 12 airs on 14 bells, signed G. Brinkman, London, 2 ft. 11½ in. high (90 cm.). **£1,800-2,000** *P*

A George III mahogany calendar bracket clock for the Spanish market, the 7 in. dial signed Juan y Melchor Brockbank Londres, Tocar/Silencio dial in the arch, the repeating movement with half hour striking and altered anchor escapement, 1 urn finial replaced, 20 in. high (51 cm.). **£1,400-1,600** *S*

The brothers John and Myles Brockbank worked in partnership until 1806.

A small ebony-veneered quarter repeating basket top bracket timepiece, the movement with 5 ringed pillars, pull quarter repeat on 2 bells, verge escapement and bob pendulum, signed Phillip Corderoy London, a brass winding key pierced engraved with tulips, 12½ in. high (32 cm.). **£2,500-£3,000** *S*

CLOCKS

Longcase and bracket clocks are in maker's name order. Any clock without a maker's name is at the end of the particular section in date order.

A large George III Scottish mahogany balloon bracket timepiece with a 12 in. enamel dial, the movement with anchor escapement, steel rod and heavy lenticular bob, signed Laur. Dalgleish Edinburgh, 25½ in. high (64.5 cm.). **£450-550** *S*

An unusual boulle bracket clock and bracket of religieuse type, with vase shaped pillars and verge escapement with cycloidal cheeks, silk suspension and bob pendulum, signed Clavier A. Paris, 22 in. high (56 cm.) and a matching ogee bracket, 11 in. high (28 cm.). **£2,000-2,500** *S*

A Gothic oak chiming bracket clock and bracket by Cornell, 83 Cheapside, London, no. 787, the twin chain fusee movement striking the quarters on 8 bells and 1 rod gong, with pendulum locking, 2 keys and pendulum, 31½ in. (80 cm.), 1860's. **£500-600** *S*

A good mahogany bracket clock by Dent, with quarter striking on 8 bells and 5 gongs, the dial with chime/silent, slow/fast and chime on 8 bells/Westminster chimes, signed Dent to the Queen 33, Cockspur St., London, with key and pendulum, 26 in. (66 cm.), c. 1880. **£900-1,000** *S*

A George II quarter repeating bracket clock, the 5 in. dial signed 'Benj. Gray, London', the movement with verge escapement, pull alarm and quarter repeat on 2 bells, in later mahogany case, 15¼ in. high. **£1,400-1,800** *Bea*

A George III mahogany striking bracket clock, the dial signed Dwerrihouse Berkeley Square, with anchor escapement, 16 in. high (41 cm.). **£1,200-1,500** *C*

Left
A mahogany and brass inlaid quarter chiming bracket clock, the twin train movement signed Frodsham, Gracechurch St., London, 1 ft. 8½ in. high (54 cm.), mid 19th C. **£700-800** *P*

A Louis XV bracket clock with 7½ in. dial signed 'Le Doux — a Amien', the 2 train 8-day movement with anchor escapement, striking on 2 bells and with outside locking-plate, the brass case all inlaid in red tortoiseshell, stained ivory and mother-of-pearl, 36 in. high overall. **£1,900-2,200** *Bea*

An ebonised chiming bracket clock, signed Thos. Gardner London, the 3 train movement chiming the quarters on 8 bells and with altered anchor escapement, 20 in. high (51 cm.). **£2,400-2,600** *S*

A George III satinwood musical bracket clock, the 8 in. repainted dial signed Grimalde London, with 6 tune selector dial in the arch, the repeating 3 train movement playing the selected tune every hour, the pin drum with 12 bells and hammers and mounted at right angles to the plates, verge escapement with lenticular bob, 26 in. high (66 cm.). **£4,000-5,000** *S*

An ebony-veneered quarter repeating bracket clock, the movement with 5 ringed pillars, pull quarter repeat and verge escapement, backplate signed Jacobus Hassenius Londini, with restoration, 13 in. high (33 cm.). **£2,200-2,500** *S*

A Regency bracket clock in mahogany, the top of pagoda form with brass ring handles and glazed Gothic panels to the sides, the front with brass scroll inlay, by Hanson of Windsor, 19 in. high by 6¼ in. wide by 11½ in. long, c. 1820. **£350-£400** *OL*

An ebony-veneered quarter repeating basket top bracket clock, the dial signed Alexander Hewitt London, the 7 pillar movement with pull quarter repeat on 5 bells, outside set up ratchets and verge escapement with lenticular bob, signed backplate, 15 in. high (38 cm.). **£3,200-3,600** *S*

Alexander Hewitt was apprenticed to Benjamin Bell in 1685 and became Free of the Clockmakers' Company.

An early walnut bracket clock, now with caddy top, the front door now modified to conform to the later added arch, twin fusee, verge escapement and numbered outside countwheel, engraved with a rose, the backplate signed Henry Jones in the Temple and with tulip engraving in the corners, 18½ in. high (47 cm.). **£5,500-6,500** *C*

A boulle bracket clock by Howell & James, Paris, with key and pendulum, 34 cm., c. 1860. **£400-£500** *S*

A small and rare quarter repeating bracket clock, verge escapement with bob pendulum and outside set up ratchets, the backplate signed Henricus Jones Londini, 10 in. high (25 cm.), with restoration, now in a black-painted rectangular case 12½ in. high (32 cm.). **£1,550-£1,750** *S*

Henry Jones, a famous maker, was Free of the Clockmakers' Company in 1663, he died in 1695.

A late Stuart ebony quarter striking bracket clock by Jont. Lowndes London, bell frets to door and side panels, signed silvered chapter-ring, triple fusee, quarter strike on 5 (formerly 6) quarter bells, verge escapement, backplate signed Jonathan Lowndes in the Pall Mall London, 16½ in. high (42 cm.). **£5,000-6,000** *C*

A walnut bracket clock, signed Jno. James London, the repeating movement with half-hour striking on 2 bells, verge escapement, bob pendulum with silk suspension and incomplete pull quarter repeat, with restoration, 21½ in. high (54.5 cm.), mid 18th C. **£2,500-£3,500** *S*

A brass inlaid mahogany bracket clock, the painted dial signed Robt. Jones, Liverpool, with pendulum, winder and door key, 15½ in. (39.5 cm.), mid 19th C. **£300-400** *S*

An ebony striking bracket clock, typical phase III case, dial signed at the base, the movement with latches to the 6 ringed pillars, rack strike and quarter repeat on 2 bells, the verge escapement with pierced backcock, the backplate signed Joseph Knibb Londini Fecit, with restorations, 12½ in. high (32 cm.). **£9,000-11,000** *C*

An 18th C. mahogany bracket clock with seconds dial and brass spandrels, 8-day striking movement by Marriott, London with a carrying handle, 15 in. high. **£1,000-1,200** *GR*

A tortoiseshell bracket clock by J. Marti, the dial with arabic numerals, with key and pendulum, 12 in. high (31 cm.), c. 1880. **£500-£600** *S*

An unusual late 18th C. grande sonnerie bracket clock, the 9 in. painted dish dial signed Meuron & Comp, the regulation dial above (work lacking), the 3 train movement with silk suspension and grande sonnerie striking on 3 bells with outside rack striking work, 24½ in. high (62 cm.), Jura. **£1,500-1,700** *S*

A mahogany bracket clock, with brass carrying handle, the dial signed Thomas Monkhouse London, movement with triple chain fusee, chiming on 8 bells with anchor escapement, 17 in. high (43.5 cm.). **£1,500-£1,700** *C*

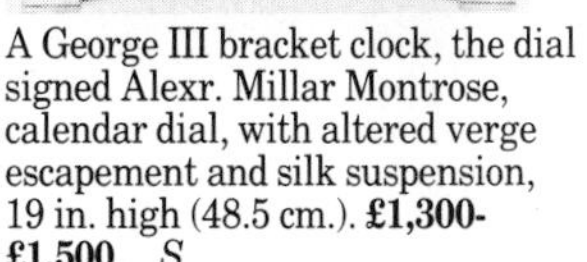

A George III bracket clock, the dial signed Alexr. Millar Montrose, calendar dial, with altered verge escapement and silk suspension, 19 in. high (48.5 cm.). **£1,300-£1,500** *S*

A George III mahogany striking bracket clock, the dial signed Robt. Newman Camberwell, movement converted to anchor escapement, 21 in. high (53.5 cm.). **£1,800-£2,000** *C*

A brass inlaid ebonised chiming bracket clock by John Moore & Sons, Clerkenwell, London, no. 11469, the 3 train movement with chain fusee, 17 in. (43 cm.), mid 19th C. **£450-550** *S*

A George III ebonised striking bracket clock by Godfrie Poy London, the dial signed behind the false pendulum aperture, movement with trip repeat, verge escapement and signature repeated on the scroll engraved backplate with securing brackets to the case, with restorations, 14¾ in. high (37.5 cm.). **£3,800-4,200** *C*

A mahogany bracket clock, the movement with twin chain fusee and anchor escapement, and numbered 6800, the painted dial signed Payne and Co., with winding handle and pendulum, 17 in. (43 cm.), c. 1850. **£400-500** *S*

A George IV mahogany chiming bracket clock, 9½ in. diam. enamel dial, 3 train quarter striking movement with anchor escapement, chiming on a series of 8 bells, the backplate inscribed Robert Roskell, Liverpool, inlaid throughout with cut brass and ebony designs, 23 in. overall (58 cm.), early 19th C. **£750-£950** *SC*

A late George III mahogany chiming bracket clock, 9 in. painted dial signed Sampson London, the 3 train movement chiming the quarters on 10 bells and with chain fusee and anchor escapement, 20 in. high (51 cm.). **£900-1,100** *S*

A Gothic revival oak bracket clock by Salsbury & Sons, 56 High Street, Guildford, with quarter striking on 8 bells and 1 gong, the dial with subsidiary chime/silent, slow/fast and Cambridge/8 bells dials in the arch, with pendulum and winder, 31 in. high (80 cm.), c. 1850. **£600-700** *S*

BRACKET CLOCKS
Case Finish

Ebony veneer	from c. 1660 to c. 1850	**Mahogany**	from c. 1730
Walnut	from c. 1670 to c. 1795	**Dials**	
		Square dial	to c. 1770
Marquetry	from c. 1680 to c. 1740	**Broken arch dial**	from c. 1720
Rosewood	from c. 1790	**Round/painted**	
Lacquered	from c. 1700 to c. 1760	**silvered**	from c. 1760

A George III mahogany musical bracket clock, signed John Thwaites Clerkenwell London No. 2601, 6 tune selector dials and 3 train movement playing the selected tune on 10 bells and with chain fusee and verge escapement, 26 in. high (66 cm.), and a mahogany bracket, 15½ in. high (39.5 cm.). **£4,500-5,500** *S*

A mahogany and inlaid bracket clock, the 6¾ in. (17 cm.) dial inscribed Geo Tupman, London, the twin train movement with circular plates, anchor escapement, 1 ft. 9 in. high (53 cm.), and its bracket, early 19th C. **£1,800-2,200** *P*

A William IV rosewood bracket clock by Vulliamy, London, the twin train movement signed Vulliamy, London, No. 1142, with anchor escapement and pull/repeat, 10 in. (25.5 cm.) high. **£1,900-£2,200** *P*

An ebony-veneered bracket clock, the 6½ in. dial bearing the signature T. Tompion, the movement with latched dial and plates, 6 ringed pillars and later chain fusees and anchor escapement, with restoration, alarum work removed, with contemporary engraved winding key, 14½ in. high (37 cm.), early 18th C. **£1,100-1,300** *S*

The style of the mounts and recessed alarum disc attached to the hour hand suggest a Dutch influence or origin.

A Regency satinwood bracket clock, with ebony stringing and moulding, the circular silvered dial signed John Todd Glasgow with deadbeat escapement, fusee and chain with maintaining power, 17 in. high (43 cm.). **£550-650** *C*

An ebonised chiming bracket clock by E. J. Vokes, Bath, the 3 train movement with chain fusee and quarter striking on 8 bells and 1 rod gong, with winder, 24 in. (61 cm.), 1860's. **£700-800** *S*

A rosewood striking bracket clock, the border signed Vulliamy London, glazed side panels, with double fusee with rack strike on bell anchor escapement and wood rod pendulum, the backplate signed, 17 in. (43 cm.) high. **£1,000-£1,200** *C*

A George III mahogany bracket clock, the chipped 7 in. enamel dial signed Vulliamy London, the movement with arched plates, chain fusees and anchor escapement, the backplate signed, 15 in. high (38 cm.). **£1,100-1,300** *S*

A William IV mahogany bracket clock, the painted dial signed J Webb, 446 Oxford St, London, the movement with pendulum locking (nut lacking), with winder, 19 in. (48 cm.), 1830's. **£300-400** *S*

A late George II brass-inlaid ebony chiming bracket clock, the dial signed Wm. Webster Exchange Alley London, the 3 train movement chiming the quarters on 8 bells and with chain fusees and verge escapement, similarly signed backplate, 18 in. high (46 cm.) and an ogee bracket, now painted grey 7½ in. high (19 cm.). **£3,500-£4,500** *S*

A mahogany bracket clock by Webster, 91 Grace Church Street, London, No. 20600, 15¼ in. high (38 cm.), c. 1870. **£400-500** *S*

A 19th C. German carved oak bracket clock, by Winterhalder, Berlin, the brass 6 in. dial with silvered chapter ring with fast, slow and strike silent subsidiary dial, twin fusee movement, Westminster quarter chiming on 5 gongs, height 20 in. **£450-500** *DS*

A George III ebonised chiming bracket clock with a calendar dial in the arch signed Weeks Coventry Street London, repeating 6 pillar 3 train movement chiming the quarters on 8 bells and with outside deadbeat escapement, 17 in. high (43 cm.). **£2,500-3,000** *S*

A Regency mahogany bracket clock, the dial inscribed 'John Wilson, London', the movement with plain backplate striking on a bell, on ball feet, 21½ in. (55 cm.). **£400-500** *SS*

A repeating rosewood and marquetry bracket clock by Winterhalder & Hofmeier with quarter striking on rod gongs, and a pull repeat, with pendulum, German, 20 in. high (51 cm.), c. 1900. **£400-500** *S*

A late Louis XIV tortoiseshell-veneered bracket clock, with ormolu dial and enamel numerals, the movement with verge escapement and outside countwheel striking on a bell in the dome, the backplate signed 'Les Frères Dumont, Besancon', 21½ in. (55 cm.) high. **£900-1,200** *SS*

An Italian ebonised bracket clock, silvered dial plate, shaped steel hands, external steel ratchets and clicks, twin going-barrels, verge escapement, with restorations, 19 in. (48 cm.) high, early 18th C. **£900-1,100** *C*

A mahogany quarter striking bracket clock by M. Winterhalder & Hofmeier, 11½ in. (29 cm.), c. 1900. **£300-400** *S*

An English bracket clock, fusee movement and original painted dial in mahogany case, 13 in. high, c. 1860. **£230-260** *IAT*

An ebonised bracket clock with quarter striking on 9 bells, the dial with subsidiary chimes/silent and Westminster/chime on 8 bells dials, with key and pendulum, 17¾ in. (45 cm.), c. 1860. **£800-900** *S*

A mahogany musical automaton bracket clock, a procession of automaton figures in the arch, the painted background with a dancer and 2 musicians, the 3 train movement with verge escapement and bob pendulum, 26 in. high (66 cm.). **£4,500-5,000** *S*

An unusual gilt-bronze mounted bracket clock, with blue enamel numerals and the movement with rectangular plates, later anchor escapement and outside countwheel, probably South German, with restoration, 29½ in. (75 cm.), early 18th C. **£1,100-£1,300** *S*

A Louis XV tortoiseshell and brass inlaid balloon-shaped bracket clock, fitted with a later English 8-day fusee movement, on matching bracket with ormolu mask corners, 54 in. high overall. **£1,500-1,800** *DWB*

A good Louis XV contreboulle clock and bracket, signed Fiacre Clement A Paris, the case stamped B. Lieutaud, 26½ in. high (67 cm.) and a matching ogee bracket, mid 18th C. **£3,200-3,600** *S*

A good and small ebonised bracket clock with quarter striking on 8 bells and 1 gong, with pendulum and key, 16¼ in. high (42 cm.), c. 1870. **£1,100-1,300** *S*

An ebonised quarter chiming bracket clock, the 3 train fusee movement with anchor escapement, gong striking, and chiming the quarters on 8 bells actuated by a pin drum, 21 in. (53.5 cm.). **£800-£900** *L*

An ormolu-mounted boulle bracket clock, 61 in. (155 cm.) high overall, 19th C. **£2,400-2,800** *C*

Right
A Victorian oak bracket clock, with 8-day striking and chiming movement. **£600-£700** *M*

A Victorian burr-elm bracket clock, the movement striking on a gong, 27½ in. (70 cm.) high, with matching wall bracket, 15 in. (38 cm.) high. **£500-600** *SS*

A late 19th C. bracket clock, in ebony and ormolu-mounted case, etched steel dial, Westminster/ Cambridge chimes on ormolu scroll feet, side carrying handles, 30 in. high. **£1,100-1,300** *HWO*

A good tortoiseshell bracket clock with quarter striking on 8 bells and 1 gong, with pendulum and keys, 53 cm., c. 1870. **£950-1,150** *S*

A late 19th C. ebonised bracket clock, with a brass and silvered face, 2 secondary dials and striking movement. **£550-600** *M*

A boulle bracket clock, the case inlaid with brass foliage on a red ground, the whole with gilt bronze foliate mounts, 18 in. high (46 cm.), c. 1880. **£500-600** *S*

A simulated rosewood mahogany bracket clock, the chain fusee movement with quarter striking on bells and gongs, with 3 keys and pendulum, 29 in. (73.6 cm.), 1890's. **£800-900** *S*

An ebonised twin chain fusee bracket clock striking the hours and the quarters on 8 bells and 4 rod gongs, with pendulum locking, with pendulum, case key and later winder, 30 in. (76 cm.), c. 1890. **£800-1,000** *S*

A twin chain fusee ebonised bracket clock, striking on 8 bells and 1 gong, with strike/silent in the arch, with pendulum, 2 winders and 2 case keys, 28¾ in. (72 cm.), c. 1890. **£600-800** *S*

A German twin fusee bracket clock, 11½ in., c. 1900. **£475-550** *TP*

A large Edwardian bracket clock with 7 in. dial, with chime/silent dial and Westminster/chime on 8 bells dials in the arch, the triple fusee movement with anchor escapement, chiming on 8 bells and striking on 1 gong, 29½ in. high. **£800-900** *Bea*

. unusual Louis XVI gilt-bronze nd marble clock, 18½ in. high 7 cm.), c. 1780, later movement. **3,000-4,000** *S*

A late Louis XV gilt-bronze mantel clock, the dial signed Stollewerk A Paris, the movement signed Moisy A Paris No. 719 and with outside countwheel and altered escapement, 18 in. high (46 cm.), c. 1770. **£3,500-4,500** *S*

A Louis XV bronze and gilt-bronze bull mantel clock, the dial signed Causard à Paris, 17 in. high (44 cm.), mid 18th C. **£3,000-£4,000** *S*

\n ormolu, bronze and marble pendules a cercles tournants' with he minute and hour rings in a blue painted sphere, the movement with in and pallet escapement, the oing train geared to the 2 circles hrough a counterwheel, with nidden keyholes behind books and yre, 39 in. high. **£3,500-4,000** *'HF*

A Louis XVI gilt-bronze mantel clock, the dial signed Lepaute Hger du Roi, supported on a central fluted column surrounded by 3 female figures, 21½ in. high (55 cm.), c. 1775. **£4,000-5,000** *S*

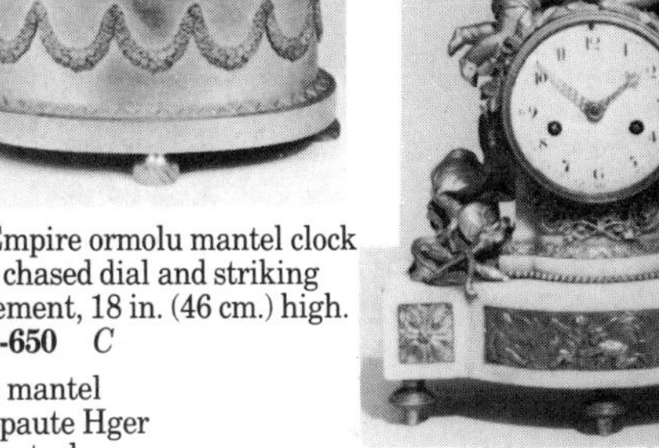

An Empire ormolu mantel clock with chased dial and striking movement, 18 in. (46 cm.) high. **£550-650** *C*

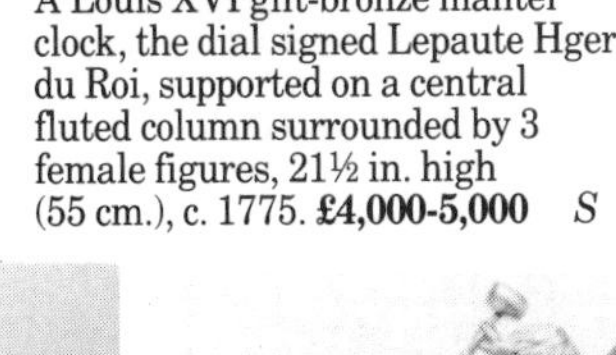

A Louis XVI ormolu and carrara marble mantel clock with dial signed Loguet à Paris with striking movement, 11 in. (28 cm.) wide. **£550-650** *C*

A Louis XVI ormolu mantel clock, signed on the dial and striking movement Delunesy à Paris and numbered 250, 12¼ in. (31 cm.) wide by 13¼ in. (33.5 cm.) high. **£2,300-2,700** *C*

Nicholas Pierre Delunesy became maître-horloger on 16 February 1769. He made the movement for the celebrated Avignon Clock, for which Pierre Gouthière cast the case, now in the Wallace Collection.

An Empire gilt-bronze mantel clock with an enamel dial, the movement with silk suspension and outside countwheel, with a plaque inscribed Envoye à Cithère, 14 in. high (35.5 cm.), c. 1810. **£1,500-2,000** *S*

An Empire ormolu mantel clock with striking movement, the base with neo-classical plaques, 16¾ in. (42.5 cm.) high. **£600-800** *C*

A Louis Philippe gilt-bronze mantel clock, the movement stamped Médaille d'Or Pons, 1827 à St. Nicholas, with outside countwheel and silk suspension, with key and pendulum, 58.5 cm., 1830's. **£700-800** *S*

A Charles X gilt-bronze mantel clock, the movement with silk suspension and outside countwheel, the dial signed Pienot Arne Rue Vivinne No., with pendulum, 17¼ in. (44 cm.), c. 1820. **£300-£400** *S*

A small Empire gilt-bronze and marble chariot mantel clock, the enamel chapter ring signed Blanc Fils Palais Royal, the movement with silk suspension and outside countwheel, on a white-veined green marble base, 15 in. high (38 cm.), c. 1810. **£2,000-2,500** *S*

The open-ended reference system
Miller's Antiques Price Guide builds up year by year to form the most comprehensive photo-reference system available. The first four volumes contain photographs of over 30,000 stock items!

A gilt-metal and bronze mantel clock, the dial signed Masson, Paris, 22 in. (56 cm.) high. **£900-£1,000** *C*

A French Empire ormolu mantel clock, on rectangular verdi-antico marble base, the French movement with countwheel strike on a bell and silk suspension, 16½ in. high, early 19th C. **£420-480** *CSK*

A Louis Philippe parcel gilt-bronze mantel clock, 28 in. (71 cm.), 1830's. **£600-700** *S*

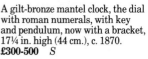

A gilt-bronze mantel clock, the movement stamped Wm. Roskell, Paris, with pendulum, 43 cm., c. 1870. **£650-750** *S*

A French mantel clock by Martin Baskett, Paris, with Sèvres panels, c. 1840. **£2,400-2,800** *SA*

Panels actually painted at Sèvres.

A gilt-bronze mantel clock, the dial with roman numerals, with key and pendulum, now with a bracket, 17¼ in. high (44 cm.), c. 1870. **£300-500** *S*

An ormolu cased French mantel clock by Henri Marc of Paris, with silk suspension, 17½ in. high, c. 1850. **£250-300** *TP*

A French bronze mantel clock, with circular black slate dial, the French movement striking on a bell, stamped S. Watenberg, Paris, 22½ in. high. **£500-600** *CSK*

A French porcelain mounted gilt-brass sculptural mantel clock, the movement with brocot type suspension and bell striking, 19¼ in. (49 cm.). **£400-450** *L*

A French ormolu and porcelain mantel clock, the twin train movement with white enamel dial, the plinth inset with porcelain plaquettes, 1 ft. 3 in. (38 cm.) high. **£600-800** *P*

A mid 19th C. French mantel clock, the movement with outside countwheel striking on a bell, on a veined marble base, 12½ in. (32 cm.) high. **£500-600** *SS*

A 19th C. French bronze ormolu mantel clock, the twin train movement with white enamel dial inscribed Gavelle, Paris, 1 ft. 4 in. (41 cm.) high. **£700-800** *P*

A gilt spelter and porcelain mantel clock, the Japy movement with half-hour striking on a bell and with outside countwheel, the case surmounted by a figure of a woman holding a basket of flowers, 18 by 24 in. (46 by 61 cm.) overall, mid 19th C. **£300-350** *SC*

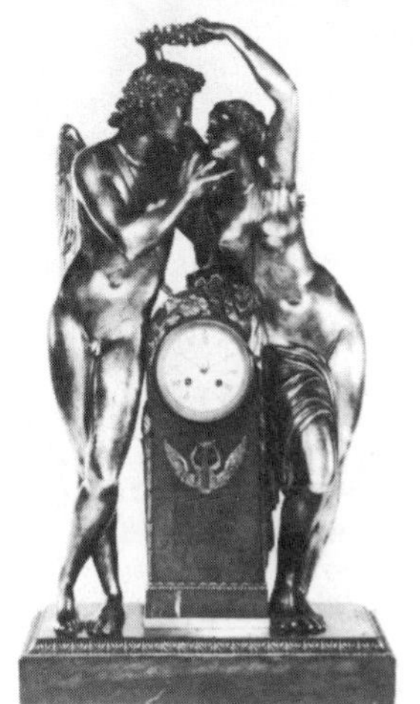
A 19th C. French gilt-bronze mantel clock of large size, the twin train movement with white enamel dial, 2 ft. 6 in. (76 cm.). **£600-700** *P*

A porcelain cased boudoir timepiece, 13½ in. high, c. 1870. **£250-300** *TP*

A French bronze and ormolu clock, 21 in., c. 1860. **£400-450** *TP*

A Palais Royal ormolu-mounted cut glass mantel clock with chased dial, striking movement and sunburst pendulum, 18½ in. (47 cm.) high. **£900-1,000** *C*

A French 8-day ormolu boudoir clock, 9½ in. high, c. 1870. **£350-£400** *TP*

A late Louis XVI white marble and gilt-bronze mantel clock, the dial signed Merra A Paria, the movement with silk suspension and outside countwheel, possibly Italian, 17½ in. high (44.5 cm.), c. 1785. **£600-800** *S*

A gilt-bronze and porcelain mantel clock, with pendulum, 16 in. high (41 cm.), c. 1880. **£350-400** *S*

A Louis Philippe ormolu and Paris porcelain portico mantel clock, the plinth with an antique 'bas relief' panel, 25½ in. (65 cm.) high, dated 1833 on the reverse. **£1,700-2,000** *C*

An unusual Charles X bronze and gilt-bronze mantel clock, the movement with silk suspension and butterfly pendulum, 17 in. high (43 cm.), c. 1830. **£3,000-£3,500** *S*

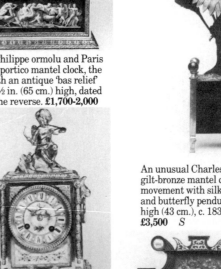

An Algerian onyx and gilt-bronze mantel clock, the dial with an enamel chapter ring, the Marti movement striking on a gong, 15 by 11 in. (38 by 28 cm.), 3rd quarter 19th C. **£400-500** *SC*

A gilt-bronze and porcelain mantel clock, with painted jewelled dial, with key and pendulum, with a plinth, 12 in. high (31 cm.), c. 1880. **£400-500** *S*

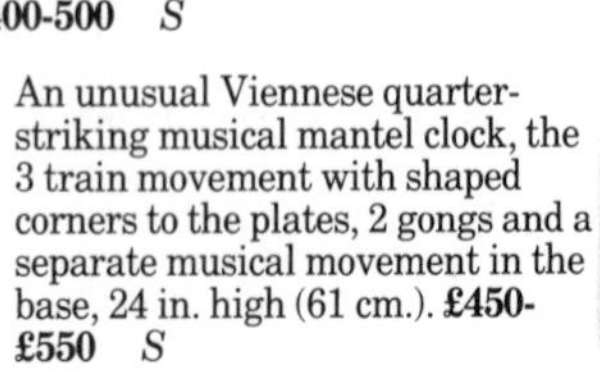

An unusual Viennese quarter-striking musical mantel clock, the 3 train movement with shaped corners to the plates, 2 gongs and a separate musical movement in the base, 24 in. high (61 cm.). **£450-£550** *S*

A brass mantel clock with quarter striking on 5 blued steel gongs, the movement numbered 122, with key, winder and pendulum, 31¼ in. (79 cm.), c. 1880. **£700-900** *S*

A gilt and patinated bronze and marble mantel clock, with a figure of Napoleon seated on a chair, 13 in. high (33 cm.), c. 1870. **£750-£850** *S*

A French boudoir timepiece in ormolu case, 6½ in. high, c. 1900. **£150-200** *TP*

A fine and impressive quarter chiming ormolu mantel clock by Edward White, London, the back with concealed panel, shuttered winding apertures and strike/silent lever, Cambridge chimes at the quarters and striking the hours on a steel gong, 1 ft. 2½ in. high. **£8,500-9,500** *P*

An ebonised cased clock by Juchy of Prague, 3 train grande sonnerie movement, 22½ in., c. 1850. **£500-£600** *TP*

A Louis XVI ormolu musical mantel clock, signed Chles Bertrand A Paris, the base containing the musical movement playing 2 tunes on 9 bells with 18 hammers, 11½ in. wide by 19¾ in. high (29 by 50 cm.). **£3,500-4,500** *C*

Joseph Charles Paul Bertrand, fl. 1772-89.

A gilt-bronze and porcelain mantel clock, the case inset with panels painted with portrait medallions on a pink ground, with pendulum and stand, 14½ in. high (37 cm.), c. 1880. **£300-400** *S*

A large brass mantel clock, the movement with outside countwheel, the dial with roman numerals and turned centre, in a drum case, with key and pendulum, 23 in. high (51 cm.), c. 1850. **£600-700** *S*

A gilt and patinated bronze and black marble mantel clock, the dial with roman numerals and snake hands, with key and pendulum, 25 in. high (64 cm.), c. 1870. **£500-£600** *S*

A 19th C. French mantel clock, the enamelled dial inscribed F. Berthoud (?) à Paris, with glazed compartment below, on marble base, 29 in. **£1,100-1,300** *GSP*

A gilt-bronze mantel clock, with pendulum and giltwood base, movement French, case probably English, 16 in. (41 cm.), c. 1860. **£400-500** *S*

A Thomas Cole porcelain-mounted strutt timepiece with platform escapement, signed Made by Thos. Cole for Barry, London, 6½ in. (16.5 cm.), 1860's. **£700-800** *S*

A gilt-bronze mantel clock, the movement with a mercury pendulum, with key and pendulum, probably American, 15 in. (38 cm.), c. 1870. **£200-300** *S*

A French clock, the case representing a silvered cannon ball on ormolu golden eagle, 14 in. high, c. 1870. **£900-1,250** *TP*

A gilt-bronze mantel clock, the movement by Aubin A Paris, no. 1003 with outside countwheel, 43 cm., c. 1870. **£350-400** *S*

A gilt-bronze and porcelain mantel clock, the movement stamped A.F., with key and pendulum, 23 in. (59 cm.), c. 1880. **£1,200-1,400** *S*

A French gilt-brass mantel clock for the Turkish market, the movement with silk suspension, outside locking plate, stamped S.N., and numbered 1817, on ebonised wooden stand, 17¾ in. (45.2 cm.). **£500-600** *L*

A 19th C. French ormolu mantel clock by LePine A Paris, the base in the form of a prison entrance with a figure incarcerated, the twin train movement with countwheel strike and white enamel dial, raised on a marble base, 1 ft. 8 in. (51 cm.). **£1,400-1,600** *P*

A gilt-bronze and porcelain mantel clock, the movement stamped G.V., with key and pendulum, 16 in. (41 cm.), c. 1880. **£700-800** *S*

A gilt-bronze and porcelain mantel clock, with pendulum, 23 in. (59 cm.), c. 1880. **£500-600** *S*

A brass and porcelain mantel clock, the dial painted with arabic numerals and birds, the sides with similar panels, with key and pendulum, 14 in. high (36 cm.), c. 1880. **£350-400** *S*

A French green onyx and ormolu cased clock, 15½ in. high, c. 1880. **£450-500** *TP*

A gilt-spelter and porcelain mantel clock, with pendulum, 20½ in. (52 cm.), c. 1880. **£700-800** *S*

A French mantel clock with striking movement within an elaborate brass case and Limoges porcelain panels with gilt wheatear decoration, 1 plaque cracked, 17 in., late 19th C. **£130-180** *WHL*

An unusual gilt-bronze mantel clock, with pendulum, 22 in. (56 cm.), c. 1890. **£600-700** *S*

A French 19th C. burr-walnut and ormolu-mounted lyre clock, the twin train movement with white enamel dial decorated with floral swags, 1 ft. 6 in. (46 cm.) high. **£600-700** *P*

A gilt-bronze and champleve enamel mantel clock by Martie & Cie, with mercury pendulum, 28 cm., c. 1890. **£450-550** *S*

A large and ornate French brass cased mantel clock, the cylindrical 8-day movement with hour and half-hour strike, 20 in. high. **£400-£500** *DDM*

A lacquered brass and champleve mantel clock, inscribed Polland Ltd, Belfast, the French movement striking on a gong, 14 in. (36 cm.), late 19th/early 20th C. **£250-300** *SC*

A plaster sculptural mantel clock, the arched case signed Lapeque, the movement now with cylinder escapement, 62 by 56 cm., dated 1901. **£250-350** *S*

A gilt-bronze and enamel lyre mantel clock, pendulum studded with brilliants, 19 in. (48 cm.), c. 1890. **£1,700-1,900** *S*

A French boulle mantel clock, 12 in. high, c. 1880. **£500-600** *TP*

An unusual silver travelling or mantel clock, the 3 in. dial signed Spink & Son Ltd, 17 & 18 Piccadilly London W., the movement with chain fusees, lever escapement and gong striking, London hallmarks for 1904, 10¼ in. high (26 cm.). **£1,500-£2,000** *S*

A French 19th C. ormolu-mounted boulle mantel clock, the enamel dial signed 'Grohe, Paris', striking on a gong, with ebonised plinth and glass dome, 12½ in. (32 cm.). **£400-£500** *S*

A boulle mantel clock, the dial signed Bozzo à Angers, with a brown tortoiseshell ground case, with pendulum, 12 in. (30 cm.), c. 1880. **£300-400** *S*

An ormolu-mounted, tortoiseshell-cased, French clock by Japy of Paris, 12 in., c. 1870. **£300-350** *TP*

A small Regency rosewood case mantel clock by Wilson, Stamford, roman numerals, 8-day movement. **£500-600** *TM*

A Georgian steeple clock by John Palmer of London, in rosewood case, 13¾ in. high, 1829. **£750-£900** *TP*

A petite sonnerie 'Neuchatel' clock, the case decorated in black lacquer with gilt foliate design, the twin train movement of 14-day duration, strike and repeat by means of a separate train with pull cord, and with verge escapement, 1 ft. 9 in. high (54 cm.), late 18th C. **£800-£1,200** *P*

A Directoire grey marble mantel clock with striking movement, plinth bearing a label inscribed '26 Oct. 1806 presented by Citizen Conisberg to Prof. Hagen', 14½ in. high (37 cm.). **£500-700** *C*

A satinwood-veneered mantel clock, the twin train movement signed 'Ganthony Cheapside', with anchor escapement, 9¾ in. high (25 cm.). **£600-700** *P*

A mantel timepiece, the gilt dial signed Parkinson & Frodsham Change Alley London, the movement with chain fusee, anchor escapement and similarly signed backplate, formerly ebonised, 10¾ in. high (27.5 cm.), early 19th C. **£700-800** *S*

A mahogany mantel clock by Joseph Jones London, with quarter striking on 8 silvered bells and 1 large bell, with 2 keys and a pendulum, 18 in. high (46 cm.), c. 1830. **£500-600** *S*

A German rococo mantel clock, the going-barrel movement with verge escapement, strike and alarm on bell, 12¼ in. high (31 cm.). **£800-£900** *C*

A large ebonised-cased library clock by Thwaites & Reed, with 3 train fusee movement, Whitehall quarter chimes, 29½ in., c. 1820. **£800-900** *TP*

A rosewood English mantel clock, the 2 train chain fusee movement with anchor escapement, gong striking and signed on the back plate Murray & Co., Royal Exchange, London, 10¾ in. (27.2 cm.). **£1,400-1,600** *L*

An ebonised mantel clock by Thomas Boxell, with twin chain fusee and striking on a single gong, with key and pendulum, 12½ in. (32 cm.). **£1,000-1,200** *S*

A mid 19th C. ormolu desk strutt timepiece of small size, by Thomas Cole, No. 799 (design 74), the cylinder movement with oval silvered dial, 3¼ in. (8 cm.) high. **£300-350** *P*

A mid 19th C. 8-day chronometer by Kelvin White & Hutton of 11 Billiter Street, London, No. 545, 11½ in high by 10½ in. wide (29 by 27 cm.). **£1,900-2,200** *S*

A mahogany mantel clock, the fusee movement with pendulum locking, the brass dial signed W. Higgins, 10 Ernest Street, Regents Park, with 3 keys and winder, 22 in. (56 cm.), c. 1840's. **£250-£350** *S*

A brass clock with new escapement, 11½ in. high, c. 1835. **£80-90** *MPA*

An oak quarter repeating grande sonnerie mantel clock, the 3 chain fusee movement striking on 9 bells, with key and pendulum, 21 in. (53.5 cm.), c. 1850. **£300-400** *S*

An ebony calendar mantel timepiece, the movement stamped D.H., the dial signed J.H. Steward, 406 Strand, London, 10¼ in. (26 cm.), c. 1870. **£300-350** *S*

An unusual French ebonised gilt-metal mounted mantel clock, the twin train movement signed A.N. Delolme, Abe unsuic, with countwheel strike and anchor escapement to the backplate, with bi-metallic compensated balance and blued helical hairspring, 1 ft. 5½ in. high (44 cm.), 19th C. **£400-£700** *P*

A French gilt-brass boudoir clock, the lever movement with engraved backplate, 'William Barker, Jeweller and Watchmaker, 164 New Bond Street, London', 9 in. high (23 cm.), c. 1870. **£400-500** *SS*

A black marble and malachite calendar mantel clock, the movement with 'open brocot' escapement, with a calendar dial with phase of the moon, day, date and month indicators, with pendulum and key, 17 in. high (43 cm.), c. 1870. **£600-700** *S*

A mahogany mantel regulator, the dial signed Frodsham, the movement with deadbeat escapement, weight driven and maintaining power on fusee, 4 wheel train and half seconds pendulum, 25 in. high (52 cm.), mid 19th C. **£850-950** *SC*

A black marble barometer mantel clock, the movement with 'open brocot' escapement, the dial above a barometer with a thermometer, with key and pendulum, 14½ in. high (37 cm.), c. 1870. **£350-400** *S*

A malachite inlaid black marble calendar mantel clock, no. 1284, with 'open brocot' escapement, 16¾ in. (42.5 cm.), c. 1880. **£450-£500** *S*

A polished slate combination mantel clock, with 'open brocot' escapement, the movement striking on a bell, and stamped E. Legrand Paris, 18½ by 17 in. (47 by 43 cm.), mid 19th C. **£400-450** *SC*

A late 19th C. walnut-cased mantel clock. **£70-100** *JMW*

An unusual French 4 glass clock with ship's wheel pendulum and visible escapement, 13¾ in. high, c. 1880. **£600-700** *TP*

An unusual mahogany-cased 4 glass battery mantel clock, inscribed Eureka Clock Co. Ltd, London, the movement with a massive bi-metallic compensated balance, with terminals for a battery, 13½ by 8½ in. (34 by 21 cm.), late 19th C. **£350-400** *SC*

A 4½ in. symphonion mantel clock, contained in glazed oak case, musical movement with single comb and centre drive, together with 2 discs, German, 11½ in. (29 cm.) high, c. 1900. **£400-450** *S*

A French figured walnut and parcel gilt mantel clock, the 2 train movement with anchor escapement, gong striking and signed J. Silvani, Paris, 10 in. (25.4 cm.). **£120-180** *L*

An American striking mantel clock with white enamel dial in a mahogany case, 14 in. high, c. 1900. **£60-70** *IAT*

A French brass-cased clock, 6½ in. high, c. 1900. **£80-100** *TP*

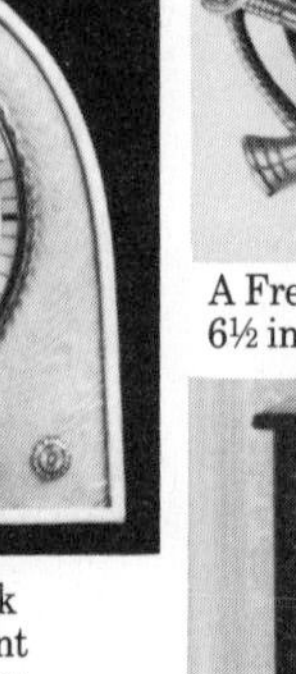

A silver, gold and enamel desk clock, enamelled in translucent pink over wavy engine-turning within a band of opaque white enamel, set with gold flowerheads, silver strut support, maker's mark for J. Britzin, Moscow, 3¾ in. high (8.5 cm.), 1908-12. **£1,100-1,300** *S*

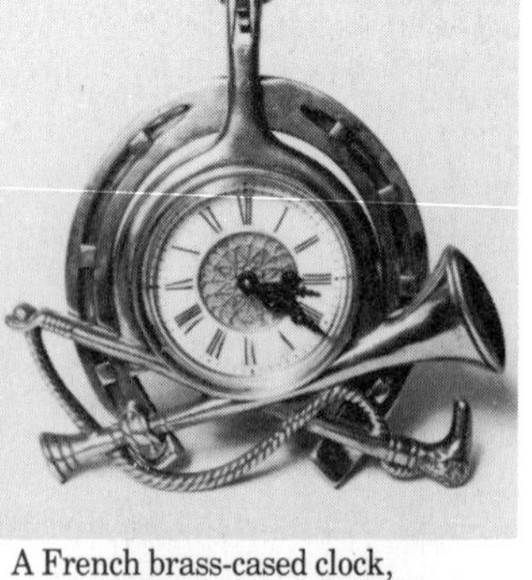

A striking mantel clock in a walnut and ebonised case, 10 in. high, c. 1890. **£60-70** *IAT*

A French ebonised and walnut mantel clock with bell striking movement, 10 in. high, c. 1890. **£70-80** *IAT*

A brass petite sonnerie carriage clock, the movement stamped in an oval Drocourt Frs Paris, strike/ repeat and alarm on 2 bells, enamel dial, corner chips, 5¼ in. high (14.5 cm.). **£700-800** *C*

A small mahogany cased 4 glass carriage clock, the movement signed Arnold & Dent 84 Strand, fusee and chain, the arched dial with signed enamel chapter-disc, arched glazed side panels, 9 in. high (22.5 cm.). **£1,800-2,000** *C*

An Edwardian mantel clock, 7 in. high. **£50-70** *IHA*

A fine French brass repeat alarum carriage clock, the 2 train movement with lever escapement, compensated balance, blued steel spiral spring, half-hour gong striking, repeating at will, numbered 8288, and bearing the trade stamp of Pierre and Alfred Drocourt, 6 in. (14.7 cm.). **£850-£950** *L*

A nickel-plated combined timepiece and barometer, the timepiece with a white enamel dial, lever escapement, the aneroid barometer with a white enamel register, rectangular polished slate base, 9 in. (23 cm.) overall, late 19th C. **£140-180** *SC*

An Edwardian balloon clock with French 8-day movement, 10¾ in. **£150-200** *TP*

A 19th C. Swiss gilt-brass petite sonnerie carriage clock by P. Girard, Chaux de Fonds, the movement with chronometer escapement, the striking and repeating work visible upon the backplate, with alarm train, 7½ in. high (19 cm.). **£2,500-2,700** *P*

An unusual gilt-metal travelling clock, the 2½ in. enamel dial signed Barwise, London, the movement with chain fusees, vertical lever escapement mounted behind the backplate and bell striking, 6 in. high (15 cm.). **£750-850** *S*

A French brass carriage clock of bamboo construction, the twin train lever movement with push repeat and alarm, the dial and sides of porcelain with a gilt ground and painted in the Chinese style, 8 in. high (20 cm.). **£950-1,050** *P*

A porcelain-mounted carriage clock, the repeating lever movement with gong striking and numbered 284, in a moulded case with outset corner columns, 6¼ in. high (16 cm.). **£1,100-1,300** *S*

An English gilt-metal travelling or mantel timepiece, the lever movement with monometallic balance, the back engraved with a view of Windsor and the side panels with other castles, 5¼ in. high (13.5 cm.). **£600-700** *S*

A small enamel-mounted alarum timepiece, with ¾ in. dial, the Swiss movement with lever escapement, alarum disc on the backplate and bell in the base, in a moulded case with guilloche red enamel corners, with a travelling case, 3 in. high (7.5 cm.). **£400-£500** *S*

An early French brass calendar alarum repeating carriage clock, the 2 train movement with lever escapement, plain brass 3-arm balance, blued steel spiral spring, contained in an early multi-piece case, 18.5 cm. **£600-700** *L*

An hour repeating alarum carriage clock, with key and leather case, 6 in. (15 cm.). **£400-500** *S*

An enamel-mounted miniature French brass carriage timepiece, the movement with lever escapement, compensated balance, numbered 662, and signed A. Dumas, the enamel dial signed Ancock, London, and decorated in the Art Nouveau style (Mignonnette number 3), A. Dumas, 44 Rue Bonaparte, Paris, 4 in. (10.2 cm.). **£750-850** *L*

A round alarum carriage clock with cylinder escapement, 5¾ in. high. **£250-280** *TP*

A gilt-bronze repeating carriage clock, the platform lever escapement with compensation balance, with key, 8¾ in. (22 cm.), c. 1880. **£500-700** *S*

A gilt-metal striking carriage clock with chaff-cutter escapement in the manner of Garnier, the movement signed Martin Baskett & Cie. A Paris, now with travelling case, 6 in. high (15 cm.). **£1,000-1,300** *C*

A late Victorian carriage clock with lever movement, 6½ in. high. **£160-190** *TP*

A French gilt-brass carriage clock, the 2 train movement with lever escapement, compensated balance, half-hour gong striking, repeating at will, numbered 7917, and bearing the trade stamp of Pierre and Alfred Drocourt, 6 in. (16 cm.). **£500-550** *L*

A miniature carriage clock in leather covered case with silver corner mounts, 3½ in. high, c. 1900. **£150-180** *TP*

A French gilt-brass repeat alarum carriage clock, the movement with lever escapement, compensated balance, gong striking, and numbered 4312, and repeating at will, 5¾ in. (14.6 cm.). **£900-£1,000** *L*

A French gilt-brass carriage clock, the twin train lever movement with push/repeat and white enamel dial, in a canalee-style case, 7 in. high (18 cm.). **£350-450** *P*

A French brass carriage clock, the movement with lever escapement and compensated balance, striking half-hourly on a gong, 7 in. (17.8 cm.). **£200-250** *L*

A French late 19th C. champleve enamel carriage timepiece, the cylinder movement No. 907 signed Boxell Brighton, the dial within a turquoise blue enamel ground with polychrome decoration, the case of Anglaise Riche design. **£1,500-£1,700** *P*

A gilt-metal chronometer carriage timepiece, inscribed Vulliamy, London, the movement with 6 screwed pillars, sunken platform escapement, Earnshaw type spring detent with bi-metallic compensated balance, 9 in. high (23 cm.). **£1,700-1,900** *P*

A silver-cased carriage clock, the movement with lever escapement and white enamel dial, 2¾ in. (7 cm.) high, and its case. **£60-80** *P*

A French export carriage clock, dial cracked, 6 in. high, c. 1880. **£160-200** *BP*

A carriage clock with cylinder movement, 5½ in., c. 1890. **£140-£180** *TP*

A French carriage clock, repeat movement, 6½ in. high. **£350-400** *TP*

An oval French carriage clock, lever movement, 6¼ in. high. **£200-£250** *TP*

A French alarm carriage timepiece with bell striking alarm, travelling case, 4½ in. high. **£125-150** *PWC*

A strike and alarum carriage clock, signed Japy Freres, 7½ in., c. 1870. **£400-450** *TP*

(l.) A French gilt-brass cased repeater carriage clock, the dial inscribed Goldsmiths Co. **£200-£250** *PWC*

(c.) A good French repeater carriage clock, the dial inscribed Clarke, Royal Exchange, London. **£400-450** *PWC*

(r.) A French gilt-brass cased carriage timepiece. **£100-140** *PWC*

A very large grande sonnerie alarum carriage clock, signed E.W. Streeter 37 Conduit Street London, with pointed tooth lever escapement, compensation balance, gong striking, the backplate with the stamp of Drocourt, numbered 9020, with the original numbered key, 8½ in. high (21.5 cm.). **£3,000-£3,500** *S*

A wing alarum lantern clock with 7 in. dial, the movement with verge escapement mounted between the 2 trains and outside alarum work, 15½ in. high (39.5 cm.), c. 1700. **£1,400-1,600** *S*

An early 18th C. brass lantern clock, the movement with verge escapement and countwheel strike and single steel hand, signed Antony Hebert, Moorefields N^ere^ Londini Fecit, 1 ft. 4½ in. (42 cm.) high. **£800-1,000** *P*

A French lantern clock, signed Bouvier A Preaux, the movement with verge escapement and outside countwheel, with restoration, alarum work lacking, 14½ in. high, 18th C. **£550-650** *S*

A brass alarum lantern clock, the posted frame with pierced cresting pieces, the dial signed Henricus Montlow Londini Fecit, single steel hand, the twin train movement with verge escapement, alarum train and countwheel strike, with restorations, 1 ft. 3½ in. high (39 cm.), 18th C. **£1,000-1,200** *P*

A brass alarum lantern timepiece, of small size, the posted frame surmounted by a bell with turned finial, the dial with matted centre, silvered alarm disc and chapter ring, signed in the roundel above the XII J^no^ Tickle, London, the movement with verge escapement and alarum train, 9 in. high (23 cm.), 18th C. **£500-800** *P*

A lantern clock, the movement with anchor escapement and outside countwheel, possibly Dutch, pendulum lacking, 15½ in. high (39.5 cm.). **£900-1,100** *S*

A late 18th C. Continental brass lantern clock, the posted movement with tapering spiral columns joined by baluster and ring turned pillars, the 6½ in. dial with countwheel strike and original anchor escapement and hand gear cut wheels, and 6 in. bell, with weight and pendulum, 17 in. high. **£450-£550** *DS*

A Japanese brass lantern clock, lacquered chapter ring, the iron movement with double foliot verge escapement and countwheel strike on bell above a wood stand with later glazed canopy, 15¼ in. (38.5 cm.) height of clock. **£2,000-£2,500** *C*

A Japanese double foliot brass lantern clock, rotating chapter ring with 2 bands of chapters, alarm pin with 8 setting holes and single steel hand, double foliot verge escapement and strike/alarm, hexagonal lead weights, 8½ in. high (21.5 cm.). **£1,000-1,500** *C*

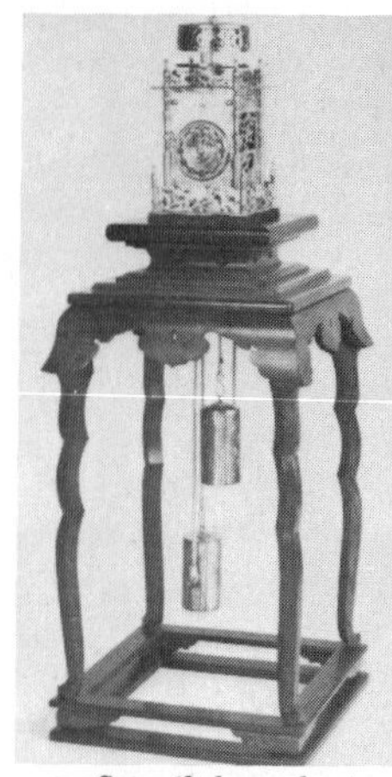

A Japanese fine gilt-brass lantern clock, verge escapement, single foliot-cum-balance, countwheel strike on 'pork pie' bell above, carved wood stand and glazed canopy, 8 in. (20.5 cm.) height of clock, 30½ in. (77.5 cm.) overall height. **£3,500-4,500** *C*

A brass lantern clock with twin chain fusee and quarter striking, with pendulum, 15 in. (38 cm.), c. 1860. **£400-500** *S*

A rare and early epicyclic skeleton timepiece, with chain fusee and anchor escapement within the frame, in a typical scrolled frame, with a plaque signed Brookhouse Derby Wm. Strutt Derby Esqr. Invt., with a glass dome, 14 in. high (35.5 cm.). **£2,200-2,600** *S*

William Strutt invented his clock in about 1830, and they were made in small numbers for a few years subsequently. Other known examples appear to be all signed by Strutt and Wigston or Strutt alone.

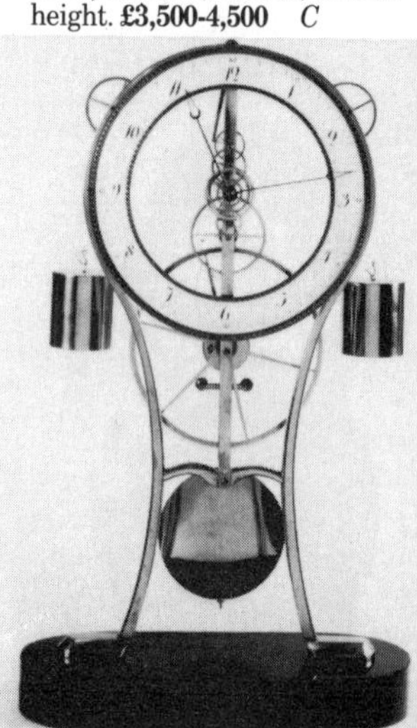

A rare weight-driven skeleton timepiece, the 5 wheel train mounted vertically and with 2 weights mounted one at each side, 16 in. high (40.5 cm.), early 19th C. **£4,500-5,500** *S*

A good skeleton clock by John Pace Bury, the movement with anchor escapement and wire fusee, with glass dome, 9¼ in. (23.5 cm.), c. 1840. **£300-400** *S*

A 19th C. twin fusee brass skeleton clock, 16 in. high. **£500-550** *JMW*

A Victorian brass skeleton clock, the twin train movement with pierced silvered chapter ring, surmounted with a bell, the plinth inscribed G. Groom, Windmill Rd, Croydon, 18½ in. (52 cm.) high. **£800-900** *P*

A Victorian brass framed Lichfield Cathedral skeleton clock, the twin chain and fusee movement with 6 spoked wheels, half deadbeat escapement and pendulum with micrometer adjustment, with glass dome, 17 in. high. **£1,000-1,200** *CSK*

A skeleton timepiece with passing strike, 19 in., c. 1860. **£450-500** *TP*

A Scott Memorial skeleton timepiece with a 4½ in. silvered chapter ring, the movement with chain fusee and anchor escapement with wood rod and cylindrical bob, 18 in. high (46 cm.). **£550-650** *S*

A 19th C. English skeleton clock, the 8-day fusee movement with passing strike, with silvered dial and glass dome, 17 in. high. **£375-£425** *IAT*

Some typical Wall Clocks with their approximate dates of manufacture.

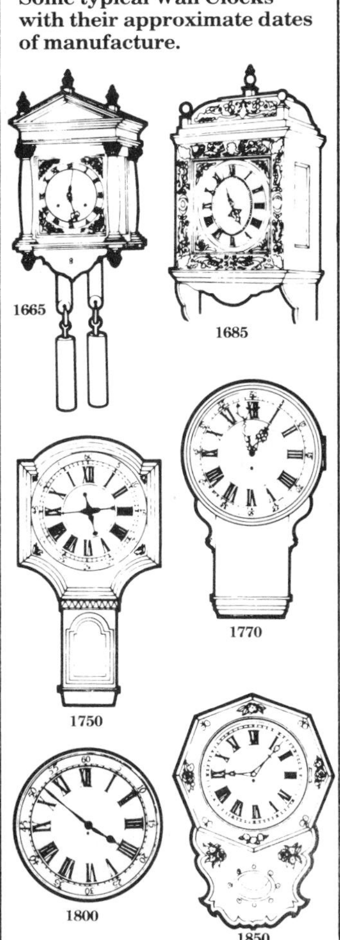

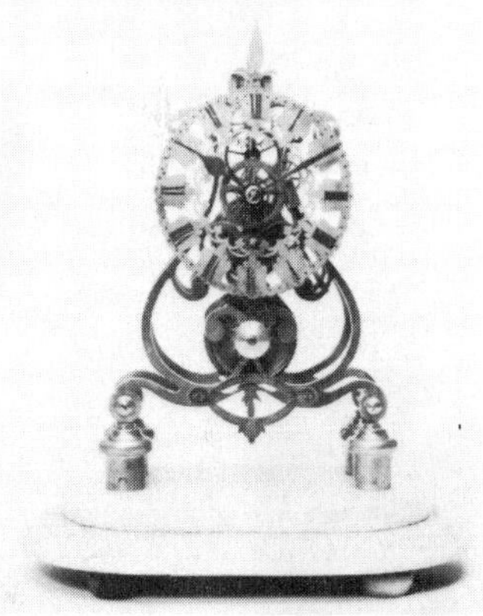

A brass skeleton timepiece with chain fusee, on a moulded white marble base, inscribed Time Passes but Friendship remains, 28th July 1864, with key, pendulum and a glass dome, 14 in. (35.5 cm.). **£300-£400** *S*

A George III mahogany hooded wall clock, twin fusee striking movement with anchor escapement, dial signed Alex[r] Cumming London, case of typical form, the bracket pulling forward to reveal a key well, with restorations, 31½ in. high (80 cm.). **£5,500-6,500** *C*

A George III black-japanned Act of Parliament wall timepiece, the 24½ in. dial signed Peter Oyen Wapping, the movement with tapering plates and anchor escapement, the case with 3 gilt finials, 2 detached, 5 ft. 2 in. high (157 cm.). **£1,800-2,000** *S*

Peter Oyen or Oyens is recorded working between 1756 and 1778.

An interesting oak tavern dial timepiece, the movement with baluster pillars, anchor escapement and tapering shouldered plates, the case carved with a genre scene, with one lead weight and a pendulum, 54 in. (137 cm.) overall, originally mid 18th C. but the partly 17th C. carved pieces applied later. **£900-1,200** *SC*

The front plate is inscribed Thwaites. This firm was founded in 1740 by Agusworth Thwaites, later becoming Agusworth and John, John Thwaites and later Thwaites and Reed.

A Friesian Stoelklok, with alarum mechanism, vertical verge escapement and Dutch striking with outside countwheel, repainted case, 30 in. high (78 cm.), c. 1800. **£1,400-1,600** *S*

A mahogany-cased 2-train fusee wall clock by Peters of Cambridge, 47 in. high, c. 1840. **£450-500** *TP*

A mahogany wall timepiece by B. Smethurst, with pendulum and weight, 43½ in. (110 cm.), c. 1850. **£600-700** *S*

A 2 weight Vienna regulator in a walnut and ebonised case, rack striking movement with 2 piece dial, 46 in. high, c. 1880. **£400-£450** *IAT*

Left
A Victorian double weight Vienna wall clock with ebony mounts, walnut cased. **£350-400** *HFM*

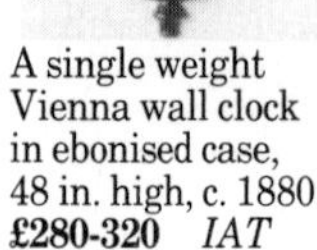

A single weight Vienna wall clock in ebonised case, 48 in. high, c. 1880. **£280-320** *IAT*

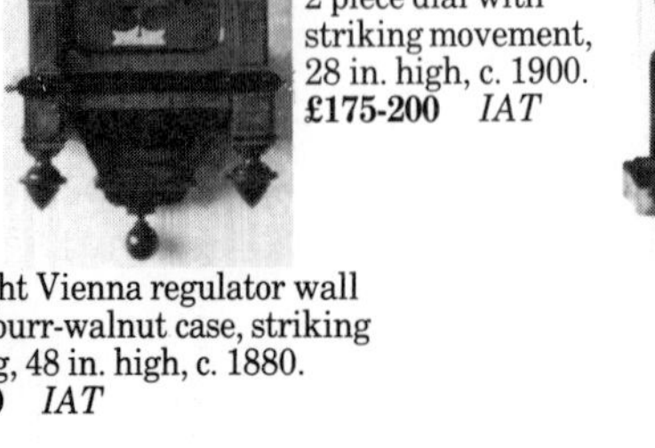

A spring driven Vienna wall clock, 2 piece dial with striking movement, 28 in. high, c. 1900. **£175-200** *IAT*

A 2 weight Vienna regulator wall clock in burr-walnut case, striking on a gong, 48 in. high, c. 1880. **£525-550** *IAT*

A German wall clock in walnut case, spring driven striking movement, 35 in. high. **£170-190** *IAT*

An American drop dial wall clock in a rosewood and ivory inlaid case, bell striking, 26 in. high, c. 1880. **£160-180** *IAT*

An English 12 in. dial wall clock, brass dial engraved Jn. Snape, London, fusee movement with verge escapement, c. 1800. **£700-£750** *IAT*

An English double fusee drop dial wall clock in mahogany case, painted dial signed Wm. Cope, Nottingham, rack striking movement on a bell, 27 in. high, c. 1860. **£400-450** *IAT*

An American drop dial wall clock in a mahogany case, 27 in. high, c. 1890. **£110-130** *IAT*

A Coalbrookdale cast iron clock barometer, in good order, 25 in. long, c. 1870. **£160-170** *FF*

A walnut cuckoo clock with half-hour striking and musical bellows, probably Austrian, 18½ by 14 in. (47 by 36 cm.), c. 1880. **£450-500** *S*

A brass-cased ship wireless operator's clock, 10½ in. **£75-95** *BP*

A Georgian wall clock in mahogany case with fusee movement by Tupman, Grosvenor Square, London. **£550-600** *JD*

An important oak-cased wall hanging clock, by Vulliamy London number 401, 5 pillar fusee movement, rise and fall adjustment at 12.00, 25 in. diam., c. 1810. **£2,200-2,400** *FHF*

An English 12 in. trunk dial clock in mahogany case, single fusee movement, dial signed J.W. Ninnes, Tunbridge Wells, 16 in. high, c. 1890. **£160-180** *IAT*

A Louis XV ormolu cartel clock with later striking movement, 32¼ in. (81.5 cm.) high. **£2,000-£2,500** *C*

A 19th C. French bronze ormolu and white marble garniture-de-cheminée, the movement stamped Vincetti & Cie, 20 in. high. **£700-£800** *GSP*

A gilt-bronze cartel clock, 27½ in. high (70 cm.), c. 1880. **£300-400** *S*

A 'jewelled Sèvres' porcelain-mounted garniture-de-cheminée, the Japy Frères movement no. 1324, with key, 47 cm., c. 1860. **£1,700-1,900** *S*

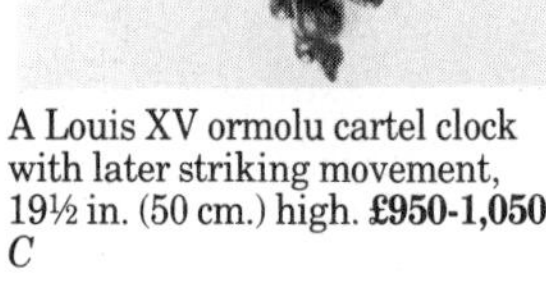

A Louis XV ormolu cartel clock with later striking movement, 19½ in. (50 cm.) high. **£950-1,050** *C*

A repeating brass and iron comptoise wall clock with half-hour striking, the dial signed Jn. Pre. Fleury à Gap, with 2 weights and pendulum, 15¼ by 9½ in. (39 by 24 cm.), 19th C. **£250-300** *S*

A composed boulle garniture, inlaid with cut brass foliage on a brown tortoiseshell ground, with pendulum, 12 in. (30.5 cm.), c. 1870. **£500-600** *S*

WALL CLOCKS
Dials

Square	to c. 1755	George II or later
Broken arch	from c. 1720 to c. 1805	early to late Georgian
Painted/round	from c. 1740	George II or later
Silvered	from c. 1760	George III or later

A bleu celeste 'Sèvres' composed clock garniture, the Japy movement no. 7590, with pendulum, 1870's. **£600-700** *S*

A composed gilt-bronze and porcelain mantel clock garniture, with key and pendulum, 15 in. (38 cm.), c. 1880. **£400-500** *S*

A gilt-bronze and champleve and cut glass clock garniture, the Japy movement striking on a gong, contained in a 4-glass case surmounted by a glass cupola, cracked, 15½ in. (40 cm.), flanked by a pair of vases, each with a cut glass body, 12 in. (31 cm.), mid 19th C. **£400-500** *SC*

An iron chamber clock in the Gothic manner, the posted frame movement with foliot verge escapement, countwheel strike with external fly, lantern pinions, possibly incorporating some early wheelwork, 27 in. (68 cm.) high. **£1,700-2,000** *C*

A champleve and gilt-bronze garniture-de-cheminée, the Richard & Cie movement no. 12293 48, with pendulum and key, the clock with a giltwood plinth, 34 cm., c. 1890. **£500-600** *S*

A German ebonised wood-cased striking table clock, the movement with iron trains, brass barrels and cage, verge escapement, key drawer to the base, with adaptations and restorations, 12½ in. (31.5 cm.), basically late 17th C. **£4,000-5,000** *C*

A gilt spelter and porcelain clock garniture, the movement with half-hour striking on a bell, the case inset with a porcelain panel and surmounted by a porcelain urn, 16½ in. (42 cm.) overall, flanked by a pair of urns, 14 in. (36 cm.), late 19th C. **£400-450** *SC*

A gilt-metal German tabernacle clock, fusee and later verge escapement with front swinging pendulum, the dial with pewter chapter-ring, the bell cupola adapted, 10½ in. high (26.5 cm.), basically early 17th C. **£4,000-5,000** *C*

A gilt-metal large Gothick table clock, the 2 train fusee movement quarter striking on 2 bells above, within the false bell, 41 in. high (104 cm.), 19th C. **£1,400-1,700** *C*

An Algerian onyx and champleve clock garniture, the French movement striking on a gong, mercuric pendulum in a 4-glass case with enamel canted sides, bearing a presentation inscription dated 1903, 12½ in. (32 cm.), flanked by a pair of lamps, fitted for electricity, 16½ in. (42 cm.) with 2 shades. **£350-400** *SC*

An architectural clock, the posted-frame brass movement formerly weight-driven, sometime converted to spring barrels with indirect wind, the verge escapement with later external pendulum, the countwheel strike on a bell above, formerly on 2 bells, possibly Dutch or Italian and originating from the early 17th C. **£2,000-2,500** *C*

A German gilt-metal hexagonal table clock of small size signed Josephus Jans Passau with chain fusee for the going, resting barrel for the alarm, with silver champleve chapter-ring, 8 cm. diam. **£3,500-4,000** *C*

A German brass hexagonal table clock, unsigned, with chain fusee for the going and resting barrels for the strike and alarm, 11.5 cm. diam. **£2,300-2,600** *C*

A hexagonal horizontal table clock with brass and iron plates, c. 1600. **£5,000-7,000** *HAD*

A Continental gilt-metal table clock, chain fusee for the going with bridge-cock verge escapement and resting barrels for the strike, enamel dial cracked, signed Johan Georg Werndle à Presburg, 5 in. high (12.7 cm.), early 19th C. **£1,000-1,200** *C*

A 17th C. square horizontal table clock, verge escapement, hour striking, with alarm. **£3,000-£5,000** *HAD*

A half-quarter repeating table clock, the movement signed Peter Hochögg, fusee and now chain, the dial with engraved gilt-plate, silver champleve chapter-ring and blued central alarm disc, 3½ in. high (9 cm.), early 18th C. **£3,100-£3,300** *C*

An unusual gilt-metal grande sonnerie desk clock in the manner of Thomas Cole, the repeating 2 train Swiss movement signed R. Golay Geneve and with vertical cylinder escapement and striking on 2 gongs, the back inscribed Horloge à grande et petite sonnerie, 5¼ in. high (13.5 cm.), with a leather travelling case. **£1,450-1,650** *S*

It is suggested that this clock was manufactured during the last quarter of the 19th C. some time after Thomas Cole's death in 1864.

A mahogany table regulator, dead-beat escapement, fusee and chain, maintaining power, 17½ in. high (44.5 cm.). **£950-1,150** *C*

A German weight-driven novelty 30-hour timepiece, 8 in. diam., c. 1900. **£75-100** *TP*

A gilt bedside alarum mechanism, with verge watch movement No. 767 by Ageron of Paris, later dial, the case stamped Japy and with silvered plaque inscribed Galerie de Valois, Palais Royal No. 164, and engraved Invt. Laresche, No. 706, shaped leather-covered box with key, length overall 103 mm., early 19th C. **£450-550** *S*

An unusual brass and mahogany coachman's timepiece, the enamel dial and plate inscribed George Littlewort by the Kings Letters Patent, London, the movement with 3 armed balance enclosed by a sliding backplate, 4 in. overall (10 cm.). **£350-400** *SC*

A rare French nightwatchman's clock, c. 1850. **£300-350** *CGC*

An 18 ct. gold and enamel box opening to reveal an oval timepiece flanked by 2 small photograph frames and a perpetual calendar, complete with gold and enamel simulated lock, the face of the timepiece bearing Garrard's retail mark, in fitted case, 7 by 3.75 by 3 cm. **£1,800-2,000** *P*

A gilt-framed picture clock, in oil on canvas in the manner of the German early 19th C. school, movement with anchor escapement, hour strike on gong and connecting to the separate going barrel assembly for the quarter strike on 2 gongs, 31½ by 27 in. (80 by 68.5 cm.). **£900-1,000** *C*

A rare French clock movement for driving slave clocks by compressed air, with deadbeat pinwheel escapement, remontoire via the third wheel and pinion to drive the pump, with (? later) electrical contacts and the original motion work for 2 slave dials, 25 in. long (64 cm.), 19th C. **£1,300-1,500** *C*

An unusual bronze clock cast as an umbrella, the centre with pierced hands, with key, 11½ in. diam. (29 cm.), c. 1880. **£350-400** *S*

A George III gilt-metal mounted mahogany musical clock with automaton, dial, cracked, signed Brockbank London, the 3 train chain fusee movement playing a tune at the hour on 8 bells followed by the strike on bell above, with securing nut for the micrometer adjusted pendulum of the anchor escapement, 24 in. high (61 cm.). **£5,000-6,000** *C*

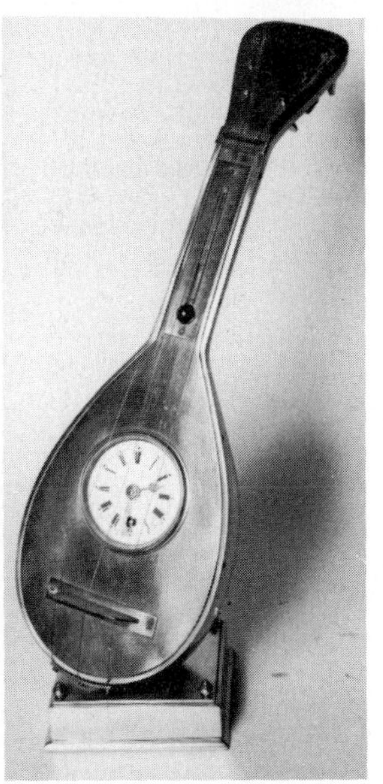

A brass-cased timepiece in the form of a mandolin, 14 in. high, c. 1900. **£200-250** *TP*

An ormolu blackamoor figure holding sedan-type timepiece, 8 in. high, c. 1830. **£100-140** *TP*

A Japanese stick clock, 3 wheel movement with plain 2 arm balance (lacking hair spring), seconds hand, with restorations, 41 cm. high, 19th C. **£750-850** *C*

A 19th C. French mystery night clock, with candle holder behind dial. **£400-600** *HAD*

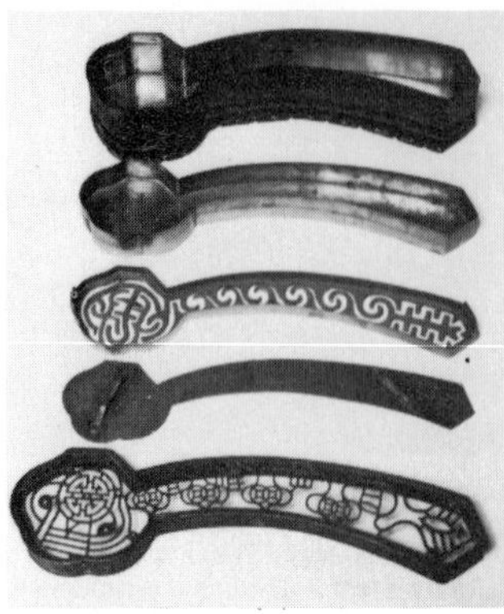

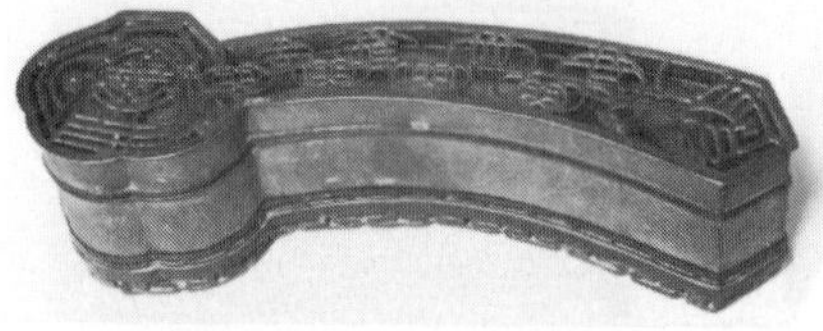

A 19th C. Chinese fire clock. **£200-£500** *HAD*

The open-ended reference system
Miller's Antiques Price Guide builds up year by year to form the most comprehensive photo-reference system available. The first four volumes contain photographs of over 30,000 stock items!

A brass lighthouse clock, applied with lion masks and window frames, supporting a revolving glass drum-cased clock face with brass pointer, English, 21 in. (53.5 cm.) high, mid 19th C. **£400-£450** *S*

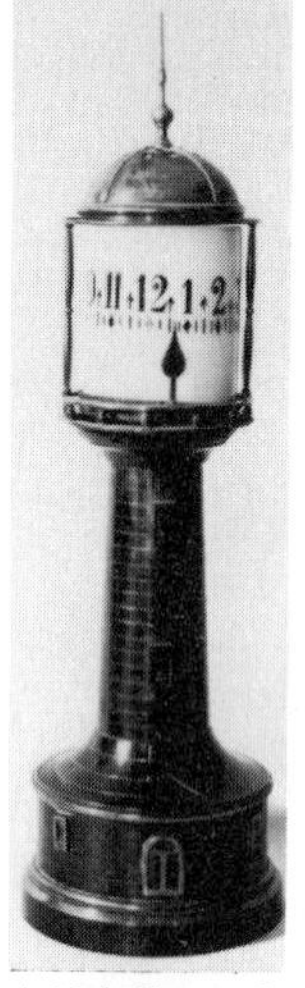

A 19th C. metal night clock, 21 in. high. **£250-300** *DWB*

A gilt-metal combined timepiece, barometer and thermometer in the form of a lighthouse, the upper storey fitted with 4 dials, on circular base, 21 in. high, mid to late 19th C. **£450-500** *PK*

A globe clock, inscribed Richards Chronosphere, patent 19460, the French movement revolving the sphere, and indicating the mean time by means of a pointer on a 24-hour chapter around the circumference, 11 in. (29 cm.). **£500-600** *L*

A brass rolling ball clock to a design by Congrieve, the movement with a wire fusee and a 30 seconds table, the hour dial flanked by a 30 second dial and a minute dial, 18½ by 17 in. (47 by 43 cm.) overall, modern. **£1,000-£1,200** *S*

An 18 ct. gold open faced quarter repeating keyless lever watch by William Alexander & Son, 109 Buchanan St., Glasgow, no. 17022, the three-quarter plate movement with compensation balance, 54 mm., London 1872. **£800-900** *S*

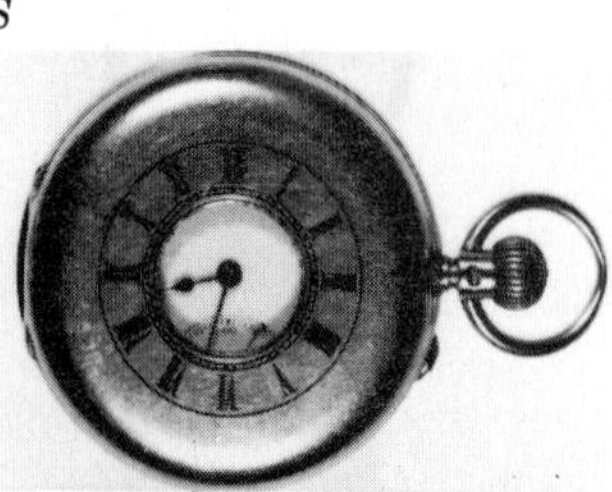

An 18 ct. gold half hunting cased keyless lever watch by Army & Navy, 117 Victoria Street, London, No. 4524, 49 mm., hallmarked London 1887. **£300-350** *S*

An 18th C. 22 ct. gold pair cased repousse verge watch by William Allam, London, No. 493, the movement with square baluster pillars, pierced cock with diamond endstone, 48 mm., London, 1776. **£900-1,000** *P*

An 18 ct. gold hunting cased lever watch by E. F. Ashley, 2 Green Terrace, Clerkenwell, No. 03239, the three-quarter plate movement with compensation balance, 49 mm., hallmarked London 1884. **£350-450** *S*

An 18 ct. gold open faced keyless lever watch by Barnby & Rust, No. 06359, the three-quarter plate movement with compensation balance, 47 mm., hallmarked London 1891. **£200-250** *S*

An 18 ct. gold half hunting cased free sprung lever watch by Barraud & Lunde, Cornhill, London 2/9504, the three-quarter plate movement with compensation balance and chain fusee, and a gold-plated chain, 49 mm., hallmarked London 1871. **£500-600** *S*

A cylinder watch by Ferdinand Berthoud, Paris, converted from verge, in gold consular case with paste set bezel, 38 mm., c. 1780. **£700-800** *P*

A quarter repeating open faced keyless lever watch by Borel Fils, gold coloured metal, 53 mm., c. 1890. **£400-500** *S*

Locate the source
The source of each illustration in Miller's can be found by checking the code letters below each caption with the list of contributors on page 12. In view of the undoubted differences in price structures from region to region, this information could be extremely valuable to everyone who buys and sells antiques.

A pair-cased watch, verge movement by Cetti of London. **£160-190** *TP*

An 18 ct. gold open-faced lever watch by Dent, 33 Cockspur Street, London, No. 24140, the full plate movement with chain fusee, 44 mm., hallmarked London 1862. **£250-300** *S*

A gold pair-cased cylinder watch no. 1162 signed Alexr. Cumming, London, the enamel dial with hair crack, both cases hallmarked 1781, the inner with casemaker's initials IL, the outer MR, 53 mm. diam. **£1,100-1,200** *S*

A gold, rose cut diamond and garnet set keyless cylinder watch, the movement signed Le Coultre & Cie. **£400-500** *P*

A gold and enamel outer case and chatelaine, with associated quarter repeating verge movement by Cabrier of London, with maker's mark PM, with large rose-diamond thumbpiece, length overall 190 mm., c. 1760. **£7,000-8,000** *S*

A gold-cased pocket chronometer by Thos. Earnshaw, London, No. 2382, the full plate movement signed Thos. Earnshaw, Invt. et Fecit No. 354, with 'Z' balance and diamond endstone, the dial signed. **£800-900** *P*

A rare silver egg-shaped cylinder watch, shaped movement signed Benjamin Gray Just. Vulliamy London ruu, diamond endstone, brass escape wheel, blued beetle-and-poker hands, case plain, 60 mm. diam. **£8,000-9,000** *C*

A silver gilt pair-cased quarter-repeating verge watch no. 1507 by Thomas Grignion of Covent Garden, London, dial chipped, 48 mm. diam., mid 18th C. **£950-£1,150** *S*

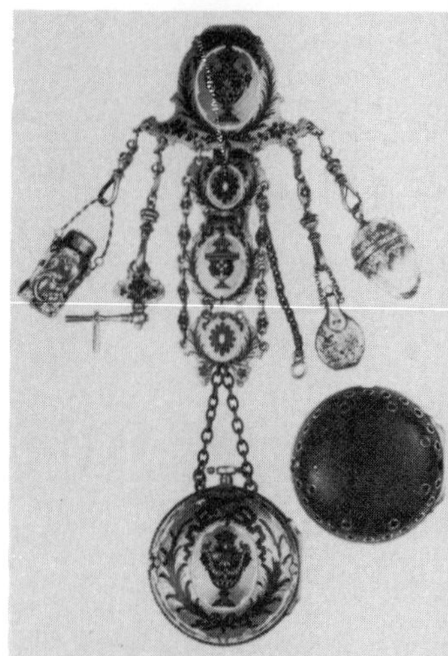

A gold and enamel pair-cased half quarter-repeating cylinder watch and chatelaine no. 1686 by Thomas Grignion of Covent Garden, London, the 4 pendant chains terminating in scent bottle, crank key, vinaigrette and small flask, and with an alternative green shagreen outer case, slight chip to dial, 48 mm. diam., c. 1780. **£5,200-£5,700** *S*

A Georgian fusee movement watch by Thos. Hawley, London, c. 1798-1828. **£100-130** *TP*

An 18 ct. gold hunting cased centre seconds keyless lever watch by J. & A. Harris, 28 Berry Street, London, No. 22160, the three-quarter plate movement with compensation balance, hallmarked London 1876, 55 mm. **£400-500** *S*

A silver pair-cased verge watch by John Hocker of Reading, both cases plain, the outer with square hinge, 57 mm. diam., c. 1710. **£650-750** *S*

A silver pair-cased verge watch, the movement signed Jos. Jackeman London 1116, silver champleve dial (lacking centre), cases plain, silver chain with fob seal and good brass crank key, 51 mm. diam. **£350-450** *C*

A silver pair-cased and repousse calendar verge watch by Simon Laches, Utrecht, with pierced cock, foot and slide plate signed, the outer case of repousse work, 55 mm. diam., early 18th C. **£850-£950** *P*

A silver pair-cased quarter-repeating verge watch by Simon Van Leeuwen of Amsterdam, with vase-shaped pillars, winged balance cock, gilt dust band, silver champleve dial, inner and outer cases pierced and engraved, 59 mm. diam., early 18th C. **£1,900-2,100** *S*

A French gold-cased calendar verge watch by Charles LeRoy A Paris, the gilt movement with pierced bridge cock, the dial signed, the bezels with a raised gold design, 51 mm. diam., late 18th C. **£250-£300** *P*

A 22 ct. gold pair-cased verge watch by Daniel de St. Leu, London, the gilt movement with pierced cock, square baluster pillars, the outer case of repousse work, London, 1763, 48 mm. diam. **£850-950** *P*

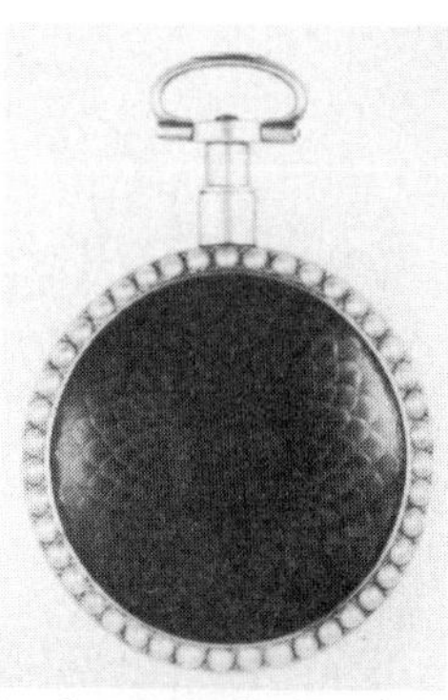

A gold and enamel cylinder watch no. 3041 by James McCabe, signed James McCabe, London, later white enamel dial, the back of the case of red translucent enamel over guilloche, 49 mm. diam., c. 1790. **£1,200-1,500** *S*

A gold hunting cased duplex watch no. 7156 by James McCabe, gilt dust cover, the front cover with engraved coat of arms and hallmarked 1811, and with 2 contemporary gilt keys with cast decoration, 57 mm. diam. **£800-£900** *S*

A gold cylinder watch, signed Tho. Mudge, W. Dutton, London, the movement with large 'scape wheel, winged masked cock with diamond endstone, dial with hair cracks, plain case hallmarked 1768 and with the casemaker's initials P M, 51 mm. diam. **£1,500-1,800** *S*

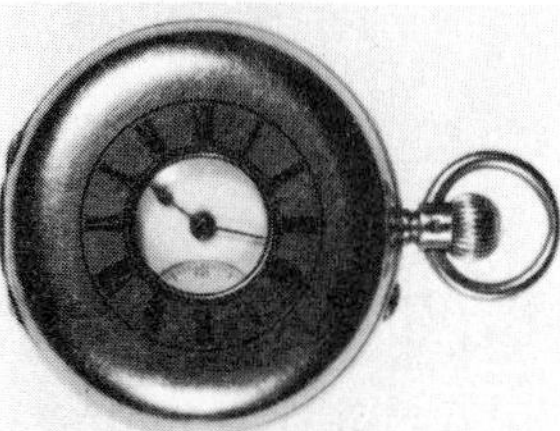

An 18 ct. gold half hunting cased keyless lever watch by R. G. Oldfield, Liverpool, no. 66314, hallmarked Chester 1897, 52 mm. **£300-350** *S*

An early 18th C. silver cased 'onion' watch by Salles AcCaen, the gilt full plate movement, signed, with silver pierced bridge cock, 57 mm. diam. **£400-450** *P*

A repousse gold pair-cased watch no. 2050 by Marmaduke Storr of London, the movement now with lever escapement, the inner case hallmarked 1736 and with casemaker's initials SD, 48 mm. diam. **£1,400-1,800** *S*

An 18 ct. gold hunting cased centre seconds keyless lever watch by T. Taylor & Son, Liverpool, 53 mm., hallmarked London 1899. **£300-400** *S*

An 18 ct. gold minute repeating watch, the keyless lever movement free sprung, subsidiary seconds dial and blued steel fleur-de-lis hands, by F. Thoms, London, and having thief-proof swivel bow, hallmarked 1903. **£1,100-1,300** *S*

An 18 ct. gold half hunting cased keyless lever watch by A. R. Trewinard, 5 Duke Street, Adelphi, London, no. 19265, the three-quarter plate movement with compensation balance, hallmarked London 1903, 48 mm. **£300-400** *S*

A slim half-sized 9 ct. gold dress watch with quarter-repeat movement, c. 1870. **£600-700** *TP*

A 9 ct. gold open dial pocket watch, c. 1890. **£90-110** *TP*

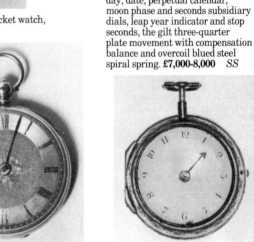

A Swiss gold minute repeating hunting cased pocket watch, with day, date, perpetual calendar, moon phase and seconds subsidiary dials, leap year indicator and stop seconds, the gilt three-quarter plate movement with compensation balance and overcoil blued steel spiral spring. **£7,000-8,000** *SS*

An 18 ct. gold pocket watch, c. 1890. **£220-250** *TP*

A late Victorian 18 ct. gold pocket watch. **£220-260** *TP*

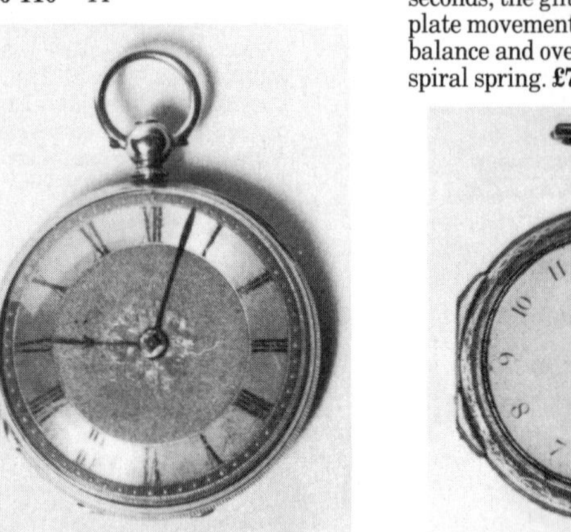

A quarter-repeating verge watch by Thomas Windmills, having 5 reeded baluster pillars, with later white enamel dial push bow repeat and in gilt copper case. **£600-800** *S*

An 18 ct. gold half hunter, c. 1900. **£340-380** *TP*

A pair-cased verge watch, c. 1826. **£120-150** *TP*

An open dial watch with fusee movement in silver case, c. 1850. **£60-70** *TP*

An 18 ct. gold pocket watch with cylinder movement, c. 1870. **£100-£130** *TP*

An 18 ct. gold key wind pocket watch with fusee movement, c. 1869. **£320-360** *TP*

A full hunter 9 ct. gold-cased watch, c. 1920. **£230-280** *TP*

An unusual mid 19th C. rosewood wheel barometer, the 11½ in. silvered dial signed J. Amadio, 6 Shorters Court, Throgmorton Str, City, the case inlaid with cut mother-o'-pearl and mounted with a bowfront thermometer with fahrenheit and reaumur scales, 44¾ in. (1.137 m.) high. **£900-£1,000** *P*

A 19th C. mahogany wheel barometer by Lewis Arnaboldi, the boxwood and ebony strung case fitted with a level, with a thermometer and a hygrometer, 43 in. (90.2 cm.) high. **£250-300** *P*

An 8 in. mahogany barometer, by Cetti & Co., c. 1810. **£285-335** *NC*

A large and unusual inlaid rosewood clock cum barometer with a hygrometer, thermometer, 12 in. dial, signed M. Pius Drescher no. 21 Mytongate Hull, the timepiece with a 6 in. repainted dial signed B. Cooke & Son Hull and 8-day fusee movement with narrow plates and anchor escapement, 53 in. (135 cm.) high. **£1,500-1,700** *S*

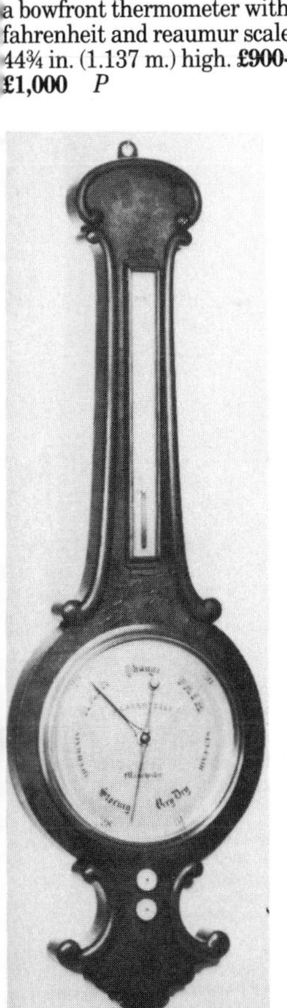

A walnut wheel barometer, the 9½ in. silvered register signed J. Casartelli, Manchester, with a thermometer, restored, 41 in. (104 cm.), 3rd quarter of the 19th C. **£180-220** *SC*

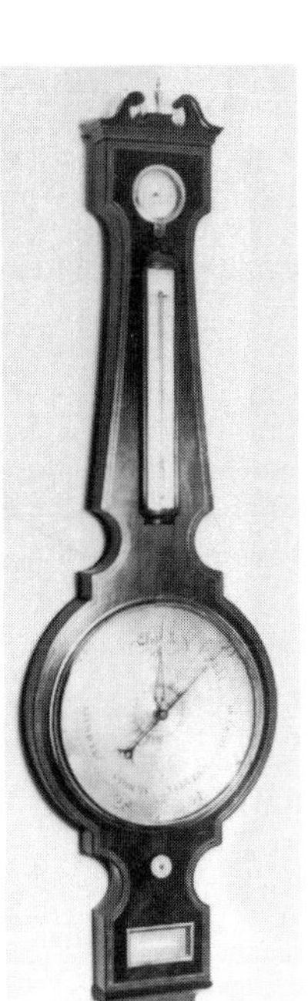

A 10 in. mahogany barometer by Guanziroli, c. 1835. **£650-750** *NC*

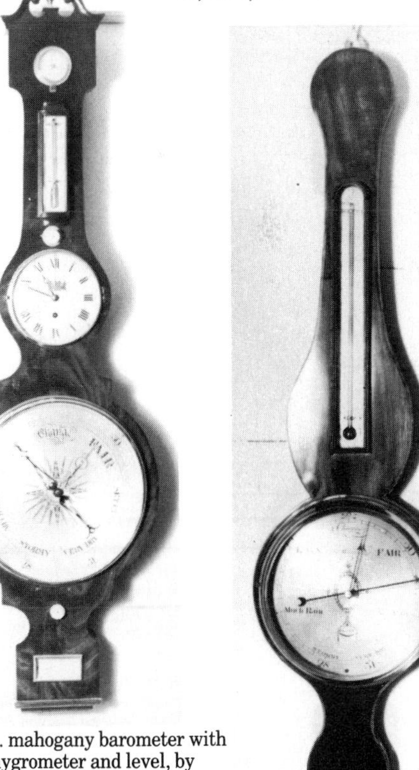

A 12 in. mahogany barometer with clock, hygrometer and level, by King of Leather Lane, c. 1840. **£1,750-1,950** *NC*

A mahogany 8 in. barometer by Chas. Malacrida, c. 1800. **£575-£675** *NC*

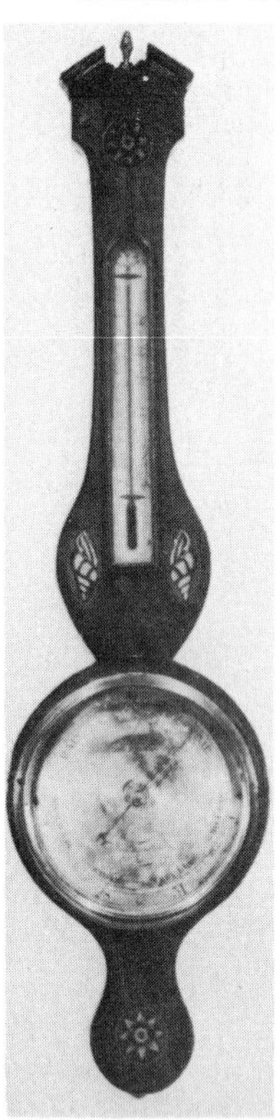

An early Victorian mahogany banjo barometer, the case inlaid, with thermometer and silvered dial signed Pastorelli, Bowling Street, Westminster, 38½ in. high. **£350-£400** *CSK*

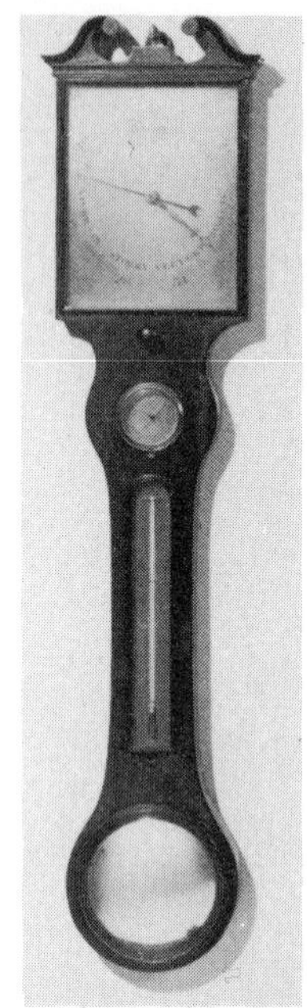

A fine mahogany wheel barometer, the silvered scale signed Tagliabue & Co., Holborn London no. 26 with hygrometer, and mercury thermometer, 38½ in. (98 cm.) high. **£2,500-3,000** *C*

A mahogany banjo clock-barometer, level signed J. Vassalli, Scarborough, hygrometer, mercury thermometer and with lever platform movement, 44 in. (112 cm.) high, late 18th C. **£700-£900** *C*

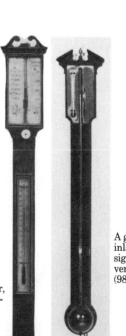

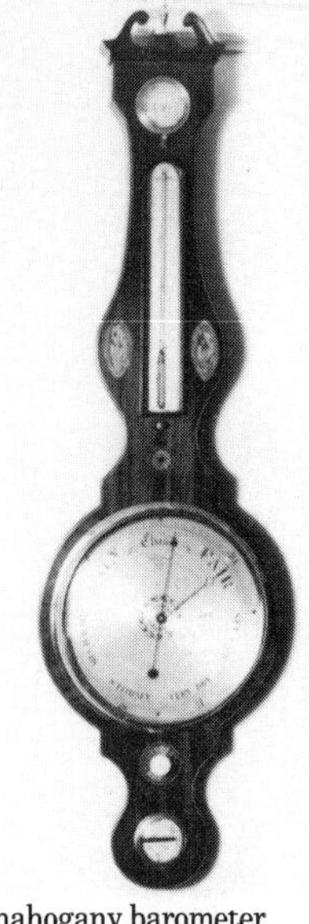

A 10 in. mahogany barometer, possibly with later inlay, unsigned, c. 1830. **£325-375** *NC*

A large rosewood mercury wheel barometer, inlaid with brass foliage, 43½ in. (110.5 cm.), mid 19th C. **£250-300** *S*

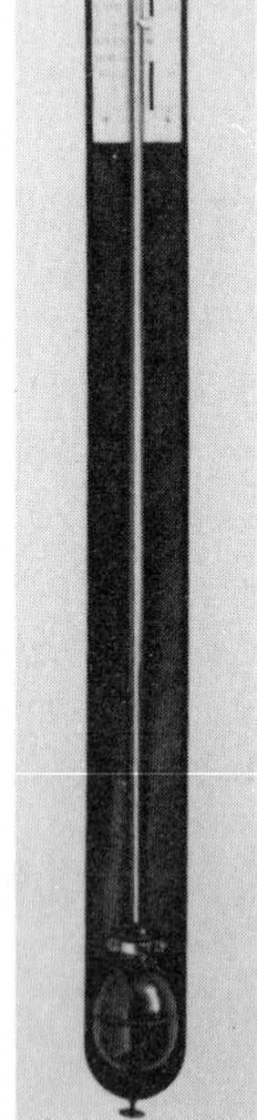

A George III mahogany stick barometer, the arched silvered register plate signed T. Blunt Cornhill London and with vernier, 37 in. (94 cm.) high, c. 1770. **£700-£800** *S*

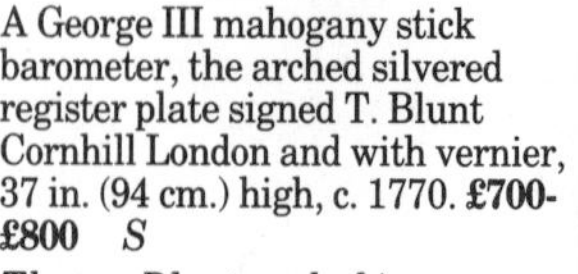

Thomas Blunt worked in partnership with Thomas Nairne from 1774; Nairne died in 1806 and Blunt in 1822.

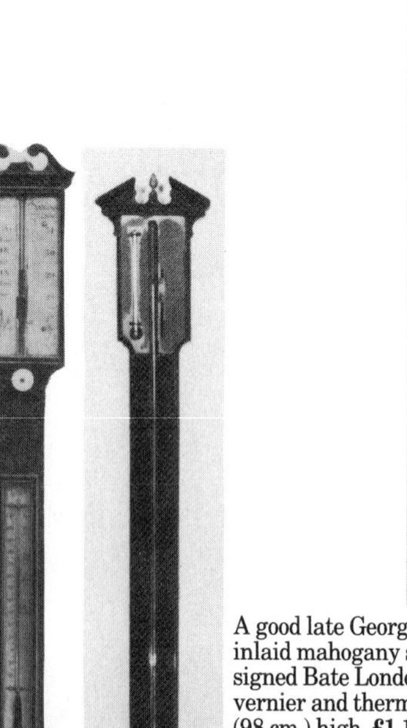

An early 19th C. mahogany stick barometer, signed Berringer, London, fitted with a thermometer, 37¾ in. (95.8 cm.) high. **£300-350** *P*

A good late George III bowfronted inlaid mahogany stick barometer, signed Bate London and with vernier and thermometer, 38½ in. (98 cm.) high. **£1,100-1,200** *S*

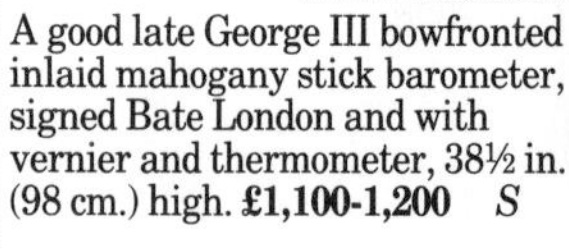

A Georgian mahogany stick barometer, the brass plate mounted with a thermometer and signed Bleuler, London, the back applied with an original trade label for I[t] & P[r] Bregazzi, Nottingham, 38¾ in. (98.5 cm.) high. **£500-550** *P*

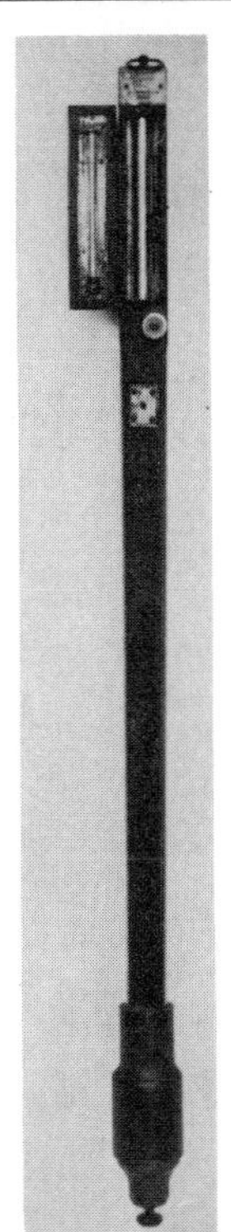

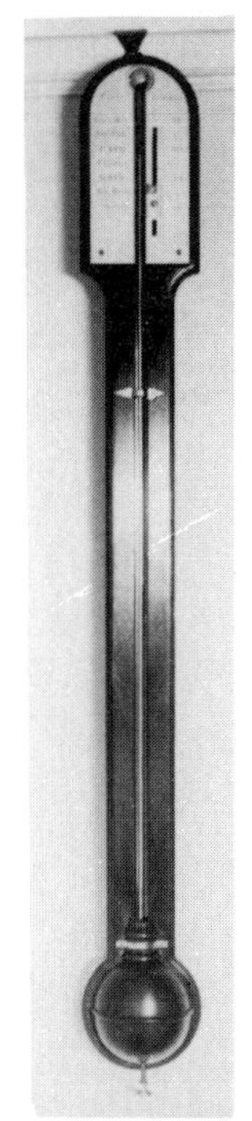

A mahogany stick barometer by Cary, c. 1790. **£685-780** *NC*

. marine stick barometer by Cary, ondon, having the silvered scales nd thermometer, maker's name ngraved on a plaque, gimbal ttings lacking, 39¼ in. (99.5 cm.). **800-900** *S*

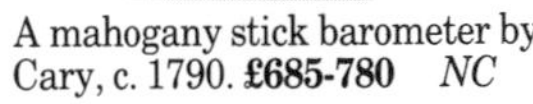

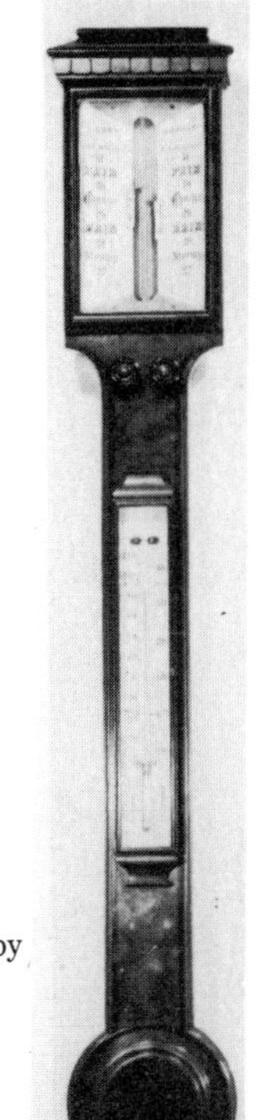

A late Victorian mahogany stick barometer, with gabled top and thermometer, the ivory scales signed Cary, London, 38 in. high. **£350-400** *CSK*

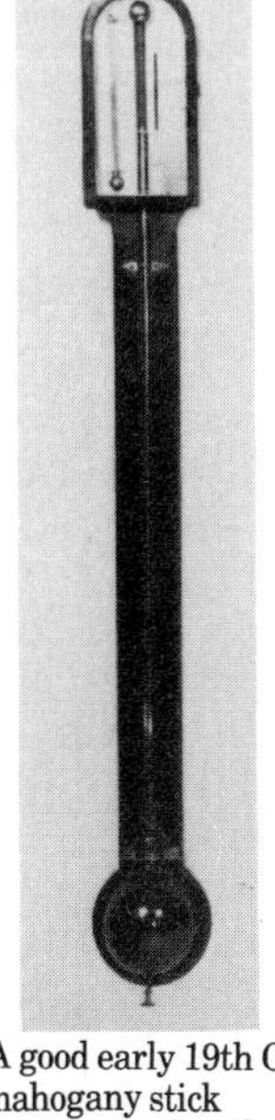

A good early 19th C. mahogany stick barometer, the silvered brass plate mounted with a thermometer and signed P. Hill, Edinburgh, 37 in. (94 cm.) high. **£400-500** *P*

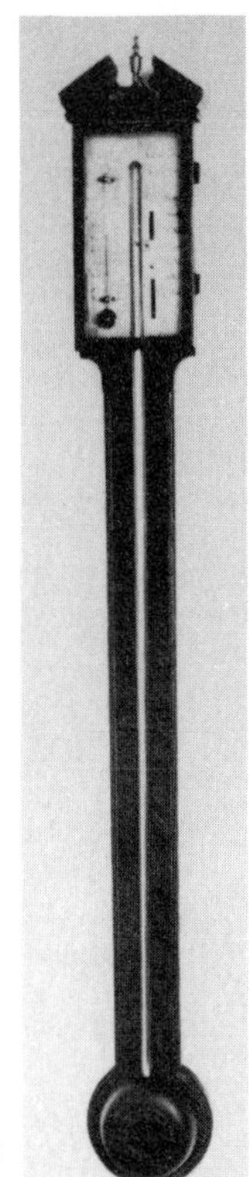

A George III mahogany stick barometer, signed A. Crioli, Fecit, with a thermometer, 39 in. (99 cm.), late 18th C. **£500-600** *SC*

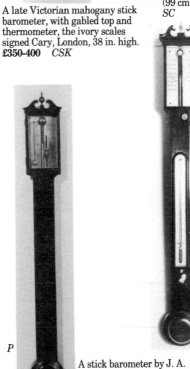

A Georgian mahogany stick barometer by Nathan Dawson, 38 in. (96.5 cm.) high. **£200-250** *P*

.n early 19th C. mahogany owfront stick barometer, the ilvered brass plate signed). Davis, Optician, Glasgow, 8⅝ in. (98 cm.) high. **£650-750** *P*

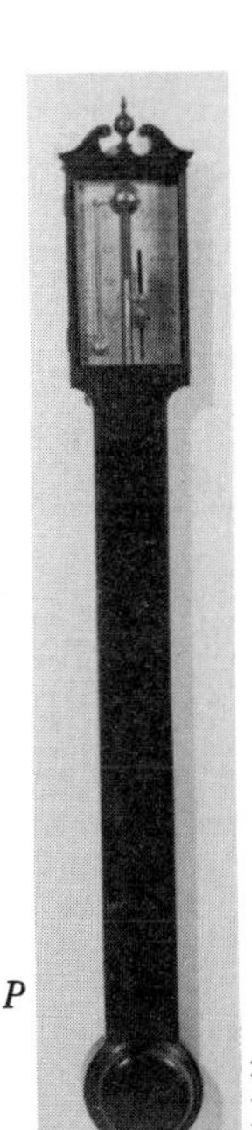

A fine walnut stick barometer, the silvered scale with mercury thermometer signed Dollond London and hinged door for adjustable vernier, 39 in. (99 cm.) high. **£1,500-2,000** *C*

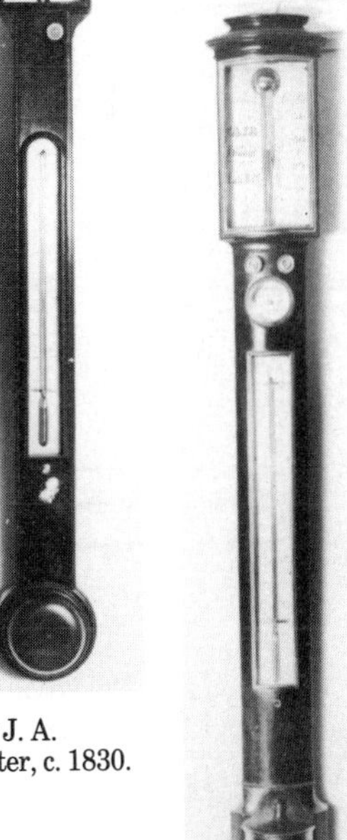

A stick barometer by J. A. Franklin of Manchester, c. 1830. **£650-745** *NC*

A mahogany bowfronted stick barometer by Dollond, c. 1835. **£1,750-1,850** *NC*

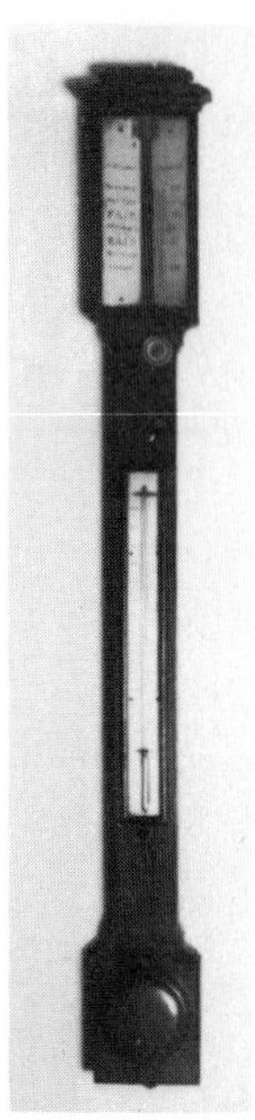

A mahogany stick barometer by J. Hughes, London, c. 1820. **£400-£475** *RD*

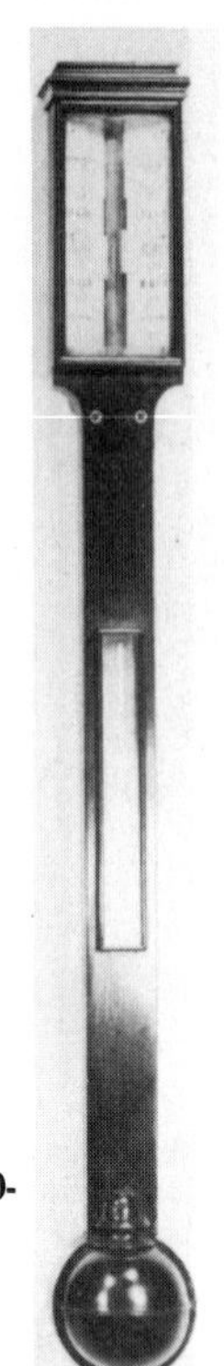

An early Victorian rosewood pillar barometer, the ivory scales signed G. Knight & Co, Foster Lane, London, with thermometer below, 37 in. high. **£350-400** *CSK*

A mahogany stick barometer by Lione and Tarone, c. 1805. **£675-£775** *NC*

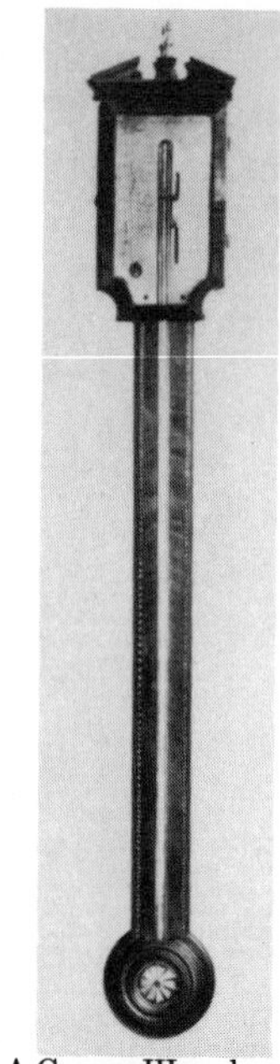

A George III mahogany stick barometer, the brass register signed Geo. Meyer, the trunk inlaid with chequer lines, with restorations, 38 in. (97 cm.), late 18th C. **£180-220** *SC*

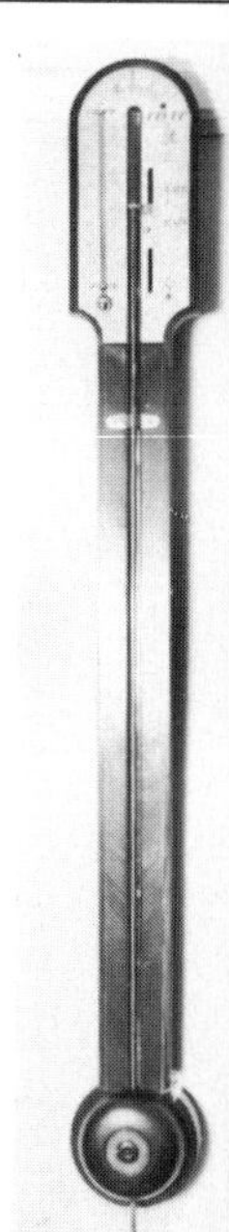

A fine mahogany stick barometer by Manticha, c. 1810. **£700-£780** *NC*

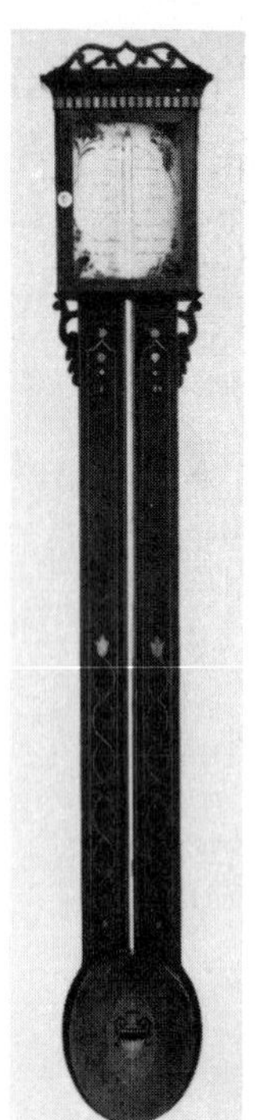

An unusual George III inlaid mahogany stick barometer, signed Geo. Purchon Glass House, with delicately painted pink and blue flowers, 39 in. (99 cm.) high. **£800-£900** *S*

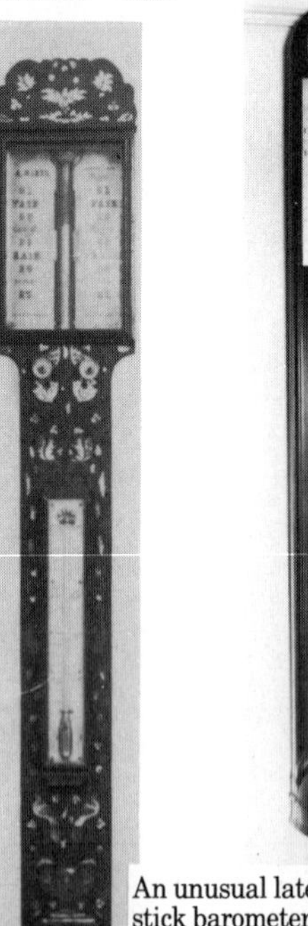

A William IV/early Victorian rosewood stick barometer, with ivory scales inscribed 'A. Rizzi, Lowerhead Row, Leeds', the case profusely inlaid with mother-of-pearl, 41 in. (104 cm.) high. **£350-£400** *SS*

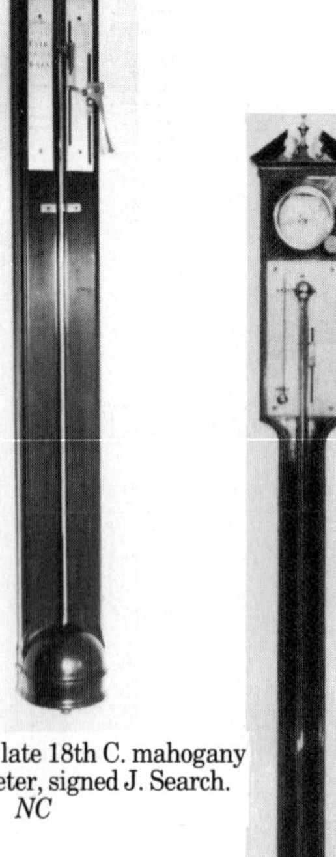

An unusual late 18th C. mahogany stick barometer, signed J. Search. **£900-1,100** *NC*

A Georgian mahogany stick barometer signed Watkins, London, the case strung with ebony and boxwood and fitted with a hemispherical cistern cover and hygrometer, 44½ in. (1.13 m.) high. **£900-1,100** *P*

An early Victorian mahogany bowfront pillar barometer, sig Troughton & Simms, London, 36 in. high. **£800-900** *CSK*

The partnership between Edwc Troughton and William Simm dates between 1826 and 1860.

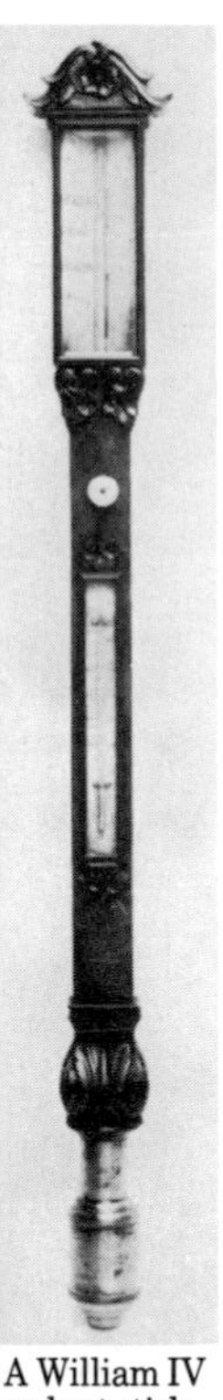

A William IV walnut stick barometer and thermometer, having ivory scales and turned brass cistern, 38¼ in. (97.5 cm.). **£400-500** *S*

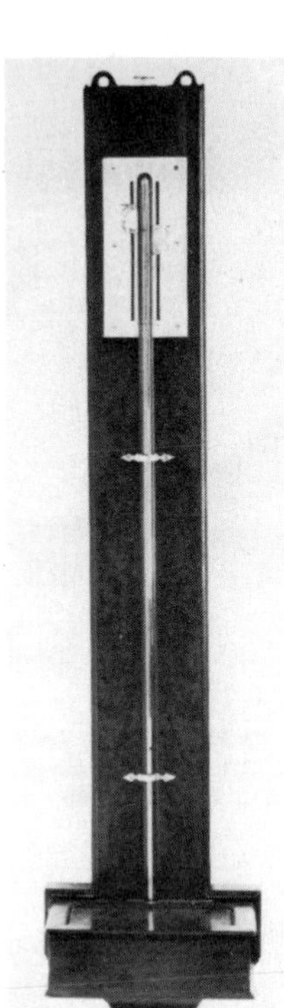

An unusual George III mahogany wall barometer, the silvered register plate signed Nairne and calibrated in French and English inches, the projecting base with a removable cover, 41½ in. (105.5 cm.) high, c. 1770. **£600-£700** *S*

A rare inlaid walnut double tube angle barometer, the 15 in. silvered register plate signed and dated Made by Cha. Orme of Ashby-de-la-Zouch 1741, the tubes calibrated in fortieths of an inch, 40½ in. high by 25 in. wide. **£3,000-4,000** *S*

For a full account of Charles Orme, a renowned but little known maker, see Nicholas Goodison, English Barometers, 1680-1860, pages 173-78, where a triple tube instrument of similar design is illustrated.
For a double tube example dated 1742 with a longer register plate and tubes at a shallower angle calibrated in hundredths of an inch see Ralph Edwards, The Shorter Dictionary of English Furniture, London, 1964, s.v. barometers, figure 11.

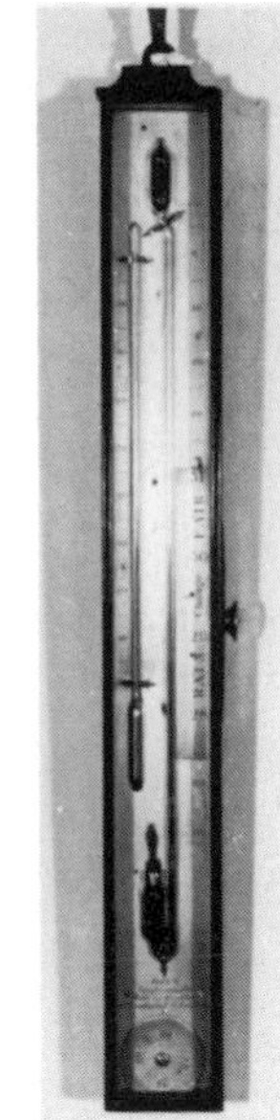

A 19th C. Adie's sympiesometer by Chrichton, London. **£700-800** *DWB*

A rare 2-day marine chronometer by William B. Crisp of 174 St. John Strt. Road, London, the spotted movement with Earnshaw spring detent, Hartnup's compensation balance, inscribed Prize Medal 1862, key with curved butterfly handle, diam. of bezel 123 mm. **£1,500-2,000** *S*

An 8-day marine chronometer, signed Barrauds, Cornhill, London no. 856, with Earnshaw spring detent escapement, now with bi-metallic compensation balance with movable screws, in original brass bound mahogany box, diam. of bezel 99 mm. **£3,200-3,600** *S*

A marine boxed chronometer by Brockbank and Atkins, London, no. 1515, the three-quarter plate 8-day movement with 5½ in. bezel, Earnshaw spring detent escapement, compensated balance, in brass bound Brazilian rosewood case, aprox. 8 by 8 in. **£2,500-£3,000** *DS*

A 2-day marine chronometer by D. McGregor & Co. of Glasgow & Greenock, the spotted movement with Earnshaw spring detent escapement, compensation balance, in brass bound rosewood carrying case, diam. of bezel 122 mm. **£950-£1,050** *S*

A 2-day marine chronometer by Parkinson & Frodsham, the movement with bi-metallic compensated balance, in a brass bowl hung in gimbals, in a mahogany 3-tier box, 6½ in. (16.5 cm.) square. **£1,100-1,300** *P*

A good 2-day marine chronometer by Lilley & Reynolds Ltd, London. **£550-650** *PWC*

An 8-day ship's table chronometer by Charles Frodsham, in burr-walnut case, 11 in. high. **£2,000-£2,500** *TP*

A brass military clinometer, dated 1945, 7¾ in. **£20-30** *CLA*

A brass, Admiralty pattern clinometer with mahogany case, 9½ in. high. **£80-100** *CLA*

A 2-day marine chronometer, the spotted movement with Earnshaw spring detent escapement, compensation balance, signed Robt. Roskell, Liverpool, diam. of bezel 104 mm. **£1,000-1,200** *S*

Miller's Antiques Price Guide builds up year by year to form the most comprehensive photo-reference system available. The first three volumes contain over 20,000 completely different photographs.

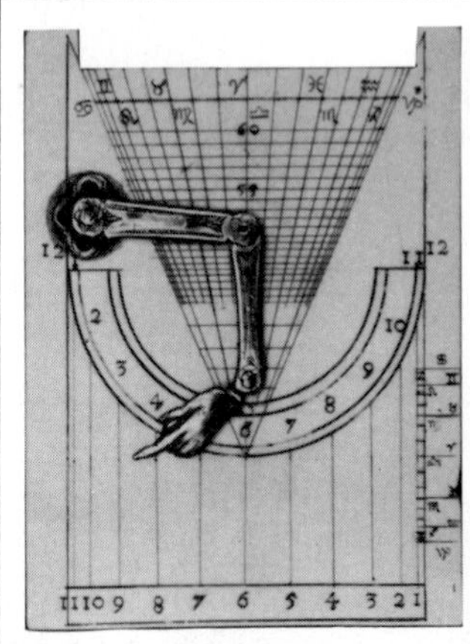

A rare ivory universal altitude dial, the ivory tablet mounted with silvered metal indicator arm and tablet engraved with latitude scale 15 to 60, radiating lines of zodiac signs and 2-hour scales, probably French, missing sun sights and plumb-bob, 3½ by 2¾ in. (90 by 70 mm.), late 16th/early 17th C. **£1,250-1,550** *S*

After the designs of Regiomontanus, published 1476. To discover the time using this instrument the finger of the indicator is adjusted to the latitude and date at which the dial is to be used. The bead on the plumb-bob is then adjusted to the date on the small zodiac scale and the dial is then held up until the light passing through the upper sight falls upon the lower sight, the plumb-bob then shows the time on the vertical hour lines.

A Miller ivory diptych dial signed Leonhard Miller, the upper leaf engraved with the cardinal points, pointer lacking, the underside with the Signs of the Zodiac, the lower leaf with inset compass, needle and glass lacking, dated 1632, the underside of the base with hour and lunar scales, volvelle lacking, length 3⅝ in. (92 mm.), 1632. **£1,300-1,500** *S*

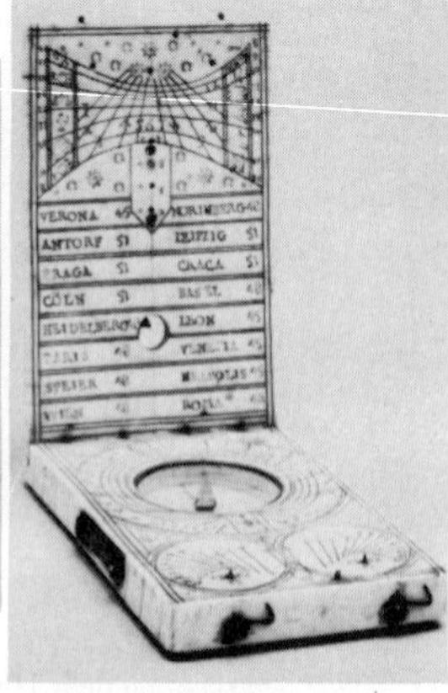

An ivory diptych dial, the upper leaf with a windrose and the cardinal points, brass pointer, the base with inset glazed compass stamped 3 in the centre and with dials for Italian and Babylonian hours, foliate, 3¾ in. (9.4 cm.) length, early 17th c. **£1,700-2,000** *S*

A wooden polyhedral dial with hand-coloured paper dials on 5 surfaces together with fixed brass gnomons, and signed D. Berringer, with inset glazed compass, length of base 4 in. (10 cm.), 18th C. **£600-£700** *S*

A good late 18th C. brass universal equinoctial ring dial, signed Cary, London, the bridge engraved with the signs of the zodiac and other scales, 6 in. (15.2 cm.) diam. **£1,400-1,600** *P*

A universal equinoctial dial, the reverse of the base with a list of towns and their latitudes and signed Johann Martin Willebrand in Augsp., 48, in original shaped box, rubbed, diam. of chapter ring 1¾ in. (4.5 cm.), c. 1725. **£1,200-£1,600** *S*

Johann Willebrand took over the Martin workshop on the death of his stepbrother in 1720, and up to the time of his own death in 1726 Willebrand's sundials were signed Johann Martin Willebrand.

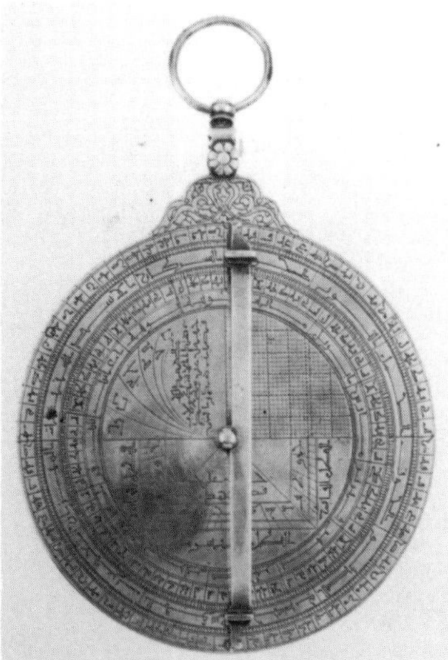

A rare and important mid 17th C. brass Maghribi Astrolabe, 17.2 cm. diam., the Rete for 30 stars, all but 2 named. The 5 plates engraved on both sides with circles of altitude, lines for unequal hours, times of Muslim prayer, and Dawn and Dusk lines. An inscription in maghribi script within the Horary quadrant reads 'Praise be to God. This astrolabe is a pious bequest to the Mosque of Quasba Hadrash'. **£12,000 +** *P*

A good 18th C. brass English circumferentor signed Thos. Heath, Londini Fecit, fitted with a silvered compass, the 12 in. (30.5 cm.) diam. cut away baseplate engraved on the circumference with a 0-360° scale, contained in a fitted oak case, 15⅜ in. (39.1 cm.) wide with a tripod universal attachment, a levelling plate with 3 adjusting screws and a companion plane-table circumferentor surveyor's dial with bubble level. **£1,300-£1,500** *P*

A brass universal equatorial dial by Adie & Son of Edinburgh, silvered chapter ring and folding latitude quadrant, brass gnomon, in original case, diam. of chapter ring, 65 mm., early 19th C. **£400-£500** *S*

A French brass large universal equinoctial dial signed Butterfield A Paris, with inset glazed magnetic compass, hinged chapter circle, folding gnomon, quadrant scale and level indicator, lacking plumb, 150 by 170 mm. **£3,000-4,000** *C*

A rare brass equatorial dial by Edmund Culpeper, with hinged hour scale, folding gnomon, the base signed Edm. Culpeper Londini Fecit, in original velvet lined fishskin covered case, length overall 67 mm., early 18th C. **£1,300-1,500** *S*

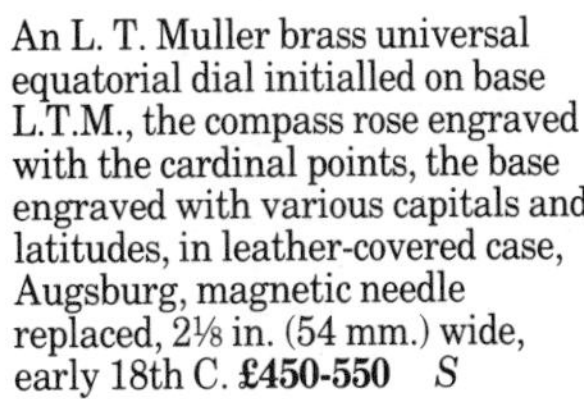

An L. T. Muller brass universal equatorial dial initialled on base L.T.M., the compass rose engraved with the cardinal points, the base engraved with various capitals and latitudes, in leather-covered case, Augsburg, magnetic needle replaced, 2⅛ in. (54 mm.) wide, early 18th C. **£450-550** *S*

A brass universal equatorial dial, signed Ramsden, London, on the chapter ring, the whole raised on 3 levelling screws, diam. of chapter ring 4½ in. (11.5 cm.), late 18th C. **£700-800** *S*

A good John Davis & Son brass miner's dial, two spirit levels, inscribed Davis & Son, London & Derby, no. 293, flanked by 2 open sights (detachable to accept brackets for the sighting telescope), mahogany case, English, 11½ in. (29 cm.) long, late 19th C. **£300-£350** *S*

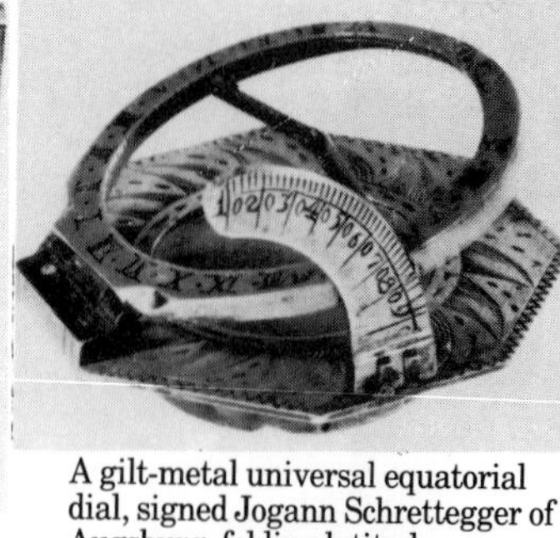

A gilt-metal universal equatorial dial, signed Jogann Schrettegger of Augsburg, folding latitude quadrant, diam. of chapter ring 1¾ in. (4.5 cm.), 18th C. **£250-300** *S*

A 19th C. brass equinoctial dial, the hinged equinoctial plate with folding spring loaded gnomon and folding latitude arc, contained in a mahogany case, 6½ in. (16.5 cm.) square. **£400-500** *P*

A W. & S. Jones brass, ivory and wood table orrery, the wooden table applied with paper printed with the months, signs of the Zodiac, a pictorial representation of the solar system titled 'A Table of the Principal Affections of the Planets published by W. & S. Jones 30 Holban London', operated by brass and ivory handle at the side, English, base cracked, 12½ in. (31.5 cm.) diam., late 18th C. **£1,200-1,400** *S*

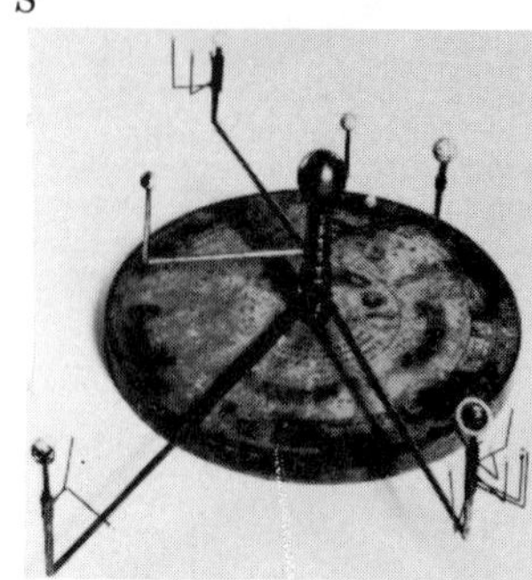

A W. Jones brass ivory and wood orrery with brass and ivory spheres, English, diam. of base 7¾ in. (19.5 cm.), c. 1800. **£600-£700** *S*

A late Stuart surveying compass with engraved rose and scale, brass bezel set in wood case, the hinged cover with hollows for the detachable sights, now lost, 150 by 147 mm. **£200-300** *C*

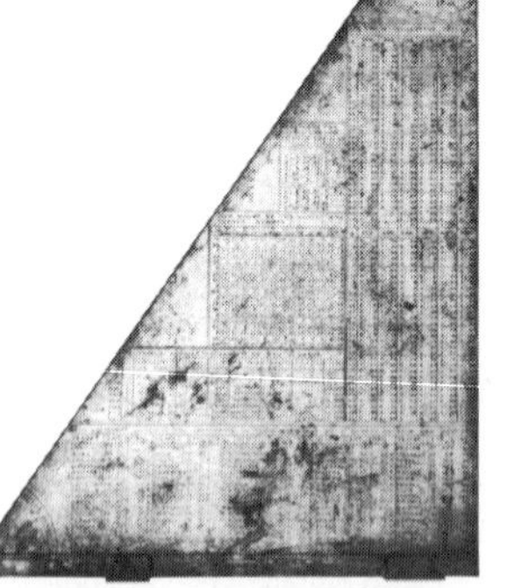

A large sundial gnomon, designed by G. Fullarton, the triangular heavy gauge brass plate engraved with maker's name within cartouche G. Fullarton Designavit et Soli Fulgenti Consecravit Anno 1744, on 2 brass supports, English, 18 in. (46 cm.) high, dated 1744. **£600-700** *S*

A 19th C. brass and iron orrery signed G. Phillip & Son, 32 Fleet Street, London, with wheel, rack and pinion gear mechanism, mounted with a 3 in. (1.6 cm.) diam. terrestrial globe and sun by R. Scholte & Co., Berlin. **£350-£400** *P*

A 19th C. orrery, unsigned, the brass movement mounted on a circular base, 17 in. (43.2 cm.) diam., covered with a printed and varnished zodiac calendar and sky representation, the printed paper gores defective, 18½ in. (47 cm.) wide, and with an ebonised octagonal stand, 35½ in. (90.2 cm.) high. **£1,700-2,000** *P*

A 3 in. pocket globe, signed Newton's New & Improved Terrestrial Pocket Globe, No. 56, Chancery Lane, London, and inscribed below Pub. Jan. 1, 1817, in fishskin-covered outer case, the inside of the lid lined with paper gores of the planets with signs of the Zodiac and months of the year, English, dated 1817. **£700-800** *S*

brass armillary sphere, ntaining terrestrial globe, sun d moon, the whole on turned ass column and base, 15 in. 3 cm.) high, good condition. **£700-00** *S*

Make the most of Miller's

When buying or selling, it must always be remembered that prices can be greatly affected by the condition of any piece. Unless otherwise stated, all goods shown in Miller's are of good merchantable quality, and the valuations given reflect this fact.

Pieces offered for sale in exceptionally fine condition or in poor condition may reasonably be expected to be priced considerably higher or lower respectively than the estimates given herein.

Our section on large globes has this year been moved to the Furniture section which is ordered alphabetically.

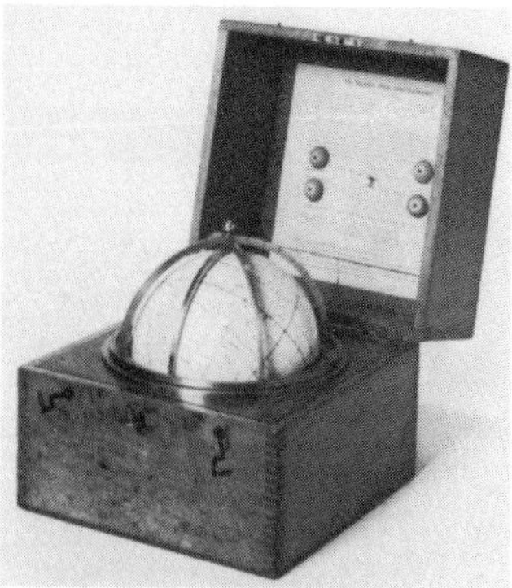

An unusual celestial globe designed for star finding to determine latitude and time, marked Cary & Co., Makers to the Admiralty, 7 Pall Mall, London, in a mahogany case, the lid with operating instructions, 8¾ in. (22.2 cm.). **£300-350** *P*

6 in. Stanley brass transit eodolite, the sighting telescope ounted with spirit level, vertical rcle of degrees with verniers and agnifiers, magnetic compass and orizontal circle of degrees with rniers and 2 spirit levels, nglish, 15 in. (380 mm.) high, 1900. **£750-850** *S*

A lacquered brass transit theodolite signed G. Adams, Invr. London with double altitude and azimuth scales controlled by rack and pinion, in case, transit pinion missing, sighting tube 9½ in. long. **£3,500-4,000** *CSK*

A large T. Cooke & Sons transit theodolite No. 16743, on rotating stage with vernier and spirit level, complete with fitted case, accessories and large mahogany tripod, English, 13½ in. (34 cm.) high, early 20th C. **£400-500** *S*

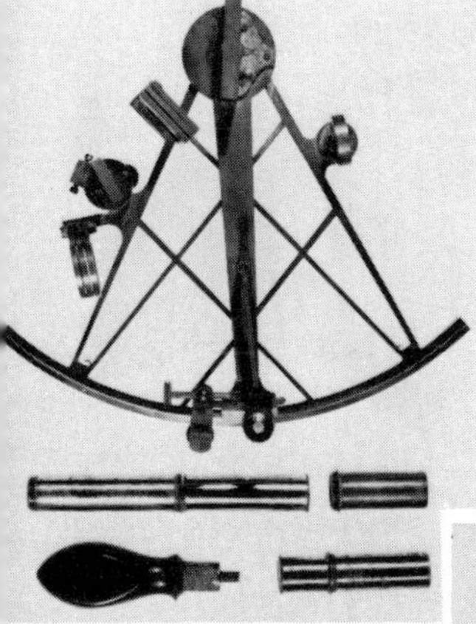

brass sextant with unusual evelled platina scale, signed on e radius limb Dollond London, in riginal shaped mahogany box, amaged, with associated sighting ıbes, radius 7 in. (17.8 cm.), nglish, early 19th C. **£1,100-1,200** *S*

A Troughton & Simms 'Y' brass theodolite inscribed 'Diff. of Hypo & Base', above compass rose, spirit balance and silvered circle of degrees, in fitted mahogany case, English, 10 in. (25.5 cm.) high, mid 19th C. **£500-600** *S*

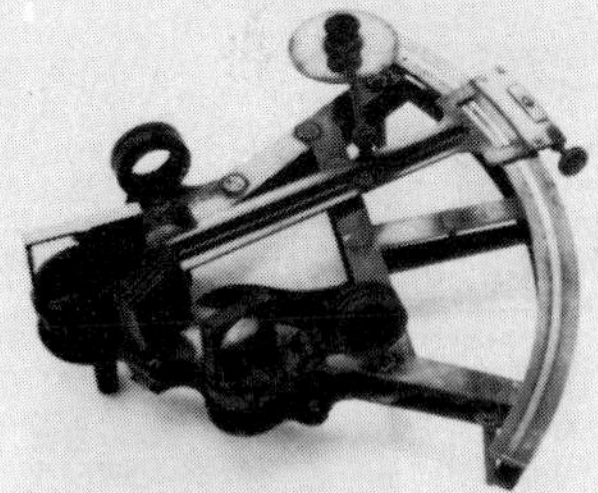

A Troughton brass double frame sextant, No. 1047 by Troughton of London, signed on the arc, with platina scale and vernier with magnifier, 2 sets of coloured filters, in mahogany box with 4 sighting tubes, radius 8 in. (203 mm.), English, 1815-16. **£1,200-1,300** *S*

A letter from the National Maritime Museum dating the instrument is attached.

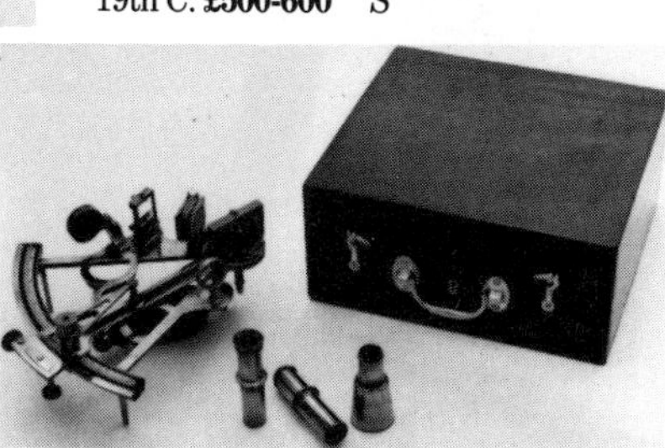

A late 19th C. brass sextant inscribed Castle and Pagan, Hull, with 'ivory and ebony' scale, spare telescopes and coloured shades, fitted box, 9¾ in., c. 1875. **£250-£300** *DDM*

A Winter miniature brass sextant, signed Winter, late Cail, Newcastle upon Tyne, the T-shaped frame with platina scale and vernier with hinged magnifier, 3⅜ in. (8.5 cm.) radius, 19th C. **£550-600** *S*

A German sextant in case dated 1944. **£60-70** *JMW*

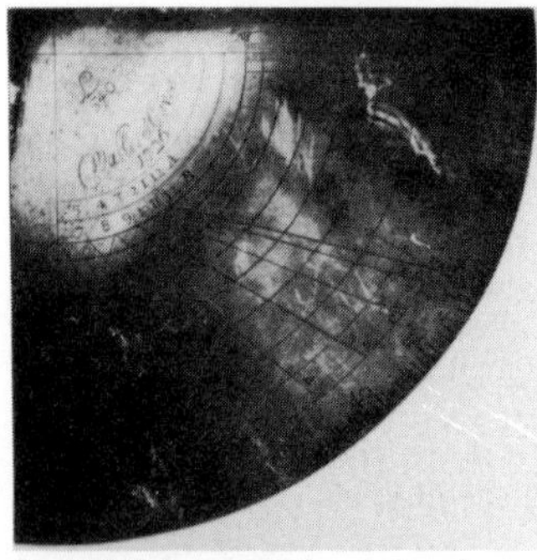

An 18th C. brass quadrant signed and dated Walter Hayes, 1726 and engraved with calendar scales, a 0-90° arc and other divisions for latitude 54°. 00′, 9¹¹⁄₁₆ in. (14.5 cm.) radius. **£180-250** *P*

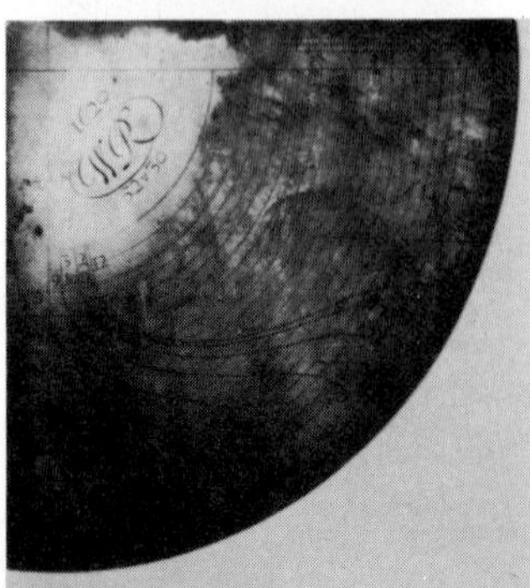

A 17th C. brass quadrant signed and dated WR, 1620 and engraved with calendar and zodiac scales, a 0-90° arc and other lines and division for latitude 52°. 30′, 9¹¹⁄₁₆ in. (14.5 cm.) radius. **£160-£250** *P*

A Keohan brass sextant, with silver 0-160° scale, ebony handle, in shaped mahogany case with 2 telescopes, pin-hole sight and filter eyepiece, English, 7½ in. (19 cm.) radius, late 19th C. **£300-400** *S*

Thomas Keohan is listed in the London Directories as instrument maker at Commercial Road and Upper East Smithfield from 1863 to 1870.

A good 18th C. ebony and brass mounted quadrant by John Goater, the frame inset with an ivory plate engraved Goater at No. 141, Wapping, the brass arm engraved with a masonic emblem, fitted with an index glass, horizon glass and second mirror for back observation, the arm 17¾ in. (45 cm.) radius. **£600-700** *P*

A Finch brass sector, signed I. Finch fecit, engraved with numbers, chords, sines, tangents and secants, English, length of arm 12 in. (305 mm.), mid 18th C. **£850-£950** *S*

A Robert Bate ebony octant, the ebony frame inset with maker's plaque, with 2 telescopes, English, 9¾ in. (24.8 cm.) radius, c. 1830. **£350-400** *S*

A 17th C. Dutch brass quadrant signed Jan Cornelisen Fecit, fitted with an adjustable pinnule, mirrors, the coloured shades lacking, the grand alidade having a spring clamp but no vernier, the engraved scales marked Boeren, Beneden Honiz and Zenit, 12⅞ in. (32.7 cm.) radius. **£1,100-1,200** *P*

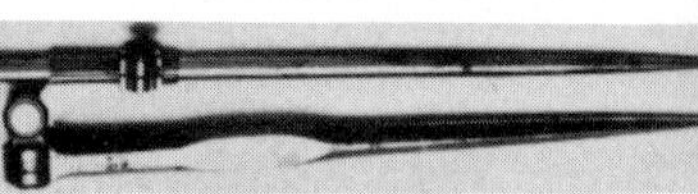

A good pair of brass and steel triangulation compasses, in a fitted leather case, 7¼ in. (18.4 cm) long. **£140-180** *P*

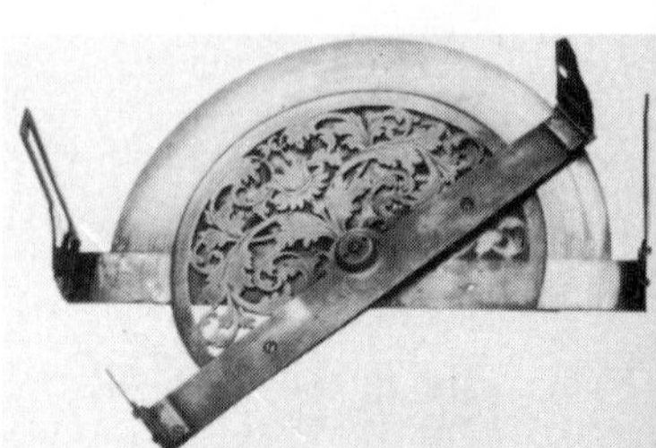

A rare brass graphometer signed Michael Scheffelt, Ulm fecit, dated beneath the alidade 1719, with outer degree scale and folding sights, overall diam. 338 mm., 1719. **£2,600-3,000** *S*

Born in February 1652 in Ulm, South Germany, Michael Scheffelt worked as a clerk, maker of fireworks and latterly as a teacher of mathematics. According to Zinner there are only 6 signed instruments by him. He died in July 1720.

An unusual 18th C. brass pedometer, the silvered dial signed Nairne and Blunt, London, driven via a gear drive from the steel tyred 4 baluster spoke wheels, 5¾ in. (24.6 cm.) diam., in a fitted case 9¼ in. (23.5 cm.) wide. **£600-£700** *P*

An unusual hand-enamelled tinplate arithmometer, finished in green and yellow, probably German, 6½ in. (16.5 cm.), c. 1900. **£250-300** *S*

A dry card binnacle compass, the 3½ in. diam. printed compass cased in brass drum case, 11½ in. (290 mm.) high, mid 19th C. **£300-£350** *S*

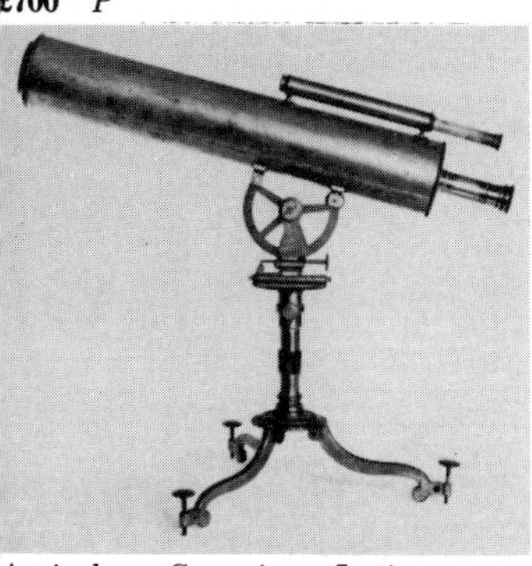

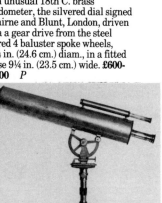

A 4 in. brass Gregorian reflecting table telescope, signed on the eye piece B. Martin Fleet Street, London, the tube with sighting telescope, English, length of tube 24 in. (61 cm.) c. 1770. **£1,950-£2,150** *S*

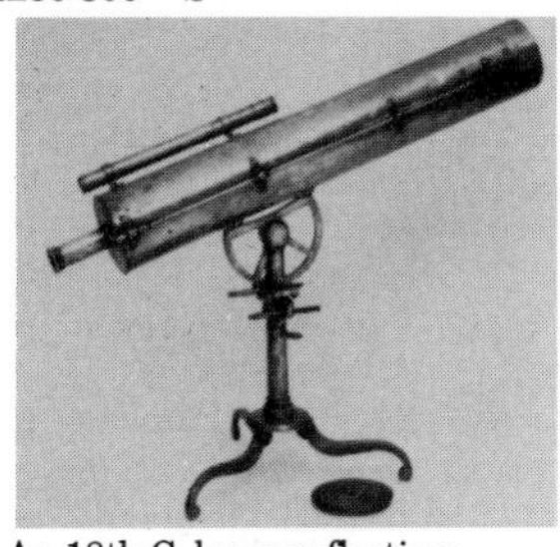

An 18th C. brass reflecting telescope, unsigned, of Gregorian type, having a 5 in. (12.7 cm.) diam. barrel, 31¾ in. (80.6 cm.) long with screwthread rod focusing, 24 in. (61 cm.) high in horizontal position. **£800-900** *P*

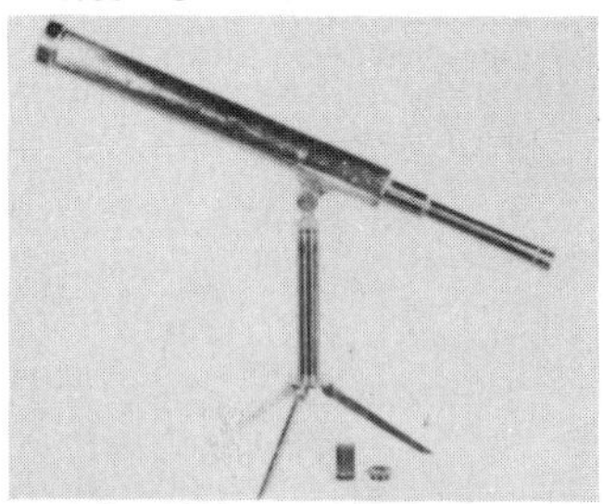

A fine 1¾ in. astronomical telescope by J. E. Ramsden, London, in fitted mahogany case, tube length 16 in. **£700-800** *CSK*

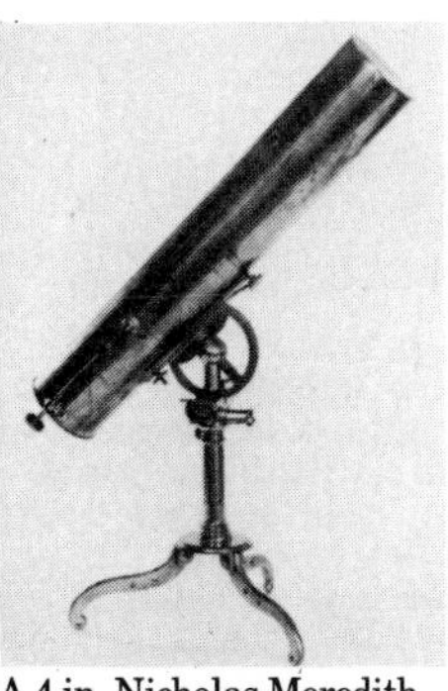

A 4 in. Nicholas Meredith Gregorian reflecting table telescope, signed round the eyepiece Meredith, Bond Street, London, with long screw focusing, English, length of tube 24 in. (61 cm.), c. 1800. **£400-500** *S*

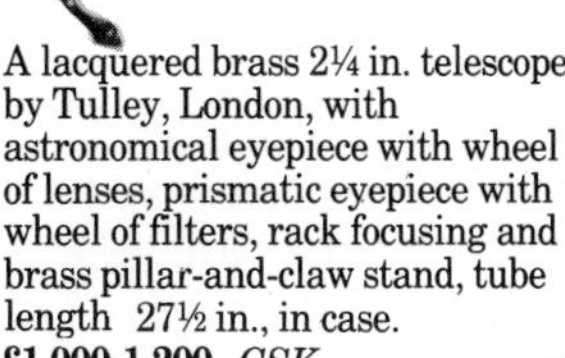

A lacquered brass 2¼ in. telescope by Tulley, London, with astronomical eyepiece with wheel of lenses, prismatic eyepiece with wheel of filters, rack focusing and brass pillar-and-claw stand, tube length 27½ in., in case. **£1,000-1,200** *CSK*

A 2½ in. William Harris & Co. brass refracting telescope on stand, in oak case with 2 oculars, together with mahogany tripod, English, length of tube 44 in. (112 cm.), mid 19th C. **£300-350** *S*

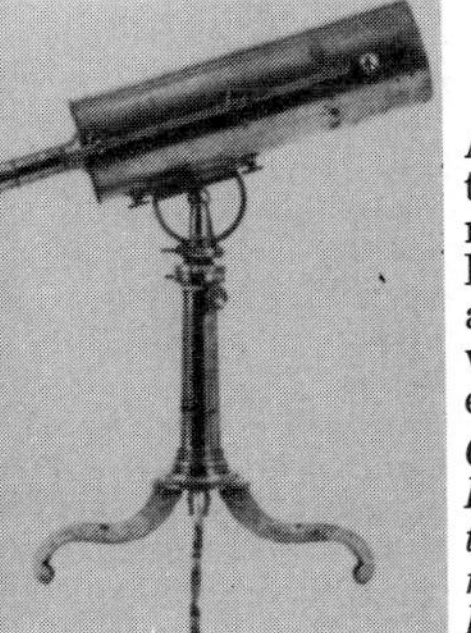

A Tulley Gregorian reflecting telescope, on stand, with 4¼ in. reflector, inscribed Tulley, Islington, London, on a trunnion and tripod base, English, complete with case, 22 in. high (56 cm.), early 19th C. **£1,300-1,500** *S*

Charles Tulley operated in the Islington area of London between the dates 1782-1846, he is also noted for purchasing the business of Benjamin Martin.

A 3 in. Dollond brass table telescope, signed round the eyepiece Dollond London, the tube with rack and pinion focusing, in mahogany case with 4 eyepieces and a coloured filter, with trade label, English, length of tube 43 in. (109 cm.), mid 19th C. **£500-600** *S*

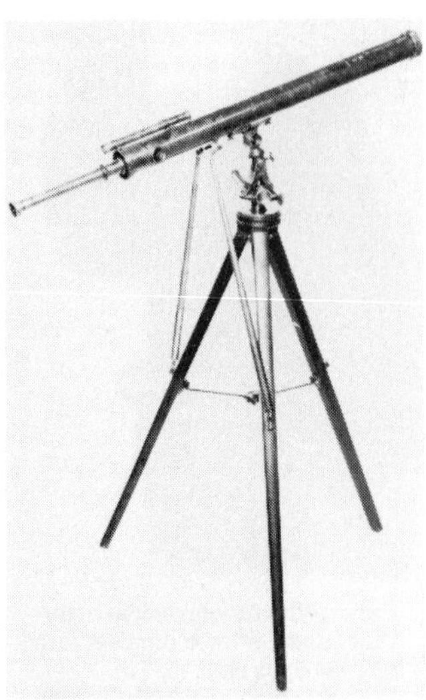

A 2¾ in. Abrahams brass refracting telescope, the tube with rack and pinion focusing to the eyepiece, length of tube 43 in. (109 cm.), English, mid 19th C. **£1,000-1,200** *SC*

An early 19th C. 2 draw ivory and Old Sheffield gilt-metal monocular signed ADAMS London and dated 1803, 2½ in. high (6.3 cm.). **£180-£220** *P*

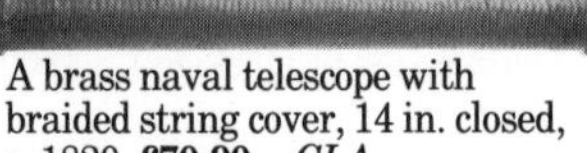

A brass naval telescope with braided string cover, 14 in. closed, c. 1820. **£70-90** *CLA*

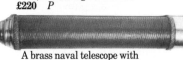

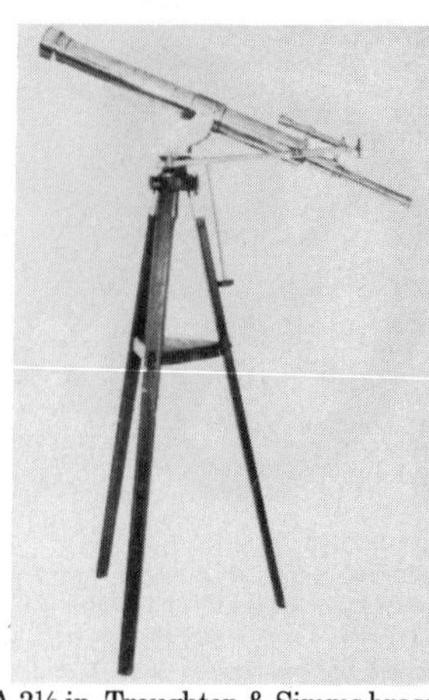

A 3½ in. Troughton & Simms brass astronomical telescope on stand, with rack and pinion focusing to the eyepiece, with slow motion azimuth racked circle, in mahogany case with 5 eyepieces, English, c. 1900. **£800-900** *S*

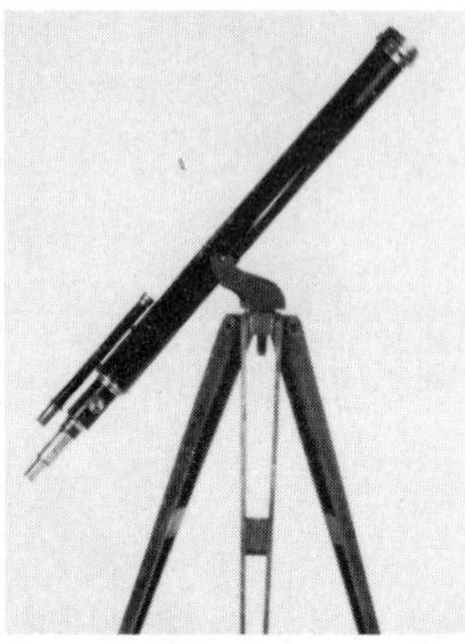

A 4 in. T. Cooke & Sons anodised brass astronomical refracting telescope on stand, on oak tripod, in painted case with 2 draw tubes, 2 oculars, 4 filters and objective shade, English, length of tube 48 in. (122 cm.), early 20th C. **£500-£600** *S*

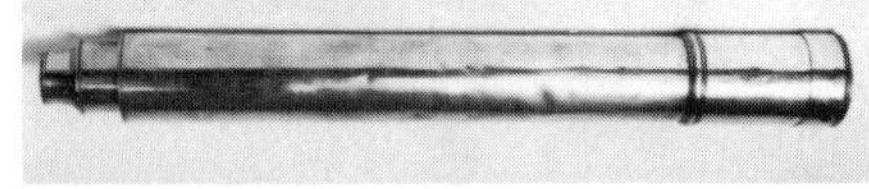

A brass naval 'day and night' telescope signed J. Hughes, 39 in. extended, c. 1830. **£90-120** *CLA*

Joseph Hughes was a mathematical, philosophical and nautical instrument maker working from Ratcliff Cross, London, from 1822-46.

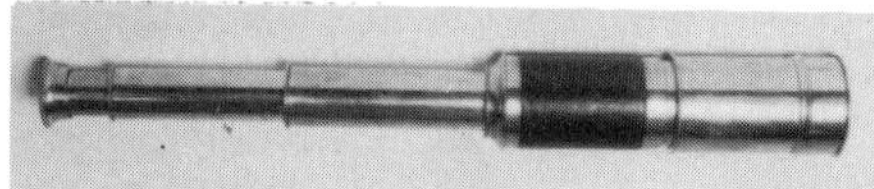

A brass telescope, 15 in. extended, c. 1860. **£50-70** *CLA*

Use the Index!

Because certain items might fit easily into any of a number of categories, the quickest and surest method of locating any entry is by reference to the index at the back of the book. This has been fully cross-referenced for absolute simplicity.

An improved double and single microscope by G. Adams, Fleet Street, with 1 ocular, objective lenses in rotating mount, spring stage with bull's-eye, stage forceps and sub-stage condenser with accessories drawer, 17 in. high. **£1,000-1,200** *CSK*

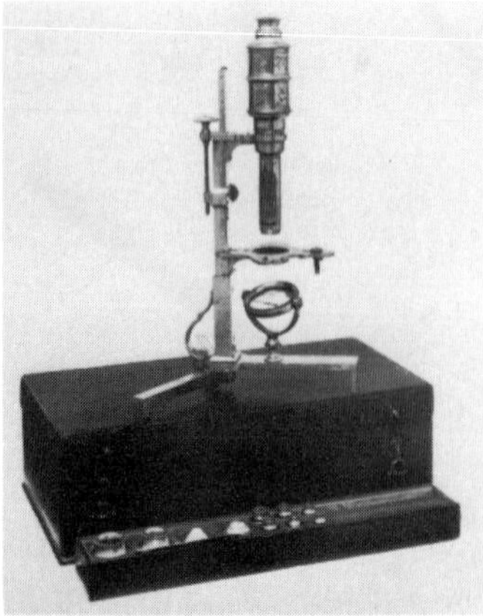

A George Adams brass compound microscope, signed on the stage Geo: Adams Inst. Maker to His Majesty, fixed stage, in original mahogany box with most accessories, length of box 13¾ in. (34 cm.), late 18th C. **£3,000-£4,000** *S*

A Baker brass binocular microscope, signed on the base Baker, 244 High Holborn London, in mahogany case with oculars, objectives, and other accessories, English, 17 in. high (43 cm.), c. 1880. **£700-800** *S*

A lacquered brass binocular microscope by R. & J. Beck, with mechanical stage, 6 oculars, 3 Beck objectives and other accessories, in fitted mahogany case, 13½ in. high. **£400-500** *CSK*

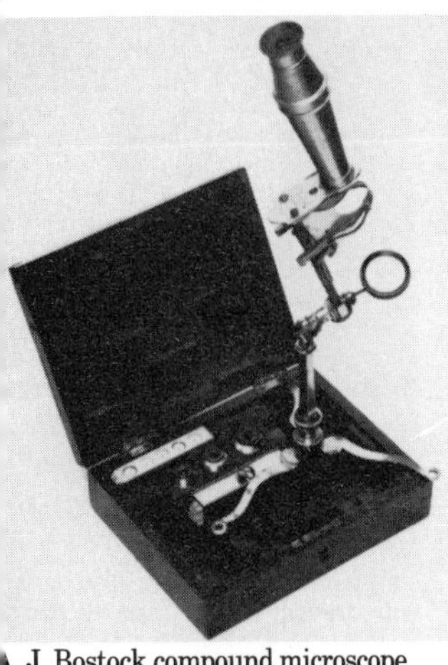

. J. Bostock compound microscope f the Watkins type, 6 numbered bjectives on rotating disk, later nirror, contained in mahogany box vith brass holder for slides, and 3 ieberkuhn, length of box 7¼ in. 18 cm.), 18th C. **£1,300-1,500** *S*

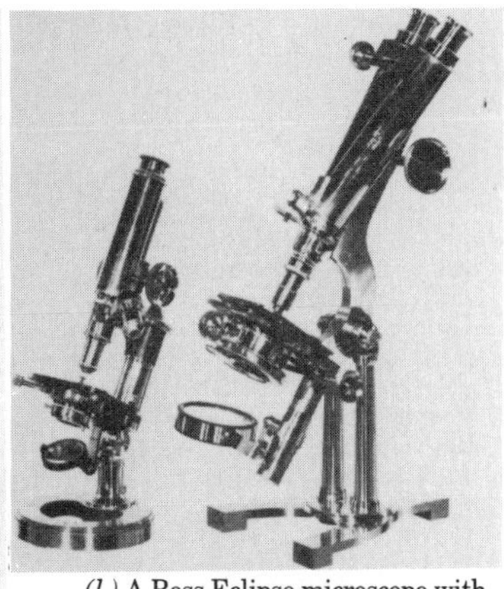

(l.) A Ross Eclipse microscope with coarse and fine focusing, 2 objectives, 2 oculars, condenser and sub-stage mirror in circular brass base, in mahogany case, 10 in. high. **£140-160** *CSK*

(r.) A binocular microscope by J. B. Dancer, No. 402, with Wenham prism, 2 pairs of oculars, 4 objectives, polariser and analyser, mechanical stage, sub-stage mirror, 17½ in. high. **£850-950** *CSK*

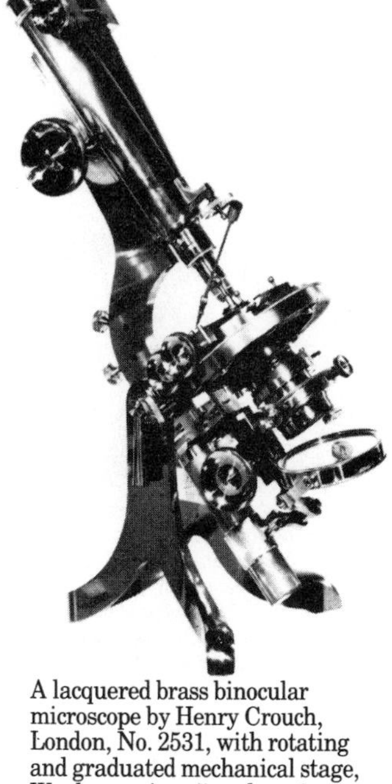

A lacquered brass binocular microscope by Henry Crouch, London, No. 2531, with rotating and graduated mechanical stage, Wenham prism, 5 oculars, 6 objectives, condenser, polariser and analyser, stand and stage bull's-eyes, in mahogany case, 18 in. high. **£1,000-1,200** *CSK*

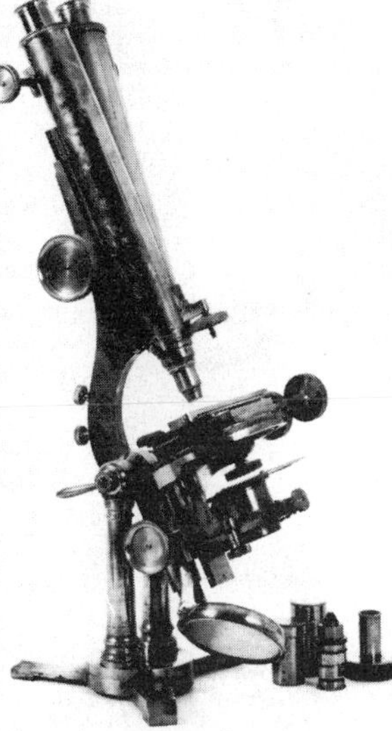

A large brass binocular microscope, possibly by H. Crouch, the Lister-limb construction with dual rack and pinion adjustment to the eyepieces, rack and pinion coarse focusing, polariser, live box and 3 objectives by Ross, Swift and Beck, with 2 boxes of slides, English, c. 1870. **£800-900** *S*

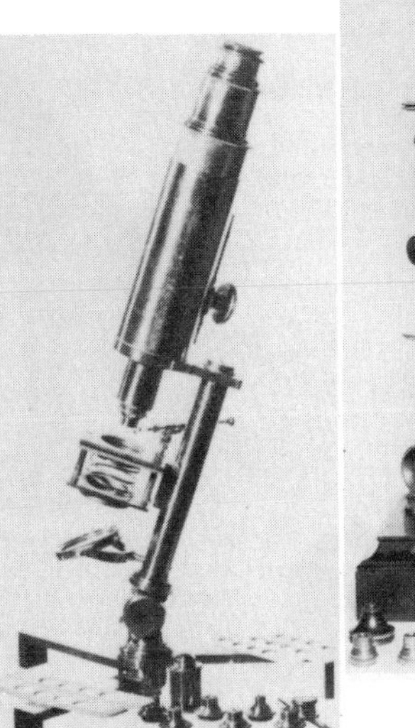

A lacquered brass 'New Improved Compound' microscope signed Davis, Cheltenham, with 7 objectives, live box, lieberkuhn, hand magnifier, bull's-eye, substage mirror, spring stage, in case with instruction booklet, 16 in. high. **£1,000-1,200** *CSK*

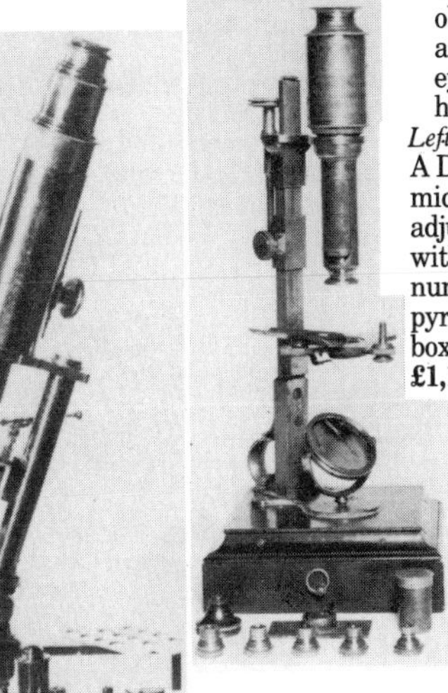

Left
A Dollond brass Cuff-type microscope, signed Dollond London, adjustable mirror below, cracked, with drawer containing 6 numbered objectives, in associated pyramid mahogany box, height of box 17¼ in. (44 cm.), c. 1800. **£1,100-1,300** *S*

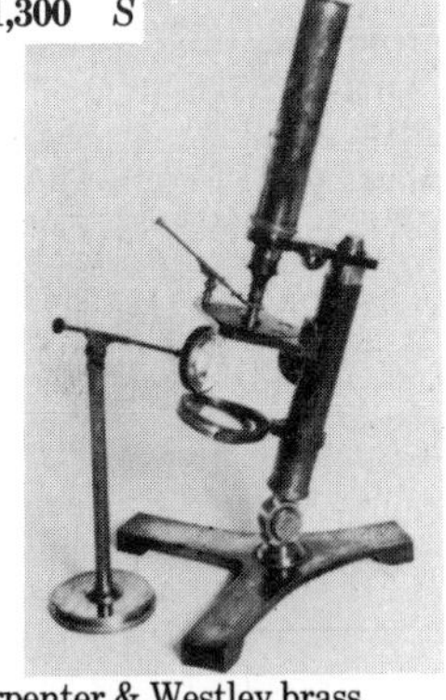

A Carpenter & Westley brass monocular microscope, the bar-limb construction with coarse focusing by rack and pinion, fine focusing by lever and screw, cut-away square stage with concave reflector below, on tripod base, signed Carpenter & Westley, 24 Regent St, London, in mahogany and walnut case with 2 oculars, 2 objectives, sprung stage, tweezers, forceps, wheel of stops and live box, with a mahogany cabinet with a quantity of specimen slides, English, 13 in. high (330 mm.), c. 1835. **£700-800** *S*

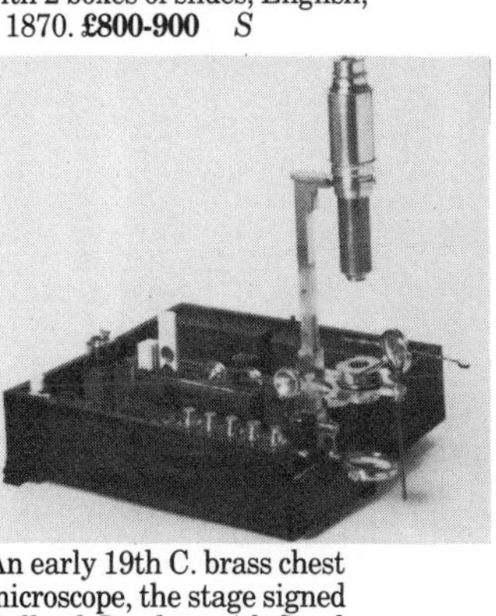

An early 19th C. brass chest microscope, the stage signed Dollond, London, with fitted case and accessories including 6 objectives, 2 sets of slides, sprung slide plate, bull's-eye condenser, etc., 11½ in. wide (29.2 cm.). **£950-£1,050** *P*

Left
A lacquered brass microscope by Dollond, London of 'Jones Most Improved' type with 2 oculars, lieberkuhn objective, live box, sub-stage condenser and mirror, fish-plate, specimen sticks, etc., in case, 18 in. high. **£1,400-1,500** *CSK*

An Ellis-type aquatic microscope, with sliding focusing screwing into the lid of a fishskin-covered box containing stage, objective, lieberkuhn, 3 aquatic lenses, tweezers and stage forceps, lacking reflector, English, case 5⅛ in. wide (130 mm.), c. 1870. **£250-300** *S*

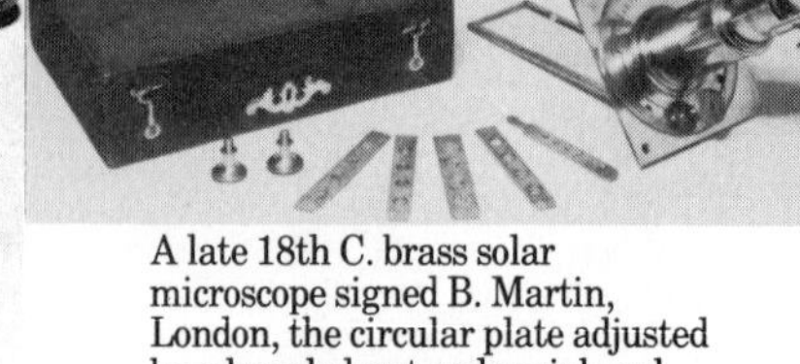

A late 18th C. brass solar microscope signed B. Martin, London, the circular plate adjusted by a knurled nut and peripheral gear, contained in a fishskin-covered case, 10⅜ in. wide (26.3 cm.), with accessories. **£1,300-£1,500** *P*

A fine Cuff-type microscope by Dollond, London with 1 ocular, 6 objectives and accessories, on base with drawer, 13½ in. high. **£1,600-£1,800** *CSK*

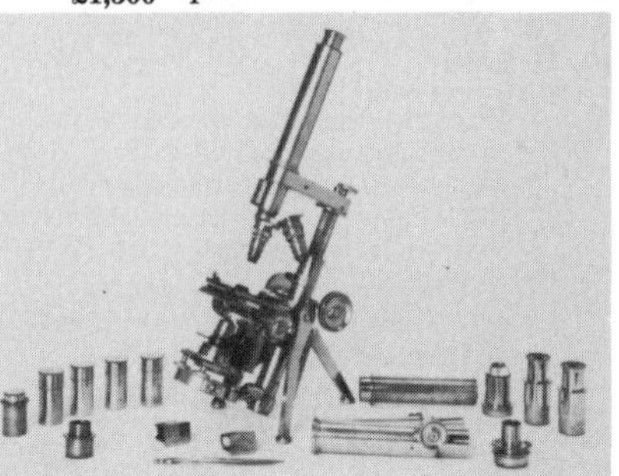

A quality mid 19th C. brass compound monocular microscope signed Powell & Lealand, 170 Euston Road, London, in a mahogany case, fitted out with a binocular attachment and numerous accessories including a parabolic illuminator, polarising lens, opaque object prism, 19⅝ in. high (49.8 cm.). **£1,000-1,100** *P*

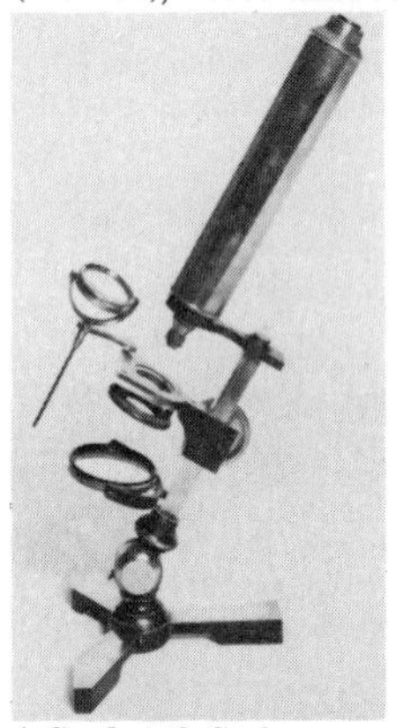

A Gardner & Co. brass monocular microscope, with concave reflector on compass joint above tripod base, in case with objective, stage forceps and condenser, live box and tweezers, 14 in. high (355 mm.), Scottish, c. 1840. **£650-750** *S*

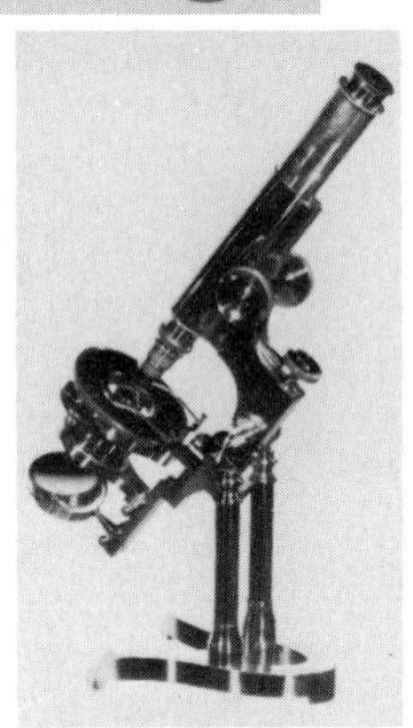

A lacquered brass microscope by Ross, No. 5261, of improved Ross-Zentmayer type, 11½ in. high. **£350-£400** *CSK*

A Powell & Lealand 'iron' student's microscope with lacquered brass body on japanned iron stand, 1 ocular, 1 objective and sub-stage mirror 15¾ in. high. **£350-400** *CSK*

A microscope by A. Ross, London, No. 471, with correction collar objective, Watson variable eyepiece, 3 other eyepieces, 18 in. high. **£750-850** *CSK*

A good Victorian brass monocular microscope by Andrew Ross, London, No. 110, in upright glazed mahogany cabinet with 18 drawers including various slides and tools, 28½ in. **£850-950** *GSP*

A fine lacquered brass monocular microscope by A. Ross, London, No. 605, sub-stage marked Made by A. Ross, London, Registered July 20th 1849, with accessories, in double-sided opening mahogany case, 17 in. high. **£700-800** *CSK*

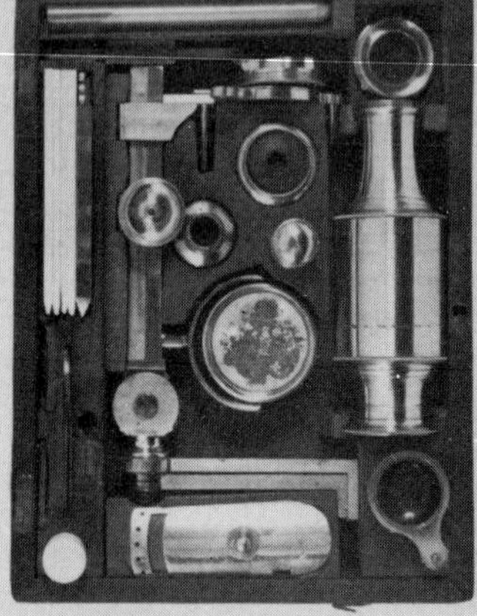

A good brass compound microscope, of pillar construction, rotating nosepiece containing 6 numbered objective lenses, on folding tripod base, with accessories, minimum height 6½ in. (16.5 cm.), in fitted mahogany case 8 in. long (20 cm.), English, c. 1800-30. **£800-900** *S*

An early 19th C. Cary-type brass monocular microscope, unsigned, in a fitted case, complete with bull's-eye condenser, a set of objectives and some slides, 7¾ in. wide (19.7 cm.). **£350-400** *P*

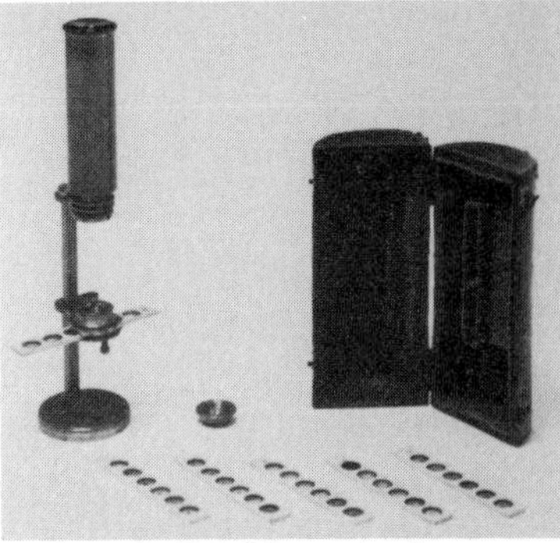

An early 19th C. brass simple monocular microscope, unsigned, in a case containing slides and accessories, 5⅗ in. long by 2⅖ in. diam. (14.3 by 6.1 cm.). **£180-220** *P*

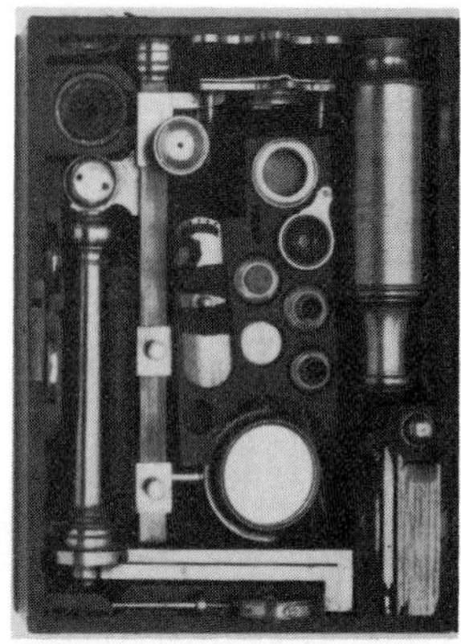

A good 19th C. brass compound monocular microscope, unsigned, constructed on the principle of 'Joneses' Most Improved', in a fitted case, with extensive range of accessories, including objectives, slides, forceps and bull's-eye condenser, 12 in. (30.5 cm.) wide. **£850-950** *P*

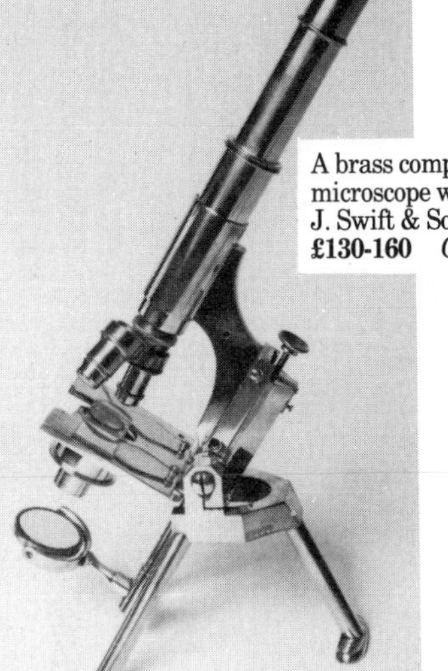

A brass compound monocular microscope with 2 objectives, by J. Swift & Son, 15 in. high, c. 1880. **£130-160** *CLA*

A chest microscope of Nairne type with ocular, 6 objectives, fish-plate, spring stage, stage bull's-eye, sub-stage mirror and other accessories, hinged in (later) mahogany case, 11½ in. wide. **£800-900** *CSK*

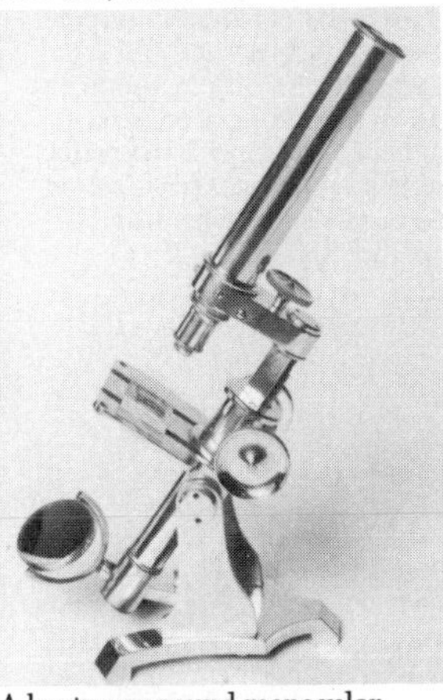

A brass compound monocular microscope with mahogany case, c. 1860, 12 in. **£120-150** *CLA*

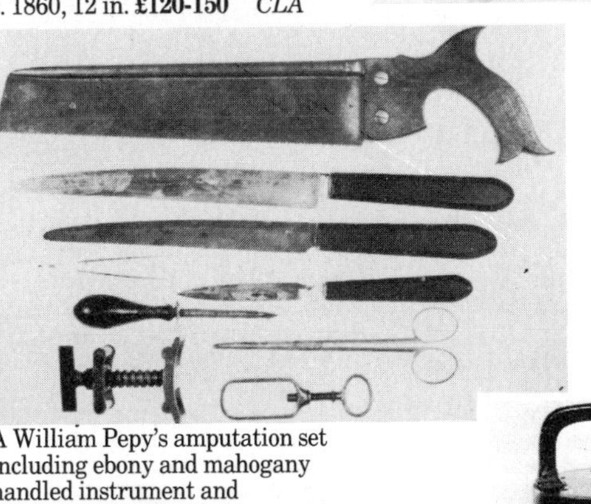

A William Pepy's amputation set including ebony and mahogany handled instrument and tourniquet, needles and knives, in fitted mahogany case (incomplete, saw by Stodart), English, 17 in. (432 mm.) wide, mid 19th C. **£250-£300** *S*

A 19th C. brass scarificator, stamped Thompson, London, fitted with 16 blades, an adjustment screw, trigger and release button; also a smaller scarificator by the same maker having 4 blades. **£200-£250** *P*

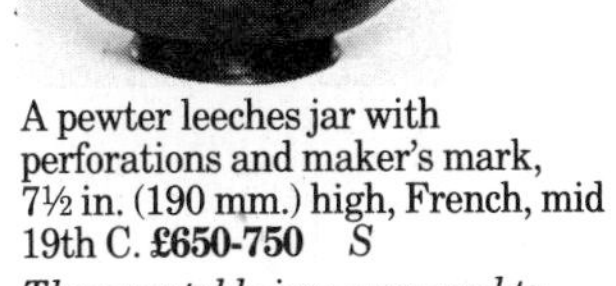

A pewter leeches jar with perforations and maker's mark, 7½ in. (190 mm.) high, French, mid 19th C. **£650-750** *S*

These portable jars were used to carry leeches from the local apothecary to a private sickroom.

A Hutchinson trepanning set, with crown saws, scalpel, Hey's saw, double-ended spring forceps, double-ended elevator, trephine brush and lancet, 10¾ by 5½ by 2 in. (27.3 by 14 by 5 cm.), c. 1840-50. **£450-500** *S*

William Hutchinson, Son & Coy, razor, surgical and veterinary instrument makers of Sheffield, 1825-79. During the American Civil War a ship bound for the U.S. was wrecked and was later found to have been carrying quantities of surgical instruments marked 'W. H. Hutchinson'.

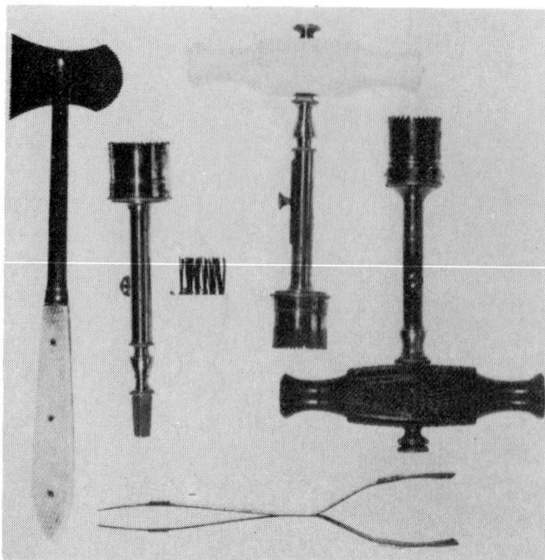

A cased set of Maw & Stevenson trepanning instruments, comprising an ivory handled trephine with 2 interchangeable blades, an ivory handled Hey's saw, ivory brush and steel elevator (incomplete), in case, 8¾ in. (220 mm.) wide, with another trephine with diamond pattern ebony handle, English, mid 19th C. **£550-600** *S*

(l.) A 19th C. brass ear trumpet, signed 'F. C. Rein sole inventor & maker, 108 Strand, London', the body applied with the maker's label and a similar brass ear trumpet by the same maker. **£100-130** *P*

(c.) A 19th C. tortoiseshell ear trumpet of vase shape by F. C. Rein & Son, London, fitted with a silver plated extension tube, 12⅞ in. (32.7 cm.) long, and a brass telescopic 'patent' ear trumpet by the same maker. **£160-200** *P*

(r.) An unusual pair of late 19th C. simulated tortoiseshell ear trumpets by F. C. Rein, connected with an adjustable head band and another ear trumpet by the same maker having a telescopic action, 13¼ in. (33.7 cm.) long fully extended. **£120-140** *P*

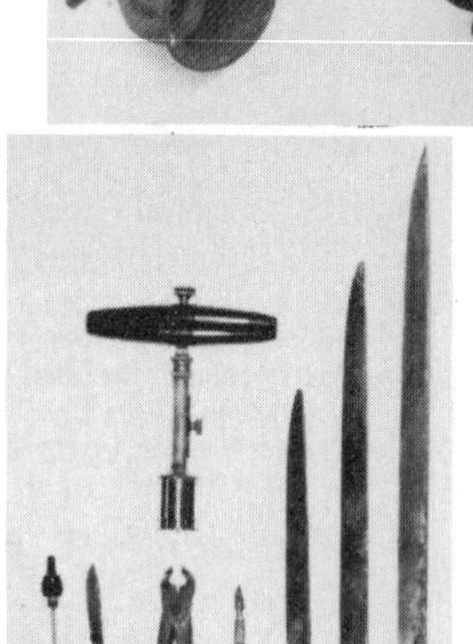

A surgeon's general purpose instrument set, the mahogany case red velvet-lined and fitted, English, 19½ by 7½ by 2¾ in. (42 by 19 by 7 cm.), c. 1860. **£550-600** *S*

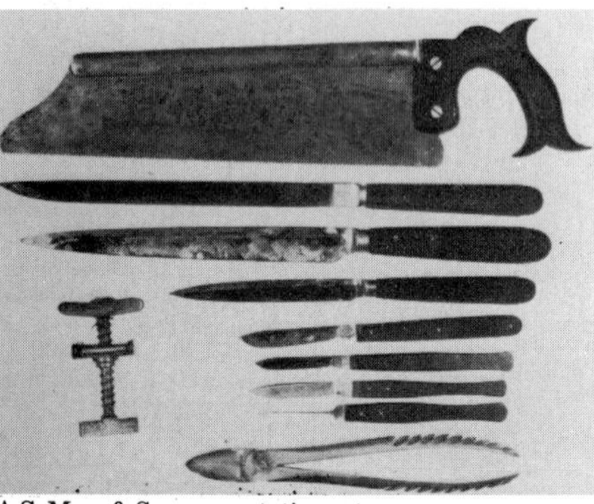

A S. Maw & Sons amputation set including long and short Liston-type amputation knives, large saw, bone cutters, tourniquet and scalpels, in case, English, 16½ in. (420 mm.) wide, 1850-75. **£350-£400** *S*

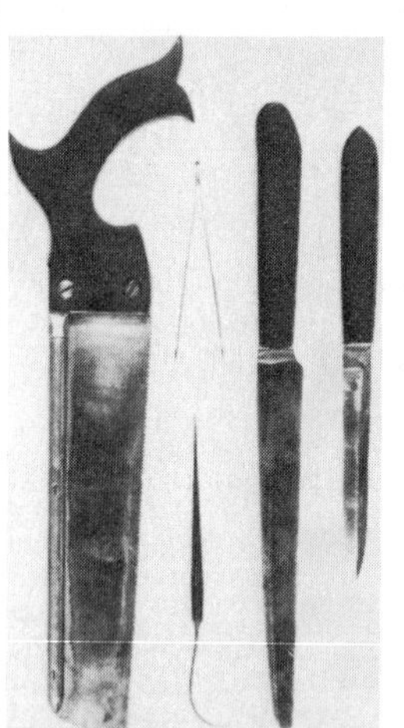

A William Pepy's amputation set, the fitted mahogany case containing ebony-handled steel instruments including torniquet, forceps, needles and thread, English, 14¾ by 7 by 2½ in. (37.5 by 18 by 6.5 cm.), mid 19th C. **£300-£350** *S*

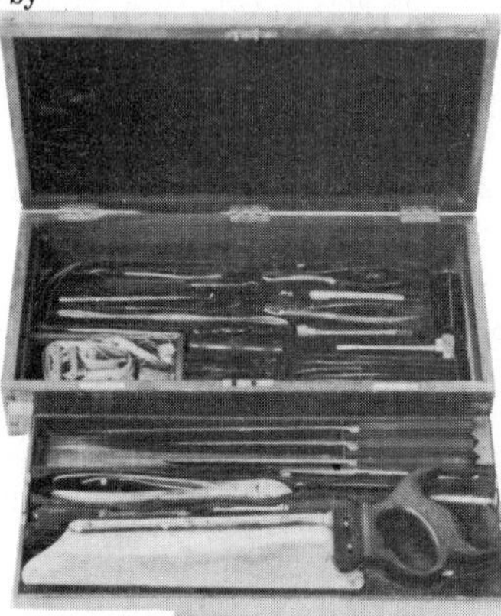

A good J. Milliken general purpose surgeon's instrument set, the brass-bound oak case with 2 layers of instruments, many with chequered ebony handles, 17¼ by 8½ by 3¾ in. (44 by 21.5 by 9.5 cm.), English, 1870-80. **£600-700** *S*

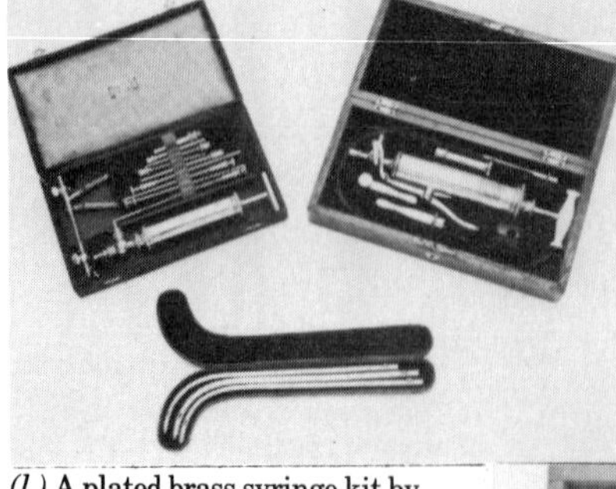

(l.) A plated brass syringe kit by P. Harris & Co. Ltd., contained in a fitted case, 10 7/16 in. (26.5 cm.). **£60-£70** *P*

(c.) A good set of 3 silver catheters by Arnold & Sons, possibly Henry Cuzner, London, 12 in. (30.5 cm.) long, 1874, 1½ oz. **£60-80** *P*

(r.) A late 19th C. brass syringe by Lynch & Co., London, contained in a fitted case, with ivory and treen fittings and attachments, 11 11/16 in. (30 cm.) wide. **£70-90** *P*

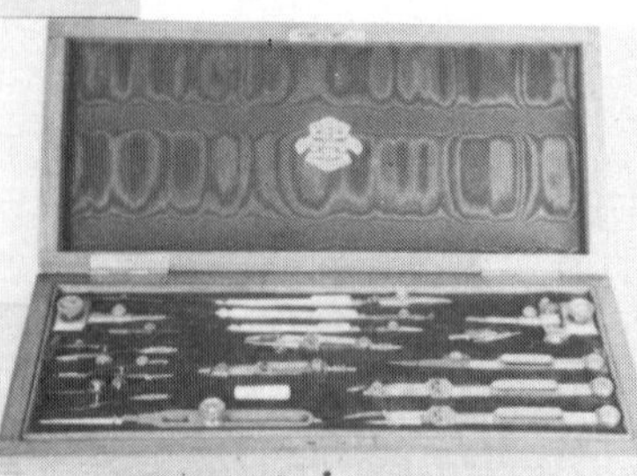

A set of drawing instruments in case, c. 1900. **£80-120** *JMW*

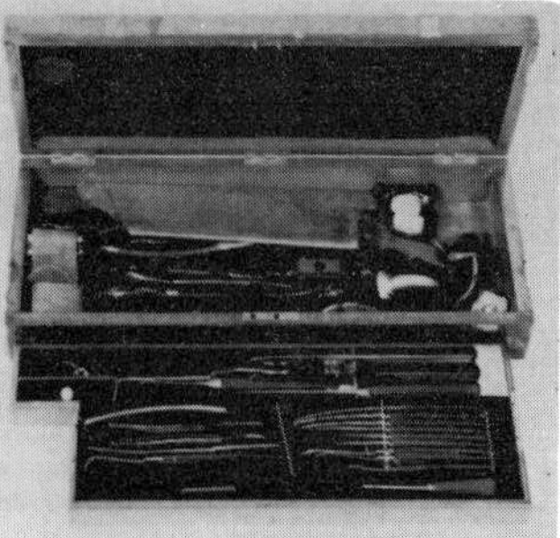

A Maw, Son & Thompson general purpose surgeon's instrument set, the brass-bound mahogany case with fitted interior and lift-out tray, English, 17 by 6½ by 3 in. (43 by 16.5 by 7.8 cm.), c. 1880. **£500-£550** *S*

A brass-bound mahogany medicine chest, the fitted interior with pill bottles, a drawer in the base containing bottles, flasks and glass mortar and pestle, English, when closed 9 in. (23 cm.) high, c. 1830. **£400-500** *S*

A fine quality George III mahogany and brass-bound domestic medicine chest, the lower compartment fitted with a glass pestle and mortar, 3 silver-metal topped measures, 3 bottles and other accessories, the chest 12⅛ in. (30.8 cm.) high. **£900-1,000** *P*

A Georgian period apothecary cabinet of fine quality, fitted with 16 bottles including Leamington examples, the drawer fitted with additional bottles together with scales. **£500-600** *LE*

A good 19th C. brass-bound mahogany domestic medicine chest, opens to reveal a compartment for 16 bottles, the drawer below containing compartments for scales, bottles and other accessories, 12⅛ in. (30.8 cm.) wide. **£280-340** *P*

A mahogany medicine chest with lid opening to reveal compartments, including 4 glass canisters and a glass ear syringe, with hinged front panel opening to reveal 6 bottles and 7 drawers, English, 13 in. (33 cm.), c. 1830. **£350-400** *SC*

A Blake's walnut-veneered medicine chest with fitted interior with 30 glass compound bottles, 6 with brass lids, some bottles replaced, 2 drawers below containing glass measuring flask and hanging scales, the lid interior applied with brass plaque engraved Blakes 47 Piccadilly Corner of Albany, English, 19¼ in. (490 mm.) wide, c. 1800. **£700-800** *S*

An S. Maw & Sons mahogany medicine chest, the fitted interior with 17 compound bottles, 2 ointment jars, measuring flask, set of brass hanging scales with weights and bandages, English, 8¼ in. (21 cm.) wide, c. 1860. **£500-£600** *S*

A 20th C. brass patent 'rolling' parallel rule with mahogany box, 18 in. **£40-50** *CLA*

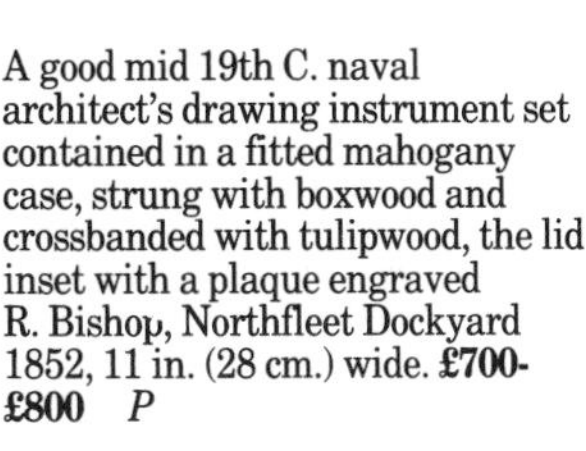

A good mid 19th C. naval architect's drawing instrument set contained in a fitted mahogany case, strung with boxwood and crossbanded with tulipwood, the lid inset with a plaque engraved R. Bishop, Northfleet Dockyard 1852, 11 in. (28 cm.) wide. **£700-£800** *P*

A Thomas Blunt necessaire complete with brass pen, dividers, 2 compasses with 2 accessories, ivory protractor and sector signed T. T. Blunt London, in fishskin-covered case, English, 6¾ in. (170 mm.) high, c. 1820. **£200-£300** *S*

A good 19th C. Sike's hydrometer signed Potter, Poultry, London, contained in a velvet-lined fitted rosewood case, 5¾ in. (14.6 cm.) wide, with thermometer by Dring & Fage, 145 Strand, London, and glass measure and a companion leather bound volume of instructions and tables. **£75-85** *P*

A magnifying glass in turned boxwood frame, German, 4¾ in. (12 cm.) diam., early 17th C. **£110-£150** *S*

A 19th C. mahogany and brass fitted mechanical air pump by Wm. Elliott, 227 High Holborn, London, the base 13½ in. (34.3 cm.) long, max. height 15½ in. (39.3 cm.). **£350-400** *P*

An important early Wimshurst electrostatic machine, 23½ in. high. **£550-650** *T*

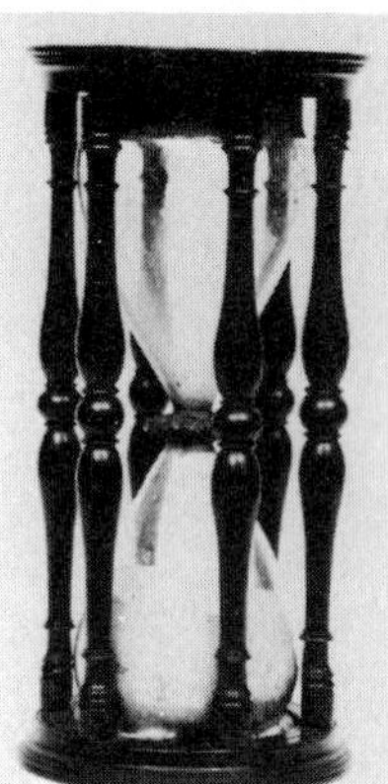

An unusually large sandglass, within turned-wood frame, 13½ in. (34 cm.) high, probably 18th C. **£1,300-1,500** *C*

An early 18th C. brass-mounted sand clock with 15-minute glass, 8 in. (20.3 cm.) high. **£200-250** *P*

A late 19th C. German Wimshurst machine, 'Die Influenz-Maschinen', complete with an original instruction book, overall height 11 in. (28 cm.). **£200-250** *P*

An unusual Edwardian period barograph by Bailey of Birmingham contained in a rosewood case with drawer and bracket below. **£1,300-£1,500** *LE*

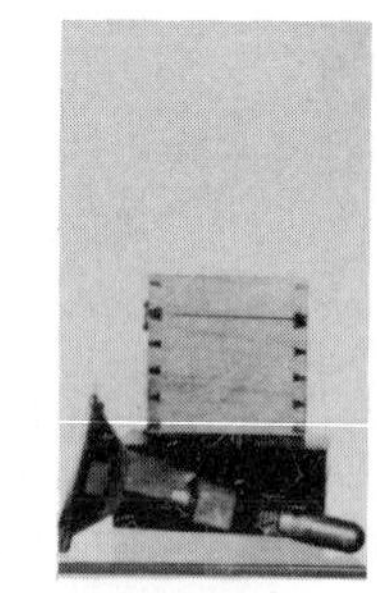

A quarter-plate sliding box wet-plate camera with brass-bound Petsval-type lens with rack focusing by McCrossan, Glasgow. **£450-500** *CSK*

A very rare Gaudin all-metal daguerreotype camera made by 'Lerebours à Paris' with 2 washer stops, hinged rear plate-clamp and ninth-plate mask, mounted in walnut box with tray and internal divisions for accessories. **£5,500-£6,500** *CSK*

Designed by Alexis Gaudin in 1841 and made commercially by Lerebours of Paris, the all-metal cylindrical camera was sold mounted within a wooden accessory box, giving the appearance of a box-form camera. Fox Talbot used a similar camera, c. 1845 for making portraits according to his own calotype process.

A whole-plate Ottewill's Patent mahogany sliding box wet-plate folding camera with Ross brass-bound portrait lens, plaque — 'T. Ottewill's Registered Camera 25 May 1853 — No. 151'. **£2,500-£3,000** *CSK*

A Horne & Thornthwaite rail-mounted stereoscopic camera, probably for daguerreotype use, with mahogany focusing screen/plate holder, 3 plate holders and swivelling base mounted on folding mahogany rail, in fitted wood case. **£4,000-4,500** *CSK*

Although researches have proved inconclusive, the thinness of the plate holders and absence of silver-wire plate supports (common in wet plate slides) suggests a one-time daguerreotype usage for this camera.

A whole-plate wet-plate view camera by Claudet Houghton & Son, 89 High Holborn, London with Ross No. 7 Symmetrical 9 in. lens with wheel stops, screw focusing, revolving back, focusing screen and 1 dark slide holder. **£350-450** *CSK*

A Negretti & Zambra wet-plate stereoscopic outfit, with Petzval-type lens with rack focussing. **£2,500-3,000** *CSK*

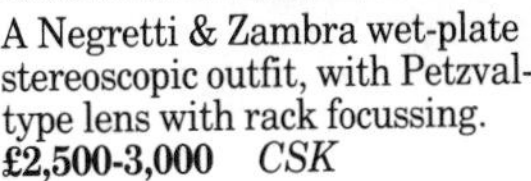

A 21 by 27.5 cm. French wet-plate tailboard camera with Houghton's Holborn Special 8½ by 6½ Portrait Lens with rack focusing and Waterhouse stops. **£250-300** *CSK*

A fine whole-plate Dallmeyer sliding box wet-plate studio camera, No. 1078, with No. 4A portrait lens with rack focusing — No. 16009, set of Waterhouse stops, screw focusing, swing and tilt back and 1 wet-plate slide holder, 52 in. high approx. **£1,900-2,400** *CSK*

An ordinary Kodak box form roll film camera, No. 1170, in polished wood casing, with lens, string-cocked sector shutter and Patent dates for 1889 and 1890, lacks front panel. **£300-350** *CSK*

A 12 by 16 cm. Krugener's Delta walnut falling-plate camera by Dr. R. Krugener with rapid rectilinear lens, sliding focusing, guillotine shutter and 10 plate holders. **£200-£300** *CSK*

A J. Robinson the 'Luzo' box camera, 6 by 6 cm., Aplanat 70 mm. f/11 lens, rotary shutter in front of lens, in case, English, c. 1889. **£700-800** *S*

A quarter-plate Royal Mail 15 exposure postage stamp copying camera by W. Butcher & Sons, with spring loaded guillotine shutter. **£300-350** *CSK*

A 6 by 13 cm. stereo block-notes camera by L. Gaumont & Cie, Paris, No. 5114, with Krauss Tessar-Zeiss 80 mm. f/6.3 lenses in guillotine shutter, 2 filters and film-pack adapter, lacks focusing screen. **£180-240** *CSK*

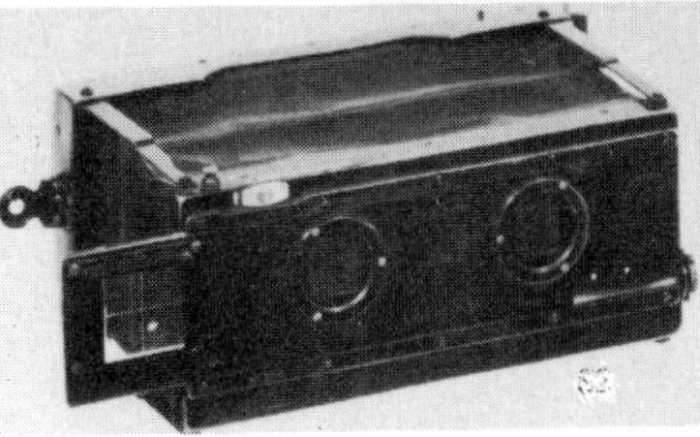

A half-plate Shew Xit stereoscopic folding strut camera with Ross 6 in. rapid symmetrical lenses, T-P roller blind shutter and Adams' aluminium clip-on prismatic viewfinder, in canvas case. **£500-£600** *CSK*

A Lancaster's mahogany stereoscopic tailboard camera with Dallmeyer brass-bound landscape lenses, and blue cloth bellows. **£250-300** *CSK*

A 6 by 9 cm. Kalos internal strut camera with lens in guillotine shutter, cloth bellows, Kalos dark slide and 4 cut film sheaths. **£400-£450** *CSK*

A 6 by 13 cm. Groothoek stereoscope camera with Shaap & Co's Patent with black enamelled lenses with detachable caps with wheel stops fitted in reversible panel, focal-plane shutter, film pack adaptor, 6 s.m.s. **£260-320** *CSK*

A fine amboyna Brewster-pattern stereoscope with rack focusing, ebonised eyepieces and dealer's plaque 'London Stereoscopic Company, 110 Regent Street'. **£130-180** *CSK*

A J. H. Dallmeyer tailboard camera, 4¾ by 6½ in., with Dallmeyer No. 4 stigmatic series II f/4.5 lens, T & P time & inst. shutter, The Westminster retailer's stamp, black bellows, together with 2 plates, English, c. 1910. **£250-£300** *SC*

An 18 by 13 cm. walnut tailboard camera in dovetailed casing with brass-bound combinable lens by Arthur Chevalier, Paris, twin rack focusing adjustment, revolving back and converted focusing screen. **£450-550** *CSK*

The lens fitted is of daguerreotype pattern and although certain modifications have been made, various features in the camera's construction suggest a one time daguerreotype usage.

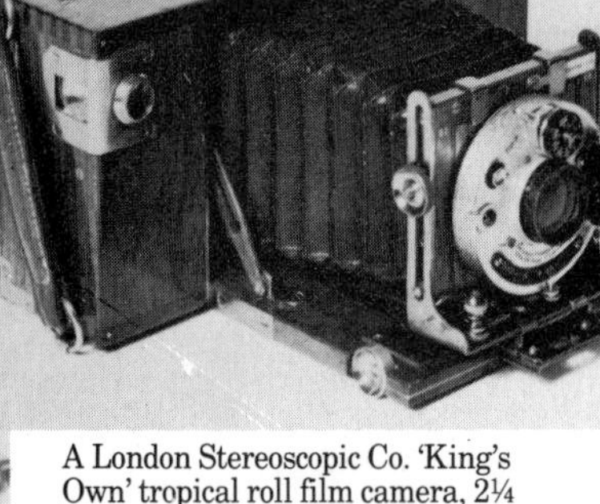

A London Stereoscopic Co. 'King's Own' tropical roll film camera, 2¼ by 3¼ in., with Bausch & Lomb r.r. f/6.3 lens in shutter, speeds 1-1/300 sec., in original leather carrying case, English, c. 1910. **£500-550** *S*

A half-plate Meagher stereoscopic tailboard camera with Dallmeyer brass-bound landscape stereo lenses, each with wheel stops. **£250-300** *CSK*

Use the Index!

Because certain items might fit easily into any of a number of categories, the quickest and surest method of locating any entry is by reference to the index at the back of the book. This has been fully cross-referenced for absolute simplicity.

A quarter-plate una tropical hand-and-stand camera by James A. Sinclair & Co. Ltd., London, with Ross combinable 9½ in. f/11 lens in N.S. Perfect shutter, Meyer & Gorlitz wide angle Aristostigmat 3⅛ in. f/1.9 lens in N.S. Perfect shutter, matching film pack adaptor and 8 d.d.s. in fitted leather carrying case. **£400-500** *CSK*

A stereoscopic mahogany tailboard camera by The American Optical Company, New York, brass reinforcements, tilting back and cloth bellows. **£250-300** *CSK*

\ quarter-plate triple extension
ropical hand-and-stand camera in
»rass reinforced teak casing with
Tessar 15 cm. f/4.5 lens in
Compound shutter, 3 d.d.s., in
itted leather carrying case. **£300-
£350** *CSK*

A 6 by 9 cm. tropical Deck Rullo focal-plane camera by Contessa-Nettel in teak casing with Tessar 12 cm. f/4.5 lens, focusing screen, with accessories. **£350-400** *CSK*

A fine Albion Albumenising Company of Glasgow whole-plate mahogany and brass camera, with Newman's patent pneumatic leaf shutter, with 5 aperture leaves for shutter, a case of 7 Waterhouse stops, a focusing screen magnifier, and 3 d.d.s., all in original case. **£180-250** *P*

Reputedly used by a firm of Glasgow shipbuilders.

A quarter-plate Adams Minex tropical reflex camera by A. Adams & Co. in brass reinforced teak casing with 5 lenses, focusing magnifier, filters, revolving back, with accessories and Adams crocodile grained leather combination case. **£1,800-2,200** *CSK*

. good Soho tropical reflex camera,
by 4 in., with Ross 6½ in. f/4.5
ns, cloth focal-plane shutter, teak
ody with lacquered brass fittings,
leather carrying case with 2
lock-form double plate holders,
nglish, c. 1910. **£950-1,050** *S*

A 9 by 12 cm. kinegraphe twin-lens reflex camera by E. Francais, Paris, with bayonet-fitting taking lens — No. 19066, spring-cocked rotary shutter, nickel-plated fittings and one d.d.s. **£550-650** *CSK*

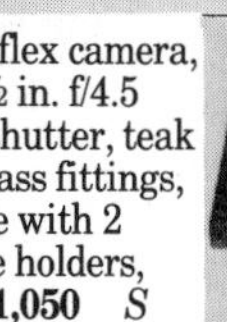

A Sanderson tropical hand-and-stand camera, 3¼ by 4¼ in. with Maximar 13.5 cm. f/6.8 lens, 2 double plate holders, English, c. 1910. **£250-300** *S*

A quarter-plate Marion's Soho
tropical reflex camera with Cooke
7.3 in. lens, green leather bellows
and focusing hood, film-pack
adaptor and 2 d.d.s., in fitted
leather carrying case. **£800-900**
CSK

A postcard-size tropical Soho reflex camera by Marion & Co. Ltd., London, with Tessar 18 cm. f/4.5 lens, red leather bellows and focusing hood, matching film-pack adaptor, 3 d.d.s. and several cut-film sheaths, in leather case. **£1,100-1,300** *CSK*

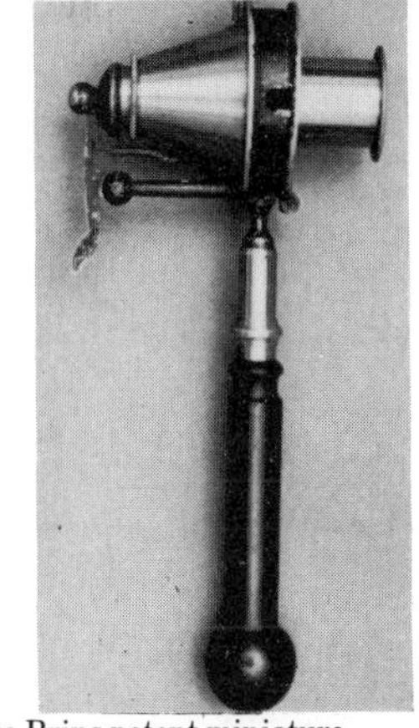

A rare Brins patent miniature detective camera for 25 mm. diam. circular exposures, 30 mm f/3.5 lens with simple shutter, the brass body engraved Brin's Patent No. 17143/828 with turned ebony handle, English, c. 1891. **£1,600-£2,000** *S*

The Brins Patent camera with plate removed and shutter open can be used as a spy-glass, however, the image is reversed.

A quarter-plate Rouch's Eureka magazine-load detective camera, in black hide-covered wood casing with Rouch Instantaneous Doublet brass-bound lens, key-wind roller-blind shutter, in leather carrying case; and an instruction book for a Beck Frena camera. **£200-300** *CSK*

A very rare Leica 250 FF 'Reporter' camera, serial no. 150072, early 1936, with Leitz Elmar f/3.5 50 mm. lens, with lens cap, a leather case, an Elmar 5 cm. hood, and 2 spare 250-exposure cassettes. **£2,000-2,500** *P*

This camera is one of 246 Leica 250FF 'Reporters' produced between 1933 and mid 1936. However, at a later date this example had the slow-speed dial removed and 1/1000 second speed added; it was also adapted to take a flash bracket.

A Leica I 'Model A', No. 47688, 24 by 36 cm. with Leitz Elmar 50 mm., f/3.5 lens, focusing in meters, in case, German, c, 1930. **£200-250** *S*

A W. Watson mahogany studio camera and tripod, 8½ by 8½ in., with Doulcon lens No. 32430 and Waterhouse stop slit, together with set of Waterhouse stops in case, English, c. 1880. **£300-400** *S*

A Carl P. Stirn waistcoat camera, the flat circular brass casing engraved C. P. Stirn's Photographische Camera No. 10397 D.R.P. No. 38391, 15 cm. diam., in original box, c. 1886. **£550-600** *S*

A 2 by 2 Marion's all-metal miniature camera with Petzval-type lens, detachable gravity shutter, hinged plate clamp at rear, 12 plate holders, in fitted wood carrying case with mounting point for camera. **£800-900** *CSK*

A 2 by 2 all-brass miniature box-form camera with miniature Petzval-type lens with rack focusing, brass-bound focusing screen, and 2 unexposed daguerreotype plates (lacks plate holders); together with accessories, and a booklet Art of Photography 1854 by Dr. G. C. Hermann Halluer detailing various early photographic processes. **£2,000-£3,000** *CSK*

A Parvo 35 mm. hand-cranked cine camera by J. Debrie, Paris, Sie. 51 No. 515, in mahogany casing with Krauss/Zeiss Tessar 3.5 cm. f/3.5 lens, through-the-lens viewfinder, 1 film cassette and machined-duralumin mechanism frame. **£250-300** *CSK*

A fine Stirn's waistcoat detective camera No. 12073, 6-exposure model in nickel-plated casing with button-hole-type lens, exposure indicator and instructions, in maker's case. **£450-500** *CSK*

A Leica IIIg, Serial No. 980662, with Leitz Summaron f/2.8 35 mm. lens, in original case, 1959. **£300-£400** *P*

A large mahogany studio camera by Dr. Staeble & Co., Munich, with Dallmeyer 3D Petzval-type brass-bound portrait lens No. 15640, with 1 Waterhouse stop, full rack and screw adjustments and repeating back, 52 in. high approx. **£200-£250** *CSK*

An early daylight contact printer, with double hinged lid holding the paper and negative opening to interior with 4 adjustable mirrors, the base with 2 drawers for storing a cloth screen and accessories, English, 18½ in. (470 mm.) wide, mid 19th C. **£70-100** *S*

A 35 mm. Moy & Bastie's patent cine camera, the chain driven hand cranked mechanism with rack and pinion focusing to the lens mount, lens missing, English, c. 1910 **£250-300** *SC*

A walnut and ebonised megalethoscope viewer by Carlo Ponti, Venice, with sliding box focusing, the whole revolving through 90°, 35 in. long and 25 in. high. **£1,800-2,200** *CSK*

Invented by Carlo Ponti in 1862, the megalethoscope used specially prepared photographs on thin paper mounted in curved frames. They were viewed by reflected light to provide daytime scenes and by transmitted light to produce a view of the same scene at night.

A Negretti & Zambra walnut table stereoscope with sliding focusing to the eyepieces, 2 hinged mirror lined flaps and handle revolving a chain of glass stereo slides, English, 17 in. (430 mm.) high, late 19th C. **£250-300** *S*

A Smith, Beck & Beck achromatic stereoscope with rack and pinion focusing to the brass-mounted eyepieces, hinged mirror and card holder, English, case 8 in., 200 mm. wide, late 19th C. **£200-250** *S*

A Polyorama Panoptique et Diagraphique paper transparency viewer, with 6 artist-drawn views of Paris and Versailles, for 'day' and 'night' viewing, French, c. 1850. **£400-450** *P*

A rare W. C. Hughes choreutoscope, with double plate-holder and brass disc with 3 projections turned by lever to operate the shutter and move the slide, English, 13¼ in. (335 mm.) long, c. 1870. **£400-500** *S*

A Kinora viewer, the hand-cranked mechanism flicking a reel of still photographs viewed through lens and black metal eye-shade, with 9 reels of film, handle missing, English, 11 in. (280 mm.) long, c. 1910. **£250-300** *S*

A mahogany slide cabinet opening to 21 drawers containing approximately 350 specimen slides, and including 18 photographic slides, many by J. B. Dancer, English, c. 1880. **£300-350** *S*

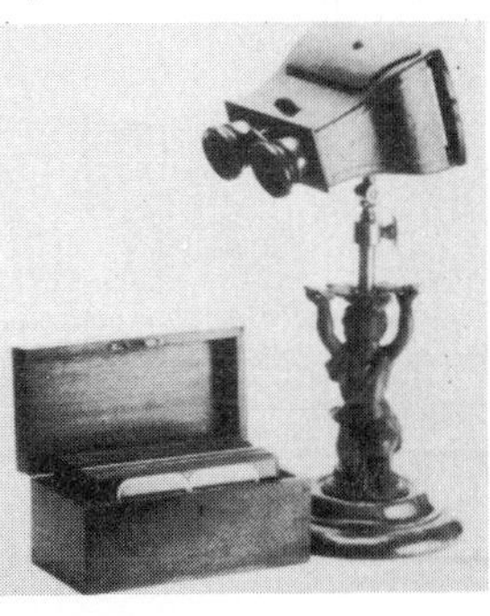

A Victorian stereoscopic viewer, with milled screw focusing on adjustable brass column, 16¾ in. high, together with 23 topographical slides in mahogany box. **£280-340** *Bea*

A fine walnut graphoscope, with stereoscopic lenses and sliding card holder, large magnifier, drawer containing small quantity of stereograms. **£200-250** *S*

THE STATE OF THE SILVER MARKET

The price of any piece of silver offered for sale depends upon three main factors; the weight of metal used in i manufacture, the skill and artistry with which the raw silver has been transformed into a rare object of use an beauty and its date of manufacture. In this respect, objects made of precious metals occupy a unique place in th broad spectrum of antiques, because they are subject to two quite different, and sometimes opposed, market force Where two of these set a premium on rarity, beauty and workmanship, the other concerns itself solely with th world demand for the raw material.

Under normal circumstances, the premium set upon quality and rarity divides the silver market into two distinct parts; pieces which are endowed with these virtues remaining largely unaffected by 'melt' prices, the remainder — mediocre quality and late goods — commanding only a few pounds per ounce over the constantly fluctuating price of bullion silver. In times of crisis, therefore, the price of all silver wares may rise as high as £20 per ounce, while the 'art' premium remains unaffected, or may even drop a little as individuals seek to convert their silverwares into cash.

The past year has seen some fluctuation in the melt price of silver, between £3-8 per ounce, but not nearly enough to disturb the differential between the two ends of the market. There has, however, been a greater volume of goods passing through auction rooms than during the year before — mainly mediocre quality pieces which have sold at prices reflecting their melt values.

Better quality wares have shown a steady, if unremarkable, upward trend, as have the larger and more ostentatiou pieces of Victorian electro-plate, while small collectables hav remained fairly static unless they have been of particular fine quality.

The year ahead promises no major swings in either directio (assuming no world crises in the commodity market). Neve theless, the discriminating buyer should find opportunity f sound, if unspectacular, investment, particularly among th goods put up at auction.

A George I oval cake basket, with reed and tie borders, shaped moulded rim and detachable chequer pattern handle with trefoil terminals, by Edward Feline, 1725, 13½ in. (34.3 cm.) long, 59 oz. **£6,000-7,000** *C*

A George II heavy cake basket, the swing handle engraved with armorials in a foliate cartouche, John Jacob, London, 1738, 12¼ in. (31 cm.) wide, 53 oz. 7 dwt. (1,660 gm.). **£2,500-3,500** *S*

A George II heavy oval fruit basket, the sides pierced with quatrefoils, saltires and scrolling foliage, Samuel Courtauld, London 1750, 13¾ in. (35 cm.) wide, 56 oz. 11 dwt. (1,760 gm.). **£3,000-£4,000** *S*

SILVER

The silver section has been arranged in alphabetical subject order: e.g. baskets, followed by beakers, followed by bowls, etc. Each category is then arranged in chronological order. There is also a miscellaneous category at the end of the section. The quickes way of finding any item is by means of the comprehensive and fully cross-referenced index.

A Central American circular dessert basket, maker's mark Gueixa, Guatemala, 34 cm. diam., mid 18th C., 795 gm. **£900-1,000** *S*

A George III shaped oval cake basket, engraved with a later coat-of-arms, by L. Courtauld and G. Cowles, 1770, 15½ in. (39.3 cm.) long, 57 oz. **£2,200-2,600** *C*

The arms are those of Bacon impaling Shield.

A George III oval basket, engraved with later armorials, marked on body and handle, Aldridge & Green, London, 1769, 14 in. (35.5 cm.) wide, 27 oz. 15 dwt. (860 gm.). **£900-1,200** *S*

The arms are those of Hoare impaling Ainslie for Henry Charles Hoare (1790-1852), 2nd son of Sir Henry Hoare, 3rd Bt.

A George III oval cake basket, by P. A. and W. Bateman, 1802, 15¾ in. (40 cm.) long, 49 oz. **£1,500-£1,700** *C*

A George III oval neo-classical cast and pierced fret oval sugar basket, with a red glass liner, repaired, maker John King, London, 1772, 15 oz. **£400-500** *WW*

A George III boat shaped sweetmeat basket, pricked with ribbon-tied tassels, further bright cut with 2 oval cartouches, with gilt interior, John Robins, London, 1794, 6⅛ in. (15.6 cm.) wide, 7 oz. 13 dwt. (237 gm.). **£400-500** *S*

A George III boat shaped sweetmeat basket, John Warner of Cork, 6¼ in. (15.8 cm.) wide, c. 1790, 9 oz. 16 dwt. (303 gm.). **£650-700** *S*

An early George III oval cake basket, maker William Plummer, London, 1767, 15 in. overall, 35 oz. **£1,300-1,500** *WW*

A George III boat shaped sugar basket, 1793 by Samuel Godbehere and Edward Wigan, 5 in. (12.7 cm.). **£500-600** *L*

A pair of George III oval salts, with blue glass liners, 1775 by Robert Hennell I, 1775, 3.25 in. (8.3 cm.). **£300-400** *L*

A pair of George III oval sweetmeat baskets, Thomas Pitts, London, 1804, 6½ in. (16.4 cm.) overall width, 20 oz. 4 dwt. (628 gm.), excluding 2 blue glass liners. **£550-£650** *S*

A William IV shaped circular cake basket, by Barnard and Co., 1830, 13⅞ in. (35.2 cm.) diam., 47 oz. **£1,200-1,500** *C*

A William IV shaped circular cake basket, by Henry Wilkinson & Co., Sheffield, 1832, gilding later, 13 in. (33.1 cm.) diam., 45 oz. **£1,500-£1,700** *C*

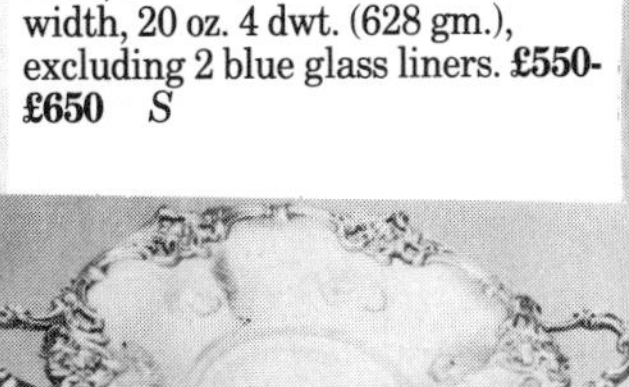

A William IV cake basket, the centre engraved with script initials, on 4 matted leaf supports, Birmingham 1837 by Robinson, Edkins & Aston, 13.75 in. (34.9 cm.) across handles, 16 oz. **£250-350** *L*

A Victorian shaped oval basket, marked on body and handle, W. R. Smily, London, 1852, 14¼ in. (36 cm.) wide, 32 oz. 6 dwt. (1,001 gm.). **£600-700** *S*

A Dutch 2-handled oval cake basket, A. de Hass, Sneek, 1890, 40.7 cm. over handles, 57 oz. 7 dwt. (1814 gm.). **£1,000-1,200** *S*

A suite of 5 early 20th C. Viennese oval neo-classical dessert baskets, 5¾ to 13¼ in. **£1,000-1,200** *WW*

A pierced boat shaped fruit basket, maker's mark D?. London, 1916, P.O.D.R. number: 577413, 12¾ in. (35 cm.), 32 oz. 4 dwt. (1,001 gm.). **£800-900** *S*

A silver basket, Chester, 11 in., c. 1907, 18 oz. **£200-250** *IHA*

A Charles II tapering cylindrical beaker, also pricked with the initials S/RM and the date 1674, maker's mark RD above a mullett flanked by 2 pellets in a shield, London, 1672, 3¾ in. (9.4 cm.) high, 5 oz. 2 dwt. (158 gm.). **£1,200-£1,500** *S*

A Hungarian parcel-gilt beaker, maker's mark only apparently HR conjoined below a crown, probably for Johannes (Hans) Retsch sr. (Brasso), 13.3 cm. high, c. 1640, 116 gm. **£900-1,000** *S*

A silver-gilt beaker and cover by Gottfried Ihme, the matching domed cover centred by a thaler and ball finial, marked on body and lid, maker's mark, Breslau, 24.6 cm. high, c. 1730, 855 gm. **£2,500-3,000** *S*

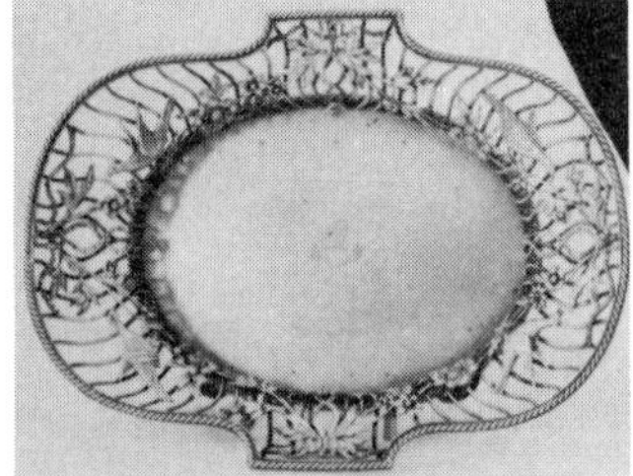

A shaped oval fruit basket on 4 cast and pierced foliate panel supports, the underside engraved with a later inscription, William Comyns, 1907, 13½ in. (34 cm.), 38 oz. 10 dwt. (1,197 gm.). **£1,000-1,200** *S*

A pair of Charles II plain beakers, engraved with a later crest and motto and with gilt interiors, by Jacob Bodendick, 1678, 4 in. (10.1 cm.) high, 17 oz. **£3,000-£4,000** *C*

The crest and motto are those of Sterling.

A German parcel-gilt rummer shaped beaker embossed in baroque style, maker's mark HH conjoined, Rosenberg no. 4268, Nuremburg, 10.5 cm. high, c. 1680 75 gm. **£1,400-1,600** *S*

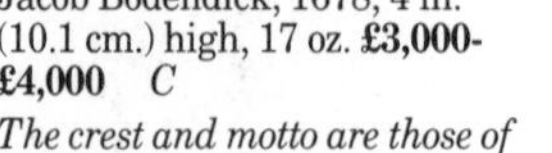

A Dutch silver beaker, with a later presentation inscription dated 1735, Groningen, 1681, maker's mark HS, 5¼ in. (13.3 cm.) high, 4 oz. 6 dwt. **£1,200-1,500** *C*

A German silver-gilt beaker, maker's mark apparently that of Hans Jakob Baur III, Augsburg, 9.3 cm. high, c. 1685, 140 gm. **£800-£900** *S*

A Swedish parcel-gilt beaker, Lars Pihl, Vastervik, 4¼ in. (11.1 cm.) high, c. 1735, 4 oz. 12 dwt. (145 gm.). **£500-600** *S*

A William and Mary tapering cylindrical beaker, pricked with initials EHB and dated 1692, 1691, maker's mark IC crowned, 3½ in. (8.9 cm.) high, 4 oz. 14 dwt. **£1,000-£1,300** *C*

A Channel Islands beaker, engraved with initials APD Jersey, maker's mark PD, 3⅝ in. (9.2 cm.) high, c. 1745, 3 oz. 11 dwt. **£500-£600** *C*

A parcel-gilt beaker by G. I. Serebyanikov, maker's mark, Moscow, 1762, 18.4 cm. high, 278 gm. **£900-1,000** *S*

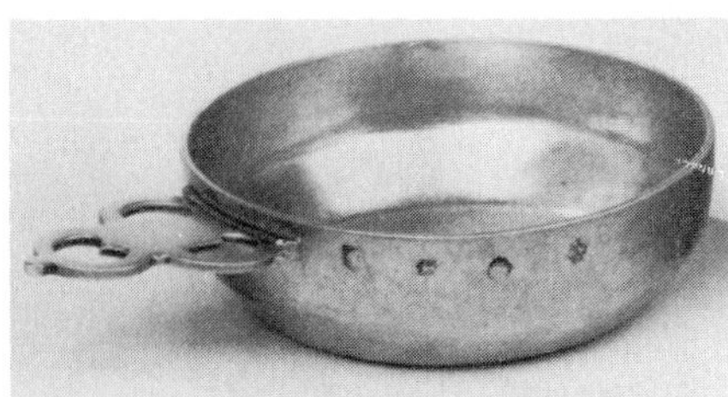

A Charles II silver bleeding bowl with pierced flat trefoil handle, probably 1660, maker's mark WH a star above a pellet in annulet below, 5⅛ in. (12.9 cm.) diam., 7 oz. 13 dwt. **£3,000-4,000** *C*

A small plain bleeding bowl, struck on the handle with initials AH, Provincial, maker's mark only, WL struck thrice, late 17th C., 2 oz. **£500-700** *C*

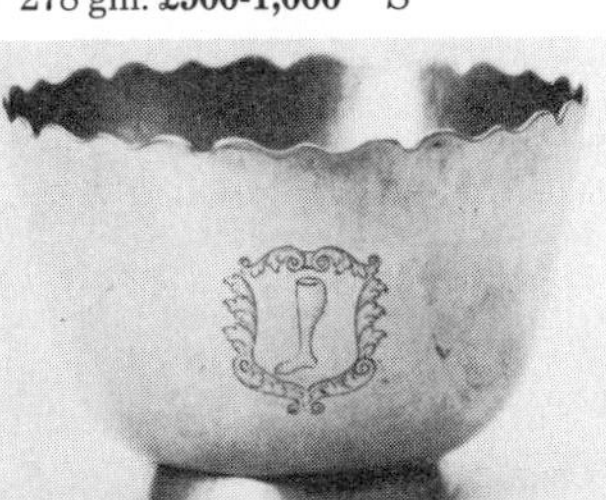

A Queen Anne circular bowl, David King, Dublin, 1708, 3¾ in. (9.4 cm.), 4 oz. 4 dwt. (130 gm.). **£1,400-1,600** *S*

The arms are those of Shirgley.

An agate bowl with silver-gilt mounts, unmarked, probably German, 4¼ in. (10.5 cm.), mid 17th C. **£800-900** *S*

A rare Charles II silver bleeding bowl, London 1681, 8¾ oz. **£1,900-£2,200** *T*

A George II hemispherical broth bowl, later engraved with armorials, William Aytoun, Assay Master Archibald Ure, Edinburgh, 1733, 6 in. (15.2 cm.) diam., 7 oz. 17 dwt. (243 gm.). **£1,400-1,600** *S*

A Queen Anne bleeding bowl, marked on body and handle, maker's mark badly struck, probably Alice Sheene, London, 1712, 6¾ in. (17.1 cm.), 5 oz. 18 dwt. (183 gm.). **£1,650-1,850** *S*

A Louis XV 2-handled ecuelle on rim foot, the rim engraved 'ROBERT + SENELAR', Lille, 1749, maker's mark LDT, crown above, 5 in. (12.7 cm.) diam., 7 oz. 2 dwt. **£3,800-4,400** *C*

A George II plain circular bowl, by William Townsend, Dublin, 7 in. (17.8 cm.) diam., c. 1736, 18 oz. 10 dwt. **£1,900-2,100** *C*

The arms are those of Wright of Cranham, Co. Essex, impaling another.

A large 18th C. Indian kuft work on silver bowl of Mogul design, the inside later engraved 'To Mr. & Mrs. De Bunsen, with best wishes, from, Prince Bhanurangsi', 13.5 in. (34.3 cm.). **£600-700** *L*

Make the most of Miller's

When buying or selling, it must always be remembered that prices can be greatly affected by the condition of any piece. Pieces offered for sale in exceptionally fine condition or in poor condition may reasonably be expected to be priced considerably higher or lower respectively than the estimates given herein.

An 18th C. French sugar bowl, cover, stand and sifter, Lyon, c. 1770, maker's mark GB a winged mask below and a crown above, 15 cm. high, 33 oz. **£4,500-5,500** *L*

A George III sugar bowl by Wm. Fountain and Daniel Pontifex, 1792. **£350-450** *DWB*

A pair of presentation fruit bowls, Birmingham, 1937, by Joseph Gloster Ltd., 30.8 cm. across handles, 47 oz. **£300-350** *L*

A Victorian circular bowl, Frederick Elkington for Elkington & Co., Birmingham, 1880, stamped: 15151, 5¼ in. (13.5 cm.) diam., 20 oz. (622 gm.). **£300-400** *S*

A Russian sugar box, marked on base and lid, maker's mark I.C.R. (Latin), Moscow, 5¼ in. (13.6 cm.) wide, c. 1775, 9 oz. 18 dwt. (310 gm.). **£850-950** *S*

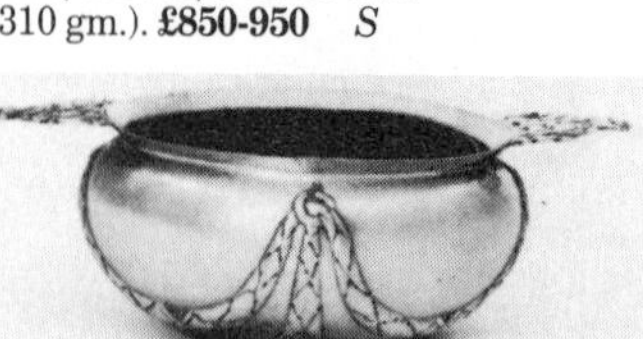

A German circular 2-handled bowl, maker's mark G.R. (Scheffler, Goldschmiede Rheinland-Westfalens, no. 1275), Vreden, 21.6 cm. wide overall, c. 1785, 275 gm. **£1,000-1,100** *S*

A silver-mounted rock crystal bowl and cover carved in the form of a feathered duck, unmarked, probably Austro-Hungarian, 9 in. (23.2 cm.) high, 8¼ in. (21 cm.) long, late 19th C. **£3,000-3,500** *S*

A Victorian pedestal fruit bowl, Horace Woodward & Co. Ltd., London, 1898, stamped: 72690, 7½ in. (19.3 cm.) high, 26 oz. 13 dwt. (828 gm.). **£500-600** *S*

An oval covered sugar bowl by Christian Friedrich Schultz, maker's mark, Celle, 12.5 cm. high, c. 1780, 235 gm. **£1,200-1,400** *S*

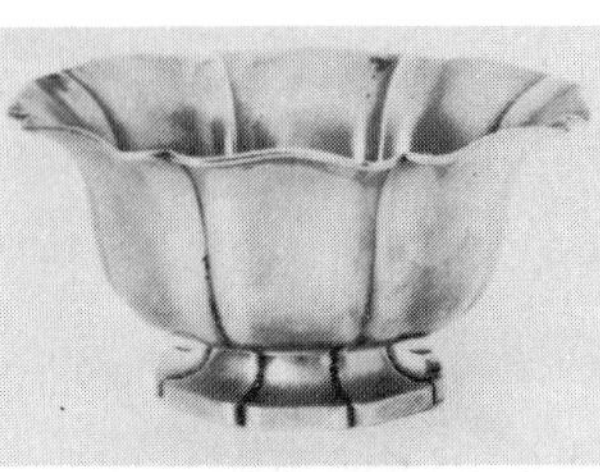

A Victorian shaped circular bowl, William Bateman, probably for Rundell, Bridge & Co., London, 1839, 8¼ in. (20.9 cm.) diam., 18 oz. 9 dwt. (571 gm.). **£600-700** *S*

A large circular rose bowl in early 18th C. taste, with gilt interior, Elkington & Co. Ltd., London, 1903, 24 in. (61 cm.) over handles, 255 oz. 6 dwt. (7,923 gm.). **£3,500-£4,000** *S*

A silver-mounted mazer bowl, by Omar Ramsden, 1927, also engraved 'OMAR RAMSDEN ME FECIT', the bowl cracked, 6¾ in. (17.2 cm.) diam. **£600-700** *C*

A Charles II oval tobacco box, the cover pierced and etched with a border of emblems of France, Ireland, England and Scotland, the centre with a portrait bust of Charles I, inscribed 'Vivat Rex Cvrrat Lex Floret Grex', all on a gilt ground, marked on base with maker's mark only BB a crescent below (Jackson, p. 143), London, 3⅜ in. (8.6 cm.) wide, c. 1680. **£900-£1,000** *S*

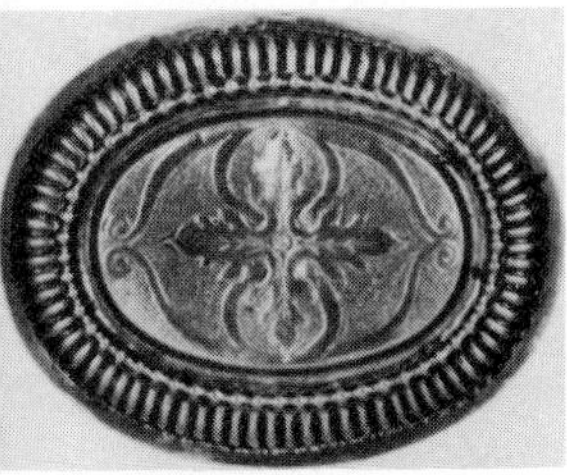
A late 17th C. German oval snuff box, by Elias Grische, Breslau, 8.5 cm. long, c. 1690, 2 oz. **£300-£400** *P*

A very unusual silver-gilt mounted mother-of-pearl sentry box, probably German, 4 in. (10 cm.) high, early 18th C. **£850-950** *C*

An unusual octagonal silver-gilt snuff box, with double-opening cover and base, with gilt interior, possibly Dutch, 3½ in. (9 cm.) long, mid 18th C. **£450-550** *C*

A German box, maker's mark apparently that of Andreas Ropenack, Brunswick, 8.3 cm. diam., c. 1680, 114 gm. **£550-650** *S*

A Queen Anne tobacco box, engraved on the underside 'Lawrence Parker', the detachable cover engraved with the owner's armorials, William Fleming, London, 1703, 3⅞ in. (9.8 cm.) wide. **£1,400-1,600** *S*

A silver and tortoiseshell snuff box, applied with a raised pierced and chased silver panel, on a tortoiseshell ground, apparently unmarked, probably Scandinavian, 2½ in. (6.5 cm.) diam., c. 1750. **£250-300** *S*

An 18th C. Dutch parcel-gilt oblong snuff box, maker's mark DS in oval punch, Rotterdam, probably 1767, inside of cover with later Victorian inscription, 8.25 cm. long. **£250-£300** *P*

An 18th C. Continental snuff box, the cover engraved with a cartouche of 2 squirrels beside a tree enclosed by rococo scrolls, unmarked, probably Scandinavian, 8 cm. long, c. 1740, 5 oz. **£90-130** *P*

An 18th C. Spanish silver-gilt snuff box, by Francisco Sanchez Bueno Taramas, Cordoba, 7.75 by 6 cm., c. 1760, 4 oz. **£300-400** *P*

A note in the box explains 'This box was taken from a Spanish officer killed in the Peninsular War'.

An unusual Danish silver-mounted rectangular snuff box set with panels of stained grey agate, by Jorgen N. Brosboll, Vejle, 1757. **£600-700** *C*

A tobacco box and cover by Hendrik Fortman, later initialled and dated, maker's mark, Leiden, 1767, 15.2 cm. high, 505 gm. **£2,600-3,000** *S*

An 18th C. Dutch tobacco box, the cover embossed with hunting scenes, by Carolus Wilhelmus Ten Ham, Amsterdam, 1766, 16 cm. long, 6.5 oz. **£500-600** *P*

An 18th C. Dutch tobacco box, by Jacob Abram Barbie, The Hague, 1772, 14 cm. long, 6 oz. **£600-700** *P*

A South African plain tobacco box, maker's mark only IC for Johannes Combrink, Cape Province, 4 in. (10.2 cm.) diam., c. 1800, 6 oz. 10 dwt. **£800-900** *C*

A Russian silver-gilt lined shaped oblong snuff box nielloed overall with buildings, figures and lattice-work, 3¼ in., c. 1830. **£100-130** *CSK*

A George III oblong snuff box by Samuel Pemberton, Birmingham, 1806, 6.75 by 4.6 cm. **£130-160** *P*

An unusual 19th C. Russian silver-gilt and niello snuff box, maker's mark probably DK, Moscow, 1823, 7.9 by 5.25 cm. long. **£400-450** *P*

A tobacco box and cover by Johannes Janse(n), maker's mark, Rotterdam, 1774, 18.9 cm. high, 544 gm. **£1,900-2,200** *S*

An early 19th C. Scottish mounted horn table snuff mull, fitted with a snuff brush and spoon on chain, marked on the spoon only IE, probably by James Erskine, Aberdeen, 17 cm. long, c. 1800. **£300-350** *P*

A George III small snuff box by Wardell & Kempson, Birmingham, 1811, 5.5 cm. long. **£70-90** *P*

An early 19th C. Italian snuff box, the green hardstone body with silver-gilt foliate scroll mounts, by Camillo Picconi, Rome, c. 1815. **£200-250** *P*

A George IV silver-gilt snuff box, the cast cover depicting in high relief the Roman philosopher Seneca (Nero's tutor) lecturing his followers, having opened his veins with a knife, by Edward Farrell, 1824, 8.5 cm. long, 7.5 oz. **£800-£1,000** *P*

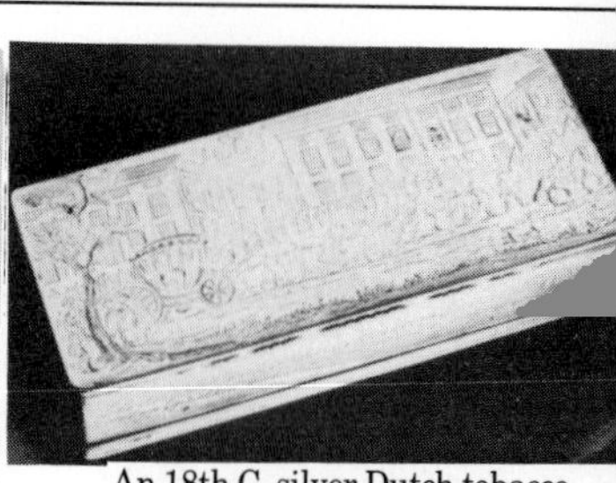
An 18th C. silver Dutch tobacco box, with engraved inscriptions, dated 20th September 1787, with a contemporary engraving and initials M.S.M. applied at a later date, 6 by 2½ by 1¼ in. high, 8 oz. 5 dwt. **£850-950** *AG*
This box commemorates the restoration to power of Willem V in 1787 after King Frederick, Willem II of Prussia (Princess Wilhelmina's brother) had sent 20,000 Prussian troops to quell the uprising.

A Russian silver nielloed gilt-lined shaped oval snuff box, maker's mark indistinct, Suzdal, 1¾ in., 1783-1814. **£150-200** *CSK*

A William IV 'pedlar' snuff box by Francis Clarke, 1835, 8 by 4.5 cm., 3 oz. **£250-300** *P*

A George IV oblong table snuff box by A. J. Strachan, 1824, 8 by 5.5 cm., 4.5 oz. **£200-250** *P*

A Victorian table snuff box, the lid engraved with a presentation inscription, gilt interior, marked on base and lid, William Dudley, Birmingham, 1850, 4⅛ in. (10.4 cm.) wide. **£450-500** *S*

A Continental oblong snuff box enamelled in dark blue, unmarked, probably Austrian, 8 by 4.5 cm., c. 1870. **£150-200** *P*

A 19th C. French niello snuff box, bearing French export marks and later Russian marks, 8.75 by 5.25 cm., c. 1870, 5 oz. **£350-400** *P*

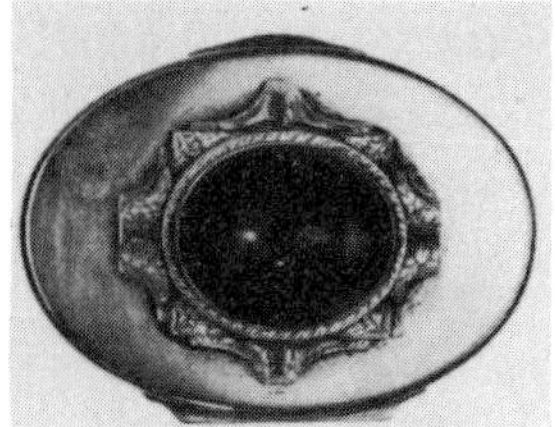

A Victorian silver-gilt oval snuff box, the cover set with a large amethyst probably by William Smiley, maker's mark WS in oval punch, 1873, 7.25 cm. long. **£120-£150** *P*

A parcel-gilt freedom casket and silver-mounted plate glass plinth, engraved with the arms of the Skinners' Company of London, John Bodman Carrington for Carrington & Co., London, 1900, 7¾ in. (19.5 cm.) wide, 47 oz. 19 dwt. (1,491 gm.). **£1,500-1,700** *S*

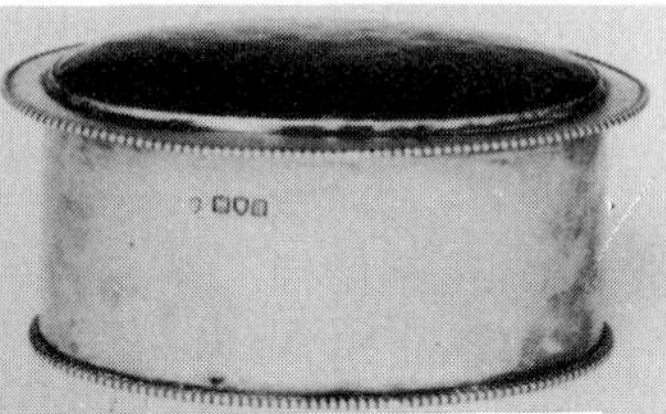

A Guild of Handicraft Ltd. silver and enamelled box and cover designed by Charles Robert Ashbee, the cover decorated with a blue and green enamelled plaque, stamped 'C.R.A.', London hallmarks for 1903, 6 cm. high. **£280-360** *P*

A Victorian card case richly chased, with a raised view of Westminster Abbey, Nathaniel Mills for N. Mills & Son, Birmingham, 1843, 4 in. (10.1 cm.) high. **£200-250** *S*

A Victorian card case with a raised view of St. Paul's Cathedral, by Nathaniel Mills, Birmingham, 1843, 4 in. (10.1 cm.). **£250-300** *S*

A small card case with Abbotsford on one side and Kenilworth on the other, by N. Mills, Birmingham, 1849, 3¼ in. (8.6 cm.) high. **£150-£200** *S*

A shaped card case, one side with a view of Holy Trinity, New York and the other with simulated filigree-work enclosing trophies of love, unmarked, U.S.A., 3½ in. (9 cm.) high, c. 1850. **£100-150** *S*

A Victorian card case decorated on one side with a view of Osborn House, Hillard & Thomason, Birmingham, 1869, 3¾ in. (9.6 cm.) high. **£180-220** *S*

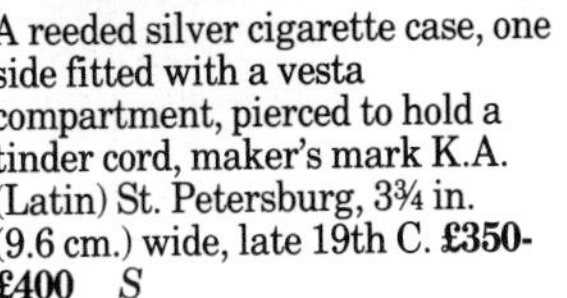

A reeded silver cigarette case, one side fitted with a vesta compartment, pierced to hold a tinder cord, maker's mark K.A. (Latin) St. Petersburg, 3¾ in. (9.6 cm.) wide, late 19th C. **£350-£400** *S*

A Russian cigarette case, decorated in relief, 11 cm. long, c. 1910, 6.5 oz. **£150-200** *P*

A Russian cigarette case, applied with gold (coloured metal) facsimile signatures and a red-enamelled boss with Cyrillic letters, maker's mark, IKK, 11 by 7.25 cm., c. 1910. **£180-220** *P*

A Russian cigarette case, decorated in relief, the back plain and the thumbpiece cabochon-set, 11.5 cm. long, c. 1910, 6.5 oz. **£150-200** *P*

A Victorian vesta case unusually modelled as an ancient Egyptian man, by E. H. Stockwell, 1876, 8 cm. high, 3.5 oz. **£200-250** *P*

An unusual 19th C. Continental niello vesta case, unmarked, probably French, 6 cm. long, c. 1880. **£140-180** *P*

A German vesta case modelled as a baby girl in bonnet, holding a rattle, bearing English import marks for 1892, 6.75 cm. high. **£150-180** *P*

A novelty vesta case by Sampson Mordan & Co., with slide-action propelling pencil and penknife at one end and vesta compartment at the other, 1901, 8 cm. long. **£150-£180** *P*

A Charles II small octagonal silver spice box of fluted cushion form, the hinged interior with detachable perforated inner coyer, unmarked, 1 in. (2.5 cm.) diam., c. 1680. **£400-£500** *C*

An early 17th C. Continental parcel-gilt miniature book with 2 clasps, the 8 hinged leaves contained therein engraved on both sides with biblical scenes, probably engraved at a later date, probably German, 2.5 by 3.6 cm., c. 1620. **£220-280** *P*

A miniature cylindrical silver nutmeg grater by Samuel Pemberton, Birmingham, 1793, 1¼ in. high (3 cm.). **£180-220** *C*

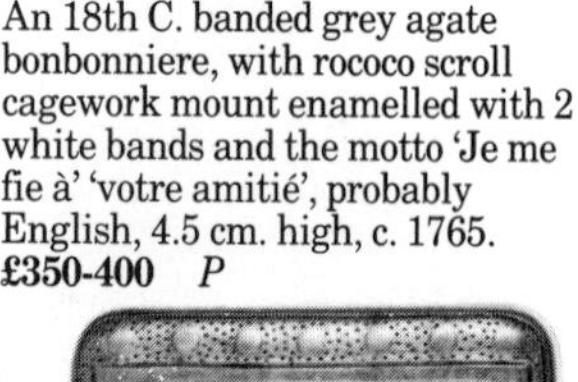

An 18th C. banded grey agate bonbonniere, with rococo scroll cagework mount enamelled with 2 white bands and the motto 'Je me fie à' 'votre amitié', probably English, 4.5 cm. high, c. 1765. **£350-400** *P*

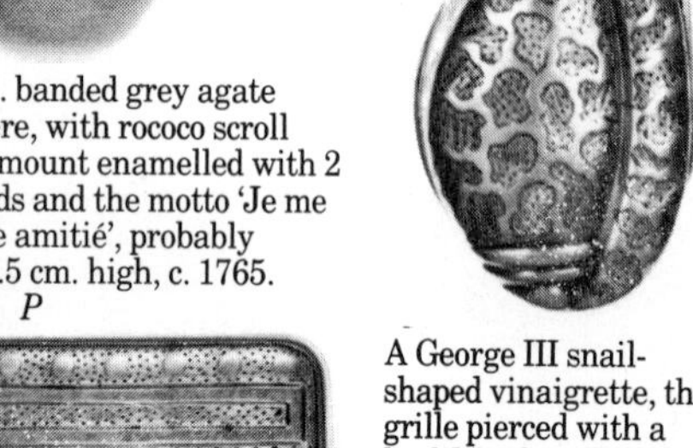

A George III snail-shaped vinaigrette, the grille pierced with a leaf, Matthew Linwood, Birmingham, 1804, 1½ in. wide (4 cm.). **£500-600** *S*

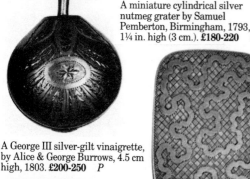

A George III silver-gilt vinaigrette, by Alice & George Burrows, 4.5 cm high, 1803. **£200-250** *P*

A George III vinaigrette, the grille pierced with musical instruments, Matthew Linwood, Birmingham, 1808, 1⅜ in. wide (3.6 cm.). **£250-300** *S*

A George III oblong vinaigrette, gilt interior and floral and foliate grille, marked on base and lid, Phipps & Robinson, London, 1803, 1¾ in. wide (4.5 cm.). **£400-500** *S*

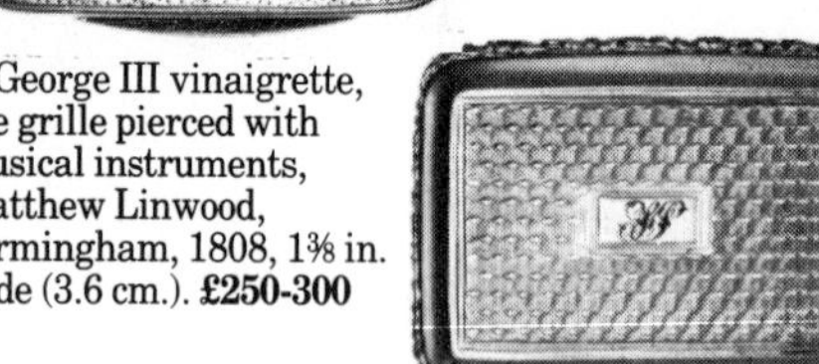

A George IV silver-gilt vinaigrette, the grille pierced with a cornucopia, by Thomas Newbold, Birmingham, 1821, 3.25 cm. long. **£150-200** *P*

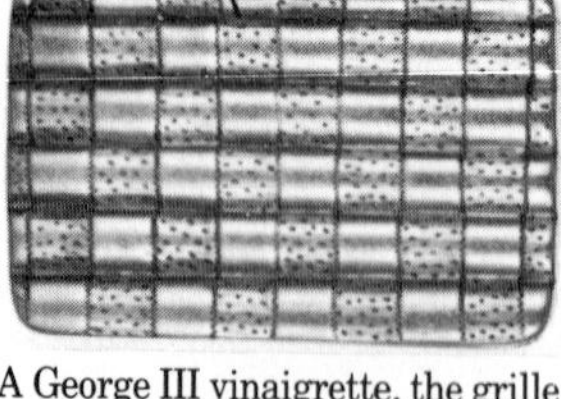

A George III vinaigrette, the grille pierced with flowers and foliage and inscribed 'G.B. Proctor', fully marked, Joseph Willmore, Birmingham, 1812, 1⅝ in. wide (4.1 cm.). **£150-200** *S*

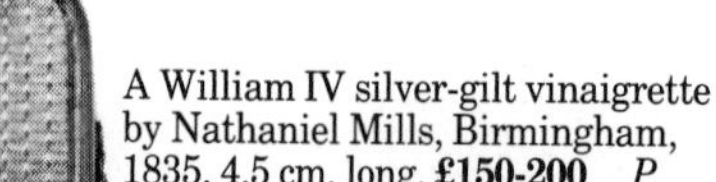

A William IV silver-gilt vinaigrette by Nathaniel Mills, Birmingham, 1835, 4.5 cm. long. **£150-200** *P*

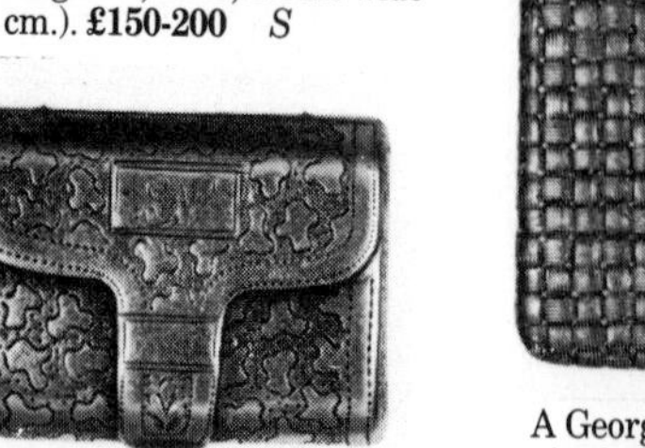

A George III purse vinaigrette by John Shaw, Birmingham, 1816, 3 cm. long. **£150-200** *P*

A George III silver-gilt oblong vinaigrette, the grille pierced to resemble filigree, Joseph Taylor, Birmingham, 1817, 1¾ in. wide (4.4 cm.). **£200-250** *S*

A George IV vinaigrette by Thomas Newbold, Birmingham, 1822, 4 cm. long. **£150-200** *P*

n unusual George IV vinaigrette silver-gilt by Joseph Willmore, ondon, 1821. **£650-750** *T*

A German fish spice box with red cabochon eyes, K. Kurz, Kesselstaft, importers' mark of Singleton, Benda & Co., London, 1903, 5½ in. long (13.8 cm.). **£300-£350** *S*

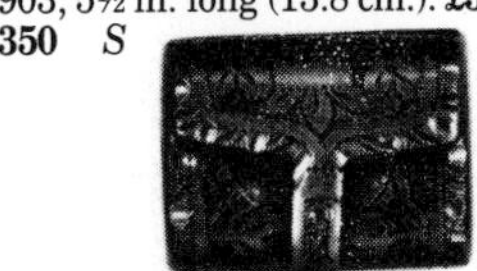
A William IV small purse vinaigrette by Thomas Shaw, Birmingham, 1834, 2.1 cm. long. **130-180** *P*

A pair of 19th C. Austrian neo-classical 4 light candelabra, 25 in. **£1,600-2,000** *WW*

A pair of 7 light candelabra, silver coloured metal, Continental, loaded, 57.5 cm. high, 20th C. **£1,600-1,800** *S*

An early Victorian castle-top vinaigrette by Nathaniel Mills, the cover chased in low relief probably with a side view of Windsor Castle, Birmingham, 1837, 4 cm. long. **£450-500** *P*

A silver-gilt bezoar stone case opening into halves to reveal the bezoar stone, 2¾ in. (7 cm.), 19th C. **£400-500** *S*

Bezoar stones, the gall stones of certain ruminants, were treasured in the Middle Ages as they were believed to act as antidotes to poison. Cases of this type were also made for ambergris balls performing the same function as pomanders.

An articulated fish spice box, probably Indian, 5½ in. long (13.7 cm.), late 19th/early 20th C. **£200-250** *S*

A German articulated fish spice box with red cabochon eyes, silver coloured metal, Simon Rosemau, Bad Kissingen, c. 1900, also struck with the post-1893 French import mark, 5 in. long (12.6 cm.). **£280-£360** *S*

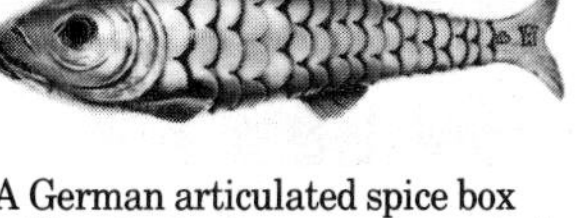
A German articulated spice box with red cabochon eyes, importer's mark of J.G. Smith for J. G. Smith & Co., proprietors of the Continental Daily Parcels Express, London, 1899, 4¾ in. long (12 cm.). **£280-360** *S*

A Victorian vinaigrette by Edward Smith, Birmingham, 1843, 3.75 cm. long. **£150-200** *P*

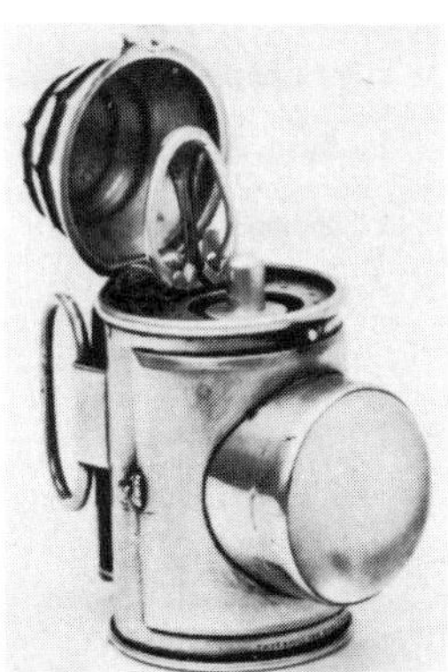
A Victorian necessaire/vinaigrette with hinged lid and gilt backed clear glass 'light' concealing a pill compartment, fitted with the following silver/steel items: a pair of folding scissors, a tape measure, 2 cotton reels, a bodkin (one other missing), a handle with screw-on button hook and awl, Thomas Johnson, London, 1873, P.O.D.R. mark for 8th September 1869, engraved: 'Thornhill 144 Bond Street', 3 in. high (7.6 cm.). **£600-£700** *S*

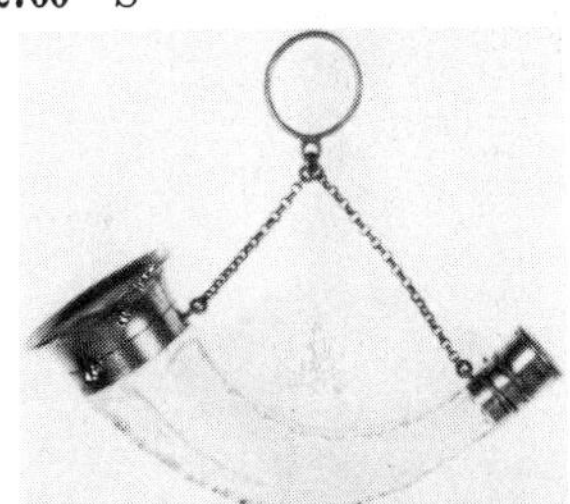
A 19th C. silver-gilt mounted glass combined vinaigrette and scent bottle bearing French import marks, 10 cm. long, c. 1870. **£120-£160** *P*

A Victorian combined vinaigrette and scent bottle by Sampson Mordan, one end detachable, 10.5 cm. long, 1874. **£180-240** *P*

An important pair of Charles II candlesticks, with maker's mark I.B. for Jacob Bodendick 1674, 24.5 cm. overall height, weight 45 oz. **£50,000+** *P*

A pair of silver-gilt 2 light candelabra, applied with cast and chased figures in 18th C. costume, and with detachable nozzles, 1966 by C. J. Vander Ltd., 27.8 cm. overall height, 96 oz. **£1,500-£2,000** *L*

A pair of William III candlesticks, later crested with later nozzles, th underneath with sets of initials, maker R.S. London 1695, 8½ in., 22 oz. all in. **£3,500-4,000** *WW*

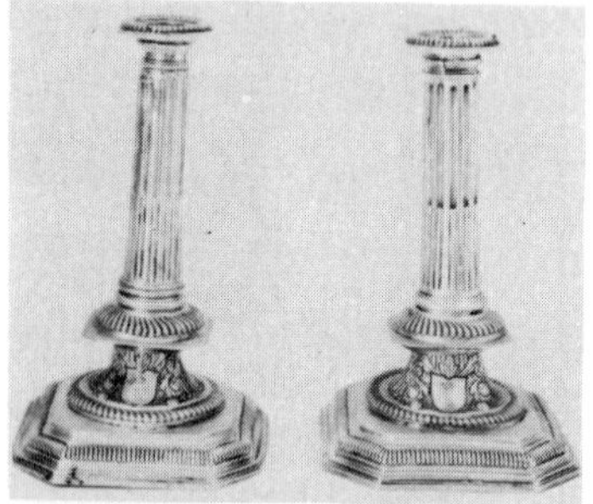

Two William III table candlesticks engraved at a later date with a crest and earl's coronet, one William Denny & John Backe, London, 1700, the other unmarked, 10½ in. high (26.7 cm.), c. 1700, 51 oz. 12 dwt. all in. **£2,000-2,500** *S*

A pair of William III table candlesticks, marked on bases and sconces, Joseph Bird, London, 1701, 6½ in. high (16.8 cm.), 28 oz. 9 dwt. (884 gm.). **£5,000-6,000** *S*

A pair of Queen Anne tapersticks, Thomas Folkingham, London, 1710, 4 in. high (10.1 cm.), 7 oz. 19 dwt. (247 gm.). **£4,500-5,000** *S*

A pair of Queen Anne candlesticks, marked on bases and sconces, Thomas Farren, London, 1709, 6¾ in. high (17.4 cm.), 22 oz. 10 dwt. (699 gm.). **£7,500-8,500** *S*

A pair of George II table candlesticks, marked on bases and one sconce, James Gould, London, 1731, 6¾ in. high (17.2 cm.), 24 oz. 17 dwt. (772 gm.). **£3,000-3,500** *S*

Four George II table candlesticks, marked on bases, 1 sconce and 2 nozzles, 2 George Wickes, 1745, 2 Edward Wakelin, 1752, all London, 8½ in. high (22 cm.), 80 oz. 17 dwt. (2,514 gm.). **£5,500-6,500** *S*

The arms are possibly those of Lynch.

A George II taperstick, maker's mark apparently IH, London, 1737, 4¼ in. high (11 cm.), 4 oz. 8 dwt. (136 gm.). **£600-700** *S*

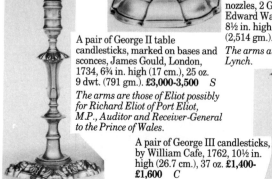

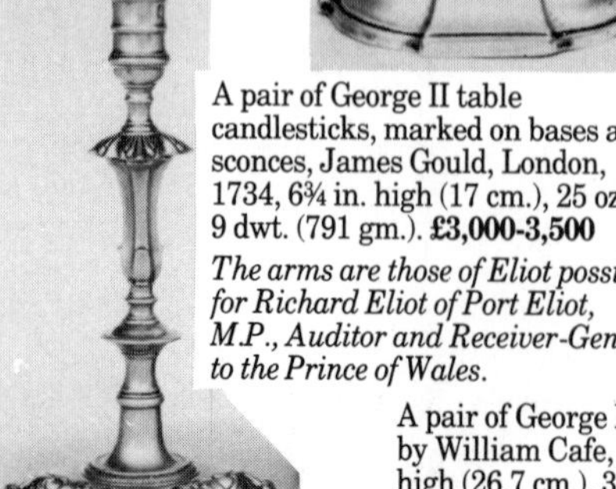

A pair of George II table candlesticks, marked on bases and sconces, James Gould, London, 1734, 6¾ in. high (17 cm.), 25 oz. 9 dwt. (791 gm.). **£3,000-3,500** *S*

The arms are those of Eliot possibly for Richard Eliot of Port Eliot, M.P., Auditor and Receiver-General to the Prince of Wales.

A pair of George III candlesticks, by William Cafe, 1762, 10½ in. high (26.7 cm.), 37 oz. **£1,400-£1,600** *C*

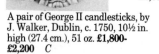

A pair of George II candlesticks, by J. Walker, Dublin, c. 1750, 10½ in. high (27.4 cm.), 51 oz. **£1,800-£2,200** *C*

A set of 4 George II cast candlesticks, by John Cafe, London, 1751, 9½ in. high, 89½ oz. **£4,500-5,000** *M*

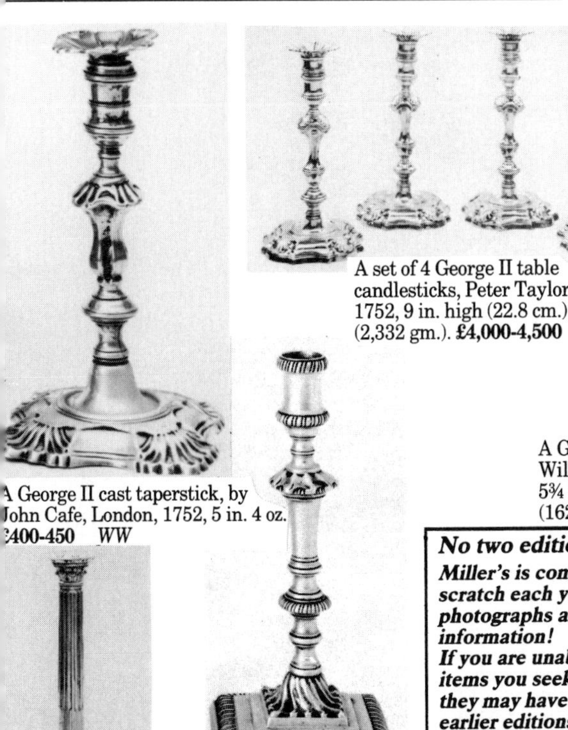

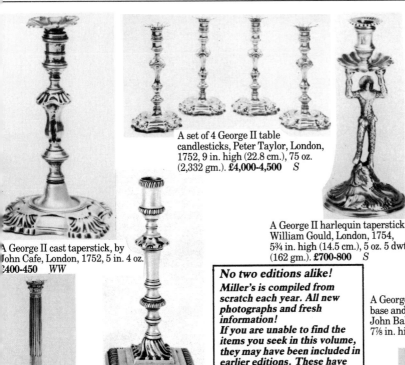

A set of 4 George II table candlesticks, Peter Taylor, London, 1752, 9 in. high (22.8 cm.), 75 oz. (2,332 gm.). **£4,000-4,500** *S*

A George II harlequin taperstick, William Gould, London, 1754, 5¾ in. high (14.5 cm.), 5 oz. 5 dwt. (162 gm.). **£700-800** *S*

A George II cast taperstick, by John Cafe, London, 1752, 5 in. 4 oz. **£400-450** *WW*

A George III taperstick, marked on base and nozzle, James Stamp & John Baker, London, 1768 (loaded), 7⅞ in. high (20 cm.). **£350-450** *S*

No two editions alike!
Miller's is compiled from scratch each year. All new photographs and fresh information!
If you are unable to find the items you seek in this volume, they may have been included in earlier editions. These have now been reprinted to satisfy demand; details at the back of this book.

A pair of George III tapersticks, William Cafe, London, 1765, 6⅛ in. high (15.5 cm.), 11 oz. 19 dwt. (370 gm.). **£1,500-1,700** *S*

A pair of George II table candlesticks, marked on bases and nozzles, Peter Werritzer, London, 1757, 11¾ in. high (30 cm.), 28 oz. 5 dwt. (877 gm.). **£1,000-1,200** *S*

A set of 6 George III candlesticks, Sheffield, 1801-02 by John Green & Co. and 2 plated branches. **£3,300-£4,000** *DWB*

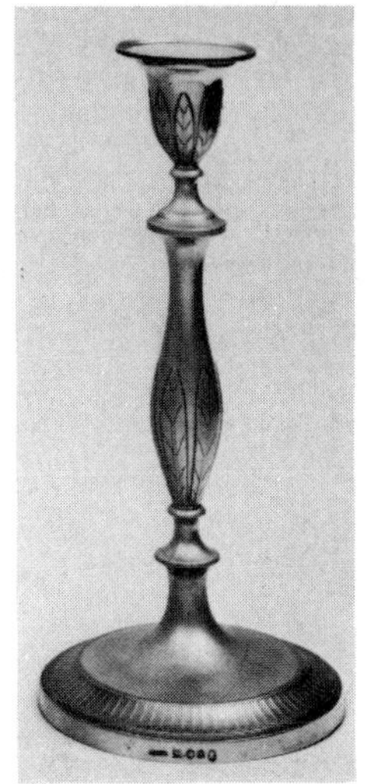

A pair of George III table candlesticks, marked on bases and nozzles, Green, Roberts, Mosley & Co., Sheffield, 1794 (loaded), 11⅝ in. high (29.5 cm.). **£1,400-£1,600** *S*

A Georgian silver taperstick. **£400-£450** *BHW*

A set of 4 George III cast candlesticks, all bearing an engraved crest, fully hallmarked, 2 by Robert Makepeace and Richard Carter and 2 by John Carter, London, 1776, 12 in. high, 113 oz. **£3,300-4,000** *M*

(l. & r.) A pair of late 18th C. Sheffield plate candlesticks, 10 in. **£80-120** *WW*
(c.) A pair of early George III

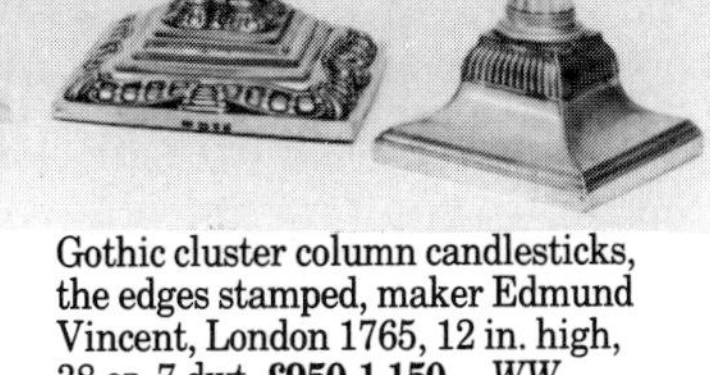

Gothic cluster column candlesticks, the edges stamped, maker Edmund Vincent, London 1765, 12 in. high, 38 oz. 7 dwt. **£950-1,150** *WW*

A set of 4 George III telescopic candlesticks, by John Roberts and Co., Sheffield, 1806, 8¼ in. high (21 cm.). **£3,000-3,500** *C*

A George III 7 light candelabrum, fully marked, Joseph Preedy, London, 1806, 26 in. high (66 cm.), 316 oz. (9,796 gm.). **£7,000-8,000** *S*

Grimwade records this unregistered maker's mark (No. 3670) as perhaps being that of John Parker II. There is little doubt, however, that this is the mark of Joseph Preedy. A cup and cover bearing this same maker's mark, London, 1802, and engraved on the base 'Executed by J. Preedy, Great Newport St., London, was sold at Sotheby's Gleneagles Hotel, 26th August, 1971, lot 144.

A set of 4 George III table candlesticks, marked on bases and nozzles, Smith, Smith & Creswick, Sheffield, 1808 (loaded), 12 in. high (30.5 cm.). **£1,000-1,300** *S*

A set of 3 Queen Anne casters, by Simon Pantin, 1710, 9 and 7¼ in. high (22.9 and 18.7 cm.), 34 oz. **£3,000-4,000** *C*

The arms are those of Bucknell.

A set of 4 19th C. German candlesticks, 12 in. high. **£1,200-£1,400** *WW*

A pair of unusual Victorian silver-gilt candlesticks in Gothic taste, by John Keith, 1851, some stones missing, 11¾ in. high (29.9 cm.), gross 45 oz. **£3,000-3,500** *C*

The most likely designer of these candlesticks is James Brooks (1825-1901), an architect and friend of Augustus Pugin. Two pairs of copper gilt altar candlesticks of similar form but less elaborate finish by him were included in the exhibition 'Victorian Church Art' at the Victoria and Albert Museum 1971-72 (G25 and G27).

A set of 3 Queen Anne octagonal casters, marked on bases and covers, Joseph Ward, London, 1713, 8½, 7 and 6¾ in. high (20.7, 17.7 and 17 cm.), 20 oz. 15 dwt. (643 gm.). **£2,000-3,000** *S*

A set of 3 early 18th C. casters, each engraved on one side with a coat-of-arms headed by a Viscount's coronet, the blind example London, 1702 or 09, the other two marked on bodies and one cover, John Chartier, London, 1700, 9 and 6¾ in., high (22.7 by 17 cm.), 34 oz. 18 dwt. (1,085 gm.). **£6,000-7,000** *S*

John Chartier entered two marks as a largeworker between April, 1698 and May, 1699.

A pair of George I casters, marks struck on base by Thomas Bamford, London, 1719, 6½ in. high, 16 oz. **£1,000-1,400** *GM*

A set of 3 casters, engraved later with a crest and motto, by David Tanqueray, one 1713, one 1714 and the other with worn marks, 11 and 9 in. high (28 and 22.8 cm.), 51 oz. **£1,800-2,200** *C*

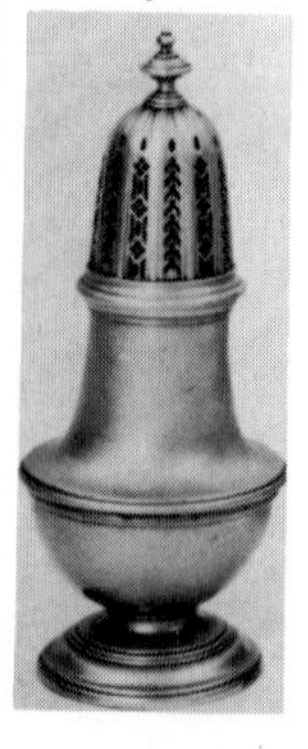

A George II vase-shaped caster, marked on base and cover, Peter Archambo, London, 1730, 5½ in. high (14 cm.), 5 oz. 15 dwt. (178 gm.). **£550-650** *S*

A Danish baluster caster with a matching bayonet cover, maker's mark only, Peter Norman (Randers), c. 1750, 6½ in. high (16.7 cm.), 5 oz. 7 dwt. (170 gm.). **£550-650** *S*

A silver-gilt sugar caster, Wakely & Wheeler, London, 1902, excluding fitted case with green velvet and silk lining and label: 'James Ramsay/goldsmith/8 High St/Dundee', 9¼ in. high (23.5 cm.), 12 oz. (373 gm.) **£350-400** *S*

A George III epergne, engraved with 2 crests and a motto, by Thomas Pitts, 1768, 13¾ in. high (34.9 cm.), 99 oz. **£3,000-4,000** *C*

A silver-gilt and agate sweetmeat stand, the square grey agate bowl with blackish inclusions, unmarked, probably German, 6½ in. high (16.5 cm.), c. 1850. **£300-350** *S*

A Guild of Handicraft Ltd. silver sugar caster, pierced cover surmounted with amber stone, maker's mark, London, 1924, 16 cm. **£250-350** *S*

A William IV silver-gilt centrepiece, engraved 3 times with a coat-of-arms, coronet, Garter motto and supporters, and 3 times with a crest, by William Theobalds and Lockington Bunn, 1835, 21 in. high (53.3 cm.), 148 oz. **£5,000-£6,000** *C*

The arms are those of Lowther.

A George III epergne, engraved with a coat-of-arms, by William Holmes, 1790, 16¾ in. high (42.5 cm.), 147 oz. **£2,500-3,000** *C*

The arms are those of Porter impaling Carr.

A Victorian 2 tier shaped circular cake stand, showing traces of gilding, Robert Garrard for R. J. & S. Garrard, London, 1838, 12 in. high (30.5 cm.), 61.6 oz (1,918 gm.). **£850-950** *S*

A pair of shaped circular pedestal fruit stands, the fluted bowls flat-chased in Regence style with scalework, foliage and scrolls, the Goldsmiths & Silversmiths Co. Ltd., Birmingham, 1941, 9 in. high by 11½ in. diam. (23.2 by 29.5 cm.), 108 oz. 6 dwt. (3,368 gm.). **£1,350-£1,450** *S*

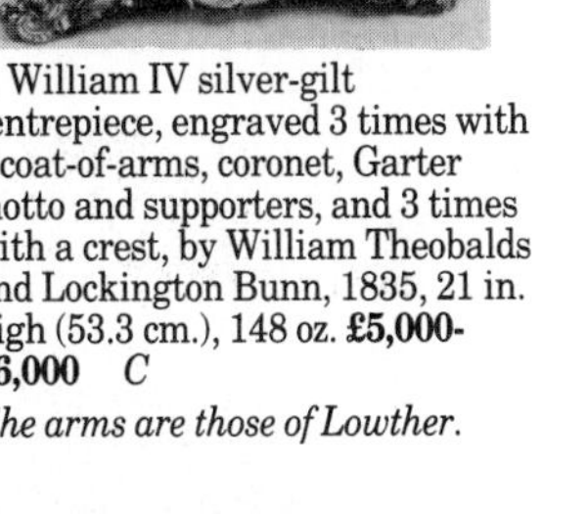

A pair of Victorian circular dessert stands, complete with 2 circular frosted glass dishes enriched with cut key pattern bands, John Hunt & Robert Roskell for Hunt & Roskell, London, 1865, both stamped: 'Hunt & Roskell late Storr & Mortimer 3599', 9¼ in. overall height (23.5 cm.), 40 oz. 8 dwt. (1,256 gm.). **£600-700** *S*

A large Victorian parcel-gilt 6-light Pompeian pattern centrepiece and mirror plateau, designed by A. A. Willms, 29¼ in. high (74.4 cm.) with branches, 24¼ in. high (61.8 cm.) with dish and holder, the plateau 17 in. diam. (43.5 cm.), Frederick Elkington for Elkington & Co., Birmingham, 1875, the centrepiece stamped: 754, P.O.D.R. mark for 3rd May 1862 (6), the plateau stamped: 1142, 13,005 gm. (418 oz. 3 dwt.) of weighable silver. **£7,000-8,000** *S*

The original Pompeian pattern dessert service was manufactured by Elkington & Co. in parcel-gilt silver with enamel embellishments for their exhibit at the International Exhibition of 1862.

A silver epergne marked Birmingham 1926, 11½ in. **£300-£350** *TP*

A pair of George III coasters, Richard Morton, Sheffield, 1791 (loaded), 4¾ in. diam. (12 cm.). **£600-700** *S*

A fine pair of George III silver-gilt coasters of large size, Digby Scott & Benjamin Smith for Rundell, Bridge & Rundell, also stamped: 'Rundell Bridge et Rundell aurifices Regis et Principis walliae Londini fecerent', London, 1806, 7 in. diam. (17.7 cm.), 63 oz. 15 dwt. (1,982 gm.) all in. **£10,000-12,000** *S*

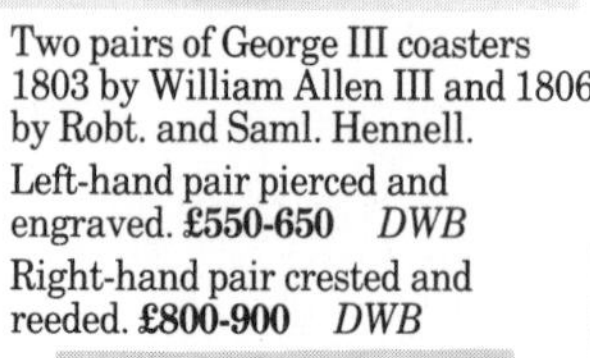

Two pairs of George III coasters 1803 by William Allen III and 1806 by Robt. and Saml. Hennell.

Left-hand pair pierced and engraved. **£550-650** *DWB*

Right-hand pair crested and reeded. **£800-900** *DWB*

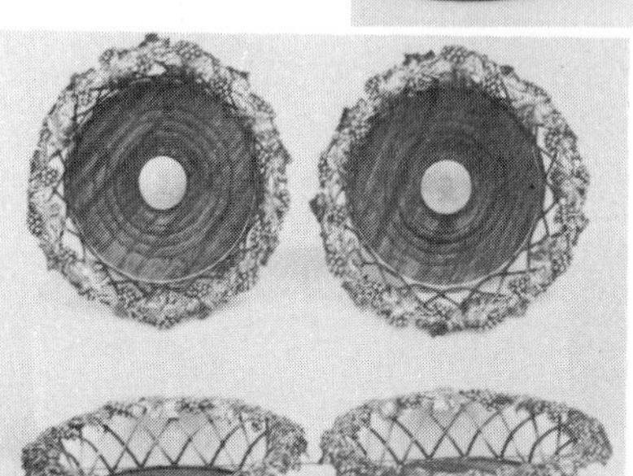

A set of 4 William IV silver-gilt wine coasters engraved with a crest, by E., J. and W. Barnard, 1835. **£5,000-6,000** *C*

A Queen Anne plain tapering cylindrical chocolate pot, engraved with a lozenge-of-arms with baroque cartouche, by Benjamin Pyne, 1707, 10 in. high (25.4 cm.), gross 23 oz. **£5,000-6,000** *C*

A George II plain tapering cylindrical coffee pot engraved with a coat-of-arms within foliage mantling, by Edward Pocock, 1729, 9 in. high (22.9 cm.), 28 oz. gross. **£3,500-4,000** *C*

A George II plain tapering cylindrical coffee pot engraved with a coat-of-arms in rococo cartouche, by George Methuen, 1744, 9¼ in. high (23.5 cm.), gross 27 oz. **£2,000-£3,000** *C*

The arms are probably those of Stewart of Nateby Hall, Co. Lancs. impaling Archbold.

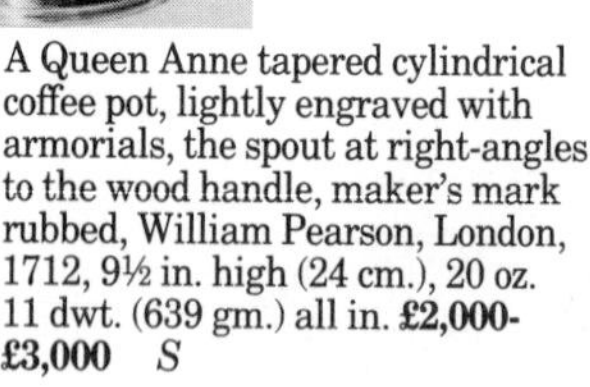

A Queen Anne tapered cylindrical coffee pot, lightly engraved with armorials, the spout at right-angles to the wood handle, maker's mark rubbed, William Pearson, London, 1712, 9½ in. high (24 cm.), 20 oz. 11 dwt. (639 gm.) all in. **£2,000-£3,000** *S*

A Hungarian coffee pot by Johannes Georgius Puskailler, Neusohl, 7½ in. high (19.2 cm.), c. 1745, 14 oz. 1 dwt. (438 gm.) all in. **£1,400-1,500** *S*

A Queen Anne chocolate pot, the spout at right-angles to the wood handle, marked on body and lid, no maker's mark, Dublin, 1706/07, 10⅞ in. high (27.5 cm.), 32 oz. 19 dwt. (1,021 gm.), all in. **£4,000-£5,000** *S*

A George II silver coffee pot, the domed cover (not hallmarked) hinged and with turned finial, maker Thomas Whipham, London, 1743, 9¼ in. high, 24½ oz. **£900-£1,000** *NSF*

A set of 3 George II silver casters, the covers (not hallmarked) pierced and with turned finials, some damage, maker Christian Hilliard, London, 7¼ and 5¼ in., c. 1740 (no date letter). **£400-500** *NSF*

A Channel Islands plain tapering cylindrical coffee pot, by Pierre Amiraux of Jersey, maker's mark struck twice, 9⅞ in. high (25.1 cm.), c. 1745, 33 oz. **£9,000-10,000** *C*

A George II tapered cylindrical coffee pot, engraved with armorials within a rococo cartouche, marked on body, base and lid, William Cripps, London, 1748, 9½ in. high (24.2 cm.), 26 oz. 11 dwt. (823 gm.) all in. **£2,500-3,000** *S*

A George II baluster coffee pot, marked on body and lid, Thomas Wallis, London, 1756, 10 in. high (25.3 cm.), 28 oz. 13 dwt. (891 gm.) all in. **£1,800-2,000** *S*

A George II small baluster coffee pot engraved on one side with a crest, marked on body and cover, maker's mark I.B., London, 1758, 8 in. high (20 cm.), 15 oz. all in. **£800-1,000** *S*

No two editions alike!
Miller's is compiled from scratch each year. All new photographs and fresh information!
If you are unable to find the items you seek in this volume, they may have been included in earlier editions. These have now been reprinted to satisfy demand; details at the back of this book.

An early George III baluster coffee pot, marked on body and lid, William Shaw II, London, 1762, 10⅛ in. high (25.6 cm.), 24 oz. 8 dwt. (756 gm.) all in. **£1,500-£1,700** *S*

A George III pear-shaped coffee pot, by John Payne, London, 1763, 11½ in., 32 oz. all in. **£900-1,000** *WW*

An 18th C. Irish provincial coffee pot, John Nicholson of Cork, c. 1775, 11 in. high (28 cm.), 30 oz. 19 dwt. (962 gm.) all in. **£2,000-£2,500** *S*

The arms are those of Cuthbert, Inverness.

A George III plain pear-shaped coffee pot, engraved with a coat-of-arms and a crest within floral cartouches, by T. Whipham and C. Wright, 1767, 11 in. high (28 cm.), 30 oz. gross. **£2,000-£3,000** *C*

The arms are those of Goddard.

A George III baluster coffee jug, by Daniel Smith and Robert Sharp, 1770, 27 cm., 25 oz. **£500-600** *L*

A baluster silver chocolate pot by Jakob (Johann) Wilhelm Kolb, maker's mark, Augsburg, 1771-73, also struck with a French control mark, 26.7 cm. high, 570 gm. all in. **£2,000-2,500** *S*

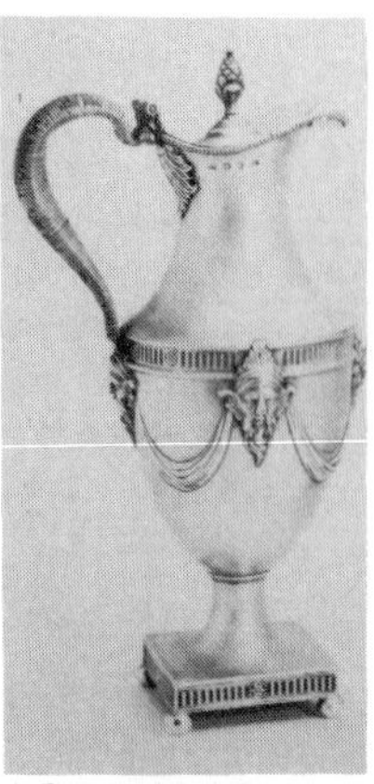

A George III coffee pot and hot milk jug, marked on bodies and covers, Richard Morton & Co., Sheffield, 1776, 11¾ in. high (30 cm.), 44 oz. (1,368 gm.) all in. **£2,200-2,600** *S*

A plain baluster chocolate pot by Jakob (Johann) Wilhelm Kolb, maker's mark, Augsburg, 1779-81, 27 cm. high, 680 gm. all in. **£2,200-£2,600** *S*

A vase-shaped coffee pot and milk jug by Nicolas-Theodore Cailliez, coffee pot 29.5 cm. high, milk jug 18.7 cm. high, both maker's mark, Paris, c. 1800, 1,090 gm. all in. **£1,500-2,000** *S*

A George III oval vase-shaped coffee pot, marked on base and lid, R. & D. Hennell, London, 1800, 11⅞ in. high (30 cm.), 28 oz. 13 dwt. (888 gm.) all in. **£1,100-1,300** *S*

An Italian vase-shaped coffee pot, Geatano Pane, Naples, 10¾ in. high (27.2 cm.), c. 1825, 22 oz. 18 dwt. (710 gm.), all in. **£950-£1,050** *S*

A George IV 3-piece coffee set, coffee pot with silver handle and button, stamped: 251, and lampstand with detachable burner, 10¾ in. overall height (27 cm.), milk jug stamped: 99, and sugar basin, Paul Storr for Storr & Mortimer, London, 1829-30, some also stamped: 'Storr & Mortimer', 64 oz. 1 dwt. (1,992 gm.) all in. **£4,000-4,500** *S*

The arms are those of Elliot, Minto, Co. Roxburgh.

A Victorian baluster coffee pot, crested, otherwise quite plain, domed cover with button finial, Robert Garrard, London, 1843, 10 in. high (25.5 cm.), 25 oz. 17 dwt. all in. **£700-800** *SC*

A Victorian octagonal baluster coffee pot, E. & J. Barnard for Edward Barnard & Sons, London, 1853, stamped: 133/U, 10½ in. high (26.7 cm.), 25 oz. 2 dwt. (780 gm.) all in. **£450-550** *S*

A German coffee pot, silver coloured metal, struck with pseudo French hallmarks, 23 cm. high, late 19th C., 37 oz. (1,156 gm.). **£600-700** *S*

A Victorian tapered cylindrical coffee pot in typical mid 18th C. Irish style, maker's mark J.S., Dublin, 1894, 11 in. high, 35 oz. all in. **£800-900** *SI*

A Charles II small porringer, maker's mark GW, 1674, crescent below, 2¼ in. high (5.7 cm.), 1 oz. 10 dwt. **£500-700** *C*

A Charles II tumbler cup, York, 1680, by Thos. Mangy, 3¼ in. diam., 6¼ oz. **£650-750** *A*

An important James II 2-handled porringer by R. I. London, c. 1687, 4¼ in. high, 15 oz. **£1,000-1,200** *GM*

A Queen Anne plain 2-handled porringer, engraved on the underside 'HM Baptized y 6th of Dec: 1704', by Francis Garthorne, 1705, 3 in. high (7.6 cm.), 5 oz. **£900-1,000** *C*

A Continental silver-gilt chalice, engraved under foot 'LE CALIS POIS 19 ONS ED 1622', maker's mark only DH conjoined, probably French or Flemish, 9⅛ in. high (23.2 cm.), early 17th C., 16 oz. **£3,000-4,000** *C*

A rare 17th C. skillet, London, 1649, 10 oz. **£1,100-1,300** *WHL*

A late 17th C. silver-gilt porringer, Hull town mark (3 coronets), stamped twice, maker's mark for Abraham Barachin, the inside of the foot prick-marked 'Frog Hal 1689', 9¼ in. wide overall, 4¾ in. high. **£750-850** *DDM*

A parcel-gilt silver chalice, probably Dutch, 2¾ in. high, early 17th C., 4 oz. **£550-600** *EEW*

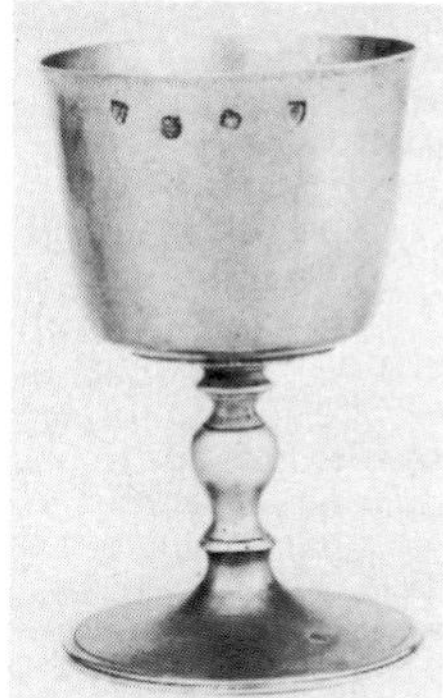
A Charles II plain wine cup pricked with initials NEV and dated 1671, 1670, maker's mark PD, 3 pellets above cinquefoil below, 5⅝ in. high (14.2 cm.), 7 oz. 14 dwt. **£5,500-£6,500** *C*

A pair of George III plain vase-shaped goblets, with a presentation inscription dated 1807, by John Wakefield, 1807, 6¼ in. high (15.8 cm.), 20 oz. **£700-800** *C*

A George I small plain silver-gilt 2-handled cup, engraved with the Royal Arms and initials of George I, by David Willaume I, maker's mark only struck 4 times, 2⅝ in. high (6.7 cm.), c. 1715, 4 oz. 15 dwt. **£2,200-2,500** *C*

A Norwegian 2-handled pedestal cup, inscribed, silver coloured metal, stamped: 'H. Moller/ Trondhjem', 25.5 cm. high, c. 1900, 41.4 oz. (1,288 gm.). **£350-400** *S*

A Channel Islands plain wine cup, engraved with initials IAB and dated 1687, Jersey, maker's mark AH a fleur-de-lys above struck twice, 4¾ in. high (12.1 cm.), 6 oz. 15 dwt., c. 1685. **£2,000-3,000** *C*

A pair of Regency ostrich egg cups, the egg painted with a crest and motto, maker's mark AD, 8 in. high (20.3 cm.), 1814. **£900-1,000** *C*

A pair of Victorian campana-shaped goblets, gilt interiors, Samuel Keely, Birmingham, 1842, 6¾ in. high (17 cm.), 22 oz. 10 dwt. **£450-£550** *S*

An embossed 2-handled racing cup by Hyans London, 1853, 'Durban Race Cup', 130 oz., 16 in. **£850-£950** *GM*

A Victorian bell-shaped goblet, Josiah Williams & Co., of Bristol, Exeter, 1877, 7¾ in. high (19.7 cm.), 9 oz. 6 dwt. (289 gm.). **£280-360** *S*

A Commonwealth 2-handled porringer and cover, the base pricked with initials, 1659, maker's mark perhaps FW for Field Whorwood (cf. Jackson, p. 125), 12 oz. 10 dwt. **£3,000-4,000** *C*

A set of 12 bell-shaped goblets in late 18th C. style, gilt interiors, maker's mark NL in a lozenge, London, 1968, 5¼ in. high (13.6 cm.), 69 oz. (2,146 gm.). **£1,450-1,650** *S*

A Charles II 2-handled cup and cover engraved with the arms of Wynne, the base inscribed I.S./I.W. 1682, maker I.M., 3 pellets above and below, London, 1681, 6 in. diam., 28 oz. **£4,500-5,500** *WW*

The Wynne family lived in the Taunton area in the late 17th C.

A parcel-gilt double cup (doppelkopf), the ring handle with 3 rectangular panels, each cast and chased with a human headed monster, Swiss or German, 10.6 cm. diam., 7.5 cm. high, 1st quarter of the 14th C., 290 gm. (all in).

Sold for **£132,000** March, 1983 *S*

This hitherto unknown piece of early 14th century silver ranks with another, as yet unpublished, found walled up in the former Imperial castle of Karlstein, Czechoslovakia, as the most important discovery of mediaeval secular vessels of the last 100 years. The exact place of discovery is not recorded, but some indication of its source can be obtained from the coat-of-arms which decorates it and from comparable surviving pieces. These point to Switzerland or the upper Rhine. The double cup is very similar to 2 others of slightly later date with undoubted Swiss provenance.

In view of the extreme rarity of comparable 14th century secular silver, it is difficult to arrive at a precise dating. The best indication of period is the presence of the grotesque monsters on the handle of the double cup. These look back to the 13th century and imply a date early in the 14th century; this dating is confirmed by the early type of helm on the crest inside the bowl of the double cup, which closely resembles those shown on the Manessesche Handschrift of c. 1300.

The double cup can be recognised as this early on account of the human headed monsters on the handle. The inscription, with the names of the three Kings, Caspar, Melchior and Waltazar on the cover has an amuletic significance in warding off evil, and similar inscriptions are recorded on the mounts of German 14th century drinking horns and on the Three Kings Mazer Cup at Corpus Christi College, Cambridge (ill. Jones, Cambridge Plate, p. 41).

The coat-of-arms in the form of three Jewish hats is recorded as used by various families, among them the Zurich family von Magelshofen (W. Merz and F. Hegi, Die Wappenrolle von Zürich, Zürich pl. XXII no. 430). The family of Judden of Westphalia uses as its arms, gules, three Jewish hats argent, with crest or, three Jewish hats sable. For contemporary representations of the Jewish hats, see a psalter from the diocese of Basel or Constance (ill. Juif Medieval au miroir de l'art chrétien, figs. 111 and 158) and on the Mainz Gospels of c. 1260 (ill. ibid. fig. 137). The double cup differs from the late 14th and 15th century examples in that it has a low base and no stem; most later examples have bowls of mazer wood, rock crystal or serpentine and stand on taller bases.

A William III 2-handled gilded racing cup and cover, London, 1699, 11½ in. high, 61 oz., in original 2-handled storage case. **£2,000-2,500** *GM*

A George III silver-gilt campana-shaped 2-handled cup and cover, marked on body and cover, William Bateman, London, 1818, engraved: 'Michah Furniss, Manchester', 19 in. high (48.5 cm.), 114 oz. 13 dwt. (3,565 gm.) all in. **£1,500-£2,000** *S*

The Stand Cup, value 100 guineas, was run at Chester Race Course on Wednesday, 5th May, 1819. As the inscription records, it was won by Mr. Houldsworth's 4-year-old chestnut filly, Torelli, by Cerberus, out of Miss Cranfield. The odds for Torelli were 6 to 4 on.

A George III 2-handled vase-shaped cup and cover, by Charles Aldridge, 1796, 13¾ in. high (34.8 cm.), 53 oz. **£700-900** *C*

Two George I silver-gilt butter dishes formed as scallop shells, one by Ambrose Stevenson, the other by Edmund Pearce, maker's marks only, 10 oz. 18 dwt., c. 1715. **£1,600-£1,800** *C*

A George III 2-handled cup, cover and stand, maker's mark WH probably for William Holmes, 1800, 20 in. high (50.8 cm.), 140 oz., in fitted wood case. **£3,000-4,000** *C*

The arms are those of Capt. David King.

Four William IV silver-gilt shell-shaped butter dishes, engraved with a crest, by J. E. Terrey, one 1833, three 1836, gilding later, 23 oz. **£1,500-1,700** *C*

A George IV silver-gilt 2-handled cup and cover, by Benjamin Smith II, 1826, 16½ in. high (41.9 cm.), 160 oz., on circular wood plinth. **£4,500-5,500** *C*

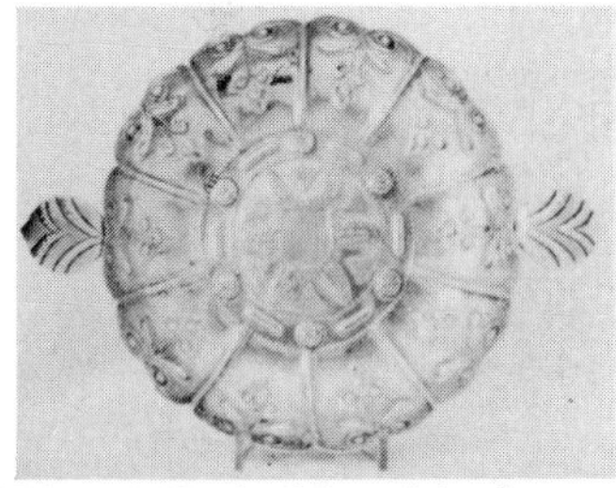
A Charles I shaped circular sweetmeat dish, W. Maundy, London, 1630, 8⅜ in. (21.2 cm.) over handles, 3 oz. 16 dwt. (117 gm.). **£750-850** *S*

A Charles I circular sweetmeat dish, maker RC in shield with circles, London, 1632, old repairs, 4½ oz. all in. **£1,200-1,500** *WW*

A rare and early 17th C. Communion cup and paten, struck 7 times with the maker's mark only, Robert Williamson, York, inscribed 'Ye Gyfte of ye good Queene 1585' with crest and Latin inscription, 10½ in. high overall, 16 oz. **£800-1,100** *DDM*

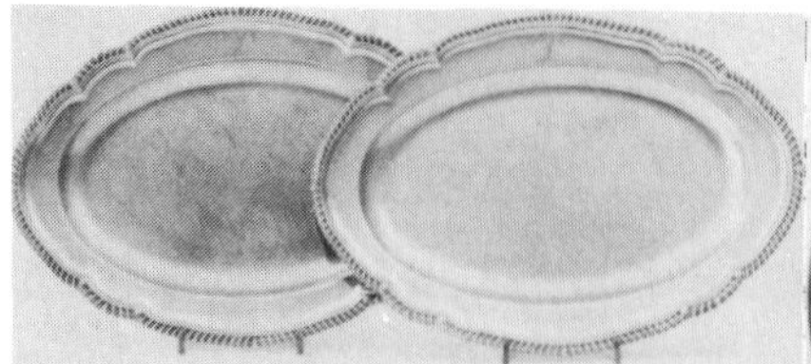

A pair of George II shaped oval meat dishes, Edward Wakelin, London, 1757, 15 in. wide (38.2 cm.), 70 oz. 18 dwt. (2,197 gm.). **£1,200-1,400** *S*

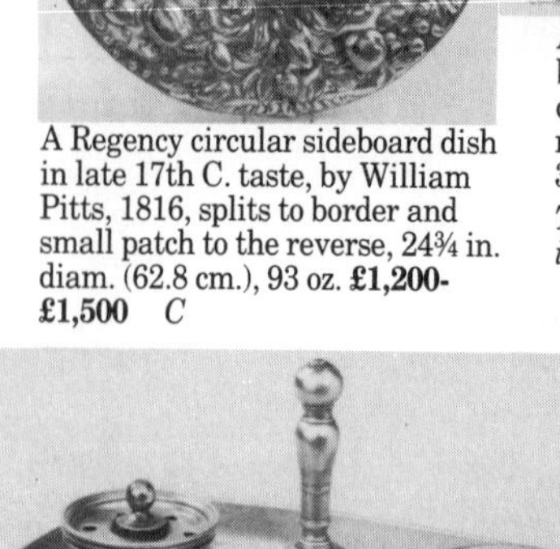

A Regency circular sideboard dish in late 17th C. taste, by William Pitts, 1816, splits to border and small patch to the reverse, 24¾ in. diam. (62.8 cm.), 93 oz. **£1,200-£1,500** *C*

A George II shaped oval ink-stand, by David Willaume II, 1743, the cover to the ink pot a later replacement, 10 in. long (25.4 cm.), 39 oz. **£2,700-3,500** *C*

The arms are those of Podenham impaling Robinson.

A German silver-gilt oval dish, struck with 3 pseudo-hallmarks, 45.9 cm. long, c. 1880, 31 oz. (966 gm.), excluding ebonised wood stand. **£700-900** *S*

A Queen Anne plain oblong inkstand, by John Chartier, 1705, the ink pot and cover by Robert Calderwood, Dublin, c. 1760, the bell unmarked, engraved with a later coat-of-arms, coronet and crest, 11½ in. long (29.2 cm.), 52 oz. **£3,000-4,000** *C*

A George IV silver-gilt travelling inkwell, the screw-on cover rotating to operate a plunger, engine-turned, glass-lined, fully marked except for finial, Archibald Douglas, London, 1825, 5 in. high (12.5 cm.). **£1,300-1,600** *S*

A George III shaped rectangular 3-bottle inkstand, the stand fully marked, one lid with lion passant only, Thomas Daniell, London, 1774, 9½ in. long (24.4 cm.), 18 oz. 3 dwt. (564 gm.), of weighable silver. **£750-850** *S*

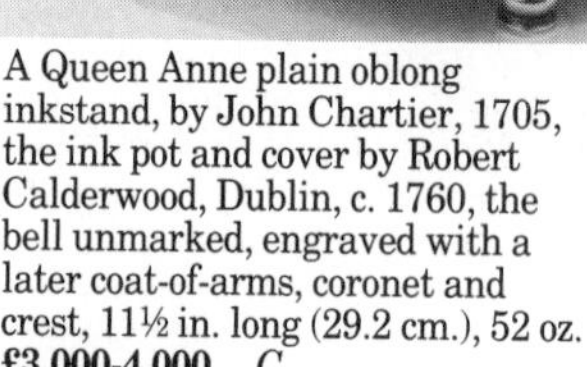

A George II rectangular inkstand, the pounce pot Richard Cooke, 1800, the remainder Fuller White, 1754, all London, 12¼ in. long (31.4 cm.), 52 oz. (1,529 gm.), excluding clear glass liner. **£1,600-£1,800** *S*

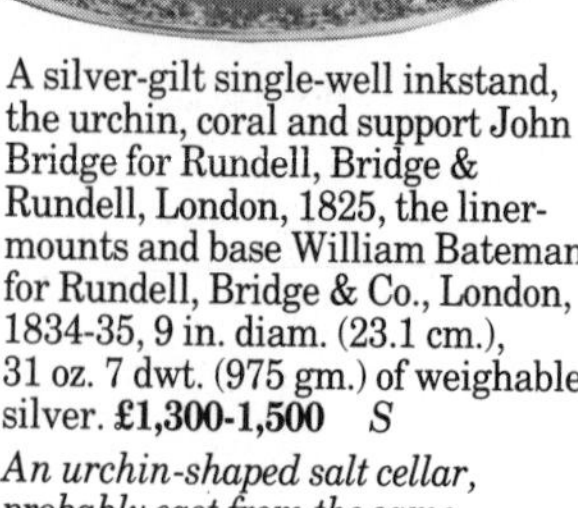

A silver-gilt single-well inkstand, the urchin, coral and support John Bridge for Rundell, Bridge & Rundell, London, 1825, the liner-mounts and base William Bateman for Rundell, Bridge & Co., London, 1834-35, 9 in. diam. (23.1 cm.), 31 oz. 7 dwt. (975 gm.) of weighable silver. **£1,300-1,500** *S*

An urchin-shaped salt cellar, probably cast from the same pattern, John Bridge for Rundell, Bridge & Rundell, predecessors of Rundell, Bridge & Co., London, 1825, is in the Victoria and Albert Museum. For an illustration see Culme & Strang, Antique Silver & Silver Collecting, London, 1973, p. 66.

A George III silver-gilt inkwell in the form of a Roman oil lamp with serpent handle, fully marked, Digby Scott & Benjamin Smith probably for Rundell & Bridge, London, 1804, the interior of the lid scratched in freehand script: 'Rundell & Bridge', 6 in. diam. (15.1 cm.), 10 oz. 17 dwt. (337 gm.). **£1,700-1,900** *S*

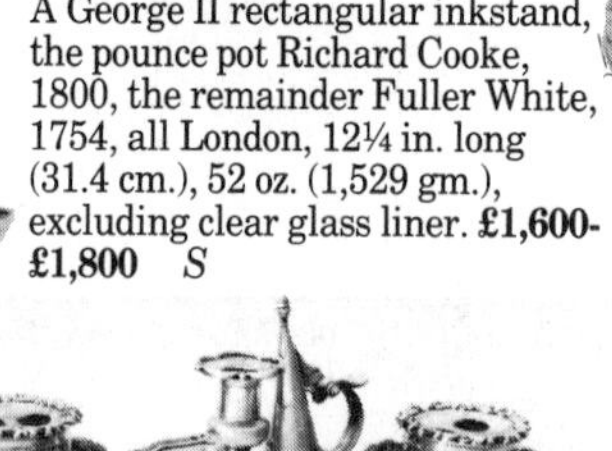

A large William IV rectangular 2-bottle inkstand, fully marked, T.J. & N. Creswick, Sheffield, 1830, 12¾ in. long (32.4 cm.), 51 oz. 2 dwt. (1,589 gm.) of weighable silver. **£1,000-1,200** *S*

A George IV 2-handled oval inkstand containing 2 silver-mounted glass bottles and central circular box surmounted by a taperstick, with detachable nozzle by John Houle, 1827, with extinguisher by John Angell, 1823, weight without bottles 42 oz. **£1,200-1,400** *C*

Make the most of Miller's

Unless otherwise stated, any description which refers to 'a set' or 'a pair' includes a valuation for the entire set or the pair, even though the illustration may show only a single item.

\ William IV shaped oblong
nkstand, the moulded pen
lepressions engraved with
ırmorials and a crest, fully
narked, Joseph & John Angell,
.ondon, 1836-37, 13¾ in. wide
35 cm.), 51 oz. 14 dwt. (1,602 gm.)
ıf weighable silver. **£1,400-1,600**
;

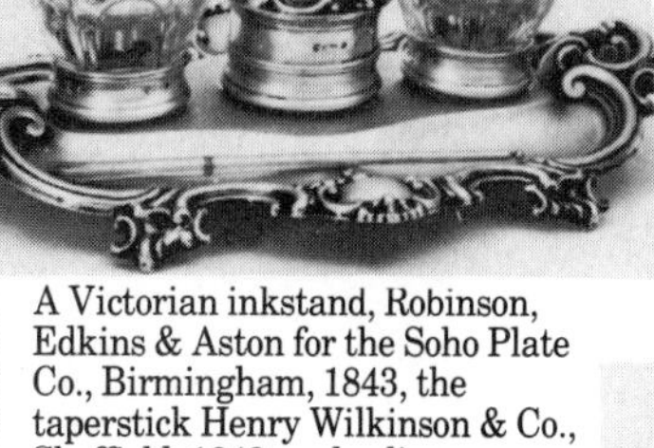

A Victorian inkstand, Robinson, Edkins & Aston for the Soho Plate Co., Birmingham, 1843, the taperstick Henry Wilkinson & Co., Sheffield, 1842, and a dip pen, S. Mordan & Co., London, c. 1870, 12 in. long (30.5 cm.), 22 oz. 18 dwt. (712 gm.) of weighable silver. **£600-£700** *S*

A Victorian oval inkstand engraved with stylised Egyptian wings and fitted with 2 pen depressions, the centre with a sarcophagus-shaped container fitted with 2-glass inkwells and a box, maker's mark HW, Birmingham, 1874, 11¾ in. wide (29.7 cm.), 34 oz. 11 dwt. of silver. **£500-600** *SC*

A large William IV shaped oval
3-bottle inkstand in mid 18th C.
style, the gallery sides and bottle
holders pierced with foliage below
applied gadroon borders, fully
marked, Edward Cornelius Farrell,
London, 1836, 12¾ in. long
(32.4 cm.), 59 oz. 7 dwt. (1,845 gm.)
of weighable silver. **£3,000-3,500**
S

A Walker & Hall Victorian silver inkstand fitted with 2 cut glass bottles with silver mounts flanking a detachable chamber candlestick with snuffer, Sheffield, 1898, 10½ in., 20 oz. **£400-500** *WHL*

A Victorian rectangular inkstand, one hinged cover lacking, the detachable taperstick complete with nozzle and unmarked conical extinguisher, C. T. & G. Fox, London, 1884, 9¾ in. long (25 cm.), 31.8 oz. (990 gm.) of silver. **£750-£850** *S*

\ large shaped rectangular 2-bottle
nkstand, Walker & Hall Ltd.,
ˌheffield, 1907, 14¼ in. long
36 cm.), 50 oz. 15 dwt. (1,578 gm.)
ıf weighable silver. **£600-700** *S*

A silver-gilt and jade-mounted desk set, by Charles Boyton, London, 1915, the inkstand 11¼ in. (28.5 cm.) overall. **£2,100-2,500** *C*

A rare Elizabeth I silver-gilt mounted tigerware jug, the spreading circular foot mount stamped with egg-and-dart ornament, the neck mount engraved with strapwork panels, with 3 applied masks, with dolphin and scroll thumbpiece, with later strap to the handle engraved with foliage, Norwich, 1568, maker's mark a five-petalled rose, 9 in. high (22.8 cm.). **£20,000-25,000** *C*

. silver-mounted salt-glazed
:oneware jug, the whole covered in
ıottled 'tiger' glaze, the silver
ollar chased with a band of floral
:rapwork, cover altered, part later,
over with impressed marks,
ͽopard's head crowned, lion
assant, date letter for 1570 and
ıaker's mark possibly for William
ocknidge, 8 in. (20 cm.), late
6th C. **£900-1,100** *SS*

A silver-mounted tigerware jug, stamped thrice with an incuse H, 5½ in. high (14 cm.), late 16th C. **£600-700** *C*

A silver-mounted salt-glazed stoneware jug of 'Malling' shape, covered in a finely mottled 'tiger' glaze, foot cracked, 7¾ in. (19.5 cm.), late 16th/early 17th C., mount 19th C. **£200-300** *SS*

A German fluted pear-shaped hot milk jug, by Johann Georg Renner, Hanover, 8 in. high (20.3 cm.), c. 1730, 20 oz. gross. **£5,500-6,500** *C*

The arms are those of Beaufort, of Utrecht and Northern Brabant.

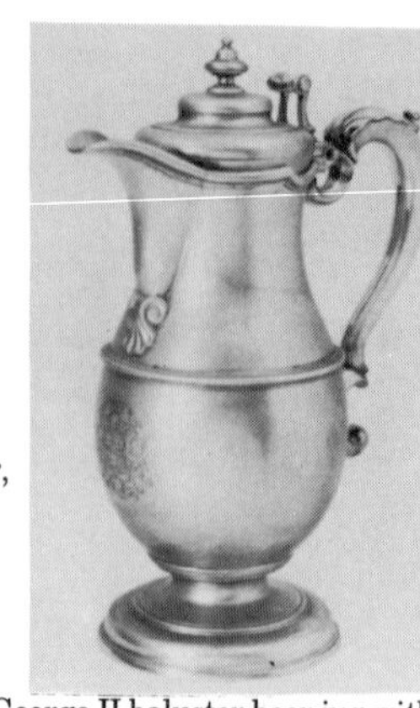

A George II baluster beer jug with detachable hinged cover, marked on base and cover, John Swift, London, 1736, 12½ in. high (31.8 cm.), 59 oz. 5 dwt (1,842 gm.). **£6,000-7,000** *S*

The arms are those of Hamilton.

A George II pear-shaped jug and cover, by W. Shaw and W. Priest, 1753, the handle with ivory inserts and the cover with detachable baluster finial, 11½ in. high (29.2 cm.), 36 oz. gross. **£2,500-£3,000** *C*

The arms are those of Trafford impaling another.

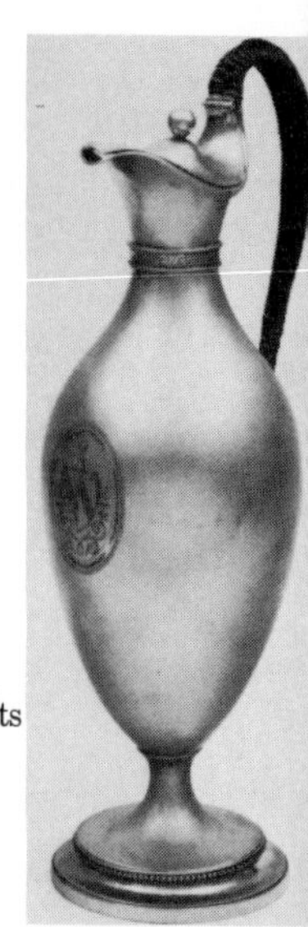

A George III wine ewer, marked on base and cover, Wakelin & Taylor London, 1784, 13½ in. high (34.3 cm.), 27 oz. 11 dwt. (856 gm.) all in. **£1,200-1,500** *S*

A fine and unusual Louis XVI silver-gilt helmet-shaped ewer, Paris, 1783, 12 in. high, 46½ oz. **£2,600-3,000** *T*

A George III vase-shaped hot water jug, with entwined snake handle and beaded borders, the domed cover with reclining figure finial, by John Robins, 1774, 13 in. high (33 cm.), 30 oz. gross. **£800-900** *C*

A George III beer jug, William Fountain, London, 1807, 7 in. high (18 cm.), 36 oz. **£700-800** *S*

A Victorian claret jug, by Martin Hall & Co., 1874, the foot loaded 30 cm. **£550-650** *L*

A Victorian silver-mounted 'rock crystal' engraved glass claret jug, by F. B. Macrae for the Army & Navy Co-operative Society, London, 1887, 8½ in. (21.7 cm.). **£500-600** *S*

A German enamelled silver group, painted in translucent enamel with flesh tints, turned wooden base, 2½ in. (6.5 cm.), late 16th C. **£450-£550** *S*

A silver-gilt miniature group of the Madonna and Child, Spanish, 2½ in. (6.3 cm.), c. 1600. **£250-£300** *S*

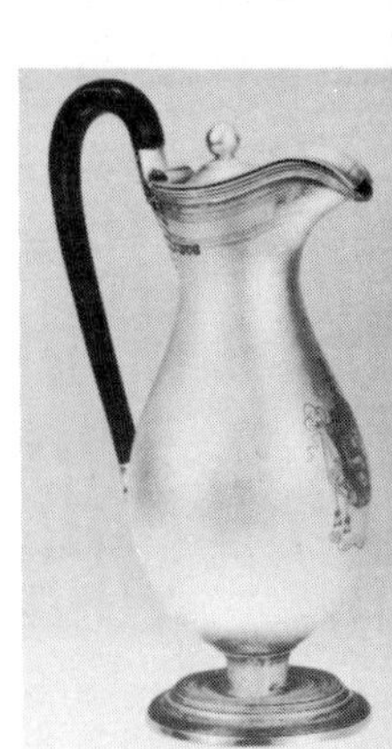

A late Victorian claret or hot water jug, maker's mark of D. & J. Wellby overstriking another, 1897 11 in. (28 cm.), 26 oz. all in. **£400-£500** *L*

A South German silver-gilt figure of God the Father, as an old man sitting on a cloud, 7½ in. (19 cm.) high, late 17th C. **£700-800** *S*

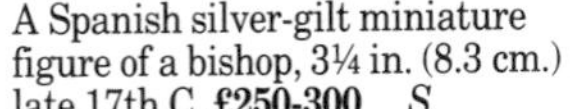

A Spanish silver-gilt miniature figure of a bishop, 3¼ in. (8.3 cm.) late 17th C. **£250-300** *S*

A South German silver figure of a kneeling putto, 4 in. (10 cm.), c. 1700, wooden stand. **£500-600** *S*

A silver-gilt model of a warrior on horseback, the horse with a well-modelled detachable head, unmarked, on a wood stand, 14 in. (35.4 cm.) high overall, 19th C., 66 oz. (1,820 gm.) (excluding stand). **£1,600-2,000** *S*

A large German model of a cockerel with detachable head, pseudo-hallmarked, 55.5 cm. high, c. 1880, 105 oz. (3,269 gm.). **£1,300-1,500** *S*

A Victorian model of a pomeranian, on a weighted base inscribed in dark-blue enamel 'Woossie/1883', James Barclay Hennell for R. Hennell & Son, London, 1883, 4 in. (9.8 cm.) long. **£400-450** *S*

(c.) A pair of German chased silver coloured metal figures of a prince and a knight with ivory faces, English import mark for 1907, 9½ in. high. **£800-900** *GSP*

(l. & r.) A pair of German chased silver coloured metal figures of a lady with ivory face, and the companion figure of a cavalier, English import mark for 1907, 5½ in. high. **£600-700** *GSP*

A German nef parcel-gilt, B. Nerseheimer & Sohne, Hanau, importer's mark of Berthold Muller for B. Muller & Son of London, Chester, 1906, 20 in. (51.5 cm.) high, 19½ in. (49.5 cm.) overall length, 54 oz. 13 dwt. (1,699 gm.). **£1,600-1,800** *S*

A German 3-masted nef with full-blown sails, B. Neresheimer & Sohne, Hanau, importer's mark of B.H. Muller for Berthold Muller & Son, London, 1914, 14 in. high by 13½ in. long (66 by 65 cm.), 126 oz. 9 dwt. (3,932 gm.). **£4,500-5,000** *S*

A large German 2-masted nef, B. Neresheimer & Sohne, Hanau, importer's mark of Berthold Muller for B. Muller & Son, London, 1910, 25 in. high by 22 in. overall length (63.7 by 56 cm.), 135 oz. 10 dwt. (4,214 gm.). **£4,500-5,000** *S*

A Charles II baluster chinoiserie mug, dated 1687, loop handle, maker's mark a goose in a dotted circle, London, 1684, 3¼ in. (8.5 cm.) high, 3 oz. **£500-550** *S*

A German figure of a knight in armour, import marks for London, 1907, 9½ in. high. **£350-400** *DWB*

A Charles II small plain mug, 1683, maker's mark IC, 2¼ in. (5.7 cm.) high, 1 oz. 10 dwt. **£500-£700** *C*

A Charles II plain tapering cylindrical mug, engraved with a coat-of-arms within foliage mantling, 1684, maker's mark SH conjoined, 3 in. (7.6 cm.) high, 5 oz. 4 dwt. **£750-850** *C*

A George II mug, maker's mark apparently I.E., a crown above, a crescent below, London, 1728, 3¼ in. (8.2 cm.) high, 6 oz. 6 dwt. (195 gm.). **£700-800** *S*

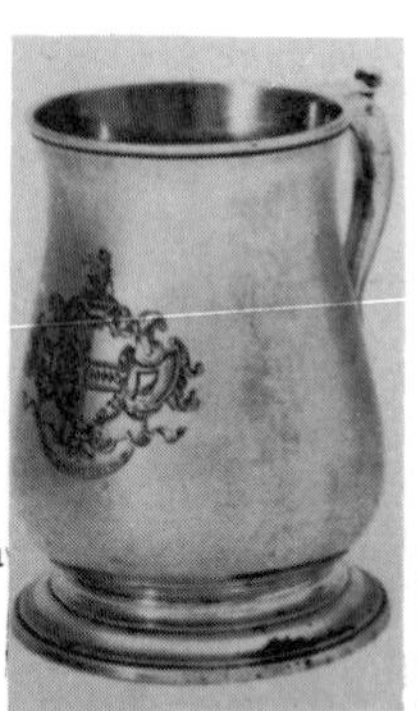

A George II baluster mug, R. Gurney & T. Cook for Richard Gurney & Co., London, 1748, 4¾ in. (12.5 cm.) high, 15 oz. 4 dwt. (472 gm.). **£750-850** *S*

A pair of George II baluster mugs engraved with a crest, William Grundy, London, 1757, 4¾ in. (12 cm.) high, 25 oz. 17 dwt. (801 gm.). **£2,000-2,500** *S*

A Victorian mug, 'S' scroll leaf decorated handle, E. and J. Barnard, London, 1853, 5¼ in. (13 cm.) high, 12 oz. **£300-400** *S*

A George II plain brandy saucepan by Sampson Bennet of Falmouth, maker's mark only struck thrice, c. 1730, 3 oz. 8 dwt. gross. **£700-£800** *C*

For an account of this maker see T. A. Kent, The Goldsmiths of Falmouth, Proceedings of the Silver Collectors' Society, 1974-76. According to this writer, 'Bennet was certainly the most prolific of the Falmouth goldsmiths, and numerous examples of his work, usually sturdy and somewhat unsophisticated, have survived. In particular, brandy saucepans and tea pots have been noted'.

A Georgian brandy saucepan on stand with burner, body with short spout, slightly domed cover with button finial, and side handle, with heart-shaped reinforcing plate, each piece later unobtrusively numbered, full marked, Emes & Barnard, London, 1818-20, 8 in. (20 cm.) overall, 15 oz. 4 dwt. **£500-£600** *SC*

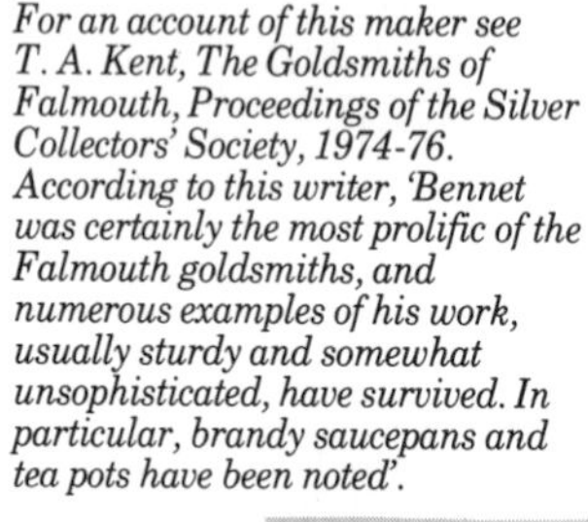

A George IV baluster brandy saucepan and cover, Emes & Barnard, London, 1824, 7¾ in. (19.8 cm.) high, 22 oz. 2 dwt. (687 gm.) all in. **£700-800** *S*

Eight Regency plain circular salt cellars by Paul Storr, six 1810, two 1811 (2 with worn gilding and corrosion to the interior), with 8 shell and hour-glass pattern salt spoons, 1812, maker's mark TB, 83 oz. **£6,500-7,500** *C*

Four George II large silver salt cellars by Robert Calderwood, Dublin, c. 1743, 41 oz. **£2,000-£2,500** *C*

A set of 6 George III shaped oval salt cellars, engraved with the arms of Queen Anne and the crest of Smith, maker's mark AL, London, 1774, 3¾ in. (9.7 cm.) wide, 28 oz. 13 dwt., excluding blue glass liners. **£900-1,000** *SC*

This apparently unrecorded maker's mark could perhaps relate to Augustine le Sage who made a pair of meat dishes with similar borders in the same year.

A set of 4 George IV shaped circular salt cellars, engraved with a crest and Earl's coronet by Paul Storr, 1820, 48 oz. **£6,000-7,000** *C*

A William and Mary salver on foot, marked on salver and foot, maker's mark SH, a cinquefoil below, London, 1693, 8¾ in. diam. (22.7 cm.), 11 oz. **£600-800** *S*

A 16th C. Portuguese silver-gilt tazza, c. 1580, the border probably added in the 18th C., 33.25 cm. diam., 36.25 oz. **£7,000-8,000** *P*

A William and Mary circular salver, 1689, maker's mark RC in dotted circle, probably for Robert Cooper, the foot unmarked, 10¾ in. diam. (27.3 cm.), 19 oz. 12 dwt. **£800-1,000** *C*

The arms are those of Stanhope impaling Cotton.

A William and Mary plain circular salver, by David King, Dublin, 1699, 14½ in. diam. (36.8 cm.), 36 oz. **£3,500-4,000** *C*

The arms are those of Moore quartering another.

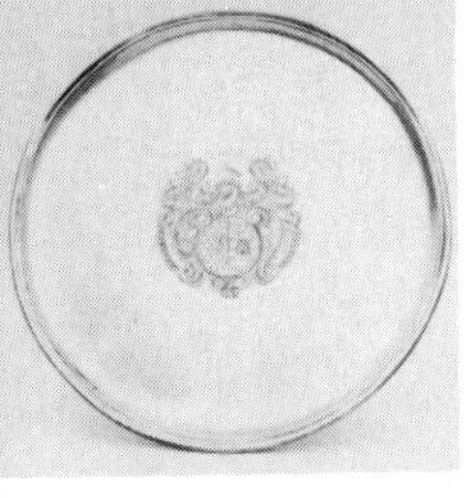

A Queen Anne circular salver on foot, marked on base and foot, Robert Smith, Dublin, 1708-09, 12⅛ in. diam. (30.7 cm.), 29 oz. 11 dwt. (916 gm.). **£2,000-2,500** *S*

The arms are possibly those of Wykes of Cocktree, Co. Devon, impaling Treweek of Penzance, Co. Cornwall.

A small George I circular tazza, by Samuel Wastall, London, 1722, 5¾ in. diam., 6 oz. **£450-550** *WHL*

A pair of George II plain shaped square waiters, by Matthew Alanson, Dublin, c. 1732, 6¼ in. square (15.9 cm.), 19 oz. 8 dwt. **£2,000-2,500** *C*

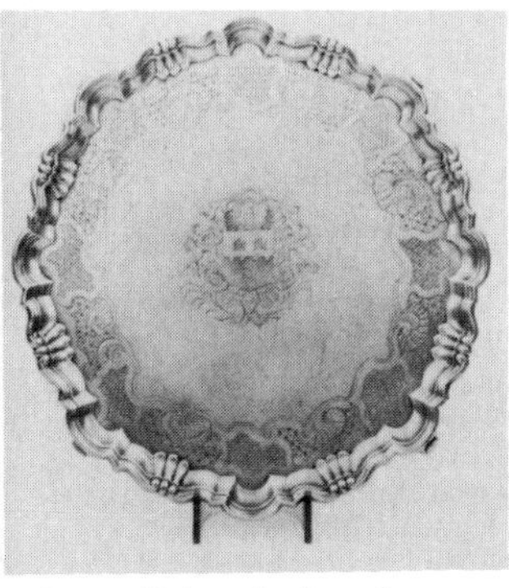

A George II shaped salver, George Hindmarsh, London, 1736, 13½ in. diam. (34 cm.), 40 oz. 2 dwt. (1,246 gm.). **£1,200-1,500** *S*

The arms are those of Yates.

A George II plain circular salver, 1739, maker's mark lacking, 9⅝ in. diam. (24.5 cm.), 20 oz. **£900-£1,300** *C*

The arms are those of Blake, Co. Galway, one of the 12 'tribes' of Galway.

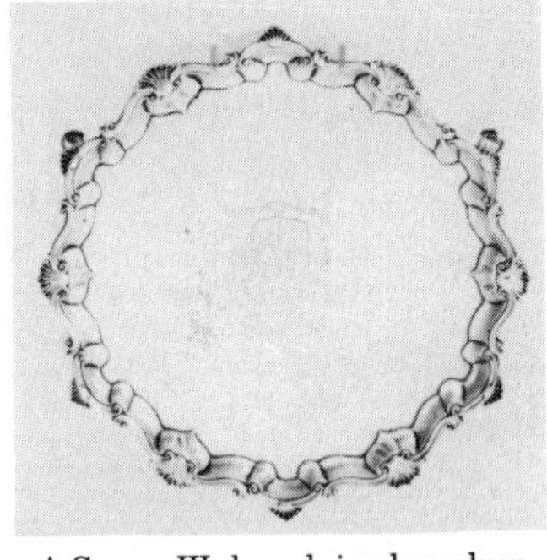

A George III shaped circular salver, later inscribed and dated, Richard Rugg, London, 1764, 12⅞ in. diam. (32.7 cm.), 29 oz. 14 dwt. (920 gm.). **£600-800** *S*

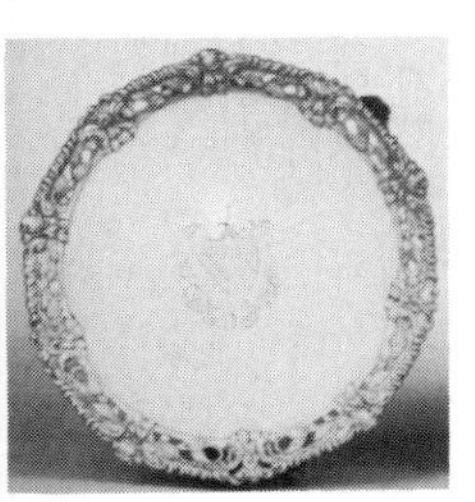

A set of 4 George III shaped circular salvers, 1764, maker's mark TH.RM, probably for T. Hannam and R. Mills, 8½ in. diam. (21.6 cm.), 62 oz. **£2,800-£3,600** *C*

A George III circular salver, marked on base and rim John Carter, London, 1768, 16¼ in. diam. (41.5 cm.), 60 oz. 19 dwt. (1,895 gm.). **£2,000-2,500** *S*

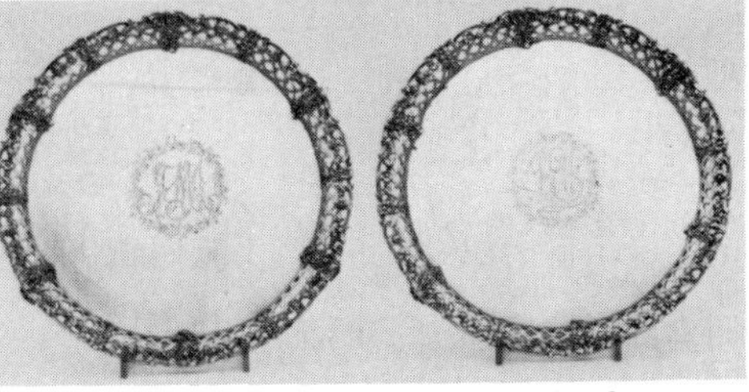

A pair of George III circular salvers, Elizabeth Cooke, London, 1769, 10¼ in. diam. (26 cm.), 42 oz. 7 dwt. (1,312 gm.). **£1,100-1,300** *S*

A salver by Ebenezer Coker, London, 1770, clear marks, 13 in. diam., 32 oz. **£750-850** *Wor*

A set of 3 George III shaped circular salvers, by R. Jones and J. Scofield, 1776, two 8⅛ in. (20.5 cm.) and one 12⅝ in. (32 cm.) diam., 62 oz. **£2,000-2,500** *C*

The arms are those of Rose impaling Nevill.

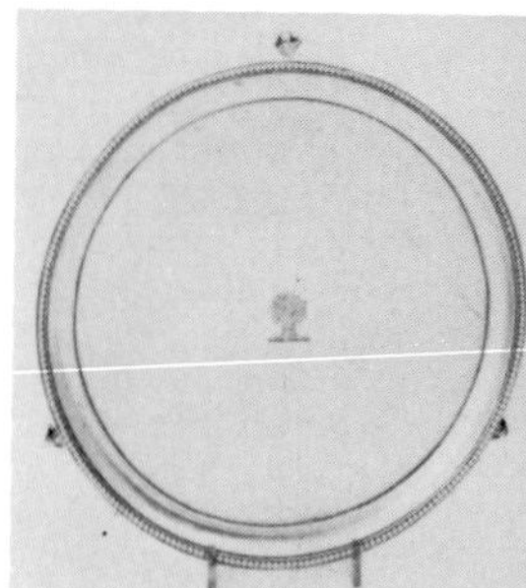

A pair of George III circular salvers, on ball and claw feet, Smith & Sharp, London, 1779, 7 in diam. (17.8 cm.), 19 oz. (589 gm.). **£600-700** *S*

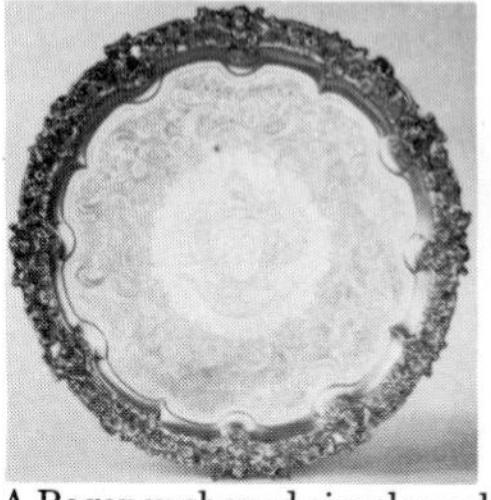

A Regency shaped circular salver engraved with a coat-of-arms within rococo cartouche, by William Bennett, 1810, the border and feet unmarked, 19 in. diam. (48.3 cm.), 141 oz. **£2,500-3,000** *C*

A pair of George III circular salvers, Crouch & Hannam, London, 1783, 8¼ in. diam. (21 cm.), 25 oz. 6 dwt. (784 gm.). **£600-700** *S*

A George III presentation silver salver with later presentation inscription, London, 1807, Thomas Hannam and John Crouch, 17 in. diam., 88 oz. **£800-900** *EBB*

A Regency shaped circular salver on 4 lions' mask, paw and scroll feet, engraved slightly later with a monogram, by Paul Storr, 1813, 17⅛ in. diam. (43.5 cm.), 119 oz. **£7,000-8,000** *C*

A George III oval salver, by Elizabeth Jones, 1794, 16¼ in. long (41.3 cm.), 39 oz. **£1,800-2,200** *C*

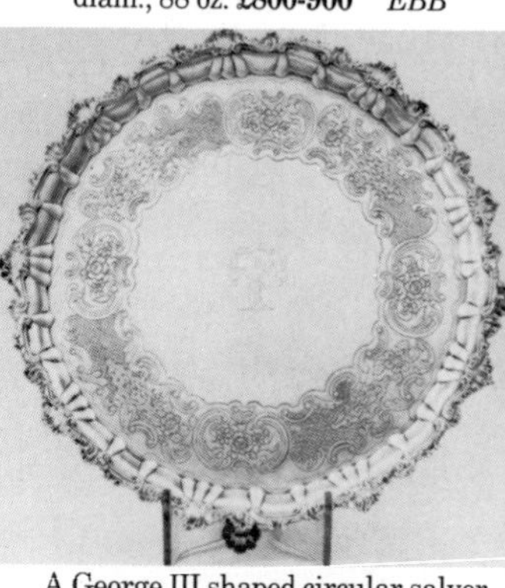

A George III shaped circular salver, James Le Bass, also stamped Law, Dublin, 1816, 17¾ in. diam. (45 cm.), 94 oz. 4 dwt. (2,920 gm.). **£1,500-2,000** *S*

A George IV large shaped circular salver engraved with an inscription, a coat-of-arms and a view of the Lambeth Water Works with Neptune reclining on a shell in the foreground, by J. E. Terrey, 1825, the border apparently unmarked, 28⅛ in. diam. (61.1 cm.), 202 oz. in fitted wood case. **£3,000-3,500** *C*

A George IV large shaped circular silver salver, the reverse with an inscription dated November, 1825, by Joseph Cradock, 1825, the border and feet unmarked, 24¼ in. high (61.6 cm.), 178 oz. **£5,000-£6,000** *C*

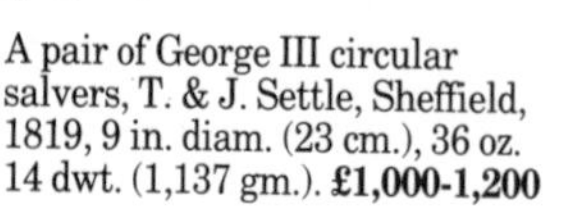

A Victorian salver, Sheffield, 1883, maker's mark defaced and with retailer's mark of Elkington & Co, 12½ in. (31.7 cm.), 29 oz. **£400-£500** *L*

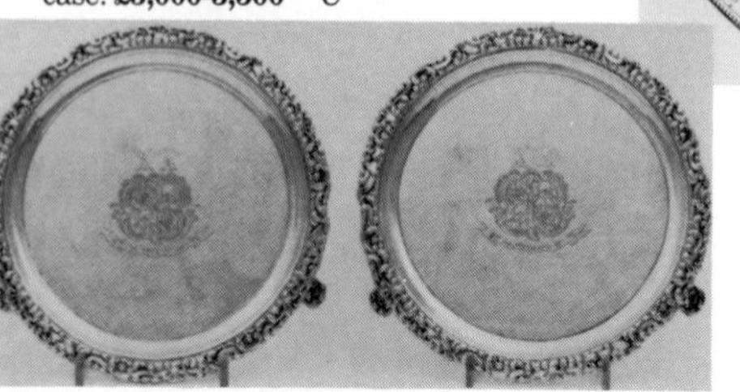

A pair of George III circular salvers, T. & J. Settle, Sheffield, 1819, 9 in. diam. (23 cm.), 36 oz. 14 dwt. (1,137 gm.). **£1,000-1,200** *S*

A Victorian shaped circular salver, James Charles Edington, London, 1841, 18¼ in. (46.5 cm.) wide, 85 oz. (2,643 gm.). **£1,100-1,500** *S*

Two Victorian shaped circular salvers, Robert Hennell for R. Hennell & Son, London, 1855, stamped: 'C.F. Hancock Bruton St. London', 10 in. diam. (25.7 cm.), 60 oz. 4 dwt. (1,872 gm.). **£750-£850** *S*

Two George II matching oval sauceboats, one Francis Nelme, 1735, the other Gabriel Sleath, 1743, both London, 8½ in. (21.5 cm.), 31 oz. 4 dwt. (967 gm.), **£1,500-2,000** *S*

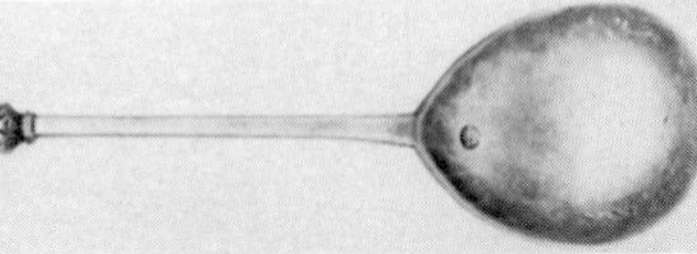
A Henry VIII Maidenhead spoon, with fig-shaped bowl and flattened hexagonal stem, the finial bearing traces of gilding, 1534, maker's mark a sprig, unrecorded by Jackson. **£1,000-1,500** *C*

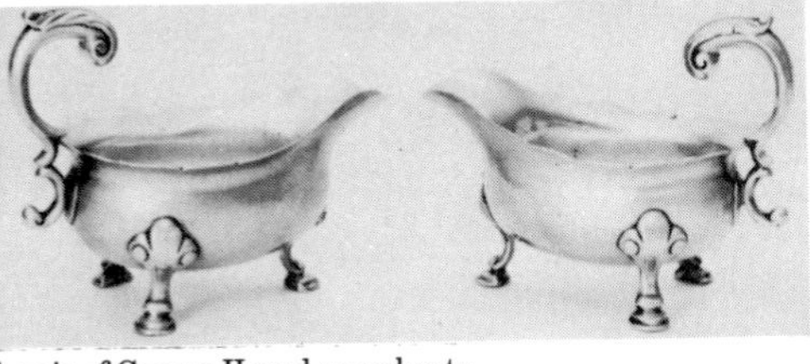
A pair of George II oval sauceboats, William Cripps, London, 1745, 6¼ in. (16 cm.), 22 oz. 6 dwt. (691 gm.). **£1,200-1,500** *S*

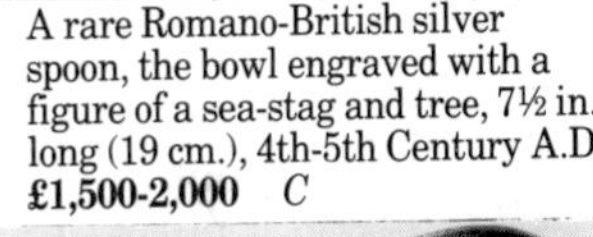
A rare Romano-British silver spoon, the bowl engraved with a figure of a sea-stag and tree, 7½ in. long (19 cm.), 4th-5th Century A.D. **£1,500-2,000** *C*

A rare pair of George III silver sauceboats, by Carden Terry, Cork, 1780, 16 oz. **£2,000-2,500** *GM*

A Henry VIII slip-top spoon, maker's mark a pheon ?, London, 1540, 6⅜ in. long (16.2 cm.), 1 oz. 6 dwt., (40 gm.). **£1,800-2,000** *S*

A Henry VIII Maidenhead spoon, London, 1534. **£550-600** *A*

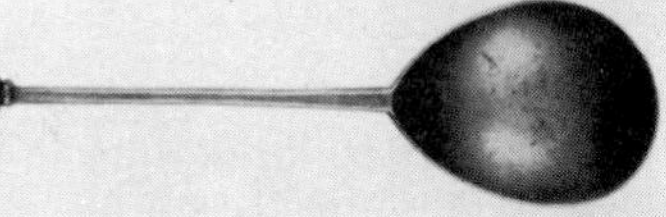
A 16th C. seal-top spoon, silver-gilt, the bowl back engraved IN, John Eydes, Exeter, c. 1580, 6 in. long (15.2 cm.), 1 oz. (31 gm.). **£700-£800** *S*

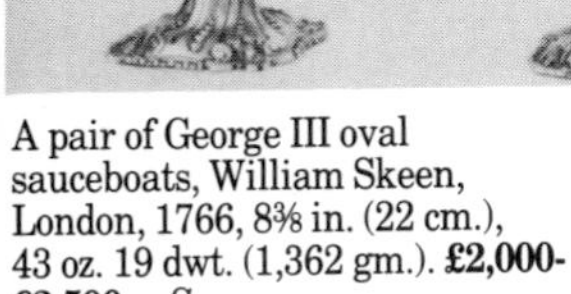
A pair of George III oval sauceboats, William Skeen, London, 1766, 8⅜ in. (22 cm.), 43 oz. 19 dwt. (1,362 gm.). **£2,000-£2,500** *S*

An Elizabeth I apostle spoon — St. James the Less, London, 1602, by William Cawdell. **£500-550** *A*

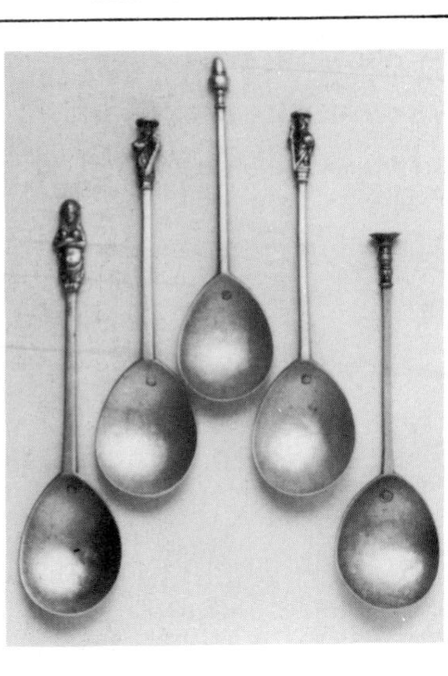
(1.) An Elizabeth I Buddha top spoon, pricked with initials SC SR, c. 1600, struck in the bowl and thrice on the stem with a bird (?), probably for Peter Quycke of Barnstaple. **£800-900** *C*

(2.) An Elizabeth I apostle spoon surmounted by the gilt figure of St. Simon, pricked with initials IP and dated 1659, 1592, maker's mark a crescent enclosing W for William Cawdell. **£1,000-1,200** *C*

(3.) An Elizabeth I acorn top spoon, 1593, maker's mark a crescent enclosing a mullet for William Cawdell. **£1,300-1,500** *C*

(4.) A James I apostle spoon surmounted by the figure of St. Bartholomew with St. Esprit nimbus, 1617, maker's mark a crescent enclosing a mullet. **£700-£800** *C*

(5.) A James I seal top spoon, pricked with initial RF AP 1620, Truro, c. 1620. **£600-700** *C*

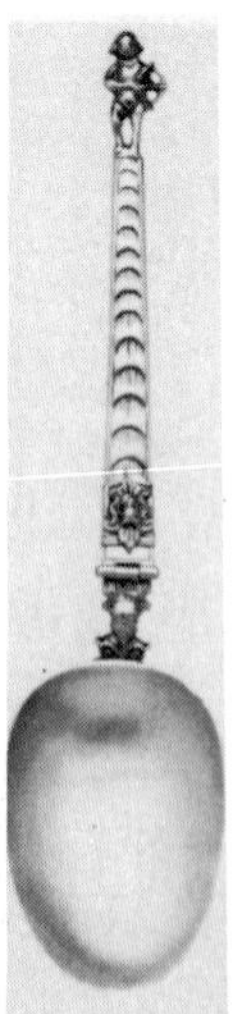

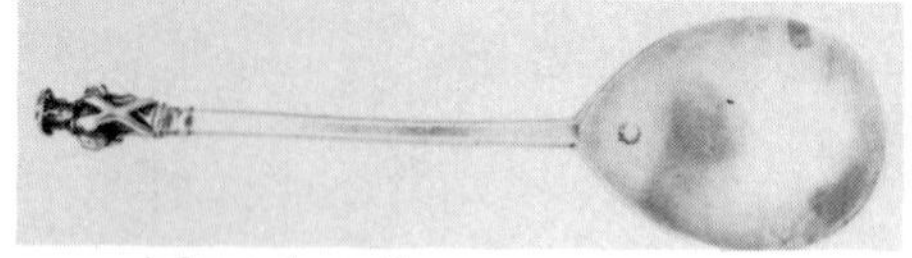

A James I apostle spoon surmounted by the gilt figure of St. Andrew, 1607, maker's mark C enclosing W, possibly a variation of William Cawdell's mark. **£600-£800** *C*

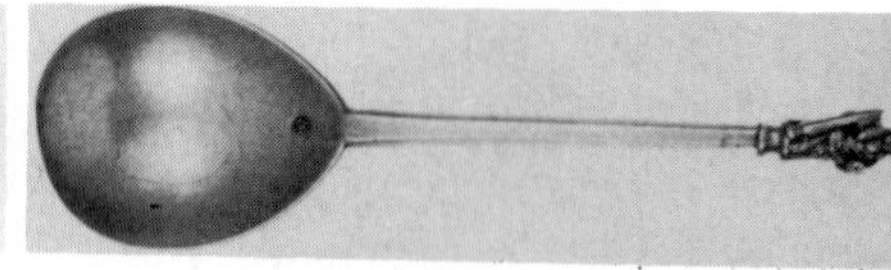

An early 17th C. apostle spoon, St. Matthias, struck in the bowl IP in a circle and on the stem I Parnel, 7¼ in. (18.6 cm.), c. 1630. **£600-£700** *S*

According to present research John Parnell, who in the past was thought to have worked in Barnstaple, was in fact an inhabitant of Truro from about 1614 until his death in 1666.

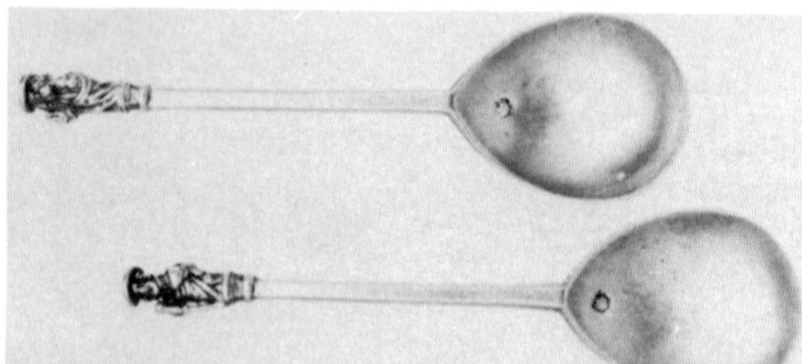

A Continental combined folding spoon and fork, with Cupid finial, probably French or Belgian, 17th C., marked with a fleur-de-lys above a device. **£500-600** *C*

Two James I apostle spoons surmounted by the gilt figures of The Master and St. James the Greater, by William Cawdell, 1609. **£3,500-4,000** *C*

Four Charles I apostle spoons surmounted by the gilt figures of St. James the Less, St. Philip, St. Simon Zelotes and St. Thomas, each with St. Esprit nimbus, one missing, by Richard Crosse, 1634. **£4,500-5,000** *C*

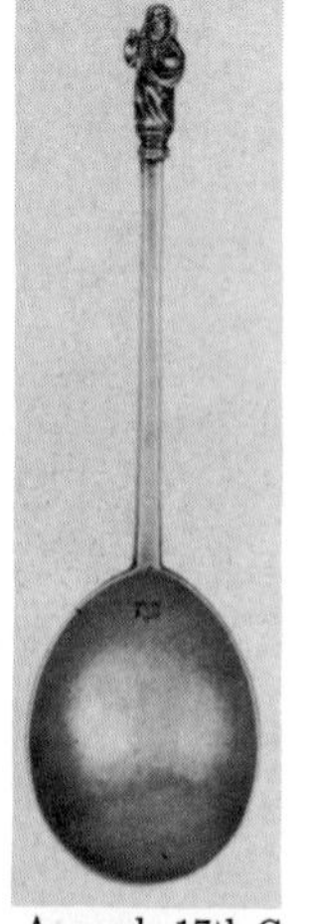

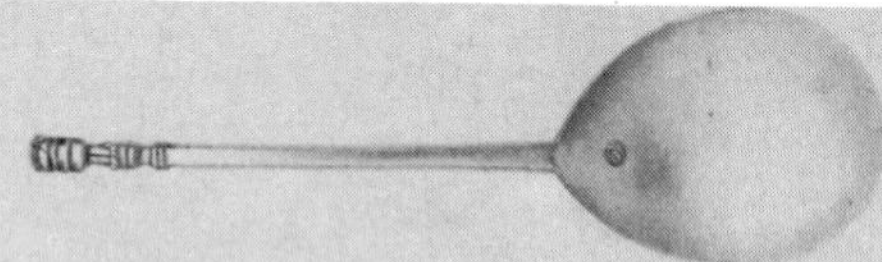

A Lion-Sejant spoon, pricked with initials ET IH and dated 1644, the bowl struck with a mark, AB conjoined, the back of the bowl struck with a turreted tower, probably c. 1640. **£400-500** *C*

For similar spoons see the Ellis catalogue, pp. 24-26, where the marks are tentatively attributed to Aberystwyth.

An early 17th C. apostle spoon, St. John, the terminal gilt, marked in the bowl AB in a shield and thrice on the stem with a small castle or x, 7 in. long (18.1 cm.), c. 1630-50. **£600-700** *S*

For a group of AB and castle mark spoons, including one of St. John pricked with the date 1647, see the Ellis catalogue pp. 23-27 and lot 27, where they were ascribed to Aberystwyth. This origin has now been discounted in favour of the West Country, perhaps in the Bristol area.

A Commonwealth Puritan spoon, initialled on the terminal reverse, Stephen Venables, London, 1655, 6¾ in. long (17.4 cm.), 1 oz. 10 dwt. (46 gm.). **£700-800** *S*

A 17th C. stump-end spoon, maker's mark only, struck in the bowl and on the stem, RF a mullet below, 7 in. long (17.6 cm.), 1 oz. 12 dwt. (50 gm.), c. 1650. **£600-£700** *S*

A pair of Queen Anne dognose terminal tablespoons engraved TES 1726 by John Elston, Exeter, 1709. **£150-200** *WW*

A Commonwealth St. Matthew apostle spoon, Poole, 1652. **£600-£700** *WW*

A set of 6 James II trefid spoons initialled DWE, maker's mark IK a rosette below, London, 1685, 8 in. long (20.1 cm.), 12 oz. 4 dwt. (380 gm.), **£1,300-1,500** *S*

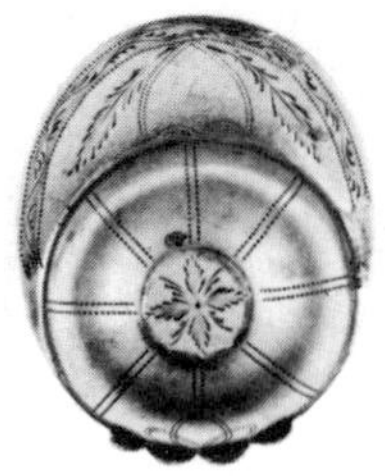

A George III jockey cap caddy spoon, Joseph Taylor, Birmingham, 1799. **£250-300** *S*

A George III hand caddy spoon, Josiah Snatt, London, 1811. **£200-£250** *S*

A William IV eagle wing caddy spoon, probably die-stamped, Joseph Willmore, Birmingham, 1832, 3 in. (7.7 cm.) long. **£500-£600** *S*

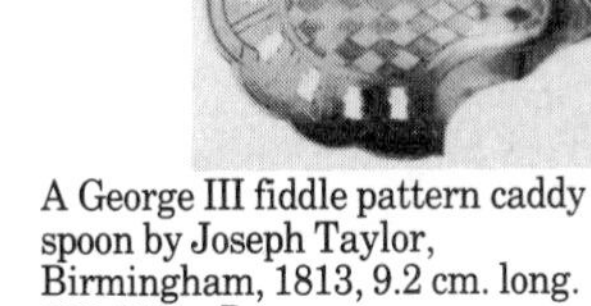

A George III fiddle pattern caddy spoon by Joseph Taylor, Birmingham, 1813, 9.2 cm. long. **£80-100** *P*

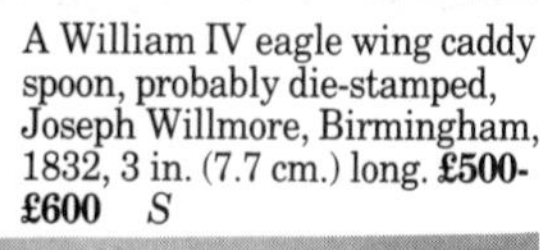

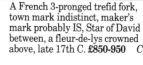

A French 3-pronged trefid fork, town mark indistinct, maker's mark probably IS, Star of David between, a fleur-de-lys crowned above, late 17th C. **£850-950** *C*

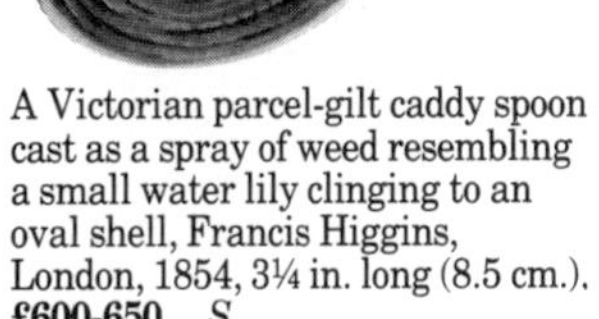

A Victorian parcel-gilt caddy spoon cast as a spray of weed resembling a small water lily clinging to an oval shell, Francis Higgins, London, 1854, 3¼ in. long (8.5 cm.). **£600-650** *S*

A caddy spoon of this pattern was shown by Francis Higgins at the Great Exhibition of 1851.

A pair of Victorian caddy spoons with small pricked Old English pattern handles, J. & F. Pairpoint, London, 1880. **£80-100** *S*

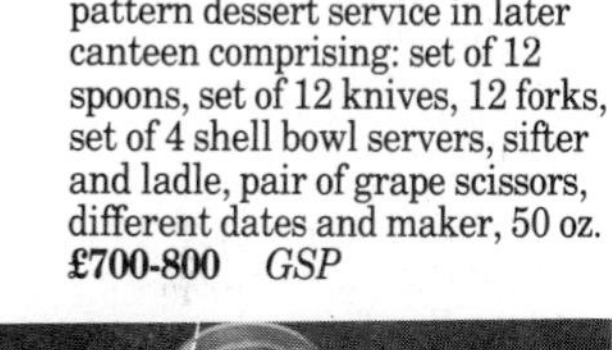

A George III gilt-silver thread pattern dessert service in later canteen comprising: set of 12 spoons, set of 12 knives, 12 forks, set of 4 shell bowl servers, sifter and ladle, pair of grape scissors, different dates and maker, 50 oz. **£700-800** *GSP*

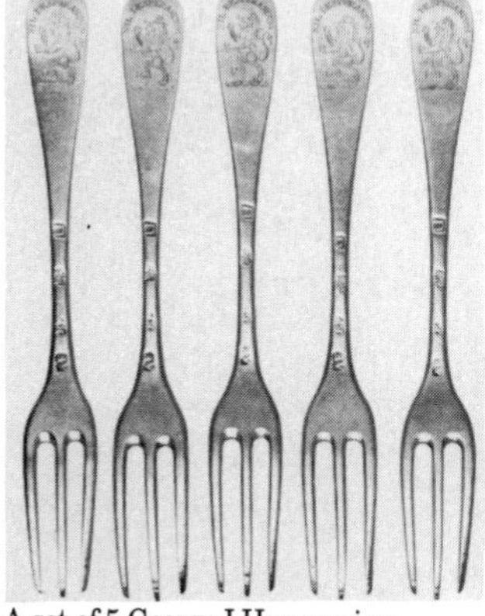

A set of 5 George I Hanoverian pattern dessert forks by Alexander Edmonstoune, Edinburgh, 1724, assay master Edward Penman, 4 oz. 15 dwt. **£2,500-3,000** *C*

The crest is that of Ogilvie.

A William IV Scottish service of fiddle pattern cutlery for 6 place settings, comprising 6 table forks, 6 table spoons, 6 dessert forks, 6 dessert spoons, 6 teaspoons, soup ladle, gravy spoon and a butter knife, 60 oz. **£600-700** *L*

Glasgow, 1834 and 1835, by Robert Gray and Son, except 3 dessert forks Glasgow 1845 by D. C. Rait, and the butter knife Glasgow, 1835, by A. McMillan.

A 57-piece Victorian Old English and feather edged pattern silver table service, 105½ oz. **£950-£1,100** *PWC*

A fine pair of Victorian fish servers, 1856 by Francis Higgins, 13.5 in. (34.3 cm.) length of slice, 12.5 oz. **£550-650** *L*

A parcel-gilt tankard by Hans Christoph Mehrer I, marked on base and lid, maker's mark, Augsburg, 1653-55, 13 cm. high, 378 gm. **£2,500-3,000** *S*

A peg tankard by Jon Jorgensen Feiff, later engraved with various names and the date 1670, the scroll handle with shield terminal, maker's mark only struck twice (Stavanger), 18.6 cm. high, c. 1680, 910 gm. **£4,000-4,500** *S*

An unusually small Charles II chinoiserie tankard flat-chased with a group of 4 figures from an Oriental court attended by a child and a sunshade bearer, engraved at a later date with a crest on the lower terminal, marked on body, handle and cover, maker's mark WA in monogram in a shield (Jackson, p. 136, line 2), London, 1683, 4 in. (10.2 cm.) high, 9 oz. 6 dwt. (286 gm.). **£25,000-27,000** *S*

A Charles II chinoiserie tankard, the almost cylindrical body flat-chased with birds, insects and figures amid stylised bamboos, fully marked, maker's mark TC a fish above, London, 1683, 7 in. (17.8 cm.) high, 25 oz. 7 dwt. (785 gm.). **£9,000-10,000** *S*

A William III tapered cylindrical tankard, marked on body, lid and handle, John Fawdery I, London, 1699, 7 in. (18 cm.) high, 27 oz. 3 dwt. (841 gm.). **£1,900-2,100** *S*

An early Queen Anne tapered cylindrical tankard, inscribed on the scroll handle, marked on body, lid and handle, Robert Timbrell, London, 1702, 7¾ in. (19.7 cm.) high, 26 oz. 10 dwt. (821 gm.). **£1,800-2,000** *S*

A Queen Anne tankard engraved with armorials, David King, Dublin, 1704-05, the handle by another, 8¼ in. (21 cm.) high, 30 oz. 7 dwt. (943 gm.). **£1,100-1,300** *S*

A George I tapered cylindrical tankard, the scroll handle engraved with owner's triad A/R *M, fully marked Hugh Arnett & Edward Pocock, London, 1726, 6¾ in. (17.2 cm.) high, 21 oz. 12 dwt. (670 gm.). **£1,100-£1,300** *S*

A George II tankard of plain tapering form with a moulded girdle, marked 1742 by Thomas Whipham, 17.3 cm. high, 26 oz. **£1,000-1,200** *L*

A George II plain cylindrical tankard engraved with a later coat-of-arms, by Fuller White, 1753, 7½ in. (18.9 cm.) high, 24 oz. **£1,100-1,400** *C*

The arms are those of Coleman impaling Freeman.

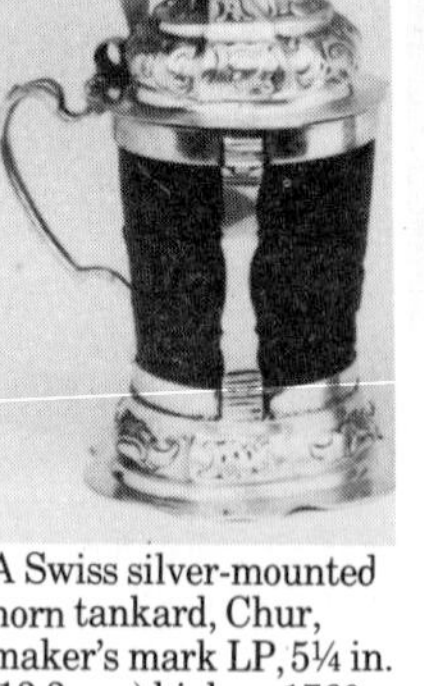

A Swiss silver-mounted horn tankard, Chur, maker's mark LP, 5¼ in. (13.3 cm.) high, c. 1760. **£1,200-1,500** *C*

An early George III baluster quart lidded tankard by Fuller White, 7¾ in., London, 1761, 26 oz. **£1,100-1,400** *WW*

A George III baluster tankard, engraved 'C/I.I/1774', marked on base and cover,? William Tuite, London, 1774, 8½ in. (21.3 cm.) high, 28 oz. 6 dwt. (880 gm.). **£1,200-1,400** *S*

A George III silver tankard by John Langlands, Newcastle, 1769, 8 in. high, 26 oz. **£700-£850** *T*

An early George III baluster tankard, maker's mark I*M, for Jacob Marsh or John Moore (Grimwade 3658), 1770, 21.5 cm., 28 oz. **£900-£1,000** *L*

A George III lidded quart tankard, Newcastle, 1772, maker John Langlands, 8 in. high, 32 oz. **£600-£700** *DDM*

A George II baluster quart lidded tankard by Edward Feline, London, 1743, 8 in., 34.5 oz. **£1,400-1,600** *WW*

A peg tankard by Johan Salomon Hind, maker's mark, Bergen, 19.3 cm. high, c. 1800, 820 gm. **£1,700-1,900** *S*

A George III tankard, handle with heart terminal, by Peter, Ann and William Bateman, London, 1800, 8 in., 26½ oz. **£900-1,100** *DWB*

A fine Regency silver-gilt tankard, matted and applied with vignettes of bibulous putti reclining, drinking, sporting with goats and feasting, marked on body and lid, William Elliot, London, 1813, 8 in. (20.5 cm.) high, 58 oz. **£3,500-£4,500** *SC*

A large George III tankard, chased in relief with a spirited battle scene, Britannia standard, marked on body, cover and finial-nut, maker's mark erased, other marks partially erased, apparently London, 1819, 15½ in. (39.3 cm.) high, 92 oz. 6 dwt. (2,870 gm.). **£1,700-2,000** *S*

The partial erasure of the hallmarks and the obliteration of the maker's mark on this piece, probably the result of misguided elements in the antique silver trade of 80 or 100 years ago, cannot mask the unmistakable hand of Edward Cornelius Farrell. Working to the instructions of Kensington Lewis, the dynamic and ambitious retail silversmith of St. James's Street, Farrell produced a range of silver and silver-gilt plate between 1815-16 and 1827 unrivalled before or since for its overwhelming decorative qualities.

A large German silver-mounted ivory tankard carved in relief, lid detached, 18 in. (46.2 cm.) high, unmarked, late 19th C. **£5,500-£6,000** *S*

An early George I oblong tea caddy, fully marked, Gundry Roode, London, 1714, 4⅞ in. (12.3 cm.) high, 7 oz. 8 dwt. (229 gm.). **£1,200-£1,400** *S*

A Dutch vase-shaped tea caddy, the cap pierced later, Henrk Hoorn, Amsterdam, 1700, 4 in. (10.5 cm.) high, 4 oz. **£600-800** *S*

A pair of George I oblong tea caddies, John Farnell, London, 1719, 4⅜ in. (11.7 cm.) high, 20 oz. 8 dwt. (632 gm.). **£1,300-1,500** *S*

A pair of George II plain oblong silver tea caddies and a sugar box, the caddies each with sliding base, by Samuel Taylor, 1750, the covers to the caddies unmarked, in fitted brass-mounted shagreen case, 31 oz. **£3,500-4,000** *C*

The arms are those of Lodyington or Lodington.

A set of 3 George II oblong tea caddies, marked on bases and covers, Pierre Gillois, London, 1758, 4½, 5 and 5¼ in. (12, 12.6 and 13 cm.) high, 21 oz. 6 dwt. (660 gm.), excluding recovered snake-skin fitted case with contemporary silver mounts. **£2,000-3,000** *S*

The arms are those of Hunter.

A pair of George II inverted pear-shaped tea caddies and a sugar basin and cover, by Samuel Taylor, 1759, 2 covers unmarked, in fitted silver-mounted shagreen case, the lockplate with maker's mark IW, 23 oz. **£1,700-2,000** *C*

The arms are those of Hitch or Hicke impaling another.

A pair of George III tea caddies, marked, Samuel Taylor, London, 1760, 4¾ in. high, 10 oz. 10 dwt., fitted marquetry case. **£900-1,100** *S*

A set of 3 George III tea caddies, the detachable beaded lids with wild strawberry buttons, the 2 rectangular examples tin lined, marked on bases and lids, Daniel Smith & Robert Sharp, London, 1761, 5 in. (12.7 cm.) high, 31 oz. 8 dwt. (976 gm.) all in. **£1,500-£2,000** *S*

A good George III silver chinoiserie tea caddy engraved with an armorial and Chinese hieroglyphic, London, 1772, maker Aaron Lesturgeon (Grimwade), 3¾ in., 16 oz. **£1,700-2,000** *GSP*

A George III oval tea caddy, maker probably Hester Bateman (but effaced), London, 1780, 12.7 oz. **£800-900** *WW*

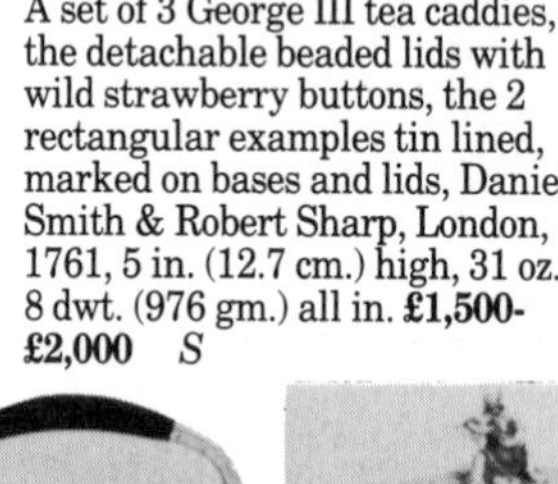

A Regency oblong tea caddy, maker's mark IC, 1810, 5¼ in. (13.4 cm.) high, 25 oz. **£1,000-£1,300** *C*

An oval tea kettle and lampstand, Harrison Brothers & Howson, Sheffield, 1900, 14 in. (36 cm.) high overall, 53 oz. 7 dwt. (1,653 gm.), all in, excluding wood box. **£500-£600** *S*

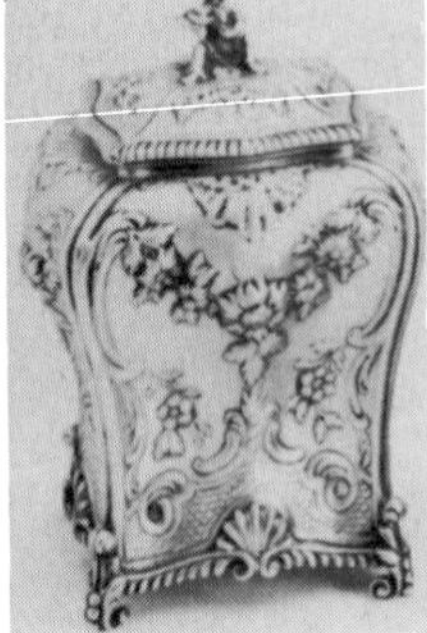

A Victorian tea caddy in 18th C. style, marked on base and cover, C. T. & G. Fox, London, 1849, 5½ in. (14.2 cm.) high, 10 oz. 14 dwt. (332 gm.). **£500-600** *S*

A George III large 2-division tea caddy by Crispin Fuller, 1811. **£600-700** *DWB*

A George II tea kettle, lampstand and kettle salver, Shaw & Priest, the stand James Morison, all London, 1753, 107 oz. 4 dwt. (3,323 gm.) all in. **£3,200-3,500** *S*

The arms are those of Sheppard.

A Victorian tea kettle on lampstand in 18th C. taste, fully marked, William Comyns, London, 1899, 15¼ in. (38.7 cm.) high, 74 oz. 11 dwt. (2,318 gm.), **£1,200-1,400** *S*

(l.) A George III octagonal tea pot by Robert Hennell, 1793, 15 oz. 8 dwt. **£700-800** *C*

(r.) A George III shaped oval tea caddy with the mark of Robert Hennell, overstruck by another, 1780, 14 oz. 1 dwt. **£1,100-1,300** *C*

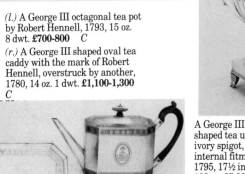

A George III two-handled vase-shaped tea urn, with stained green ivory spigot, with cylindrical internal fitment, by Paul Storr, 1795, 17½ in. (44.5 cm.) high, gross 102 oz. **£5,000-6,000** *C*

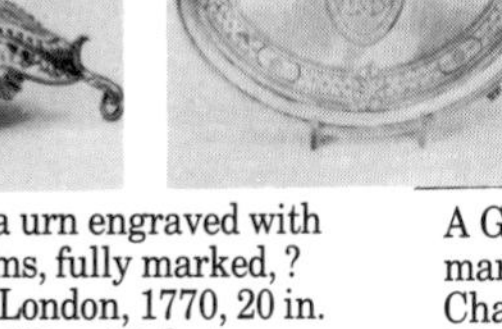

A George III tea pot and stand, marked on base, lid and stand, Henry Chawner, London, 1788, 28 oz. (870 gm.) all in. **£2,000-£2,200** *S*

The arms are those of Douglas of Mains, Co. Dumbarton for R. S. Douglas.

A bullet-shaped tea pot, engraved on one side with a coat-of-arms, and on the other with a crest, apparently unmarked, 5 in. (12.7 cm.) high, early 18th C., 14 oz. 19 dwt. (464 gm.) all in. **£600-700** *S*

A George III tea urn engraved with later coat-of-arms, fully marked, ? William Tuite, London, 1770, 20 in. (50.7 cm.) high, 92 oz. 11 dwt. (2,878 gm.). **£1,500-1,700** *S*

The arms are those of Lee.

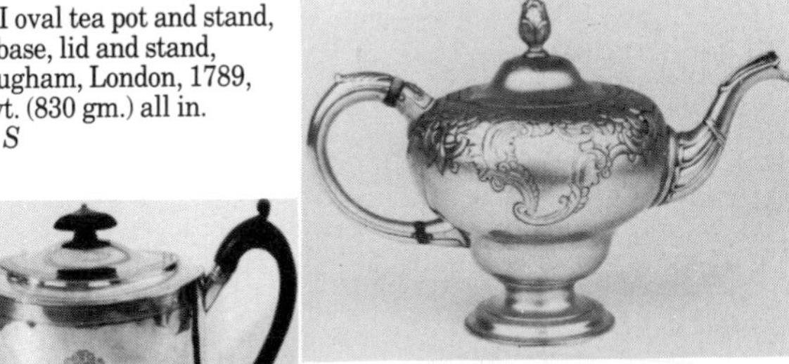

A George III oval tea pot and stand, marked on base, lid and stand, Charles Hougham, London, 1789, 26 oz. 14 dwt. (830 gm.) all in. **£800-900** *S*

A George II inverted pear-shaped tea pot by Ker and Dempster, Edinburgh, 1755, Assaymaster Hugh Gordon, gross 20 oz. **£600-£800** *C*

A Dutch inverted pear-shaped tea pot by Johannes Jansen, Rotterdam, 1776, gross 11 oz. 15 dwt. **£800-1,000** *C*

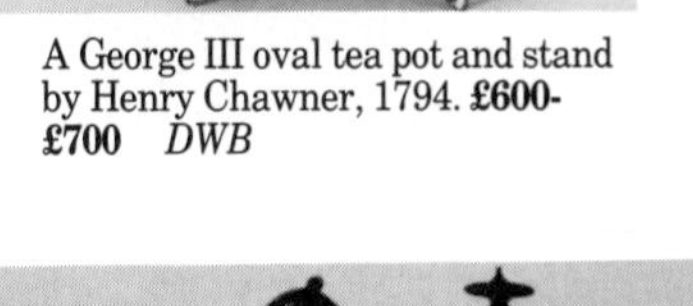

A George III oval tea pot and stand by Henry Chawner, 1794. **£600-£700** *DWB*

An oval tea pot, maker's mark I.W. for John Warner, John Williams or James Warner of Cork, 6⅞ in. (17.5 cm.) high, c. 1795, 20 oz. (620 gm.) all in. **£800-900** *S*

A George III oval tea pot and stand, the stand on 4 supports, R. & D. Hennell, London, 1799, 19 oz. 4 dwt. (595 gm.) all in. **£550-650** *S*

A Victorian crested tea pot, John Tapley, probably for Rundell, Bridge & Co., London, 1837, stamped: 58, scratched: 5775, 5¾ in. (14.7 cm.) high, 23 oz. 2 dwt. (998 gm.) all in. **£650-750** *S*

A George III oval tea pot on stand, makers Peter, Ann and William Bateman, London, 1799-1800, 17.5 oz. all in. **£600-700** *WW*

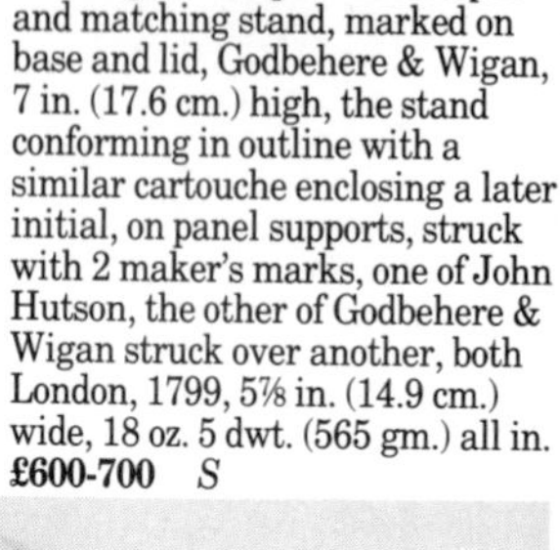

A George III shaped oval tea pot and matching stand, marked on base and lid, Godbehere & Wigan, 7 in. (17.6 cm.) high, the stand conforming in outline with a similar cartouche enclosing a later initial, on panel supports, struck with 2 maker's marks, one of John Hutson, the other of Godbehere & Wigan struck over another, both London, 1799, 5⅞ in. (14.9 cm.) wide, 18 oz. 5 dwt. (565 gm.) all in. **£600-700** *S*

A George III circular tea pot, engraved under the base 'MARION NEILSON, DRIMSYNIE, LOCHGOILHEAD, N.B.', by Paul Storr, 1809, with later silver handle, gross 38 oz. **£2,200-2,500** *C*

A French oval tea pot, maker's mark D. above a star, Provincial, 5¾ in. (14.5 cm.) high, c. 1800, 19 oz. 10 dwt. (615 gm.) all in. **£500-600** *S*

A Regency circular tea pot, engraved with a coat-of-arms and a crest, by Paul Storr, 1810, gross 33 oz. **£1,700-1,900** *C*

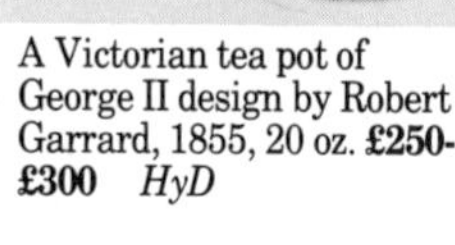

A Victorian tea pot of George II design by Robert Garrard, 1855, 20 oz. **£250-£300** *HyD*

A George III compressed circular tea pot, replacement fibre handle, marked on base and lid, George Burrows, London, 1819, 6¼ in. (16.2 cm.) high, 25 oz. 14 dwt. (799 gm.) all in. **£350-450** *S*

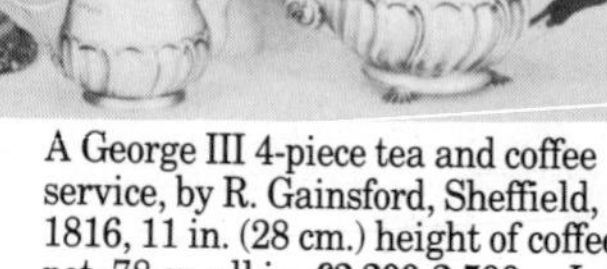

A George III 4-piece tea and coffee service, by R. Gainsford, Sheffield, 1816, 11 in. (28 cm.) height of coffee pot, 78 oz. all in. **£2,200-2,500** *L*

A George III 4-piece tea service, the tea pot by John Robbins, the stand by William Bennett, the sugar bowl by John Beldon, and the milk jug by William Abdy II, all 1804, 15.5 cm. height of tea pot, 37 oz. all in. **£1,100-1,400** *L*

A George III 3-piece tea set and tea pot stand, the milk jug and sugar basin with gilt interiors, R. & S. Hennell, London, 1807, 40 oz. 5 dwt. (1,251 gm.) (all in, excluding stand). **£850-950** *S*

A George III oblong 3-piece tea set, Charles Fox, the tea pot overstruck by Alice & George Burrows, London, 1811, 45 oz. (1,395 gm.) all in. **£600-800** *S*

A George IV 3-piece tea set, T. & J. Settle, Sheffield, 1821, 54 oz. 17 dwt. (1,705 gm.) all in. **£600-£700** *S*

A matching 3-piece tea set and coffee jug on lampstand complete with burner, milk jug and sugar basin, Alice & George Burrows, 1817, the latter overstruck by Joseph Angell, a sugar basin cover and tea pot, Joseph Angell, 1825, the coffee jug, stand and burner, 10½ in. (26.7 cm.) overall height, William Burwash, 1815, all London, 97 oz. 7 dwt. (3,027 gm.) all in. **£1,100-1,300** *S*

A George III 3-piece 'Jester' tea set, the scroll handles with hooded jester head thumbpieces, James le Bas, retailer William Law, Dublin, 1817, and a pair of floral chased sugar tongs, Charles Murray, Dublin, 1824, 57 oz. **£1,100-1,300** *SI*

A George IV bachelor's 4-piece tea and coffee set, fully marked, William Elliott, London, 1825-26, 47 oz. 2 dwt. (1,460 gm.) all in. **£1,700-2,000** *S*

A George IV 5-piece tea set by Paul Storr, 1822, 120½ oz. **£12,000-£14,000** *P*

A George IV silver circular tea pot, the repousse and chased flower and scroll decorated banded body with spreading foot with scalloped edge, 11 in. wide, London, 1825, a George III silver pumpkin-shaped sugar basin, 9 in. wide, London, 1816, and a matching William IV silver cream jug, 6½ in. wide, London, 1835, 56 oz. 5 dwt. **£750-850** *DSH*

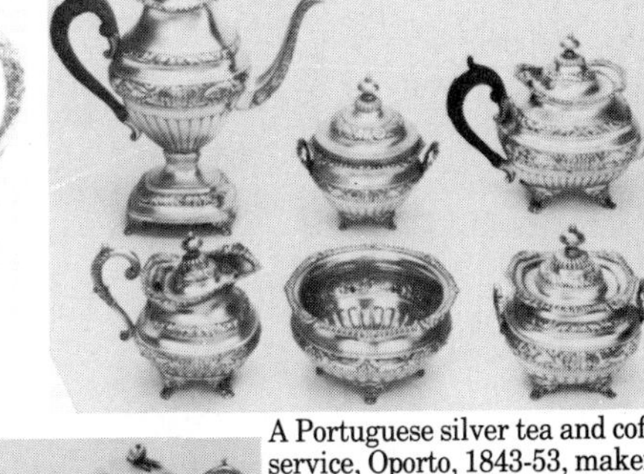

A Portuguese silver tea and coffee service, Oporto, 1843-53, maker's marks APS in monogram, height of coffee pot 13½ in. (34.4 cm.), 160 oz. gross. **£2,200-2,800** *C*

A William IV 4-piece cottage pattern tea and coffee set, J. & A. Savory for A. B. Savory & Sons, London, 1835-36, 73 oz. 15 dwt. (2,293 gm.) all in. **£1,400-1,600** *S*

A silver-gilt compressed circular matching 3-piece tea set, fully marked, Robert Hennell II, 1819, the milk jug and sugar basin, Charles Gordon, 1831, all London, and a pair of sugar tongs, Robert Gainsford, Sheffield, 1828, 80 oz. 2 dwt. (2,483 gm.) all in. **£2,800-£3,000** *S*

A William IV Irish 4-piece tea and coffee service and similar sugar tongs, Dublin, 1830, the tongs 1829, by Edward Power, 9½ in. (24.2 cm.) height of coffee pot, 103 oz. **£2,800-3,200** *L*

This service is believed to have belonged to Henry Wellesley, 1st Baron Cowley, 1778-1847, brother of the Duke of Wellington.

A Victorian silver 3-piece tea set, 1869, maker Martin Hall & Co., 48 oz. **£750-850** *GSP*

A Victorian tea service, Dublin, 1838. **£800-900** *DWB*

A William IV silver 4-piece tea set with melon-shaped bodies well chased with flowers and foliage, 1831 and 1834, maker's initials J.H. (perhaps James Hobb), 78½ oz. **£1,600-1,800** *GSP*

A Victorian silver tea and coffee service, by Hunt & Roskell, late Storr & Mortimer, 1855, coffee pot 9½ in. high, 68 oz. **£1,800-2,200** *NP*

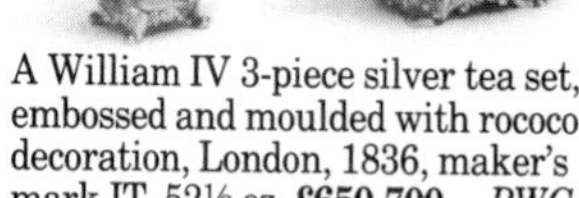
A William IV 3-piece silver tea set, embossed and moulded with rococo decoration, London, 1836, maker's mark IT, 52½ oz. **£650-700** *PWC*

A Victorian lemonade set of jug, 6 tumblers and a stand, by Martin, Hall & Co., 1872, 10½ in. (26.7 cm.), 179 oz. **£2,200-3,000** *L*

A Victorian 4-piece tea and coffee service by W. & H. Stratford, Sheffield, 1873, 9¼ in. (23.5 cm.), 74 oz. **£1,100-1,300** *L*

A Victorian 4-piece tea service, fully marked Sheffield, 1880, by Martin, Hall & Co., height of hot water jug 11 in. (28 cm.), 78 oz. **£1,300-1,500** *L*

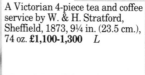

A Victorian 3-piece tea set chased with blooms and scrolls incorporating two cartouches, one initialled, Martin Hall & Co., Sheffield, 1865, 54 oz. 12 dwt. all in. **£700-800** *SC*

A Victorian presentation 3-piece tea service by Henry Wilkinson of Sheffield, 1858, height of tea pot 8½ in. (21.6 cm.), 49 oz. **£650-750** *L*

A Victorian pear-shaped tea and coffee service by Robert Garrard, 1865 and 1868, coffee pot 9½ in. (24.1 cm.), 109 oz. gross. **£2,000-£2,500** *C*

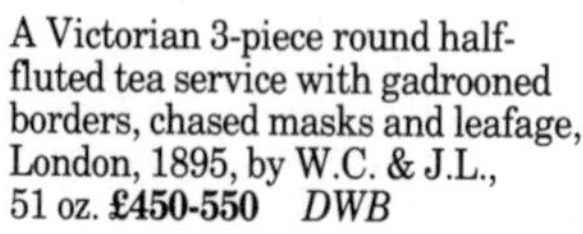
A Victorian 3-piece round half-fluted tea service with gadrooned borders, chased masks and leafage, London, 1895, by W.C. & J.L., 51 oz. **£450-550** *DWB*

matching 5-piece tea-set, the bodies part chased with hevron lobing below everted foliate shell and gadroon orders, the coffee pot and hot water jug by Walker & Hall, heffield, 1922, the tea-set by C. S. Harris, London, 1901-03, 03 oz. 17 dwt. all in. **£850-950** *SC*

A composite 5-piece tea service, tray 24½ in., Sheffield, 1901, 104 oz., tea pot and jug Sheffield, 1901, sugar bowl and milk jug London, 1892, gross weight 76 oz., maker's marks RB and SH. **£1,300-£1,600** *DDM*

A 4-piece tea service, by Joseph Gloster Ltd., Birmingham, 1906, height of coffee pot 23.2 cm., 60 oz. all in. **£550-600** *L*

A 5-piece circular tea and coffee set, James Dixon & Sons, Sheffield, 1925-26, 81 oz. 7 dwt. (2,521 gm.) all in. **£950-1,050** *S*

An oval 3-piece tea service with fluted bodies, scrolling handles and pedestal bases, Sheffield, 1930, 25 oz. **£300-400** *DDM*

A silver 3-piece tea service, marks for Birmingham, 1932, height of pot 5½ in., 32 oz. **£360-400** *TP*

A 4-piece tea service by Joseph Gloster Ltd., Birmingham, 1937, height of hot water jug 22 cm., 73½ oz. all in. **£400-500** *L*

A 4-piece tea and coffee service, Sheffield, 1937, 50 oz. gross. **£400-£500** *DDM*

A 4-piece tea service, Sheffield, 1938 and 1940, by Munsey & Co. of Cambridge, height of hot water jug 21 cm., 58 oz **£500-600** *L*

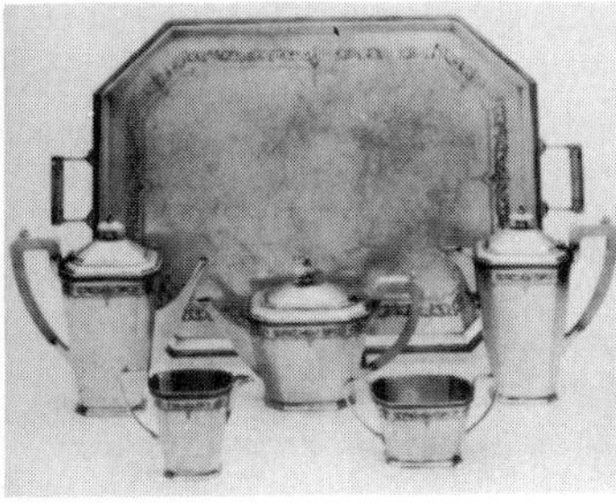

A 6-piece tea and coffee set, Mappin & Webb, Sheffield, 1941/44/45, 198 oz. 10 dwt. (6,153 gm.) all in. **£2,000-2,500** *S*

A French silver-gilt tea and coffee set, by A. A. Hebrard of Paris, height of coffee pot 12 cm., 50 oz., London import marks for 1968. **£850-950** *P*

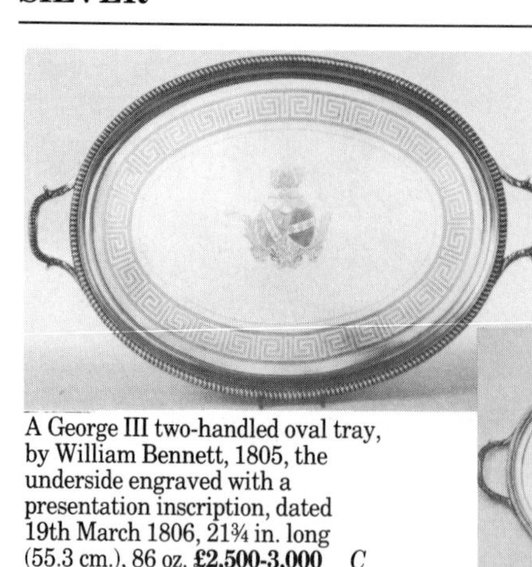

A George III two-handled oval tray, by William Bennett, 1805, the underside engraved with a presentation inscription, dated 19th March 1806, 21¾ in. long (55.3 cm.), 86 oz. **£2,500-3,000** *C*

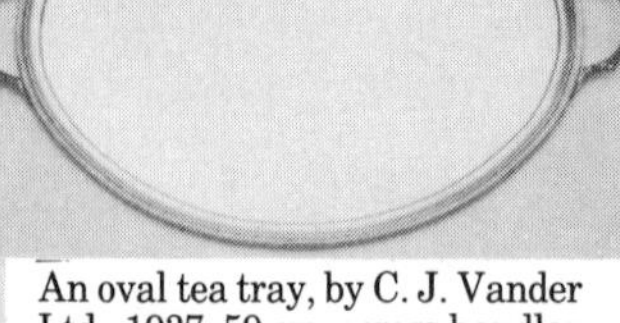

An oval tea tray, by C. J. Vander Ltd., 1937, 59 cm. across handles, 69 oz. **£600-700** *L*

A George II two-handled oval soup tureen and cover, by Eliza Godfrey 1747, the original engraving erased, with liner, engraved with the Levinge crest, by Robert Garrard, 1852, 14¼ in. (36.2 cm.) long, 149 oz. **£7,500-8,500** *C*

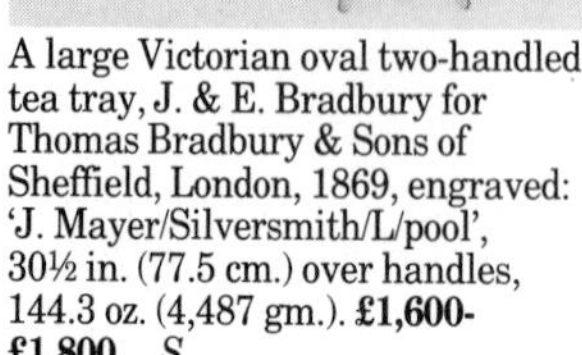

A large Victorian oval two-handled tea tray, J. & E. Bradbury for Thomas Bradbury & Sons of Sheffield, London, 1869, engraved: 'J. Mayer/Silversmith/L/pool', 30½ in. (77.5 cm.) over handles, 144.3 oz. (4,487 gm.). **£1,600-£1,800** *S*

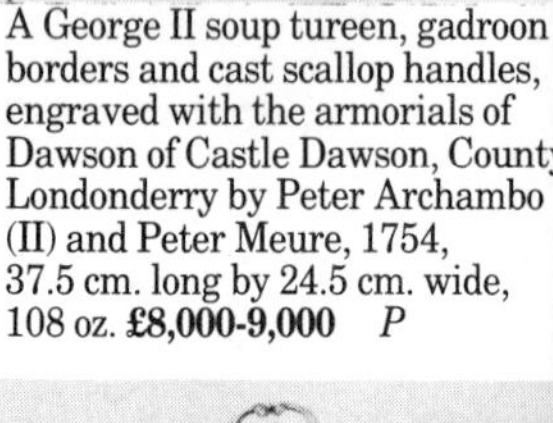

A George II soup tureen, gadroon borders and cast scallop handles, engraved with the armorials of Dawson of Castle Dawson, County Londonderry by Peter Archambo (II) and Peter Meure, 1754, 37.5 cm. long by 24.5 cm. wide, 108 oz. **£8,000-9,000** *P*

A pair of George III plain-shaped oval sauce tureens and stands, engraved with the Royal arms, crown and initials of George III, by Thomas Heming, 1763, length of stands 8⅞ in. (22.5 cm.), 47 oz. **£6,000-7,000** *C*

A George III soup tureen and cover, Andrew Fogelberg, London, 1777, 10 in. diam. (25.2 cm.), 97 oz. 1·7 dwt. (3,043 gm.). **£3,500-4,500** *S*

A pair of George III oval sauce tureens and covers, marked on bases and covers, William Fountain, London, 1803, 9½ in. wide (24.4 cm.), 56 oz. 1 dwt. (1,737 gm.). **£1,600-2,000** *S*

A George III plain oval entrée dish and cover, by Paul Storr, 1793, the finial unmarked, 12⅛ in. long (30.8 cm.), 34 oz. **£1,200-1,400** *C*

A pair of George III oblong entrée dishes and covers, fully marked, William Stroud, London, 1805, 12½ in. wide (32 cm.), 131 oz. 16 dwt. (4,085 gm.). **£1,500-1,700** *S*

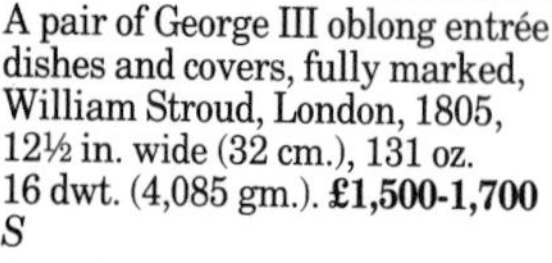

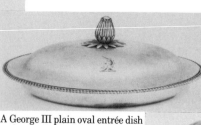

A pair of George III plain two-handled oval entrée dishes and covers, engraved with the Royal Monogram and Crown of Queen Charlotte and with a coat-of-arms and crest, by Robert Garrard, 1803 one cover with worn marks, 14¾ in. long (37.5 cm.), 70 oz. **£2,000-£2,500** *C*

The arms are probably those of Wallace.

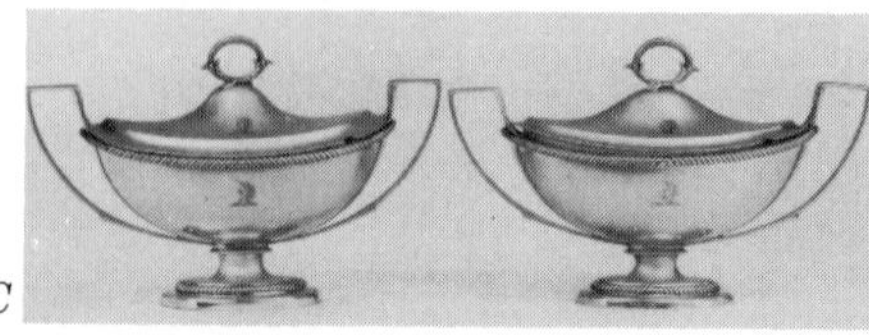

Two George III plain two-handled boat-shaped sauce tureens and covers, engraved with the Errington crest, by Lewis Pantin III, 1799, one cover by William Pitts, 1789, 42 oz. **£1,100-1,300** *C*

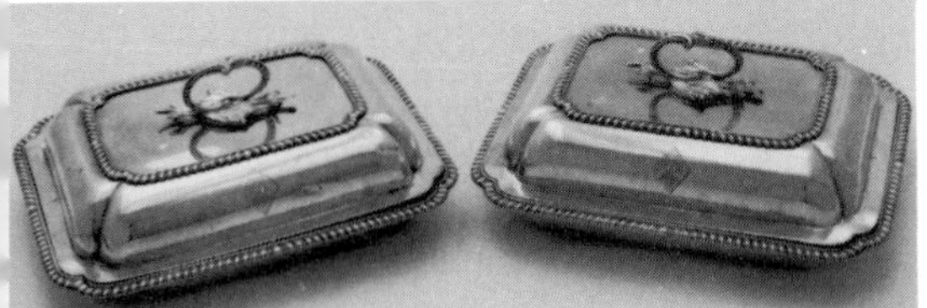

A pair of George III rectangular entrée dishes with covers, gadrooned edges and replacement (probably earlier) unmarked scroll handles, maker Robert Garrard, London, 1806 and 1808, 11 in., 106 oz. **£850-950** *DDM*

A George III oblong bacon dish, marked on base, lid and ring handle, Benjamin & James Smith, London, 1809, 10 in. wide (25.5 cm.), 41 oz. 19 dwt. (1,300 gm.). **£700-800** *S*

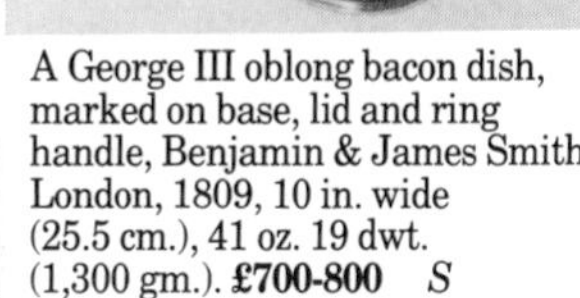

A set of 4 George III shaped oblong entrée dishes, John Houle, London, 1812, 11¾ in. wide (29.8 cm.), 137 oz. 6 dwt. (4,256 gm.). **£2,200-£2,600** *S*

A George IV shaped circular entrée dish and cover, marked on base, cover and handle, Paul Storr for Storr & Mortimer, London, 1829, 11¾ in. diam. (29.8 cm.), 64 oz. 8 dwt. (1,996 gm.), and a Sheffield plated heater base and liner, 10⅛ in. diam. (25.8 cm.), c. 1830. **£3,500-4,000** *S*

A Victorian oval soup tureen and cover, marked on base and cover, Marshall & Sons, Edinburgh, 1843, 16¼ in. wide (41.3 cm.), 98 oz. 15 dwt. (3,070 gm.). **£3,500-4,000** *S*

A set of 4 Victorian shaped circular entrée dishes and covers, by Robert Garrard, 1849, 11½ in. diam. (29.3 cm.), 213 oz. **£5,000-6,000** *C*

A Victorian circular breakfast dish, Hunt & Roskell, London, 1872, 12½ in. (32 cm.) wide over handles, 97 oz. 12 dwt. (3,025 gm.) all in. **£1,500-1,700** *S*

An Edward VII replica of the Warwick vase, by Barnard & Co., 1903, 8¼ in. high (20.9 cm.), 66 oz. **£700-800** *C*

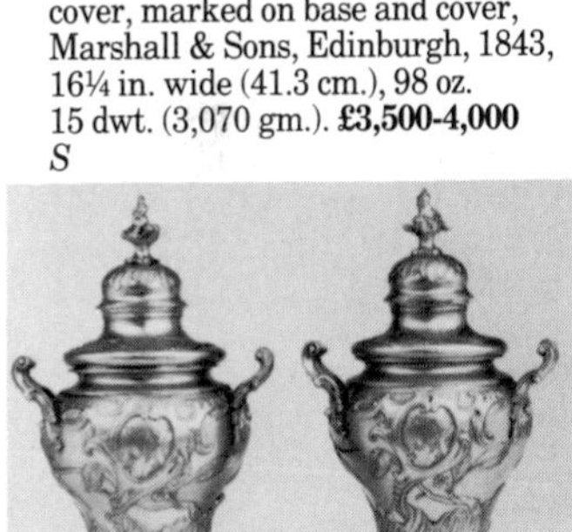

A pair of George III silver-gilt two-handled inverted pear-shaped condiment vases and covers, by John Swift, 1762, the gilding later, 8 in. high (20.3 cm.), 25 oz. **£850-£1,050** *C*

A George III matched set of 3 wine labels, inscribed and by respectively, Lisbon, maker's mark TH, Claret, maker Richard Binley, Port, maker Margaret Binley, 2 in. wide (5 cm.), all c. 1770. **£150-£160** *P*

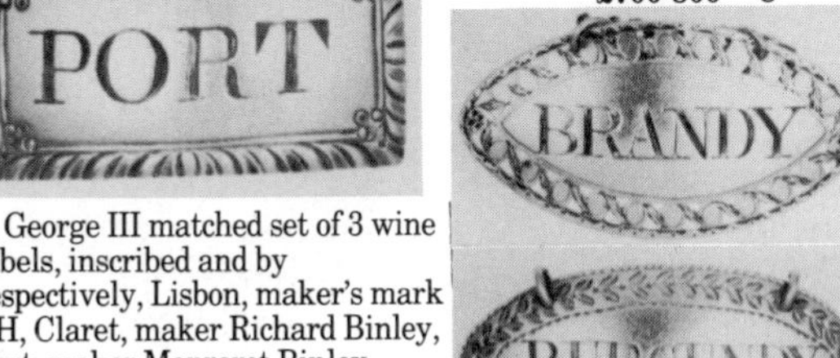

A George III eye-shaped wine label by T. Phipps and Edward Robinson II, inscribed Brandy, 2 in. (5 cm.), 1791, a 2nd wine label, inscribed Burgundy, 2 in. (5 cm.), maker's mark only James Phipps I, c. 1770. **£250-300** *P*

A rare George III Irish cast wine label by Benjamin Taitt, inscribed Sherry, 2 in. wide (5 cm.), Dublin, c. 1775. **£210-260** *P*

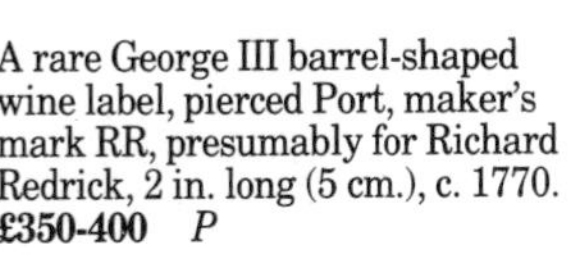

A rare George III barrel-shaped wine label, pierced Port, maker's mark RR, presumably for Richard Redrick, 2 in. long (5 cm.), c. 1770. **£350-400** *P*

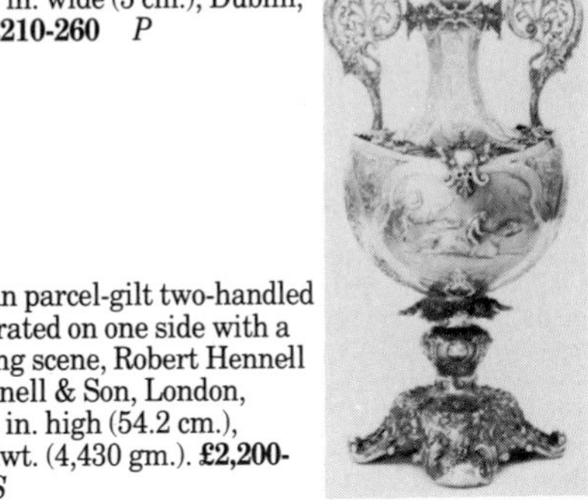

A Victorian parcel-gilt two-handled vase, decorated on one side with a horse racing scene, Robert Hennell for R. Hennell & Son, London, 1859, 21¼ in. high (54.2 cm.), 142 oz. 9 dwt. (4,430 gm.). **£2,200-£2,600** *S*

A George III unusual heraldic and festoon wine label, by Susanna Barker, engraved with a Scottish crest, inscribed Port, 2 in. wide (5 cm.), c. 1785. **£500-600** *P*

A single George III heraldic and festoon wine label, inscribed Madeira, maker's initials T.A., possibly for Thomas Adcock, struck over another maker's mark, possibly that of John Steward (?), 2 in. wide (5 cm.), c. 1790. **£65-75** *P*

A George III Irish wine label, incised Champaigne, by James Keating, Dublin, maker's mark only struck twice, 5 cm. long, c. 1795. **£85-95** *P*

Four octagonal labels comprising: 2 with engraved titles 'Madeira' and 'White Wine' by T. Phipps and E. Robinson, 1797, another with engraved title 'Claret' by R. Peppin, 1822, another with engraved title 'Port' by John Robins, 1794. **£250-300** *C*

A George III Irish cast wine label by John Ebbs, inscribed Claret, maker's mark and also the assay master William Law, Dublin, 1806, 2 in. wide (5 cm.), also a George III scroll wine label with bright cut border, inscribed Sweet Wine, 2 in. wide (5 cm.), c. 1790. **£150-200** *P*

A set of 4 George III heraldic and festoon wine labels, inscribed respectively W. Wine, Madeira and Port, bearing the maker's initials T.W., possibly Thomas Watson, struck over the initials of Hester Bateman (?), incused King's Head, 2 in. wide (5 cm.), c. 1785. **£250-£300** *P*

Four wine labels, 3 with engraved titles 'Geneva', 'Rum' and 'Brandy', by P. and A. Bateman, 1792 and 1793, and another with engraved title 'Rum', by William Bateman I, 1815. **£320-400** *C*

A pair of George III cast silver-gilt wine labels by Digby Scott and Benjamin Smith II, engraved respectively Port and Hock, 2⅛ in. wide (5.5 cm.), 1804. **£300-350** *P*

A George III label, with engraved title 'I. Whisky', by Robert Garrard I, 1809. **£80-100** *C*

Six shaped oval labels with pierced titles 'Claret', 'Lisbon', 'Port' (2), 'Madeira' and 'Sherry', by Charles Rawlings, 1819 and 1822. **£180-£220** *C*

A rare George III barrel-shaped wine label, by Susanna Barker, 1792, 1⅝ in. long (4 cm.). **£220-£280** *P*

A set of 3 George III sauce labels, possibly by Robert Garrard I, 1806, inscribed respectively Cayenne, Soy and Ketchup, 1⅛ in. wide (3 cm.). **£90-110** *P*

A pair of George III wine labels by Hester Bateman, inscribed respectively Soutern and Hock, marks punched differently on each label, 2 in. wide (5 cm.), c. 1795. **£170-200** *P*

A George III large single cast silver-gilt wine label by Benjamin Smith II and James Smith, pierced Port, with heavy chain, 1809. **£350-£400** *P*

A matching pair of George III cast heraldic wine labels, pierced for Claret and Madeira, one with a wing damaged, maker's mark obscured, probably by Phipps & Robinson, 1812 and 1815, 4.25 cm. high by 4 cm. long. **£360-420** *P*

A pair of George III Irish cast wine labels and a single matching example by John Ebbs, inscribed respectively Malmsey and Moselle, Dublin, 1818, and Vindegrave, c. 1815, all measuring 2⅛ in. wide (5.5 cm.), and punched with the mark of William Law. **£200-250** *P*

A pair of George IV cast sauce labels, respectively Harvey and Lemon, by J. R. (Josephus Read?), 1823, 1⅜ in. wide (3.5 cm.), another pair similar, pierced respectively Chili and Cayenne, by Mary Ann & Charles Reilly, c. 1825. **£110-140** *P*

A George IV shaped oval label, with engraved title 'Madeira', by W. and A. Mitchell, Glasgow, 1828. **£90-110** *C*

A set of 5 Regency silver-gilt wine labels with titles 'Cape', 'Claret', 'Sherry', 'Port' and 'Madeira', by Paul Storr, three 1811, two 1814, 7 oz. 4 dwt. **£2,500-3,000** *C*

A set of 4 George III cast wine labels, pierced respectively for Madeira, Claret, Sherry and Port, one inscribed on back 'Merino Society to C.T. Tower Esq.–', by Thomas and James Phipps, 1815, 5.5 cm. long, 2.75 oz. **£350-400** *P*

Eight labels of shaped escutcheon form with pierced titles, 'Bucellas', 'Hollands', 'Madeira' (2), 'Rhenish', 'Sherry' (2) and 'Shrub', 7 by John Reily, 1823 and 1825, one by C. Reily and G. Storer, 1822. **£350-£400** *C*

A matching pair of George IV/ Victorian wine labels, pierced respectively Burgundy, maker's mark disfigured, 1823, and Port, by Charles Reilly & George Storer, 1840, 2⅛ in. wide (5.5 cm.). **£140-£180** *P*

A George IV collected set of 6 wine labels, comprising, respectively inscribed, Brandy and Rum, 2⅛ in. wide (5.5 cm.), Lisbon, Hollands, Brandy and Madeira, 1¾ in. wide (4.5 cm.), 5 by Joseph Taylor, Birmingham 1823/1825, and one by Taylor & Perry, Birmingham, 1829. **£300-350** *P*

A Queen Anne silver snuffers-stand and a pair of snuffers, by George Lewis, 1703, 9 oz. 6 dwt. **£3,000-4,000** *C*

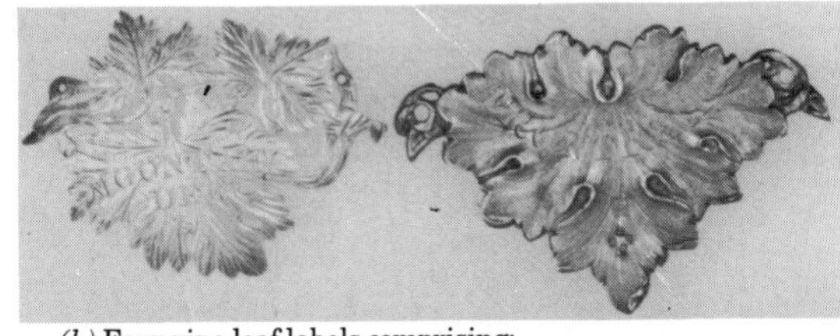

(l.) Four vine leaf labels comprising: 'Madeira', by Taylor and Perry, Birmingham, 1830, 'Bucellas', Birmingham, 1834, maker's mark omitted, 'Mountain Dew', by William Kingdon, 1842, 'Cognac', by G. Angell or G. Adams, 1856. **£160-200** *C*

(r.) Two Victorian large vine leaf labels, with pierced titles 'Barsac' and 'Frontignac', by J. and H. Lias, 1846. **£100-150** *C*

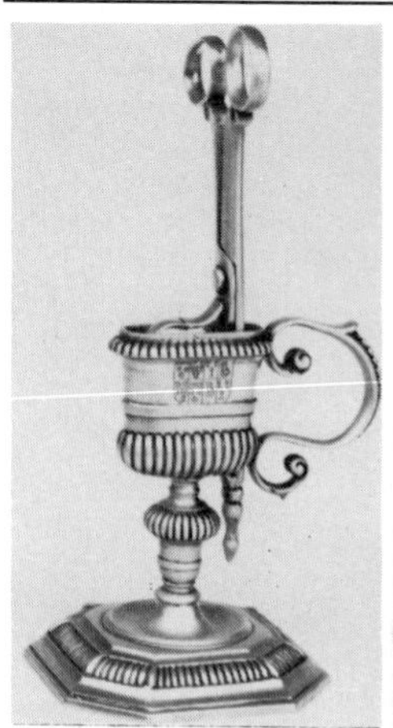

A Queen Anne snuffers-stand and a pair of snuffers, by Thomas Brydon, 1704, 9 oz. 13 dwt. **£6,500-7,000** *C*

A pair of George IV snuffers, fully marked, Emes and Barnard, London, 1823, 6 oz. all in. **£300-£400** *S*

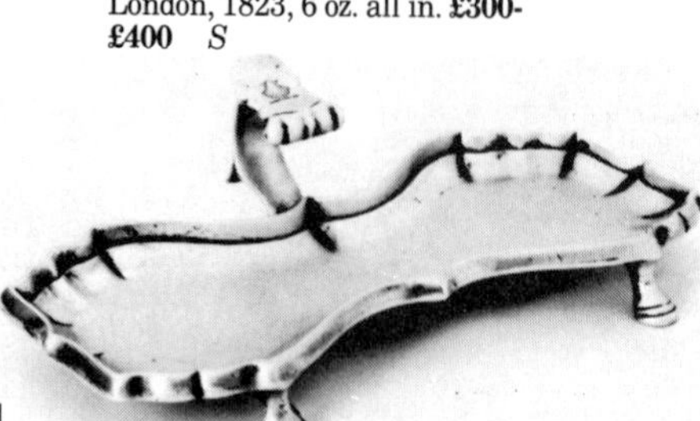

A George II shaped oblong snuffers tray, William Gould, London, 1735, 7 in. long (18.2 cm.), 9 oz. 5 dwt. (286 gm.). **£450-550** *S*

An amusing child's rattle modelled as a 'pussy' cat in short jacket and baggy trousers, with mother-o'-pearl handle, 11 cm. long. **£60-70** *P*

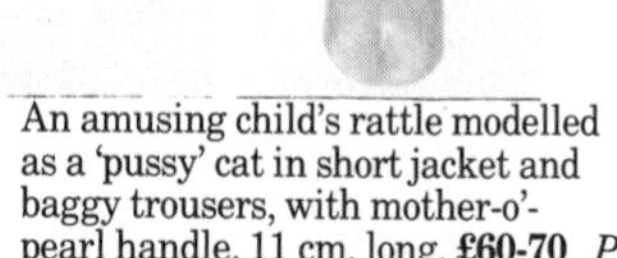

A rare pair of silver sugar tongs designed by the architect William Burges, the rounded top enclosing a wrought steel spring embellished with gilded studs, engraved 'Willielmus Burges' and with traces of gilding, hallmarks for Jes Barkentin of Barkentin and Krall, London, 1870, 11.5 cm. long. **£1,800-2,200** *P*

These tongs were almost certainly designed and commissioned by Burges for use by himself.

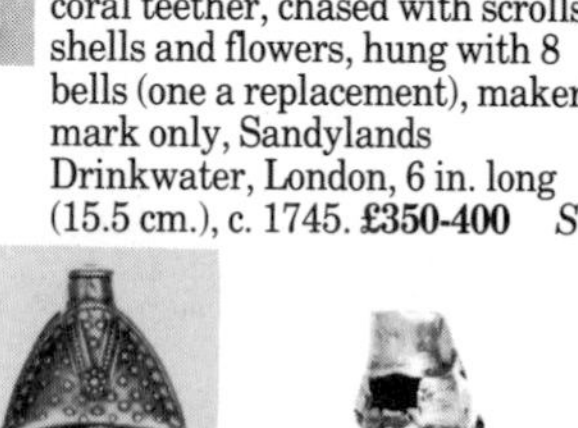

A silver-gilt child's rattle with coral teether, chased with scrolls, shells and flowers, hung with 8 bells (one a replacement), maker's mark only, Sandylands Drinkwater, London, 6 in. long (15.5 cm.), c. 1745. **£350-400** *S*

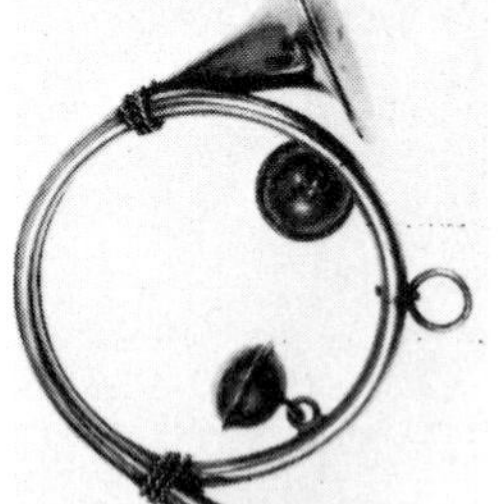

A 19th C. German musical whistle and rattle, punched only with a '13', 9 cm. long, c. 1840. **£150-200** *P*

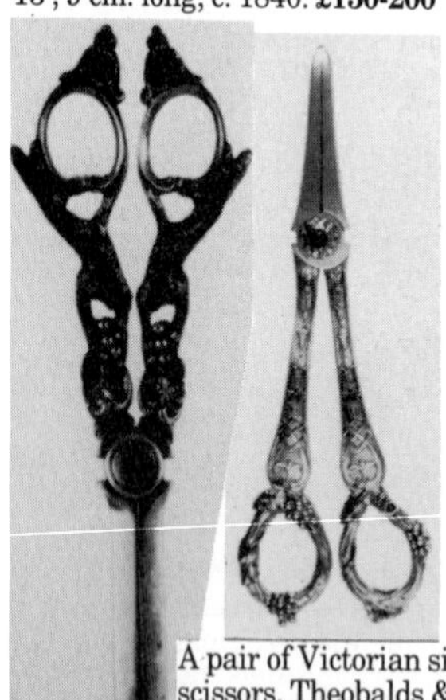

A pair of Victorian silver-gilt grape scissors, Theobalds & Atkinson, London, 1839, 7 in. long (18.3 cm.). **£250-300** *S*

An unusual pair of Edwardian grape scissors, the handles modelled as leaping foxes, by Walker & Hall, Chester, 1906, 3.75 oz. **£90-110** *P*

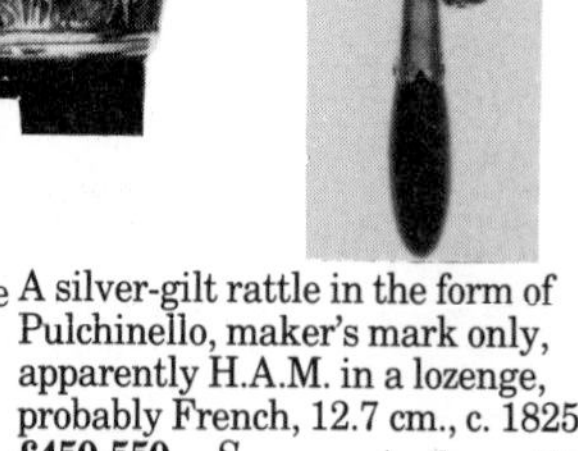

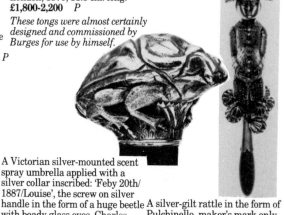

A Victorian silver-mounted scent spray umbrella applied with a silver collar inscribed: 'Feby 20th/1887/Louise', the screw on silver handle in the form of a huge beetle with beady glass eyes, Charles Dumenil, London, 1886, 37½ in. long (94.5 cm.). **£450-500** *S*

A silver-gilt rattle in the form of Pulchinello, maker's mark only, apparently H.A.M. in a lozenge, probably French, 12.7 cm., c. 1825. **£450-550** *S*

A silver-gilt rattle with coral teether, with shells, flowers and foliage on matted grounds, complete with pendant ring and 8 bells, maker's mark only, T.M. below a crown, 6¼ in. long (16 cm.), c. 1740. **£450-500** *S*

A pair of silver-gilt cast sugar nips and a similar mote spoon, both unmarked, probably early 19th C., 2 oz. **£140-150** *P*

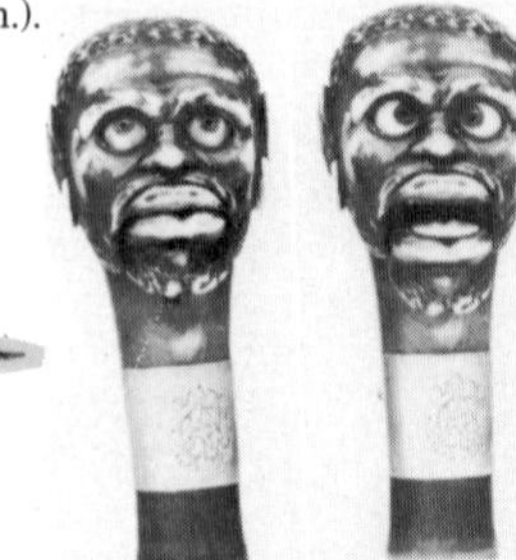

A novelty walking cane, the ivory grip carved and stained as the head of a negro who, at the touch of a button, rotates his eyes and flicks his tongue, maker's mark F.B. in a rectangle, London, 1880, 35½ in. long (90.2 cm.). **£500-600** *S*

A pair of dish rings, in mid 18th C. Irish style, William Comyns for W. Comyns & Sons Ltd., London, 1902, 8 in. diam. (20.2 cm.), 31 oz. 6 dwt. (973 gm.). **£450-500** *S*

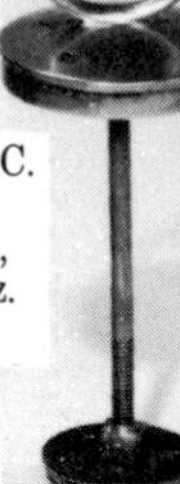

A rare George IV cork-pull with ring handle, by George Pearson, 9 cm. long, c. 1825. **£80-110** *P*

A small Irish dish ring, Dublin, 1904, by Edmond Johnson Ltd., ½ in. (11.5 cm.), 6 oz. **£200-250**

A pair of wine wagons, the coasters by J. and T. Settle, Sheffield, 1815, the carriages by C. Reily and G. Storer, 1846. **£1,800-2,200** *C*

A George III 6 bottle cruet of rare crescent form, London, 1784, probably by William Abdy, marks rubbed (dissimilar stoppers). **£350-£400** *WHL*

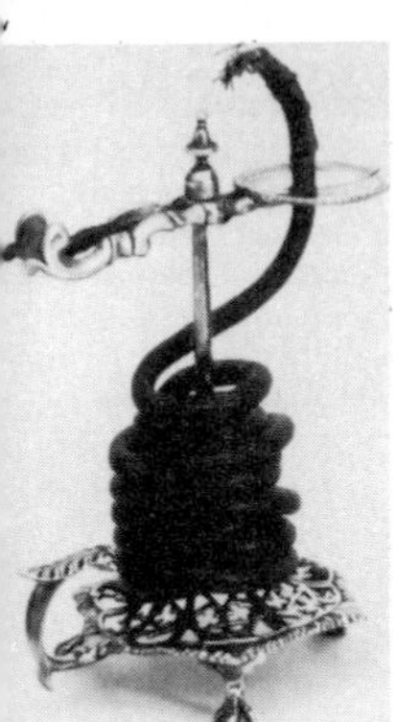

A George III wax jack, marked on base and taper holder, maker's mark WC, possibly for William Cafe, London, 1768, 6⅛ in. high (15.5 cm.), 5 oz. 5 dwt. (162 gm.) all in. **£700-800** *S*

A George IV silver cruet stand, stand 13 oz., maker John Angell, London, 1825. **£450-550** *T*

A French toothpick holder, maker's mark apparently that of Marc-Augustin Lebrun, Paris, 13.2 cm. high, c. 1820, 270 gm. **£400-500** *S*

A parcel-gilt pipe by Johan Wilhelm Ohlsson, maker's mark, Lidköping, 67 cm. high, c. 1840, 252 gm. of silver. **£500-600** *S*

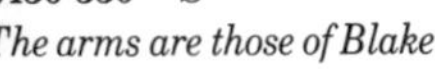

A travelling railway carriage lamp, W.F. Wright for Wright & Davies, London, 1896, 6 in. long (15.2 cm.). **£450-550** *S*

The arms are those of Blake.

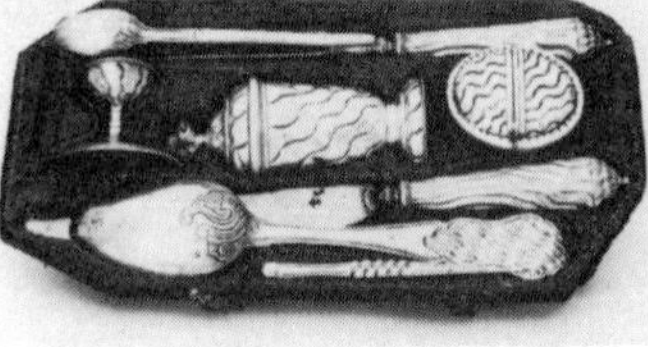

A German silver travelling set in contemporary leather case, by various makers, unidentified Nuremburg, c. 1760, 230 gm., excluding knife, fork and fitted case. **£1,500-2,000** *S*

A Hungarian silver-gilt belt, applied with garnets and beryls, unmarked, 76.5 cm. long, c. 1700, 410 gm. all in. **£1,200-1,600** *S*

A William IV silver-gilt dressing table set, all flat chased with a crest, helm and order flanked by foliage on a matted ground, fully marked, Reily & Storer, also 20 shaving, manicure and other implements, the majority Paul Storr for Storr & Mortimer, all London, 1833, 47 oz. 17 dwt. (1,483 gm.) all in of weighable silver. **£2,500-3,000** *S*

A George III bosun's whistle inscribed 'Honble/Mr. De Burgh' on one side and 'Belmont/Hampshire' on the other, Matthew Ferris, London, 1776, 5⅜ in. (13.6 cm.) long. **£500-550** *S*

A George III cow creamer, later gilt, John Schuppe, London, 1763, 5¾ in. (14.6 cm.) long, 4 oz. 4 dwt. (130 gm.). **£2,400-2,800** *S*

A pair of silver wall lights, 8¼ in. (21 cm.), 18th C. **£800-850** *S*

A Russian silver stirrup cup in the form of a rough-haired dog, gilt interior, 3¼ in. marks '84, A.C.', 19th C., 5 oz. **£600-700** *WHL*

Four Portuguese shaped oval sconces, one with 19th C. Lisbon town-mark, the others unmarked, possibly late 17th C., height of back plates 13½ in. (34.2 cm.), weight without branches 58 oz. **£1,100-£1,300** *C*

A Victorian egg cruet for 6, by Richard Hennell, 1857, 23.9 cm. overall length, 31 oz. **£500-600** *L*

A George III circular silver wine cooler with half reeded body, having grapevine border, with satanical horned mask handles, London, 1806, makers R. & S. Hennell, slight damage, 10 in., 62 oz. **£900-1,100** *WSW*

A Fabergé silver note pad holder, Workmaster Julias Alexandrovitch Rappoport, St. Petersburg, 1892, 13.3 cm. **£350-450** *Bon*

A silver-mounted loadstone, with silver binding, overall height 87 mm., late 18th C. **£800-900** *S*

A set of 31 Charles II silver gaming counters, 2.5 cm. diam., with inscribed portraits of the Kings and Queens of England (including the odd English and foreign prince), in contemporary silver drum-shaped counter box, by Simon Van De Passe, 2.5 cm. high, c. 1660. **£950-£1,050** *P*

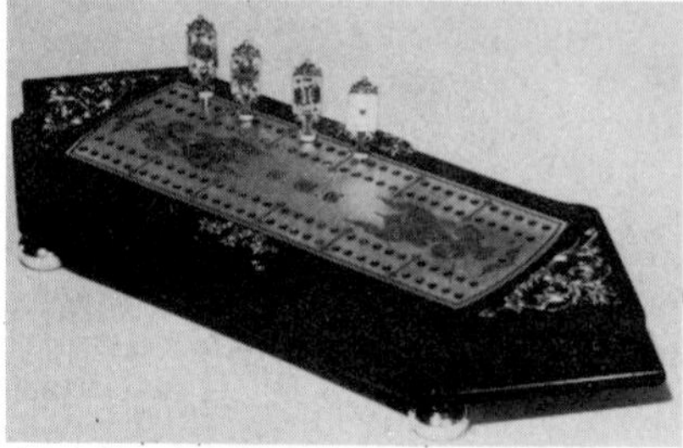
A late Victorian silver-mounted wooden cribbage board, the 4 pegs applied with enamel playing card finials, Jack; Queen, King and Ace of Hearts, by T. Latham & E. Morton, Birmingham, 1892, 27 by 9.7 cm. **£280-360** *P*

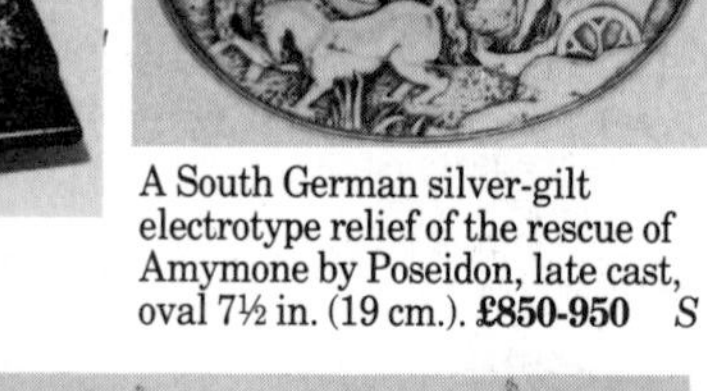
A South German silver-gilt electrotype relief of the rescue of Amymone by Poseidon, late cast, oval 7½ in. (19 cm.). **£850-950** *S*

SILVER MARKS

Owing to shortage of space, tables of Silver marks have been omitted from this edition of Miller's. Remember that marks for Birmingham, Chester, Edinburgh, Exeter, London, Sheffield and York are to be found in Miller's Guide 1983 (Volume IV) pages 516-519 and in Miller's Guide 1982 (Volume III) pages 431-434.

A pair of electroplated 5-light candelabra, maker's mark HW & Co., perhaps for Henry Wilkinson & Co., 58 cm. overall height. **£400-£500** *L*

A good pair of Sheffield plate candlesticks, 11½ in., c. 1850's. **£180-220** *IHA*

A silver-plated cruet stand, tops silver hallmarked 1906. **£150-£160** *FD*

A Victorian electroplated cruet stand by Dr. Christopher Dresser, the base struck with design registration mark for 11th June, 1878, maker's mark of Hukin and Heath, and stamped Designed by Dr. C. Dresser, 3⅝ in. (9.2 cm.) overall height. **£250-300** *L*

An 18th C. Old Sheffield plate snuff box, 6.5 by 4.75 cm., c. 1765. **£90-110** *P*

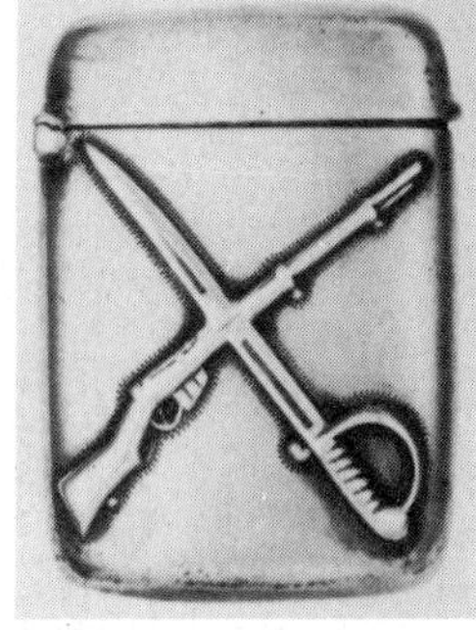

A vesta case, the cover applied with a crossed sword and rifle, 5.5 cm. long. **£40-45** *P*

(l.) A vesta case embossed with a portrait of King Edward VII, Birmingham, 1901, 5 cm. long. **£45-50** *P*

(r.) A late Victorian vesta case, embossed with a portrait of 'Charley's Aunt', inscribed on back 'From Charley's Aunt Dec. 21st 1895', by Walker & Hall, Sheffield, 1895, 4.5 cm. long. **£50-55** *P*

A 19th C. plated tobacco jar with liner, 8 in. **£120-150** *JMW*

A fine Victorian wine jug by Elkington & Co., 13½ in. **£500-£550** *WW*

A Sheffield plate tea pot and stand, 13¼ in. high, c. 1860. **£50-60** *MPA*

A Victorian patented silver-plate claret jug, the patented self-opening mechanism with a bunch of grapes weight, 13¼ in. (33.6 cm.) overall height. **£250-300** *L*

(l.) A spirit kettle on stand with hardwood handle and finial, supported on 3 curving legs with incomplete burner, 11 in. high. **£80-100** *DDM*

(c.) A large early Victorian tea urn with applied scroll and leaf handles, finial and rim, with ornate tap, 18 in. high. **£180-220** *DDM*

(r.) A late Victorian spirit kettle on lamp stand, with plain burner, 15 in. high. **£120-150** *DDM*

A Sheffield plate tea machine, with 3 compartments for black tea, green tea and coffee, English, 23⅜ in. (60 cm.), c. 1810. **£1,800-2,200** *S*

Examples of these tea machines are scarce and 'were quite the largest and most expensive of all articles made in Old Sheffield Plate'.

A late Sheffield tea urn, 18¼ in. (46.4 cm.). **£300-350** *L*

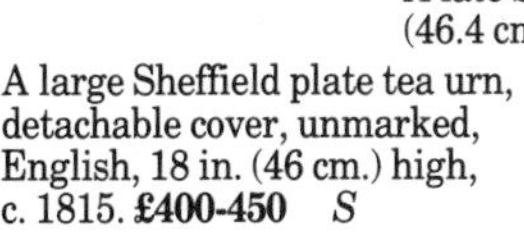

A large Sheffield plate tea urn, detachable cover, unmarked, English, 18 in. (46 cm.) high, c. 1815. **£400-450** *S*

A Sheffield plate tea urn, English, 16½ in. (42 cm.) high, c. 1820. **£400-450** *S*

A good Victorian 4-piece tea and coffee service by Elkington & Co., 10 in. (26.7 cm.) height of coffee pot. **£200-250** *L*

A fine Sheffield plate candle snuffer and tray, 10½ in., c. 1830. **£75-100** *IHA*

A Victorian large 4-piece tea and coffee service. **£250-300** *DDM*

A Christofle electroplated coffee set designed by Lino Sabattini, each piece stamped 'Christofle France Collection Gallia', tea pot numbered O L 750, 15 cm. ht. of coffee pot, c. 1960. **£170-200** *S*

A Victorian silver-plated tray, 27 in. **£140-160** *FD*

A silver-plated entrée dish, with 2 liners, 12 in., c. 1860. **£100-150** *IHA*

A pair of Sheffield plate sauce tureens and covers, with everted scroll and shell rims, crested, 8¾ in. (22.2 cm.) overall, c. 1835. **£900-1,100** *S*

A pair of oval sauce tureens and covers, engraved with trailing leaves and ferns below the everted beaded collar, covers also engraved, by Elkington & Co., struck with their date letter for 1879, 8 in. (20.5 cm.) overall. **£400-450** *SC*

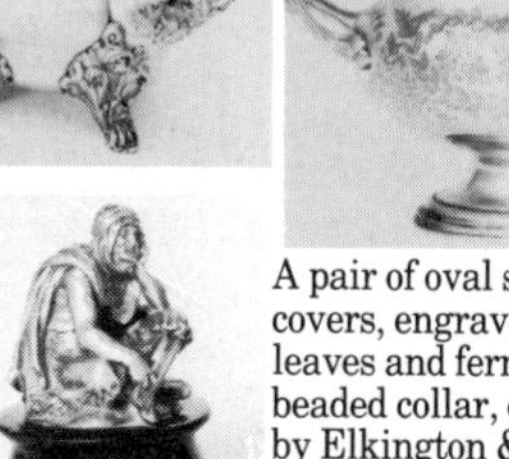

A silver-plated figure of a seated Arab-Bedouin, French produced, stamped 'Fanniere Fres'. **£90-110** *P*

A set of 4 entrée dishes and covers complete with heater bases, the dishes overlaid with flowers and foliage, the reversible covers with applied floral under-borders and engraved with a crest and motto below the top mounts, one handle a replacement, 13¾ in. (35 cm.) overall, c. 1820. **£850-950** *SC*

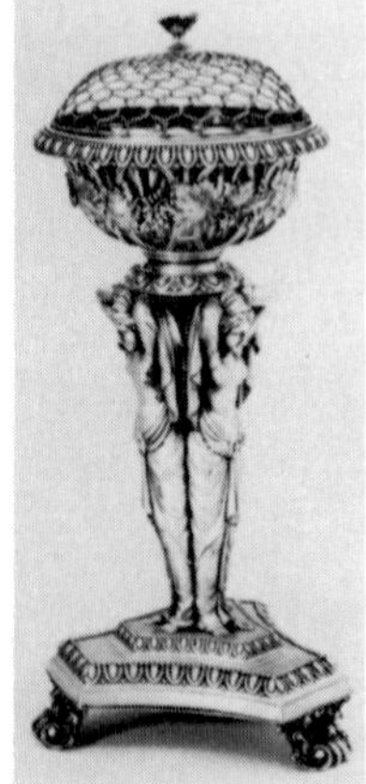

A Sheffield plate dessert stand, struck twice with the crown mark and once with a heart-shaped (? workman's) mark, English, 17 in. (43 cm.) high, c. 1830. **£800-900** *S*

A Sheffield plate oval verriere, English, 11¾ in. (30 cm.) wide, c. 1805. **£500-600** *S*

A Victorian cast electroplated table bell modelled as Old Mother Hubbard by Elkington & Co., 1857, 11.5 cm. high. **£120-150** *P*

A sweetmeat stand with parcel-gilt electroplated copper electrotype pedestal, 6 in. (15.4 cm.) high, Elkington & Co., Birmingham, 1874, stamped: 861/M, fitted with a circular blue-stamped agate bowl, 6½ in. (16.8 cm.) diam. **£150-200** *S*

A faceted clear glass bottle encased in gold floral trellis, the cap inscribed on white enamel band Gage de mon amitie, with original glass stopper, 2⅜ in. (6 cm.) high, c. 1765. **£800-900** *C*

A faceted clear glass bottle encased in gold architectural scroll settings, cap inscribed on white enamel band Marque de mon amitie, original stopper, slight damage to enamel band, 2⅞ in. (7.4 cm.) high, c. 1765. **£700-800** *C*

A clear glass bottle in boldly scrolling cagework mount in matt and polished gold, the cap inscribed on white enamel band Gage de mon amitie, 3⅛ in. (8 cm.) high, c. 1765. **£1,200-1,400** *C*

A Chinoiserie clear glass bottle with faceted neck and sides, and gold cagework mounts, cap inscribed on white enamel band L'amour nous unis, small restoration to mount, cap possibly associated, in contemporary fishskin case, the bottle 2⅞ in. (7.3 cm.) high, c. 1765. **£750-850** *C*

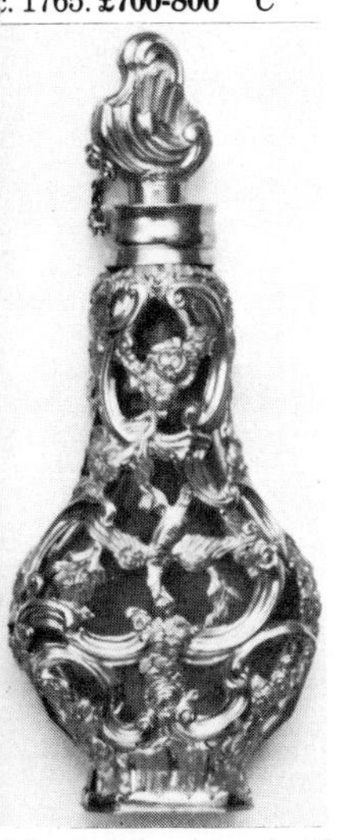

A neo-classical clear glass bottle with 2 enamel medallions, mounted in floral cagework, with associated engraved gold cap and original glass stopper, 2¾ in. (7 cm.) high, c. 1770. **£800-900** *C*

A faceted clear glass bottle encased in gold cagework, with chained gold stopper, in original fishskin case, the bottle 3¼ (8.3 cm.) high, c. 1765. **£1,100-1,300** *C*

A late 18th C. Swiss miniature gold and enamel scent bottle, 1¾ in., cased. **£550-650** *T*

An unusual gold-mounted amber scent bottle, the red amber overlaid with pierced and chased gold mounts, 8.5 cm. high, late 19th C. **£900-1,000** *S*

A small gold snuff box, apparently unmarked, English or Dutch, 6 cm. wide, c. 1725. **£3,000-3,500** *S*

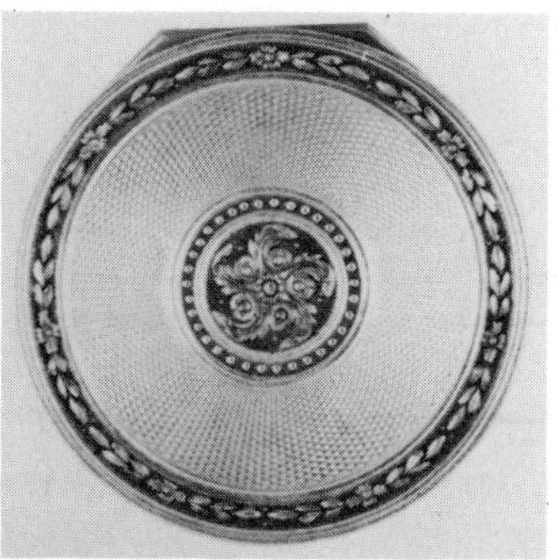

A George III two-colour gold circular snuff box by George Hall, 1798, 7 cm. diam., approx. 4.5 oz. **£2,200-2,500** *P*

A George III 18 ct. gold oval snuff box by Jacob Amedroz, 1805, 5.75 cm. long, approx., 1.5 oz. **£1,000-1,200** *P*

A Mexican three-colour gold cheroot case, assay master Antonio Forcada y la Plaza, Mexico City, in later case, 7 cm. high, 1791-1818. **£1,600-2,000** *S*

A Swiss four-colour gold pill box, maker's mark rubbed, Geneva, 1½ in. (4 cm.) diam., c. 1825. **£450-£500** *S*

A three-colour 18 ct. gold presentation snuff box by A. J. Strachan, the interior of the lid with a presentation inscription, maker's mark, London, 1825, 8.5 cm. wide. **£2,300-2,600** *S*

A Russian gold coloured metal cigarette case by Karl Faberge, workmaster Henrik Wigstrom, 9 by 6.25 cm., c. 1910, approx. 6 oz. **£2,100-2,500** *P*

A circular gold-mounted grey composition snuff box set with a miniature of a young boy in Van Dyck costume by John Smart, few pieces of inlay missing, some damage to miniature, 2½ in. (6.4 cm.) diam., c. 1780. **£1,100-£1,300** *C*

An Austrian enamelled gold presentation snuff box, with a micro-mosaic plaque, maker's initials IK, 3⅝ in. (9.3 cm.) long, early 19th C. **£1,500-2,000** *C*

A Victorian 18 ct. gold snuff box, with inscribed lid and reeded sides, the interior engraved with a list of donors, Alfred Taylor, Birmingham, 1853, 3 in. (7.5 cm.) long, 2 oz. 16 dwt. (87 gm.). **£750-850** *S*

A 19th C. Swiss gold snuff box, stamped with French import marks for 1864-93, 8 by 5.5 cm., c. 1865, approx. 3 oz. **£750-850** *P*

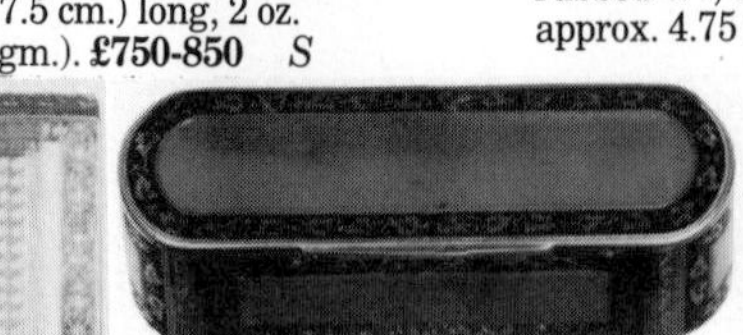

A Swiss oblong engine-turned gold snuff box, on a blue enamel ground, some damage to enamel, Neuchatel, 3⅝ in. (9.2 cm.) long, 19th C. **£600-700** *C*

A modern 9 ct. gold oblong snuff box by Asprey & Co., 8 by 4.5 cm., 2.5 oz. **£350-400** *P*

A French gold snuff box with later roman micro-mosaic plaque, Paris, restricted warranty mark 1798-1838, maker's initials LFR, the back of the lid engraved 'Castellani in Roma', 3½ in. (9 cm.) long. **£2,500-3,000** *C*

A 19th C. Continental gold and enamel snuff box, probably Swiss, 7.5 by 4.5 cm., c. 1840, approx. 2.25 oz. **£500-600** *P*

A 19th C. gold box with engine-turned sides and base, stamped '18 and bearing a maker's mark, rubbed W?, 8 by 5 cm., c. 1840, approx. 4.75 oz. **£1,000-1,200** *P*

An 18 ct. gold snuff box with cabochon sapphire thumbpiece, 5. by 3.75 cm., approx. 2.25 oz. **£550-£600** *P*

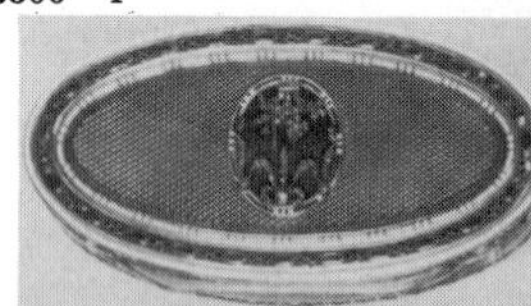

A Louis XVI oval gold and enamel snuff box with later applied rose-diamond set basket-of-flowers on red enamel medallion, by Nicolas Marguerit, Paris, 1778-79, with th poincons of J. B. Fouache, 3½ in. (9 cm.) long. **£3,000-4,000** *C*

A Swiss octagonal gold and enamel snuff box, painted after Prudhon bordered by split pearls, by Georges Remond et Cie, 3 in. (7.6 cm.) long, early 19th C. **£2,000-3,000** *C*

A Swiss oval gold snuff box, the black enamel body with a grisaille musical trophy, gilt flowers and instruments, the flange numbered 1049, 2⅞ in. (7.4 cm.) long, c. 1840 **£1,800-2,000** *C*

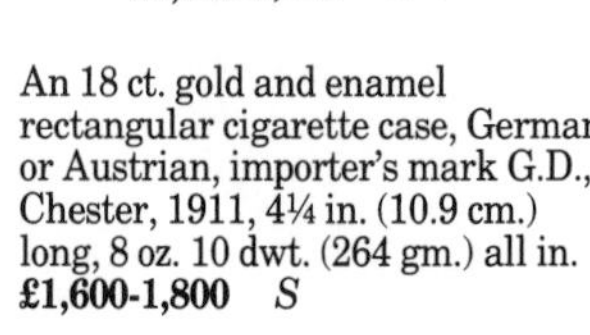

An 18 ct. gold and enamel rectangular cigarette case, German or Austrian, importer's mark G.D., Chester, 1911, 4¼ in. (10.9 cm.) long, 8 oz. 10 dwt. (264 gm.) all in. **£1,600-1,800** *S*

A Louis XVI gold and blonde tortoiseshell snuff box, the flange engraved Ve George Beaulieu à Paris, Paris, 1770, with the poincons of Julien Alaterre, 3½ in. (9 cm.) long. **£1,800-2,000** *C*

Veuve George Beaulieu was the wife of P. F. M. de Beaulieu, maitre 1763-92 and widow of the well-known orfevre Jean George. Beaulieu signed his boxes with his wife's name for the distinction of this association.

An 18th C. gold-mounted tortoiseshell box, the cover set with an enamel plaque of a lady, probably English, 8.2 cm. diam., c. 1760. **£800-900** *P*

A circular gold-mounted tortoiseshell box, with brightly coloured gouache miniatures, signed H. Sallembier and dated 1815, the flange with decharge of J.B. Fouache, Paris, 2¾ in. (7 cm.) diam., 1774-80. **£900-1,000** *C*

Henri Sallembier (c. 1753-1820) was a Parisian painter and engraver.

A vari-coloured gold vinaigrette, the cover with plaited hair compartment in chased green and red gold, unmarked, 1⅛ in. (2.8 cm.) long, c. 1820. **£400-600** *C*

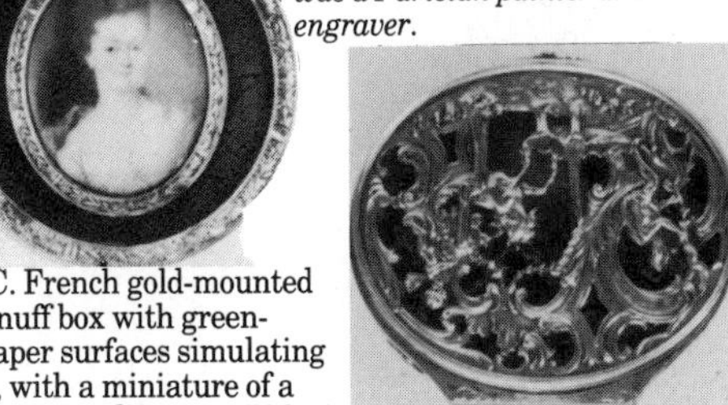

An 18th C. French gold-mounted circular snuff box with green-stained paper surfaces simulating shagreen, with a miniature of a lady, Paris, 6 cm. diam., c. 1786. **£350-400** *P*

An oval mottled agate snuff box with gold cagework mounts, the sides with scroll cartouches, base mount missing, crack to cover, 2⅜ in. (6 cm.) long, 18th/19th C. **£800-1,200** *C*

A large gold and enamel snuff box, the lid inset with an earlier French enamel plaque, marks rubbed, 8 cm. long, late 19th/early 20th C. **£3,500-4,000** *S*

A 19th C. gold vinaigrette of engine-turned design, the rose diamond set Imperial crown, probably applied at a later date, unmarked, 3 cm. diam., c. 1820. **£350-400** *P*

A George III gold-mounted ivory patch box, the blue enamelled cover set with a memorial panel of plaited hair, enclosed by a border of pearls, in original fitted red leather case, 8.75 by 3.5 cm., c. 1790. **£180-£200** *P*

An 18th C. French gold-mounted oval tortoiseshell snuff box, the cover set with a miniature of a lady by Luke Sullivan, 1769, 8.6 cm. long, c. 1770. **£600-700** *P*

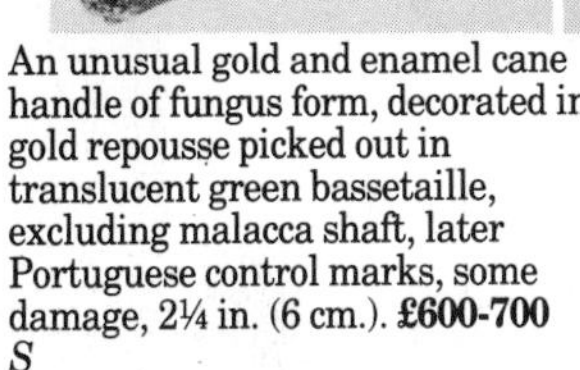

An unusual gold and enamel cane handle of fungus form, decorated in gold repousse picked out in translucent green bassetaille, excluding malacca shaft, later Portuguese control marks, some damage, 2¼ in. (6 cm.). **£600-700** *S*

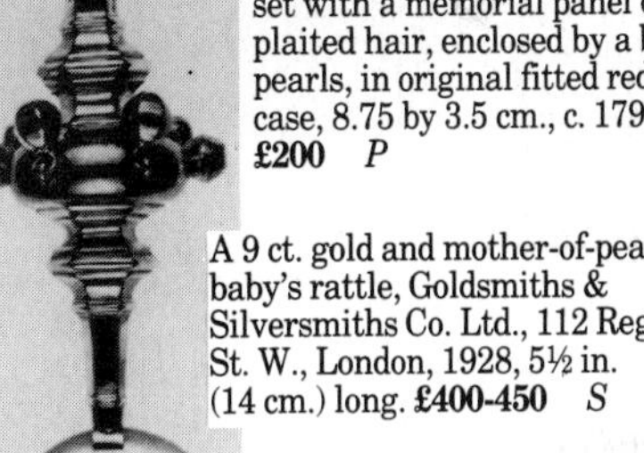

A 9 ct. gold and mother-of-pearl baby's rattle, Goldsmiths & Silversmiths Co. Ltd., 112 Regent St. W., London, 1928, 5½ in. (14 cm.) long. **£400-450** *S*

An English gold, enamel and velvet book cover containing 'Peacock's Historical Almanack for 1833', in the manner of A. J. Strachan, 4¼ in. (11 cm.) long, c. 1833. **£550-650** *S*

A gold fob seal, with foxes, birds and foliate-chased superstructure, the agate matrix engraved with a coat-of-arms, 19th C. **£500-600** *Bon*

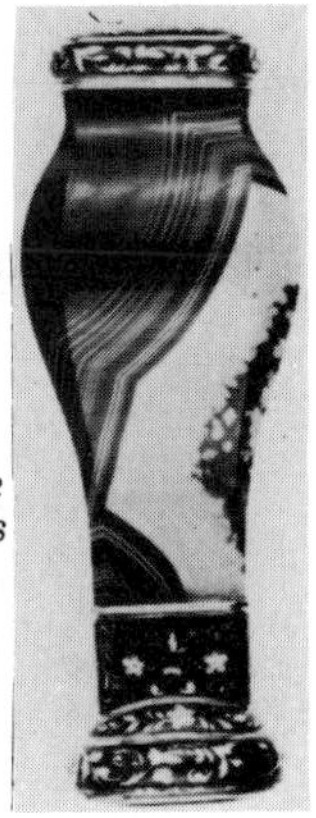

A gold, enamel and hardstone desk seal, North Italian or Swiss, slight damage to enamel, 7.5 cm. high, c. 1830. **£600-700** *S*

This type of enamel decoration, using only black and white with the gold or just gold on black enamel, is to be seen on snuff boxes from Turin. Swiss taille d'epargne enamelling, on the other hand, tends to use more colours although with very similar plumy scroll and flower patterns.

GLASS

During the course of the past year the glass market has reflected, albeit cautiously, the general increase in th availability of money.

Prices have tended to rise right across the board, even in those areas which fell back during the tougher part of th depression. More glass is appearing in auction rooms, both in specialist and general sales, and the present buyer' market is felt to be contributing to a reawakening of interest in collectable glass.

Bohemian glass, particularly, has made a noticeable recovery. The high prices paid by Arab buyers prior to the revolution have not yet fully returned, but there are positive indications that the more flamboyant pieces of all kinds are set for a healthy revival.

Good quality slag glass and, particularly, marked pieces of press moulded glass are attracting the attention of an increasing number of collectors. Larger pieces of the best quality are becoming fairly scarce, which is always an indicator of imminent price increases.

Still undervalued in the view of many authorities are many 18th C. drinking glasses and early 19th C. cut glass tablewares. Bought with care, these are likely to prove a sound investment, as are large, early decanters. Smaller liqueur decanters, on the other hand are attracting relatively little interest.

All in all, the market is healthy, with marked interest being shown in better quality wares of all kinds, particularly those having special or unusual features.

An early sealed wine bottle, of clear dark green tinted metal, neck with string rim, applied seal with the impressed initials IAL, chip on base, small chip on seal, 8 in., c. 1670-80. **£850-950** *S*

(l.) A wine bottle with seal 'All Souls Common Room', 280 mm. high, c. 1780. **£30-35** *Som*

(r.) A Ricketts patent bottle, 3-piece seal 'Donneraile House', 285 mm. high, c. 1820. **£40-50** *Som*

Two west country wine bottles of green bottle glass:—

(l.) Seal 'R. Densham Upton 1810', 285 mm. high. **£140-160** *Som*

(r.) Seal, crown and letter 'C' for Coham, 293 mm. high, c. 1770. **£90-£110** *Som*

A dated seal bottle, the seal inscribed 'E. Geldart. Norwich. 1784', 10½ in. **£90-120** *SC*

(l.) A green spirit flagon with loop handle, metal mount, cork and metal stopper, 195 mm. high, c. 1825. **£80-85** *Som*

(c.) A similar blue bottle, 195 mm. high, c. 1825. **£75-80** *Som*

(r.) A similar pair of amethyst bottles, 195 mm. high, c. 1825. **£200-220** pair *Som*

A pair of good square bottles, each engraved on one side 'John Stevens 1787' and on the reverse side 'Exeter', above a sunflower, 20.5 cm. high by 9 cm. square, c. 1780. **£160-180** *Som*

(l.) An emerald green bottle with wrythen moulded decoration, 140 mm. high, c. 1840. **£90-100** *Som*

(r.) A similar blue wine bottle, 100 mm., c. 1840. **£80-90** *Som*

Four green glass wine bottles, applied with a seal inscribed Joseph Wilson, 1839, the recessed foot moulded with the name H. Ricketts & Co., Glassworks, Bristol. **£150-200** *Bea*

(l.) An amethyst wine bottle with annulated pouring ring, possibly Scottish, 295 mm., c. 1840. **£90-£100** *Som*

(l.c.) An early green heavy crown glass wine bottle with single neck ring, possibly Alloa, 285 mm., c. 1800. **£65-70** *Som*

(r.c.) A pair of blue wine bottles with vertically faceted neck and body, triangular cut neck ring, 295 mm., c. 1870. **£180-200** *Som*

(r.) A green wine bottle with vertically faceted neck and body, cut pouring lip, 242 mm. high, c. 1845. **£95-100** *Som*

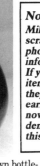

A good Nailsea brown bottle-glass bottle with opaque white looping, 240 mm. high, c. 1810. **£160-180** *Som*

A pair of green wrythen moulded wine bottles with everted lips, 11 in. high, c. 1860. **£160-180** pair *Som*

A dated seal wine bottle in dark green metal, applied with a seal inscribed 'JAs OAKES.BURY.1788', 10 in. **£90-120** *SC*

No two editions alike!
Miller's is compiled from scratch each year. All new photographs and fresh information!
If you are unable to find the items you seek in this volume, they may have been included in earlier editions. These have now been reprinted to satisfy demand; details at the back of this book.

A Nailsea pitcher in brown bottle-glass with splashes of opaque white, with crude applied handle, 200 mm. high, c. 1800. **£160-180** *Som*

A pair of early 19th C. amethyst glass bottles of slender shouldered form, 10 in. **£90-110** *WHL*

(l.) A turquoise green spirit bottle, the body and neck with flat cut fluting and cut neck ring, cut steeple stopper, 193 mm. high, c. 1840. **£60-65** *Som*

(r.) An unusual large turquoise green square decanter with faceted ball stopper, the body engraved 'R' within a star surround, 200 mm. high, c. 1800. **£180-200** *Som*

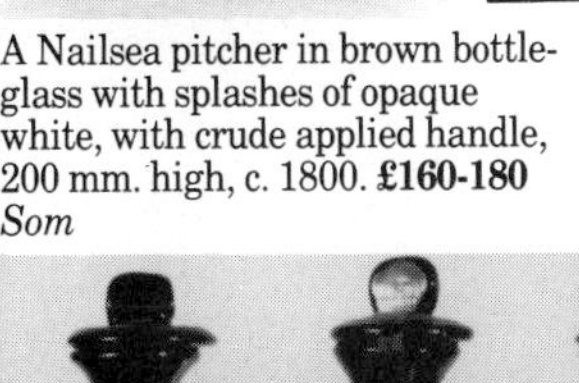

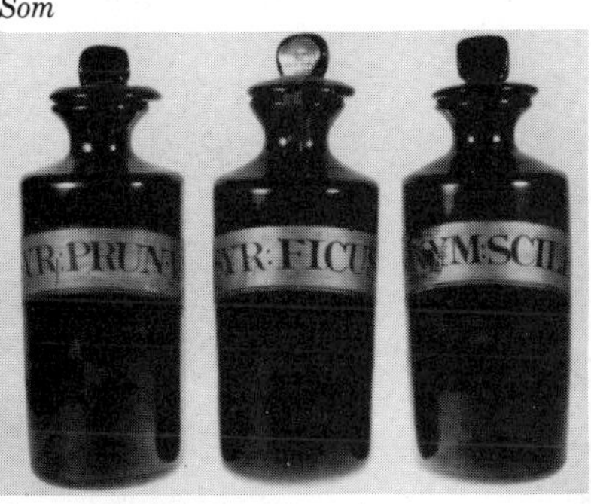

Three early Bristol apothecaries bottles with gilt contents labels, long peg stoppers, c. 1800. **£150-£180** the set *Som*

A set of 3 coloured wine bottles, amethyst, green and blue, with wrythen moulded bodies and necks, plated mother-of-pearl stoppers, 'Whiskey', 'Gin' and 'Brandy', in a later wooden trefoil stand, height of bottles less stoppers, 318 mm., c. 1840. **£400-450** the set *Som*

(l.) A Bristol blue cruet bottle, 'Kyan', with pouring lip and cut faceted stopper, 111 mm., c. 1790. **£70-75** *Som*

(c.) A pair of Bristol blue cruet bottles with gilt 'Anchovy' and 'Soy', 111 mm., c. 1790. **£120-140** *Som*

(r.) A Bristol blue cruet bottle, 'Kyan', in good gilt surround, with lozenge stopper, 95 mm., c. 1790. **£70-75** *Som*

A set of 3 coloured wine bottles, amethyst, green and blue, with wrythen moulded bodies and necks, in a silver-plated trefoil stand, height of bottles 315 mm., c. 1840. **£400-450** *Som*

Three square spirit bottles, cut overall with diamonds and with pouring necks, cut ball stoppers, in a trefoil Sheffield plated stand, 190 mm. high, c. 1820. **£140-160** *Som*

A 3-bottle tantalus, the round spirit bottles with base and neck fluting, with single neck rings, the bodies engraved 'Rum', 'Brandy' and 'Gin', with mushroom stoppers, in a Sheffield plated trefoil frame, bottles 225 mm. high, c. 1825. **£160-180** *Som*

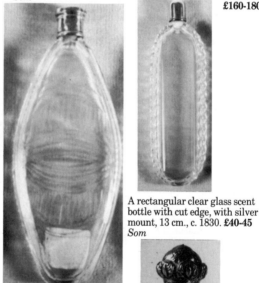

An oval clear glass scent bottle, with strawberry diamond cutting and serrated edge, with silver mount, 10 cm., c. 1770. **£80-90** *Som*

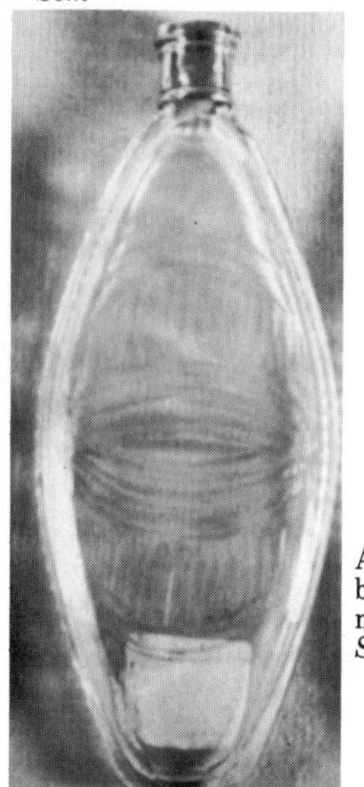

An oval flat clear glass scent bottle with flat cutting, with silver mount, 13 cm., c. 1780. **£35-40** *Som*

A rectangular clear glass scent bottle with cut edge, with silver mount, 13 cm., c. 1830. **£40-45** *Som*

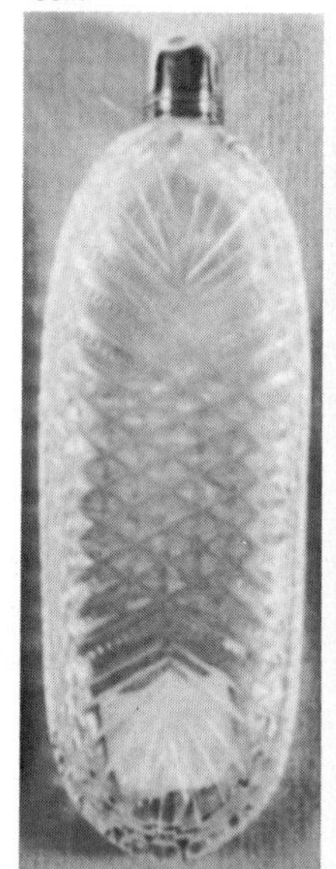

A rectangular clear glass scent bottle, diamond and facet cut, with silver mount, 13 cm., c. 1820. **£45-£50** *Som*

A pear-shaped flattened clear glass scent bottle with monogrammed gold top, 8.8 cm., c. 1850. **£90-95** *Som*

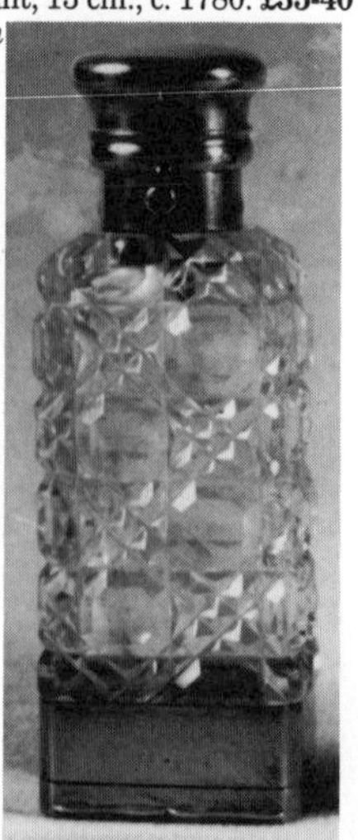

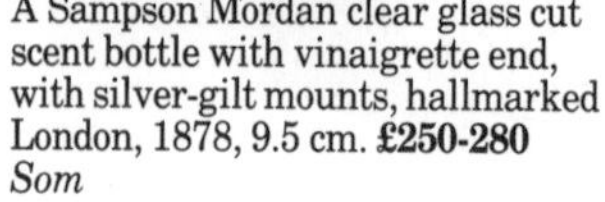

A Sampson Mordan clear glass cut scent bottle with vinaigrette end, with silver-gilt mounts, hallmarked London, 1878, 9.5 cm. **£250-280** *Som*

A long scent bottle with white latticinio panels divided by opaque blue borders, with embossed silver mount, 11.5 cm., c. 1860. **£150-£160** *Som*

A Sampson Mordan hexagonal clear glass scent bottle with embossed silver-gilt mount, with monogram and circle of turquoises, 8 cm., c. 1880. **£170-180** *Som*

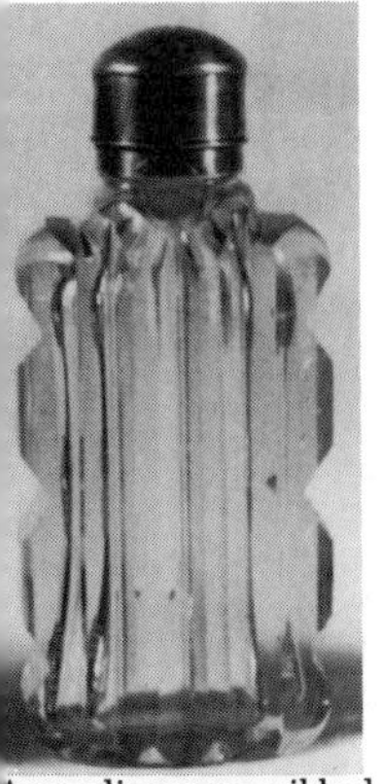

A vaseline green ribbed and cut scent bottle, with silver mount, 8 cm., c. 1880. **£60-65** *Som*

An octagonal clear glass scent bottle, with silver mount, hallmarked London, 1883, 7 cm. **£45-50** *Som*

A pale green cut scent bottle, with silver mount, hallmarked Birmingham, 1888, 6.5 cm. **£35-£40** *Som*

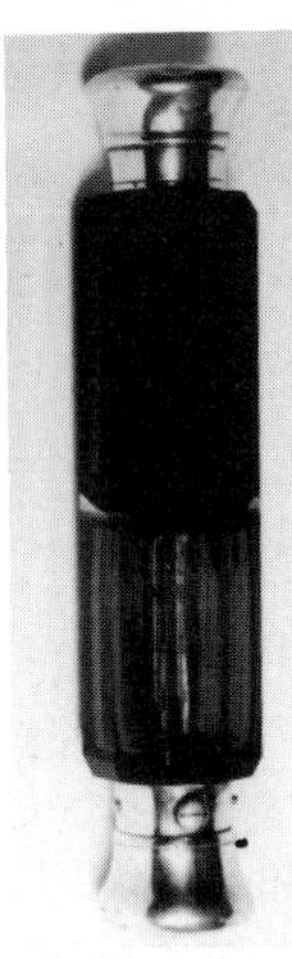

A cranberry glass double-ended perfume bottle with silver tops, 5½ in. long, c. 1840. **£50-60** *BP*

A French scent bottle with blue and white zig-zag pattern, gilt-brass mount, 8 cm., c. 1850. **£130-140** *Som*

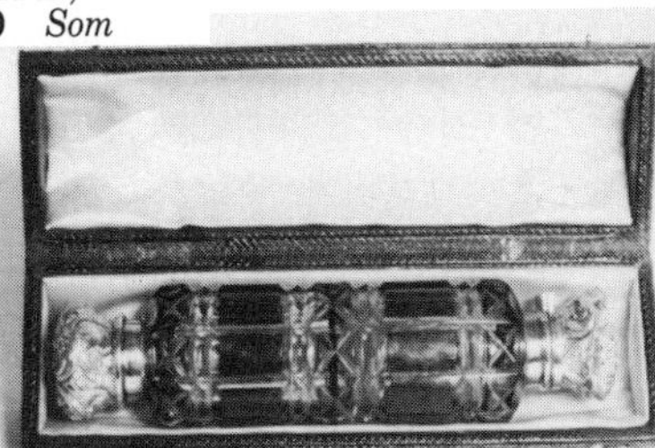

A clear glass Oxford lavender scent bottle, with floral decoration, 12.3 cm., c. 1860. **£25-30** *Som*

A green overlay cut glass double-ended perfume bottle, 5½ in., c. 1850. **£80-100** *BP*

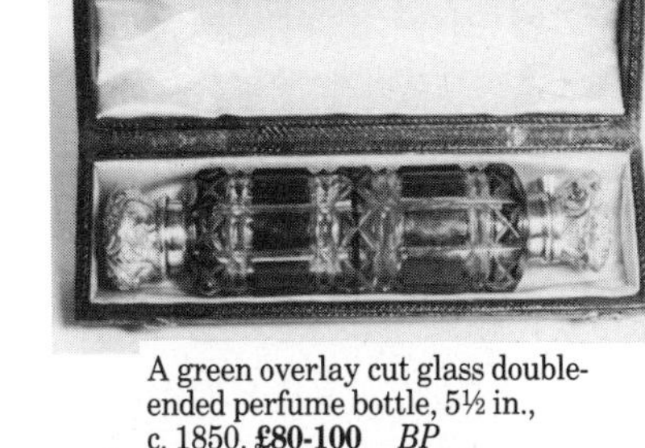

A clear glass Oxford lavender scent bottle with enamelled rose and gilt decoration, 13 cm., c. 1860. **£25-£30** *Som*

A blue overlay cut glass double-ended perfume bottle with silver tops, 5½ in., c. 1860. **£70-90** *BP*

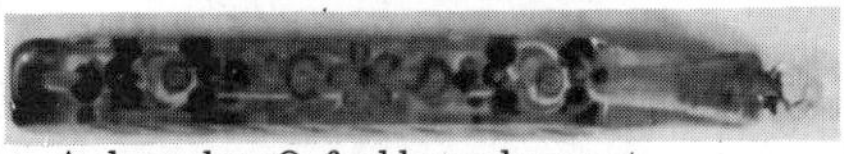

A heavy blue cut scent bottle, with silver mount, 9.5 cm., c. 1860. **£55-£60** *Som*

A round flat amber scent bottle, cut with strawberry diamonds with plated mount, 7 cm., c. 1860. **£35-£40** *Som*

A green overlay scent bottle, with embossed silver mount, 8.5 cm., c. 1860. **£70-75** *Som*

A blue overlay scent bottle, with embossed silver mount, 8.8 cm., c. 1870. **£45-50** *Som*

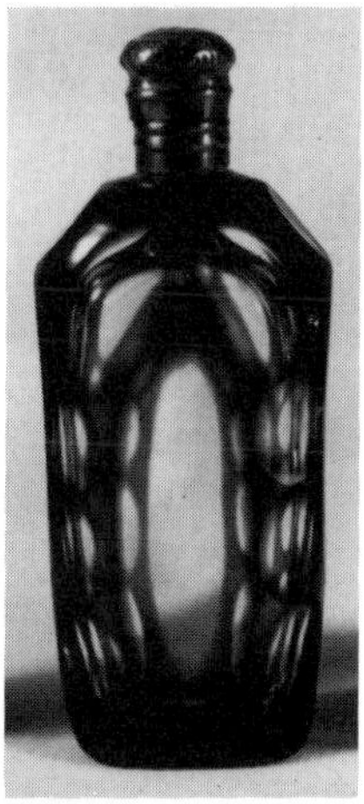

An amethyst glass scent bottle, with cut flutes and strawberry diamonds, 6 cm., c. 1860. **£45-50** *Som*

A green overlay scent bottle, with embossed gilt-brass mount, 9 cm., c. 1860. **£65-70** *Som*

A red glass scent bottle with faceted sides, with plain silver mount, cap marked 'Thos. Maw & Sons', 8.5 cm., c. 1880. **£55-60** *Som*

An amber Oxford lavender scent bottle, with jewelled, enamelled and gilt decoration, 19 cm., c. 1880. **£40-45** *Som*

A blue cut scent bottle, with silver-gilt mount, 9 cm., c. 1880. **£90-£100** *Som*

A red glass smelling salts bottle, with silver mount, marked Birmingham, 1897, 7.5 cm. **£40-£45** *Som*

A blue overlay scent bottle, with plated mount, 8.5 cm., c. 1880. **£55-£60** *Som*

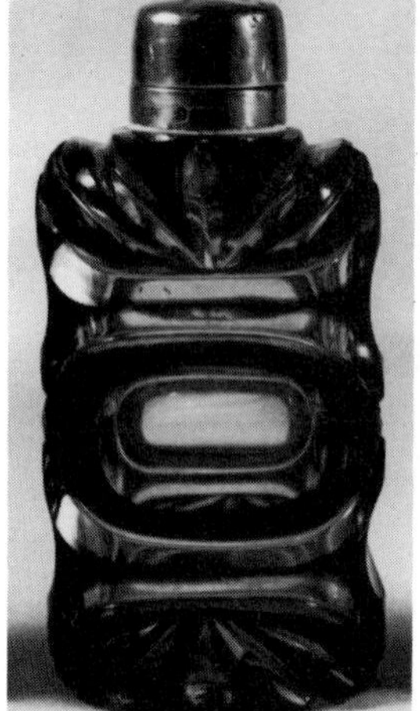

A blue overlay scent bottle, with silver mount, hallmarked Birmingham, 1903, 9 cm. **£75-80** *Som*

A cameo glass scent bottle carved with plants and a bee in opaque white on a sapphire blue ground, with hinged silver top, Birmingham, 1880 or 1885. **£500-£600** *L*

An English cameo scent bottle, the deep amber body overlaid in white, the silver top with Chester hallmark for 1884, 7.5 cm. **£180-£240** *P*

An English cameo ovoid scent bottle, the red glass overlaid in white and carved with lilies growing from water and flying insects, the silver screw top with London hallmark for 1884 and maker's mark of Sampson Mordan in fitted velvet case, 14 cm. **£850-£950** *P*

A clear glass 'cut' cornucopia scent bottle, with embossed silver mount and finger ring, 5 cm., c. 1880. **£65-£70** *Som*

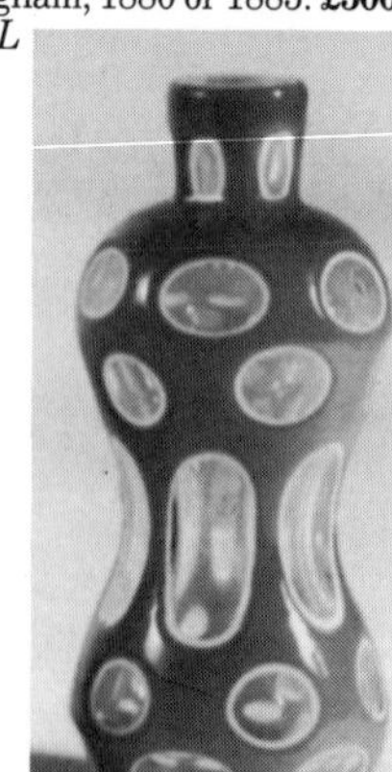

A Bohemian, waisted pink overlay scent flask, 8.5 cm., c. 1860. **£60-£65** *Som*

An Irish 'turnover rim' bowl, cut with facets with 5 constrictions, square foot with 'lemon squeezer' base, 8½ in., c. 1800. **£200-300** *S*

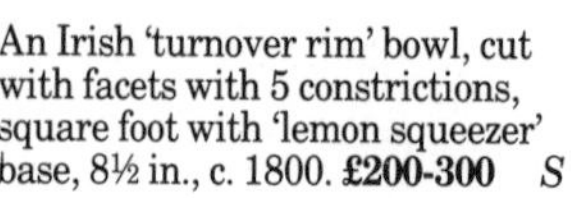

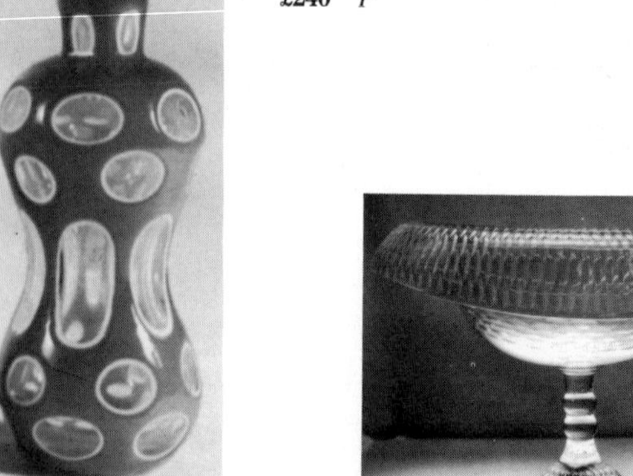

An Irish canoe bowl with turned over rim, cut with elongated hexagons, the bowl cut with shallow ovals, bobbin knop stem, square domed 'lemon squeezer' foot, 230 mm. high, c. 1800. **£400-450** *Som*

An Irish cut fruit bowl, with arch-and-angle rim and flat-cut diamonds, on a sliced stem, thick oval foot, small chips on rim, 6¾ in. high by 12¾ in. across, c. 1800. **£350-400** *S*

An Irish oval salad bowl, with scalloped rim cut with a band of shallow diamonds, supported on a heavy baluster stem, moulded foot, 9¼ in. high by 13½ in. across, c. 1790. **£450-500** *S*

A late Georgian cut glass bowl, 8 in. diam. **£90-125** *BP*

A late Georgian Irish cut glass bowl, 5½ in. **£60-100** *BP*

A 19th C. pink glass overlay bowl with handle, 7 in. long. **£80-90** *SA*

An Irish 'turnover rim' fruit bowl, cut with a band of diamonds, the rim with a band of prisms and hexagonal diamonds, lobed foot with basal moulded rosette, 8¼ in. high by 12 in. across, c. 1800. **£400-£450** *S*

A good Irish bowl of heavy dark metal, cut with shallow diamonds, cut rim, star cut base, 5¾ in. high by 9¾ in. diam., c. 1790. **£200-£250** *Som*

A rare bowl by William Beilby, with a white enamel diaper and rococo scroll decoration and worn gilt rim, bearing possible bethrothal initials 'ML' and dated 1765, on a circular foot, 2¾ in. high. **£1,500-1,700** *AG*

Until now only 3 other bowls were known to be in existence, one in the Corning Glass Museum, U.S.A., the second in the Victoria and Albert Museum, London, and the third in the Laing Art Gallery, Newcastle-upon-Tyne.

A sweetmeat-glass, carrying handle with raspberry-prunt terminals, minute chip to fold on rim, 13 cm. high, c. 1730. **£120-160** *C*

A good Irish 'canoe' salad bowl, with cut arch-and-angle rim and shallow polished diamonds, on a heavy baluster stem, moulded foot, small chips on the rim, 9¼ in. high by 13¾ in. wide, c. 1790. **£500-£550** *S*

A Nailsea 'end of the day' glass bowl and cover, 5 in. diam., c. 1870. **£20-30** *BP*

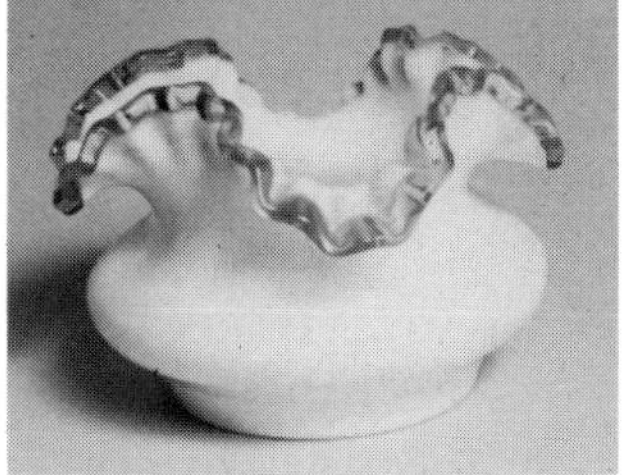
A Stourbridge blue and opaque white glass bowl, 5½ in. diam., c. 1880. **£20-25** *BP*

A 19th C. pink glass overlay basket, 7½ in. **£60-70** *SA*

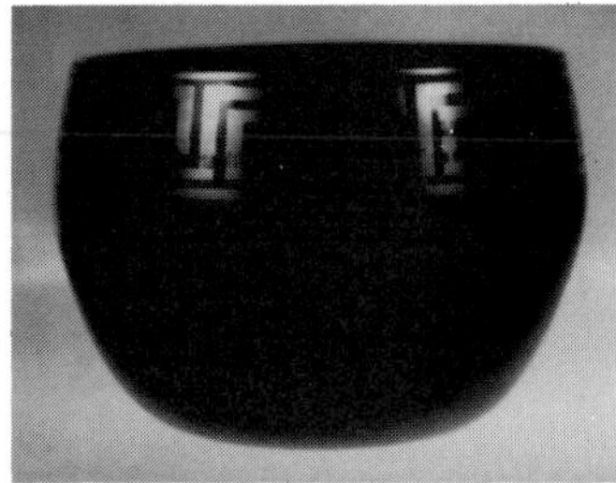
A rare blue finger bowl with Greek key decoration, signed underneath 'I. Jacobs Bristol', 80 mm. high, c. 1790. **£400-450** *Som*

A pair of early 19th C. finger bowls decorated with flowers, leaves and swags, 4¾ in. wide. **£60-70** *DSH*

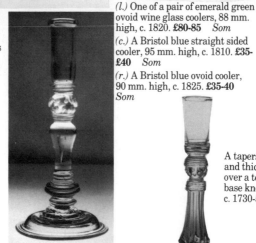

(l.) One of a pair of emerald green ovoid wine glass coolers, 88 mm. high, c. 1820. **£80-85** *Som*

(c.) A Bristol blue straight sided cooler, 95 mm. high, c. 1810. **£35-£40** *Som*

(r.) A Bristol blue ovoid cooler, 90 mm. high, c. 1825. **£35-40** *Som*

A taperstick with cylindrical nozzle and thickened rim, on a ball knop over a teared baluster section and base knop, on a terraced foot, 5 in., c. 1730-50. **£200-250** *S*

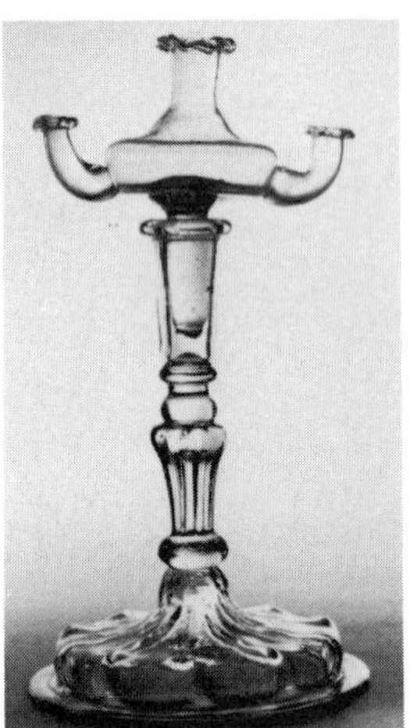

A pedestal-stemmed candlestick and detachable oil-lamp, the candlestick with a slender nozzle and everted rim, the oil-lamp of compressed form with 2 curved spouts with folded rims and with an applied vermicular collar to the rim, 29 cm. overall height, late 17th/early 18th C. **£600-800** *S*

A fine taperstick, the socket with folded rim, on a composite stem with collar, air beaded knop, inverted baluster, annulated and angular knops, domed folded foot, 155 mm. high, c. 1745. **£300-350** *Som*

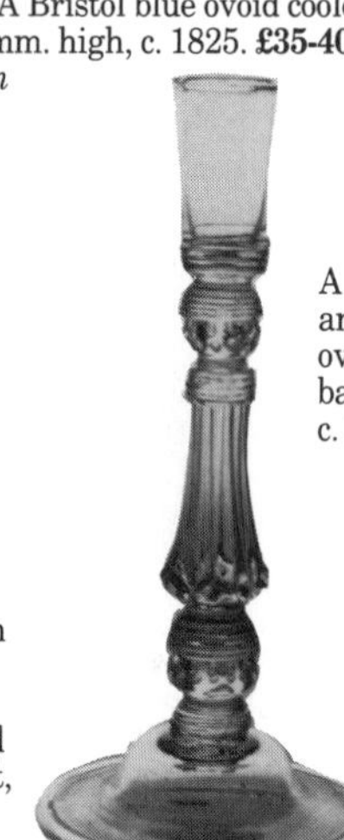

A candlestick, the nozzle on an inverted pedestal stem flanked by a series of collars and beaded ball knops, domed and folded foot, 10¾ in., c. 1745. **£300-400** *S*

A pair of cut candlesticks, the spirally cut urn-shaped bodies on square cut feet, cut nozzles with collar below, 265 mm. high, c. 1810. **£170-200** *Som*

A Swedish ormolu and cut glass 7-light chandelier, the circular base suspended by ormolu fillets above a central blue glass dish, 42 in. (107 cm.) high, early 19th C. **£2,500-3,000** *C*

A Baccarat moulded glass candlestick, 7½ in., c. 1920. **£50-£80** *BP*

A large Venetian coloured glass chandelier, fitted for electricity, 30 in. diam. by 43 in. high (76 by 109 cm.). **£700-800** *L*

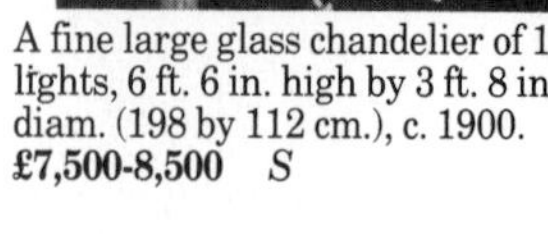

A fine large glass chandelier of 18 lights, 6 ft. 6 in. high by 3 ft. 8 in. diam. (198 by 112 cm.), c. 1900. **£7,500-8,500** *S*

A cut glass chandelier with faceted baluster stem and reservoir, 10 faceted S-shaped branches, 55 in. (140 cm.) high, 19th C. **£5,000-6,000** *C*

A gilt-metal and opaque glass chandelier, fitted for electricity, the whole sectionalised for use as a smaller chandelier if required, 25 in. diam. by 43 in. high (64 by 109 cm.), late 19th C. **£1,300-£1,500** *L*

A good 5-light glass chandelier, approx. 31 in. high. **£350-400** *PWC*

An enamelled decanter and stopper by William and Mary Beilby, decorated in white enamel with 'Madeira' in a cartouche, the reverse with a bell-flower spray, facet-cut spire stopper, 28.8 cm., c. 1765. **£2,500-3,000** *L*

A good 6-light glass chandelier, approx. 40 in. high. **£350-400** *PWC*

A good cruciform decanter, with string ring, 239 mm. high, c. 1730. **£120-140** *Som*

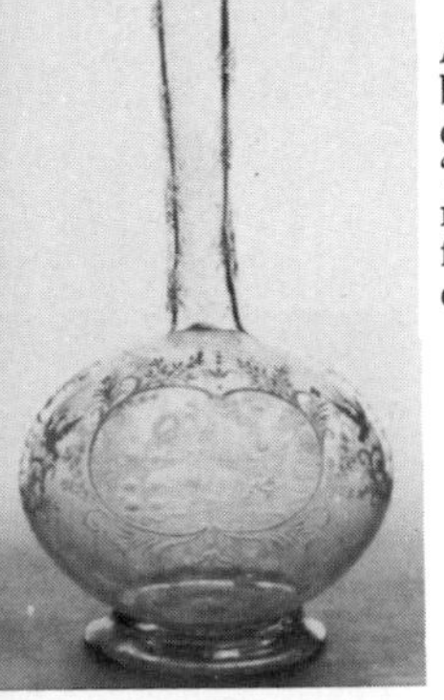

A Nuremburg engraved bottle decanter, with Cupid and a sunflower flanked by trees, the reverse with Cupid seated, the neck with a spiral band of berried foliage, 26.5 cm. high, c. 1720. **£600-800** *SC*

A good 18th C. decanter, the mallet body engraved 'Port', in a cartouche surrounded by fruiting vine, lozenge lunar cut stopper, 240 mm. high, c. 1780. **£200-250** *Som*

A Bristol green full size club-shaped decanter with lozenge stopper, 230 mm. high less stopper, c. 1780. **£130-150** *Som*

A rare spirit decanter, the barrel body with wide band of hand trailing at shoulder and base of body, probably Bristol, 170 mm. high, c. 1780. **£50-60** *Som*

(l.) A Bristol blue barrel-shaped decanter, the body with gilt wine label, 'Brandy', with ball stopper, 170 mm. high. **£120-140** *Som*

(r.) A similar decanter of lighter tint, 185 mm. high. **£120-140** *Som*

A good pair of Bristol blue decanters, the ovoid bodies with gilt simulated wine labels 'Rum' and 'Hollands', the lozenge stoppers with gilt initials, 19 cm. high, c. 1790. **£300-330** pair *Som*

A good Bristol blue ovoid decanter with 3 triangular neck rings, target (bull's-eye) stopper, height less stopper 230 mm., c. 1800. **£130-£150** *Som*

Three Georgian decanters in good condition:—

(l.) Irish decanter of ovoid shape with flute moulded base, 3 annulated neck rings and moulded target stopper, 220 mm. c. 1800. **£75-80**

(c.) An ovoid decanter with cut fluted base and 3 neck rings, target stopper, 237 mm. c. 1800. **£75-80**

(r.) A plain ovoid decanter with 3 neck rings and mushroom stopper, 123 mm. c. 1800. **£75-80** *Som*

A set of 3 Bristol blue decanters, the ovoid bodies with gilt simulated wine labels, 'Brandy', 'Rum' and 'Hollands', gilt stoppers, in a black lacquer stand, height of bottles less stopper 180 mm., c. 1790. **£350-£400** *Som*

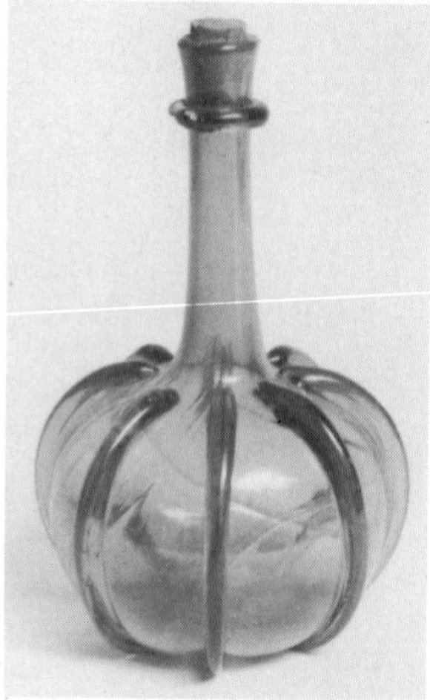

A Continental amethyst glass carafe, 8½ in. high, c. 1800. **£60-£80** *BP*

A pair of cut glass decanters and stoppers of Prussian form, cut with bands of fluting, diamonds, horizontal grooves and facets below blaze-cut mushroom stoppers, slight chipping, 9½ in. (24 cm.), c. 1820. **£300-350** *SS*

A Bristol blue decanter and stopper, 8½ in., c. 1820. **£50-75** *IHA*

A good pair of Bristol green ovoid decanters with 3 neck rings and plain hollow mushroom stoppers, height less stoppers 228 mm., c. 1830. **£300-320** *Som*

A rare blue carafe with vertical moulded ribbing, with cork/metal stopper, 230 mm. high, c. 1830. **£120-130** *Som*

A Victorian magnum decanter, diamond cut overall with notched neck, engraved with crest, monogram on reverse, 295 mm. high, c. 1860. **£100-120** *Som*

An amethyst carafe of onion shape with flat mushroom stopper, 220 mm. high, c. 1840. **£120-140** *Som*

A magnum decanter of ovoid shape with band of cut diamonds, base fluting and cut neck rings with mushroom stopper, 10¼ in. high, c. 1825. **£180-200** *Som*

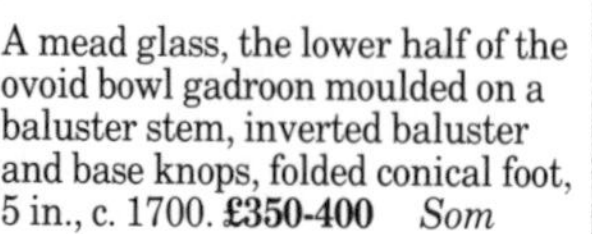

A mead glass, the lower half of the ovoid bowl gadroon moulded on a baluster stem, inverted baluster and base knops, folded conical foot, 5 in., c. 1700. **£350-400** *Som*

GLASS

Drinking glasses have been ordered in line with the E. Barrington Haynes system (see Pelican Books 'Glass' by E. Barrington Haynes).

Group I	**Baluster Stems**	**1685-1725**
II	**Moulded Pedestal Stems**	**1715-1765**
III	**Balustroid Stems**	**1725-1755**
IV	**Light (Newcastle) Balusters**	**1735-1765**
V	**Composite Stems**	**1740-1770**
VI	**Plain Straight Stems**	**1740-1770**
VII	**Air Twist Stems**	**1740-1770**
VIII	**Hollow Stems**	**1750-1760**
IX	**Incised Twist Stems**	**1750-1765**
X	**Opaque Twist Stems**	**1750-1780**
XI	**Mixed and Colour Twist Stems**	**1755-1775**
XII	**Faceted Stems**	**1760-1800**
XIII	**Other glasses with short or rudimentary stems: Dwarf Ales; Jelly Glasses; Rummers; Georgian Ales; wines and drams; 18-19th C.**	

An Anglo-Venetian ale, the flared conical bowl with lower zone of wrythen ribs, with a short true baluster, folded conical foot, 5⅝ in., c. 1690. **£550-600** *S*

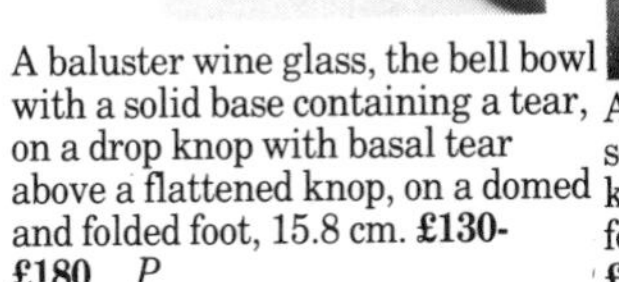

A baluster wine glass, the bell bowl with a solid base containing a tear, on a drop knop with basal tear above a flattened knop, on a domed and folded foot, 15.8 cm. **£130-£180** *P*

A goblet, the conical bowl with solid base set on a wide angular knop and teared base knop, conical foot with wide fold, 7 in., c. 1700. **£400-500** *S*

An acorn knopped goblet, the wide ovoid bowl set on a fine teared acorn knop over a base knop, domed and folded foot, 8¼ in., c. 1700. **£400-500** *S*

A baluster wine glass, the rounded funnel bowl with teared solid base, set on a cyst over a bladed knop and base knop with central elongated air bubble, domed and folded foot, 5¾ in., c. 1710. **£400-£500** *S*

A heavy baluster wine glass, the conical bowl with solid section and tear, base collar, on a stem with an inverted baluster and base knops, folded conical foot, 153 mm. high, c. 1720. **£450-500** *Som*

A goblet, the slightly flared bucket bowl, set on collars over an annulated knop, teared inverted baluster and base knop, domed and folded foot, 7¼ in., c. 1710-20. **£350-£450** *S*

An early cordial, the small waisted bowl set on a collar, the stem with central swelling and base knop, conical foot, 6⅜ in., c. 1725. **£280-£340** *S*

A baluster goblet, the funnel bowl supported on a ball knop enclosing a tear above a short plain section, on a folded conical foot, 16.5 cm. high, c. 1715. **£180-220** *C*

A heavy baluster wine glass, the round funnel bowl on a stem with an air tear, inverted baluster and base knops, folded conical foot, 4⅝ in., c. 1700. **£480-520** *Som*

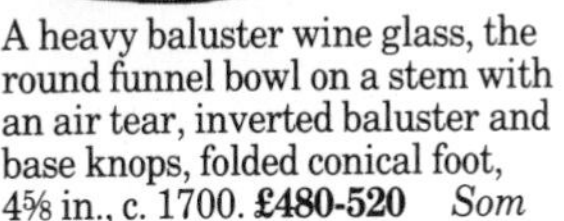

An unusual early wine glass, the flared trumpet bowl with basal hollow tapering section over a short inverted baluster stem, folded conical foot, 6 in., c. 1720. **£90-£150** *S*

A large heavy baluster wine glass, the trumpet bowl on a drawn stem with a teared knop and base knop, folded conical foot, 7½ in., c. 1720. **£450-500** *Som*

A baluster wine glass, the flared bowl with solid base set on a flattened knop over a teared inverted baluster and base knop, folded domed foot, 6¾ in., c. 1720. **£180-220** *S*

A pedestal stemmed wine glass, the bell bowl on a cushion knop above a tapering 4-sided stem with elongated tear and folded conical foot, 16 cm. high, c. 1720. **£250-£300** *C*

An engraved German wine glass, the funnel bowl decorated with a band of laub-und-bandelwerk, with hollow angular knopped stem to the basal knop, folded conical foot, probably Thuringian, 6½ in. (16.5 cm.), c. 1740. **£80-100** *SS*

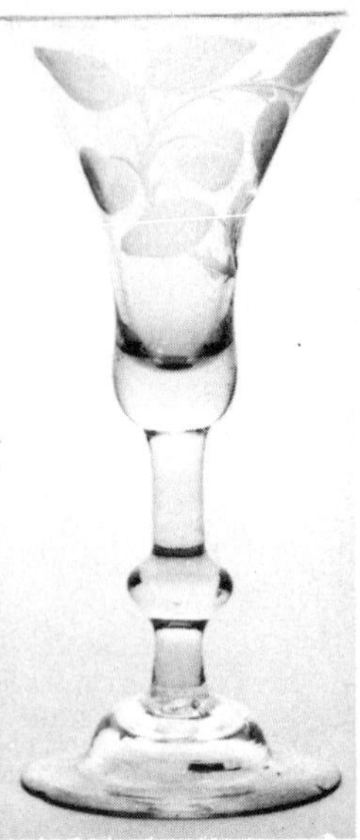

A rare cider balustroid goblet, the bowl engraved with spray of fruiting apple, the stem with central flattened knop, domed foot, foot rim chipped, 8⅛ in., c. 1745. **£500-600** *S*

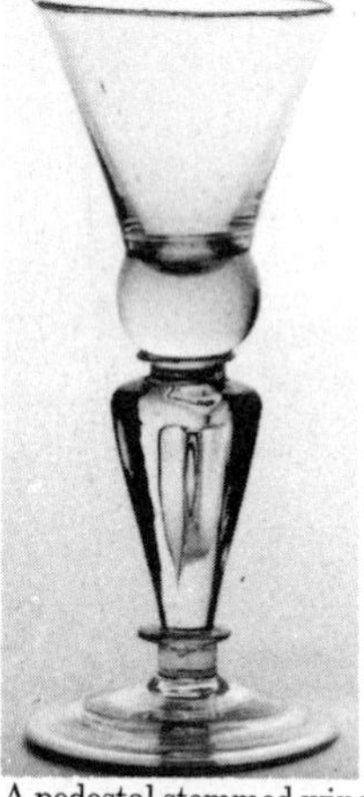

A pedestal stemmed wine glass, the thistle bowl with solid base set on a teared 4-sided pedestal stem flanked by collars, folded conical foot, 6½ in., c. 1720. **£300-350** *S*

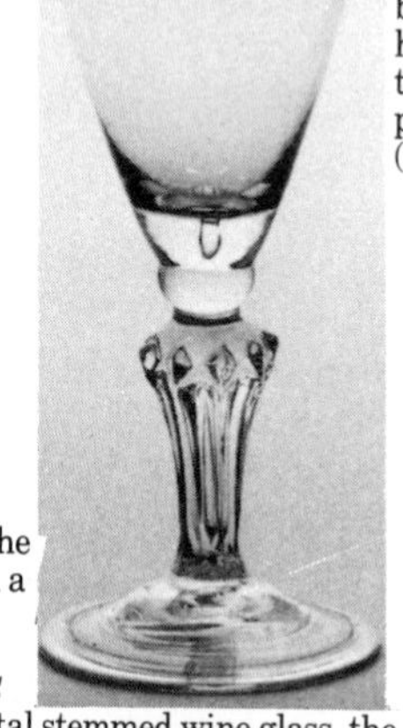

A pedestal stemmed wine glass, the pointed round funnel bowl with basal cyst, folded conical foot, 5⅞ in., c. 1735. **£250-300** *S*

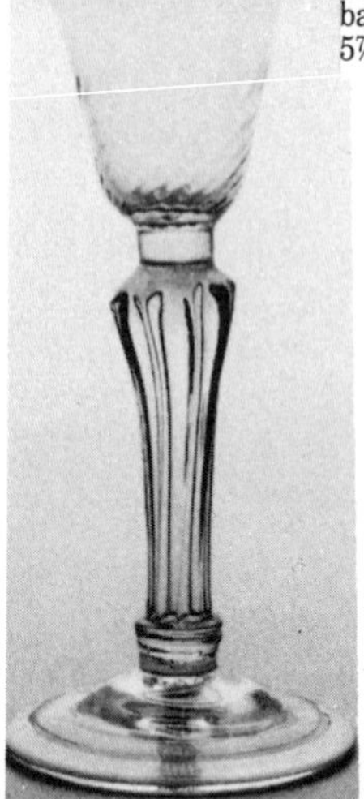

A pedestal stemmed wine glass, the small rounded funnel bowl moulded with a band of wrythen ribs round the base, folded conical foot, 6¾ in., c. 1740. **£200-250** *S*

A mead glass, the stem with annulated knop and base knop, folded conical foot, 4¾ in., c. 1730. **£550-650** *S*

A Georgian ale glass, the dimpled straight funnel bowl set on a blade collar and wrythen inverted baluster stem, folded conical foot, 5¼ in. (13.5 cm.), c. 1750. **£70-90** *SS*

A Georgian wrythen ale glass, two-thirds of the round funnel bowl moulded with bold spiral ribs and set on a short knopped stem and folded conical foot, 5 in. (12.5 cm.), mid 18th C. **£150-200** *SS*

A wine glass, the ogee bowl engraved with a rose and a bird on a branch, set on a stem with a single central knop and conical folded foot, 14 cm., mid 18th C. **£90-£130** *Bea*

A Newcastle 'friendship' wine glass, the round funnel bowl engraved and inscribed Amecitiae, the stem with an angular knop above a teared baluster and basal knop, on conical foot, 17.5 cm. **£500-600** *P*

A Newcastle wine glass, the round funnel bowl engraved with a band of fruiting vine, on a stem with collar, beaded, angular, inverted baluster and base knops, plain conical foot, 185 mm., c. 1750. **£500-550** *Som*

A diamond-engraved Newcastle wine glass signed by K. Poster ?, the bell bowl engraved with an elaborate armorial, on an angular knop above a teared knop, short plain section, hollow inverted baluster and teared basal knops, the baluster knop indistinctly signed, 18.5 cm. **£500-600** *P*

A large wine glass, the trumpet bowl on a drawn plain stem, with air tear, plain domed foot, 200 mm., c. 1750. **£90-120** *Som*

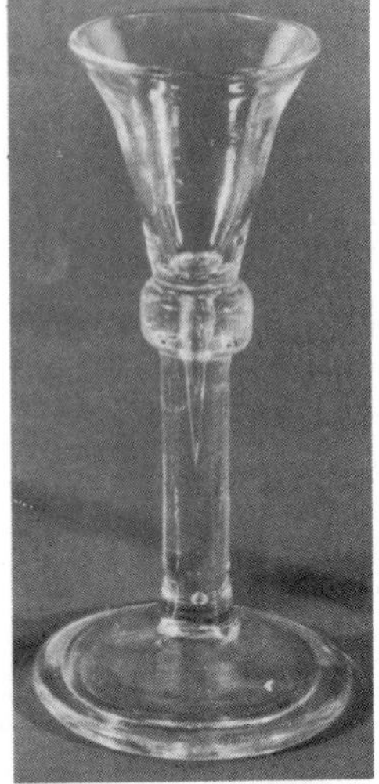

An early 18th C. wine glass with trumpet-shaped bowl, cylindrical knop and double teardrop stem on raised folded foot, 5½ in. high. **£60-£80** *DSH*

A rare diamond-point engraved glass, the small flared bowl decorated with a repeated floral motif and supported on a plain stem with base knop, folded conical foot, 6½ in., c. 1750. **£600-700** *S*

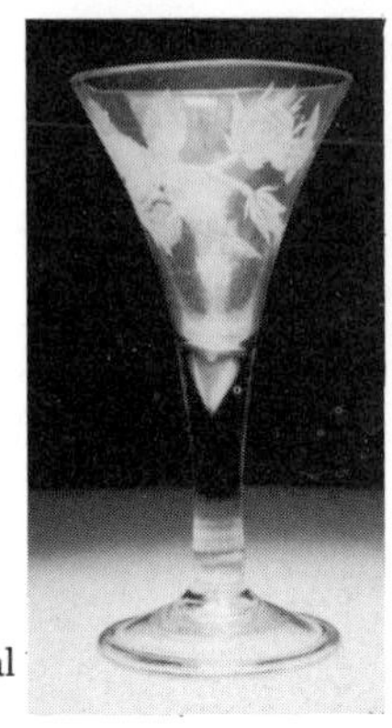

Right
A Williamite wine glass, on teared stem and domed foot, engraved with a portrait of William III with a ribbon inscribed 'THE GLORIOUS MEMORY OF KING WILLIAM', the reverse inscribed 'LIBERTY & PROPERTY', foot trimmed, 6¼ in., c. 1750. **£550-£650** *S*

Left
An unusual Jacobite wine glass, the trumpet bowl engraved with a rose, and 2 buds on one stalk, a moth on the reverse, drawn plain stem with an air tear, folded conical foot, 152 mm., c. 1750. **£320-350** *Som*

A Jacobite wine glass, the ovoid bowl engraved with a Jacobite rose, unopened bud and thistle, on a plain drawn stem, plain conical foot, 122 mm., c. 1750. **£280-310** *Som*

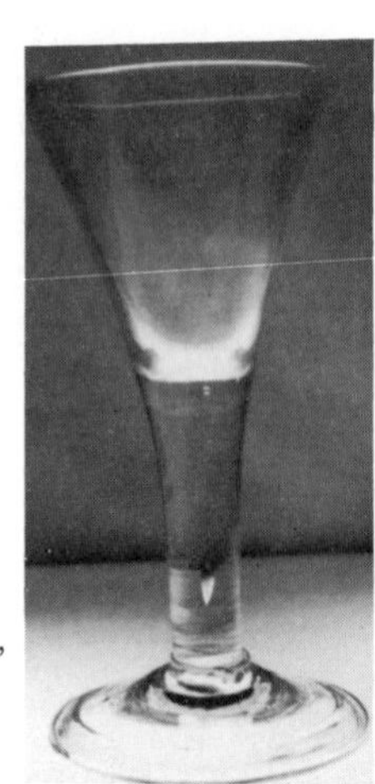

A large goblet, the trumpet bowl on a plain drawn stem with air tear, folded conical foot, 220 mm., c. 1750. **£120-140** *Som*

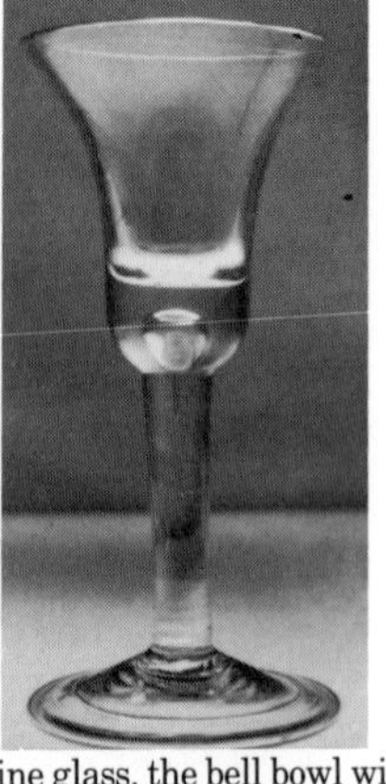

A wine glass, the bell bowl with air tear, plain stem and folded conical foot, 165 mm., c. 1750. **£70-90** *Som*

A large goblet with bell bowl containing air tear, plain stem, plain conical foot, 200 mm., c. 1750. **£100-120** *Som*

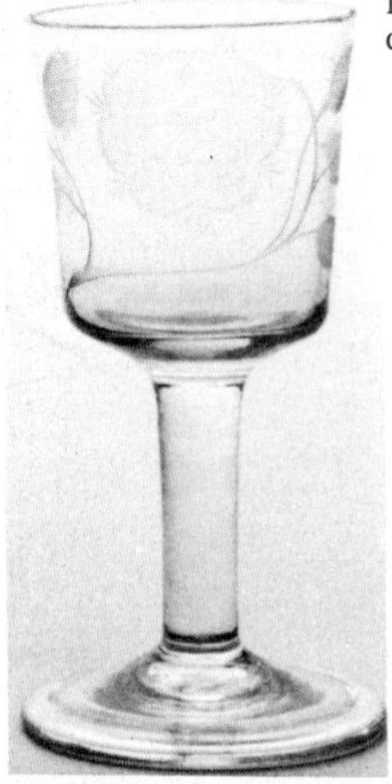

A Jacobite goblet, the bucket bowl engraved with 7-petalled rose and one bud, the reverse with moth, columnar stem, folded conical foot, 6⅝ in., c. 1750. **£350-400** *S*

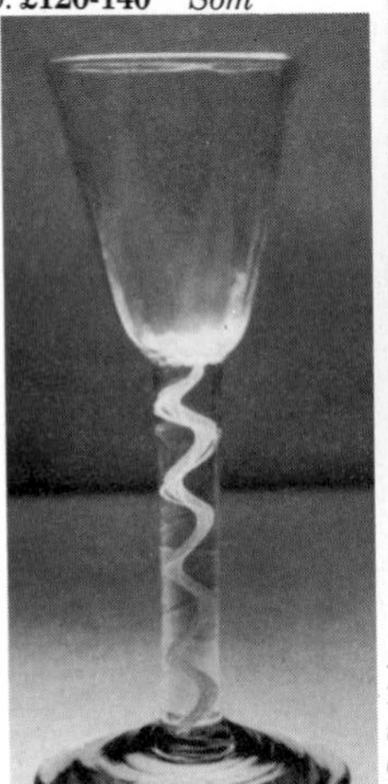

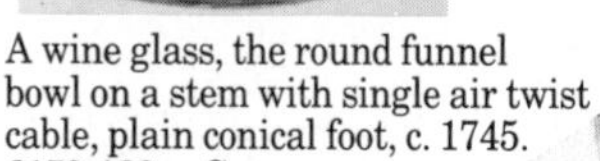

A wine glass, the round funnel bowl on a stem with single air twist cable, plain conical foot, c. 1745. **£150-180** *Som*

A wine glass, the pan top bowl on a multi-spiral air twist stem with shoulder and central knops, plain conical foot, 155 mm., c. 1745. **£160-180** *Som*

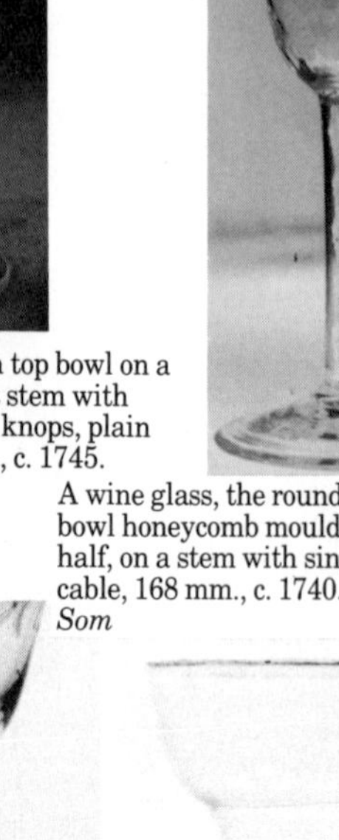

A wine glass, the round funnel bowl honeycomb moulded on lower half, on a stem with single air twist cable, 168 mm., c. 1740. **£150-180** *Som*

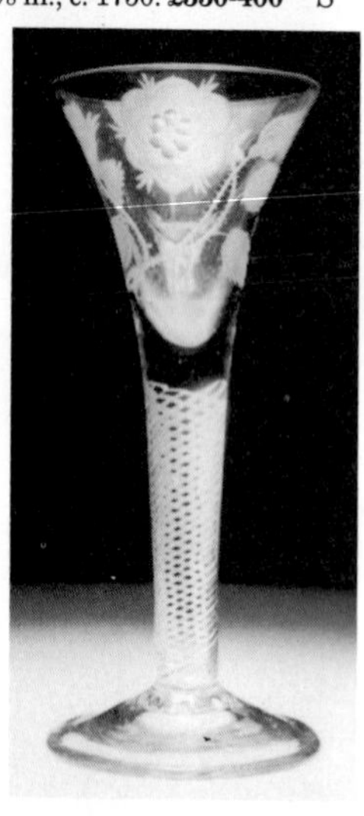

A good Jacobite wine glass, the round funnel bowl engraved with rose and 2 buds, star on reverse, on a drawn multi-spiral air twist stem, plain conical foot, 165 mm., c. 1745. **£450-500** *Som*

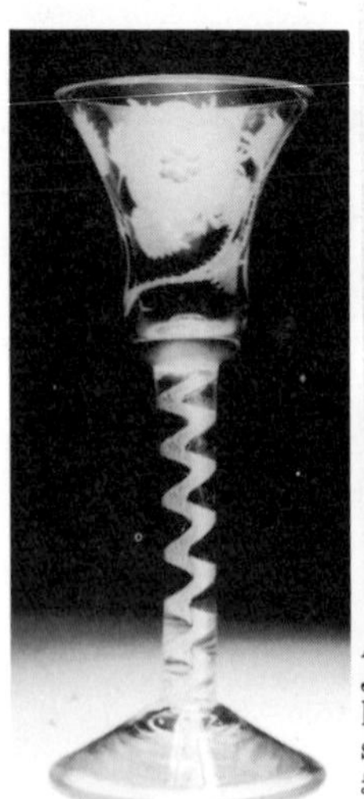

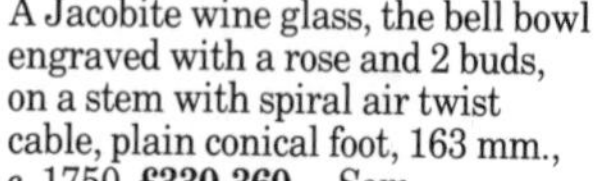

A Jacobite wine glass, the bell bowl engraved with a rose and 2 buds, on a stem with spiral air twist cable, plain conical foot, 163 mm., c. 1750. **£330-360** *Som*

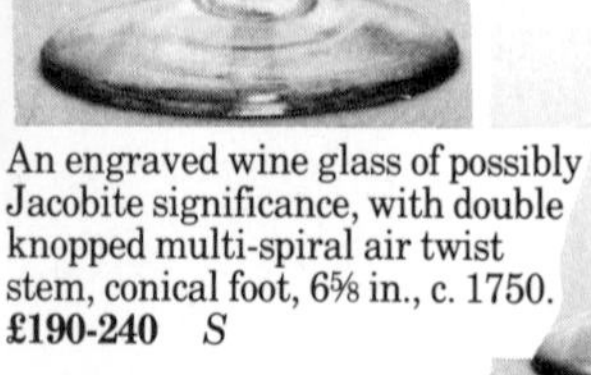

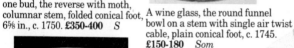

An engraved wine glass of possibly Jacobite significance, with double knopped multi-spiral air twist stem, conical foot, 6⅝ in., c. 1750. **£190-240** *S*

A large wine glass, the pan topped bowl set on a multi-spiral air twist stem with central swelling, conical foot, foot trimmed, 8¼ in., c. 1750. **£150-200** *S*

A good Jacobite glass, the round funnel bowl wheel engraved with an oval portrait medallion of the Young Pretender beneath the inscription 'AUDENTIOR IBO', the reverse decorated with an entwined thorny rose and thistle, raised on a single series air twist stem, with 2 inverted baluster knops and a conical foot, 6 in. (15.5 cm.), c. 1750. **£2,000-2,200** *SS*

For a similar glass see E. Barrington Haynes 'Glass', plate 52A.

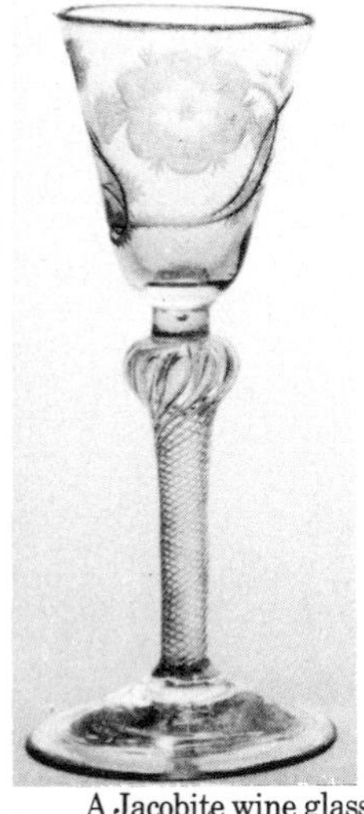

A Jacobite wine glass, engraved with rose and 2 buds, inscribed Fiat, multi-spiral air twist stem, small chip to footrim, c. 1750. **£280-£320** *S*

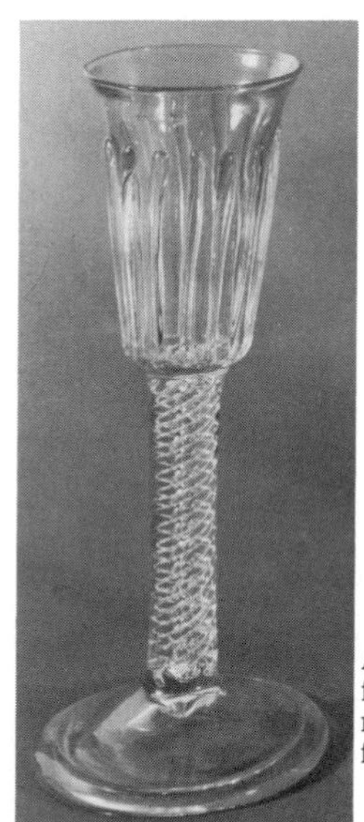

A mid 18th C. wine glass, the bucket-shaped bowl with trailed decoration, on multiple air twist stem and folded foot, 7 in. **£250-£300** *DSH*

A mid 18th C. wine glass with flared, collared funnel bowl, on multiple air twist stem and raised foot, 5½ in. **£60-90** *DSH*

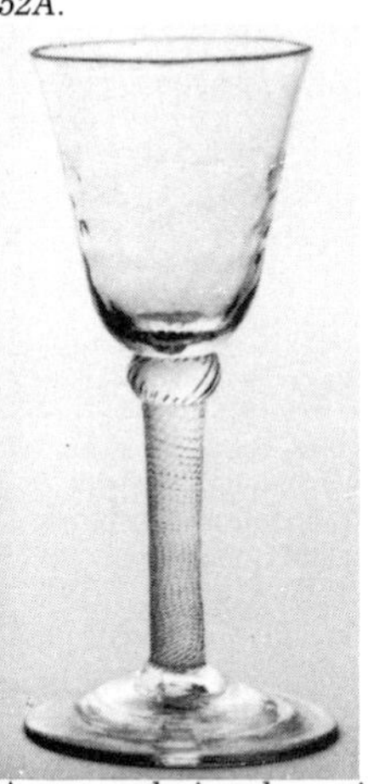

An unusual wine glass, with an incised twist stem with shoulder knop, conical foot, 6⅜ in., c. 1750. **£150-200** *S*

A mid 18th C. cordial with flared bucket-shaped bowl on multiple air twist stem and folded foot, 6 in. **£55-75** *DSH*

A cordial, the ribbed flared bowl set on a double series air twist stem, conical foot, foot trimmed, 6½ in., c. 1750. **£90-120** *S*

A mid 18th C. wine glass with tall bell-shaped bowl, on double knopped multiple air twist stem and domed foot, 7 in. high. **£70-£90** *DSH*

An incised twist stem wine glass with round funnel bowl and plain conical foot, 145 mm., c. 1750. **£200-220** *Som*

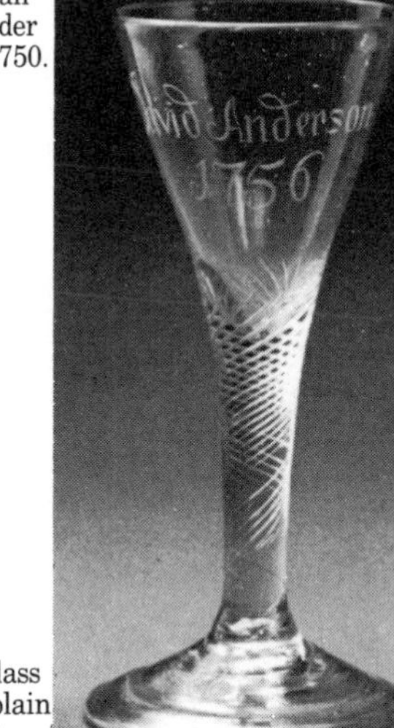

A dated and inscribed wine glass, the drawn trumpet bowl wheel engraved 'David Anderson 1756', raised on a single series air twist stem and conical folded foot, 6½ in. (16.5 cm.), 1756. **£120-160** *SS*

A wine glass, with multi-spiral air twist stem with shoulder and base knop, domed foot, 6¾ in., c. 1750. **£180-220** *S*

A mid 18th C. wine glass with bell-shaped bowl on multiple opaque twist stem and raised domed foot, 6 in. **£70-90** *DSH*

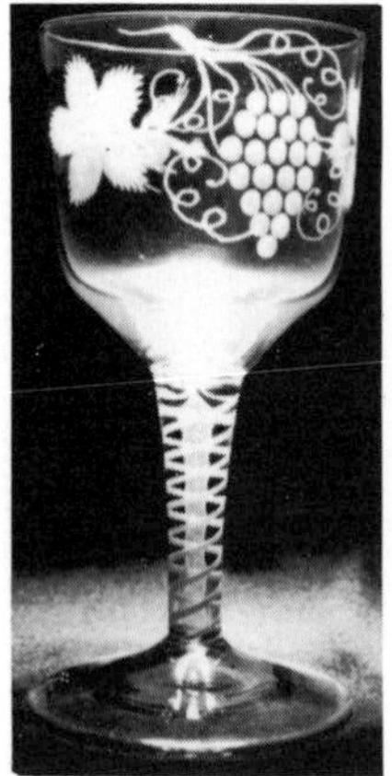

A large goblet, the ogee bowl engraved with fruiting vine, on a stem with double series opaque twist, plain conical foot, 205 mm., c. 1760. **£130-160** *Som*

A Beilby wine glass, the ogee bowl enamelled with a frieze of fruiting vine and set on a double opaque twist stem, 15 cm., 1760's. **£500-£600** *SS*

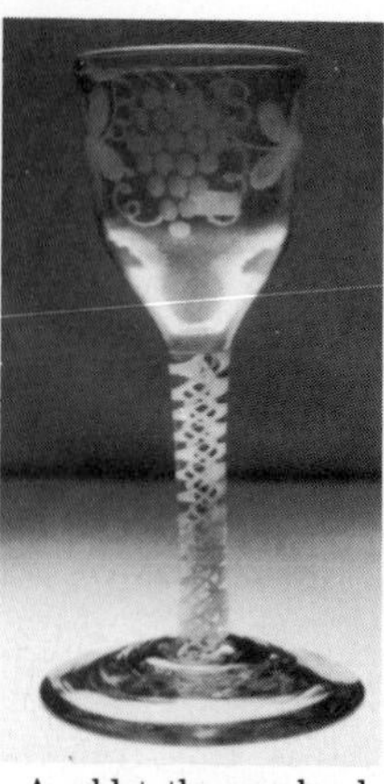

A goblet, the ogee bowl engraved with fruiting vine, double series opaque twist stem, plain conical foot, 158 mm., c. 1760. **£120-£150** *Som*

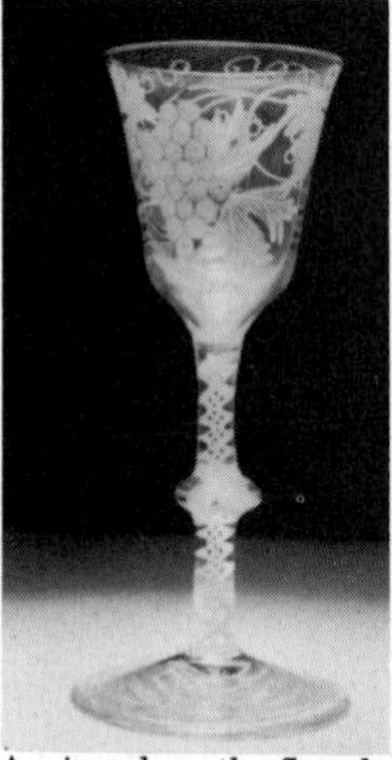

A wine glass, the flared round funnel bowl engraved with fruiting vine and bird in flight, on a stem with centre knop and double series opaque twist stem, plain conical foot, 160 mm., c. 1760. **£150-180** *Som*

A coin glass, enclosing a Dutch coin dated 1739, the stem with opaque gauze corkscrew, conical foot, 6¾ in., c. 1760. **£200-250** *S*

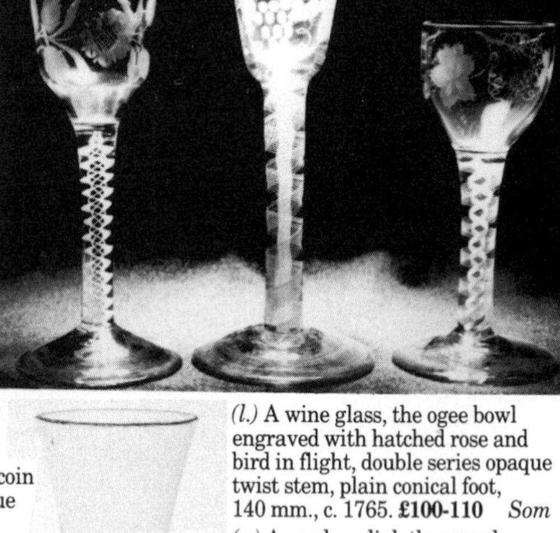

(l.) A wine glass, the ogee bowl engraved with hatched rose and bird in flight, double series opaque twist stem, plain conical foot, 140 mm., c. 1765. **£100-110** *Som*

(c.) A good cordial, the round funnel bowl engraved with fruiting vine and bird in flight, thick double series opaque twist stem, plain conical foot, 155 mm., c. 1760. **£190-200** *Som*

(r.) A wine glass, the ovoid bowl engraved with fruiting vine, on a stem with double series opaque twist, plain conical foot, 128 mm., c. 1760. **£100-110** *Som*

A ratafia, the flared bowl with band of moulded ribs round the base, double series opaque twist stem, conical foot, 6⅝ in., c. 1765. **£200-250** *S*

A small opaque twist wine glass, the ogee bowl engraved with a continuous hunting scene, double series opaque twist stem, plain conical foot, 120 mm., c. 1760. **£160-180** *Som*

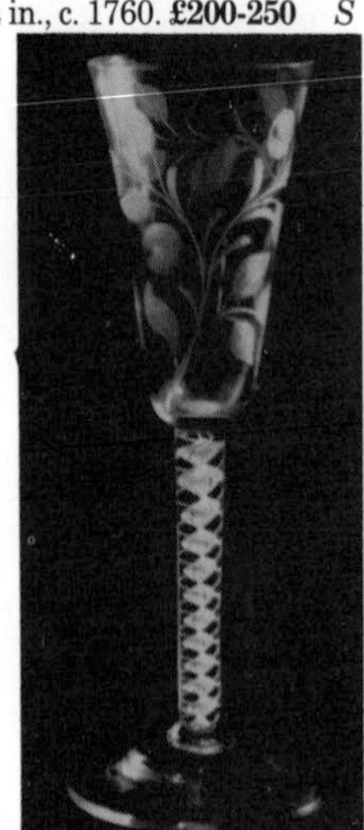

A rare cider glass, the tall round funnel bowl engraved with apples, on an opaque twist stem and conical foot, 7⅝ in., c. 1760. **£400-£500** *S*

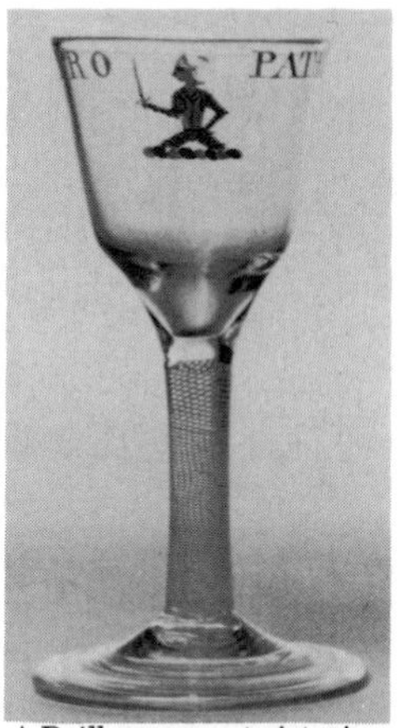

A Beilby opaque twist wine glass, the ogee bowl enamelled in white heightened in iron-red with a crest, flanked by the motto PRO PATRIA, the stem filled with opaque spiral threads and on a folded conical foot, 15 cm., c. 1765. **£1,600-1,800** *C*

The motto and crest is that of the Ogilvie family.

(l.) An ale glass, the waisted round funnel bowl engraved with hops and barley, on a double series opaque twist stem, plain conical foot, 171 mm., c. 1760. **£150-180** *Som*

(r.) A similar ale glass with deep round funnel bowl, 168 mm., c. 1760. **£140-170** *Som*

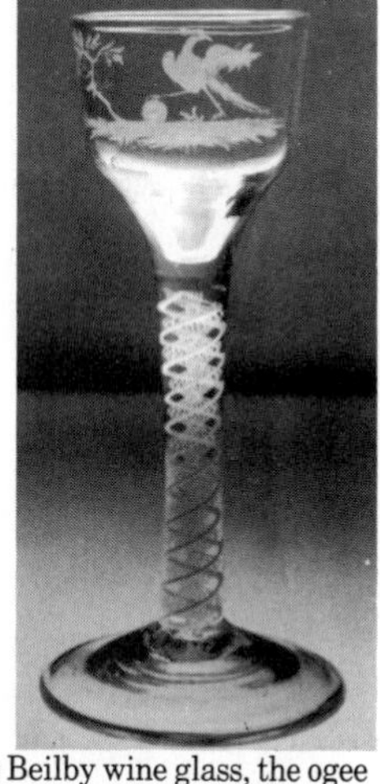

A rare Beilby wine glass, the ogee bowl decorated in white enamel with a peacock with one foot on a stone, the reverse with an insect (grub), double series opaque twist stem, plain conical foot, 149 mm., c. 1765. **£1,200-1,400** *Som*

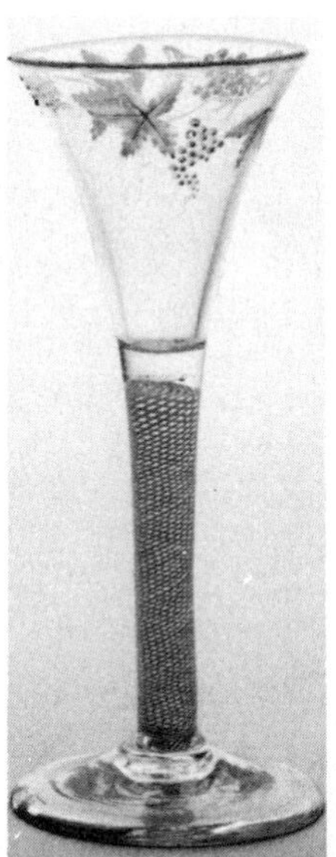

A Beilby enamelled wine glass, the drawn trumpet bowl painted in white enamel, the stem with multi-spiral opaque twists, conical foot, traces of gilding, foot chipped, 6¾ in., c. 1770. **£180-220** *S*

A gilt wine glass, possibly James Giles, the round funnel bowl with band of wrythen ribs, gilt rim, double series opaque twist stem, conical foot, small chip to foot, 5⅞ in., c. 1770. **£250-300** *S*

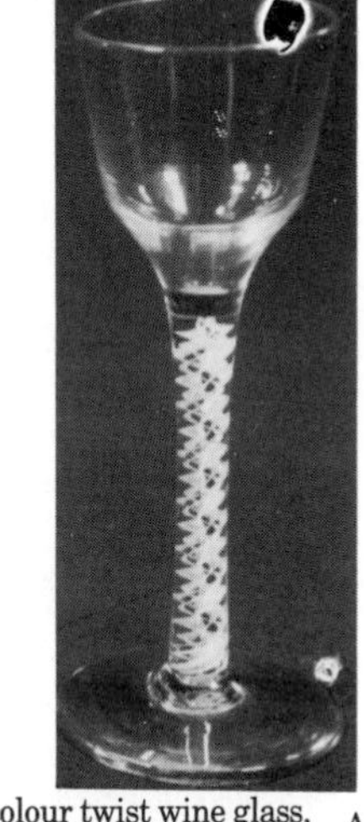

A colour twist wine glass, the ogee bowl on a stem with intertwined pink and opaque twists, plain conical foot, 153 mm., c. 1770. **£480-530** *Som*

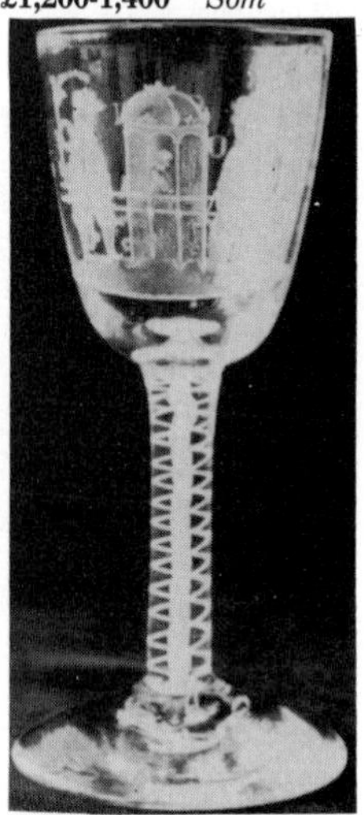

An engraved wine glass, with a sedan chair and 2 bearers, the reverse inscribed 'THE SIGN OF THE CHAIR', on a double series opaque twist stem, conical foot, 5¾ in., c. 1770. **£400-500** *S*

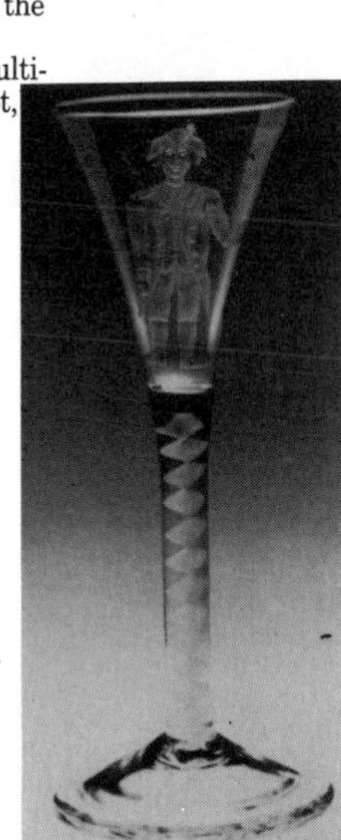

A fine Irish volunteer glass, the bowl on an opaque corkscrew twist stem and conical foot, engraved with a portrait of an ensign holding a flag inscribed 'Loyal and/ Determined', 6⅞ in., c. 1780. **£2,500-3,000** *S*

The motto probably refers to one of the Leinster corps and a similar flag also held by an ensign is depicted on the 'Volunteer Furniture' chintz, printed for the Cotton Warehouse, Dublin, by Harpur of Leixlip, Co. Kildare, around 1783 which depicts motifs representing the Provincial Review of Volunteers in Phoenix Park, Dublin, 1782.

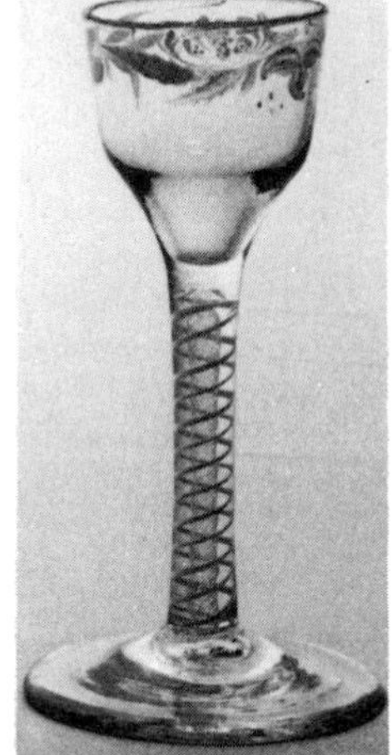

A Beilby enamelled wine glass, the ogee bowl painted in white enamel, double series opaque twist stem, conical foot, foot chipped, 5⅝ in., c. 1770. **£250-300** *S*

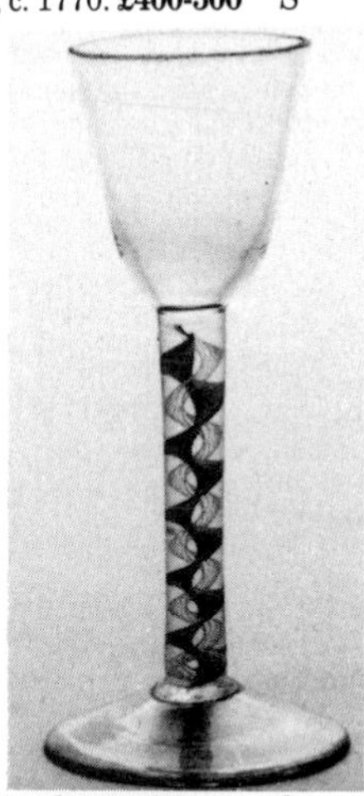

A colour twist wine glass, the stem with broad white enamel corkscrew edged in translucent green and red, 5¾ in., c. 1770. **£800-£900** *S*

(l.) A wine glass, the ovoid bowl engraved with pair of initials, bird in flight and floral sprays, drawn diamond facet cut stem, plain conical foot, 140 mm., c. 1770. **£80-£110** *Som*

(r.) A wine glass, the ogee bowl engraved with stars and printies, on a drawn stem with facet cut hexagons, terraced and cut firing foot, 132 mm., c. 1770. **£95-125** *Som*

A rare commemorative wine glass, engraved with a portrait of Sarah Siddons, on a double series opaque twist stem and conical foot, 6 in., late 18th C. **£1,400-1,700** *S*

A Bristol green wine glass, c. 1810. **£18-22** *FF*

A mid 18th C. wine glass with bell-shaped bowl decorated with vines and stars, on stem with central white multiple twist, surrounded by red, green and white twist, 6¾ in. **£400-500** *DSH*

A heavy goblet depicting an elopement scene, the ogee bowl engraved with a lover scaling ladders to reach the turret of a mansion, the stem hexagonally faceted, on conical foot, 20 cm. **£250-300** *P*

A small wine glass, the funnel bowl enamelled in white heightened in puce, gilt rim, the stem cut with hexagonal facets, on a plain foot, 11 cm., c. 1780. **£300-400** *S*

Three 18th C. Bristol green wine glasses with round funnel bowl, plain stem and plain conical foot, 125 mm., 136 mm., 145 mm., c. 1760. **£150-200** each *Som*

A fine pair of Bristol green wine glasses, the ovoid bowls set on true hollow stems with base reinforcement, plain conical feet, 137 mm., c. 1740. **£350-400** pair *Som*

(l.) A turquoise green roemer type wine glass with collar, hollow stem with strawberry prunts, plain conical foot, 100 mm., c. 1820. **£80-£90** *Som*

(l.c.) A similar green glass with trailed conical foot, 120 mm., c. 1820. **£65-70** *Som*

(r.c.) A similar glass, 126 mm., c. 1820. **£65-70** *Som*

(r.) A similar amber glass, 111 mm., c. 1820. **£40-50** *Som*

A Bristol green wine glass, c. 1800. **£20-25** *FF*

A Bristol green roemer type wine glass with ovoid bowl, hollow stem with milled collar and raspberry prunts, trailed conical foot, 115 mm., c. 1820. **£55-60** *Som*

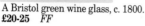

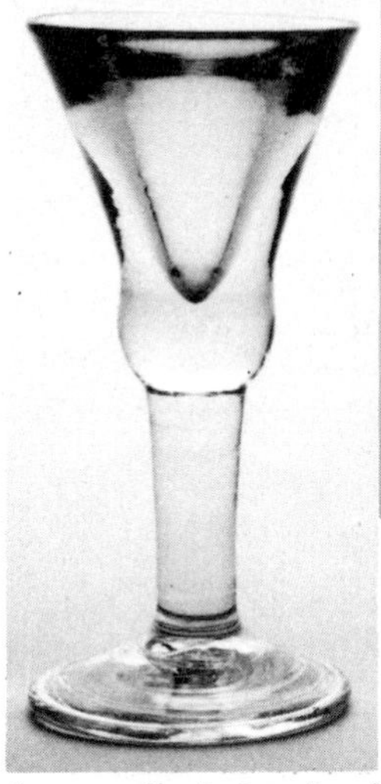

An unusual early deceptive glass, the thickened flared bowl with bulbous base set on a columnar stem, folded conical foot, 7 in., c. 1700. **£250-300** *S*

(l.) A pair of Bristol green wine glasses with conical bowls, knopped stems and conical feet, 130 mm., c. 1825. **£60-65** pair *Som*

(c.) An amethyst wine glass with ogee bowl and knopped stem, plain conical foot, 120 mm., c. 1840. **£35-£40** *Som*

(r.) A rare amber wine glass similar to left above, 120 mm., c. 1825. **£55-60** *Som*

An early 'single flint' wine glass, with an irregular flattened knop over a hollow double knopped stem, folded conical foot, 5½ in., c. 1690. **£300-350** *S*

A rummer, the ogee bowl engraved with a portrait panel of the Duke of Wellington, the reverse with a list of battles, on collared stem, 14 cm. **£350-450** *P*

A German green-tinted engraved beaker, decorated with a mirror monogram beneath a coronet, and coat-of-arms flanked by stylised flowers, Potsdam, 11 cm., c. 1700. **£300-400** *S*

A German engraved beaker, decorated in part-polished tiefschnitt, the thick base decorated with a sunflower motif, possibly Bohemian, 13.8 cm., c. 1700. **£700-£800** *S*

(l.) A green goblet with panel moulded double ogee bowl, shoulder ball knop and inverted baluster stem, plain conical foot, 157 mm., c. 1860. **£150-200** *Som*

(r.) A green wine glass, the double ogee bowl on a plain hollow stem, high conical foot, 155 mm., c. 1750. **£150-200** *Som*

A pair of Coronation rummers of King George IV, the bucket bowls engraved with an equestrian portrait of the King's Champion, the reverse with G IV R and date July 19, 1821, on annulated knop stems, 13.5 cm. **£350-400** *P*

(l.) A pair of Irish rummers, the double ogee bowls with looping and ribbon engraving, 114 mm., c. 1820. **£50-60** pair *Som*

(l.c.) An Irish rummer, the ovoid bowl engraved with vesica pattern, stars and husks, with monogram 'MW', 125 mm., c. 1800. **£40-45** *Som*

(r.c.) A set of 5 Irish rummers, the ovoid bodies panel moulded and engraved with band of laurel and circlets, 153 mm., c. 1800. **£150-£180** *Som*

(r.) A pair of Irish rummers, the ovoid panel moulded bodies engraved with vesica pattern, 123 mm., c. 1800. **£60-70** pair *Som*

A Silesian beaker of gentle campana shape, engraved probably in the workshop of Christian Gottfried Schneider, simple berry border, the foot with silver dentil mount, 10.5 cm. **£750-850** *P*

A bucket rummer, the bowl engraved with the High Level Newcastle Bridge and shipping scene below, caption 'High Level Bridge Newcastle', the reverse with an empty cartouche for a monogram, knife edge knopped stem, plain conical foot, 173 mm., c. 1830. **£150-180** *Som*

A pair of rummers, the bucket bowls engraved with a view of Sunderland Bridge framing the sailing ship 'Maria of Rye', the reverse with cypher JAB below a rose and thistle branch, on bladed knop stems, 14.5 cm. **£250-300** *P*

A rummer, the double ogee bowl engraved 'Queen Caroline For Ever', on bladed knop stem, 13 cm. **£200-£250** *P*

A rummer, the bucket bowl engraved 'The Queen' denoting Queen Victoria, the reverse with branches of rose and thistle, the stem with a single tear, 15.5 cm. **£180-240** *P*

A goblet, the large straight-sided bowl on short stem over domed foot, honeycomb moulded overall, 5⅝ in., mid 18th C. **£150-200** *S*

A small wine glass, the bucket bowl engraved with Masonic symbols and a monogram on reverse, 112 mm., c. 1820. **£60-70** *Som*

A Bohemian engraved and stained ovoid goblet and cover, thick foot with scalloped edge, matching cover, 35 cm., c. 1840. **£350-£450** *S*

A rare Williamite goblet, engraved with an equestrian portrait of William III, the reverse inscribed 'TO THE GLORIOUS PIOUS/AND IMMORTAL MEMORY OF THE GREAT AND GOOD KING WILLIAM WHO FREEDUS FROM POPE AND POPERY KNAVERY AND/SLAVERY BRASS MONEY AND WOODEN SHOES/AND HE WHO REFUSES THIS TOAST MAY BE/DAMMED CRAMMED AND RAMMED DOWN THE GREAT GUN OF ATHLONE', on a columnar stem and conical foot, 7⅝ in., late 18th/early 19th C. **£850-1,050** *S*

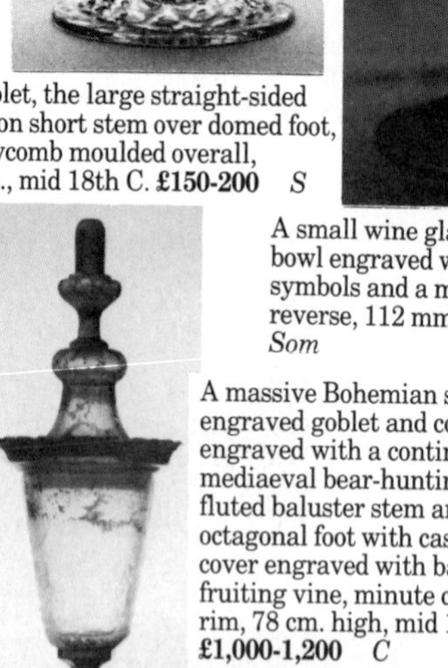

A massive Bohemian stained-ruby engraved goblet and cover, engraved with a continuous mediaeval bear-hunting scene, on a fluted baluster stem and spreading octagonal foot with castellated rim, cover engraved with bands of fruiting vine, minute chip to foot rim, 78 cm. high, mid 19th C. **£1,000-1,200** *C*

A large Bohemian overlay goblet, the translucent green ground decorated in gilding, 36 cm., mid 19th C. **£300-350** *SS*

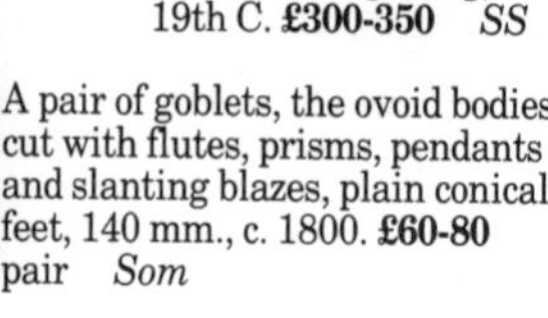

A pair of goblets, the ovoid bodies cut with flutes, prisms, pendants and slanting blazes, plain conical feet, 140 mm., c. 1800. **£60-80** pair *Som*

An early jelly glass, the trumpet bowl on a cushion knop with air beads, domed terraced foot, 110 mm., c. 1740. **£70-85** *Som*

(l.) An 18th C. syllabub, with pan top bowl and domed foot, ribbed overall, 100 mm., c. 1750. **£35-40** *Som*

(l.c.) An 18th C. syllabub, with base collar and domed folded foot, ribbed overall, 110 mm., c. 1740. **£35-40** *Som*

(r.c.) An 18th C. syllabub, with conical foot, ribbed overall, 118 mm., c. 1780. **£25-30** *Som*

(r.) A rare jelly glass, with base knop and domed foot, reticulated overall, 112 mm., c. 1740. **£45-50** *Som*

A jelly glass with ribbed pan-topped bowl set on a bladed knop over a domed and folded foot, 5⅞ in., c. 1750. **£90-120** *S*

(l.) A sweetmeat, the lipped double ogee bowl base cut, on a knopped cut stem, plain domed foot, 143 mm., c. 1750, possibly later cut, c. 1770. **£60-65** *Som*

(r.) A fine sweetmeat, the double ogee bowl and domed foot rib-moulded, on a moulded Silesian stem, 158 mm., c. 1750. **£120-140** *Som*

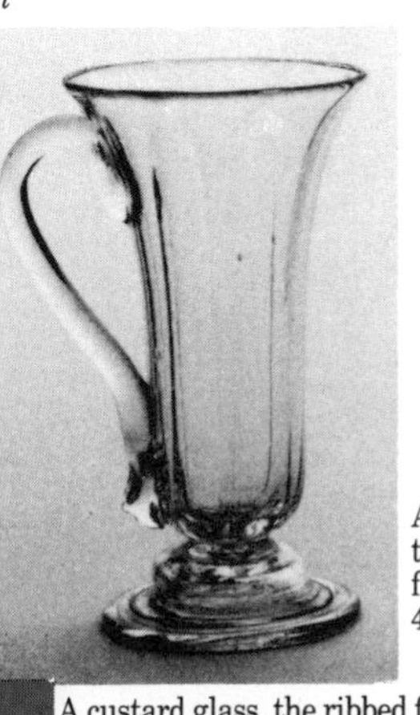

A custard glass, the ribbed flared bowl set on a small domed and terraced foot, applied scroll handle, 4½ in., c. 1750. **£90-120** *S*

A deceptive firing glass, the thickened flared bowl set on a thick flattened knop, thick terraced foot, 4 in., c. 1740-60. **£190-230** *S*

(l.) An 18th C. jelly glass, the trumpet bowl with cushion knop and domed foot, ribbed overall, 90 mm., c. 1750. **£35-40** *Som*

(l.c.) An 18th C. jelly glass, with ribbed knop and conical foot, 95 mm., c. 1780. **£12-15** *Som*

(r.c.) An 18th C. jelly glass, with base collar and folded conical foot, 94 mm., c. 1770. **£20-25** *Som*

(r.) A rare miniature jelly glass, with plain conical foot, 70 mm., c. 1770. **£20-25** *Som*

A Jacobite firing glass, engraved with rose, closed and opening buds, oak leaf, star and the motto Redeat, thick conical foot, 3 in., c. 1750. **£800-900** *S*

A sweetmeat, the double ogee bowl rib-moulded and with serrated rim, on a moulded pedestal stem, plain domed foot with cut edge, 148 mm., c. 1750. **£60-80** *Som*

(l.) A pair of octagonal bowl jelly glasses with cushion base knops and plain domed feet, hatched engraved decoration round rims, 100 mm., c. 1770. **£100-120** pair *Som*

(r.) An octagonal bowl jelly glass with plain domed foot, 98 mm., c. 1770. **£50-60** *Som*

A bonnet glass with unusual decoration, the double ogee bowl rib moulded at base, with scant blaze cutting round upper half, domed moulded foot, 73 mm., c. 1770. **£25-30** *Som*

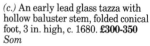

A tall sweetmeat, the ogee bowl with collar on a moulded Silesian stem with base annulated collar, domed folded foot, 187 mm., c. 1750. **£120-150** *Som*

(l.) A sweetmeat, with ribbed double ogee bowl, knopped baluster stem, domed folded ribbed foot, 5⅞ in., c. 1740. **£120-150** *Som*

(c.) An early lead glass tazza with hollow baluster stem, folded conical foot, 3 in. high, c. 1680. **£300-350** *Som*

(r.) A heavy Irish sweetmeat, with cut double ogee bowl, moulded pedestal stem, domed scalloped foot, 5⅝ in., c. 1775. **£130-150** *Som*

A dentil sweetmeat, the plain double ogee bowl with dentil rim, shoulder knopped with opaque twist stem, plain conical foot, 85 mm., c. 1760. **£80-100** *Som*

A sweetmeat, the ovoid bowl cut with flat diamonds, cut rim, on a moulded Silesian stem and domed rib-moulded foot, 145 mm., c. 1770. **£80-90** *Som*

(t.) A ruby red glass pipe with knopped stem, 50 mm., c. 1880. **£70-80** *Som*

(b.) An opaque white glass pipe with translucent green rim and knopped stem, 43 mm., c. 1860. **£70-75** *Som*

A blue-tinted enamelled flask, painted in colours, pewter screw mount, Alpenland, 14.5 cm., 18th C. **£500-600** *S*

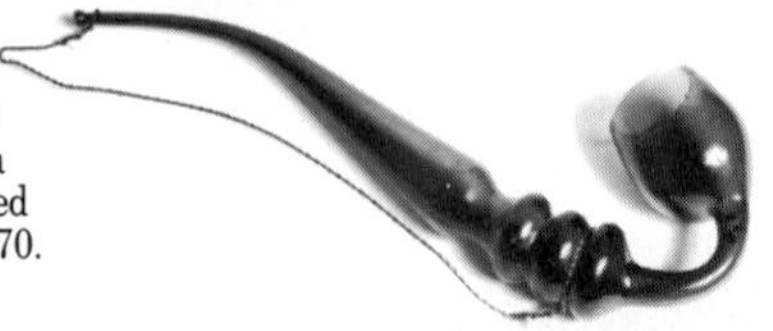

Use the Index!

Because certain items might fit easily into any of a number of categories, the quickest and surest method of locating any entry is by reference to the index at the back of the book. This has been fully cross-referenced for absolute simplicity.

A Stourbridge cranberry glass pipe, 16½ in. long, c. 1820. **£140-160** *BP*

A Stourbridge blue and white glass pipe, 14 in. long, c. 1830. **£120-£140** *BP*

A Georgian ruby glass pipe. **£75-£90** *FF*

A central European enamelled flask, painted in colours, stopper replaced, 15 cm., 18th C. **£300-£350** *S*

A 'milchglas' enamelled flask, painted in colours with floral sprays, Alpenland/Bohemia, 10.8 cm., 18th C. **£200-250** *S*

A Nailsea olive bottle glass jug with small applied handle, 8 in. high, c. 1810. **£130-150** *Som*

A central European enamelled flask, painted in colours, metal mount, 16.5 cm., 18th C. **£250-£300** *S*

A large Nailsea jug of green-tinted metal splashed overall with white, ochre and red spots, 11 in., and another jug of olive-green tint and similar form, 8 in., both early 19th C. **£400-500** *S*

A Nailsea amber glass jug, 6 in., c. 1800. **£40-50** *BP*

An Irish cut glass water jug, the body with base and neck fluting, enclosing a band of sunburst, prism and diamond panels, notched rim and strap handle, 175 mm., c. 1810. **£100-130** *Som*

A green crown glass 'Nailsea' jug with moulded wrythen body and folded rim, applied handle, 135 mm. high, c. 1830. **£55-70** *Som*

Two of a set of 3 Nailsea olive-green bottle glass jugs with opaque white decoration and white trailing round pinched rims, c. 1810.
(l.) 102 mm. **£210-230** *Som*
(r.) 135 mm. **£230-250** *Som*

A French glass wine jug, 9½ in., c. 1820. **£60-90** *BP*

A cut glass water jug with cut arched panels, prism and star cut decoration, strap handle, star cut base, 160 mm. high, c. 1830. **£80-£85** *Som*

A Stourbridge cranberry glass jug, 8 in. high, c. 1860-80. **£50-60** *BP*

A good cut glass water jug with cross cut diamonds and prism cutting, strap handle, notched rim, 180 mm. high, c. 1830. **£100-130** *Som*

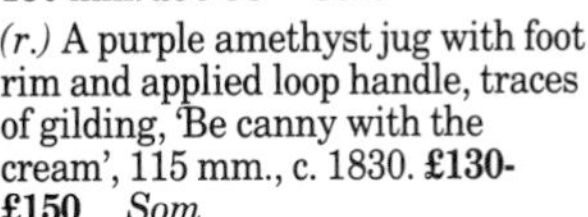

(l.) A brown amethyst mug with foot rim and applied loop handle, 130 mm. **£90-95** *Som*
(r.) A purple amethyst jug with foot rim and applied loop handle, traces of gilding, 'Be canny with the cream', 115 mm., c. 1830. **£130-£150** *Som*

A cut glass water jug, the body diamond cut, the neck bridge fluted, star cut base, the turnover rim notch cut, plain handle, 160 mm., c. 1840. **£50-60** *Som*

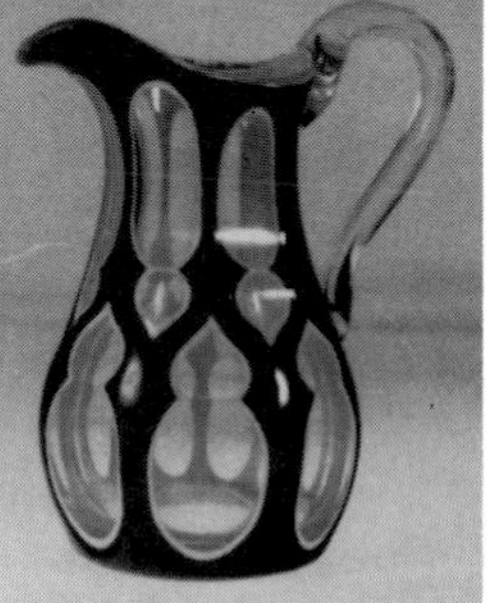

A small Bohemian jug with white and blue overlay, 100 mm., c. 1860. **£60-65** *Som*

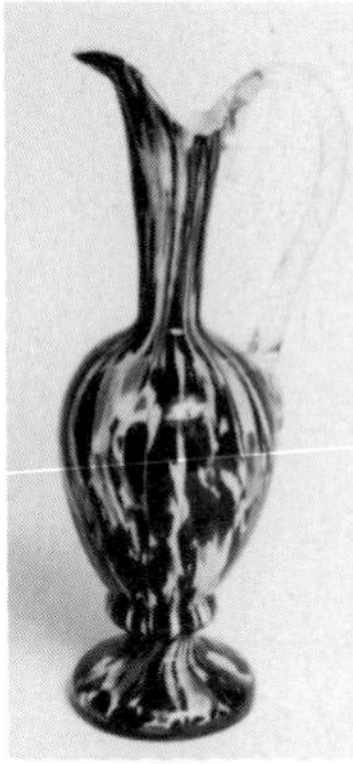

A Nailsea 'end of the day' glass jug, 9½ in. high, c. 1865. **£25-35** *BP*

(l.) An Irish pickle jar, with diamond and loop cutting, moulded pedestal foot, probably Cork, 7½ in. high, c. 1800. **£80-100** *Som*

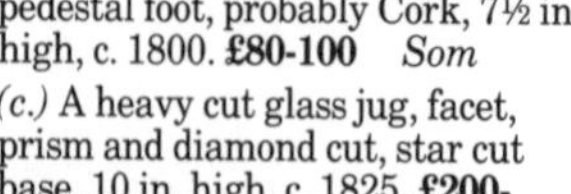

(c.) A heavy cut glass jug, facet, prism and diamond cut, star cut base, 10 in. high, c. 1825. **£200-£250** *Som*

(r.) A fine pickle jar, cut with blazes, swags and printies and scalloped rim, 6½ in. high, c. 1790. **£120-140** *Som*

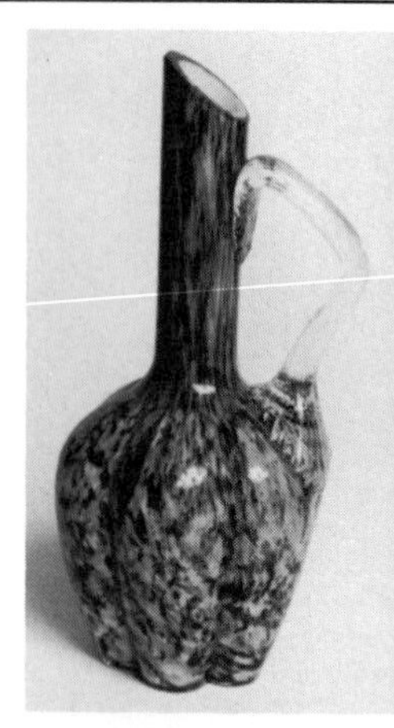

A Nailsea 'end of the day' glass jug, 7½ in., c. 1870. **£15-20** *BP*

A Stourbridge gilt and enamel blue glass jug, 8½ in., c. 1930. **£30-40** *BP*

An Irish cream boat, the heavy body cut with strawberry diamonds and prism cuts, turned over rim, heavy cut strap handle, star cut foot, 150 mm. long, c. 1825. **£50-£60** *Som*

A Baccarat miniature wheatflower weight, the flower with 12 ribbed white petals spotted in black about a red and white star centre, on a star cut base, 5 cm. diam. **£1,050-1,250** *C*

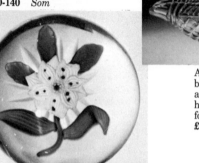

A Baccarat white double-clematis weight, with 12 ribbed petals about a red, white and blue centre including a circlet of arrow's head canes, 7.7 cm. diam. **£500-600** *C*

A Baccarat primrose type weight, with 5 heart-shaped petals in gentian blue within cupped white petals, on leafy stalk, the base star cut, 7.5 cm. **£300-350** *P*

A Baccarat garlanded primrose weight, the flower with 5 small white petals above 5 large recessed rust-red petals, within a garland on an upset muslin ground, 7.3 cm. diam. **£1,350-£1,550** *C*

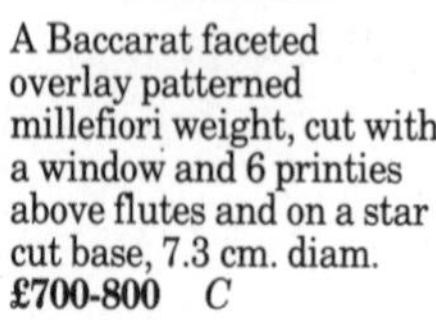

A Baccarat faceted overlay patterned millefiori weight, cut with a window and 6 printies above flutes and on a star cut base, 7.3 cm. diam. **£700-800** *C*

A Baccarat miniature yellow double-clematis weight, the flower with 12 petals about a green and white star centre, on a star cut base, 5 cm. diam. **£900-1,000** *C*

A Baccarat faceted garlanded pompom weight, the flower with many recessed white petals about a yellow stamen centre, within a garland, cut with a window and 6 printies on a star cut base, 6.7 cm. diam. **£900-1,100** *C*

A Baccarat buttercup and garland weight, outer petals turquoise, inner white, yellow stamen, encircled by a garland of crimson and white canes, and cut with a top and 6 side printies above a band of ovals, 7.5 cm. **£350-£400** *P*

A Baccarat flat-bouquet weight of cruciform type, a white bud at the base, the green stalks with 10 leaves, 9 cm. diam. **£2,000-2,500** *C*

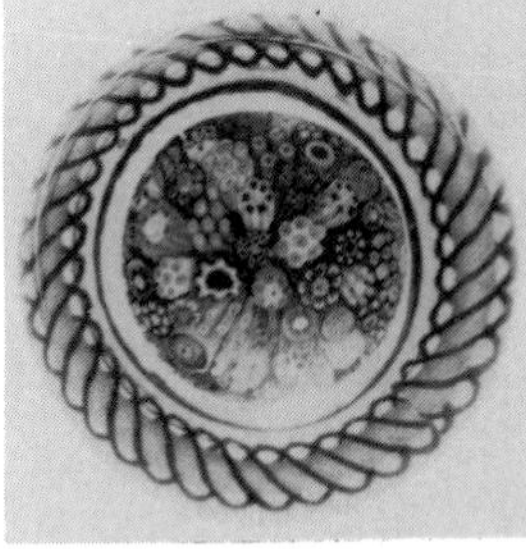
An unusual Baccarat mushroom weight, closely-packed canes centred within a red-and-white torsade, star cut base, 8 cm. **£700-750** *S*

A Baccarat apple weight, the fruit on a bed of 6 green leaves pendant from a green stalk, 6.2 cm. diam. **£700-800** *C*

A Baccarat garlanded butterfly weight, with amethyst body, black head and antennae, blue eyes and 4 brightly coloured marbled wings within a garland, on a star cut base, 8.1 cm. diam. **£1,200-1,400** *C*

A Baccarat faceted green-ground sulphide weight, the portrait of Louis Napoleon set on a translucent green ground, the sides cut with facets, 6 cm. diam. **£250-300** *C*

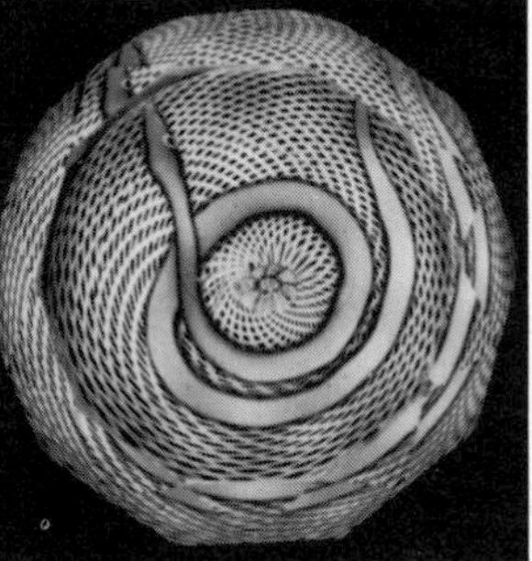
An important and very rare Baccarat snake paperweight, the all pink reptile coiled around an arrowhead cane, above a ground of spiralling latticinio threads, 7.5 cm. **£6,000-7,000** *P*

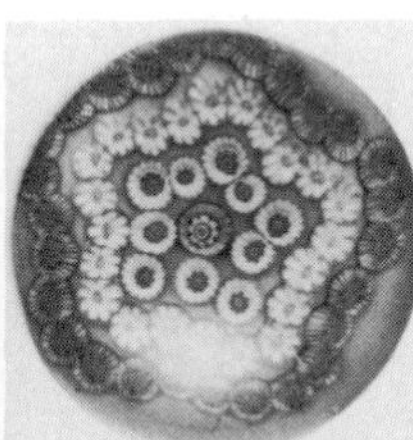
A Clichy colour ground weight, the central pale blue cane enclosed by 3 cinque-lobed rows of mainly green and white canes, on an opaque rich pink ground, 7.5 cm. **£250-£300** *P*

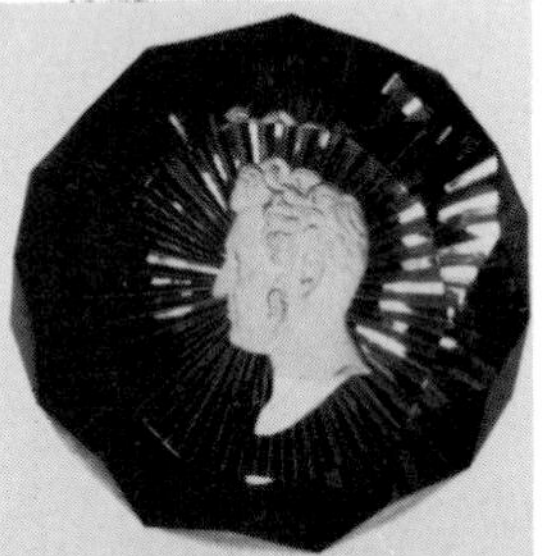
A Baccarat faceted coloured-ground sulphide weight, with a profile portrait of Louis Philippe on a translucent pink ground, with facet-cut sides and on a sunray-cut base, 7 cm. diam. **£550-£650** *C*

A Clichy blue-ground scattered millefiori weight, the brightly coloured canes including a pink rose and a central white rose set on an opaque cobalt-blue ground, 6.2 cm. diam. **£300-350** *C*

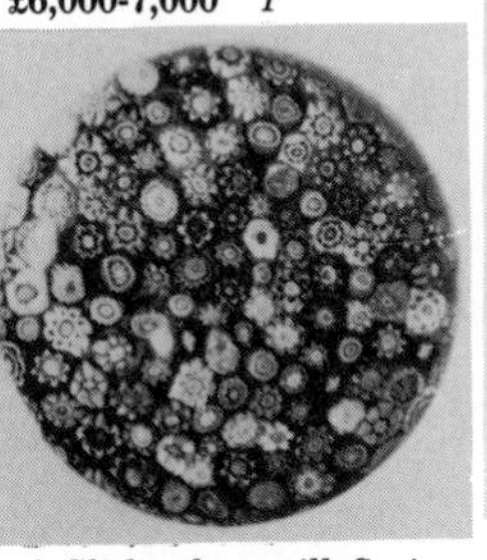
A Clichy close millefiori weight, brightly coloured including 3 pink roses, a pink and white rose, a green and white rose and a white rose, 6.5 cm. diam. **£600-700** *C*

A Clichy garlanded faceted sulphide weight with a portrait of the Virgin Mary, set within a garland of green-centred white and white-centred claret canes, the sides cut with diamond facets, 7 cm. diam. **£400-450** *C*

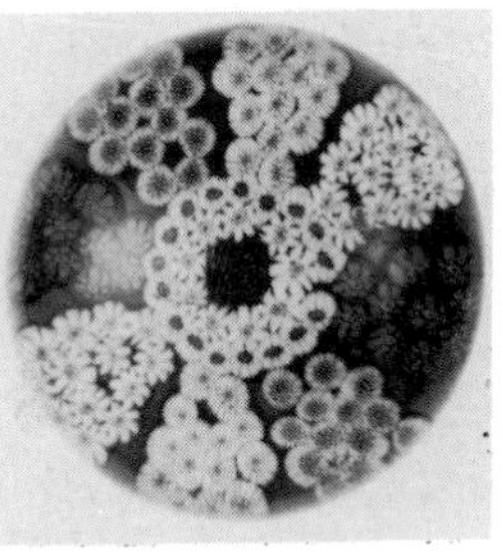
A Clichy red-ground weight with rows of predominantly white canes and 8 loops of canes in green, white, turquoise and red, 8 cm. **£600-700** *S*

A rare Clichy weight of almost crown type, clear glass with a central white and green floret, 8.5 cm. **£550-650** *S*

A rare Clichy turquoise and white overlay mushroom weight, the canes, enclosed by white staves, cut with top and 5 side printies, the base with strawberry diamond, 6.5 cm. **£900-1,100** *P*

A Clichy pansy weight, the flower with 2 large purple petals and 3 smaller yellow petals with brown spots about a green stamen centre, 7 cm. diam. **£1,000-1,300** *C*

A Clichy swirl paperweight, the alternate opaque white and turquoise spiral bands radiating from a pink and green pastry mould cane, 6.5 cm. **£250-300** *P*

A St. Louis faceted pansy weight, the top cut with square facets and the sides with 8 printies, 8.3 cm. diam. **£1,050-1,250** *C*

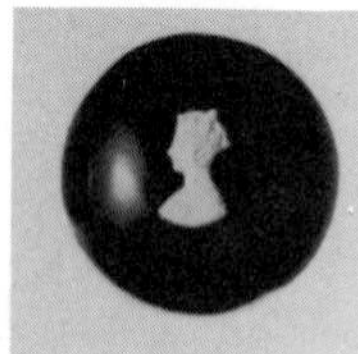
A rare Clichy sulphide weight, set with a portrait of Queen Victoria on translucent blue ground, 5 cm. **£200-250** *P*

Differing from the usual version being after the design by William Wyon for the so-called 'Gothic' series of Coinage.

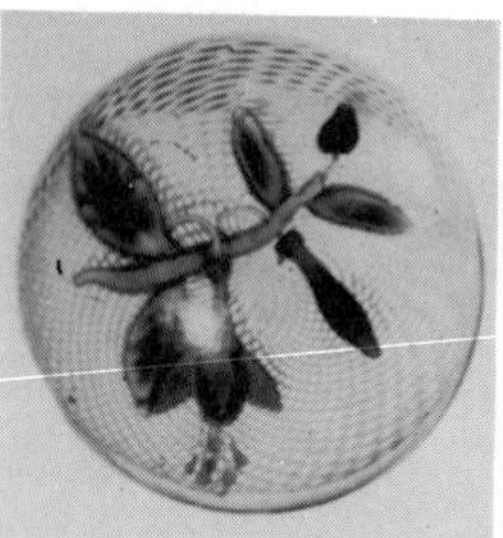
A St. Louis fuchsia weight, with a red and blue flower, 2 red buds and 4 green leaves, on a cushion of opaque spiral latticinio threads, 5.8 cm. diam. **£900-1,000** *C*

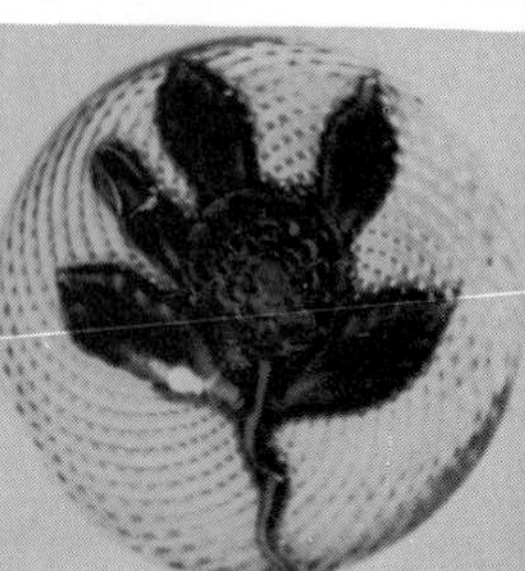
A St. Louis pink pompom weight, the flower with many recessed pink petals about a yellow stamen centre, on a cushion of opaque spiral latticinio thread, 6.7 cm. diam. **£800-900** *C*

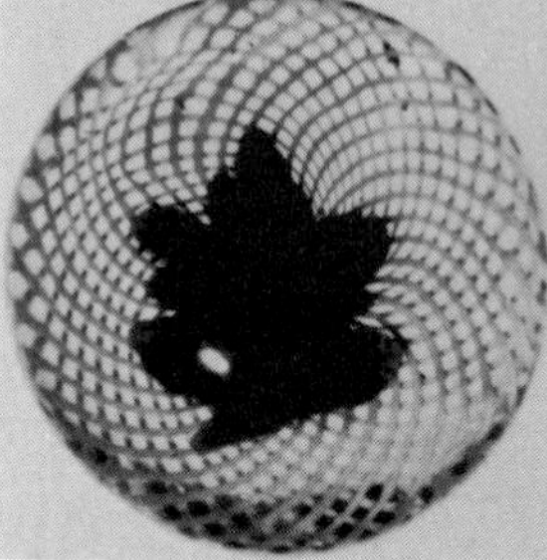
A St. Louis red double-clematis weight, the flower with 15 pointed ribbed petals about a yellow centre, resting on a cushion of opaque latticinio spiral threads, 7.3 cm. diam. **£500-600** *C*

A St. Louis faceted upright bouquet weight, the sides cut with 3 rows of graduated printies and the top with a window, on a strawberry cut base, 8 cm. diam. **£600-700** *C*

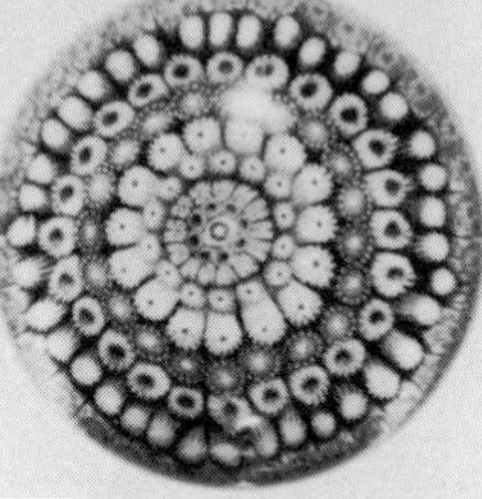
A good St. Louis close concentric millefiori weight, with 9 circles of canes in a variety of colours, 7.5 cm. **£500-£600** *P*

A St. Louis upright bouquet multi-colour weight, on star cut base 7.3 cm. diam. **£900-£1,100** *C*

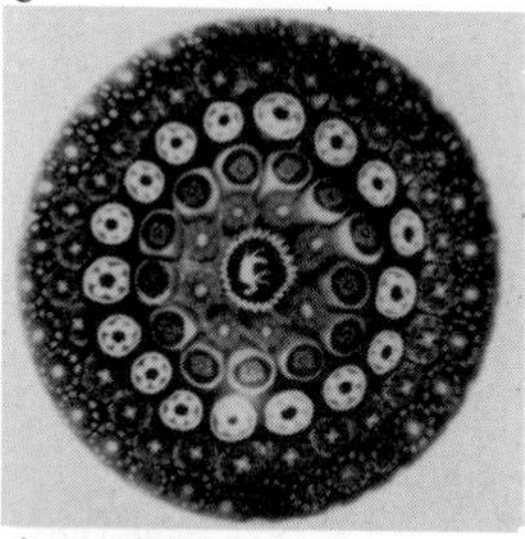
A rare dated St. Louis concentric millefiori weight with a central camel silhouette, the outer row of canes including the date SL 1847, 8.3 cm. **£1,300-1,500** *S*

It is rare to find a dated 1847 weight with a camel silhouette rather than the more usual dancing devils.

A St. Louis fruit weight, with 3 pears and 4 cherries resting on a bed of green leaves above a spiralling latticinio ground, 6.5 cm. **£300-£350** *P*

A fine St. Louis 4-colour crown weight with alternating twisted tapes in red and green, and blue and yellow, divided by spiralling latticinio thread, 6.8 cm. **£1,100-£1,300** *P*

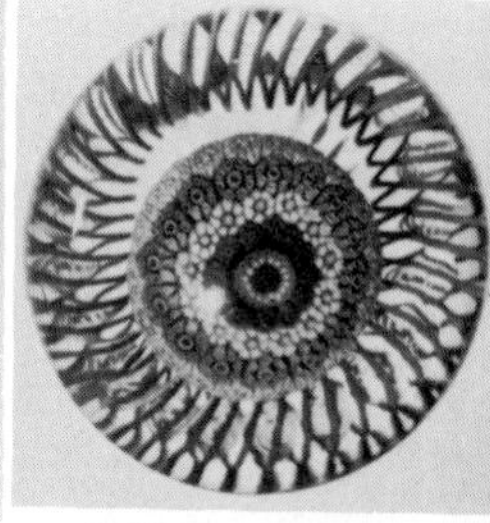
A St. Louis mushroom weight, 4 circles of canes about a central salmon-pink and blue set-up, set within a torsade of corkscrew spiral, on star cut base, 8.2 cm. diam. **£400-500** *C*

A Gillinder hexagonally-cut concentric millefiori weight with a central white silhouette of Queen Victoria, 7.5 cm. diam. **£400-500** *C*

A St. Louis mushroom weight, the red, white and blue tuft within green canes, and blue and white torsade, cut with top and 6 side printies, the base star cut, 7.7 cm. **£550-600** *P*

A St. Louis flat bouquet and garland weight, 4 florettes on leafy stalk, encircled by red and blue canes, on a tossed muslin ground, 7.5 cm. **£450-£550** *P*

A Venetian tazza with upturned rim in vetro a retorti, set over a high spreading foot with folded rim in clear glass, 18 cm. diam., late 16th C. **£500-600** *S*

(l.) A Patch stand with turned up rim, on a stem with shoulder knop, domed folded foot, 72 mm. high by 85 mm. diam., c. 1745. **£50-60** *Som*

(r.) A Patch stand with turned up rim, plain tapered stem, folded conical foot, 54 mm. high by 72 mm. diam., c. 1750. **£50-70** *Som*

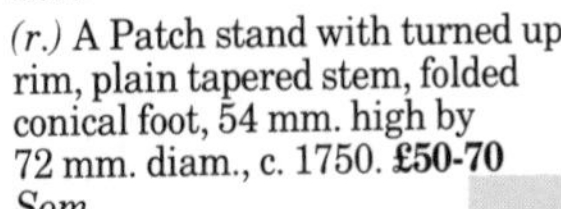

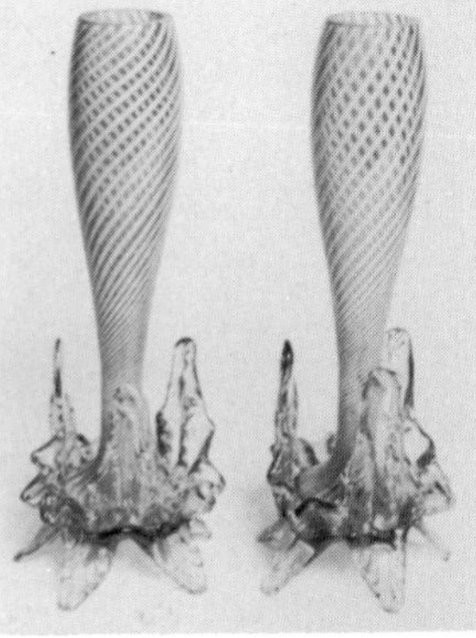

A pair of Stourbridge amber and white glass vases, 9 in., c. 1870. **£30-40** *BP*

A small cameo glass vase, the brown glass overlaid in opaque white and carved, 11.5 cm., c. 1885. **£500-600** *S*

A Facon-De-Venise tazza, with radiating panels of ladder-moulding, on a wrythen-moulded knopped stem, on a radially ribbed foot, 20 cm. diam., late 17th C. **£1,400-1,600** *C*

A Stourbridge 'end of the day' glass vase, 8 in., c. 1880. **£20-25** *BP*

A Bohemian white overlay cranberry glass vase, 19 in., c. 1850. **£250-300** *BP*

A Stevens & Williams dated cameo vase, the bright blue ground overlaid in white, the base with script Stevens & Williams mark above the date 1885, 26.5 cm. high. **£5,500-6,500** *C*

A garniture of 4 cut glass vases and covers, the square base star cut and the rim and cover with vertical flute borders, 12 and 15¼ in. (30.5 and 38.8 cm.), 20th C. **£450-550** *S*

An Orrefors 'Graal' vase, designed by Edward Hald, internally decorated in green with fish, Orrefors, Graal No. 1940K, Edward Hald, 11.5 cm. **£200-250** *P*

Edward Hald joined this Swedish glass factory as artistic director in 1917. Hald had studied painting under Matisse. He was director from 1933-44 and was inspirational in the production of some of the best decorative glass to be made in Europe.

A Bohemian white overlay cranberry glass vase with gilding (rubbed), 15 in. high, c. 1860. **£250-£350** *BP*

A pair of ormolu-mounted cut glass vases with faceted bodies, the pierced latticework covers with cone finials, 26½ in. (67 cm.) high. **£1,500-2,200** *C*

A blue-tinted sulphide vase, in translucent royal blue with a sulphide portrait of Robert Burns, inscribed 'Robert Burns, Scotland's Bard/Born 25th January 1759', John Ford & Co., Holyrood Flint Glass Works, Edinburgh, 4¾ in., mid 19th C. **£450-550** *S*

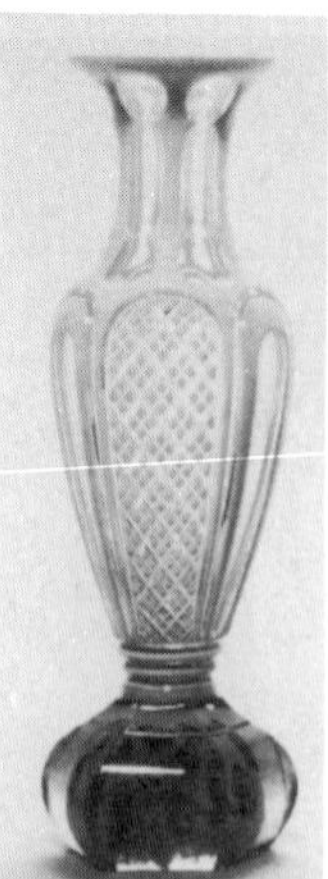

A 19th C. French glass pharmacy jar. **£120-150** *P*

A pair of Bohemian overlay paperweight vases in clear glass overlay in opaque-white, paperweight base enclosing scattered canes, 22 cm. **£450-500** *S*

A dated Lobmeyr Islamic-style enamelled vase, thickly enamelled in white and rust and gilt, base marked A. Hulb (?), 1877, 23.8 cm. **£250-300** *S*

A small Bristol blue comport or vase, 110 mm. high, c. 1830. **£35-£40** *Som*

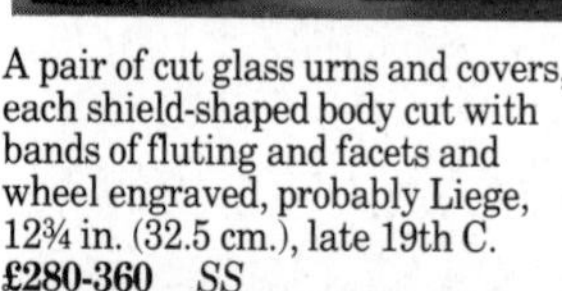

A pair of cut glass urns and covers, each shield-shaped body cut with bands of fluting and facets and wheel engraved, probably Liege, 12¾ in. (32.5 cm.), late 19th C. **£280-360** *SS*

A Victorian pressed glass hat, probably Birmingham, 2¼ in. high. **£20-30** *BP*

A pair of Georgian-style cut glass urns and covers, decorated with bands of fluting, diamonds and facets, 11½ in. (29.5 cm.), late 19th C. **£300-350** *SS*

A good pair of glass paintings, chiefly in shades of red and blue with original parcel-gilt frames, 1 ft. 10½ in. high by 2 ft. 6½ in. wide (57 by 77 cm.), early 19th C. **£1,000-1,200** *S*

An Apsley Pellat sulphide plaque, the sulphide a bust portrait of George IV, 3¾ in., c. 1820-30. **£400-450** *S*

A pair of Upper Rhenish stained glass panels, painted in vivid colours with events in the Life of Abraham, both releaded and framed with contemporary frames, 17th C. **£1,200-1,400** *S*

A Swiss stained glass panel, painted with St. Gallus and the abbot St. Omar, minor damage, 17½ in. (44.5 cm.) high, early 17th C. **£600-650** *S*

A Swiss stained glass panel with the imperial double eagle over the shields of Appenzell, some panes replaced, 17¼ in. (44 cm.) high, c. 1600. **£550-600** *S*

An opaque-white glass plaque transfer printed 'Reward', 9½ in. inc. frame, c. 1860. **£75-95** *GCA*

A pair of Stourbridge glass hats, 2½ in. high, c. 1850. **£40-60** *BP*

A Bristol blue glass hat, 3½ in. high, c. 1800-20. **£40-60** *BP*

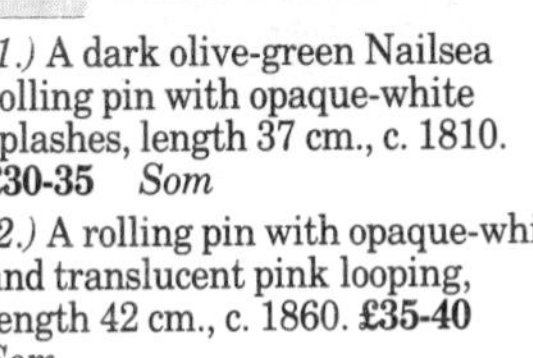

(1.) A dark olive-green Nailsea rolling pin with opaque-white splashes, length 37 cm., c. 1810. **£30-35** *Som*

(2.) A rolling pin with opaque-white and translucent pink looping, length 42 cm., c. 1860. **£35-40** *Som*

(3.) A Nailsea green crown glass rolling pin, length 44 cm., c. 1810. **£40-45** *Som*

(4.) A 'Stourbridge' brown glass rolling pin with translucent red and blue splashes, length 35 cm., c. 1860. **£35-40** *Som*

(1.) A blue rolling pin with inscription and 2 sailing ships in gilt, length 45 cm., c. 1860. **£60-£70** *Som*

(2.) A blue rolling pin inscribed 'Forget Me Not', sailing ship and The Sunderland Bridge, in gilt, length 36 cm., c. 1860. **£60-70** *Som*

(3.) A Potichomanie rolling pin with coloured print inserts, length 36 cm., c. 1880. **£60-70** *Som*

(4.) A Crown glass rolling pin with translucent blue looping, length 38 cm., c. 1860. **£55-60** *Som*

A Stourbridge vaseline glass epergne, 19½ in., c. 1860. **£150-£170** *BP*

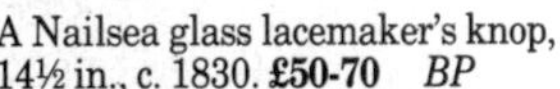

A Nailsea glass lacemaker's knop, 14½ in., c. 1830. **£50-70** *BP*

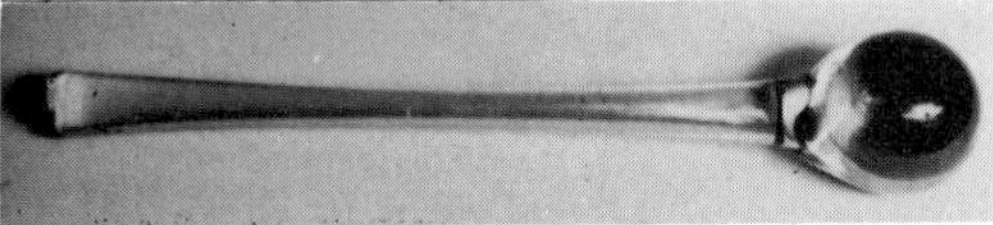

A Nailsea glass pageboy's knop, 14½ in., c. 1830. **£40-60** *BP*

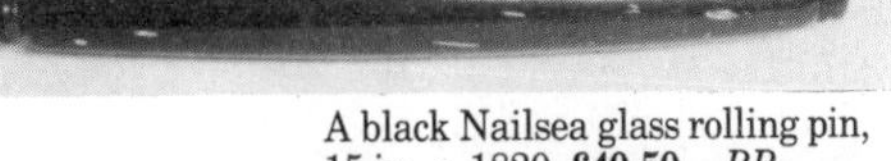

A black Nailsea glass rolling pin, 15 in., c. 1820. **£40-50** *BP*

A pair of cut lustres, cut with hobnail diamonds beneath a flared bowl hung with drops and pendants, 18.3 cm., c. 1830. **£500-£550** *S*

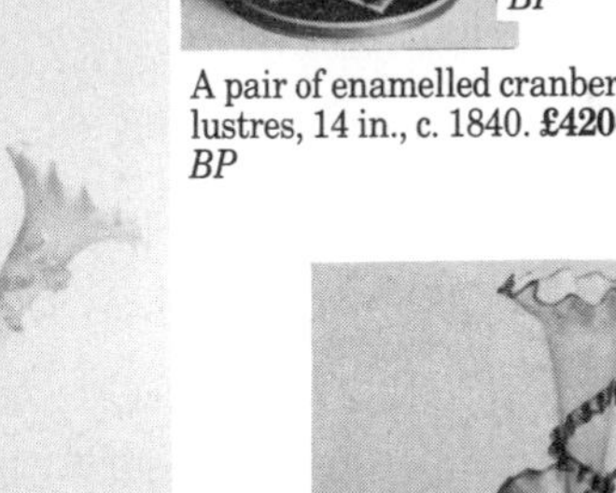

A pair of English enamelled lustres, 14 in., c. 1840. **£400-450** *BP*

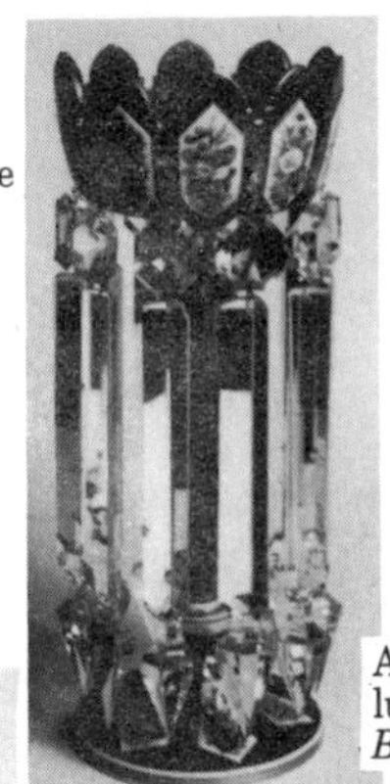

A pair of enamelled cranberry glass lustres, 14 in., c. 1840. **£420-460** *BP*

A green and cream vaseline glass epergne, 19½ in., c. 1860. **£140-£160** *BP*

A Nailsea window glass pageboy's knop, 18 in., c. 1840. **£40-60** *BP*

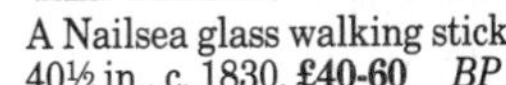

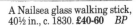

A Nailsea glass walking stick, 40½ in., c. 1830. **£40-60** *BP*

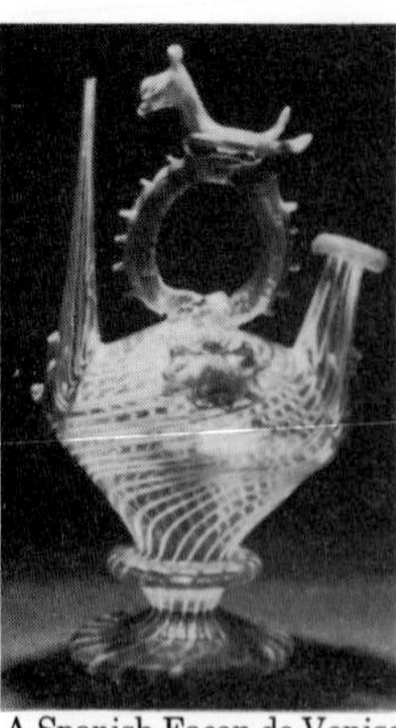

A Spanish Facon de Venise Cantir, with double-walled conical foot, of straw-coloured metal with swirling opaque-white threads, 2 applied spouts, Catalonia, 27.5 cm., 18th C. **£600-700** *S*

Two similar English cameo glass salts, almost a pair, the ruby glass overlaid in white and carved with flowers, the silver mounts and spoons marked for Birmingham, 1885, in fitted case. **£450-500** *P*

One of a set of 3 small and 2 larger oval dishes with diamond cut bodies, fan cut rims and star cut bases, 250 by 162 mm., 290 by 210 mm. Set of 5. **£200-250** *Som*

A Victorian Bristol blue cruet, the silver-plated stand with 6 blue cut condiment bottles and mustard, 11½ in. high, c. 1850. **£380-420** *Som*

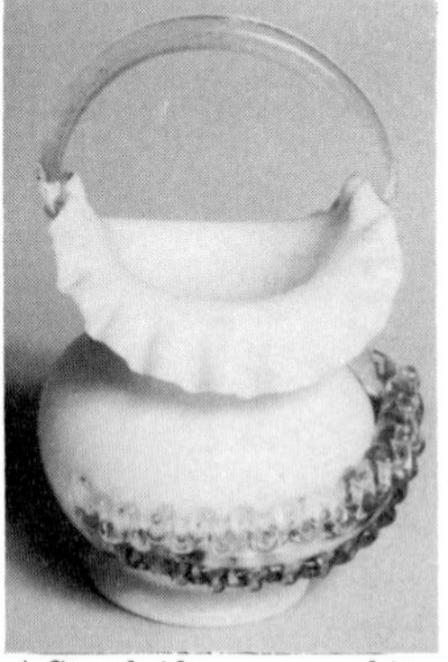

A Stourbridge opaque-white glass basket, 7 in. high, c. 1860. **£50-60** *BP*

A blue opaline washstand set, each piece enamelled beneath gilt rims, ewer cracked, late 19th C. **£180-£220** *S*

A milch glass creamer with painted floral decoration, 4½ in. high, 18th C. **£25-30** *EEW*

A fine large cut butter dish, cover and stand, the heavy metal cut with bridge flutes and diamonds, the stand with cut scalloped edge and star cut base, 150 mm. high by 255 mm. long, c. 1800. **£200-250** *Som*

A good Nailsea light green crown glass inkwell, 5 in. high, c. 1820. **£40-45** *Som*

A Stourbridge crackle-finish pink and white glass basket, 7½ in., c. 1860. **£50-60** *BP*

A Venetian amethyst glass wine barrel, 6½ in., c. 1780. **£40-50** *BP*

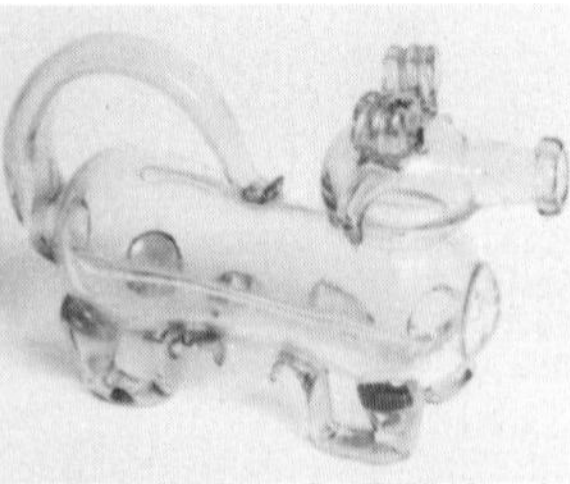

Nailsea pale blue glass gin pig, 10½ in., c. 1810-30. **£150-170** *BP*

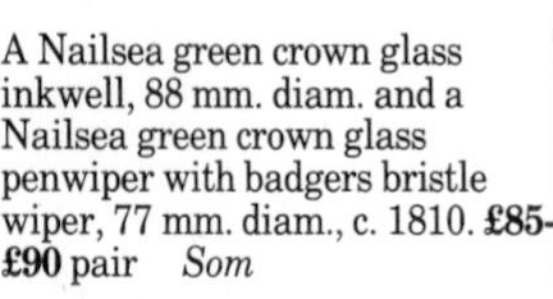

A Nailsea green crown glass inkwell, 88 mm. diam. and a Nailsea green crown glass penwiper with badgers bristle wiper, 77 mm. diam., c. 1810. **£85-£90** pair *Som*

A Nailsea green bubbled glass doorstop, 4½ in. high, c. 1840. **£40-£60** *BP*

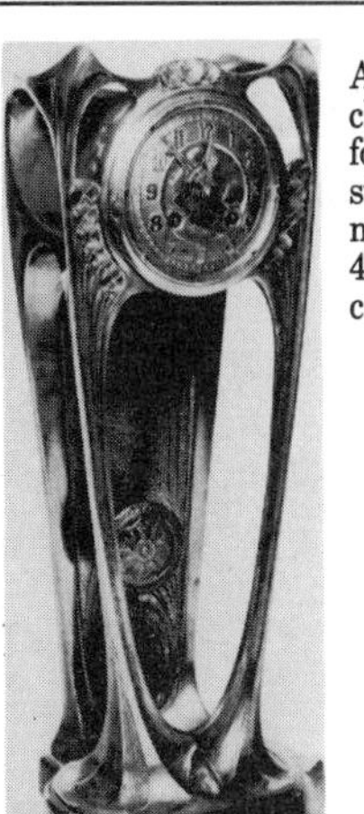

A Butzke bronze clock, cast with formalised flower and stems, signed in the maquette 'B. Butzke', 45 cm. high overall, c. 1905. **£400-450** *S*

A Liberty and Co. 'Tudric' pewter and enamel clock, designed by Archibald Knox, richly enamelled in mottled blue-green with central motif in deep red, stamped 'RD. 468106 Tudric 0609', 20.75 cm., c. 1905. **£750-850** *S*

A Liberty and Co. 'Tudric' pewter and enamel clock, designed by Archibald Knox, face detailed with deep mottled blue/green and red enamel, stamped 'Tudric 0608 Rd 468015' with Solketts mark, 14 cm., c. 1905. **£500-550** *S*

A Liberty and Co. 'Tudric' pewter and enamel clock, mottled blue and green enamelled cabochons and circular dial, stamped marks and numerals, 20.2 cm., c. 1900. **£150-£200** *S*

A Liberty and Co. 'Cymric' silver and enamel clock, the case set with 2 oval turquoise cabochons below blue and green enamelled dial, numerals replaced with the words 'Festina Lente', maker's mark, stamped 'Cymric', Birmingham, 1905, 10.5 cm. **£400-500** *S*

A Liberty and Co. silver and enamel clock, detailed in turquoise enamel, maker's mark, Birmingham, 1912, 9.25 cm. **£200-250** *S*

A Rosenburg earthenware mantel clock, painted in greens, browns and yellow, the French movement striking on a bell and signed Japy Frères, painted Rosenburg mark, 14 in. wide. **£350-400** *CSK*

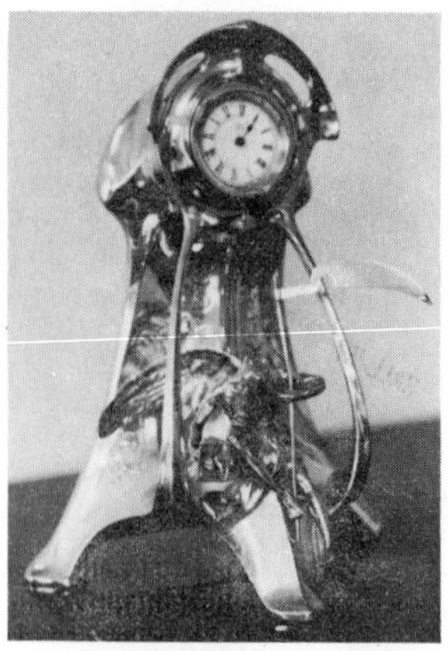

An Art Nouveau silver plated clock. **£250-300** *HWO*

An Art Nouveau clock in inlaid mahogany case with pewter chapter ring, 18 in. high, c. 1890. **£400-500** *TP*

A stained wood Art Nouveau clock, 14½ in. high, dated 1910. **£140-£160** *NP*

An ebonised and mahogany etagere by Carlo Bugatti with Moorish arch inlaid in ivory with stars, the back edge with beaten copper, 99 cm. high. **£700-750** *C*

An ebonised armchair, the design attributed to Christopher Dresser, 75 cm., c. 1880. **£550-600** *S*

A Charpentier wall mirror, indistinctly monogrammed, 54.75 cm., c. 1900. **£1,000-1,200** *S*

A Gallé fruitwood marquetry tray, inlaid mark 'Gallé', 31.75 cm. square, c. 1900. **£400-500** *S*

A Hickory secretaire cabinet in the manner of C. L. Eastlake, fall front inset with painted tiles, 183 by 96.5 by 49 cm., c. 1870. **£400-500** *S*

An Emile Gallé mahogany 3-tier occasional table, stained in green and amber with a spray of iris, dandelion and honeysuckle, upper tier signed Gallé, 87 cm. high by 82 cm. wide. **£400-450** *C*

An oak and inlaid serpentine fronted writing desk, probably designed by J. S. Henry, the right hand side fitted with pigeonholes above a central drawer with coppered handles, some glass panels broken, 109 cm. wide by 108.5 cm. high by 51 cm. deep. **£700-800** *C*

A George Walton oak armchair manufactured by Godyers Ltd. **£350-400** *C*

A small Gallé marquetry side table, hinged top opening to form 'X' shaped surface, incised 'E. Gallé Nancy' with Croix de Lorraine, 76 cm. high, 1900-10. **£650-750** *S*

An inlaid grey walnut table, probably by Wylie and Lochhead and designed by George Logan, inlaid in silver metal and mother-of-pearl, stamped 121688, 84 cm. wide by 69 cm. high, c. 1900. **£750-£850** *S*

Two J. & J. Kohn 'Fledermaus' chairs designed by Josef Hoffmann, J. & J. Kohn label, beneath upholstery, 80 cm. high, c. 1905. **£400-600** *S*

Two J. & J. Kohn 'Fledermaus' chairs, designed by Josef Hoffmann, J. & J. Kohn labels, 80 cm. high, c. 1905. **£600-700** *S*

A Liberty and Co. oak wardrobe probably designed by Leonard F. Wyburd, bearing a white printed label, Liberty, London, 198 cm. high by 91 cm. wide by 47 cm. deep, c. 1899. **£200-250** *C*

A Liberty and Co. oak wardrobe with planished copper hinges, 199 by 124.5 cm., c. 1900. **£200-250** *S*

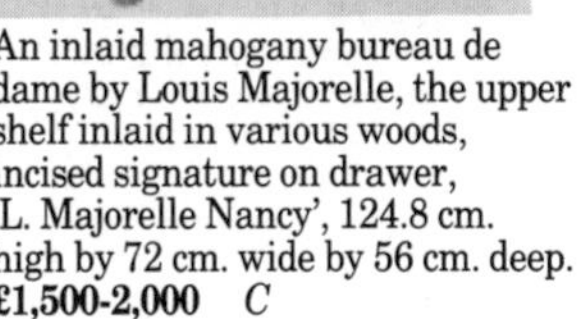

An inlaid mahogany bureau de dame by Louis Majorelle, the upper shelf inlaid in various woods, incised signature on drawer, 'L. Majorelle Nancy', 124.8 cm. high by 72 cm. wide by 56 cm. deep. **£1,500-2,000** *C*

A carved mahogany selette in the style of Louis Majorelle, with later turntable top, 75 cm. high, c. 1900. **£200-300** *S*

A Majorelle fruitwood marquetry table, the top inlaid with stylised leaves in various fruitwoods, branded mark 'L. Majorelle Nancy', 74 cm. high by 56.5 cm. deep by 72.25 cm. wide, c. 1900. **£700-800** *S*

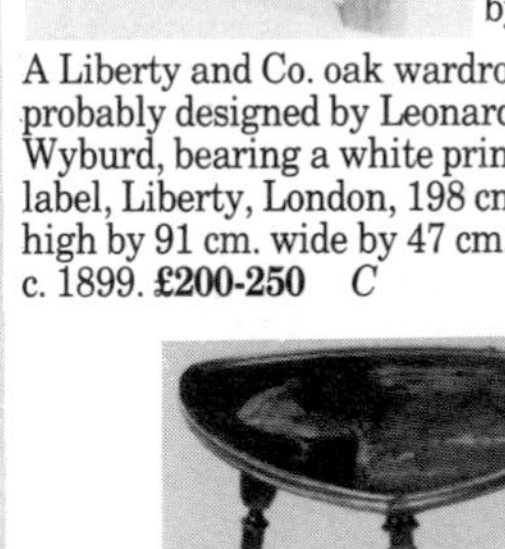

A Gallé marquetry table, the top inlaid with oak, beech and other various woods, with the legend 'Quand ce coq chante aura mon amitie pour finira', signed Gallé, 72 cm. high. **£300-£400** *P*

A French Art Nouveau fruitwood and maple vitrine in the style of Louis Majorelle, 26 in. wide. **£200-250** *CSK*

An Art Nouveau chair with stained design and mother-of-pearl inlay, 52 in. high, c. 1900. **£300-350** *TA*

An Art Nouveau oak bookshelf/ writing desk with fitted interior, 50 in. high. **£55-75** *CDE*

An Art Nouveau carved oak settle in the 'Romantic Tudor' style, the canopy carved with 5 panels and stylised Tudor Roses and the couplet 'Far from Court far from Care', 69 in. **£350-400** *WHL*

An inlaid glazed cabinet, open top with mirrored back, the whole inlaid with highly stylised foliage, 192 cm. high, c. 1900. **£800-900** *S*

A mahogany and marquetry salon suite, comprising a pair of armchairs, 4 chairs and a sofa, sofa 4 ft. 5 in. wide (135 cm.), c. 1900. **£700-800** *S*

An Austrian Art Nouveau oak bookcase cabinet in the neo-Classic style of inverted breakfront form, 81 by 80 in. (206 by 203 cm.). **£400-£450** *L*

An Argy Rousseau pâte-de-verre vase, grey with pale ruby and amethyst streaks, signed 'G. Argy Rousseau', 13 cm. high. **£800-900** *P*

Miller's is a price GUIDE Not a price LIST.

The price ranges given reflect the average price a purchaser should pay for similar items. Condition, rarity of design or pattern, size, colour, provenance, restoration and many other factors must be taken into account when assessing values. When buying or selling, it must always be remembered that prices can be greatly affected by the condition of any piece. Unless otherwise stated, all goods shown in Miller's are of good merchantable quality, and the valuations given reflect this fact. Pieces offered for sale in exceptionally fine condition or in poor condition may reasonably be expected to be priced considerably higher or lower respectively than the estimates given herein.

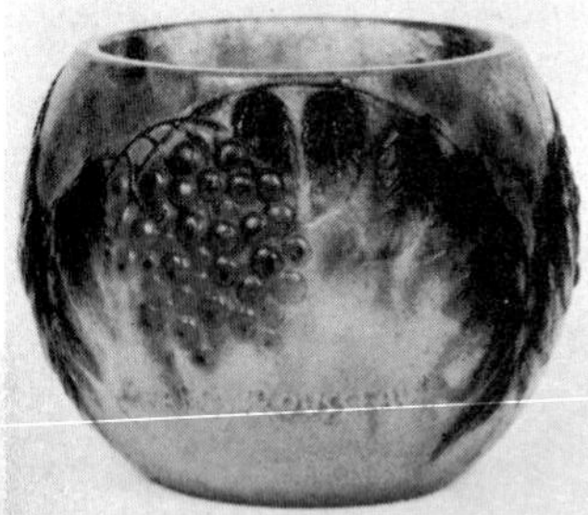

A small Argy Rousseau pâte-de-cristal bowl, moulded with sprays of red berries and green-brown branches, the body lightly streaked with purple, marked 'G. Argy Rousseau', 6.75 cm., 1920's. **£500-£600** *S*

Two Brocard etched and gilt glass vases, detailed with brown, grey and gilding, one enamelled 'G. Brocard B.S.S.', the other with gilt mark 'G. Brocard Bar. S. Seine', 14 cm., c. 1900. **£300-350** *S*

A Baccarat clear glass and bronze milieu de table moulded as a breaking wave, gilt-bronze patina, 38 cm. wide. **£2,500-3,000** *C*

A good Argy Rousseau pâte-de-verre oviform vase, the honey-coloured body moulded and modelled with grey, yellow and red, with a mottled brown border of squared spiral panels, signed 'G. Argy Rousseau', 24 cm. high. **£3,500-4,000** *P*

Three small Clutha glass vases, 2 in green glass with fine internal bubbling and scattered coppery inclusions with white streaks, the third in opaque-amber glass swirling with white, height of tallest 12.75 cm., 1880's. **£150-£200** *S*

A large green glass goblet, probably Clutha, in clear green glass with coppery internal streaks and profuse bubbling, 27.75 cm., 1880's. **£220-280** *S*

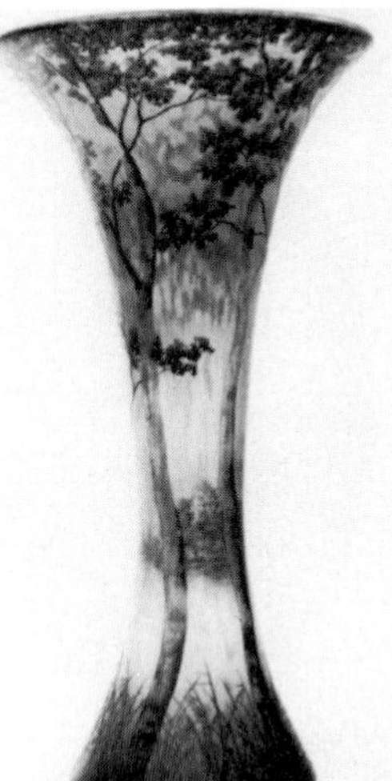

A Daum cameo glass landscape vase, enamelled in shades of green and blue, the base inscribed Daum Nancy, 15½ in. **£550-650** *WW*

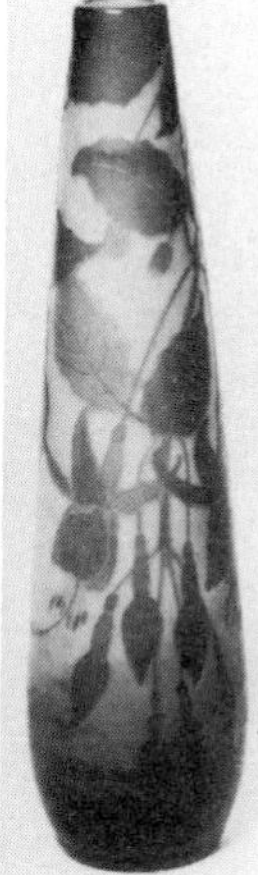

A D'Argental cameo glass vase, in amber glass overlaid with red and etched with fuchsias, cameo mark 'D'Argental', 23.5 cm., c. 1900. **£250-300** *S*

A Daum silver-mounted etched and enamelled glass bowl, the clear body overlaid in brilliant clear emerald green and etched, detailed with gilding, the rim with silver mount, stencilled mark 'Daum Nancy', 24.5 cm. diam., c. 1900. **£1,300-1,500** *S*

A Daum cameo glass vase, the pale orange and yellow mottled body overlaid with pale brown and green glass acid-etched with spiky fruit and leaves, signed in cameo 'Daum Nancy', 25 cm. high. **£500-550** *P*

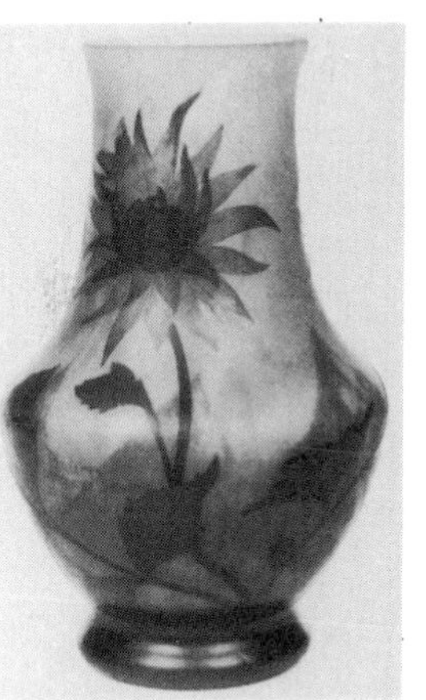

A Daum cameo glass vase, the dappled body overlaid with orange and brown glass and acid-etched with chrysanthemums, signed in cameo 'Daum, Nancy, France', 24.5 cm. high. **£350-400** *P*

A Gallé cameo glass vase, the greyish body overlaid with rich amethyst glass, engraved signature 'Gallé', 20.5 cm. high. **£1,000-£1,500** *P*

A tall Gallé cameo vase, the greyish body overlaid in white, amethyst and green, signed in cameo with interwoven 'Gallé', 60 cm. high. **£800-1,000** *P*

A Gallé cameo 'vase parlant', the body having deep blue and rust-red inclusions, overlaid with translucent brown glass, with a verse by Rollinat, signed in cameo 'Gallé', 35 cm. high. **£2,500-3,000** *P*

A Gallé cameo glass 'landscape' vase, the greyish body tinted amber at the top, overlaid with apple-green and deep ruby glass, signed 'Gallé' in cameo, 49.5 cm. high. **£1,000-1,500** *P*

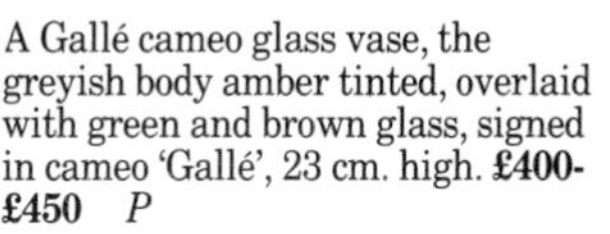

A Gallé cameo glass vase, the greyish body amber tinted, overlaid with green and brown glass, signed in cameo 'Gallé', 23 cm. high. **£400-£450** *P*

A Gallé cameo glass 'landscape' vase, the amber-tinted body overlaid with pale blue and amethyst showing as brown, intaglio signature 'Gallé', 35 cm. high. **£1,400-1,500** *P*

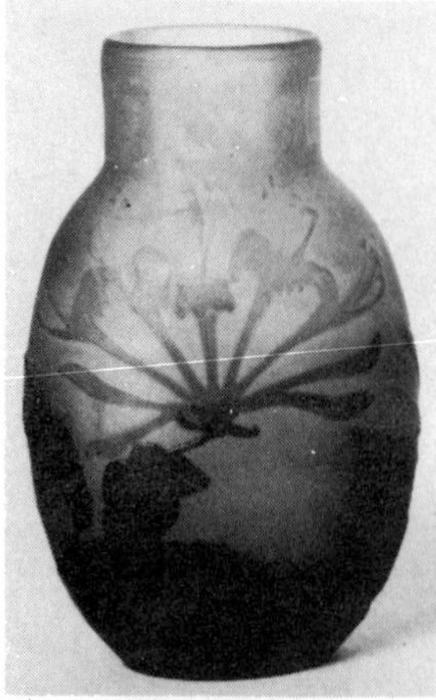

A Gallé cameo glass vase, the greyish body partially green tinted and overlaid with orange and brown, signed in cameo 'Gallé', 15 cm. high. **£250-300** *P*

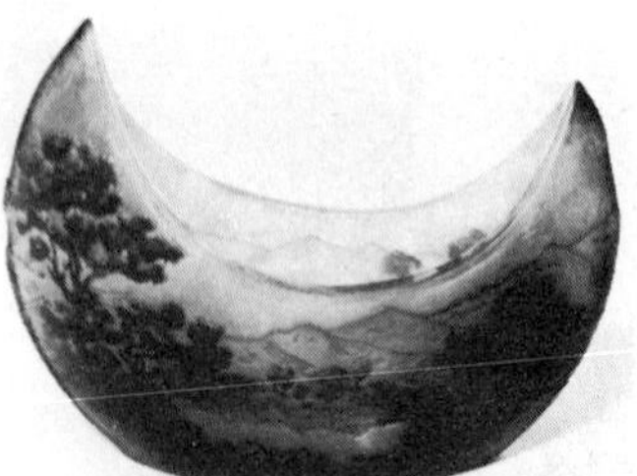

A Gallé cameo glass landscape dish, amber tinted grey glass overlaid with deep blue, cameo mark 'Gallé', 13.5 cm. maximum height, c. 1900. **£650-700** *S*

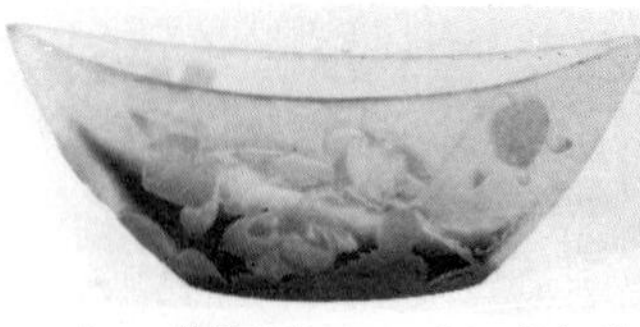

A small Gallé cameo glass dish, the body with deep inky turquoise-blue overlaid in bright pink and green, cameo mark 'Gallé', with a star, 17.5 cm. wide, c. 1905. **£300-400** *S*

A Gallé cameo glass lamp base, in green glass overlaid with brown and etched with wild grasses, cameo mark 'Gallé', 42 cm., c. 1900. **£350-400** *S*

A Gallé cameo glass vase, in grey glass tinted with pink, dark red-brown and blue, incised mark 'Gallé', 19.25 cm., c. 1900. **£400-450** *S*

A Gallé glass perfume bottle and stopper, in smoky-brown glass enamelled and gilt, with stopper, enamelled mark 'E. Gallé a Nancy', 10 cm., 1880's. **£600-650** *S*

A Gallé cameo vase, the coral and green ground overlaid in green and brown and etched with trees, cameo mark, 8¼ in. high. **£350-£400** *CSK*

A Gallé fire polished cameo glass vase, the caramel ground at the neck shading to turquoise and overlaid and etched, cameo mark Gallé, 9 in. high. **£600-700** *CSK*

A Gallé etched and enamelled green glass bottle vase, in pink, mauve and white, detailed with gilt, enamelled Emile Gallé, Depose Serie G, 10½ in. high. **£300-£350** *CSK*

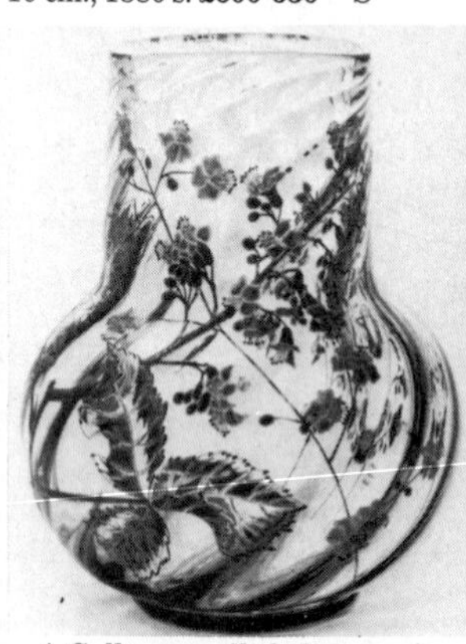

A Gallé enamelled glass vase in twisted and ribbed smoked glass, decorated in pink, green, red and black enamel, heightened with gilding, enamelled mark 'Emile Gallé a Nancy', 25 cm., 1890's. **£800-900** *S*

A Gallé double overlay glass vase, the grey ground overlaid with blue, green and amethyst, cameo mark, 8 in. high. **£500-600** *CSK*

A Gallé cameo glass vase, the pink body overlaid with orange, mauve and green glass acid-etched with nasturtiums, signed in cameo 'Gallé', 18.5 cm. high. **£700-800** *P*

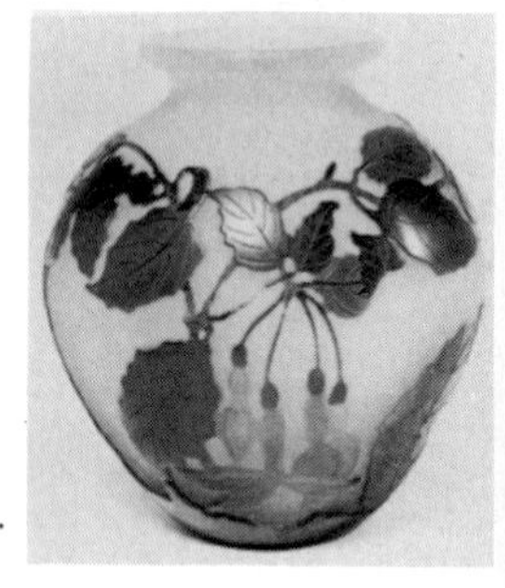

A Gallé cameo glass vase in milky amber glass, overlaid with purple-blue and etched flowering fuchsia, cameo mark 'Gallé', 13 cm., c. 1900. **£500-600** *S*

(l.) A Gallé glass landscape vase, the yellow tinted grey glass overlaid with blue and purple, cameo signature, 6 in. high, c. 1900. **£450-550** *DS*

(r.) An Art Nouveau glass vase, the yellow tinted grey glass overlaid with green and purple violets, signed Ficher, 5 in. high, c. 1900. **£70-90** *DS*

A Gallé plum overlay and mould-blown glass vase, the amber ground with purple pendant branches, cameo signature, 32.5 cm. high. **£3,500-4,500** *C*

PRICES

The pieces illustrated throughout this book have been selected to represent a broad cross section of the products of the Art Nouveau movement which are likely to be found on the market today. All the price ranges have been arrived at in consultation with a number of respected professional dealers and auction house valuers, and, as such, constitute realistic guide-lines as to the prices currently obtained.

It cannot be too strongly stressed that condition is of the utmost importance in the consideration of any price. This is particularly so in the case of Art Nouveau. Because the Art Nouveau period was relatively recent – it may reasonably be said to have ended by 1918, though a number of manufacturers continued to produce the more popular lines after that date – a great many pieces are to be found in absolutely perfect condition. Many, too, were produced in considerable quantity, and it would be unreasonable to expect a piece bearing even slight damage to realise as much as an identical, but perfect, specimen. Unless otherwise stated, all price ranges herein may be taken as representing the current market values of pieces in good showroom condition.

A Gallé cameo glass 'acorn' vase, in deep green glass mottled internally with streaks of blue-brown and bubbling, overlaid in clear brown and etched, cameo mark 'Gallé', 23.25 cm., c. 1900. **£550-650** *S*

A Lalique circular glass box and cover 'Meudon', heightened with pale blue staining, impressed on base 'R. Lalique', engraved 'France', 8.5 cm. diam. **£150-200** *P*

A large Legras cameo glass vase, milky opaque-amber body overlaid in mottled pink-brown glass with light iridescent sheen, cameo mark 'Legras', 52 cm. high, c. 1910. **£600-£650** *S*

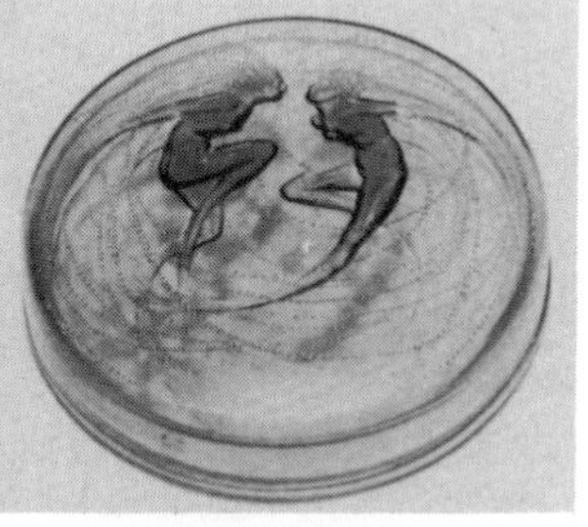

A Lalique circular glass box and cover 'Deux Sirènes' of amber colour, moulded on cover 'R. Lalique', 25.5 cm. **£500-600** *P*

A Lalique brooch, circular frosted glass over blue metallic foil, gilt-metal backing, stamped 'Lalique', 3 cm. diam., c. 1910. **£400-450** *S*

A Legras cameo glass vase, in green glass overlaid in grey and green, the mouth and neck streaked in amber, cameo mark 'Legras', 19 cm., c. 1910. **£350-£400** *S*

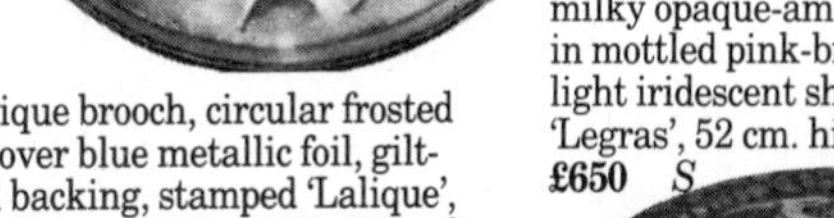

A Gallé cameo glass vase, the lemon coloured body overlaid and acid-etched with violets on leafy stems, etched 'Gallé', 16.5 cm. high. **£150-200** *P*

A Lalique circular glass box and cover 'Rambouillet', heightened with blue-grey staining, moulded on cover 'R. Lalique' and engraved on edge 'R. Lalique No.60', 8.5 cm. **£100-150** *P*

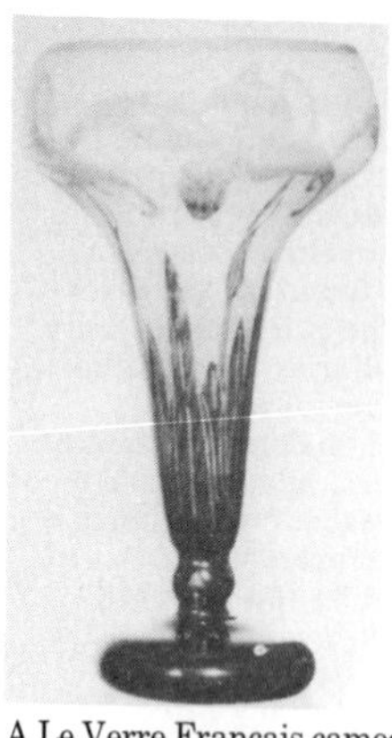

A Le Verre Francais cameo glass vase, the mottled yellow matt ground overlaid with aubergine shading to orange, polished, etched script mark, 13¼ in. high. **£70-£100** *CSK*

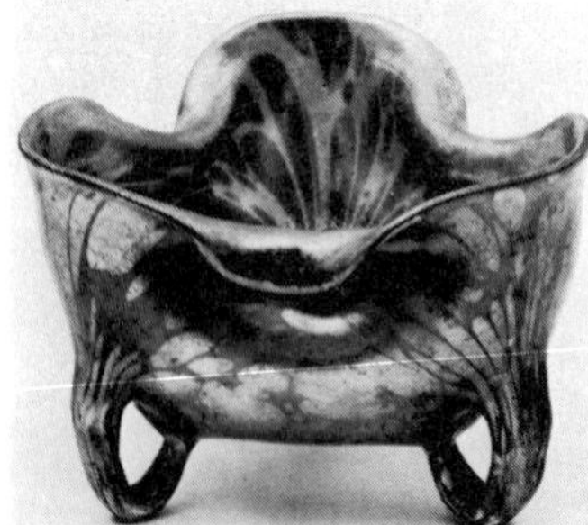

An iridescent glass bowl attributed to Loetz in amber glass decorated with splashed peacock-gold lustre, 13.5 cm., c. 1900. **£900-1,000** *S*

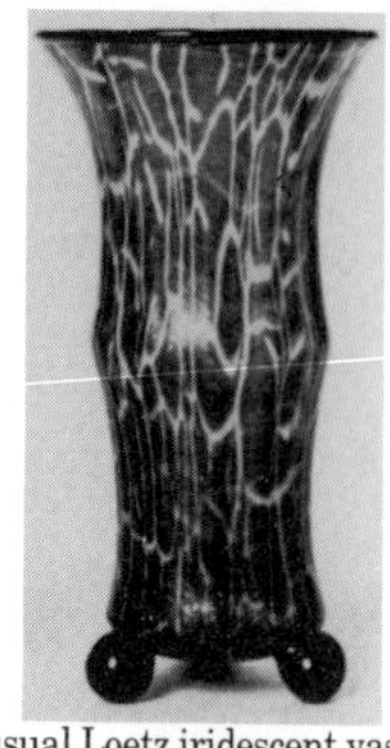

An unusual Loetz iridescent vase designed in the manner of Josef Hoffmann, the body of yellow tone covered with marbled silver-blue iridescence, 24.5 cm. high. **£150-£200** *P*

A Loetz iridescent glass vase, in pale amber glass with internal pale peacock lustre, with regular feathered trails of pale turquoise, iridescence, engraved crossed arrows mark, 31.75 cm., c. 1900. **£550-650** *S*

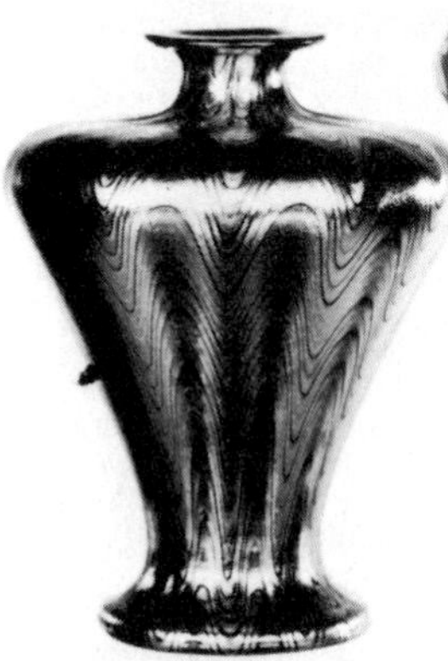

An iridescent ruby glass vase, attributed to Loetz, covered in iridescent silvery-blue and cobalt pulled thread decoration, 7¾ in. high. **£400-450** *CSK*

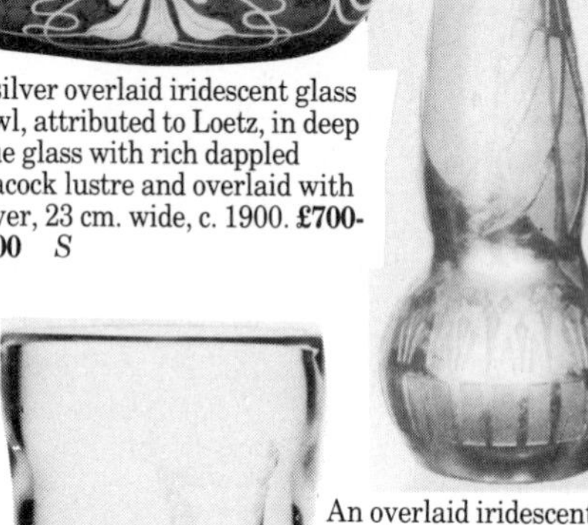

A silver overlaid iridescent glass bowl, attributed to Loetz, in deep blue glass with rich dappled peacock lustre and overlaid with silver, 23 cm. wide, c. 1900. **£700-£800** *S*

An overlaid iridescent glass vase attributed to Loetz, covered in a golden violet iridescence and overlaid with geometric gilt fretwork, 9¾ in. high. **£250-300** *CSK*

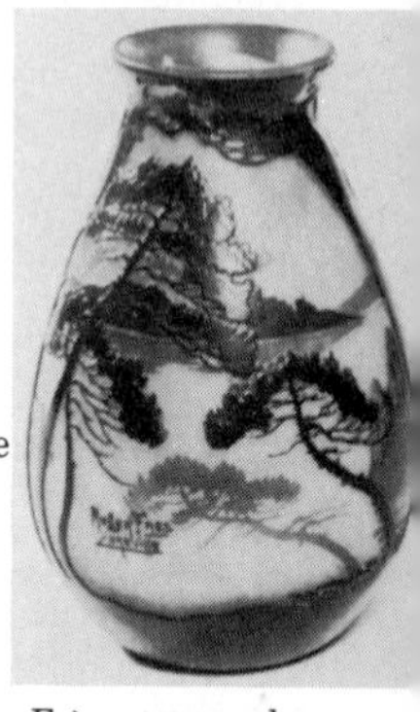

A Muller Frères cameo glass landscape vase, in pale green glass overlaid in amber, blue and black, cameo mark 'Muller Frères, Lunéville', 21.6 cm., c. 1900. **£400-£500** *S*

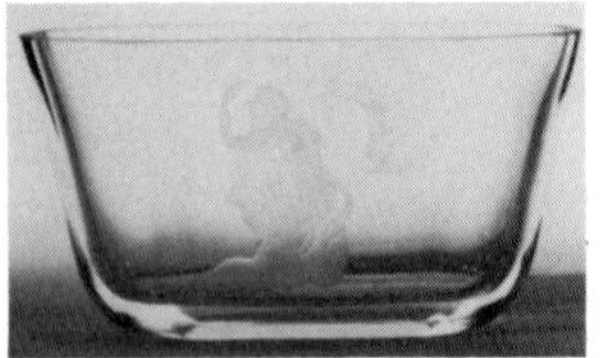

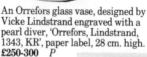

An Orrefors elliptical glass vase by Sven Palmquist, engraved on one side, 'Orrefors, Palmquist, 2397, B.I., 2B', 28 cm. long. **£70-90** *P*

An Orrefors glass vase, designed by Vicke Lindstrand engraved with a pearl diver, 'Orrefors, Lindstrand, 1343, KR', paper label, 28 cm. high. **£250-300** *P*

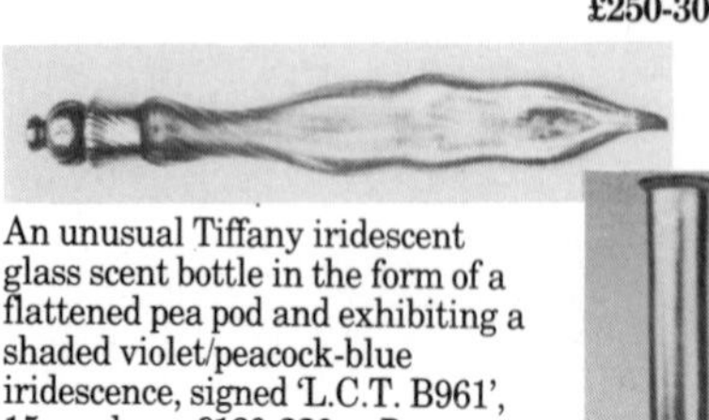

An unusual Tiffany iridescent glass scent bottle in the form of a flattened pea pod and exhibiting a shaded violet/peacock-blue iridescence, signed 'L.C.T. B961', 15 cm. long. **£180-220** *P*

A Tiffany studios Favrile glass and bronze bud vase, in green and golden iridescence, the bronze mount with 4 scroll feet, the glass inscribed L.C.T. Favrile and the base Tiffany Studios New York 715, 66.3 cm. high. **£650-750** *C*

A Tiffany iridescent glass vase, decorated with rich pink/peacock/gold lustre with trails of iridescent green leaves and stems, engraved 'L.C. Tiffany-Favrile 9661 C', 15.5 cm. high, 1908. **£350-400** *S*

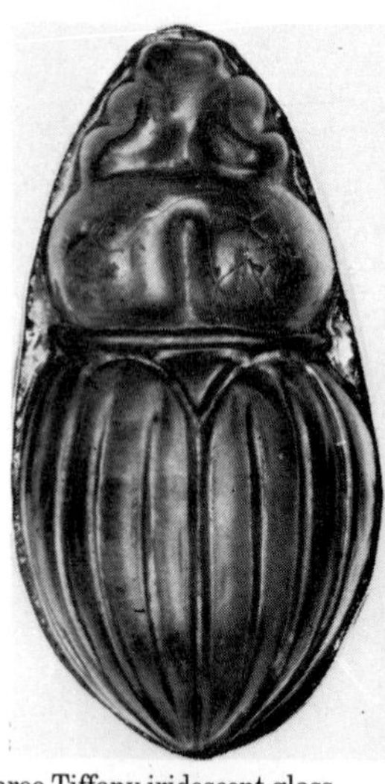

Three Tiffany iridescent glass scarabs, in amber glass with rich peacock/pink lustre, 2 mounted as gilt-metal hatpins, 4.35 cm., c. 1900. **£120-180** *S*

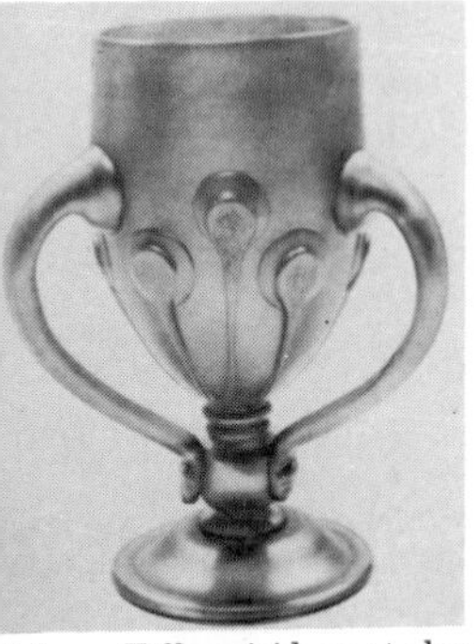

A large Tiffany iridescent glass stemmed cup, applied with teardrop trails, engraved mark 'L. C. Tiffany Favrile 8683C', 28.75 cm., 1908. **£500-600** *S*

A set of 4 Tiffany Favrile iridescent glass fingerbowls and saucers, in blue-gold iridescent glass, each piece engraved on the underside 'L.C.T.' and with 'M' prefix reference number, 15 cm. diam. of saucers. **£500-600** *S*

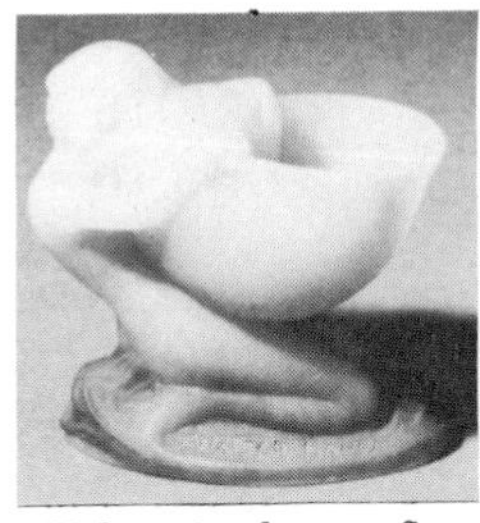

An A. Walter pâte-de-verre figure of a seated nude nymph holding a shell, in flesh coloured glass shading to yellow and green, moulded A. Walter Nancy, designer's initials JM, 10.8 cm. wide. **£1,500-2,000**

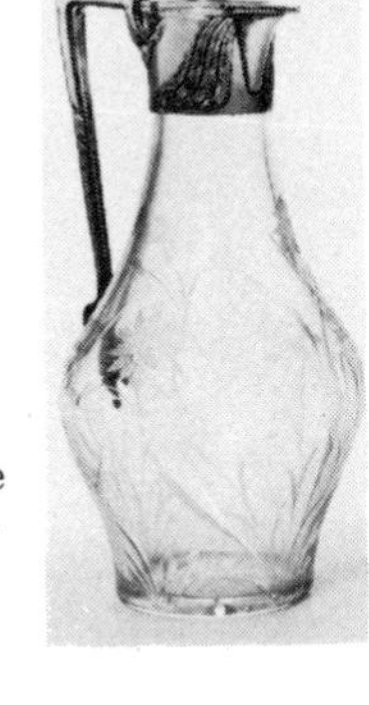

A pair of German Jugendstil claret jugs, stamped with maker's marks for Wilhelm Binder, Gmünd, and crescent moon and crown '800', 25.5 cm. high. **£800-1,000** *P*

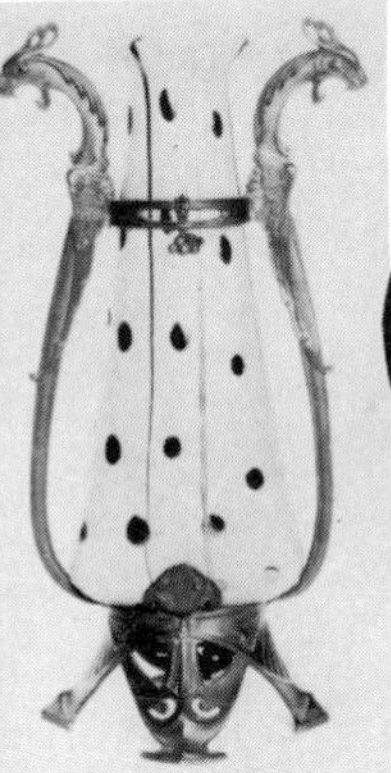

A pewter-mounted iridescent glass vase, in streaked ochre glass with a rich mother-of-pearl iridescence applied with spots and trails of deep green, with pewter mount, 36 cm. overall, c. 1900. **£200-300** *S*

An Art Nouveau glass vase with pale pink and blue overlay, 6½ in. diam. **£30-40** *BP*

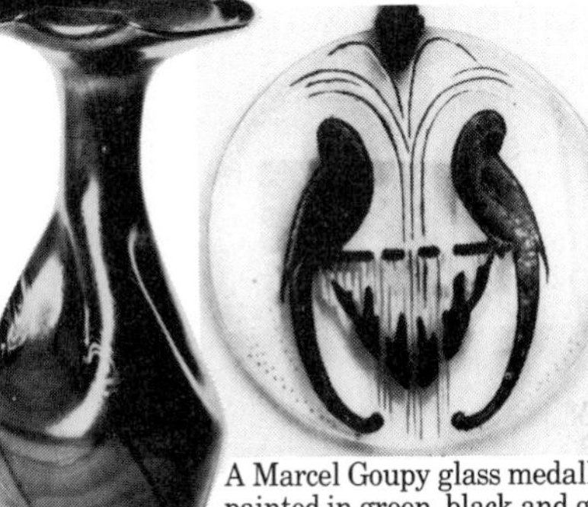

An iridescent glass vase, in mottled orange/red glass cased in a lustrous orange with trails of green/blue, 32.9 cm., c. 1900. **£200-300** *S*

A Marcel Goupy glass medallion painted in green, black and gold enamels, signed 'M. Goupy', on cord, 6 cm. diam. **£100-130** *P*

An Austrian style Art Nouveau glass claret jug, in green and clear glass, silver mounted neck, 12¾ in. high overall. **£90-120** *CDC*

An Arts and Crafts gold, silver and gem set pendant, the border enclosing an amethyst below 2 blister pearls and an opal, set with 2 further opals flanking an amethyst on gold and silver twist link suspension chain. **£400-550** *CSK*

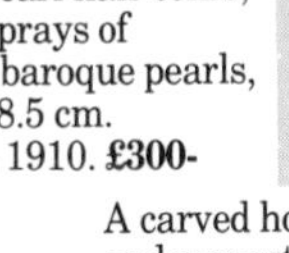

A carved horn and pearl hair comb, in the form of twin sprays of ombellifers set with baroque pearls, marked 'Partridge', 8.5 cm. maximum height, c. 1910. **£300-£400** *S*

A carved horn, silver and enamel and moonstone hair ornament, hinged on twin-pronged comb, marked 'Partridge', 11.5 cm., c. 1910. **£300-350** *S*

A gold, opal, enamel and pearl pendant, decorated with white, turquoise and fiery orange enamel over metallic foil, pendant triangular opal, with seed pearls and 3 further pearls, 5.75 cm. overall length, c. 1905. **£400-500** *S*

An Art Nouveau citrine and gold necklace, set with 7 opal-shaped citrines. **£400-450** *L*

A gold and enamel locket, the design attributed to Archibald Knox, set with pearls, the ground detailed in rich orange enamel, main body enamelled in blue-green, 4.25 cm., c. 1905. **£350-£400** *S*

An Art Nouveau gold and enamelled pendant enclosing a leaf heightened in pale green enamel shading to rose pink, the stems terminating with pearls, on chain spaced with pearls, 1.75 cm. **£100-£130** *P*

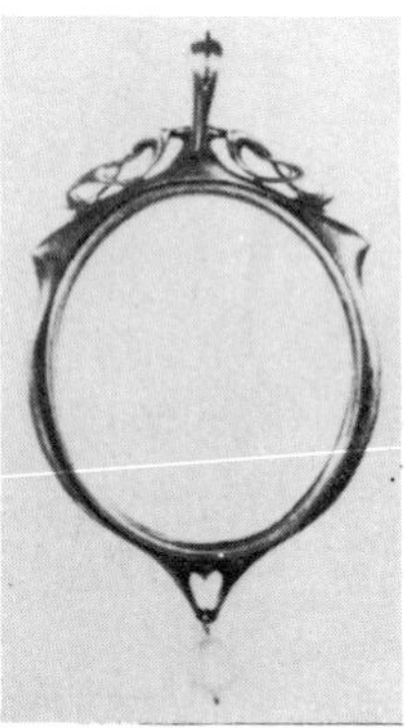

A silver locket, the design attributed to Archibald Knox, with pendant baroque pearl, 5.75 cm. overall length, c. 1905. **£200-250** *S*

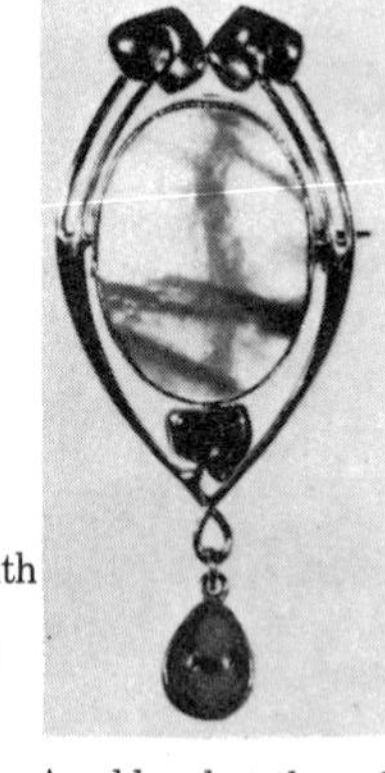

A gold and mother-of-pearl brooch, hung with turquoise in gold surround, stamped 450, maker's mark Murrle Bennett and Co. as importer, c. 1905. **£160-200** *S*

A silver and plique-a-jour enamel pendant, central oval green stone, with small pendant turquoise, 4 cm. length, c. 1910. **£110-130** *S*

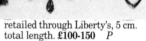

A Daum cameo glass table lamp. **£2,500-3,000** *CDC*

An Art Nouveau gold brooch centred with a triangular opal plaque beneath wirework embellishment, marked 9 ct.? and BHJ, possibly German origin, 3.75 cm. **£110-140** *P*

A Tiffany studios jewelled feather table lamp, with green glass panels above white bands, on baluster bronzed base repousse with cobweb design, 52 cm. high by 40.4 cm. diam. of shade. **£1,100-1,500** *C*

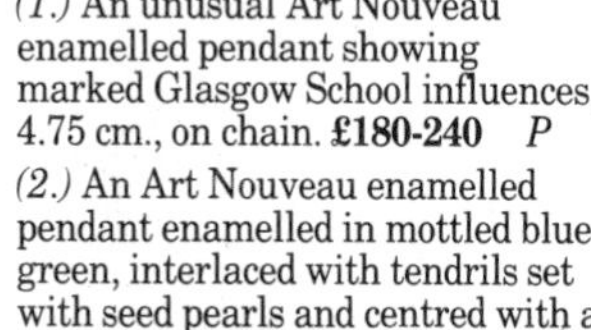

(1.) An unusual Art Nouveau enamelled pendant showing marked Glasgow School influences, 4.75 cm., on chain. **£180-240** *P*

(2.) An Art Nouveau enamelled pendant enamelled in mottled blue-green, interlaced with tendrils set with seed pearls and centred with a plaque of mother-of-pearl, with fresh water pearl drop, 4.50 cm., on chain. **£100-150** *P*

(3.) An Arts and Crafts silver and enamelled circular pendant with central plaque of mother-of-pearl flanked by panels enamelled blue-green, unmarked but probably retailed through Liberty's, 5 cm. total length. **£100-150** *P*

(4.) An Arts and Crafts silver and enamelled pendant, hallmarks for Birmingham, 1908, 5 cm. **£95-£115** *P*

(5.) A Murrle Bennett Art Nouveau ring set with a conical cabochon of turquoise, silver coloured metal stamped '950' and 'MB & Co'. **£90-£120** *P*

(6.) A gold pendant showing affinities to the designs of Van de Velde, centred with a mother-of-pearl plaque, marked 'BHJ' and '9ct.', possibly German, 3.50 cm., on chain. **£200-250** *P*

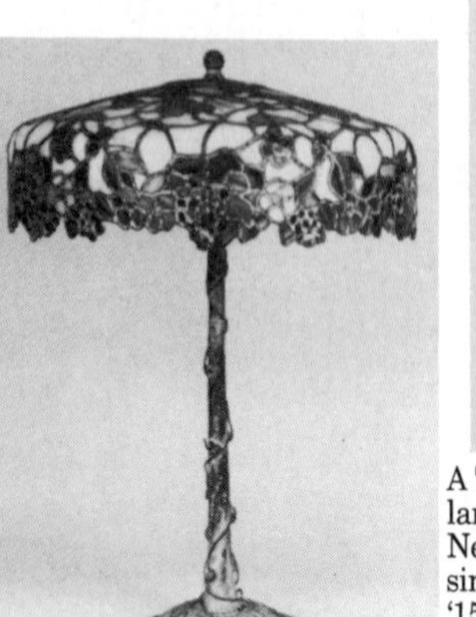

An American leaded glass and bronzed metal table lamp, the shade with polychrome and white glass floral segments, 59 cm. high. **£700-800** *C*

A Tiffany studios 'Poinsettia' table lamp, stamped 'Tiffany Studios, New York, S1432', the shade similarly marked and numbered '1558', 69 cm. high. **£3,000-4,000** *P*

A German Art Nouveau plated table lamp, the conch shell exhibiting a pale nacreous hue, stamped double-headed eagle in oval mark, 108, 29.5 cm. **£550-£650** *P*

A bronze and ivory lamp base with Gallé cameo glass shade, the shade in pink glass overlaid internally in pink and externally in green, shad with cameo mark 'Gallé', 56 cm. overall high, c. 1900. **£1,700-2,000** *S*

A Tiffany Studios bronze and iridescent glass lamp, the shades in milky iridescent glass shaded with streaks of emerald-green, base stamped 'Tiffany Studios New York 306', glass engraved 'L.C.T. Favrile', 40.6 cm., c. 1900. **£700-£900** *S*

A Miller student's lamp, the curved frosted glass shade reverse painted, the base marked 'Miller', 35 cm. high. **£180-240** *P*

A copper and brass Art Nouveau flexible stemmed reading lamp, base 6½ in. wide, c. 1910. **£30-40** *TA*

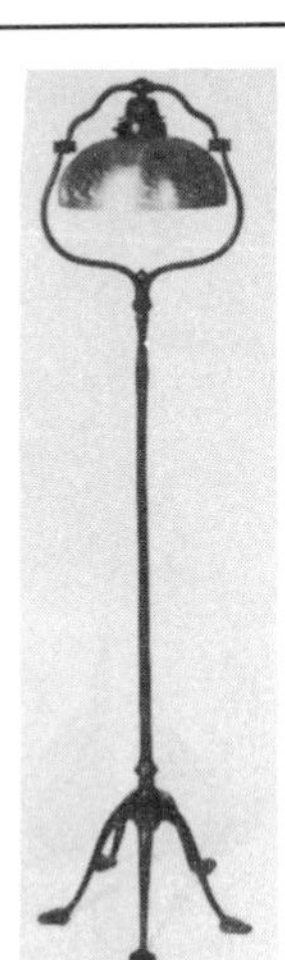

A Tiffany Studios standard lamp, the interior in opalescent-white, the shade signed 'L.C.T. Favrille', the stand stamped 'Tiffany Studios, New York, 423H', 147 cm. high. **£900-1,100** *P*

A set of 4 massive odeonesque gilt-metal and frosted glass hanging wall lights, some damage to glass and one fitting without glass, glass not shown in photograph, 158 cm. high. **£1,700-1,900** *C*

An Art Nouveau brass jardiniere, 9½ in. high. **£50-70** *BP*

A polished bronze inkwell, 26.5 max. width, c. 1900. **£150-200** *S*

A Nelson gilt-metal figure of a young woman 'L'Irise Brise', concealing small light fittings, on mottled red marble base, affixed title, plaque and artist's name 'Ant Nelson', 75.5 cm., c. 1900. **£500-£550** *S*

A small Gurschner bronze lamp base, signed in the maquette 'Gurschner', stamped below 'Gesetzl Beschutzt', 31 cm., c. 1900. **£800-1,000** *S*

An Edith F. Stewart cloisonne enamel-mounted bottle and stopper, silver-coloured metal, glass probably Powells, 19.8 cm., and a tazza set with mother-of-pearl discs, silver-coloured metal, twin handles, 16 cm. over handles, c. 1900. **£150-£200** *S*

Two large Liberty & Co. pewter biscuit boxes, designed by Archibald Knox, stamped '0237 Made in England', c. 1905. **£280-£360** *S*

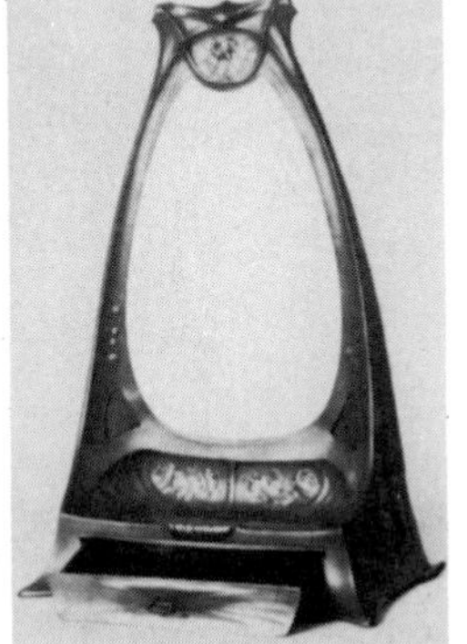

An Art Nouveau pewter dressing table mirror, with a small velvet-lined drawer, underside stamped 'Attorini & Sons Bradford, 1170', 49 cm., c. 1900. **£250-300** *S*

A Bingert Gebruder electroplated-metal and Rosenthal porcelain Turkish coffee set, coffee pot with maker's monogram, porcelain liners with Rosenthal marks, 12 cm. height of coffee pot, c. 1910. **£100-150** *S*

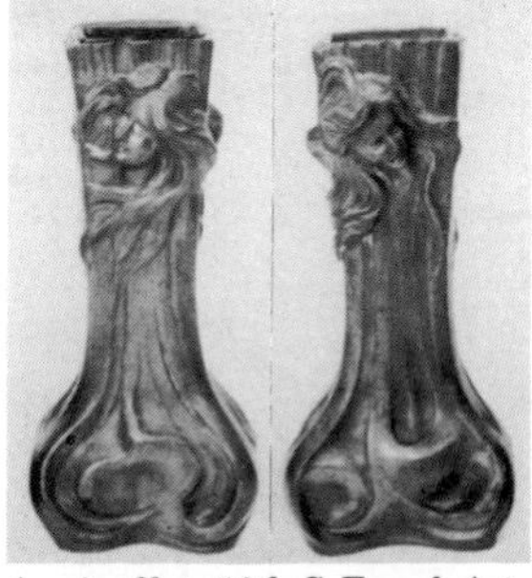

A pair of late 19th C. French Art Nouveau spelter vases, each entitled 'Flora', 11½ in. **£70-90** *WHL*

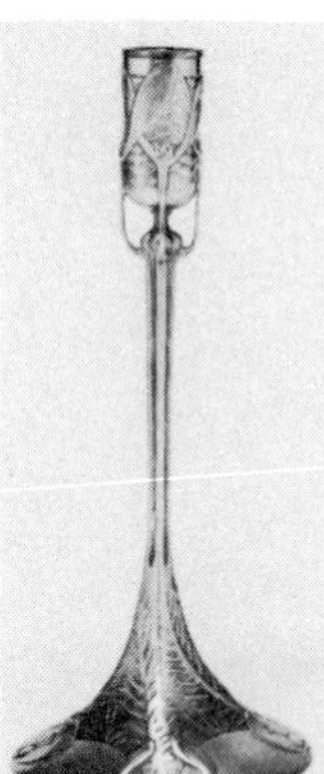

A pair of French silvered-metal candlesticks designed by Emile Gallé, unmarked, 24.25 cm. high. **£400-450** *P*

A pair of Hawksworth Eyre & Co. silver 4 light candelabra, stamped maker's marks, Birmingham, 1913, 38.5 cm. wide, 35 oz. **£600-700** *C*

A pair of Art Nouveau silver frames, maker's mark 'W.N.', Chester, 1907, 31 cm. **£450-500** *S*

An Art Nouveau miniature silver-faced photograph frame, stamped 'W.A. Birmingham 1902, Rd 40047', 12 cm. wide. **£160-190** *C*

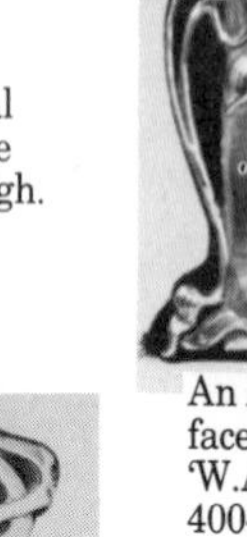

An Art Nouveau silver and enamelled picture frame embossed and hammer-textured with green and violet enamelling, A. Hutton & Sons, maker's mark for London, 1902, 20 cm. high. **£350-400** *P*

An Art Nouveau silver-faced photograph frame, cast with scrolling heart-shaped leafy sprays and poppies, enamelled in turquoise and violet, maker's mark G.A.D.W.D. Chester 1905, 6¼ in. high. **£180-220** *CSK*

An Arts and Crafts small silver-faced double photograph frame, glazed, mounted on blue plush covered wood, stamped 'W. J. H. Birmingham 1904', 12.2 cm. wide. **£160-190** *C*

A Hukin and Heath 3-piece silver picnic set, designed by Christopher Dresser, maker's marks, P.O.D.R. mark for 19th October, 1879, engraved with crest and motto 'Non Eget Arcu', London, 1879, height of tea pot 8 cm. **£250-300** *S*

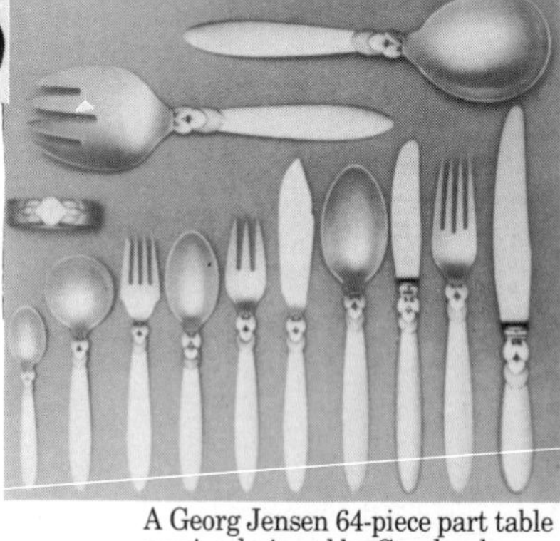

A Georg Jensen 64-piece part table service designed by Gundorph Albertus in the cactus pattern, all with firm's stamped marks, weight without table and luncheon knives and salad servers 84 oz. **£1,200-£1,400** *C*

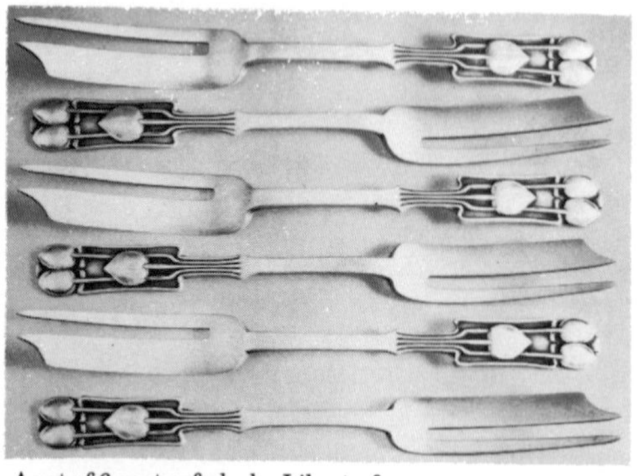

A set of 6 pastry forks by Liberty & Co., Birmingham, 1930, in original case. **£110-140** *L*

A Georg Jensen 50-piece part table service designed by Johan Rohde in the acorn pattern, all with firm's stamped marks, weight without knives 52 oz. **£2,000-£2,500** *C*

A Hukin and Heath 'Japanesque' tea pot and sugar bowl designed by Christopher Dresser, heightened with silver colour against a warm copper ground, H & H marks, numbered '2103', the pot marked 'Designed by Dr. C. Dresser', height of pot 10 cm. **£450-500** *P*

An Art Nouveau silver comport chased with roses and foliage on hammered ground, signed L. Movio 1904, makers W. Walker and B. Tolhurst, 13½ in. high, 50 oz. **£550-£600** *GSP*

Latino Movio was assistant to Gilbert Marks.

A Goldsmiths and Silversmiths Co. Ltd. silver and enamel presentation cup and cover, London, 1902, 24.9 cm. high, 25½ oz. gross. **£600-£700** *C*

A beaten pewter and ebonised wood rectangular wall mirror designed and executed by Margaret and Frances Macdonald, impressed 'Margaret Macdonald, Frances Macdonald, 1897', 69 by 60.5 cm. **£6,000-7,000** *C*

On graduation from the Glasgow school in 1894 the Misses Macdonald opened a studio at 128 Hope Street, Glasgow where they devoted themselves to the applied arts. The metal items produced by the 2 sisters were, apart from a very few examples, not only designed but worked entirely by themselves and although closely collaborating, few examples of their metal work now exist bearing both signatures. The studio closed when Frances Macdonald married Herbert MacNair in 1899.

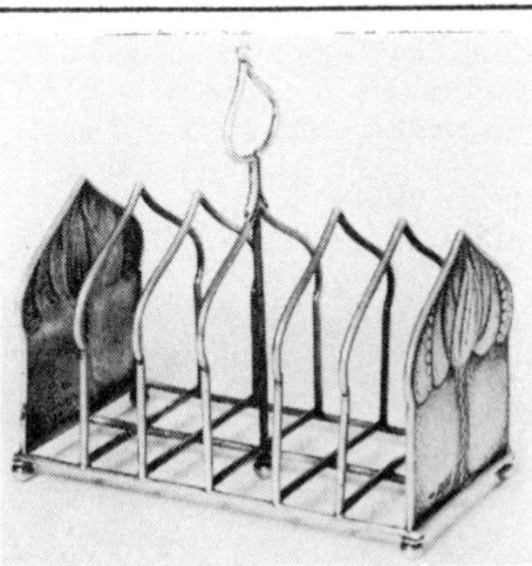

An unusual Guild of Handicrafts Ltd. silver toast rack, Guild's maker's mark for London, 1906, probably to a design by Charles Robert Ashbee, 13 cm. long, 7 oz. **£500-550** *P*

A heavy punch bowl in the Art Nouveau style, by F. Fattorini & Son Ltd., Birmingham, 1905, 31.5 cm. across handles, 37 oz. **£450-500** *L*

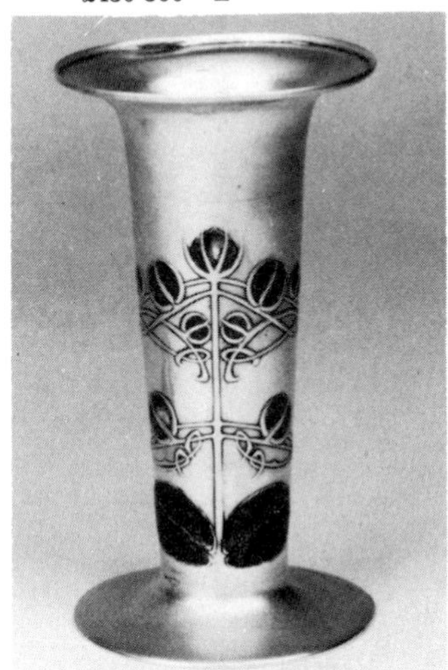

A silver and enamel flared cylindrical vase, probably designed by Archibald Knox, indistinct stamped marks, Rd. 467167, some chips to enamel, rims slightly damaged, 17 cm. high. **£150-200** *C*

A Walker and Hall silver-mounted jug, inspired by a design by Christopher Dresser, maker's mark, Sheffield, 1906, 22.25 cm. **£200-250** *S*

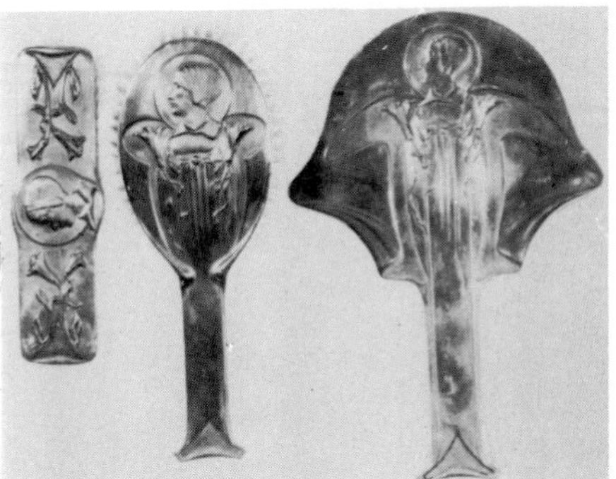

A William Hutton & Sons Ltd. 3-piece silver dressing set, designed by Kate Harris, cast with young woman in Quaker dress, maker's marks, 1900/03/04, 28.5 cm. height of hand mirror. **£400-500** *S*

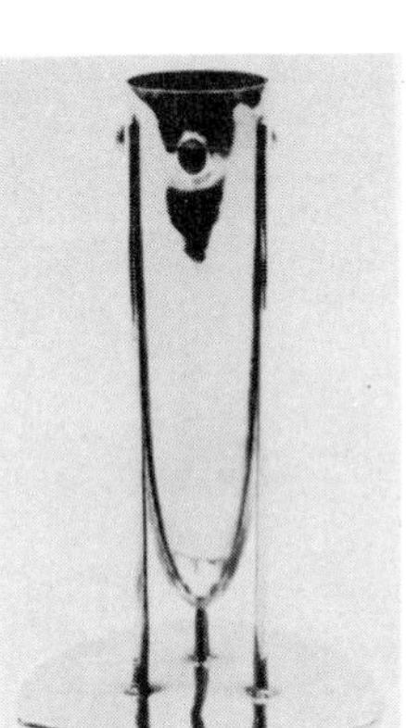

A Liberty & Co. 'Cymric' silver vase, designed by Archibald Knox, rim set with turquoises, maker's mark, stamped 'Cymric', Birmingham, 1903, 15 cm. **£300-£350** *S*

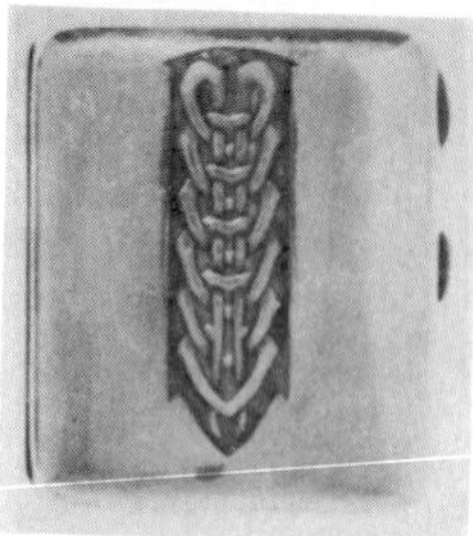

Two Liberty & Co. silver and enamel cigarette cases, detailed in turquoise enamel, one stamped 'Cymric', Birmingham, 1902, 8 by 7.25 cm. approx. dimensions. **£400-£450** *S*

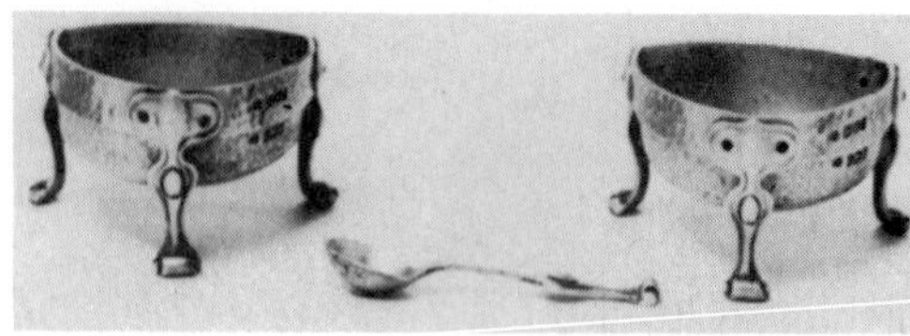

A set of 6 William Hutton & Sons silver salts, having hammer textured surfaces, with 6 silver spoons en suite, maker's mark and hallmarks for London, 1901, also Austrian importation marks, fitted case, 3.50 cm. high, 50 oz. **£150-£180** *P*

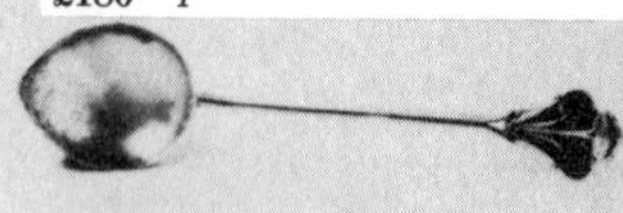

An Art Nouveau silver and enamelled christening set, each piece embellished with a blue enamelled plant form, maker's marks E. J. & S. Birmingham 1905, fitted case, height of cup 7 cm. **£90-110** *P*

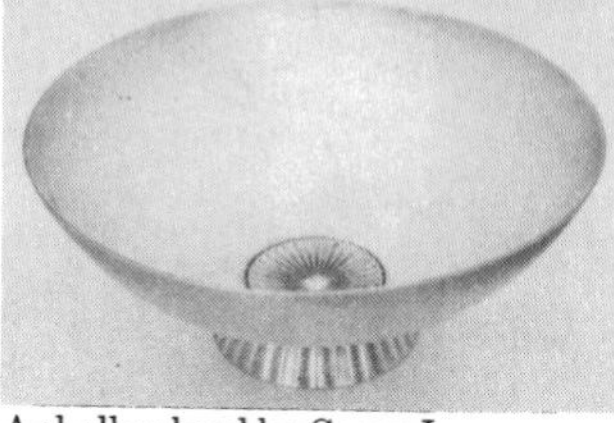

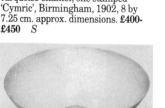

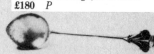

A shallow bowl by Georg Jensen, maker's mark, Denmark, stamped Sterling, silver coloured metal, 16 cm. diam., 8.8 oz. **£150-200** *L*

A WMF electroplated pewter tazza, WMF marks, 22 cm. high, c. 1900. **£350-400** *S*

A WMF electroplated dish, WMF marks, 21 cm., c. 1900. **£300-350** *S*

A WMF electroplated coffee set, cast with ivy leaves and berries, WMF marks, 29 cm. height of coffee pot, c. 1900. **£500-550** *S*

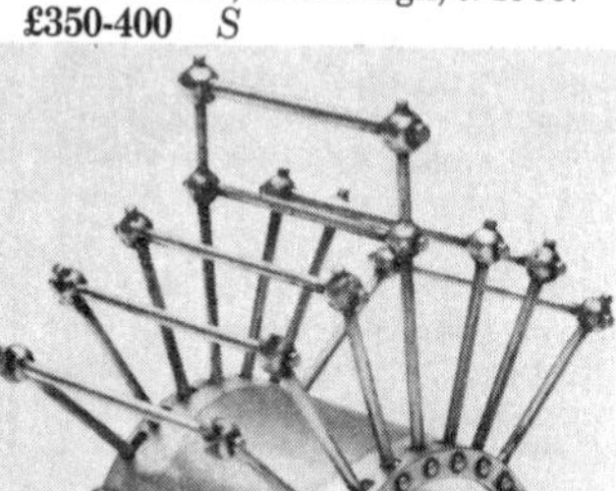

A Hukin and Heath electroplated toast/letter rack, designed by Christopher Dresser, articulated on arched base plate, maker's mark, numbered 2555, P.O.D.R. mark May 1881, 12.5 cm. **£200-250** *S*

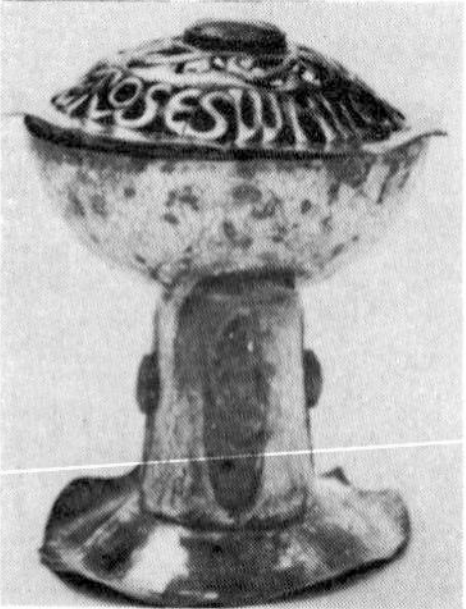

An electroplated pot-pourri casket and cover, designed by John Williams, with an enamelled floral roundel, 18.4 cm., c. 1907. **£250-£300** *S*

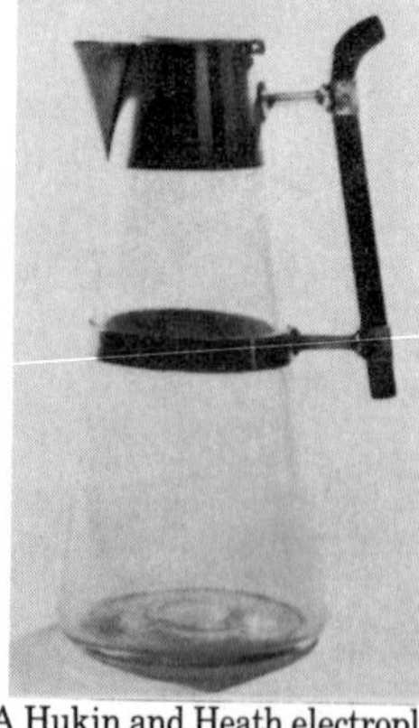

A Hukin and Heath electroplate-mounted jug, the design attributed to Dr. Christopher Dresser, with ebonised wood handle and flat hinged cover, manufacturer's mark, 24 cm., 1880's. **£280-320** *S*

(l. & r.) A pair of German Art Nouveau wine coasters, stamped mark of Wurttembergische Metallwarenfabrik (WMF), 3¼ in. high (8.2 cm.). **£100-120** *L*

(c.) A German Art Nouveau jewel casket, stamped mark of Wurttembergische Metallwarenfabrik (WMF), 7¼ in. (18.4 cm.) overall length. **£110-£150** *L*

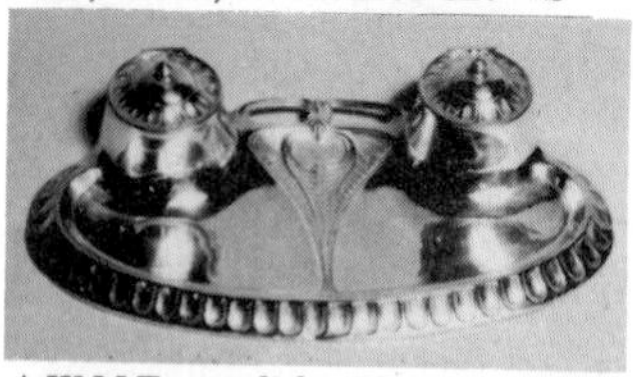

A W.M.F. standish, 13½ in., c. 1900. **£65-75** *TA*

A lithograph printed in colours by Alphonse Maria Mucha, 1912, on thin wove paper, printed by V. Newbert, Prague, very slight staining, otherwise in good condition, linen-backed, framed, 72 by 52 cm. **£800-1,000** *C*

A lithographic panneau decoratif 'Rose' by Alphonse Mucha, signed in the block, 104 by 43 cm., c. 1900. **£1,000-1,200** *S*

A lithographic panneau decoratif 'Iris' by Alphonse Mucha, signed in the block, 104 by 43 cm., c. 1900. **£450-500** *S*

A lithographic panneau decoratif 'Carnation' by Alphonse Mucha, signed in the block, 104 by 43 cm., c. 1900. **£350-400** *S*

A lithographic panneau decoratif 'Lily' by Alphonse Mucha, signed in the block, 104 by 43 cm., c. 1900. **£550-600** *S*

A study of a young woman by Alphonse Mucha, pencil and watercolour, signed in pencil 'Mucha', framed and glazed, dated '97, 24 by 16 cm. image area. **£1,300-1,500** *S*

A lithograph printed in colours 'Baie du Mont St. Michel' by A. Bergerin, c. 1920, in thin wove paper, published by Arranche, some very slight spotting, otherwise in excellent condition, paper and linen-backed, 100 by 75.4 cm. **£500-600** *C*

An Art Nouveau porcelain figure of a young woman, wearing a patterned, gilt, classical style robe, on green circular base, impressed marks, 20½ in. high. **£90-110** *CSK*

A Volkstedt Art Nouveau white glazed porcelain bust, 2 peach tinted blooms beneath her breast, on a tapering, green foliate pedestal, blue printed mark, 15 in. high. **£280-360** *CSK*

An Art Nouveau terracotta facial wall sculpture by Lambert Escaler, unsigned, 34.5 cm. high. **£150-£190** *P*

A Royal Dux Art Nouveau maiden, 9 in. **£200-300** *BP*

A lithograph printed in colours by Paul Emile Berthon, 1901, on cream wove paper, a fine impression, in good condition, framed, 51 by 36.4 cm. **£600-700** *C*

A Gallé faience model of a falcon, with blue head and yellow, blue and brown and white plumage, having bells on his legs, signed 'Emile Gallé, Nancy' and with shield monogram, 32 cm. high. **£350-400** *P*

A pair of T. & R. Boote Ltd. 'Red Indian' tiles, glazed in green, brown, turquoise and white with tube line outline, with impressed greyhound mark for Waterloo Pottery, Burslem, 21.5 by 7 cm., framed. **£80-100** *P*

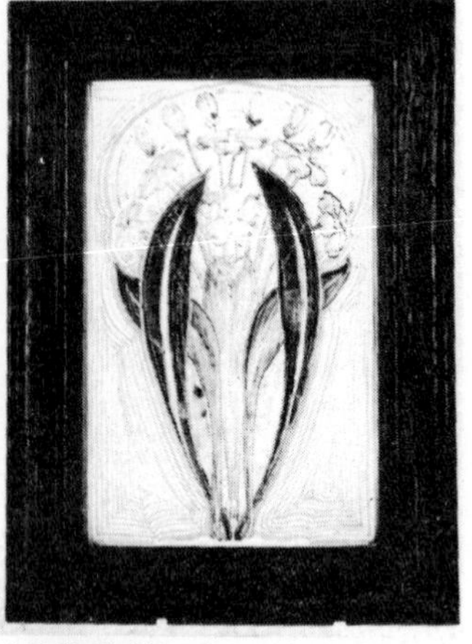

A Della Robbia plaque, incised and painted by Miss Cassandia Annie Walker, impressed mark including the date 1903, incised artist's monogram, 1903, 8¾ by 5¾ in., framed. **£80-100** *SC*

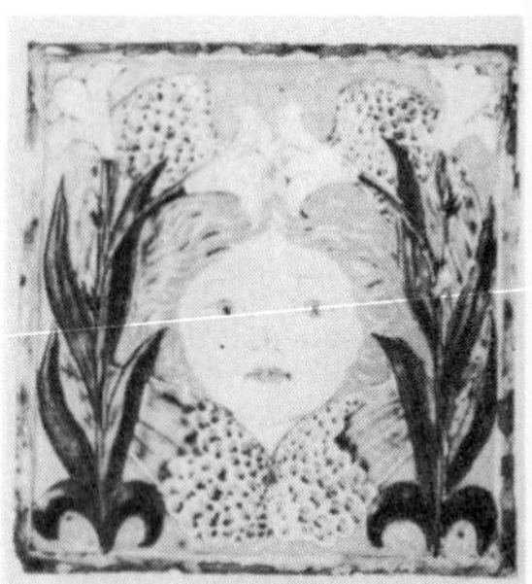

A pair of early Della Robbia plaques, modelled in low relief and coloured by Giovanni Carlo Manzoni, incised galleon mark, enclosing CM monogram and flanked by the date 1895, chips, 10¾ in. square. **£200-300** *SC*

The Della Robbia Pottery commenced production in 1894 and Manzoni is reputed to have joined the pottery between 1898 and 1899; however, these examples would appear to disprove that. It is true to say that he was approached by Harold Rathbone when Conrad Dressler left Birkenhead in order to fill the resulting vacancy, but it is not clear exactly when this occurred.

A large Della Robbia circular wall plaque, decorated in coloured slips and sgraffito technique, DR and galleon mark, dated 18/95 and initials WL.W, 47.5 cm. diam. **£120-180** *P*

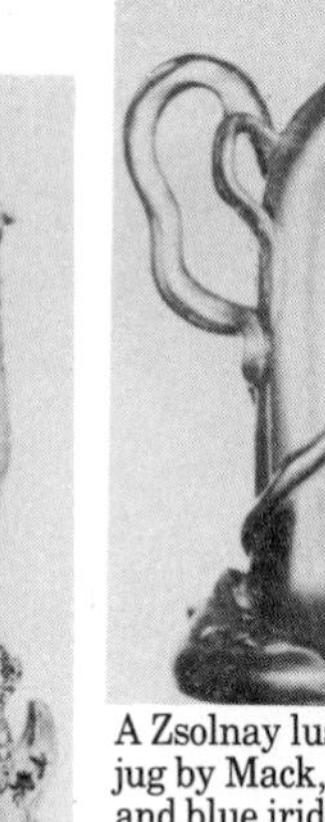

A Zsolnay lustre pottery floriform jug by Mack, covered in a green and blue iridescent lustre, signed with medallion mark in relief, numbered 5517M, 13¼ in. high. **£45-65** *CSK*

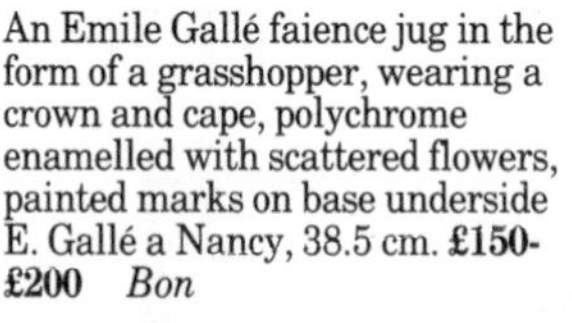

An Emile Gallé faience jug in the form of a grasshopper, wearing a crown and cape, polychrome enamelled with scattered flowers, painted marks on base underside E. Gallé a Nancy, 38.5 cm. **£150-£200** *Bon*

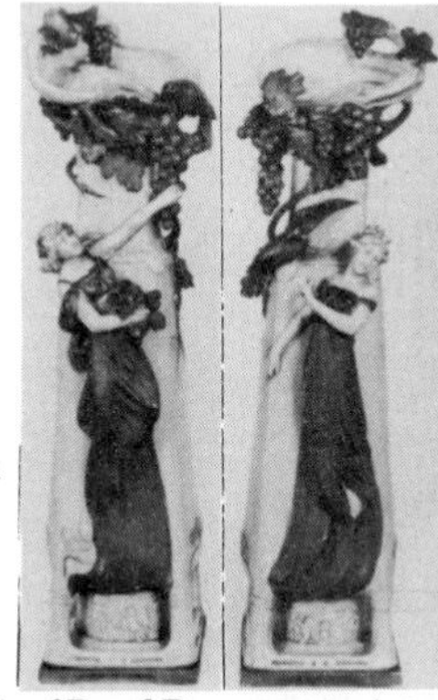

A pair of Royal Dux vases in Art Nouveau style, each of square section, applied pink triangle mark, impressed 1189-90, printed 'Made in Czechoslovakia', slight damage, 26 in. (66 cm.), 1920's. **£250-300** *SC*

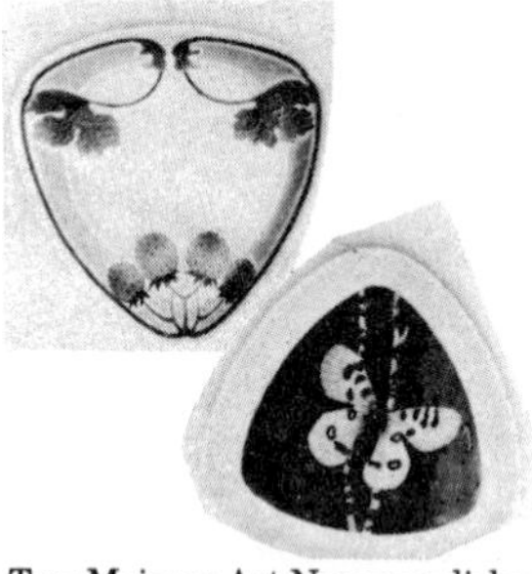

Two Meissen Art Nouveau dishes, Meissen marks, 14 cm. wide, c. 1900. **£200-250** *S*

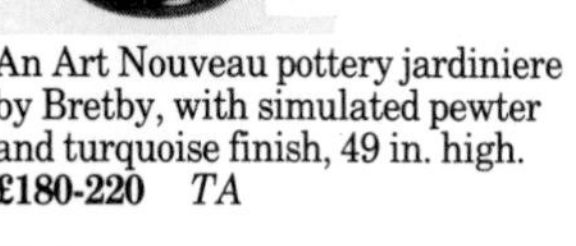

An Art Nouveau pottery jardiniere by Bretby, with simulated pewter and turquoise finish, 49 in. high. **£180-220** *TA*

A Gilbert Bayes bronze figure of an athletic naked woman, square marble base, signed on reverse 'Gilbert Bayes', 41 cm. high. **£600-£800** *P*

A Pilkington Royal Lancastrian lustre oviform vase by W. S. Mycock, with gold against a green leaf and blue ground embellished with gold and red lustre, impressed rosette mark and 'Royal Lancastrian, England', painted W.S.M. monogram, 23.5 cm. high. **£250-300** *P*

A Bouraine bronze figure modelled as naked fan dancer, with a large blue fan, signed 'Bouraine', 37 cm. high. **£600-800** *P*

A Bouval silvered and gilt bronze figure modelled as an Art Nouveau maiden, signed 'M. Bouval', and with foundry marks for 'Jollet & Cie Paris', 27 cm. high. **£400-450** *P*

A green painted gilt-bronze and ivory figure of a clown, cast and carved from a model by Chiparus, rouge marble base, inscribed Chiparus, 11½ in. high. **£70-90** *CSK*

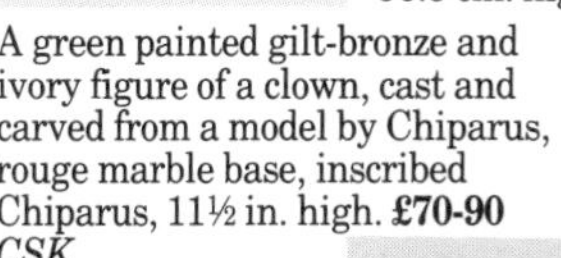

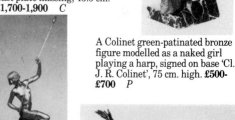

A Chiparus bronze and ivory figure modelled as an exotic dancer poised on a massive brown marble base, signed on marble 'Chiparus', 56.5 cm. high. **£3,500-4,000** *P*

A bronze figure by D. H. Chiparus of an Egyptian dancer, wearing a green and red necklace and arm bracelets, signed 'D. H. Chiparus', on marble base and bronze plaque, 72 cm. high. **£1,800-2,200** *P*

A small Chiparus bronze dancing figure, 27.5 cm., 1920's. **£400-450** *S*

A small Chiparus bronze and ivory figure of a woman, with metallic green cold painting with tiny red details, engraved mark 'Chiparus', 30.25 cm., 1920's. **£1,400-1,600** *S*

A bronze and ivory equestrian group 'Towards the Unknown' cast and carved from a model by Claire Jeanne Roberte Colinet, inscribed Cl. JR Colinet, chip to one plait, one breast plate missing, 43.5 cm. wide. **£1,700-1,900** *C*

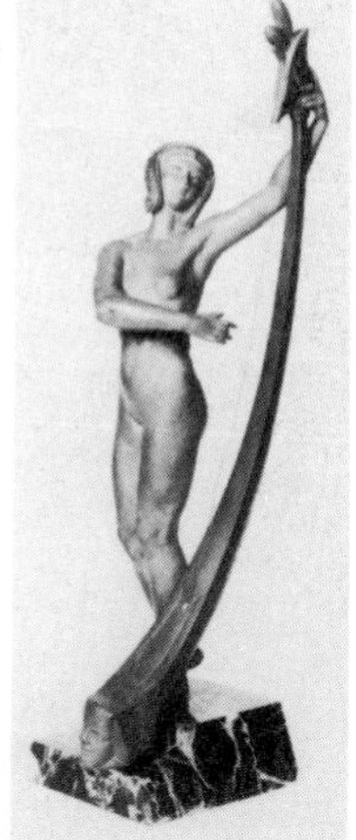

A Colinet green-patinated bronze figure modelled as a naked girl playing a harp, signed on base 'Cl. J. R. Colinet', 75 cm. high. **£500-£700** *P*

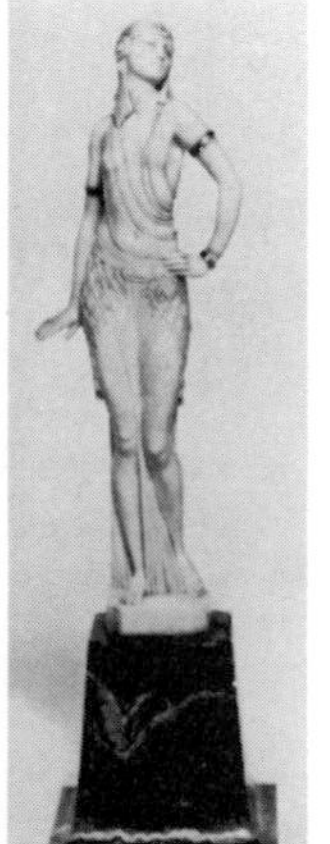

A good Descomps carved ivory of a young woman, with gold armbands and bracelet, on mottled brown marble base, ivory engraved 'Joe Descomps', 26 cm. high, 1920's. **£1,900-2,200** *S*

A Le Faguays bronze male figure of an Olympian hero, signed in the maquette 'Le Faguays', 'Cire Perdue', 'Susse Fr Ed Paris', Susse Frères foundry stamp, numbered '3', stamped 'Bronze', 66 cm., 1930's. **£500-600** *S*

A silvered bronze group of a young girl and a kid cast from a model by Joe Descomps, inscribed 'Descomps', small chips to base, 48.5 cm. wide. **£500-600** *C*

A Focht bronze male figure riding on a starbeam, signed in the maquette 'F. Focht', stamped 'Bronze', 68.5 cm., 1930's. **£800-£900** *S*

A Gerdago painted bronze and ivory figure with gilt, red and green futuristic pantaloon costume, signed 'Gerdago', AR founder's mark, 40 cm. high. **£1,200-1,400** *P*

An Art Deco bronze group signed H. Fugere, 18 in. wide, c. 1920. **£400-500** *IHA*

A Gori silvered and gilt-bronze and ivory figure of a young woman, in pyjama suit silvered and oxidised, with gilt design, base marked 'G. Gori', 30.25 cm., 1920's. **£450-£550** *S*

A Lavroff patinated bronze figure of a young woman, naked but for stockings and garters, stepped rectangular marble base, signed in the maquette, 43.7 cm., 1920's. **£300-400** *S*

A Guiraud Rivière silvered and gilt-bronze figure, mottled red-green marble base, signed in the maquette 'Guiraud Rivière', 51.75 cm. max. height, 1920's. **£5,000-5,500** *S*

A Guillemard bronze lamp, marked 'Guillemard', fitted for electricity, 39.5 cm., 1920's. **£600-650** *S*

A bronze and ivory bust by Agathon Leonard, with a gilt bronze scarf, on a green onyx base, signed 'A. Leonard', 14.5 cm. high. **£280-340** *P*

A Keck bronze and ivory figure, cold painted with metallic bronze-green, brown detailed hair, bronze base plate marked 'H. Keck fec', 33 cm., c. 1920. **£700-800** *S*

A Lorenzl polished bronze nude dancing figure, marked 'Lorenzl', 41 cm., 1930's. **£300-400** *S*

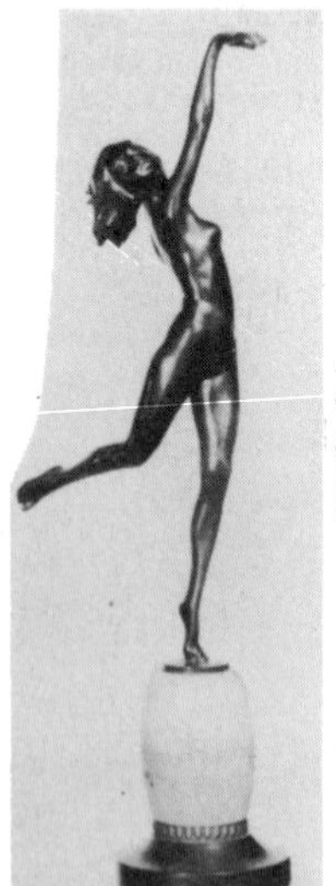

A dark bronze nude female figure cast from a model by Lorenzl, inscribed Lorenzl, 17½ in. high. **£180-240** *CSK*

A bronze and ivory figure of a temple dancer cast and carved from a model by Lorenzl, cold painted and silvered patina, inscribed Lorenzl, 36.2 cm. high. **£600-700** *C*

An unusual Lorenzl green-patinated bronze group of a pair of dancers, signed 'Lorenzl', 26 cm. high. **£500-600** *P*

Use the Index!

Because certain items might fit easily into any of a number of categories, the quickest and surest method of locating any entry is by reference to the index at the back of the book. This has been fully cross-referenced for absolute simplicity.

A gilt-bronze and ivory figure of a clown, signed C. Mimo, on a marble plinth, 8¾ in. (22 cm.), c. 1920. **£500-600** *S*

An Aurore Onu bronze nude dancing figure with a hoop, marble engraved 'Aurore Onu', 48.5 cm. high, 1930's. **£250-350** *S*

A Roland Paris bronze figure 'Pert', raised on a circular bronze base signed 'Roland Paris', 30.5 cm. high. **£200-250** *P*

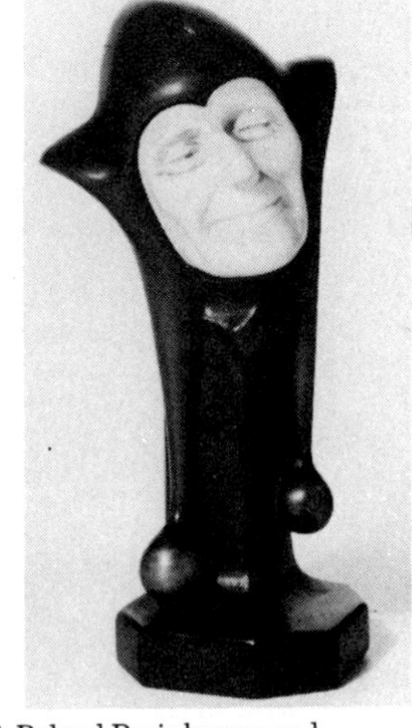

A Roland Paris bronze and alabaster bust 'The Jester', signed 'Roland Paris', 25.5 cm. high. **£280-£340** *P*

A Philippe cold painted bronze and ivory figure of a pierrette, wearing heavily-embroidered turquoise costume and cap, circular marble base, marked 'P. Philippe.R.u.M.', 38 cm., 1920's. **£2,200-2,500** *S*

A bronze and ivory figure of a cabaret dancer cast and carved from a model attributed to P. Philippe, cold painted silvery-blue and green patina, unsigned, 37.4 cm. high. **£750-850** *C*

A gilt-bronze nude study, attributed to Philippe, mottled red marble pedestal base, 58 cm., 1920's. **£250-300** *S*

A Poertzel bronze and ivory group of a woman and 2 hounds, cold painted in red-gold, marked 'Prof. Poertzel' with foundry mark 'PK', 49.5 cm., 1920's. **£3,500-4,000** *S*

An Art Deco bronze figure of 'The Charleston Girl', all-over gilded except for her shoes, collar, cuffs and base, the base inscribed F. Preiss, mottled brown marble plinth, 15 in. high. **£450-500** *PWC*

A Preiss painted bronze and ivory figure, coloured in amber and gold, on green onyx base, signed on onyx 'F. Preiss', 37 cm. high. **£1,600-£2,000** *P*

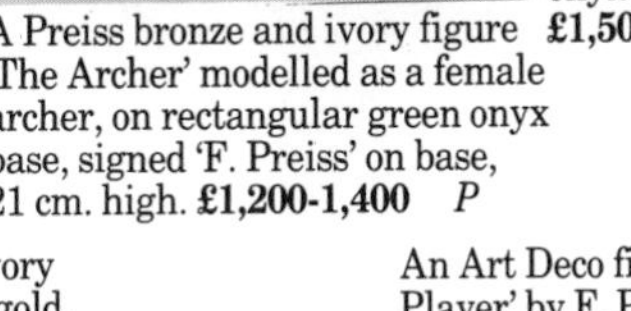

A Preiss bronze and ivory figure 'The Archer' modelled as a female archer, on rectangular green onyx base, signed 'F. Preiss' on base, 21 cm. high. **£1,200-1,400** *P*

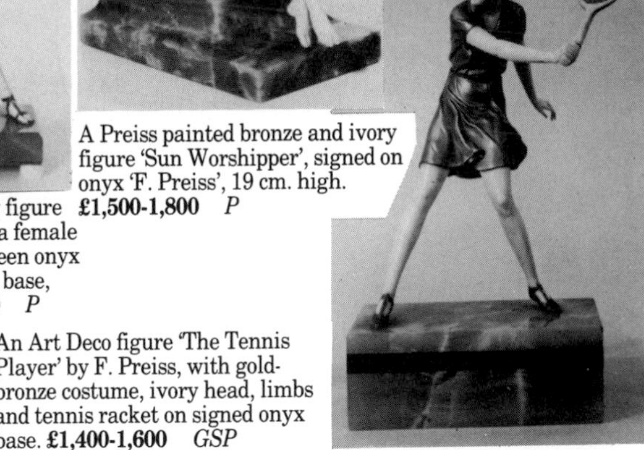

A Preiss painted bronze and ivory figure 'Sun Worshipper', signed on onyx 'F. Preiss', 19 cm. high. **£1,500-1,800** *P*

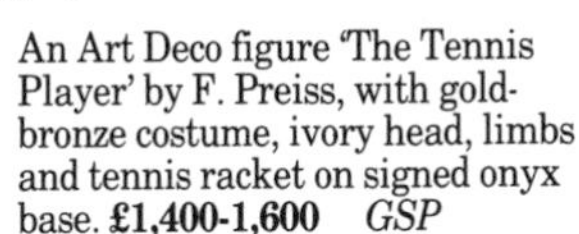

An Art Deco figure 'The Tennis Player' by F. Preiss, with gold-bronze costume, ivory head, limbs and tennis racket on signed onyx base. **£1,400-1,600** *GSP*

A bronze and ivory figure cast and carved from a model by Franz Rosse, on a square base cast as a fringed carpet, inscribed Fr. Rosse 88, 11 in. high. **£350-400** *CSK*

A bronze and ivory table lamp cast and carved from a model by P. Tereszczuk, with rectangular bronze shade fitted with a marbled glass panel, dark brown patina inscribed P. Tereszczuk, 31 cm. high. **£500-600** *C*

A bronze figure of a cabaret dancer cast from a model by Bruno Zach, cold painted polychrome and medium brown patina, bronze base inscribed Bruno Zach, 61.5 cm. high. **£4,000-4,500** *C*

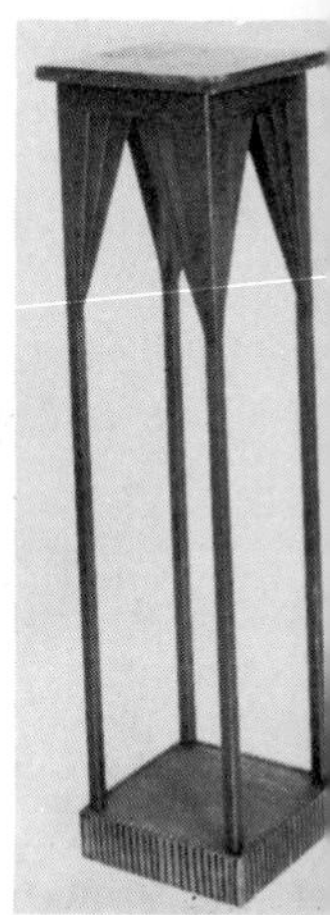

A wrought iron pedestal with brown marble top, 114.3 cm. high, c. 1925. **£250-300** *S*

A bronze and ivory group cast and carved from a model by Bruno Zach, the young woman dressed as Diana, black brown and silvered patina, inscribed 'Zach', small repair to ivory, 35 cm. high. **£1,500-£2,000** *C*

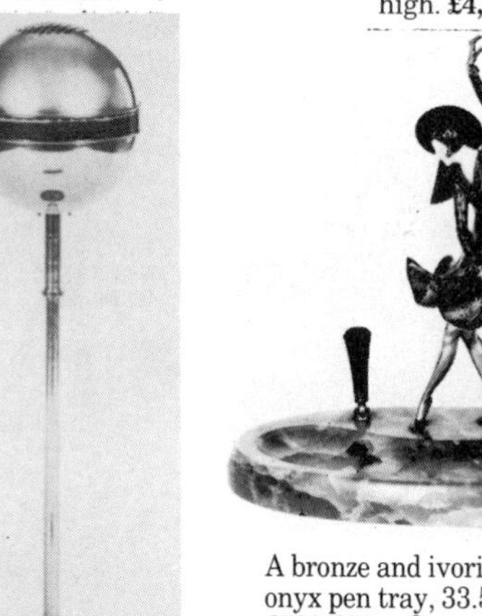

An 'Emor' radio, in chromed metal casing, on chromed metal stem, painted base, 110 cm. high, 1930's. **£400-450** *S*

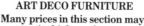

A bronze and ivorine figure on onyx pen tray, 33.5 cm., 1930's. **£500-600** *S*

An Art Deco bronze and ivory figure of a young girl, 6 in. hig **£150-200** *GSP*

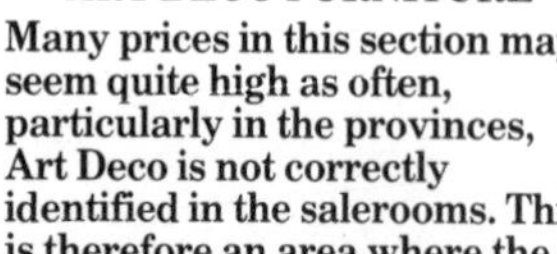

ART DECO FURNITURE

Many prices in this section may seem quite high as often, particularly in the provinces, Art Deco is not correctly identified in the salerooms. This is therefore an area where the collector with some discernment can still make some excellent purchases.

A fine Art Deco bird's-eye maple, ebonised and mirror-glazed cocktail cabinet, 163 cm. wide by 109.5 cm. high by 49.5 cm. deep. **£2,500-£3,000** *C*

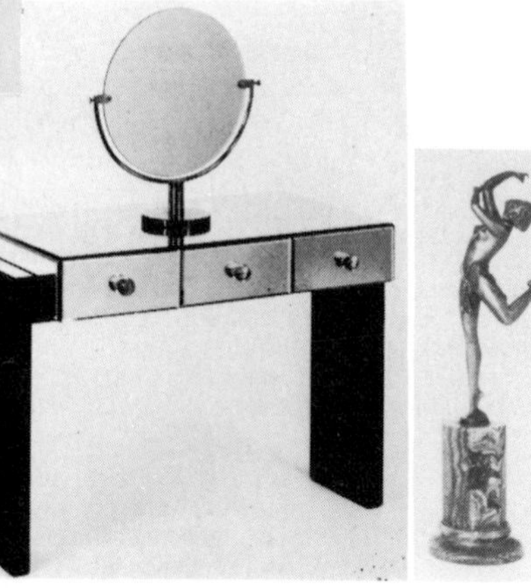

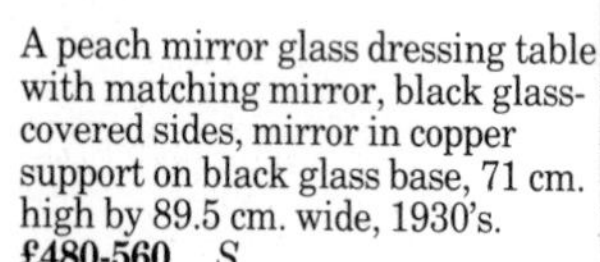

A peach mirror glass dressing table with matching mirror, black glass-covered sides, mirror in copper support on black glass base, 71 cm. high by 89.5 cm. wide, 1930's. **£480-560** *S*

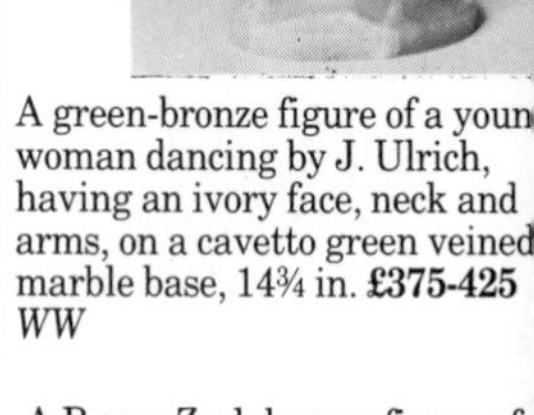

A green-bronze figure of a youn woman dancing by J. Ulrich, having an ivory face, neck and arms, on a cavetto green veined marble base, 14¾ in. **£375-425** *WW*

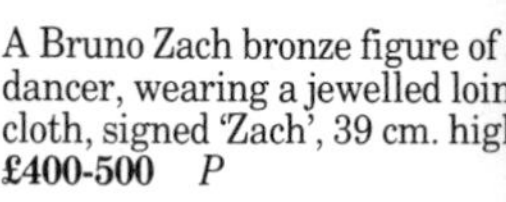

A Bruno Zach bronze figure of a dancer, wearing a jewelled loin cloth, signed 'Zach', 39 cm. hig **£400-500** *P*

A parchment covered single bed designed by Marcel Coard, the head-rest, foot-rest and siderails all covered in cream parchment, 112.8 cm. high at head, 1920's. **£350-400** *S*

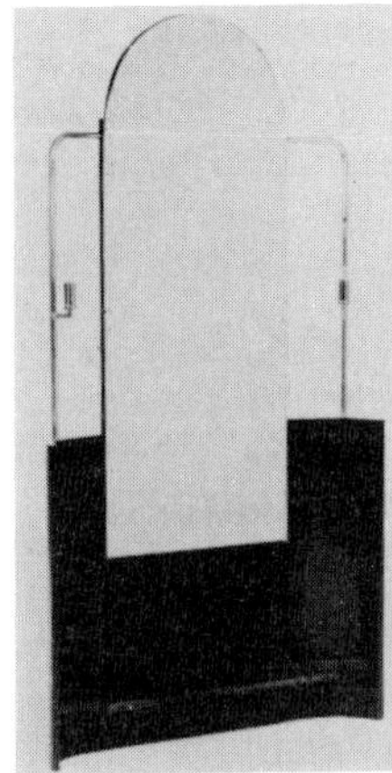

A 1930's black painted and tubular steel vanity stand, the mirror with 2 small lights on chromed tubular steel framework, 170 cm. high by 93 cm. wide. **£250-300** *S*

A plywood trolley designed by Alvar Aalto, in flat sectioned continuous plywood frame, solid white-painted plywood wheels, stamped 'Aalto design Made in Finland', 88.5 cm. wide by 46 cm. deep by 56 cm. high, c. 1930. **£400-£450** *S*

A Robert Thompson 'Mouseman' oak armchair, the backrail carved with 2 smiling masks, leather seat, carved with a mouse, 80.5 cm., 1930's. **£450-500** *S*

An Art Deco burr-maple dining suite, comprising a table, a set of 6 chairs, 4 singles, 2 carvers and a breakfront sideboard, table 4 ft. 8 in. diam. **£650-750** *EH*

A 1930's sycamore-veneered cocktail cabinet, doors fitted with bar accessories including cocktail sticks and lemon-squeezer, 112 cm. wide by 168.5 cm. high. **£600-700** *S*

An Eavestaff pianette mini-piano and stool, cream rag painted, 140 cm. wide by 90 cm. high, 1930's. **£700-800** *S*

A 1930's bar table, with 2-tier cocktail tray, descending into the interior for storage, 76 cm. diam., 99.5 cm. high with tray raised. **£150-200** *S*

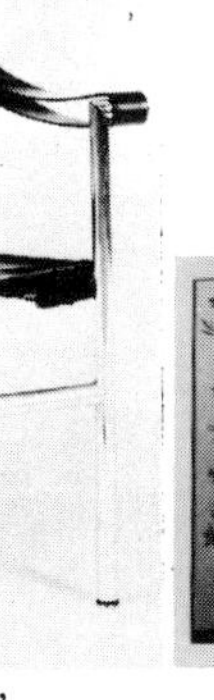

A Cassina 'Chaise Basculante', designed by Le Corbusier and Charlotte Periand, 1928-29, 70 cm. high. **£250-300** *S*

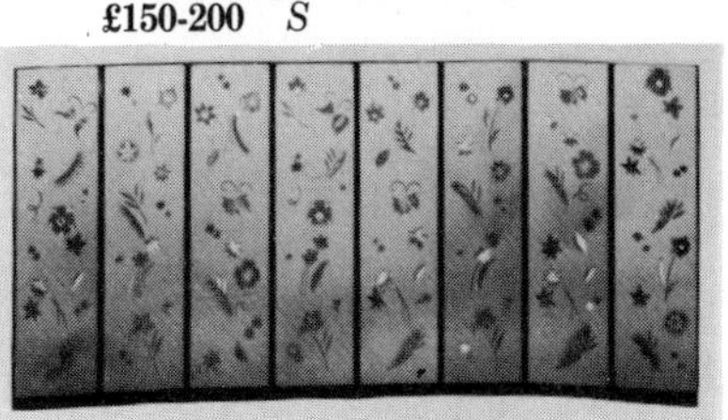

An Art Deco 8-fold mirrored glass screen, within plated brass framework, each panel 109.5 cm. high by 28 cm. wide. **£350-400** *P*

A 1930's cocktail cabinet, walnut-veneered, upper cabinet with pale wood-veneered interior, mirror backs, 156 cm. high. **£400-450** *S*

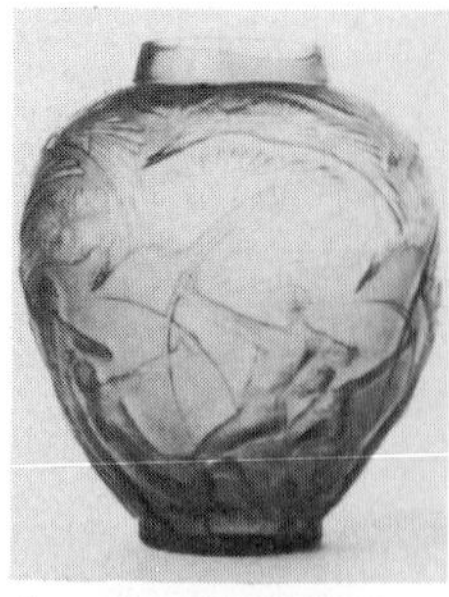

An amber glass oviform vase 'Archers', inscribed 'R. Lalique France moulded R. Lalique', 26.5 cm. high. **£750-800** *C*

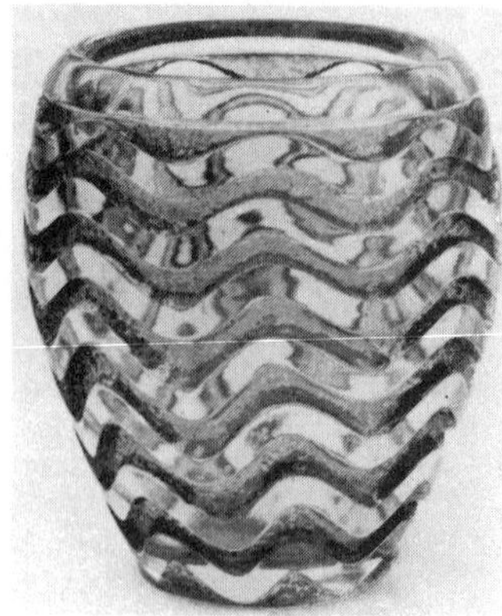

A heavy Lalique glass vase, stencilled mark 'R. Lalique', 17 cm., 1930's. **£300-350** *S*

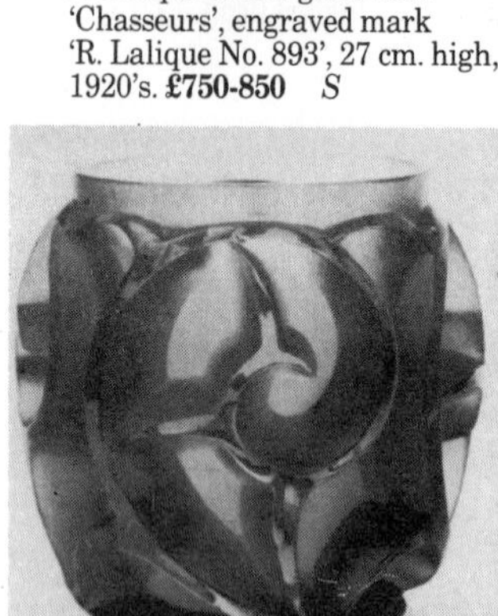

A Lalique amber glass vase 'Chasseurs', engraved mark 'R. Lalique No. 893', 27 cm. high, 1920's. **£750-850** *S*

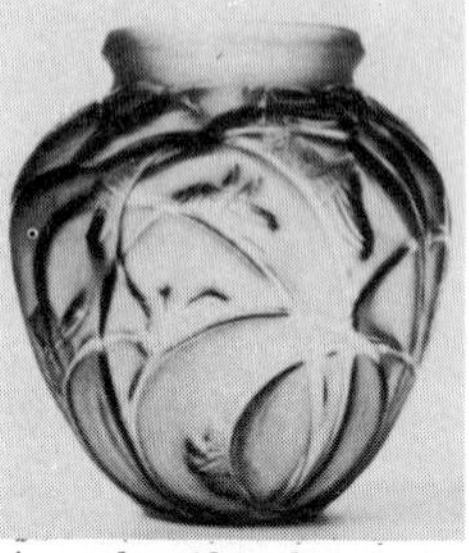

An early oviform locust vase in emerald-green glass, inscribed 'R. Lalique', 27 cm. high. **£800-£900** *C*

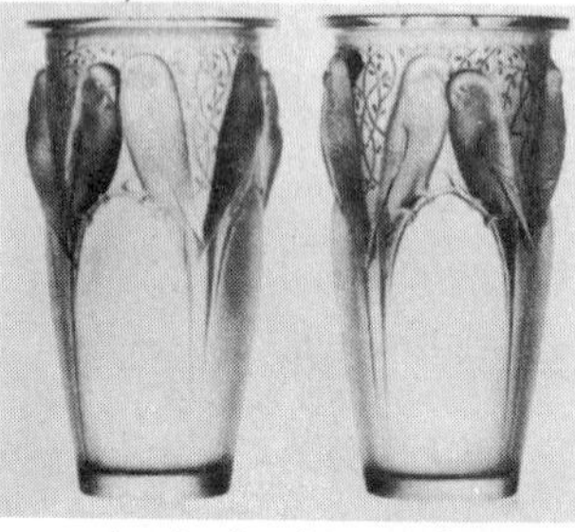

A pair of opalescent glass vases having budgerigars facing each other on stylised branches, etched mark 'R. Lalique France', one numbered 905, 9½ in. (24 cm.). **£600-700** *Bea*

A Lalique opalescent glass bowl moulded with budgerigars, heightened with blue staining, marked 'R. Lalique, France', 24.5 cm. diam. **£300-350** *P*

A Lalique frosted glass vase moulded with ibex, marked on the base 'R. Lalique, France', 20.5 cm. high. **£280-360** *P*

A Lalique amber glass vase 'Tourbillons' deeply moulded, engraved mark 'R. Lalique No. 973', 20.25 cm., 1920's. **£1,500-£1,600** *S*

A Lalique smoky-grey vase 'Ornis', engraved 'R. Lalique France', 19.5 cm. high. **£500-550** *P*

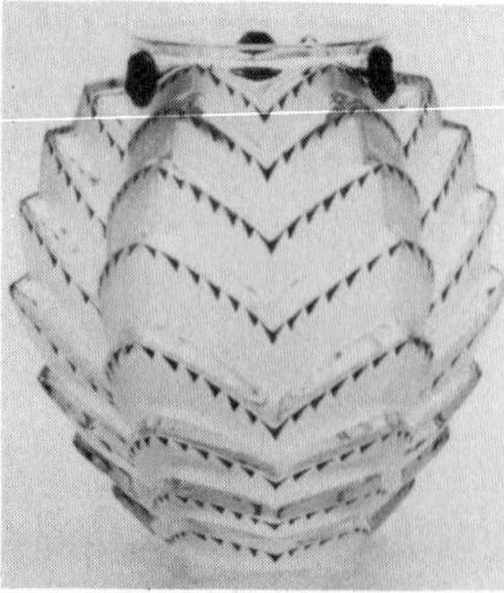

An unusual Lalique hanging lamp in the form of a stylised globe artichoke, with blue enamelled detailing, marked on bottom 'R. Lalique France', with metal rosettes, hooks and cords for suspension, 22.5 cm. high. **£150-£200** *P*

A Lalique frosted glass ceiling shade, moulded mark 'R. Lalique', 37 cm., 1930's. **£300-350** *S*

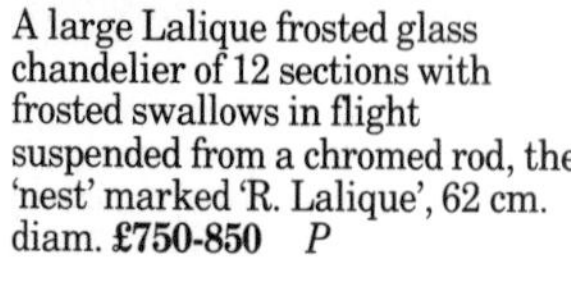

A large Lalique frosted glass chandelier of 12 sections with frosted swallows in flight suspended from a chromed rod, the 'nest' marked 'R. Lalique', 62 cm. diam. **£750-850** *P*

A matt finish glass table lamp, cerise and blue, attributed to Daum, 14 in., c. 1920's. **£350-400** *BP*

A Lalique opalescent glass figure 'Suzanne', signed on base 'R. Lalique France', 22.75 cm. high. **£450-500** *P*

A Lalique mascot 'St. Christopher', 'R. Lalique-France' markings, circular base, approx. 11.5 cm. high by 10.5 cm. wide. **£300-350** *P*

A Lalique glass hand mirror, heightened with grey staining, metal mounting rims stamped 'R. Lalique', 16 cm. diam., 1920's. **£350-400** *S*

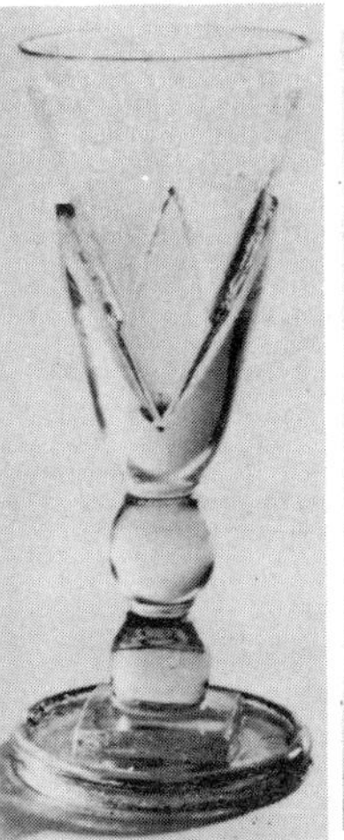

An etched glass chalice, the colourless glass deep etched with geometric motifs, part polished, part textured, engraved signature on the underside 'Marinot', 20.2 cm., c. 1925. **£2,000-2,300** *S*

A bouchon de radiateur 'Faucon' in clear polished glass fitted with a chromium plated radiator attachment, glass moulded R. Lalique etched 'France, no. 1124', minute chip to right wing, 19.7 cm. high including mount. **£500-600** *C*

An Art Deco amethyst glass decanter, 9 in. **£90-100** *FD*

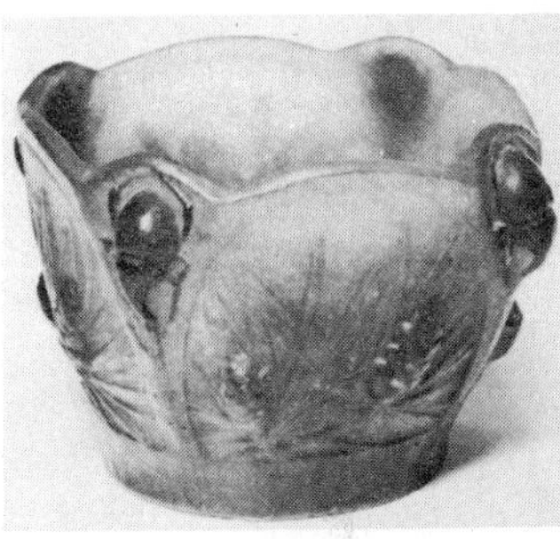

A Walter pâte-de-verre bowl, in green glass shaded to deep turquoise at the base, marked 'A. Walter Nancy' and 'H. Bergé Sc', 8.6 cm., 1920's. **£750-850** *S*

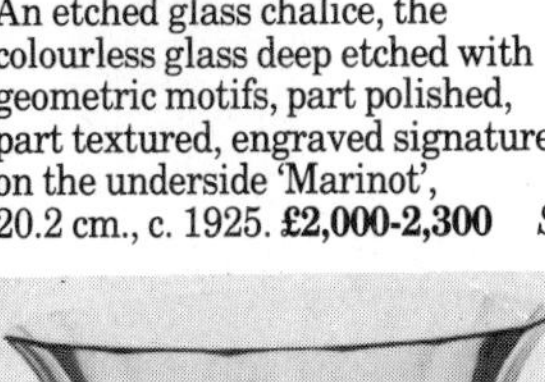

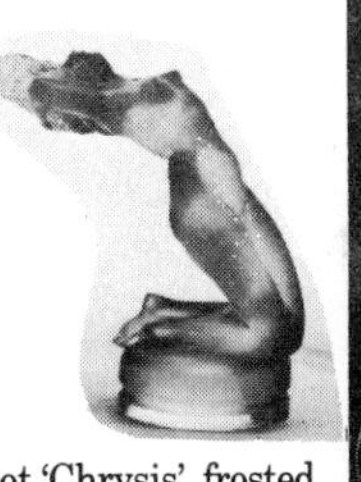

A Lalique mascot 'Chrysis', frosted glass, etched 'R. Lalique, France', under the circular base, approx. 15.5 cm. high. **£500-600** *P*

A Lalique glass cockerel, moulded 'R. Lalique France', stencilled 'Lalique France', 21.5 cm., 1930's. **£350-400** *S*

An Austrian glass vase, the design attributed to Josef Hoffmann, the olive-green, clear glass with faceted sides, unmarked but probably by Meyr's Neff or Moser of Karlsbad, 13.25 cm. high. **£150-200** *P*

A Lalique mascot 'Spirit of the Wind', some damage to base, approx. 25.5 cm. long. **£800-900** *P*

A Lalique glass moulded plaque 'The Archer', moulded and etched 'R. Lalique France', on nickel-plated Breves Gallery base fitted for illumination, 4½ in. (11.5 cm.) high. **£300-350** *CSK*

A Jean E. Puiforcat silver and rosewood 4-piece coffee service, stamped Jean E. Puiforcat and maker's mark, 72 oz. gross weight. **£1,800-2,200** *C*

An E. Viners 4-piece silver tea service, London, 1934, 55 oz. gross weight. **£500-600** *C*

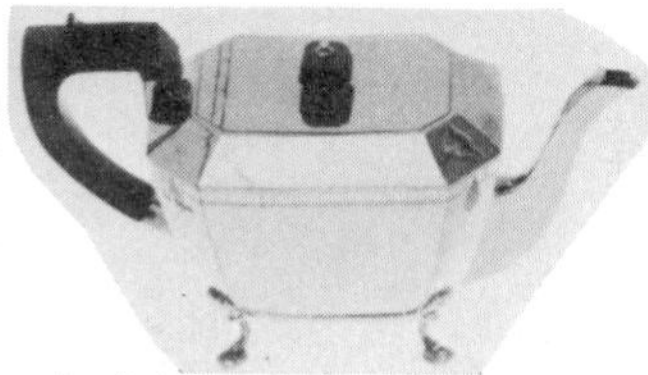

An Art Deco 4-piece silver tea service, the tea pot and hot water jug with wooden handles, all engraved with fine bands and geometric motifs, Sheffield, 1940, 60 oz. gross. **£450-550** *CSK*

A Georg Jensen 'Cactus' pattern canteen of cutlery, each piece with maker's marks and London import marks for various dates, 1936, 1930, 1931, 1932, 115 oz. (not including knives with steel blades). **£1,900-2,200** *P*

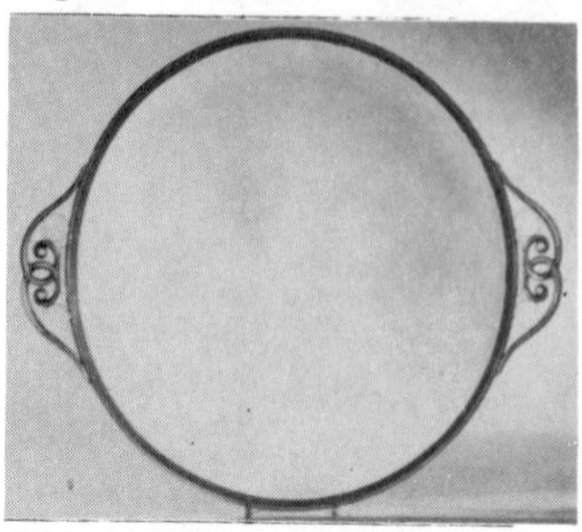

A Danish white-metal plain circular tray, engraved on the reverse with an inscription, by Georg Jensen, 15⅞ in. (40.3 cm.) diam., 68 oz., c. 1930. **£1,100-£1,400** *C*

An Omar Ramsden silver inkwell, engraved 'Omar Ramsden Me Fecit', maker's mark, London, 1927, 12.8 cm. diam. **£200-250** *S*

A silver wine taster by Jean Despres, maker's mark 'JD', engraved 'Jean Despres', 6.25 cm. diam., 1920's. **£130-170** *S*

An Omar Ramsden silver bowl, engraved 'Omar Ramsden Me Fecit', maker's mark, London, 1936, 18.5 cm. diam. **£850-950** *S*

A silver and lapis lazuli circular box and cover by Jean Puiforcat, the bowl set with circular cabochons, stamped poincon marks, impressed 'Jean E. Puiforcat', 16 cm. diam. **£1,200-1,400** *C*

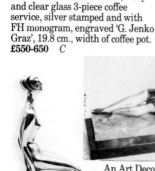

A Wiener Wekstatte silver, ivory and clear glass 3-piece coffee service, silver stamped and with FH monogram, engraved 'G. Jenko Graz', 19.8 cm., width of coffee pot. **£550-650** *C*

A silver-coloured metal evening bag in Art Deco style, blue silk interior, maker's mark CHc. P.Ch., Moscow, 9 in. (23 cm.) wide, 1908-17. **£100-140** *S*

Two Douau patinated metal vases, signed on the body 'Douau', 19.25 and 17.25 cm., 1920's. **£150-200** *S*

An Art Deco silvered metal figure, signed by Salvedo, 13 in. **£220-£280** *FD*

A pair of Sibylle May silvered-bronze bookends, signed in the maquette and monogrammed, 22.5 cm., 1920's. **£450-500** *S*

A pair of bronze Art Deco wall lights cast from models by F. Carbasius, one inscribed 'F. Carbasius', both stamped 'Brons Gieteru Deplastier A Binder Haarlem', 58.9 cm. high. **£1,200-£1,600** *C*

A bronze figure 'Faun', cast from a model by Rembrandt Bugatti, signed, stamped 'cire perdue A.A. Hebrard', numbered on base rim (Cl), 31.5 cm. high. **£1,800-2,200** *C*

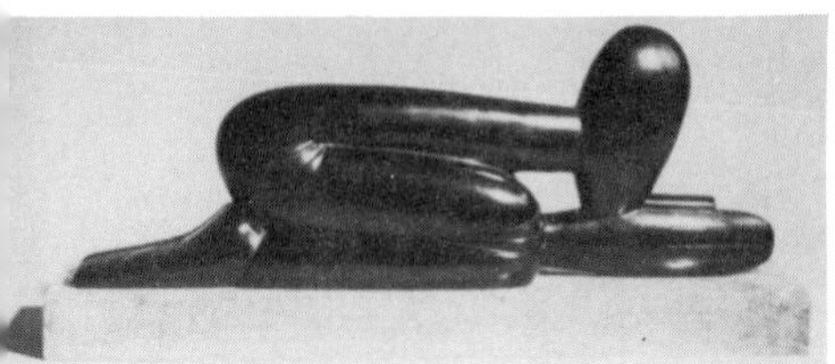

A bronze figure 'The Prayer', cast from a model of 1932 by Jean Lambert-Rucki, rich black patina, inscribed 'Lambert-Rucki 32 EA' (artist's proof) stamped founder's seal 'C. Valsuani cire perdue', 63 cm. wide. **£7,500-8,000** *C*

An Art Deco aluminium pheasant on marble base, 19½ in. **£60-75** *NP*

A Desmo jaguar SS100 'Leaping Cat' chrome plated mascot on base, stamped Desmo and Copyright on the base. **£90-110** *P*

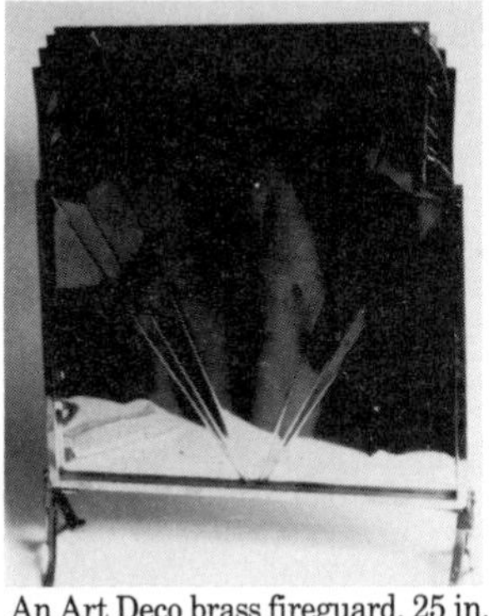

An Art Deco brass fireguard, 25 in. high. **£30-40** *BP*

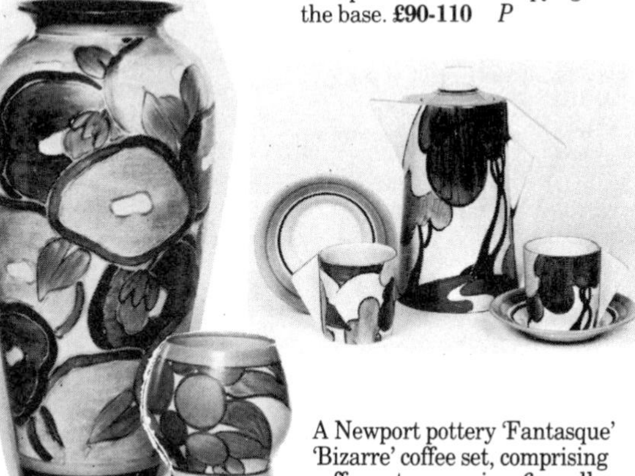

A Newport pottery 'Fantasque' 'Bizarre' vase, painted in blue, green and pink with stylised flowers, 26.4 cm., and another banded with brightly-painted stylised berries and leaves, 14.8 cm., both with printed marks, 1930's. **£200-250** *S*

A Newport pottery 'Fantasque' 'Bizarre' coffee set, comprising coffee pot, cream jug, 6 small cups with saucers, painted in bright yellow, blue-red, green and purple, printed marks, 17 cm. height of coffee pot, 1930's. **£300-350** *S*

A bronze figure by Erica Lee, signed on base 'Erica Lee' faintly dated 1921, 74 cm. high. **£480-£560** *P*

A Newport pottery 'Bizarre' 2-person tea set, in orange, blue, yellow, green, purple and black, factory marks, 12 cm. height of tea pot, 1930's. **£400-500** *S*

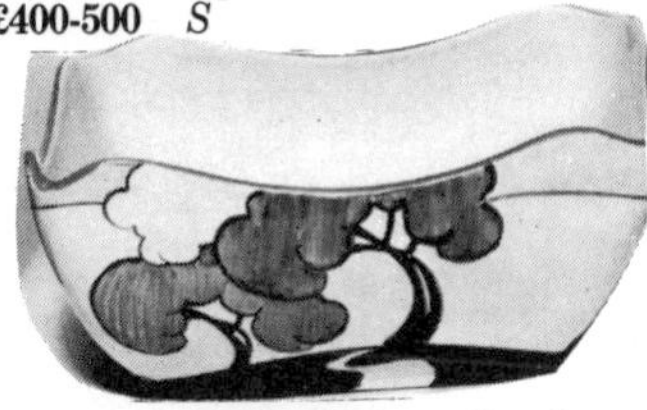

A Newport pottery 'Fantasque' 'Bizarre' bowl, painted in brilliant colours against a cream ground, printed marks, 20 cm., 1930's. **£100-150** *S*

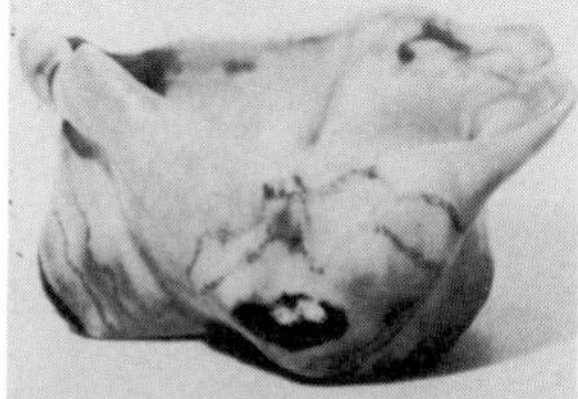

An unusual Clarice Cliff vase of abstracted tree trunk form, in a streaked turquoise and white glaze with yellow and brown, signed on base 'Le Bon Dieu — I think that I shall never see a form as lovely as a tree', 9.25 cm. high. **£100-140** *P*

A Limoges Art Deco coffee set, each decorated with broad yellow bands and bouquets of flowers, marked with a cockerel and T.L.B. for Touze, Lemaitre Frères and Blancher, 23 cm. height of pot. **£100-150** *P*

A Newport pottery 'Inspiration' 'Bizarre' vase, abstract design in blue, purple and indigo around the base, pale turquoise ground, painted marks, 20.5 cm., 1930's. **£250-300** *S*

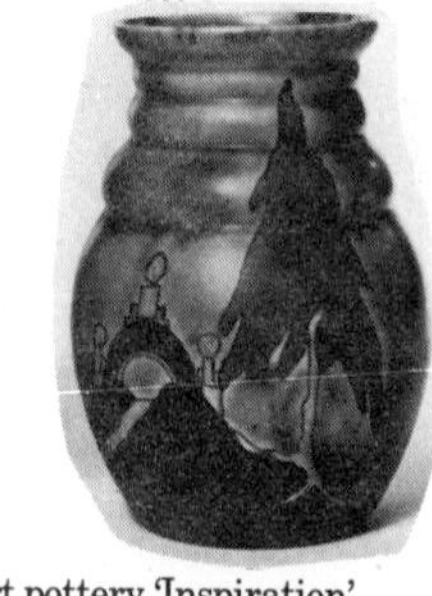

A Newport pottery 'Inspiration' 'Bizarre' vase, painted in blue, purple, beige and indigo, bright turquoise ground, painted marks, 20 cm., 1930's. **£220-280** *S*

A Fraureuth porcelain lamp modelled as a girl, standing beside a porcelain and brass lamp post that supports a fabric 'umbrella' shade, printed factory marks 'Fraureuth Kunstableitung', 51 cm high. **£95-115** *P*

A Royal Dux figure by Schaff, the girl wearing blue and gilt trousers and a string of beads, her brown hair styled to form a halo around her face, signed 'Schaff', pink triangle mark, printed Made in Czechoslovakia, 3101, 44 cm. long. **£280-340** *P*

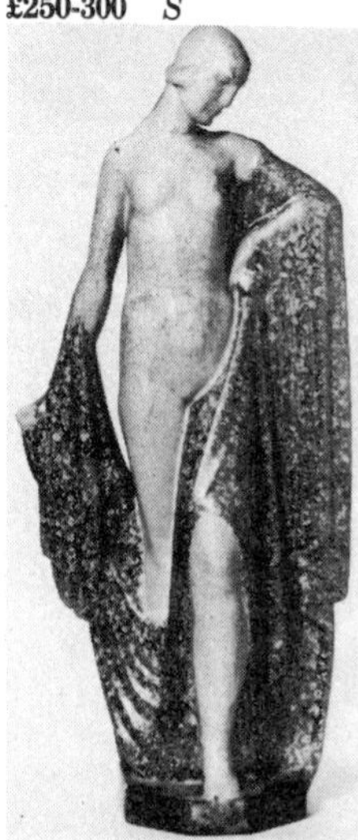

A Royal Dux figure, hollowed for use as a vase, covered with foliage, pink triangle mark, 440, 38.5 cm. high. **£120-150** *P*

A Boulogne pottery figure 'La Soie', designed by Marcel Renard, the crackled glazed body partially clad in a gilt and mauve mottled robe, impressed factory marks, signed in gilt 'Marcel Renard', 48.5 cm. high. **£280-360** *P*

A similar figure was exhibited at the Paris Exposition Internationale of 1925 and is illustrated in 'The Decorative Twenties' by Martin Battersby, on page 12 (Pub. Studio Vista 1969).

A Goldscheider 'bat girl', the blue wings veined with yellow, a blue turban on her head, on a deep turquoise oval base, inscribed Lorenzl, impressed 5230/422/16, printed factory mark, 18¾ in. high. **£300-350** *CSK*

A Lalique glass and wrought-iron lamp, on a geometric and textured iron column, attributed to Edgar Brandt, the glass scratch signed 'R. Lalique', 62 cm. high. **£1,300-1,700** *P*

A Goldscheider porcelain head of a young woman in the 1940's style, stamped Goldscheider G.U.S.A. and circular mark, impressed 507, 29.5 cm. high. **£300-400** *C*

A pottery wall mask moulded as a girl's head with a pink sun-bonnet, marked 'Royal Doulton', length top to bottom 8 in., c. 1930. **£130-160** *EEW*

A Derny earthenware figure of a baboon, matt brown-black glaze, incised signature 'Derny', 22.75 cm., 1920's. **£200-250** *S*

An amusing earthenware tea pot, in the form of an aeroplane, yellow crackled glazed with silver details, impressed ' "T. Plane" Made in England', 24 cm. long, 1930's. **£80-£120** *S*

A Richard Ginori porcelain cigarette box and cover, designed by Gio Ponti, painted with various motifs related to smoking, entertainment and travel, aubergine on white, marked 'Richard Ginori S. Cristoforo Milano Made in Italy', 11.5 cm., 1930's. **£80-120** *S*

An Art Deco cased carriage timepiece movement in burr-walnut surround, 5 in. high, c. 1920. **£100-140** *TP*

An Art Deco clock garniture in brown and cream polished stone, 15 in. wide, c. 1920. **£75-85** *NP*

A geometric carpet, design of stylised space rockets, in pastel shades of blue, purple and aubergine, maroon border, 310 by 372 cm., 1930's. **£250-350** *S*

An Art Deco diamond clip, **£350-400** *Bon*

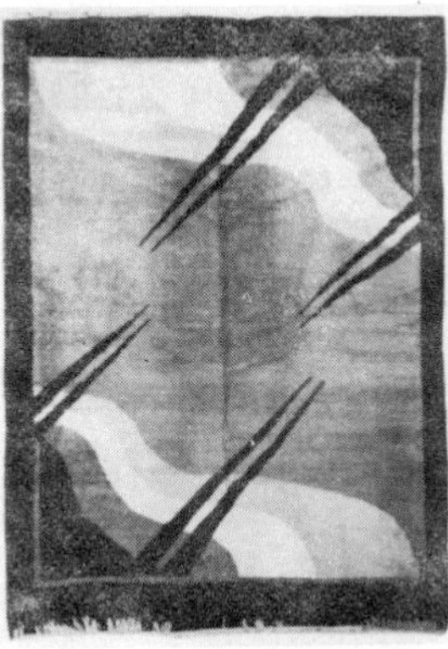

A large rug, in yellow, pink, salmon and burgundy, blue ground, burgundy border, 350 by 265 cm. 1930's. **£550-650** *S*

A Lalique glass vase lamp base, with original shade, richly detailed with blue staining, shade with interior panels of mica painted with matching design in blue and yellow, engraved mark 'R. Lalique France No. 888', 26.5 cm. height of base, 1920's. **£1,600-1,900** *S*

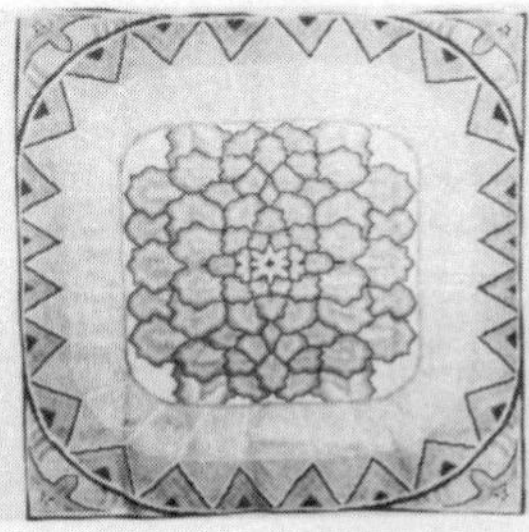

An Art Deco wool pile carpet in pink, blue, ochre and black with a border of symbol characters between a geometric centre and surround, 296 by 286 cm. **£400-£600** *C*

A Wiener Werkstatte shagreen covered cigar and cigarette box attributed to a design by Josef Hoffman with an interior compartment fitted behind a pivoting panel with brass lock plate and key, the underside stamped, 20 cm. wide. **£650-750** *C*

A sculptured wooden head carved by Emile Virgo, stained in amber and green, carved E. Virgo, 93 cm. wide. **£750-850** *C*

A multi-coloured C. Fournery advertising poster, mounted on linen, approx. 158 cm. high by 120 cm. **£150-180** *P*

An ivory, pewter and enamel-tiled rectangular wood panel 'Le Couple', by Bela Vörös, inscribed VB, 31.3 by 19.2 cm., 1940. **£1,500-1,700** *C*

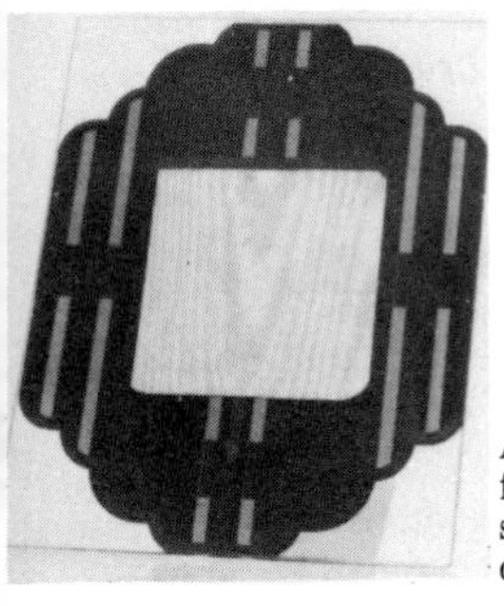

An Art Deco glass photograph frame, painted in black, red and silver with a lobed geometric linear design, 7 by 5½ in. **£50-60** *CSK*

A pair of Pieff chromed metal and smoked glass display shelves, 180 cm. high, 85.5 cm. wide. **£600-£700** *S*

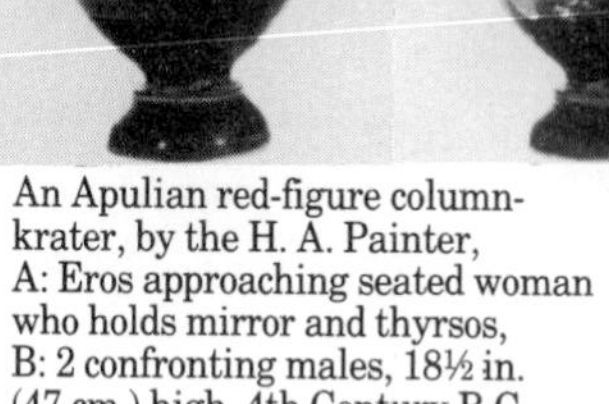

An Attic black-figure siana cup by the C Painter, 13¼ in. (33.6 cm.) diam. across handles, 2nd quarter 6th Century B.C. **£1,500-2,500** *C*

An Apulian red-figure column-krater, by the H. A. Painter, A: Eros approaching seated woman who holds mirror and thyrsos, B: 2 confronting males, 18½ in. (47 cm.) high, 4th Century B.C. **£1,700-2,000** *C*

An Attic red-figure eye-cup (Type A), repaired with some restoration 16¼ in. (41.3 cm.) diam. across handles, late 16th Century B.C. **£4,000-4,500** *C*

An Apulian red-figure oinochoe by the Baltimore Painter, Eros flying to right holding situla and casket, open and half palmettes, 10½ in. (26 cm.) high, late 4th Century B.C. **£400-450** *C*

An Attic red-figure stemless cup, by an early classical follower of Douris, 11 in. (28 cm.) diam. across handles, 2nd quarter of 5th Century B.C. **£1,900-2,100**

An Attic black-figure amphora, from the workshop of Lydos, 10¾ in. (27.4 cm.) high, 2nd quarter 6th Century B.C. **£2,400-£3,000** *C*

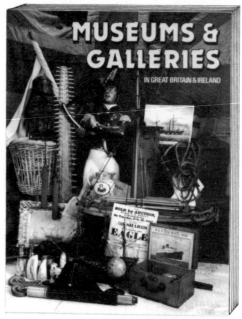

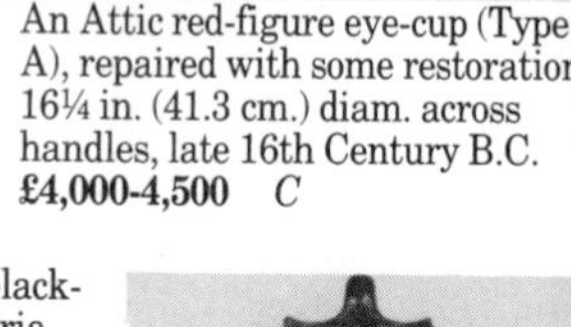

An Attic black-figure hydria, Antimenean in manner, repaired with some restoration, 19 in. (43.5 cm.) high, late 6th Century B.C. **£2,400-£3,000** *C*

An Attic black-figure lekythos, in the manner of Lydos, repaired with minor restoration, 9½ in. (24.1 cm.) high, mid 6th Century B.C. **£800-900** *C*

CHRONOLOGICAL TABLE FOR THE NEAR EAST

Pottery Neolithic	6th and 5th millennium B.C.
Chalcolithic Period	4th millennium B.C.
The Early Bronze Age	3100-2200 B.C.
The Middle Bronze Age	2200-1550 B.C.
The Late Bronze Age	1550-1200 B.C.
The Iron Age	1200-586 B.C.
The Persian Period	586-332 B.C.
The Hellenistic Period	332-30 B.C.
The Roman Period	30 B.C.-450 A.D.

A black-figure hydria, 10¾ in. (27.4 cm.) high, late 6th Century B.C. **£5,000-5,500** *C*

An Attic siana cup by the Griffin Bird Painter, repaired, 8½ in. (21.8 cm.) diam. across handles, 2nd quarter 6th Century B.C. **£350-400** *C*

A late Paestan bell-krater, close to the Painter of Naples 2585, 13 in. (33.2 cm.) high, and a Campanian bell-krater, from the workshop of the Painter of New York GR 1000, the Group of Brussels A137, rim chipped, 6¾ in. (17.4 cm.) high, 4th Century B.C. **£550-650** *C*

A Corinthian kelebe, the upper register painted in magenta and brown, the rim decorated with rays and sirens above each handle, 12¼ in. (31 cm.) high, 7th Century B.C. **£2,200-2,500** *C*

An Anglo-Saxon pottery funerary urn, 4¾ in. (12 cm.) high, c. 6th Century A.D. **£250-300** *C*

An Italo-Corinthian painted pottery amphora, 27½ in. (59.7 cm.) high, late 7th Century B.C. **£3,200-£3,500** *C*

A greenish-brown glazed frit figurine of Thoth, 2¾ in. (7 cm.) high, 4th-3rd Century B.C. **£750-850** *C*

An Etruscan bucchero quadruped caryatid bowl, repaired, 7¼ in. (18.2 cm.) high, c. 600 B.C. **£400-500** *C*

A basalt torso of an Egyptian official, with traces of a back pillar, mounted on wood, 9½ in. (22.5 cm.) high, 6th-5th Century B.C. **£1,500-£2,500** *C*

A superb black basalt figure of Horus the falcon, the base inscribed with a single line of demotic: 'Horus, Lord of Mesen-the-divine, the great god, Lord of Dr. t...', 21¼ in. high by 8 in. wide by 17¼ in. deep (54 by 20 by 44 cm.), c. 4th-3rd Century B.C., inscription Ptolemaic or Roman. **£33,000-£36,000** *C*

Mesen was the ancient capital of the XIVth Nome of the Delta and closely connected with the cult of Horus. It is probable the statue came from the modern day site of Tell Abu Seifa, eastern side of the Suez Canal.

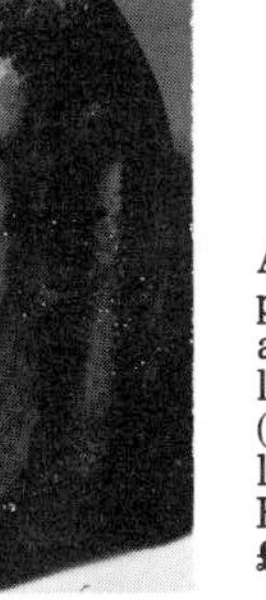

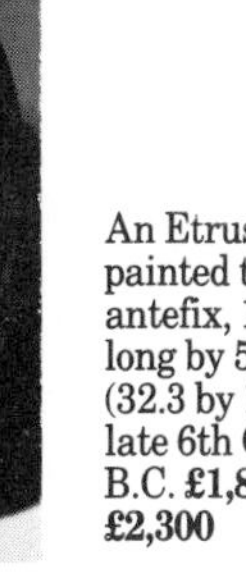

An Etruscan painted terracotta antefix, 12¾ in. long by 5¼ in. high (32.3 by 13.2 cm.), late 6th Century B.C. **£1,800-£2,300** *C*

A Romano-Egyptian painted plaster head with inlaid opaque glass eyes, and lips with traces of red ochre paint, 7½ in. (19 cm.) high, 1st-2nd Century A.D. **£1,000-£1,500** *C*

(l.) A Cypriot painted pottery figure of a quadruped, with red and black striped decoration, 3¾ in. (9.5 cm.) high, pottery flask with red and black banded decoration, 3½ in. (9 cm.) high, and the upper half of a painted terracotta Astarte plaque, 3¼ in. (8.3 cm.) high, c. 6th Century B.C. **£300-350** *C*

(c.b.) A Boeotian painted terracotta figure, 3½ in. (8.9 cm.) long, late 6th Century B.C. **£180-250** *C*

(c.t.) A Campanian black glazed bird flask, 5¼ in. (13.2 cm.) long, 4th Century B.C., a terracotta hollow backed torso fragment, 6 in. (15.2 cm.) high, c. 4th Century B.C., and a terracotta fragment of child, 2 in. (5.3 cm.) high, 2nd-1st Century B.C. **£250-300** *C*

(r.) A Greek terracotta statuette, 4 in. (10 cm.) high, 6th Century B.C. **£300-350** *C*

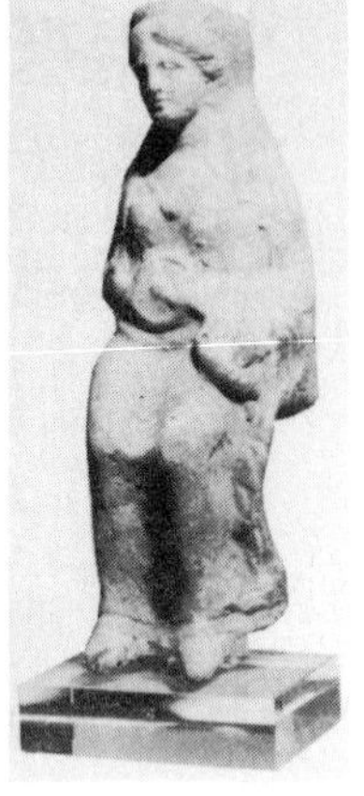

A Sicilian terracotta figure of a seated goddess, Demeter, 7¾ in. (19.8 cm.) high, mid 5th Century B.C. **£380-450** *C*

An Hellenistic painted terracott figure, 5½ in. (14 cm.) high, c. 3r Century B.C. **£400-600** *C*

An Egyptian bronze figure of Ptah, patron deity of craftsmen, on marble base, 6 in. (15 cm.) high, 6th-4th Century B.C. **£2,600-£3,000** *C*

A Phoenician terracotta figure traces of marine encrustation, 14¾ in. (37.5 cm.) high, 5th-4t Century B.C. **£300-350** *C*

A Phoenician terracotta cult figure of Tanit, traces of marine encrustation and linen wrapping, 13 in. (33 cm.) high, 5th-4th Century B.C. **£200-300** *C*

An Egyptian bronze figure of Hor-sma-towy, traces of inlaid gilding on crown, beaded collar and ib-amulet, 6¾ in. (17 cm.) high, 6th-4th Century B.C. **£1,500-£2,000** *C*

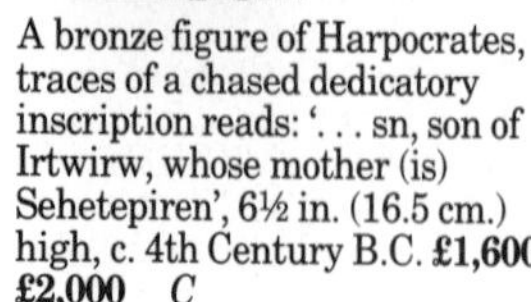

A bronze figure of Harpocrates, traces of a chased dedicatory inscription reads: '. . . sn, son of Irtwirw, whose mother (is) Sehetepiren', 6½ in. (16.5 cm.) high, c. 4th Century B.C. **£1,600-£2,000** *C*

A Canosan painted terracotta stand, pink and brown pigment traces, 6½ in. (16.5 cm.) high, 3rd Century B.C. **£400-500** *C*

(l.) Eight Luristan bronze figures, on perspex stand 2¾ in. (7 cm.) long (max.), 8th-7th Century B.C. **£400-£450** *C*

(r.) A bronze stylised ibex, 3.5 cm. high, 3 other stylised animals; and a pendant comprising twin ibex heads flanking a column, 4.3 cm. high, 8th-7th Century B.C. **£300-£400** *C*

A bronze figure of Horus the falc wearing a double crown of Upper and Lower Egypt, lower part of le missing, 4¾ in. (11.8 cm.) high, 6th-4th Century B.C. **£850-950**

A fine Greek bronze mirror and cover, the mirror a plain disc with deep concentric bands on one side, 6 in. (15.3 cm.) diam., latter half 4th Century B.C. **£6,500-7,500** *C*

An unusual bronze mirror, the central boss encircled by a crisply cast frieze of stylised animals, the massive rim with a frieze of matching animals, the smooth dark grey patina with scattered pale olive encrustation, Han Dynasty, 13.9 cm. **£1,600-1,900** *S*

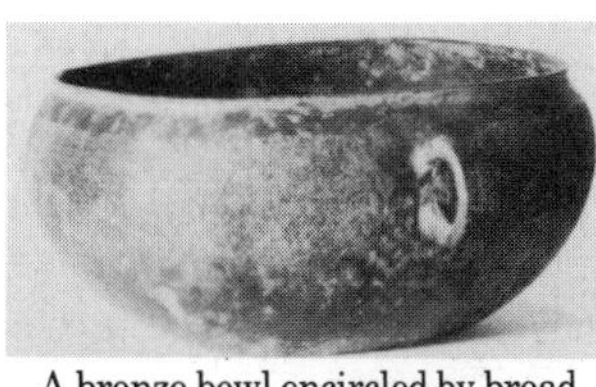

A bronze bowl encircled by broad bands of interlaced dragon scrolls, a ring handle on each side, the olive-green patina with extensive areas of paler mottling, Warring States, 15.7 cm. **£400-500** *S*

A large bronze wine vessel, yu, cast coiled snakes around the body, foot and shoulder, under a matt green patina with areas of globular malachite encrustation, damaged and partly repaired, 62 cm. high with raised handle, 35.5 cm. high at the rim, mid 1st Millennium B.C. **£1,200-1,400** *C*

A bronze double-handled bowl, on tripod cabriole legs, cast with a band of interlaced dragon scrolls in linear relief, the patina with extensive encrustation, 14 cm. long, 5th-4th Century B.C. **£450-£550** *S*

A bronze tripod brazier (jiao dou), encircled by concentric raised liner borders and horizontal lines, the dark grey patina with extensive malachite encrustation of attractive sea-green colour and with earth adhering, 35 cm., Eastern Han/Six Dynasties. **£400-£500** *S*

It is most unusual to find a jiao dou of this type with bearded human heads on the legs.

A bronze ritual vessel, decorated in intaglio low relief, overall dark green patina with some azurite encrustations, 9½ in. (24.1 cm.), Warring States. **£300-400** *S*

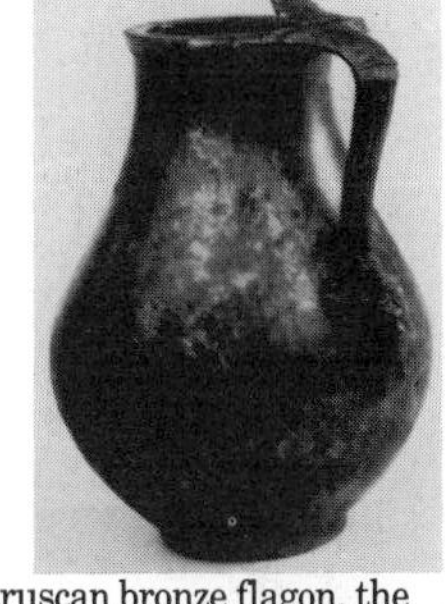

An Etruscan bronze flagon, the handle in the form of an open palmette with bird headed finials, the terminal a relief head of a young female, 6¾ in. (16.5 cm.) high, c. 4th Century B.C. **£1,000-£1,400** *C*

A Huaxiang mirror, the main field well cast in low relief, 6¼ in. (16.2 cm.), 2nd-3rd Century A.D. **£350-400** *S*

A shell amulet of a crouching animal, 2¼ in. (5.7 cm.) high, Sumerian. **£120-150** *C*

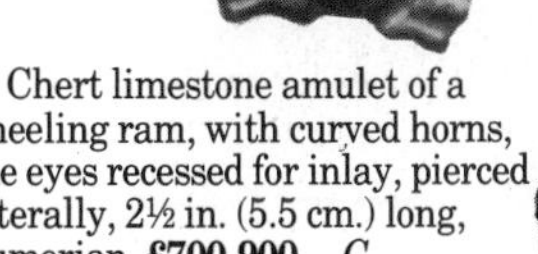

A Chert limestone amulet of a kneeling ram, with curved horns, the eyes recessed for inlay, pierced laterally, 2½ in. (5.5 cm.) long, Sumerian. **£700-900** *C*

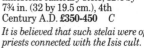

Eighteen Sumerian amulets and seals, including 2 fragmentary 'eye' idols, 3.5 cm. high (av.), Sumerian. **£350-400** *C*

A Coptic limestone bust, 16¼ in. (41.3 cm.) high, 3rd-4th Century A.D. **£450-550** *C*

A Romano-Egyptian painted limestone funerary stele, 12½ by 7¾ in. (32 by 19.5 cm.), 4th Century A.D. **£350-450** *C*

It is believed that such stelai were of priests connected with the Isis cult.

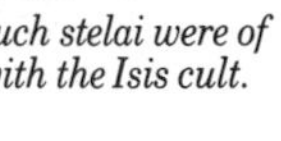

A sandstone relief fragment, 10¼ by 7 in. (26 by 17.8 cm.), Late New Kingdom. **£700-900** *C*

A Coptic limestone head, mounted, 9¾ in. (24.6 cm.) high, c. 5th Century A.D. **£350-450** *C*

An Etruscan painted limestone funerary urn, traces of blue, red and white pigment, 15¼ in. long by 13½ in. high (38.7 by 34.2 cm.), c. 3rd Century B.C. **£700-800** *C*

An Egyptian granite upper half of a seated man, 6¾ in. (17.2 cm.) high, late 12th-13th Dynasty. **£900-1,200** *C*

(l.) A brilliant blue glazed Frit Ushabti, made for the Lady of the House, . . . emkhebi, the details in black glaze, 4¾ in. (12 cm.) high, Dynasty XXI; a green glazed ushabti for Pedamenopet, 4¾ in. (12 cm.) high, Dynasty XXX; and a bronze figure of Osiris, mounted, 6 in. (15.4 cm.) high, Late Period. **£500-600** *C*

(c.) A blue-green glazed Frit Ushabti of Smenptah-psamtek, born of Ta-sherit-en-sekhmet, incised in 8 lines down the front with the late version of Ch.VI of the Book of the Dead, 8 in. (20 cm.) high, Dynasty XXVI or later. **£600-£800** *C*

(r.) A green and brown glazed Frit Royal Ushabti of Seti I, with 6 horizontal bands of hieroglyphs in dark brown glaze, repaired, mounted, 6 in. (15.2 cm.) high, Dynasty XIX. **£600-800** *C*

(l.) A baked clay tablet of rations, 4 by 2.6 cm., Third Dynasty of Ur, 2113-2006 B.C.; and a Roman pottery flask, 6½ in. (16.5 cm.) high, 1st-4th Century A.D. **£140-£180** *C*

(r.) A baked clay economic tablet recording a delivery of sheep and goats, 2¾ by 1¾ in. (7 by 4.4 cm.), Ur III, Yr. 47 of Shulgi, 2048 B.C.; and 4 fragments of baked mud bricks, 5 in. (12.7 cm.) long (max.), reign of Nebuchadnezzar. **£300-£350** *C*

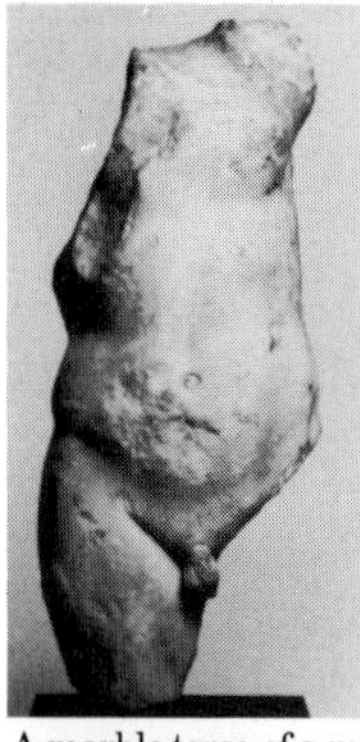

A marble torso of a man, 19½ in. (49.5 cm.) high, c. 1st Century A.D. **£800-1,300** *C*

An Archaic limestone stele, 9.5 in. (24.2 cm.) high, 2nd Dynasty. **£750-£850** *C*

A marble portrait bust, bust modern with facial restoration, 21 in. (33.5 cm.) high, probably Flavian, 1st Century A.D. **£2,000-£2,500** *C*

(l.) A Sumerian baked mud brick stamped in cuneiform with the names of 2 Queens, Urmano and his grandson Amar-sin, 10 in. (25.5 cm.) square (max.); and another similar, incomplete, early 3rd Millennium B.C. **£650-750** *C*

(r.) A Sumerian baked mud brick, with a dedicatory inscription by Amar-sin, 10 in. (25.5 cm.) square, Ur III. **£400-450** *C*

A Roman marble head of Apollo, mounted on wooden plinth, nose and part of lips restored, 10½ in. (26.8 cm.) high, 1st-2nd Century A.D. **£2,000-3,000** *C*

CHRONOLOGICAL TABLE FOR THE NEAR EAST

Pottery Neolithic	6th and 5th millennium B.C.
Chalcolithic Period	4th millennium B.C.
The Early Bronze Age	3100-2200 B.C.
The Middle Bronze Age	2200-1550 B.C.
The Late Bronze Age	1550-1200 B.C.
The Iron Age	1200-586 B.C.
The Persian Period	586-332 B.C.
The Hellenistic Period	332-30 B.C.
The Roman Period	30 B.C.-450 A.D.

An East Roman marble figure of a young male fertility god, neck repaired, on metal base, 8¾ in. (22 cm.) high, 2nd-3rd Century A.D. **£400-600** *C*

A marble portrait bust of a Roman official, bust modern with facial restoration, on marble socle, 22 in. (56 cm.) high, Trajanic, late 1st/early 2nd Century A.D. **£2,000-£3,000** *C*

An alabaster bull stele, 14 in. (35.2 cm.) high, 2nd Century B.C.-1st Century A.D. **£2,500-3,500** *C*

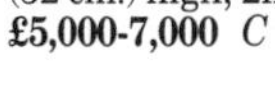

An alabaster figure, the eyebrows and eyes recessed for inlay, 12½ in. (32 cm.) high, 2nd-1st Century B.C. **£5,000-7,000** *C*

A fine South Arabian alabaster funerary plaque, the eyes inlaid with shell, pupils missing, mounted on wood, 10½ in. (27 cm.) high, 2nd-1st Century B.C. **£6,000-£7,000** *C*

A Byzantine mosaic fragment, grey-green, brown and cream coloured tesserae mounted with steel frame, 25 by 14 in. (63.5 by 35.5 cm.), c. 6th Century A.D. **£2,500-3,000** *C*

An alabaster figure, the face with incised eyebrows and the eyes inlaid with shell, pupils missing, 6¾ in. (17 cm.) high, 2nd-1st Century B.C. **£2,500-3,000** *C*

An Egyptian painted wooden boat, bearing 2 wooden figures of a reis and the deceased, each painted red, 32½ in. (82.5 cm.) long, Middle Kingdom. **£4,000-6,000** *C*

A fine Dutch brass tobacco box, richly engraved with stylised foliage, 6½ in. (16.5 cm.), c. 1700. **£700-900** *S*

A rare early 18th C. brass sponge box, 3½ in., c. 1720. **£600-650** *SA*

A similar box with pierced cover was normally for soap.

A Stucco painted wooden anthropoid mask, 15½ in. (39.5 cm.) high, Late Period. **£700-£800** *C*

A rare Dutch brass tobacco box, engraved with conventional foliage, sliding panels opening to reveal scenes from the life of Abraham, 2¼ by 5 in. (5.5 by 12.5 cm.), late 17th C. **£350-400** *S*

(l.) An 18th C. Dutch brass tobacco box, 5 in. **£140-180** *DWB*

(r.) An early 19th C. pierced brass hand lantern, 7½ in. **£170-200** *DWB*

A heavy 18th C. Dutch brass tobacco box, 6 in. high. **£95-110** *MPA*

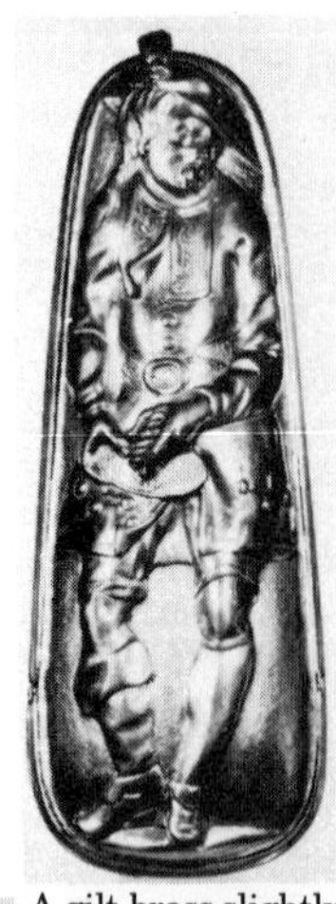
A gilt-brass slightly tapering snuff rasp, 5¾ in., probably early to mid 18th C. **£350-400** *CSK*

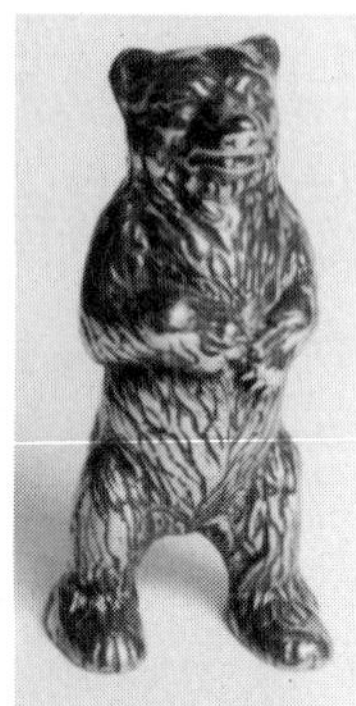
A brass bear money box, 5½ in., c. 1860-80. **£20-30** *BP*

An early 19th C. brass covered tobacco jar with tin inside case, 5½ in. high. **£15-20** *MPA*

A Victorian brass wedding casket with souvenirs and newspaper cutting for 1928, 7½ in. wide. **£50-£80** *BP*

A 19th C. Indian brass box, 6½ in. diam. **£12-15** *HA*

A Queen Mary brass Christmas box, 5 in. **£7-10** *HA*

Sent to the troops with cigarettes and photograph.

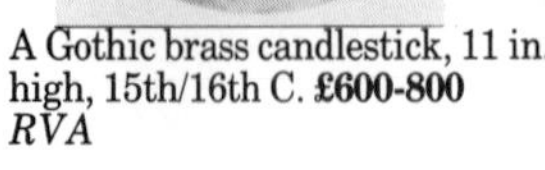
A Gothic brass candlestick, 11 in. high, 15th/16th C. **£600-800** *RVA*

A pair of Dutch brass candlesticks, the underside of each drip-pan with touch marks, 12 in. high (31 cm.), mid 17th C. **£650-750** *S*

A single Spanish brass candlestick, 9 in. high, 17th C. **£250-300** *RVA*

A pair of Dutch brass candlesticks, 8 in. high, mid 17th C. **£900-£1,000** *RVA*

A brass candlestick, 27 in., c. 1700. **£300-350** *CDE*

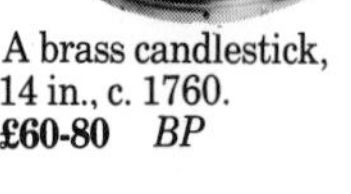
A brass candlestick, 14 in., c. 1760. **£60-80** *BP*

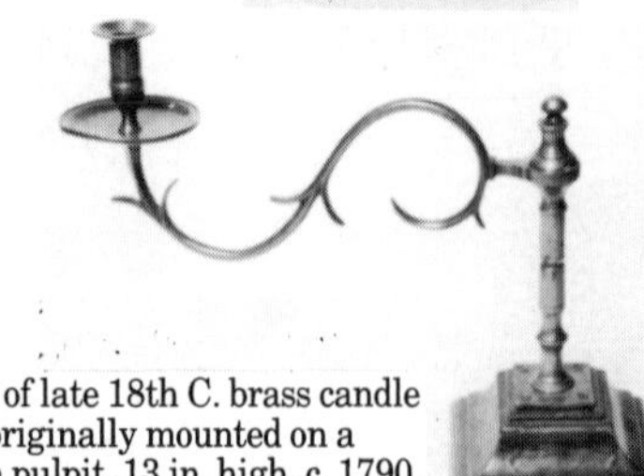
A pair of late 18th C. brass candle arms originally mounted on a church pulpit, 13 in. high, c. 1790. **£350-400** *CC*

A 17th C. Flemish pricket candlestick, 17¾ in. **£110-140** *DWB*

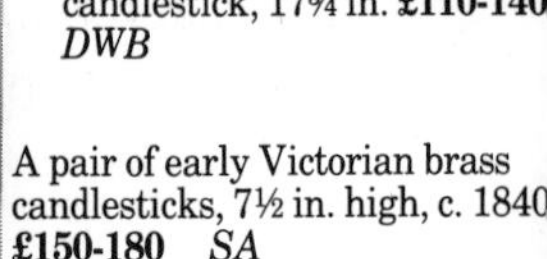
A pair of early Victorian brass candlesticks, 7½ in. high, c. 1840 **£150-180** *SA*

A pair of brass candlesticks, 7 in. high, c. 1800. **£50-60** *BP*

A pair of brass candlesticks, 8¼ in high, c. 1860. **£30-40** *BP*

A pair of brass candlesticks, 9¼ in. high, c. 1860's. **£30-40** *BP*

A pair of brass candlesticks, 11¾ in. high, 1900-20. **£50-60** *BP*

A good late 17th C. brass trifid top spoon, M.M.I.C., c. 1680. **£100-£120** *SA*

A brass fumigator, 25 in. long, c. 1750-80. **£150-200** *BP*

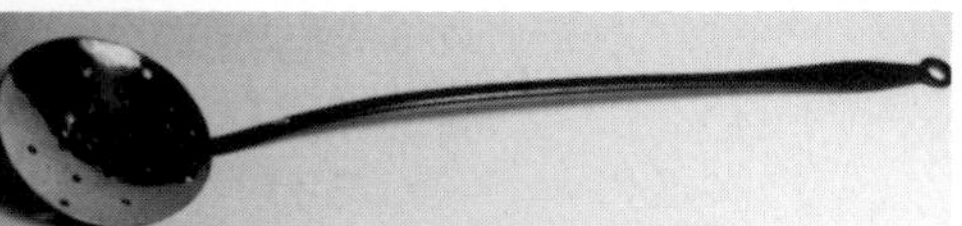
An early 18th C. brass and iron skimmer, 35 in. long. **£100-130** *BP*

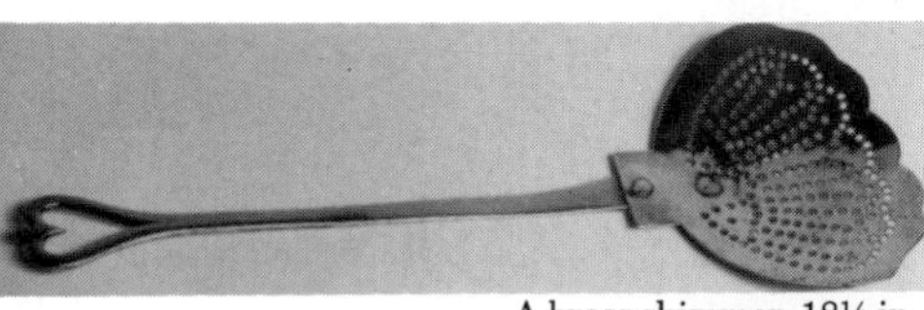
A brass skimmer, 18½ in., c. 1780-90. **£75-100** *BP*

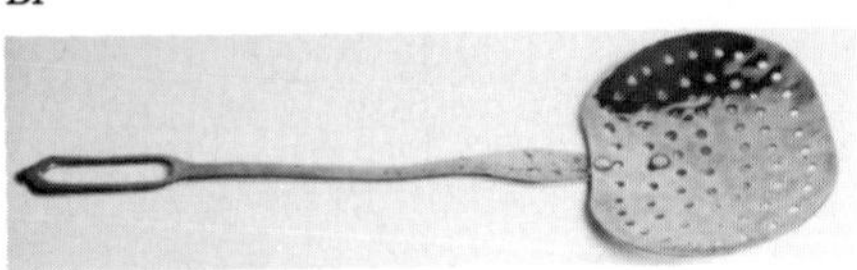
A brass skimmer, 17 in. long, c. 1780. **£50-60** *BP*

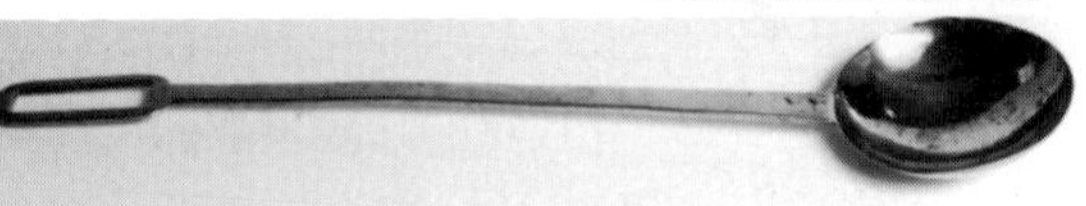
A large brass spoon, 18 in. long, c. 1800. **£40-50** *BP*

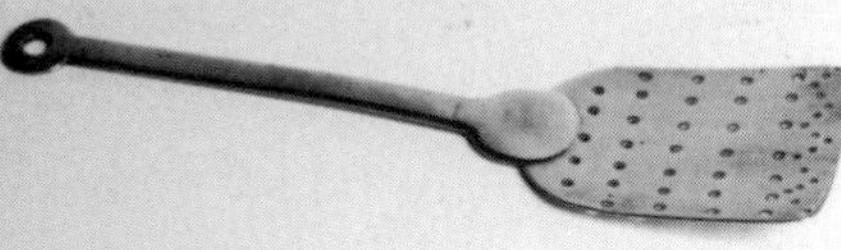
A brass fish ladle, 12 in. long, c. 1800. **£40-50** *BP*

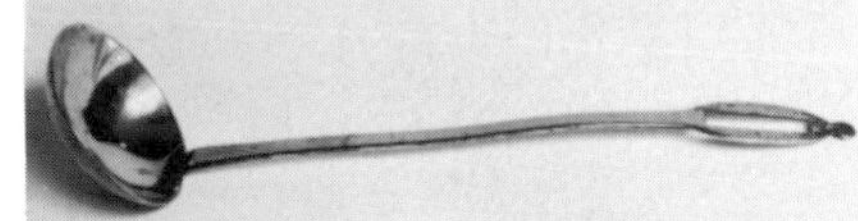
A brass ladle, 17 in. long, c. 1800. **£30-40** *BP*

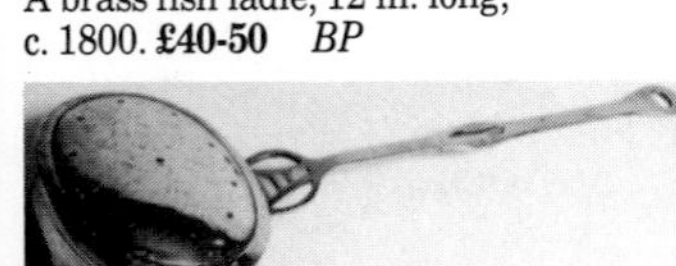
A brass chestnut roaster, 21 in. long, c. 1860's. **£80-90** *BP*

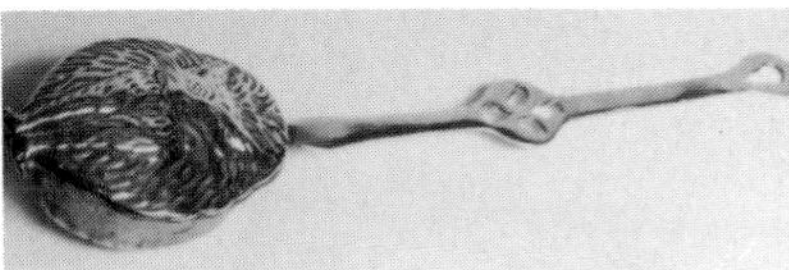
A brass 'kitten' chestnut roaster, 20 in. long, c. 1780-90. **£100-135** *BP*

A brass trivet, 7½ in. diam., c. 1900. **£40-50** *BP*

A brass footman, 9½ in., c. 1840. **£30-40** *BP*

A pair of brass fire tongs, 13 in., c. 1840. **£10-15** *BP*

A large brass and steel trivet, 13½ in. high. **£150-165** *NP*

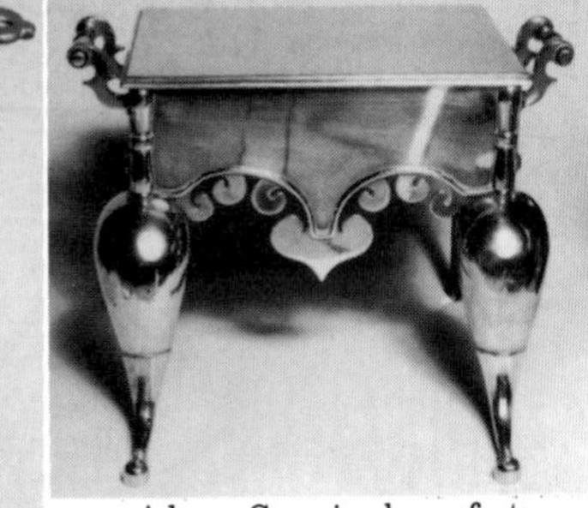
A large Georgian brass footman, 20 in. wide, c. 1790. **£250-300** *IHA*

A pair of extending brass tongs, 22 in. long max., c. 1850. **£15-20** *BP*

A brass fender, 62 in., c. 1800. **£400-450** *CDE*

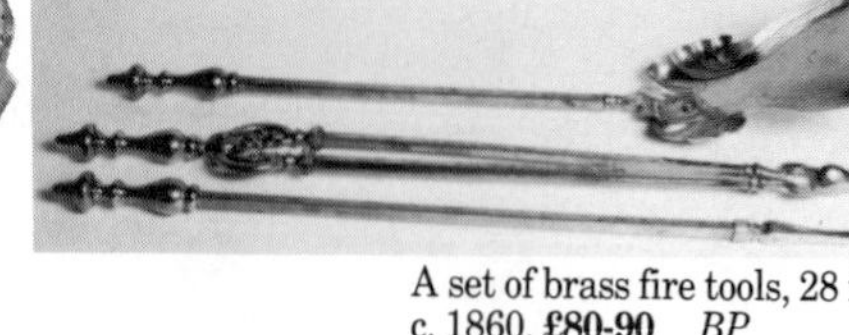

A set of brass fire tools, 28 in., c. 1860. **£80-90** *BP*

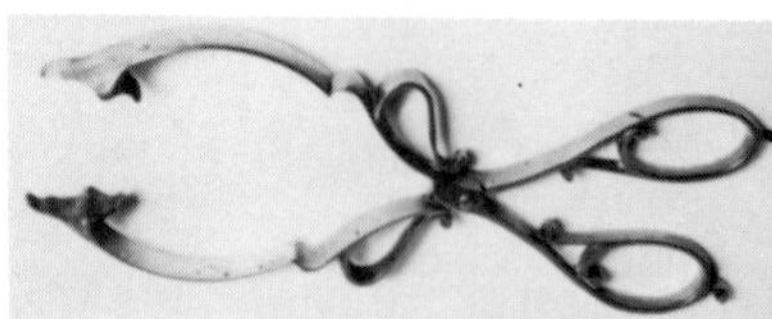

A pair of Edwardian coal tongs, 12 in. long. **£20-30** *BP*

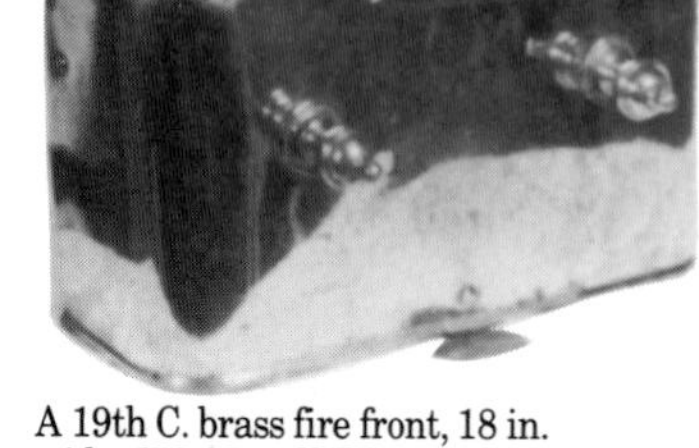

A 19th C. brass fire front, 18 in. wide. **£70-80** *JMW*

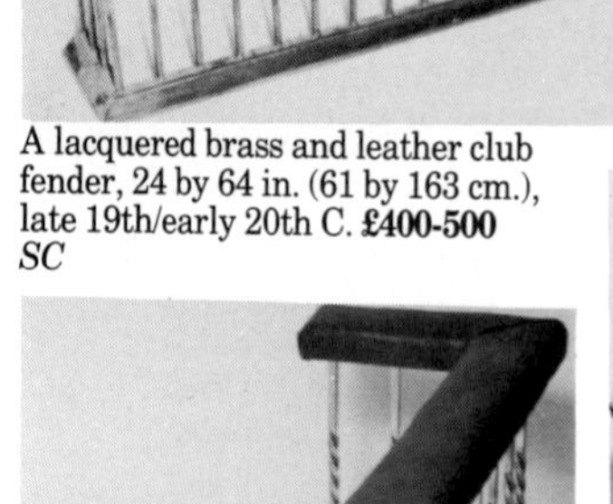

A lacquered brass and leather club fender, 24 by 64 in. (61 by 163 cm.), late 19th/early 20th C. **£400-500** *SC*

A mid 19th C. brass and steel spitjack, 13 in. **£20-24** *MPA*

A steel and brass fender, 37 in., c. 1840. **£70-90** *BP*

A Victorian brass fender, 27 in. **£50-60** *FD*

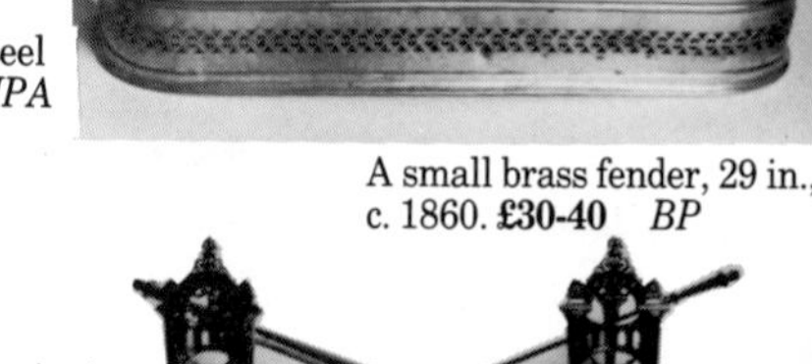

A small brass fender, 29 in., c. 1860. **£30-40** *BP*

A brass fireside set in the Adam style, 50 in. wide, c. 1865. **£500-£550** *BP*

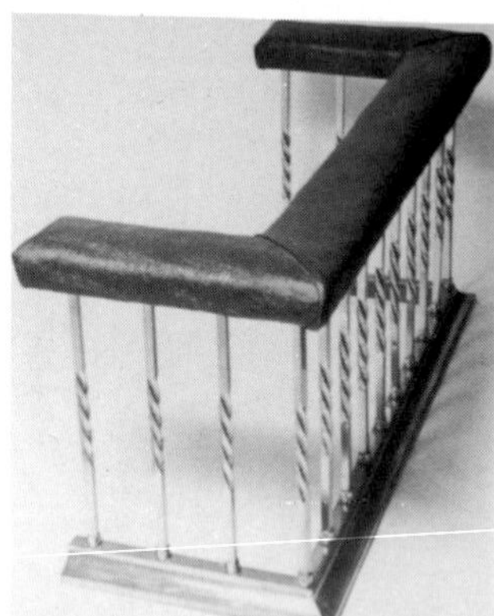

A brass club fender, c. 1875. **£220-£250** *CDE*

A Victorian brass coal helmet and shovel with fluted fan-shaped cover and ebonised handles. **£250-300** *M*

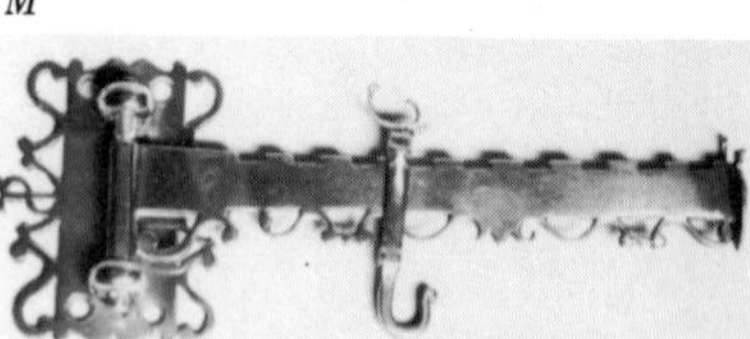

An 18th C. brass chimney crane, 11 in. **£30-40** *MPA*

A 17th C. brass mortar and pestle, 5½ in. **£230-260** *SA*

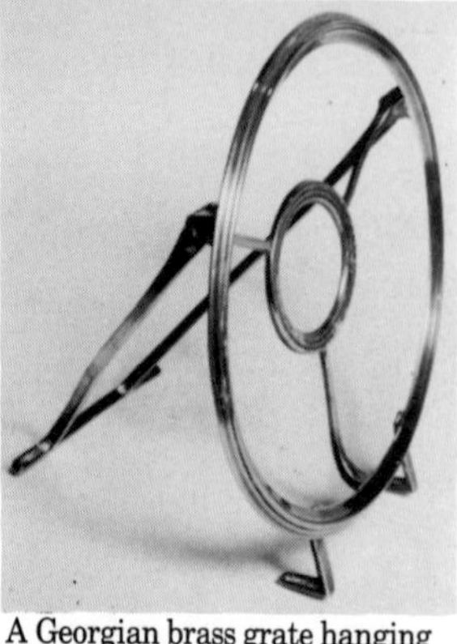

A Georgian brass grate hanging trivet, 7¼ in. diam., c. 1820. **£20-£25** *MPA*

A brass mortar with original pestle, 6 in. high, 17th C. **£100-£120** *RVA*

A rare 18th C. plain brass skillet, 13 in. long. **£95-120** *SA*

An 18th C. brass mortar, 4 in. **£25- £35** *FF*

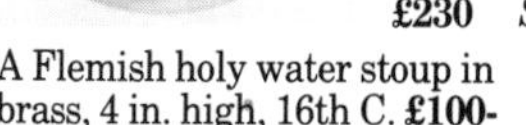

A Flemish holy water stoup in brass, 4 in. high, 16th C. **£100-£150** *RVA*

A Regency brass wine cooler with 2 pierced scroll handles, 11 in. **£200-£230** *SA*

An early 18th C. brass skillet. **£90-110** *DWB*

A 19th C. brass ice bucket, 14 in. high. **£350-450** *HWO*

A 19th C. candle holder with brass base and snuffer, and glass chimney, 7½ in. high. **£40-50** *STR*

A good pair of Powell and Hanmer all brass motor sidelamps, complete, early 20th C. **£140-160** *P*

A pair of Ducellier brass sidelamps, glass approx. 12 cm. square, complete with circular wick holders, etc., early 20th C. **£250-£300** *P*

A pair of all brass Lucas No. F141 'King's Own' veteran oil motor sidelamps, working condition, 22 cm. tall approx. **£190-240** *P*

A pair of Edwardian polished brass Lucas King of the Road No. 673 acetylene motor headlamps, as fitted to RR 'Silver Ghost', 28 cm. diam. approx. **£300-350** *P*

A pair of all brass veteran motor oil sidelamps, 4-sided, by Schön and Biedermann of Austria, 33 cm. tall approx. **£200-250** *P*

A mint pair of all brass 'Solar De Luxe Projector type 796' acetylene motor headlamps, 31 cm. diam. approx. **£600-650** *P*

A brass lantern, 16½ in. high. **£100-120** *CDE*

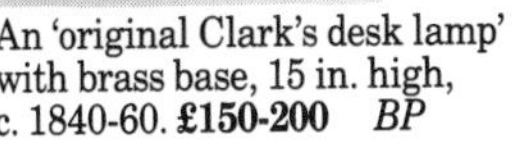

An 'original Clark's desk lamp' with brass base, 15 in. high, c. 1840-60. **£150-200** *BP*

A brass whale oil burning lamp, 15 in. high, c. 1840. **£55-65** *LG*

A Georgian brass oil lamp, 28 in. high. **£150-200** *GH*

A large pair of J. Marston & Co. Ltd. nickled-brass carriage lamps each with candle illuminant, the mount stamped J. Marston & Co. Ltd., Birmingham, the door with red glass rear lens, English, 52 in. high (132 cm.), c. 1880. **£2,500-£3,000** *S*

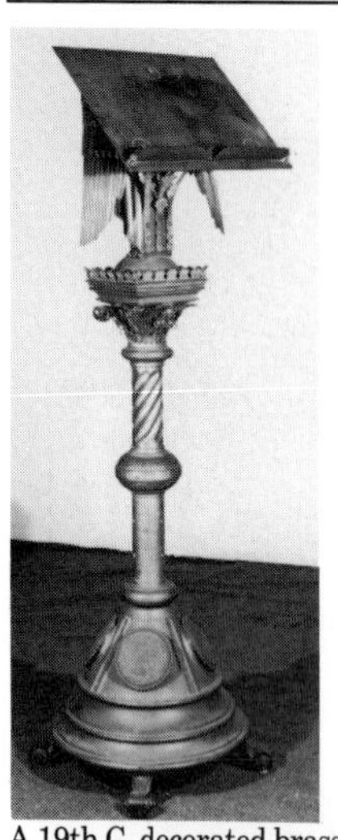
A 19th C. decorated brass lectern with copper angel surmount, 78¼ in. high. **£350-400** *DSH*

A Victorian brass-plated letter clip, 3½ in. **£8-10** *MPA*

A late 15th C. Italian repousse brass processional cross, with a Corpus Christi in the Romanesque manner, probably a later cast, God the Father and the 4 symbols of the Evangelists, 72.5 cm. high. **£850-£950** *C*

A pair of Dutch brass and iron andirons, 22 in. high. **£550-650** *S*

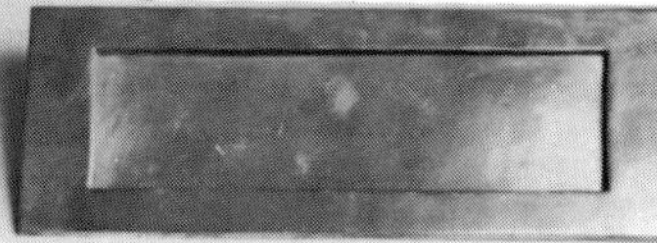
A Georgian brass letter plate, 14 in., c. 1800. **£30-45** *BP*

A brass letter plate, 9 in., c. 1920. **£25-45** *BP*

A brass ear syringe, 11½ in. extended, c. 1880. **£15-20** *BP*

A brass picture frame, 6½ in., c. 1860. **£20-30** *BP*

A brass Friendly Society staff head, 9 in., c. 1800. **£40-50** *FF*
The more ornate shapes go up to £100.

A brass and iron whip hanger, 4 in. high, c. 1850. **£20-30** *BP*

An early 19th C. brass iron stand, 9½ in. **£15-22** *MPA*

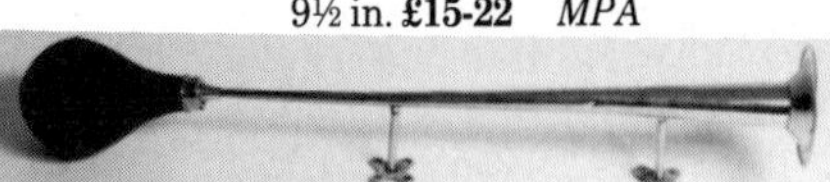
A brass motor horn, 26 in., c. 1920. **£30-40** *BP*

A late Georgian brass door knocker, 7½ in. **£70-90** *BP*

A pair of brass-mounted buffalo horn drinking goblets, 12½ in. high, c. 1830. **£200-275** *BP*

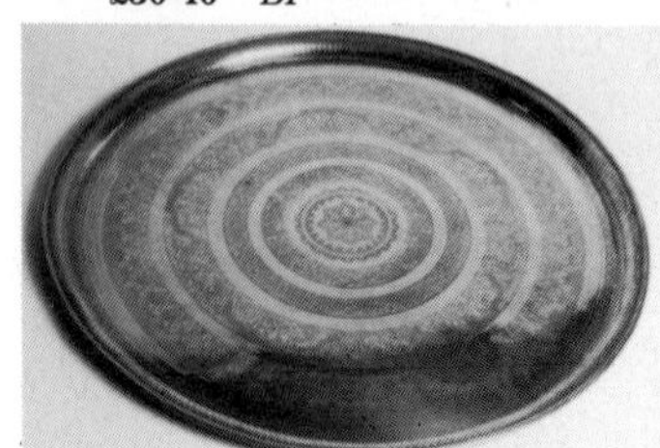
A Middle Eastern brass tray, 22½ in. diam., c. 1900-20. **£40-50** *BP*

A North African brass tray, 19 in. diam., c. 1900. **£20-30** *BP*

An 18th C. brass toffee pan, 5½ in. diam. **£40-50** *FF*

A 16th C. English brass serving dish, 23 in. diam. **£200-300** *BP*

An early 19th C. wooden handled brass kettle, 7 in. high. **£38-45** *MPA*

A Victorian brass tray, 18 in. diam. **£20-30** *BP*

A heavy, moulded glass and brass-mounted inkwell, 6 in. high, c. 1850. **£50-55** *MPA*

A Victorian brass and marble inkstand, 4½ in. square, c. 1850. **£50-60** *IHA*

A cold painted brass inkstand signed 'Müller', 11½ in. wide, c. 1930. **£140-170** *NP*

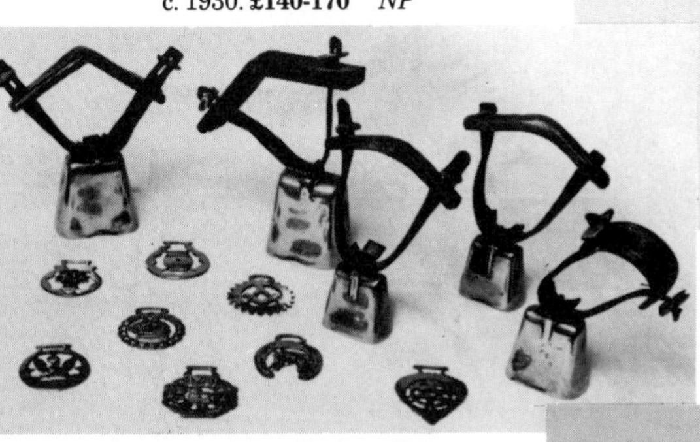

An interesting collection of 15 brass sheep bells, fitted leather collars, in sizes, together with a collection of 40 horse brasses (sample illustrated). **£350-400** *IMC*

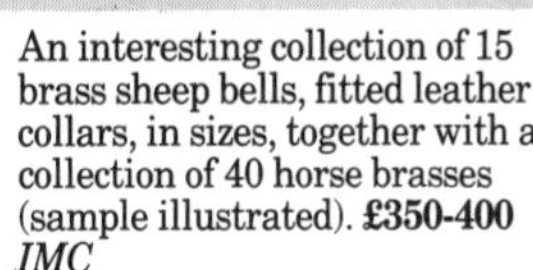

A Thurlow & Sons copper and brass water pump. **£40-50** *JMW*

A bronze group of an Arab mare and stallion by P. J. Mene, cast by Susse, 13 in. high by 21 in. long. **£1,200-1,500** *HyD*

A fine early 17th C. English bronze model of a stallion, by Francesco Fanelli, 15.5 cm. high. **£7,000-£7,500** *C*

A Victorian brass parrot cage, 72 in. high. **£500-600** *McCMB*

A collection of late 19th/early 20th C. horse brasses. **£220-300** *LS*

A North Italian bronze buffalo head, dark patina over reddish bronze, 5 in. (13 cm.), 16th/17th C. **£380-460** *S*

A pair of gilt-bronze furniture mounts, 8¼ in. (21 cm.), late 18th/early 19th C. **£180-220** *S*

A bronze figure of a hunter by Ferdinand Blundstone, rich green-brown patination, signed and dated 1934, 18¾ in. (47.5 cm.), c. 1934. **£900-1,000** *S*

F. Blundstone (1882-1951), born in Switzerland, studied in London at the Academy schools, winning a gold medal and a travelling scholarship. He exhibited abroad and at the Royal Academy.

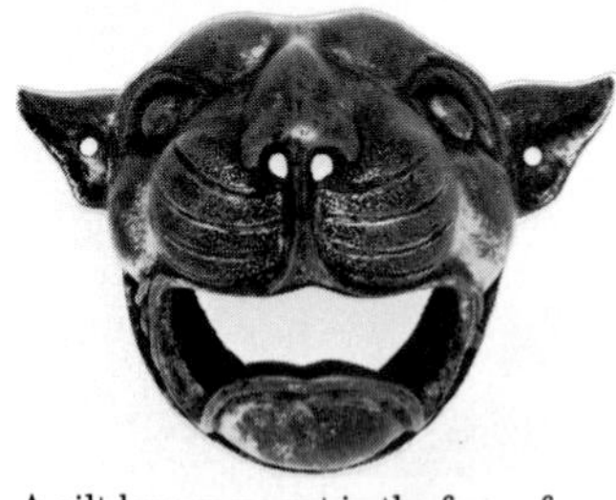

A gilt-bronze mount in the form of the head of a roaring lioness, 3½ in. (9 cm.), 19th C., Asian. **£250-£300** *S*

A bronze figure cast from a model by Rembrandt Bugatti, dark brown patina, signed on the base R. Bugatti, stamped 'cire perdue A.A. Hébrard', numbered on base rim (D4), 53 cm. wide including base. **£3,500-4,000** *C*

A pair of Italian bronze models of deer, after the Antique, marble plinth, 84 cm. high, 19th C. **£2,600-£2,800** *C*

A bronze group of 2 deer, signed P.J. Mene, 3¼ in., c. 1870. **£450-550** *S*

A bronze figure of a lion signed H. Peyrol, 20 in. **£400-450** *JD*

A bronze figure of a cockerel crowing, signed Barye, on a moulded plinth, rich golden-brown patination, 8½ in. (21.5 cm.), c. 1870. **£400-450** *S*

A 16th C. Paduan bronze model of a toad carrying a young toad on its back, one toe missing, 20.5 cm. long. **£1,200-£1,600** *C*

An amusing bronze figure of a monkey, wearing a mitre and a flowing cloak, on a textured square base, dark brown patination, with carved wood ebonised stand, 22 in. (56 cm.), late 19th C. **£280-360** *SC*

A bronze head of a man, signed Elsie Chard, 42 cm., on a green veined marble plinth, late 1930's. **£600-800** *S*

A bronze mask of Androdus by Sir William Reid Dick, on a marble plinth, 21 cm., c. 1920. **£250-300** *S*

An English bronze group of the Devil riding backwards on a bucking billy goat, in the style of Sir Alfred Gilbert, 30 cm. high, 19th C. **£4,000-4,500** *C*

French bronze bust of Flora, fter Eugene-Antoine Aizelin, nscribed AIZELIN, on a shaped quare base inscribed MAISON ARNYHAC 1 RUE DE LA PAIX ARIS, 56 cm. high, 19th C. **£350-450** *C*

A French bronze statuette of a young woman reading, after Albert Ernest Carrier de Belleuse, 40 cm. high, 19th C. **£1,500-1,700** *C*

A bronze face mask by Alphonse Legros, labelled 'A. Legros', 34 cm. high. **£350-400** *P*

A bronze bust of a young woman, signed Van der Straeten, and with the Society de Bronze Paris seal, rich red-brown patination, 13 in. (33 cm.), c. 1900. **£350-400** *S*

bronze figure of a female dancer, uggling with a porcelain ball, igned A. Gory, on red onyx marble linth, rubbed green-brown atination, 26½ in. (67.5 cm.), 920's. **£700-800** *S*

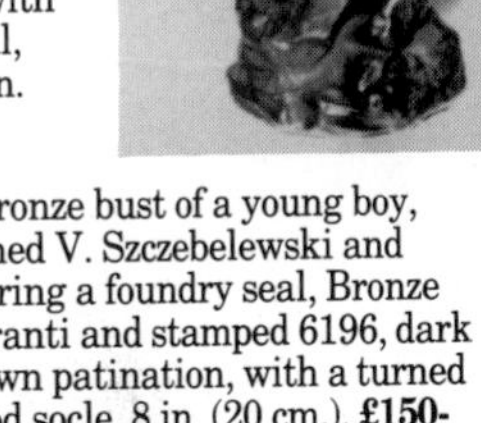

A bronze bust of a young boy, signed V. Szczebelewski and bearing a foundry seal, Bronze Garanti and stamped 6196, dark brown patination, with a turned wood socle, 8 in. (20 cm.). **£150-£200** *SC*

The sculptor is recorded as working between 1875 and 1900. A figure entitled Gamin Sifflant is illustrated in Berman's Bronzes, plate 866 and this bronze is taken from the standing figure.

A French bronze bust of Suzon after Auguste Rodin, inscribed on the reverse A. Rodin and with a serial no. 6639, on a gilt bronze socle, base-plate and marble plinth, 29 cm. high, 19th C. **£2,000-2,500** *C*

A bronze bust of a gentleman on a marble socle, 17 in. high, early 19th C. **£150-200** *EEW*

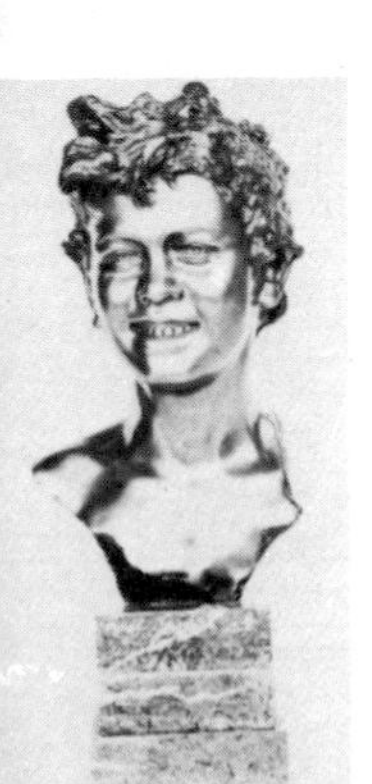

A bronze bust of a young boy, on a marble plinth, light and dark brown patination, Italian, 19 in. (48 cm.) overall, 20th C. **£100-£150** *SC*

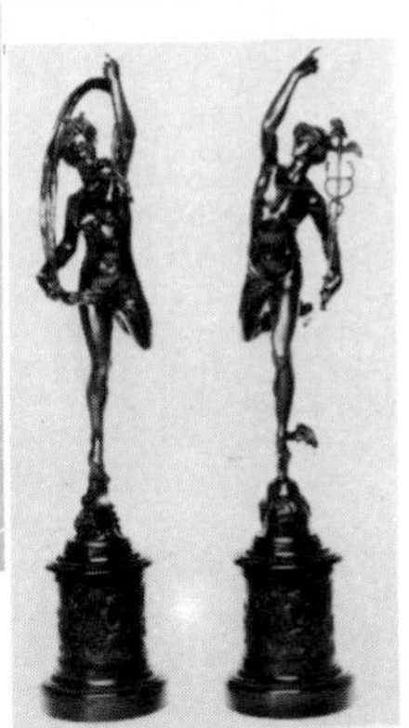

A pair of bronze figures of Mercury and Fortuna, after Bologna, rich green-brown patination, Italian, each 85 cm., c. 1880. **£600-700** *S*

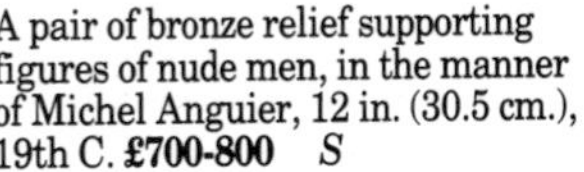

A bronze bust of a girl, signed Inez and with a founder's signature, I. Von Quifzour Fecit, 1913 indistinctly, rich mid-brown patination, 11 in. (28 cm.), c. 1913. **£200-250** *S*

A pair of bronze relief supporting figures of nude men, in the manner of Michel Anguier, 12 in. (30.5 cm.), 19th C. **£700-800** *S*

A bronze figure of the 'Little Dare Devil', signed Christine Gregory and dated 1922, 39 cm. **£200-300** *S*

An English bronze group of a seated workman with a child on his knee, after Charles Leonard Hartwell, 47 cm. high, 20th C. **£400-500** *C*

A large bronze group after T. Hillmany, of a man in a contemplative pose, a harp at his feet and a standing female figure beside him, 37 in. (94 cm.), late 19th C. **£600-700** *SC*

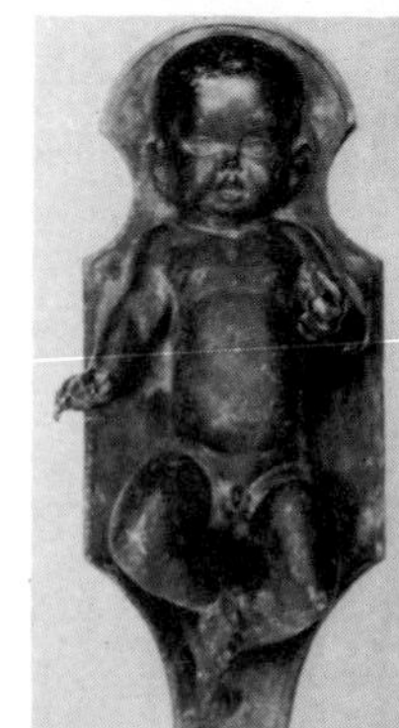
A bronze figure of a baby by Arnrid B. Johnson, weathered patination, 21 in. (53 cm.), early 20th C. **£300-£400** *S*

A late 16th or early 17th C. Italian bronze statuette of Christ in the Garden, in the style of Pompeo Leoni, areas of gilding, 18 cm. high. **£900-1,000** *C*

A bronze group by Erica Lee, signed, indistinctly dated but probably 1924, 65.5 cm. high. **£500-£600** *P*

A bronze figure cast from a model by Paul Philippe, on shaped rectangular bronze and veined marble base, inscribed P. Philippe 14¼ in. high. **£250-300** *CSK*

A Florentine gilt-bronze figure of Christ crucified, from the workshops of Antonio Susini, beard and hair finely modelled, right arm damaged, 11⅜ in. high (29 cm.), early 17th C. **£1,500-1,700** *S*

A bronze group of a shepherd and his dog entitled 'Au Loup', signed Miolin, and with a plaque stamped Salon des Beaux arts acquis par la Ville de Paris, rich yellow-brown and brown patination, 21¾ in. (55 cm.), c. 1890. **£1,800-2,000** *S*

A pair of bronze figures of Baccanalian Dancers after Louis Velentin Elias Robert, one playing cymbals, dark brown patination, 22 in. (56 cm.) overall, mid 19th C. **£350-400** *SC*

A pair of bronze figures after Jean Jules Salmson, one of Van Dyke, each holding a folder, signed Salmson, rubbed dark greenish patination, 22 in. (56 cm.), mid 19th C. **£450-550** *SC*

A bronze figure of John Bright, signed Hamo Thorneycroft 1891, brown patination, 34 cm. **£300-£400** *S*

A bronze group cast from a model by Mary Yates 'All Things Growing', dark brown patina, inscribed Mary Yates 1911, 31 cm. high. **£500-600** *C*

An unusual Rhenish bronze Corpus Christi, from a crucifix, condition generally good, but fingers missing, some original gilding, 11.8 cm., mid 14th C. **£800-900** *Bon*

A 17th C. Florentine bronze group of The Farnese Bull, after the Antique, minor damages, 47 cm. high. **£3,500-4,000** *C*

A late 17th C. Flemish gilt-bronze Figure of Christ, on a later marble base, 25.5 cm. high. **£400-500** *P*

A bronze figure of Henry of Navarre, 12½ in. high, c. 1860. **£350-400** *BP*

A bronze figure of Galileo, on plain bowfronted base, 14½ in. wide by 17¼ in. high (37 by 44 cm.), late 19th C. **£300-400** *Bea*

A bronze group of 3 bacchante playing with a goat, rich brown patination, 11½ in. (29 cm.), c. 1860. **£600-700** *S*

A pair of Louis XV gilt-bronze chenets, 10½ in. high (27 cm.), mid 18th C. **£700-900** *S*

An English or French bronze statuette of a naked young woman, on a circular plinth, marble pedestal, 32 cm. high, late 19th C. **£500-600** *C*

A bronze figure of a young woman wearing a loose fitting garment, shaped base inscribed 'F. Barbedienne Fondeur' and stamped 'Reduction Mecanique A. Collas', 8 in. wide by 8¼ in. high (20 by 21 cm.). **£150-200** *Bea*

An Austrian cold painted figure of a Moorish falconer, 14½ in. (37 cm.), c. 1900. **£600-650** *SS*

A pair of French 19th C. bronze groups inscribed Moreau, 19½ in. high overall. **£500-550** *PWC*

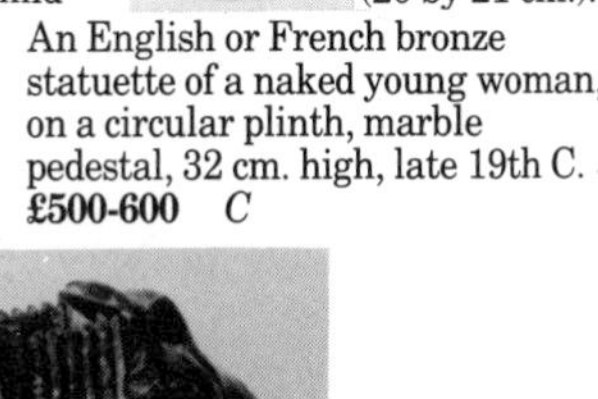

A caricature bronze-patinated metal figure, depicting a goatee-bearded figure in carpet-slippers crouched behind a large plate camera on tripod, possibly after Daumier depicting Nadar the balloonist-photographer, marked 'LSF 77' on base, 16.5 cm. high, 19th C. **£300-350** *P*

A bronze figure, unsigned, with removable fig leaf, 24½ in., c. 1880. **£400-450** *IHA*

A pair of Austrian bronze and polychrome figures of an American Indian and a cowboy astride rearing horses, 7 in. high. **£450-£500** *CSK*

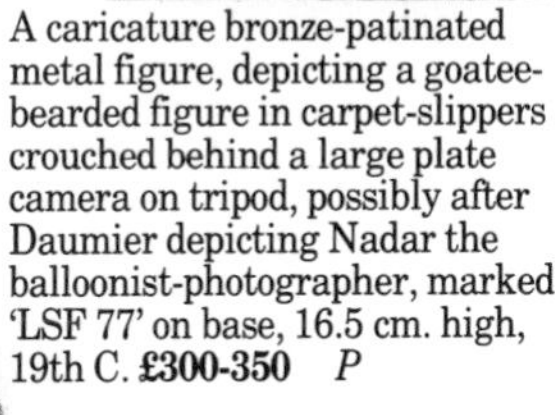

A French bronze bacchanalian group of a revelling youth and lady with 2 child musicians, 16 in. **£300-£350** *GSP*

A pair of late 17th C. bronze and wrought iron andirons, probably Flemish, 26 in. high. **£700-900** *CC*

A pair of Regence bronze and gilt-bronze chenets, 11½ in. high (29 cm.), c. 1720. **£4,000-5,000** *S*

A pair of early Louis XVI gilt-bronze wall lights, each supporting 2 leaf-cast candle branches with fluted nozzles, 19½ in. high (49.5 cm.), c. 1775. **£1,500-2,000** *S*

A pair of Louis XV gilt-bronze w lights, 15½ in. high (39 cm.), mid 18th C. **£2,000-2,200** *S*

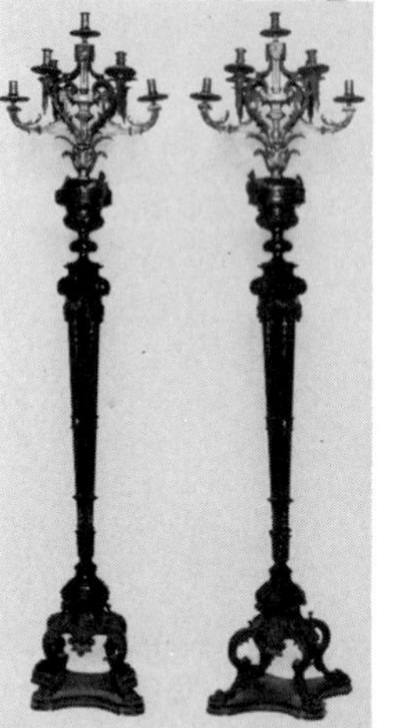
A pair of mid Victorian bronze and ormolu 7-light candelabra, 82 in. high. **£2,500-3,000** *CEd*

A good pair of bronze and gilt brass 5-light candelabra, supported by figures of winged classical females, 28¾ in. (73 cm.), early 19th C. **£1,000-1,300** *Bea*

A pair of Louis XV gilt-bron candlesticks, 10¾ in. high (27.5 cm.), mid 18th C. **£1,40 £1,600** *S*

A pair of English neo-Gothic bronze altar candlesticks, 203 cm. high, 19th C. **£3,000-3,500** *C*

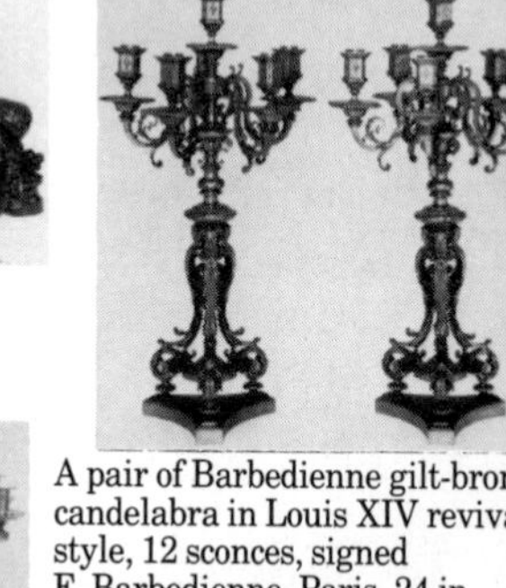
A pair of Barbedienne gilt-bron candelabra in Louis XIV reviva style, 12 sconces, signed F. Barbedienne, Paris, 24 in. (61 cm.), c. 1880. **£600-700** *S*

A pair of Empire gilt-bronze candelabra, 19½ in. high (49.5 cm.), early 19th C. **£600-£700** *S*

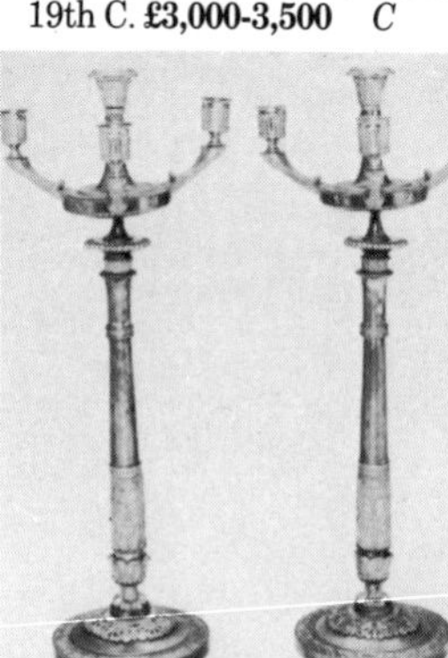
A pair of gilt-bronze table candelabra with detachable arms, 1 ft. 6½ in. high (47 cm.), c. 1820. **£500-600** *S*

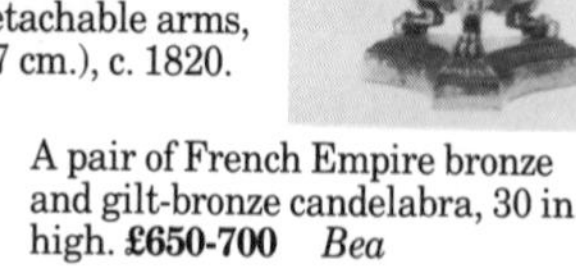
A pair of French Empire bronze and gilt-bronze candelabra, 30 in. high. **£650-700** *Bea*

A Milanese gilt-bronze casket, 8. by 14 by 8.3 cm., 16th C. **£850-£900** *SZ*

A fine 13th C. Limoges ajoure bronze base, later adapted as a pricket candlestick, the pricket of iron, 10 cm. high by 9 cm. diam. **£3,000-3,500** *C*

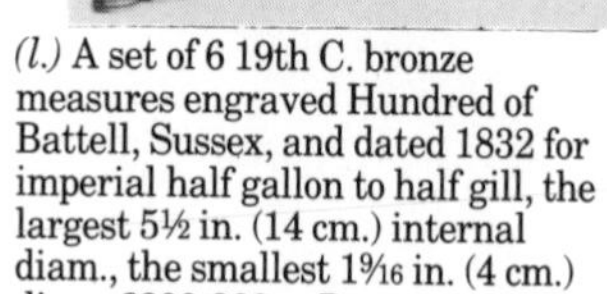
(l.) A set of 6 19th C. bronze measures engraved Hundred of Battell, Sussex, and dated 1832 for imperial half gallon to half gill, the largest 5½ in. (14 cm.) internal diam., the smallest 1⁹⁄₁₆ in. (4 cm.) diam. **£800-900** *P*

(c.) A good 19th C. bronze cylindrical gallon measure engraved Hundred of Battell, Sussex, and dated 1832, and Imperial Gallon, 9⅛ in. internal diam. (23.2 cm.). **£550-650** *P*

(r.) A rare set of 12 19th C. brass trade weights engraved Hundred o Battell, Sussex, and dated 1832, to weigh 28 lb. avoir – 4 drams and each stamped with William IV proof marks. **£1,400-1,600** *P*

A bronze quart measure, c. 1780. **£60-80** *BP*

A Tiffany bronze, nautical inkstand, designed as a sea chest, the hinged cover cast as a shell, stamped Tiffany Studios New York 1842, 5¼ in. wide. **£85-115** *CSK*

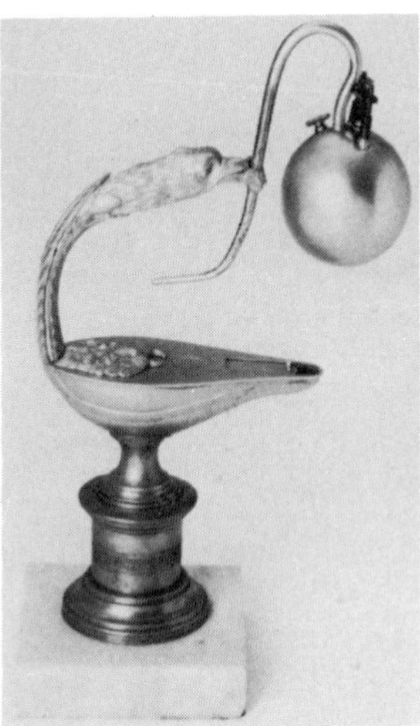
An unusual gilt-bronze cigar lighter in the form of a classical lamp, 13 in. high (33 cm.), 19th C. **£500-600** *S*

A pair of gilt and patinated bronze ewers, 22½ in. (57 cm.), late 19th C. **£300-350** *SC*

A good bronze vase, light brown-green patination, signed H. Francois Moreau, 22 in. (56 cm.), c. 1890. **£300-400** *S*

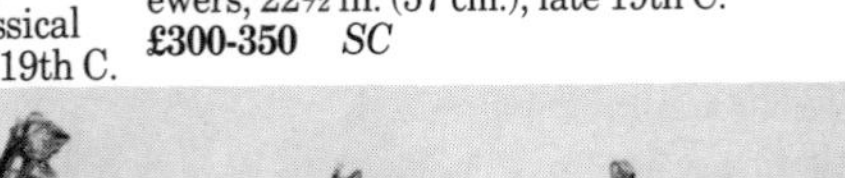

A gilt-bronze fire surround, cast with figures of boys and girls, on a cast-iron base, 16½ by 71½ in. (42 by 182 cm.), late 19th C. **£1,500-£1,600** *S*

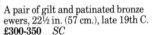

A gilt-bronze plaque of a putto sculpting a head of Venus, in moulded gilt-bronze frame, oval 5 in. (12.5 cm.), 19th C. **£100-120** *S*

A pair of gilt-bronze frames with lapis lazuli backplates, 3½ in. (9 cm.), late 18th C. **£600-650** *S*

A Roman gilt-bronze circular plaque in the manner of the Hamerani, cast in relief with the bust of Pope Innocent XI, 6$\frac{15}{16}$ in. diam. (17.6 cm.), mid 17th C. **£400-£450** *S*

An early cast bronze door knocker, 9 in. wide. **£65-80** *MPA*

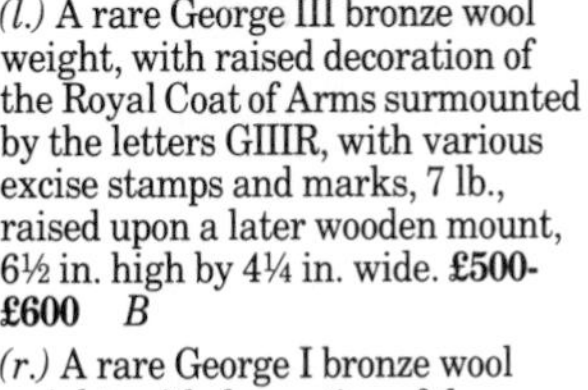
(l.) A rare George III bronze wool weight, with raised decoration of the Royal Coat of Arms surmounted by the letters GIIIR, with various excise stamps and marks, 7 lb., raised upon a later wooden mount, 6½ in. high by 4¼ in. wide. **£500-£600** *B*

(r.) A rare George I bronze wool weight, with decoration of the Royal Coat of Arms and surmounted with G.R. stamped with various excise marks, 7 lb., raised upon a later wooden mount, 6½ in. high by 4 in. wide. **£500-£600** *B*

A bronze mortar, 4 in. high, 16th C. **£100-150** *RVA*

A 12th C. North Italian bronze censer, the lid with 5 ajouré foliate panels, the edges grooved, 12.5 cm. high. **£3,000-3,500** *C*

A closely similar censer in Hungary is attributed to the Rhineland, second half 12th C.

A large bronze mortar, dated 1528, and with initial V.V., 7 in. high (17.8 cm.), c. 1528. **£1,500-2,000** *S*

A copper saucepan with close fitting lid, 20 in. **£40-60** *WHA*

A Carolean bronze mortar, 4¾ in. diam., c. 1670. **£90-110** *MPA*

An 18th C. copper saucepan, 9 in. diam. **£60-70** *SA*

A Victorian seamed copper circular kettle with cover and acorn finial, 11 in. **£50-70**

A Victorian copper warming pan with engraved cover and turned wood handle. **£35-45**

A Victorian copper one gallon harvest measure or jug with 'C' handle and plain bulbous body, stamped Loftus, 146 Oxford Street, London. 10 in. **£60-70** *DDM*

A Victorian seamed copper oval kettle with cover and brass mounts, 11 in. **£50-60**

Two small copper ship's lamps each with ribbed glass panels and stamped starboard, 6¾ in. **£15-20**

A copper coal bucket with studded base, swing handle and detachable liner, 11 in. **£70-90**

A circular brass preserve pan with swing handle, 10½ in. **£20-25**

A Victorian copper kettle with glass handle, 11 in. high. **£70-80** *FD*

A large English copper kettle, 14 in. high, c. 1800. **£125-175** *BP*

A Dutch copper coffee pot, 11 in. high. **£50-60** *MPA*

A copper-lidded cauldron with iron handle, 10½ in. diam., c. 1790. **£120-160** *LG*

An 18th C. copper tea urn with brass spout and tap, 15 in. high. **£175-200** *STR*

A copper and brass samovar, c. 1820. **£120-150** *TA*

A copper and brass samovar, 15½ in., c. 1850. **£100-150** *IHA*

A Regency copper tea urn, minus spout. **£90-110** *JMW*

A copper 2 gallon measure, 13 in. high, c. 1840-60. **£140-160** *BP*

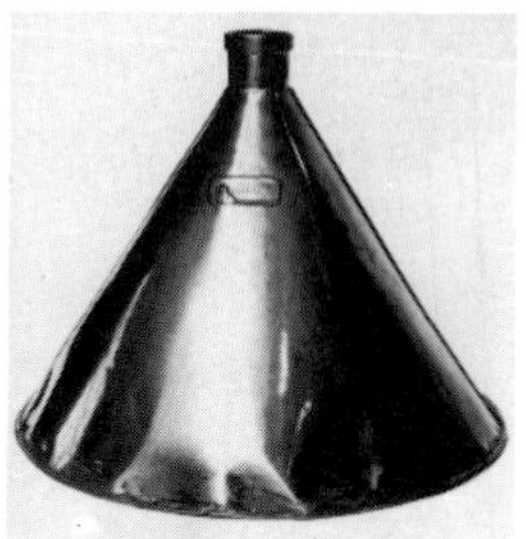

An unusual copper 2 gallon measure, 13 in. high, c. 1870. **£20-£30** *CLA*

A good set of 6 copper and brass checkpump gallon measures graduated from 5 gallons to ½ gallon. **£900-1,000** *P*

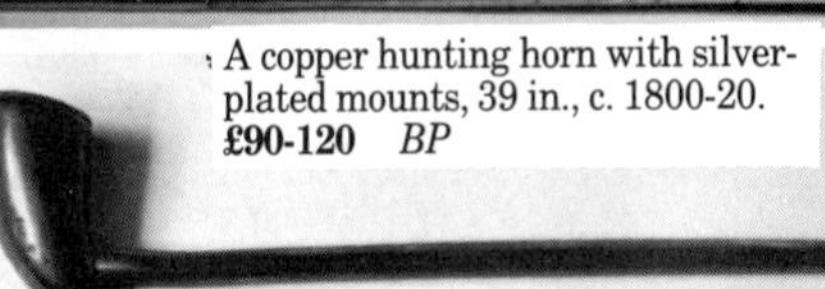

A copper hunting horn with silver-plated mounts, 39 in., c. 1800-20. **£90-120** *BP*

A rare 18th C. English copper pipe, 8 in. **£100-140** *SA*

A copper warming pan, 45 in., c. 1830. **£70-90** *BP*

A Scandinavian copper jardiniere, 9½ in. diam., dated 1727. **£65-75** *MPA*

An 18th C. copper tinder box, made in Lewes, Sussex, 5 in. diam. **£250-£280** *SA*

A copper holy water stoup, 8 in. wide, c. 1800. **£40-50** *MPA*

An unusual pair of copper chandeliers, 56 in. (142 cm.), c. 1900. **£400-600** *S*

A small 19th C. tinned copper chocolate mould, 2¼ in. high. **£7-£10** *MPA*

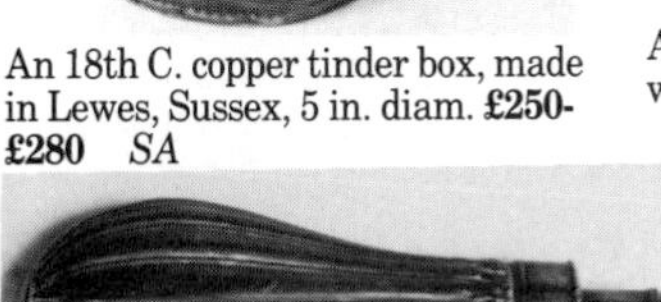

A 19th C. copper powder flask, 8 in. **£25-30** *MPA*

A copper jelly mould, 6¼ in. wide. **£55-65** *MPA*

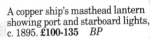

A copper table fountain, perhaps a model for a goldsmith, in German 16th C. style, 7¼ in. (18.5 cm.). **£250-350** *S*

A 19th C. copper wine funnel, 6½ in. **£25-30** *FF*

A copper wine funnel, 11½ in., c. 1860. **£15-25** *BP*

A pair of copper wall sconces, possibly designed by Gordon Russell, the drip-pans fitted with 2 candleholders, 29 cm., 1920's. **£550-£600** *S*

Gordon Russell designed a range of metalwork which was produced at the Broadway workshops during the 1920's, greatly influenced by the earlier designs of Ernest Gimson (made in brass and steel).

A copper ship's masthead lantern showing port and starboard lights, c. 1895. **£100-135** *BP*

A copper helmet scuttle with ebony handles, 19 in. long. **£75-100** *STR*

A 14th C. Gothic gilt copper pinnacle niche, originally housing a statuette, the back faced with a pierced sheet of copper, 48 cm. high. **£900-1,100** *C*

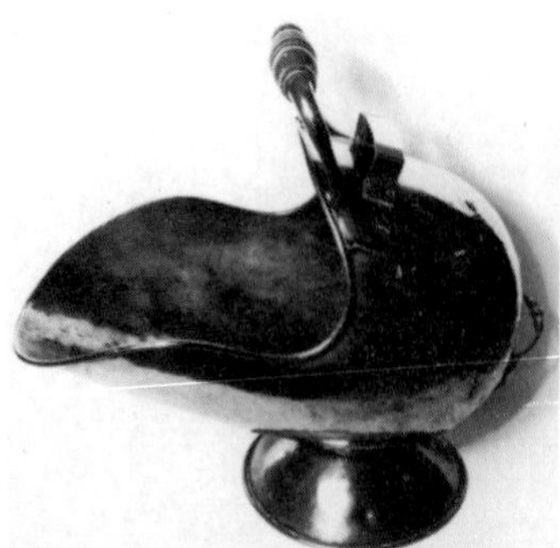
A Georgian copper coal scuttle. **£80-100** *FD*

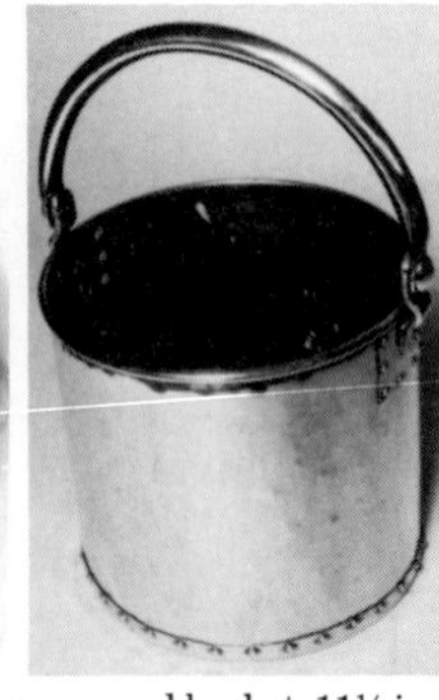
A copper coal bucket, 11½ in. diam., c. 1850. **£80-100** *LG*

A pair of Louis XVI ormolu candlesticks with later nozzles, 11 in. high (28 cm.). **£950-1,150** *C*

A heavy copper and brass coal box, the top surmounted by a flambeau finial, on foliate feet, 18 by 16½ in. (46 by 42 cm.), late 19th/early 20th C. **£180-220** *SC*

A fine rectangular Arts and Crafts copper and wrought iron fire screen, 35 by 24 in. **£70-80** *CGC*

A pair of ormolu candelabra on agate plinths, 17 in. wide (43 cm.), late 18th C. **£1,300-1,500** *C*

A pair of Louis XV ormolu and Chinese porcelain 3-branch candelabra, the porcelain 18th C., possibly German or Austrian, 10½ in. high (27 cm.). **£2,000-£2,300** *C*

A pair of ormolu 5-light candelabra in the Régence style, 22¼ in. high (56.5 cm.), early 19th C. **£1,800-£2,000** *C*

A pair of 19th C. French ormolu 6-light candelabra, 54 cm. high. **£850-950** *P*

A pair of 8-light ormolu candelabra of Louis XVI design, each formed as a Bacchanalian putto, supporting a pair of cornucopiae, 26¾ in. high (68 cm.), 19th C. **£1,000-1,200** *C*

An ormolu chandelier hung with anthemion chains, possibly Russian, 60 in. high (152.5 cm.), 1820-40. **£4,600-5,400** *S*

A pair of Louis XV ormolu twin-branch wall lights, 15 in. high (38 cm.). **£650-750** *C*

A fine pair of Victorian ormolu 7-light candelabra, 33 in. high. **£1,200-1,500** *CEd*

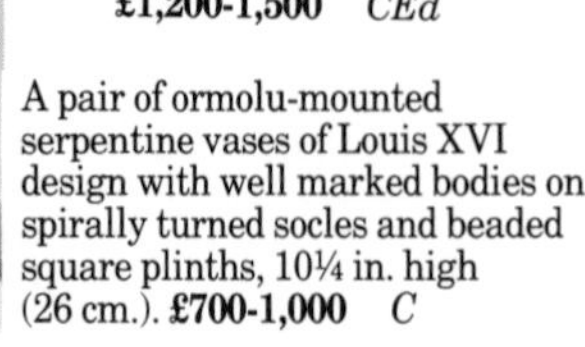
A pair of ormolu-mounted serpentine vases of Louis XVI design with well marked bodies on spirally turned socles and beaded square plinths, 10¼ in. high (26 cm.). **£700-1,000** *C*

A set of 4 Louis XV-style ormolu 2-light wall appliques. **£250-300** *PWC*

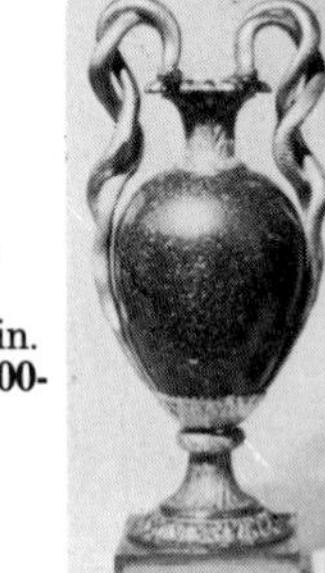
A pair of ormolu-mounted porphyry urns of Louis XVI design, drilled, 20 in. high (51 cm.). **£4,000-£5,000** *C*

A set of 4 ormolu twin-branch wall lights of Régence design, fitted for electricity, 13 in. high (33 cm.). **£5,000-6,000** *C*

A pair of ormolu-mounted blue-glass cassolettes, 9 in. high (23 cm.). **£400-600** *S*

A garniture of 3 ormolu-mounted Chinese peach-bloom vases, 8½ and 8 in. high. **£1,100-1,300** *C*

A French ormolu relief, from a piece of furniture, 15¼ in. (40 cm.), late 18th C. **£180-220** *S*

A pair of Louis XIV ormolu furniture mounts, one damaged, 7¾ in. (20 cm.), c. 1700. **£200-250** *S*

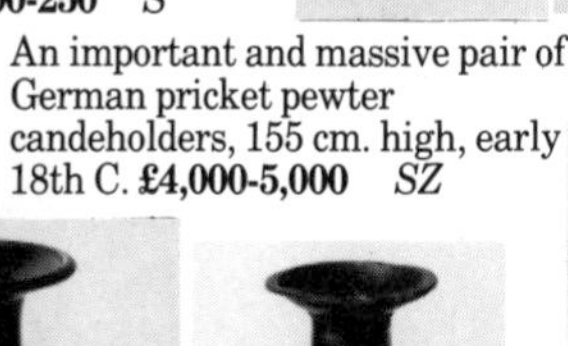

An important and massive pair of German pricket pewter candeholders, 155 cm. high, early 18th C. **£4,000-5,000** *SZ*

A pair of French Louis XV-style ormolu chenets. **£800-900** *PWC*

A pair of Louis XV ormolu chenets, 15 in. wide (38 cm.). **£1,300-1,600** *C*

A pewter candlestick, 8 in., c. 1800. **£35-40** *CLA*

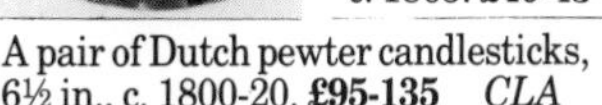

A pair of Dutch pewter candlesticks, 6½ in., c. 1800-20. **£95-135** *CLA*

A 2-handled pewter loving cup, c. 1865. **£40-45** *CLA*

A pewter chamberstick, 6 in. wide, c. 1800-30. **£45-55** *CLA*

A pewter footed wine cup, c. 1830. **£40-45** *CLA*

A pewter pint wine cup with touches of Yates Birch and Spooner of Birmingham, c. 1800. **£40-45** *CLA*

A pair of pewter candlesticks, 8¾ in., c. 1790. **£120-140** *CLA*

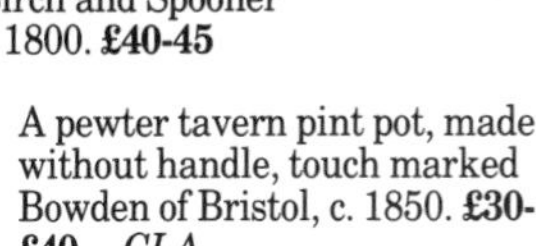

A pewter tavern pint pot, made without handle, touch marked Bowden of Bristol, c. 1850. **£30-£40** *CLA*

A pair of pewter candlesticks, 8¼ in., c. 1800. **£100-150** *CLA*

A possibly unique Jersey 'pot' flagon of unlidded type C form with type C handle and verification seal, 10 in. high, c. 1790-1800. **£180-£235** *CLA*

Woolmer states no type C pots or quarts have ever been found.

A fine series of French pewter wine measures, double litre to decilitre, c. 1850. **£450-550** *CLA*

A pewter quart tavern tankard inscribed under base 'Royal Oak, Knightsbridge', c. 1850. **£50-55** *CLA*

A pewter beer jug with a domed shaped cover, solid thumb-piece and scroll handle, 8 in., c. 1740. **£400-480** *SA*

A German unusually large pewter coffee pot, with oak handle, 12½ in., c. 1790-1800. **£175-225** *CLA*

A pewter ale jug with a rare covered spout, 8 in. high, c. 1810. **£200-240** *CLA*

A small pewter ewer with Bristol City Arms, c. 1780. **£30-40** *BP*

A pewter pepper shaker, 4 in., c. 1830. **£30-35** *CLA*

An Empire-style pewter coffee pot, 10½ in. high, c. 1830-50. **£140-£170** *CLA*

A pewter litre measure, Flemish or French, 9 in., c. 1830. **£110-140** *CLA*

A pewter bellied pint tavern measure, c. 1800-30. **£40-60** *CLA*

A good Baltic tankard, maker's touch of 'HCB', dated 1745, probably Denmark, 21 cm. high, mid 18th C. **£650-750** *SZ*

A pewter quart tavern tankard with touch of Gaskell & Chambers of Birmingham, c. 1860. **£45-55** *CLA*

A pewter 'chopin' sized tappit hen, 8¼ in., c. 1780. **£360-420** *CLA*

A good Scottish pewter tappit hen with plonck and beaker, 11½ in. high, c. 1780. **£400-450** *CLA*

'Plonck' — an internal pimple to mark the level of liquid for the given measure. Large tappit hens have beakers which fit inside the neck when not in use.

A pewter pepper pot, 4 in., c. 1830. **£30-35** *CLA*

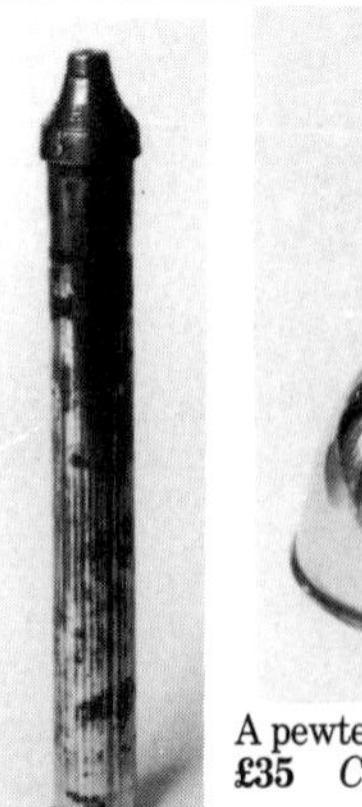
A pewter candlemould, 9½ in., c. 1830. **£20-25** *CLA*

A pewter funnel, 5 in., c. 1800. **£25-£35** *CLA*

A pewter porringer or wine taster, 7 in., c. 1760. **£110-130** *CLA*

A pewter salt dish, 3 in. diam., c. 1780-1800. **£20-30** *CLA*

A pewter wine funnel, 6½ in., c. 1780-1800. **£30-40** *CLA*

A large broad rimmed multiple reed pewter charger 'hallmark' 'E.T.', 20¼ in., c. 1670. **£380-450** *CLA*

A French pewter food bottle (Sustenteur Lucotte) Paris, 8 in., c. 1870. **£40-50** *CLA*

A fine Scottish pewter circular rosewater dish, by Richard Weir, Edinburgh, with copper and enamel boss to the centre bearing the arms of James VI and I, 17½ in. diam. (44.5 cm.), c. 1605. **£9,000-10,000** *C*

A pair of circular dinner plates, engraved with a spray of wrigglework flowers, and with initials, by James Hitchman, London, 9¼ in. diam. (23.5 cm.), c. 1705. **£350-400** *C*

A pewter plate warming dish, with touch of Samuel Cocks of London, 9⅜ in. diam., c. 1800-20. **£45-65** *CLA*

An early 16th C. latten 'monk's head' spoon, 6 in. **£40-50** *CLA*

A pewter tobacco jar, 6½ in., c. 1760-80. **£45-55** *CLA*

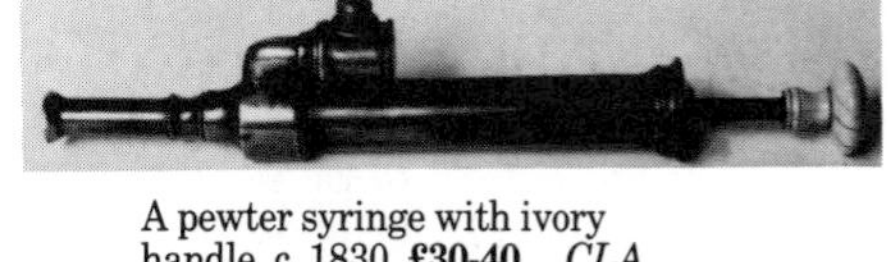
A pewter syringe with ivory handle, c. 1830. **£30-40** *CLA*

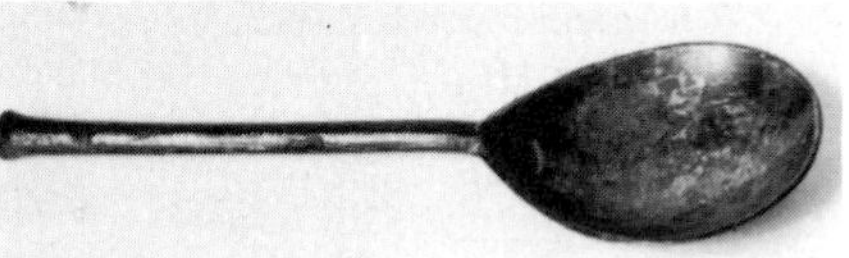
A very rare pewter Low Countries stump-end spoon, 6½ in., c. 1660. **£50-60** *CLA*

A pewter dessert mould, 8¼ in., c. 1850. **£45-55** *CLA*

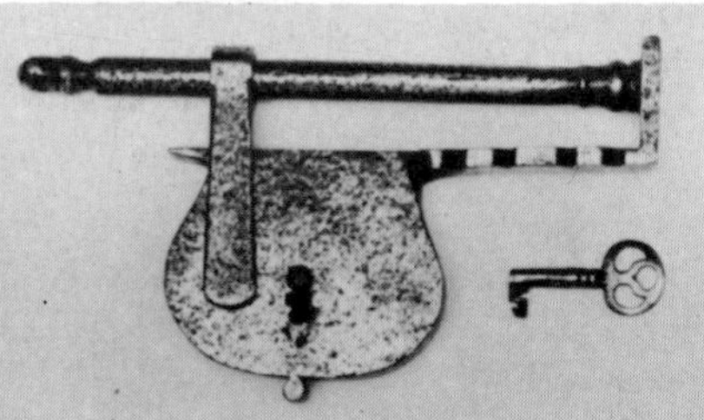
A Spanish padlock and key, 37 cm. wide, 18th C. **£200-250** *SZ*

Three padlocks of drum shape with screw type keys, 10 to 13 cm., 17th/18th C. **£350-400** *SZ*

A George III pewter hexagonal tea caddy, engraved and inlaid with variously shaped brass panels, the front inscribed Immortal Nelson, 5¼ in. wide (13 cm.). **£400-500** *C*

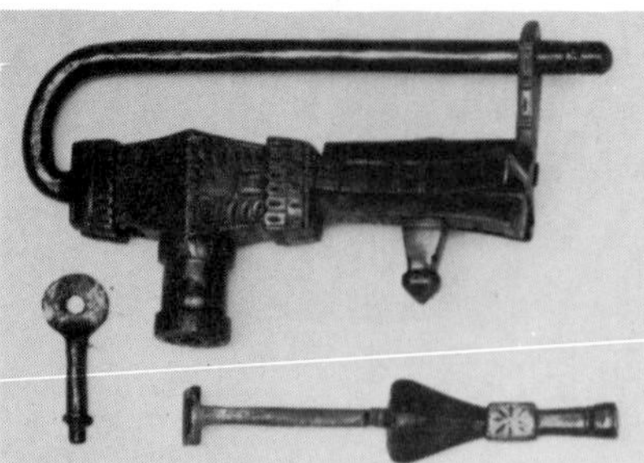
A Hispano-Mauresque padlock with 2 keys, 29 cm. wide, 18th C. **£280-320** *SZ*

A French padlock with key, keyhole cover decorated with clover leaf, 16 cm. high, early 18th C. **£150-180** *SZ*

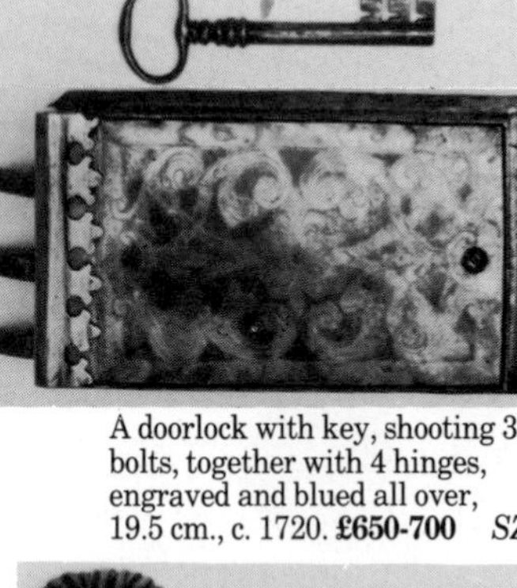
A late Gothic doorlock, shooting one bolt, 29 cm. wide, 16th C. **£1,600-1,800** *SZ*

Three padlocks of cylindrical form, 9.5 to 13 cm. long, 17th & 18th C. **£180-220** *SZ*

A rare German Gothic door lock, 11 in. high, 15th C. **£600-700** *RVA*

A doorlock with key, shooting 3 bolts, together with 4 hinges, engraved and blued all over, 19.5 cm., c. 1720. **£650-700** *SZ*

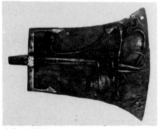

A late Gothic doorlock, shooting 2 bolts, 33 cm. wide, 16th C. **£350-£400** *SZ*

A doorlock shooting 2 bolts and one latch, lockcase of brass repousse with cartouches and signed 'IG', 20 cm. wide, c. 1730-40. **£520-580** *SZ*

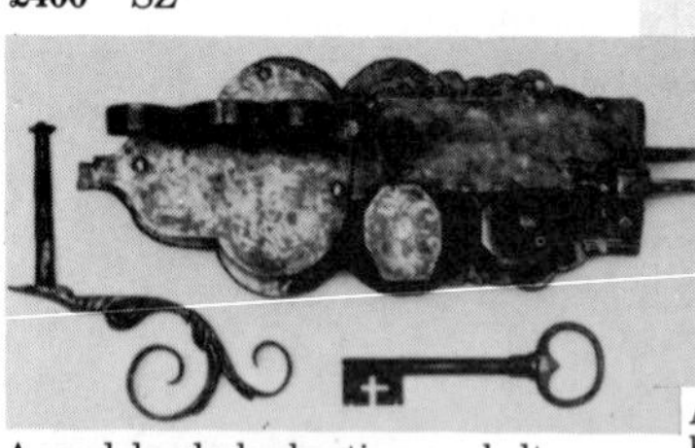
A good doorlock, shooting one bolt and with one latch, with its 2 handles and associated key, 31 cm. wide, 17th C. **£450-500** *SZ*

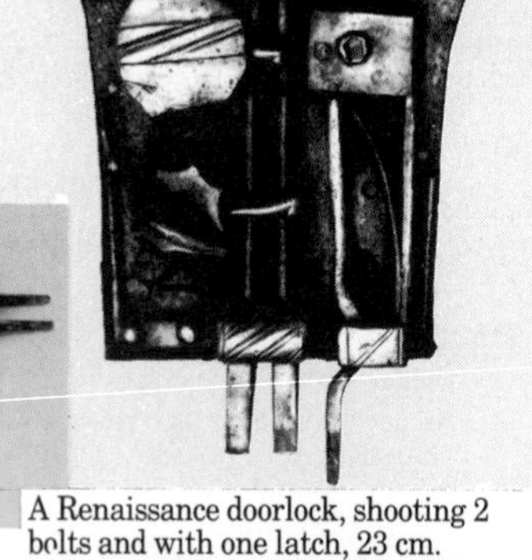
A Renaissance doorlock, shooting 2 bolts and with one latch, 23 cm. wide, late 16th C. **£350-400** *SZ*

A late Gothic chestlock with 2 latches, 20 cm. high, 16th C. **£200-£250** *SZ*

A doorlock, shooting 2 bolts, 32 cm. wide, early 18th C. **£250-300** *SZ*

A late Gothic chestlock with 2 latches, 23 cm. high, 16th C. **£200 £250** *SZ*

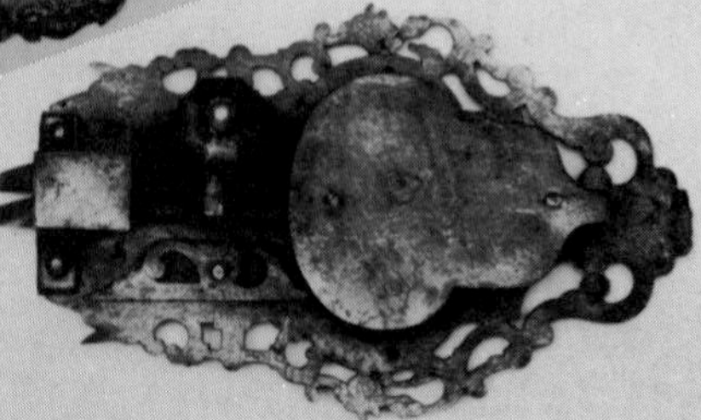
A fine doorlock, shooting 2 bolts, pierced and etched all over with scrolling foliage, 30 cm. wide, 17th C. **£300-350** *SZ*

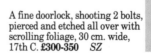

A late Gothic chestlock and key with associated hasp, 25 cm. wide, 16th C. **£200-250** *SZ*

A French chestlock, shooting 2 bolts and with triple toothed latch, 21 cm. high, early 18th C. **£700-£750** *SZ*

A chestlock with 2 latches, 18 cm. high, dated '174?', mid 18th C. **£220-260** *SZ*

A late Gothic Spanish chestlock with pierced plate, 17 cm. wide, 16th C. **£150-200** *SZ*

A 16th C. iron lock, 12½ in. long. **£70-90** *HB*

A 17th C. iron lock and key, 10½ in. high. **£50-65** *MPA*

An early 17th C. iron lockplate and hasp, 16 in. (hasp). **£90-100** *HB*

A wrought iron grille, probably a locksmith's sign, centred by a door key, 7 in. (17.8 cm.), late 17th C. **£220-280** *S*

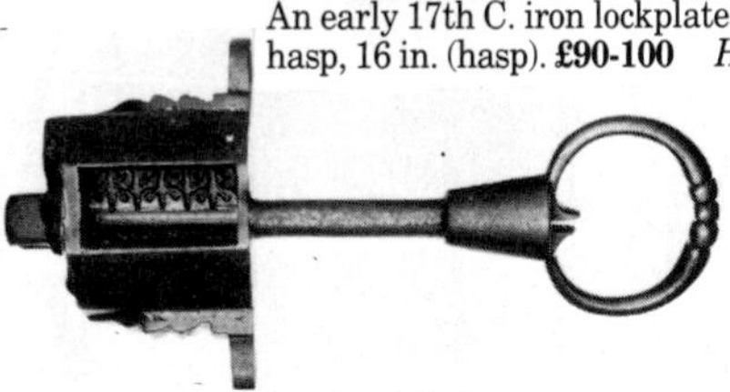

A French key and chamber, 7½ in. (19 cm.), 17th C. **£250-300** *S*

An 18th C. iron lock, 7 in. deep. **£25-30** *HB*

Eight Roman bronze keys, 4.5 to 8.2 cm., 1st to 4th C. A.D. **£600-£650** *SZ*

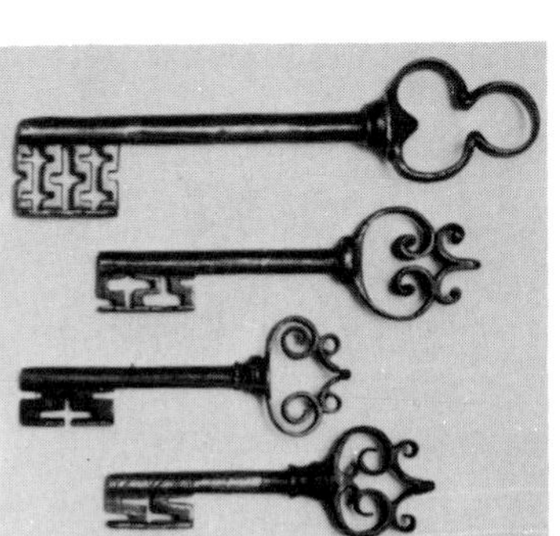

Four keys with hollow shafts and scrolled bows, 14 to 16 cm. long, 17th C. **£300-350** *SZ*

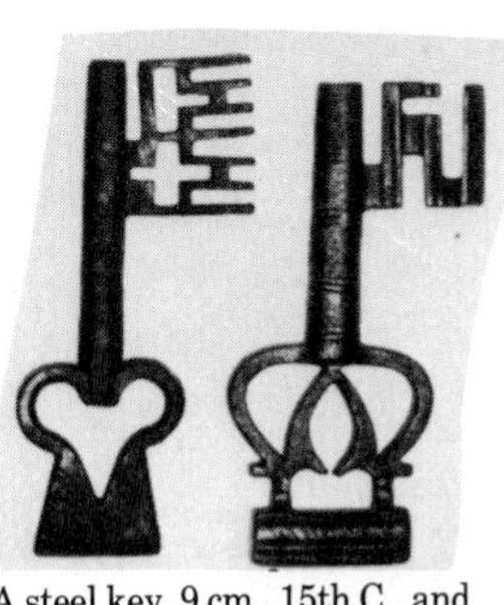

A steel key, 9 cm., 15th C., and another, 6.2 cm., 15th C. **£80-90** *SZ*

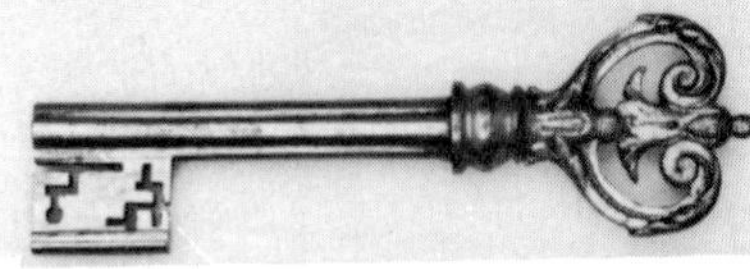

A French steel key and another of bronze, 12 and 10.5 cm., 17th C. **£150-200** *SZ*

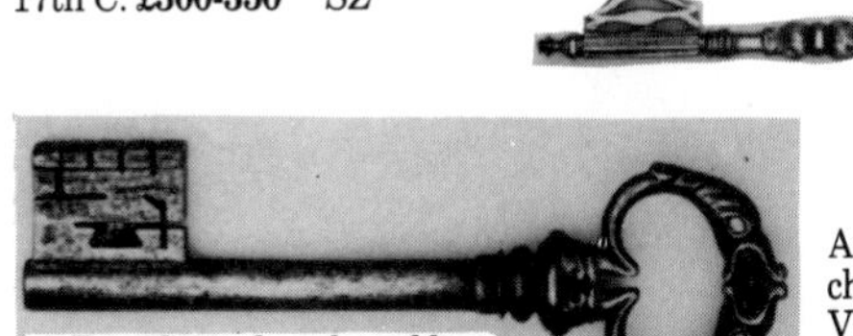

A French steel cupboard key, 13.4 cm., and another similar but smaller, 7.2 cm., both 17th C. **£300-£350** *SZ*

An ecclesiastical gilt-bronze chamberlain's key, probably Vatican, 17 cm., 19th C. **£250-£300** *SZ*

Four Roman bronze keys for lifting, 5 to 8.1 cm., 1st to 4th C. **£650-£700** *SZ*

Two gilt chamberlain's keys, inferior casts, 12 and 15 cm. long, 19th C. **£180-240** *SZ*

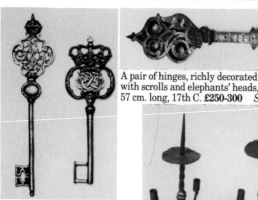

A pair of hinges, richly decorated with scrolls and elephants' heads, 57 cm. long, 17th C. **£250-300** *SZ*

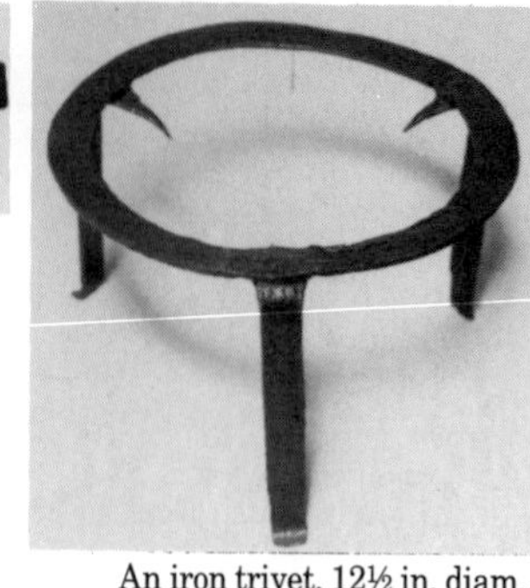

An iron trivet, 12½ in. diam., c. 1660. **£20-25** *LG*

A pair of Spanish wrought iron pricket candlesticks, 16 in. high, 15th C. **£600-800** *RVA*

An 18th C. iron swivel hook, 15 in. **£6-8** *MPA*

An early 19th C. wheelwright's shave, 11 in. wide. **£8-12** *MPA*

A Georgian iron footman, 14 by 12½ in., c. 1770. **£60-70** *AL*

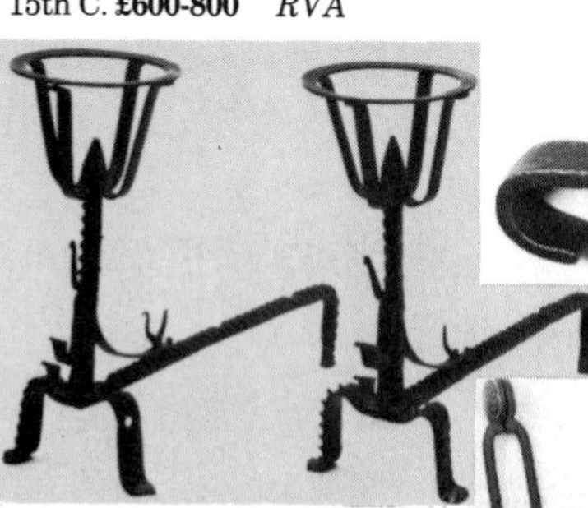

A pair of Italian andirons, 47 by 58 cm., 18th C. **£300-350** *SZ*

An 18th C. adjustable iron pot hook, 14-20 in. long. **£14-16** *MPA*

An 18th C. wrought iron trivet, 11½ in. high, c. 1780. **£30-40** *LG*

A wrought steel footman, 12 in. wide, c. 1790. **£50-60** *LG*

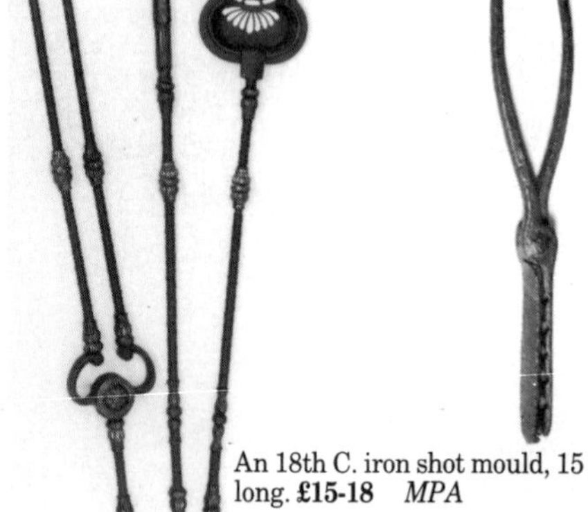

An 18th C. iron shot mould, 15 in. long. **£15-18** *MPA*

A set of 3 early 19th C. parcel gilt-steel fire-irons, 34 in. long. **£500-£600** *McCMB*

A Georgian polished steel footman, 10 in. wide, c. 1800. **£65-80** *MPA*

A steel footman, 12 in. high, c. 1850. **£55-60** *LG*

A good George III-style polished steel fire basket, 31 by 40 in. (79 by 102 cm.), late 19th/early 20th C., and a polished steel ember kerb, 54 in. wide (137 cm.), late 18th C. **£700-900** *SC*

An 18th C. steel branding iron, 11¾ in. **£15-18** *LG*

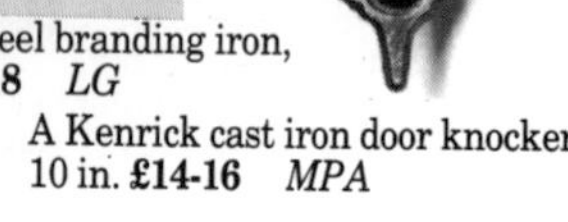

A Kenrick cast iron door knocker, 10 in. **£14-16** *MPA*

An early 19th C. cast iron boot scrape, 8½ in. high. **£25-28** *MPA*

A Victorian iron Kenrick cork press, 9 in. long, c. 1870. **£35-38** *MPA*

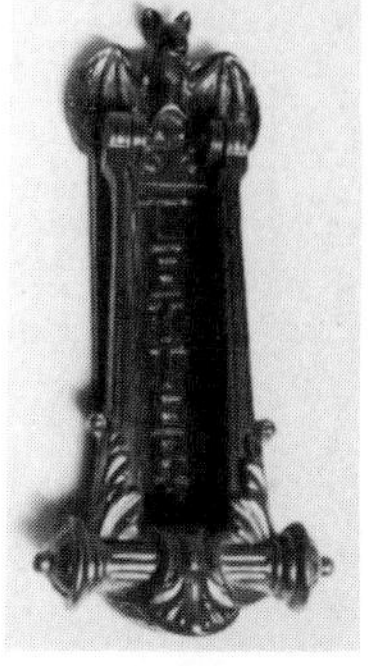

A Kenrick cast iron combination letter plate and door knocker, 9½ in., Edwardian. **£14-16** *MPA*

A Kenrick iron knocker, 7¼ in., c. 1900. **£14-16** *MPA*

An iron sheep's bell with pine yoke, c. 1830. **£30-35** *AL*

A pair of 19th C. French polished steel coasters on wheels, 8¼ in. diam. **£190-£225** *MPA*

An early 19th C. cast iron tobacco jar with Napoleon finial, 9 in. high. **£35-45** *MPA*

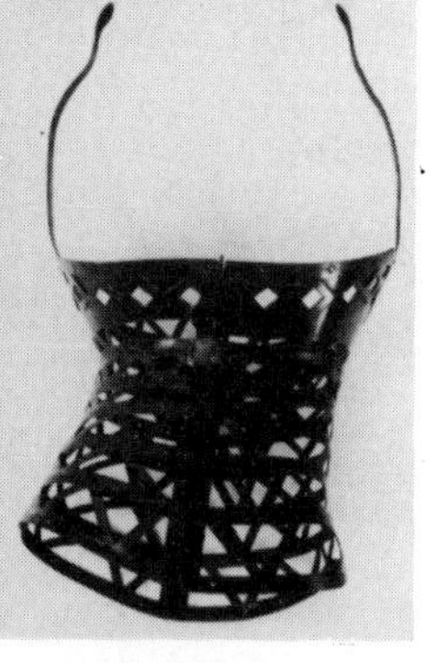

A 16th C. steel corset, the frame constructed of riveted interlaced bands, the 2 sections hinged with pins and having a waist measurement of 26 in. (66 cm.). **£250-300** *P*

A 'Thousand-Eyes' lantern, 34 cm. high, c. 1800. **£450-500** *SZ*

A painted cast iron umbrella stand, reg. mark, 27 in., c. 1880. **£75-85** *TA*

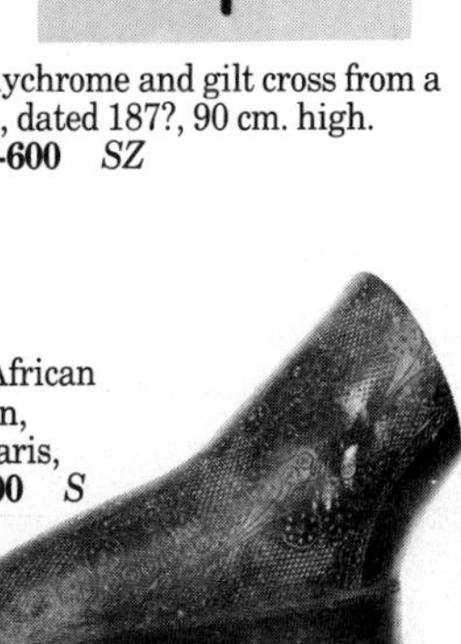

A polychrome and gilt cross from a tomb, dated 187?, 90 cm. high. **£550-600** *SZ*

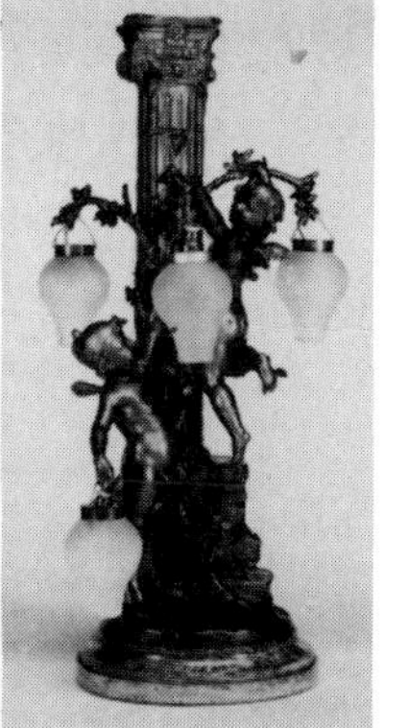

A spelter group of 2 cherubs, with hanging lanterns, on a marble base, signed indistinctly, fitted for electricity, with 4 glass shades, 23 in. (58 cm.), c. 1890. **£400-500** *S*

A French spelter figural table lamp, 28 in., c. 1880. **£200-225** *TA*

A spelter figure of a North African Arab girl, bronzed patination, indistinctly signed Jottot, Paris, 78.7 cm., 1890's. **£1,200-1,400** *S*

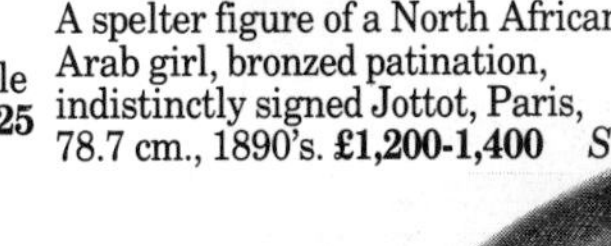

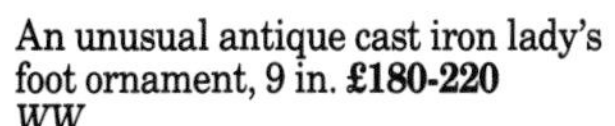

An unusual antique cast iron lady's foot ornament, 9 in. **£180-220** *WW*

A pair of spelter figures, 17½ in. high, c. 1880. **£110-130** *CDE*

A drum-shaped strongbox with key and suspension chain, 22 cm. high, 18th C. **£350-400** *SZ*

A good pair of lead garden figures of Summer and Autumn, represented by Ceres and Bacchus, perhaps English, 45 in. high (114 cm.), early 18th C. **£9,000-£10,000** *S*

Four Tudor period lead panels, 12 in. square. **£60-70** each *HB*

A lead tobacco jar with negro's head finial, 6 in. high, c. 1820. **£35-£40** *MPA*

A pair of mid Victorian lead doorstops, 'Mr. & Mrs. Slocum and family', 12 in. high. **£40-60** *STR*

A 19th C. carbon filament light bulb. **£100-150** *HAD*

A 19th C. Middle Eastern folding portable ink and pen stand. **£100-£200** *HAD*

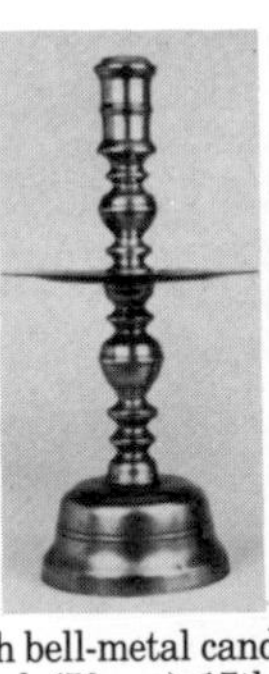
Two Dutch bell-metal candlesticks, 19½ in. high (50 cm.), 17th C. **£500-£700** *C*

A rare lead fire mark, 'Bristol Universal Fire Office', c. 1775. **£1,700-2,000** *P*

A fine specimen of an extremely rare mark, one of only several known.

An 18th C. bell-metal mortar, 4 in. diam. **£30-35** *MPA*

A pair of sheep shears, 9½ in. long, c. 1800. **£12-15** *LG*

Ten bell-metal London County Council standard imperial cylindrical measures, 2 signed Bate London, all with Middlesex deleted by-line and stamped with proving marks, in wooden case, Bate measures c. 1830, others dated 1879. **£250-300** *S*

A bell-metal footman, 12 in. wide, 19th C. **£20-40** *STR*

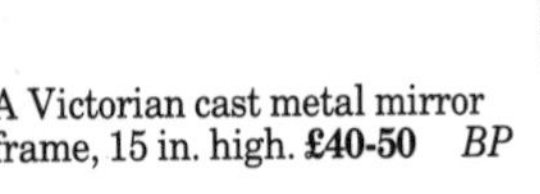
A Victorian cast metal mirror frame, 15 in. high. **£40-50** *BP*

An Artie note changer, the mahogany cabinet with 15 change drawers, the front secured by brass hinge and original padlock, American, 15 in. high (38 cm.), c. 1900. **£180-240** *S*

An Allwin de luxe, 7 win/lose chutes within concentric circles, German, 25 in. high (63.5 cm.), c. 1928. **£90-120** *S*

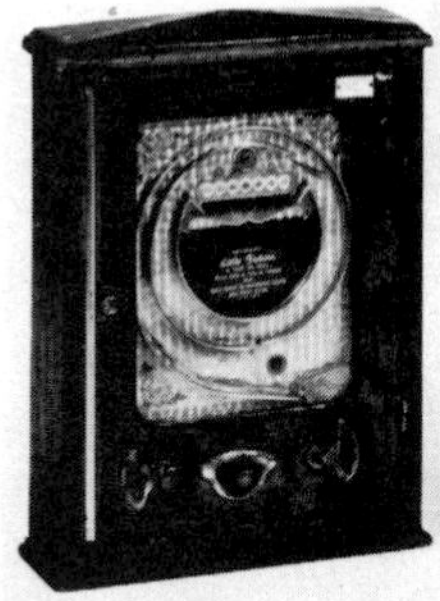

An Allwin Little Fivewin, 7 win/lose chutes within concentric circles, English, 26 in. high (66 cm.), c. 1930. **£90-120** *S*

The Mystic Hand Amusement Machine, English, 80 in. high (203 cm.), c. 1908. **£280-340** *S*

A 'pussy' shooter, the coin operated machine brightly painted with chromed revolver to the front, cast iron cat targets, by British American Novelty Co. Ltd., lacking a glass panel, not operative, 76 in. high (193 cm.), c. 1935. **£380-460** *S*

A Roulette Bussoz amusement machine, with coin slots and pay-out below, French, 26 in. high (66 cm.), c. 1915. **£160-240** *S*

A 'gipsy' fortune teller, card chute at the base, 76 by 39 in. (193 by 99 cm.), late 1930's. **£250-300** *SC*

A gipsy fortune telling machine in oak case, 2 ft. 6 in. wide by 6 ft. high. **£400-500** *CDC*

A Jennings Bandit, the cast-alloy Art Deco-style cabinet with raised score card, 3 fruit and bells tumblers, American, 23 in. high (58.5 cm.) c. 1931. **£450-500** *S*

A rare prohibition gambling machine, in the guise of a 'Ball Gum Atom Vendor', metal body electric blue with coin slot, windows displaying cigarette prizes, American, 6 in. high (15 cm.), c. 1930. **£180-240** *S*

A Brooklands totalisator bandit, cast alloy and oak casing coin slot and 3 numbered tumblers, English, 24 in. high (61 cm.), c. 1939. **£150-200** *S*

A 'Spiritualist' room automaton, containing room, with movements including revolving dog, descending lamp shade, curtain opening to reveal skeleton, flying furniture, in painted wooden case, 70 in. high (178 cm.), c. 1935. **£200-£300** *S*

A 'haunted churchyard' automaton, depicting a drunkard on a grave, a devil rises, a corpse rises from its grave, and ghosts appear, the whole contained in oak case, 70 in. high (178 cm.), late 1930's. **£200-£300** *S*

A 'twenty-one' gambling machine, cast alloy and oak casing with numbered tumblers operated by handle, house and draw options, score card below, American, 13½ in. wide (34 cm.), c. 1930. **£100-150** *S*

A novelty merchantman crane amusement machine, by Exhibit Supply Co., containing model of ship's hull with grab crane within to select prize, American, 6 ft. high (183 cm.) c. 1935. **£250-300** *S*

The 'guillotine' automaton, with castle facade, central doors, which open to reveal a decapitation scene, oak casing, converted for decimalisation, 70 in. high (178 cm.), c. 1930's. **£500-550** *S*

A mutoscope by the International Mutoscope Reel Co., containing reel of photographs entitled 'No Account Count' and starring Charlie Chaplin, American, repainted mauve and blue, 74 in. high (188 cm.), c. 1905. **£500-£550** *S*

A Brookland's racer, painted blue and gold with cast details picked out in red, the wheel in 3 sections, lithographed with racing cars, 3 'brake' buttons below, lever to the front, English, working order, 15½ by 14 in. (39 by 35 cm.), c. 1930. **£200-250** *SC*

An Ahren's 'test your strength' machine, with leather punch ball, lacking wooden panel at back, English, 6 ft. 7 in. high (201 cm.), c. 1920. **£300-400** *SC*

An auto-stereoscope, the table model with stylised Art Deco oak casing, contemporary cards depicting Tarzan and Jane, and a girl with an egg basket, operational, 39 in. high (99 cm.), c. 1930. **£250-£300** *S*

The French execution automaton, opening to reveal the guillotine decapitation of a kneeling gentleman, and bearing plaque to one side for S. Withers, Birmingham, c. 1935. **£350-450** *S*

A seascape musical automaton with small model of a paddle steamer negotiating rough seas, under glass dome with painted background, on ebonised stand containing small musical movement, French, 16 in. high (41 cm.), late 19th C. **£180-220** *S*

A musical automaton of a rocking paddle steamer, with a train crossing a bridge in the background, on ebonised base with painted glass dome, 21 high. **£400-500** *CSK*

A rabbit-in-lettuce musical automaton, the fur-covered rabbit emerges and waves his ears to the sound of a small cylindrical musical movement, French, 8 in. high (20 cm.), c. 1910. **£400-450** *S*

An automaton bear violinist in a plush-covered egg, the egg opening to allow the bear to rise and play his violin. **£500-£600** *CSK*

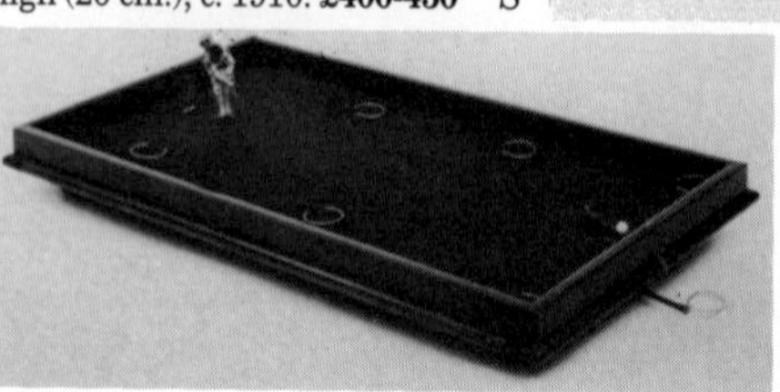
A Jacques automaton cricket board, the baize playing surface with painted lead batsman figure of W. G. Grace, in original cardboard box, English, 34 in. long (87 cm.), c. 1900. **£250-300** *S*

A 19th C. singing bird automaton, with original penny-in-the-slot, 22 in., c. 1860. **£1,100-1,200** *SA*

A pussy cat tea party automaton, with manivelle mechanism operated by handle to the front, the 2 seated kittens sip tea beneath the rose arbour while the mother cat moves from side to side, probably German, 11 in. long (28 cm.), c. 1900. **£400-450** *SC*

A musical automaton figure, 19½ in. high. **£600-800** *CSK*

A coin-operated monkey pianist automaton, the musical and clockwork mechanism concealed within the stained oak base, coin slot to the top of piano, probably French, 16 in. high (40.5 cm.), late 19th C. **£450-550** *S*

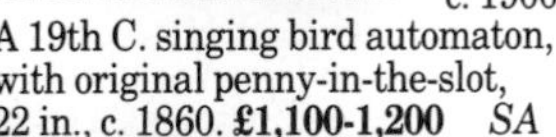

A hand operated viola player, the bisque head impressed 103 1, with open/closed mouth, fixed blue glass eyes, mohair wig, wooden arms, playing a tune when the stomach is pressed, in original clothes, French, 14½ in. (37 cm.), c. 1890. **£600-£700** *S*

A bisque headed pull-along toy with fixed blue eyes and long blond hair pigtail, wearing original suit with wooden hands and composition legs and moving his head and hands as the wheels turn, 12 in. high. **£280-340** *CSK*

A musical tambourine player automaton probably by Descamps, the Jumeau head impressed F, with closed mouth, fixed brown glass eyes, blonde mohair wig, holding a tambourine, in the original dress, standing on a box containing a musical mechanism, French, overall height 18 in. (46 cm.), c. 1880. **£2,800-3,400** *S*

A French musical automaton of girl with powder puff and mirror, 19th C. **£600-800** *HAD*

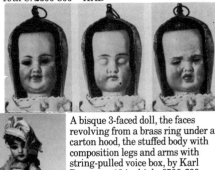

A bisque 3-faced doll, the faces revolving from a brass ring under a carton hood, the stuffed body with composition legs and arms with string-pulled voice box, by Karl Bergman, 12 in. high. **£500-600** *CSK*

A doll by Alt Beck & Gottschalck, bisque head with sleeping eyes and open mouth with teeth, impressed monogram mark to back of head, '1362 Made in Germany', 25 in. long, c. 1890's. **£150-180** *WHL*

A Cuno and Otto Dressel poppy doll, with shoulder head on cloth body and composition lower arms, c. 1912. **£250-345** *HAD*

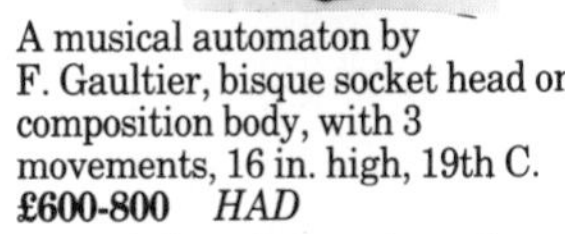

A musical automaton by F. Gaultier, bisque socket head on composition body, with 3 movements, 16 in. high, 19th C. **£600-800** *HAD*

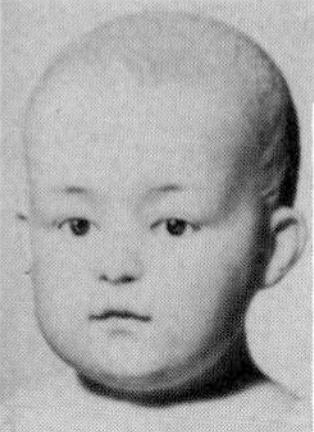

An unusual bisque shoulder head boy doll, possibly Gebruder Heubach, the shoulder plate impressed 4 Germany, with blue intaglio eyes, blonde flocked hair (worn), with white kid body, china lower arms, 15 in. high (38 cm.). **£200-250** *SC*

A Cuno & Otto Dressel poppy doll, with shoulder head on cloth body and composition lower arms, c. 1912. **£250-300** *HAD*

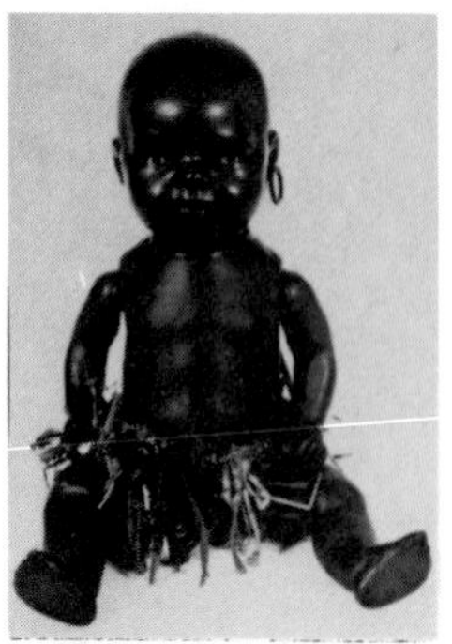

A Heubach bisque negro character doll, the head impressed 3996/0, with sleeping brown eyes and jointed curved limb composition body, lacking an ear-ring, 13 in. high (33 cm.). **£150-250** *S*

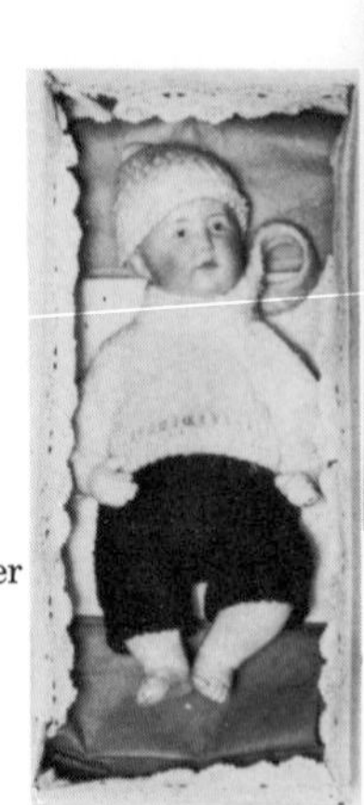

A good Heubach bisque character boy doll, with square trademark, impressed 77 59, with painted intaglio eyes and features, curved limb composition body, in original outfit and box, 9½ in. long (24 cm.). **£200-300** *S*

A Heubach Koppelsdorf black bisque doll impressed 399.4D.R.G.M., weighted black glass eyes, pierced ears, and curved limb composition body, unclothed, 19½ in. (49.5 cm.), c. 1910. **£200-£250** *S*

A Gebruder Heubach bisque character doll impressed 1407 3, with fixed pale blue glass eyes, a[s] blonde mohair wig and protrudin[g] ears, ball-jointed wood and composition body, German, 13 in. (33 cm.), c. 1910. **£400-500** *S*

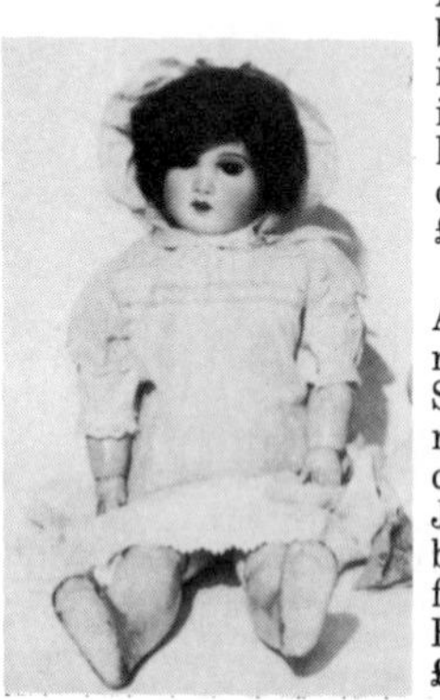

A Heubach doll with bisque head and moulded body, with sleeping eyes, moving tongue, impressed mark 'Heubach-Koppelsdorf 342-10, Germany', 25½ in. long, c. 1920 or earlier. **£150-200** *WHL*

A Jumeau bisque doll stamped in red Déposé Tête Jumeau Bte S.G.D.G. 11, with red check marks, real hair over cork pate, the jointed composition body with blue Jumeau Medaille d'Or stamp, with bisque hands, in original clothes, fourth finger right hand restored, French, 23½ in. (60 cm.), c. 1885. **£1,900-2,200** *S*

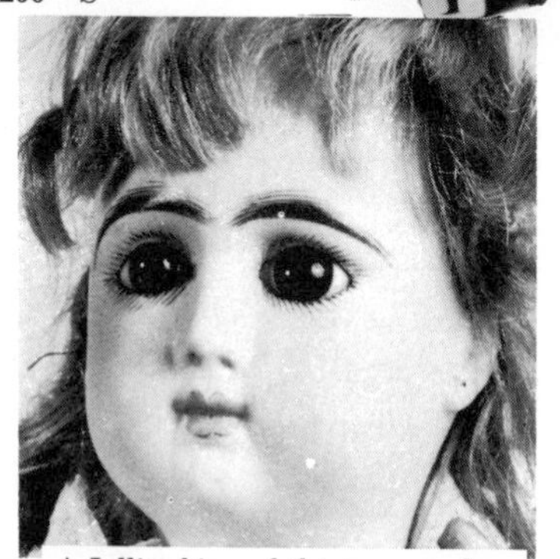

A Jullien bisque bébé, impressed Jullien 3 with fixed brown glass eyes, pierced ears, ash-blonde mohair wig and jointed wood and composition body, French, 12½ in. (32 cm.), c. 1885. **£1,000-1,200** *S*

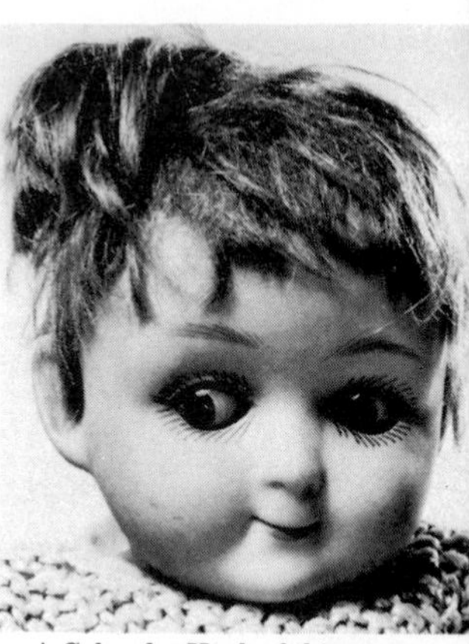

A Gebruder Heubach bisque 'googley'-eyed doll impressed 3/0, with weighted brown eyes, brown mohair wig, 5-piece composition body, ice-green knit outfit and hat, German, 8 in. (20 cm.), c. 1910. **£500-550** *S*

A Mascotte bébé impressed M 9, with closed mouth, fixed blue glass eyes, pierced ears, auburn real hair wig and jointed wood and composition body, blue-stamped Jumeau Medaille d'Or, in original dress, French, 20 in. (51 cm.), c. 1900. **£1,500-1,800** *S*

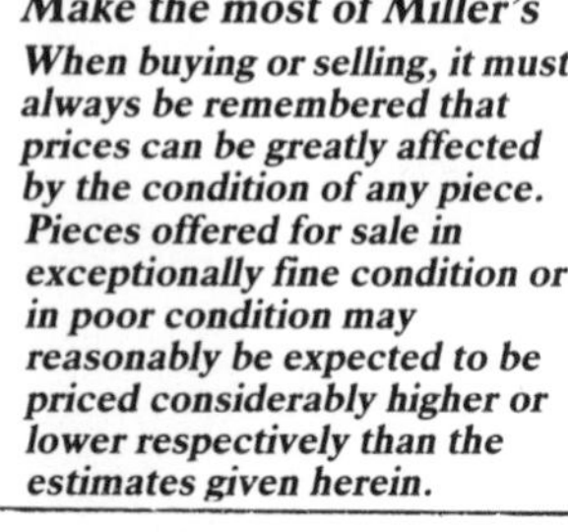

Make the most of Miller's

When buying or selling, it must always be remembered that prices can be greatly affected by the condition of any piece. Pieces offered for sale in exceptionally fine condition or in poor condition may reasonably be expected to be priced considerably higher or lower respectively than the estimates given herein.

A Jumeau bisque doll impressed 8, real hair wig and jointed wood and composition body with blue Bébé Jumeau Bte S.G.D.G. Déposé stamp on buttocks, in cream net dress, fine hairline on right temple, little finger right hand repaired, hand paint scuffed, French, 20 in. (51 cm.), c. 1895. **£450-550** *S*

A Jumeau bisque bébé, marked in red 'Tête Jumeau', with jointed wood and composition body, original blonde wig, re-dressed, hairline crack above one ear, French, 26 in. high (66 cm.), late 19th C. **£1,000-1,200** *SC*

A bisque-headed bébé with fixed blue eyes, pierced ears, blonde wig and fixed wrist, jointed composition body wearing original dress, and original underclothes and matching hat, marked A? and with printed label and stamped Jumeau, Medaille d'Or Paris, 16½ in. high. **£1,900-2,300** *CSK*

A French bisque head doll by Jumeau with original blonde mohair wig, fixed blue paperweight eyes, the jointed composition body stamped Jumeau Medaille d'Or Paris, redressed, marked Déposé Tête Jumeau Bte S.G.D.G. 12, one lower leg replaced, 62 cm. **£1,000-£1,200** *P*

A fine bisque swivel neck Parisienne, probably by Jumeau, with pale blue eyes, long blonde wig, white kid leather body, dressed, impressed J, 10½ in. high (26.5 cm.). **£700-800** *S*

A bisque-headed doll with fixed eyes, pierced ears and blonde wig, the jointed composition body wearing original clothes, with shoes and socks, marked 22 5X DEP and with paper label on the body, stamped on the body Jumeau Medaille d'Or Paris, 17 in. high. **£500-650** *CSK*

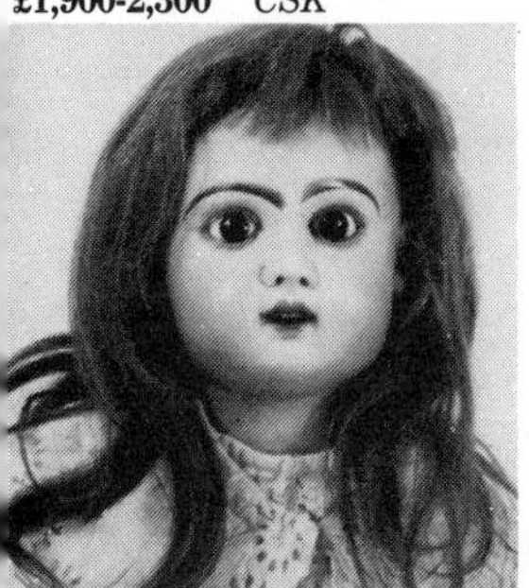

A Jumeau bébé, the bisque head impressed 12, with paper Diplome d'Honneur label to the torso, sleeping brown eyes, open mouth, composition body with jointed wrists, dressed, head severely cracked, 27½ in. high (70 cm.). **£450-500** *S*

A bisque-headed musical automaton by Jumeau, standing on tip-toe, closed mouth, stamped on head 'TÊTE JUMEAU BTE SGDG', 19th C. **£2,500-3,500** *HAD*

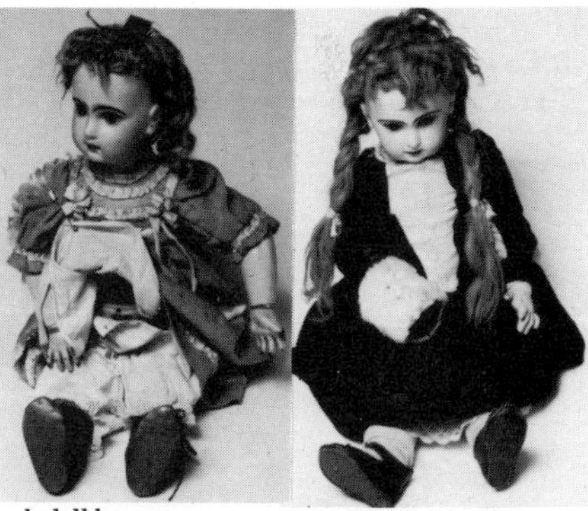

A French phonograph doll by Jumeau with bisque head, fair hair wig, 6 teeth, cylinder fitted inside body, 25 in. high, c. 1895. **£2,500-£3,500** *HAD*

A bisque-headed doll by Jumeau on jointed composition body, with blue paperweight eyes, closed mouth and pierced ears, dressed in original clothes, all underclothing monogrammed, marked on head DÉPOSÉ, TÊTE JUMEAU Bte S.G.D.G. 14 16X and on body BÉBÉ JUMEAU, Diplome d'Honneur, 32 in. high. **£4,500-£5,500** *HAD*

A Jumeau phonograph doll stamped Tête Jumeau in red, fixed brown glass eyes, blonde mohair wig and wood and composition jointed body, containing a Lioret System No. 4774, with 7 discs, the seventh title missing, the movement missing one reproducer support, French, 26 in. (66 cm.), c. 1895. **£1,800-2,200** *S*

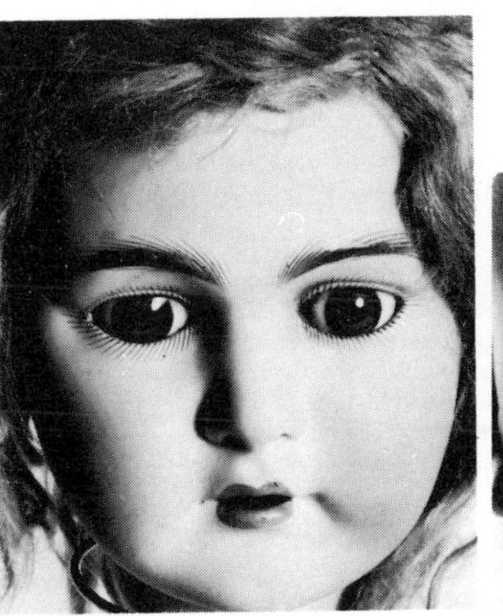

A large Kammer & Reinhardt/ Simon & Halbig bisque doll impressed 90, weighted blue glass eyes, ash-blonde mohair wig, ball-jointed composition body in pale pink dress, stringing perished, German, 32 in. (81 cm.), c. 1890. **£400-500** *S*

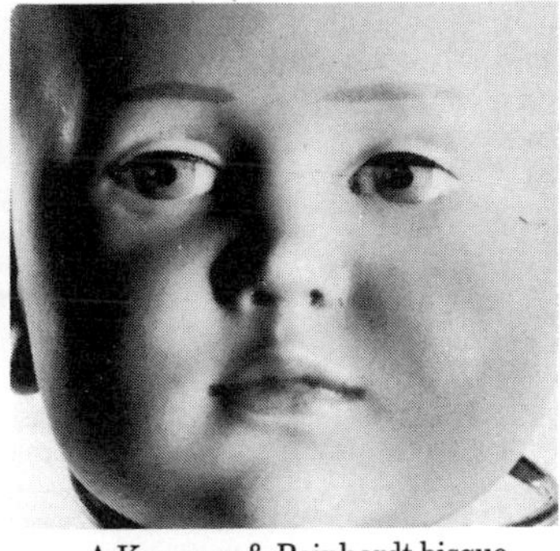

A Kammer & Reinhardt bisque character boy doll impressed 101 43, with closed mouth, painted blue eyes and jointed wood and composition body, unclothed, stringing perished, German, 17 in. (43 cm.), c. 1910. **£750-850** *S*

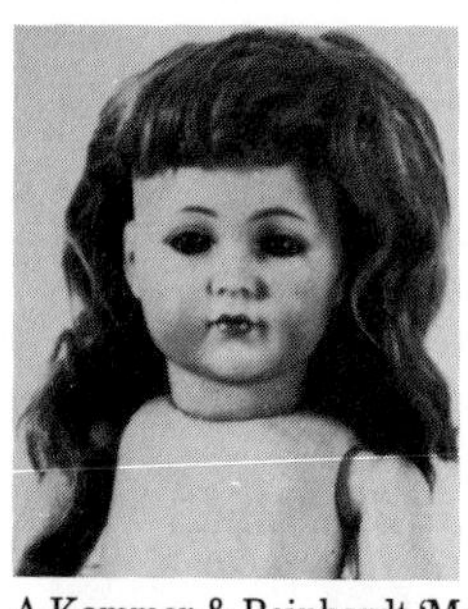

A Kammer & Reinhardt 'Mein Liebling' bisque doll, impressed 11746, with original blonde wig, sleeping blue eyes, good jointed composition body, lacking clothes, 18 in. high (46 cm.). **£1,600-2,000** *S*

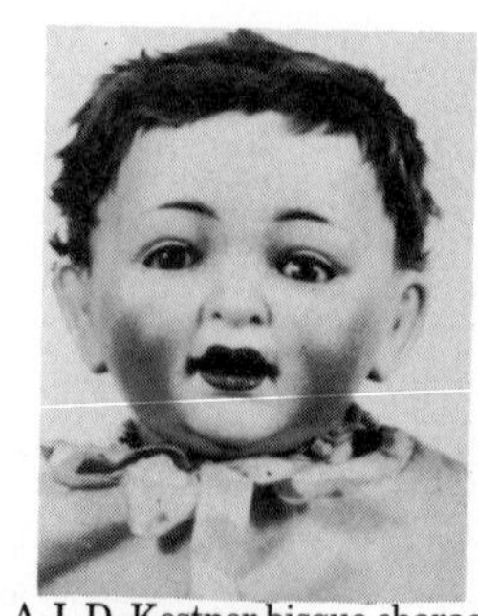

A J. D. Kestner bisque character doll, sleeping eyes, open closed mouth, curved limb composition body, loose stringing, some cracks to the body, 14 in. high (36 cm.). **£400-500** *S*

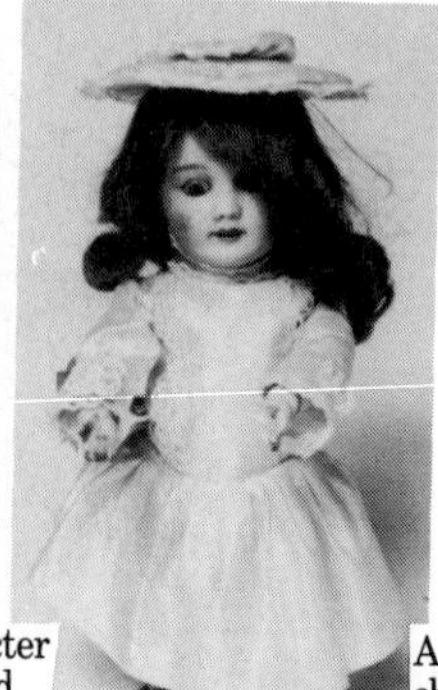

A clockwork walking doll by Limoges, on a tin painted body with elaborate boots with wheels under the feet, wound by key on the side, c. 1890. **£250-450** *HAD*

A J. D. Kestner bisque 'googly-eyed' character doll impressed 173-6, weighted brown glass eyes, mohair wig and jointed bent limb composition body, in white cotton dress, stringing perished, German, 15½ in. (39.5 cm.), c. 1910. **£1,200-£1,500** *S*

A J. D. Kestner bisque 'googly-eyed' doll impressed 173-3½, with smiling closed mouth, weighted blue glass eyes, mohair wig, and 5-piece composition body, hairline on forehead, German, 12½ in. (32 cm.), c. 1912. **£800-900** *S*

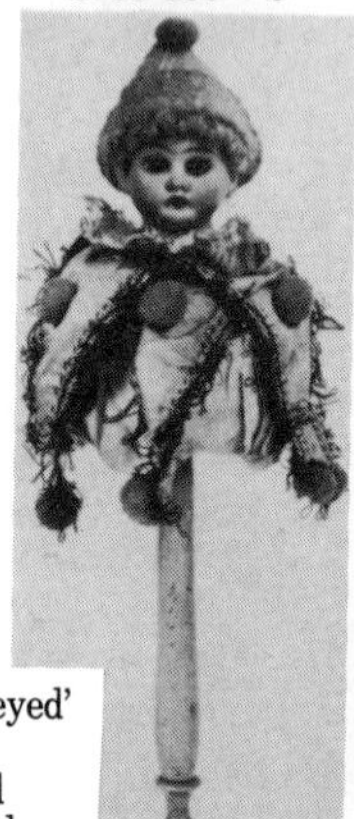

An Armand Marseille bisque poupard, impressed 3200/10/Ox, with fixed eyes, open mouth and short wig, in harlequin outfit, the softwood whistle stick operating the primitive musical movement, 13 in. long overall (33 cm.), c. 1890. **£170-190** *S*

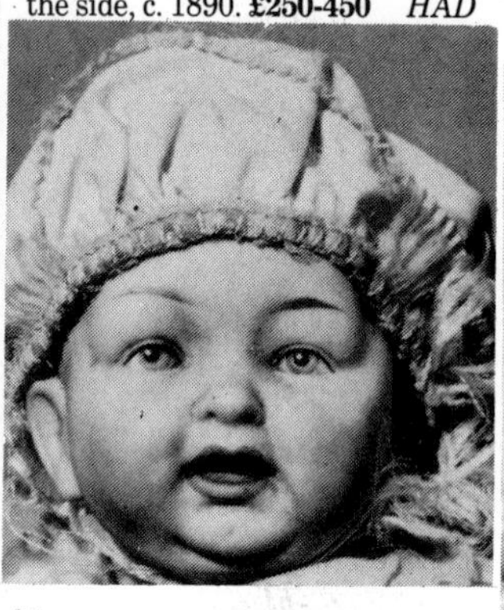

A character doll, probably by Kestner, the head impressed 1421, with kid body with composition lower limbs, dressed in original clothes, German, 10 in. high (26 cm.), c. 1910. **£300-350** *SC*

A large wax baby doll, probably by Pierotti, lashed blue eyes, short wig, with a rag body and wax lower limbs, shoulder plate broken to the rear, a thumb and index finger missing, dressed in original cream silk dress, bonnet and cape, 26 in. high (66 cm.), c. 1860. **£450-500** *S*

A fine Kathe Kruse 'The German Child' rag doll, signed Kathe Kruse and numbered 33565B, the head seamed in 3 places, with well painted features, dressed in original school outfit, one side of satchel damaged, excellent condition, German, 17 in. high (43 cm.), c. 1929. **£400-500** *S*

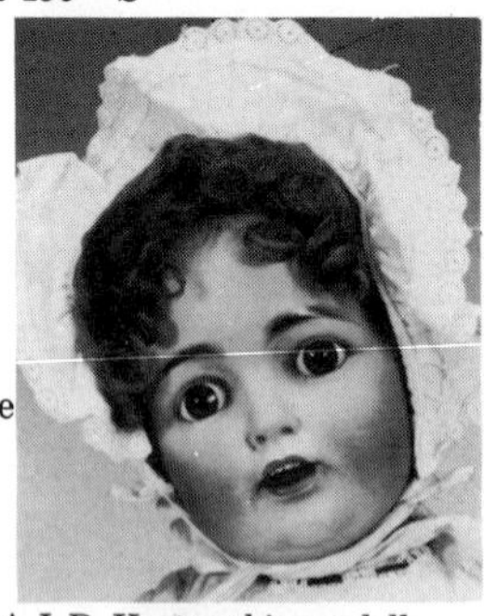

A J. D. Kestner bisque doll impressed 260 70/79, with open mouth and teeth, weighted blue glass eyes, hair wig and the composition body with hole for voice box, jointed arms, right little finger missing, German, 25 in. (64 cm.), c. 1910. **£350-400** *S*

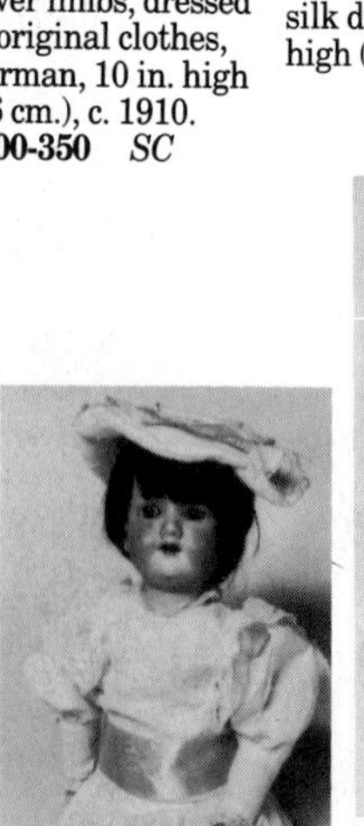

An Armand Marseille doll, model 390, with sleeping eyes, open mouth, fully jointed body and limbs, dark hair. **£120-£160** *WHL*

A Marotte shoulder bisque doll, impressed on the back 3200, with open mouth and teeth, fixed blue glass eyes, pierced ears and ear-rings, mohair wig, in original outfit, playing a tune as the conical body is turned, in original box which bears the label Marotte Folie à Musique No. 6184, marque deposée, article Français, 12½ in. (32 cm.), c. 1900. **£600-700** *S*

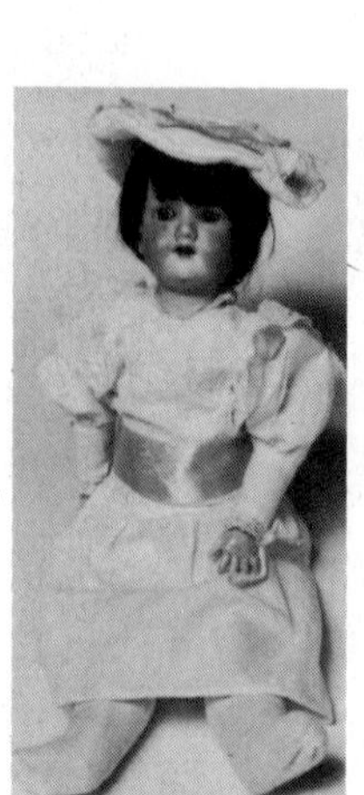

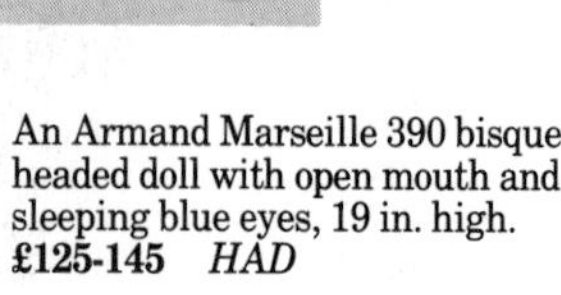

An Armand Marseille 390 bisque-headed doll with open mouth and sleeping blue eyes, 19 in. high. **£125-145** *HAD*

A bisque-headed character doll by Melitta, dressed in sailor clothes, size 12, 22 in. long, c. 1910. **£200-£250** *HAD*

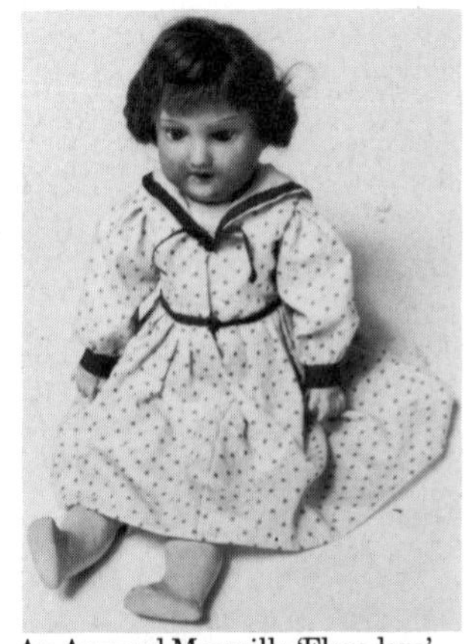
An Armand Marseille 'Floradora' bisque-headed doll on jointed composition and wood body, marked D R G M 246/1, 14 in. high, c. 1900. **£100-125** *HAD*

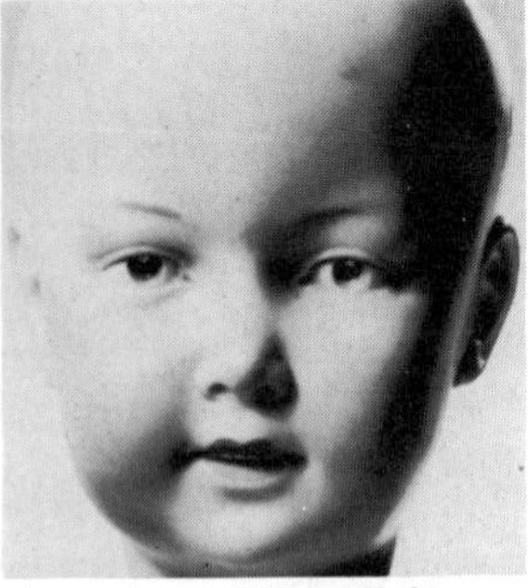
A rare Armand Marseille bisque character boy doll, impressed A.5.M., intaglio grey eyes, wig socket and jointed wood and composition body, unclothed, German, 15½ in. (39.5 cm.), c. 1910. **£400-500** *S*

Two bisque-headed closed mouth 'dream baby' dolls by Armand Marseille, in original clothing, c. 1924. **£300-450** *HAD*

A bisque-headed girl doll by SPBH (Schoenau & Hoffmeister), bisque socket head, open mouth, 4 teeth, sleeping eyes, jointed composition body with 10 joints, 28 in. high, c. 1910. **£150-200** *HAD*

A bisque-headed character baby doll, probably by Schuetzmeister & Quent, 11 in. high, c. 1912. **£100-£150** *HAD*

An Armand Marseille 370 bisque shoulder plate headed doll on stuffed cloth body, 16 in. high. **£100-120** *HAD*

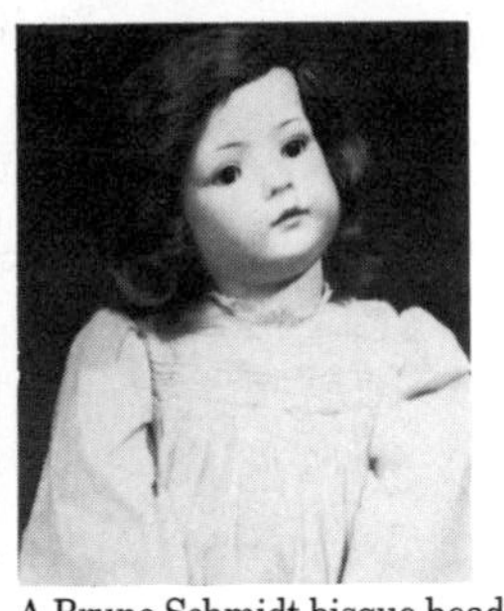
A Bruno Schmidt bisque head doll, with brown mohair wig, sleeping brown eyes, closed mouth and jointed composition body, marked BSW 2072 6, 62 cm. **£1,300-1,500** *P*

A bisque-headed doll by Simon and Halbig, in later clothing, 19 in. high, c. 1910. **£250-£350** *HAD*

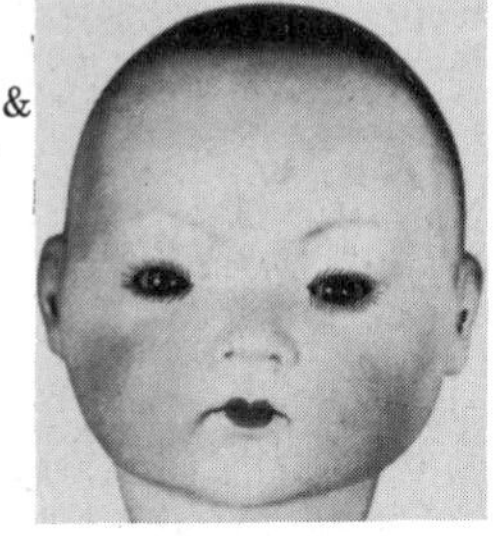
An Armand Marseille 'Oriental' baby doll, impressed 353/4k, with closed mouth, weighted brown eyes and tinted hair, curved limb composition body, 2 chips to base of neck, 15 in. high (38 cm.). **£400-£450** *S*

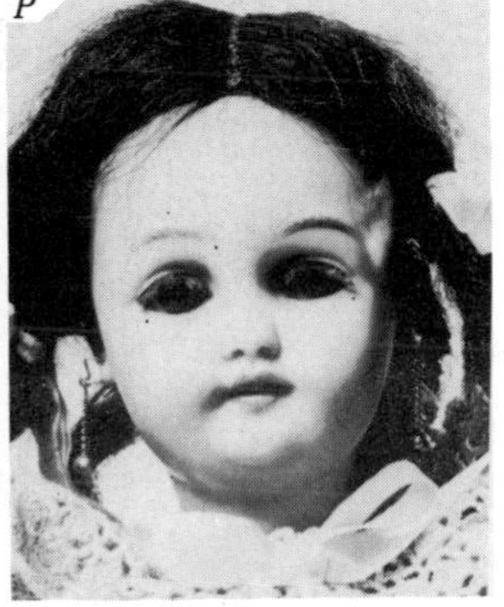
A Simon & Halbig bisque 'walking' doll, impressed 1039, with weighted blue 'flirty' eyes, long dark real hair ringlets, the jointed wood and composition body with straight 'walking' legs which turn her head from side to side, finger right hand missing, German, 14 in. (35.5 cm.), c. 1890. **£400-450** *S*

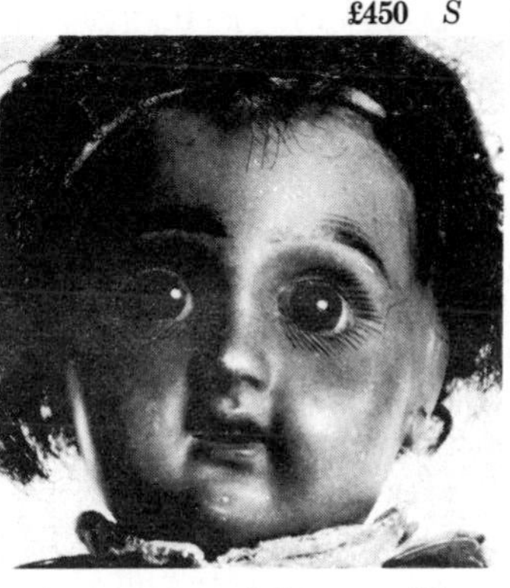
A bisque mulatto doll impressed I, probably by Jules Steiner, with fixed brown glass eyes, black mohair wig and jointed wood and papier mâché body in original dress, small chip base of neck, firing mark on wig cavity, French, 10 in. (25.5 cm.), c. 1890. **£300-£400** *S*

A fabric toy, by Steiff, dressed as a sailor, c. 1910. **£30-60** *HAD*

A musical automaton by Lucien Bontemps, 4 different movements, head signed SIMON & HALBIG, 21 in. high. **£1,200-1,500** *HAD*

A bisque-headed bébé, with pierced ears and hair wig with fixed wrist, composition body in original frock, marked F.R.?, probably by Jules Nicholas Steiner, 14 in. high. **£850-£950** *CSK*

(l.) A Jules Steiner mechanical doll, the bisque head with blonde mohair wig, fixed blue paperweight eyes, pierced ears and open mouth, the kid-covered body with composition lower limbs, when wound the doll moves her head and limbs and cries, 45 cm. **£600-700**
(r.) A Jumeau bisque head musical automaton of a young girl with blonde mohair wig, fixed blue paperweight eyes, pierced ears with ear-rings and closed mouth, redressed, as the music plays she turns her head and raises each hand, marked Tête Jumeau Bte. S.G.D.G. 3, 33 cm. high, base 11 cm. **£950-1,050** *P*

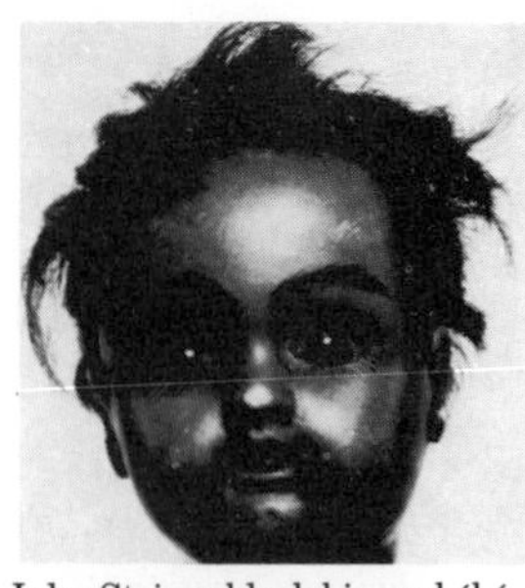

A Jules Steiner black bisque bébé doll, impressed J. Steiner Bte. S.G.D.G. Paris FIre, Al, fixed eyes, mohair wig, pierced ears and jointed composition body, both hands missing, stringing loose, nose rubbed, French, 8 in. (20 cm.), c. 1890. **£250-300** *S*

A bisque-headed bébé premier pas, with fixed blue eyes, heavy brows, blonde wool wig and carton body with composition hands and feet, by Steiner, shop label on the body reading Nain Bleu E. Chauviere Capucines 27 Paris, 18 in. high. **£650-750** *CSK*

A pair of googly-eyed costume dolls, possibly by Wilken & Strobel, the small all-bisque figures in original German peasant costume, fixed blue eyes, loose stringing, 5 in. high (13 cm.). **£220-280** *S*

A small fabric doll by Norah Wellings, 9 in. high, c. 1920. **£15-£25** *HAD*

A French shoulder bisque doll, with inset fixed blue eyes, cork pate with blonde wig, later wired and padded body, French, 10¼ in. high (26 cm.), late 19th C. **£120-180** *SC*

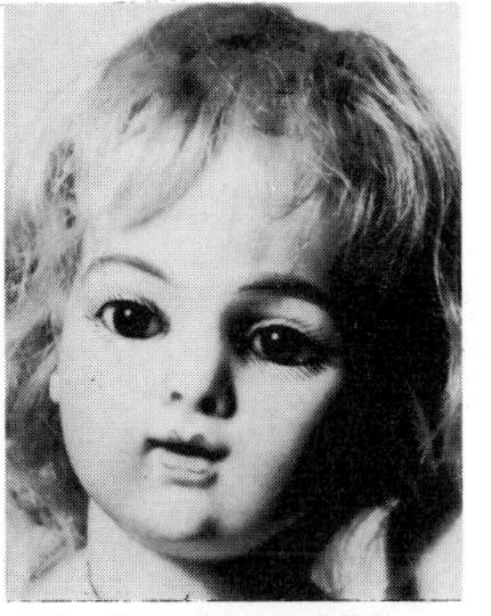

A Bru Jeune bisque doll impressed Bru.J.ne 4, fixed brown glass eyes, pierced ears, real hair wig, the kid body bearing Bru label (slightly torn), with bisque moulded breastplate and forearms, wood lower legs, unclothed, hairline crack on face, fingers damaged, French, 12½ in. (32 cm.), c. 1875. **£1,300-1,500** *S*

A dancing dolls manivelle musical automaton, with winding handle at the side, French, 16½ in. wide (42 cm.), c. 1900. **£300-350** *S*

A composition headed walking doll, on wood and composition body, probably Dutch, c. 1930. **£70-90** *HAD*

An oriental bisque 'My Dream Baby' impressed O Germany J.G.A 1½ R, weighted brown eyes, curved limb composition body, German, 12¾ in. (32.5 cm.), c. 1925. **£400-450** *S*

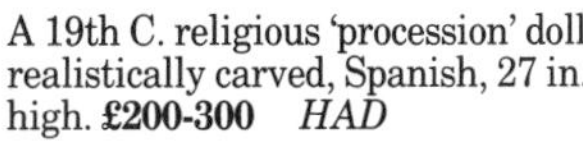

A 19th C. religious 'procession' doll, realistically carved, Spanish, 27 in. high. **£200-300** *HAD*

A shoulder-parian bisque 'walking' doll, with blue eyes, moulded blonde hair, moulded 'shirt' shoulder-plate, the conical body containing the mechanism which enables her 2 metal feet to walk when wound, German, 11 in. (28 cm.), c. 1865. **£200-250** *S*

A wax shoulder doll, hair inserted in tufts, fixed eyes, the stuffed fabric body with wax lower limbs, features slightly rubbed, lower legs damaged, dressed in original gown (damaged), bonnet and shoes, probably German, 23 in. high (59 cm.), c. 1870. **£350-400** *S*

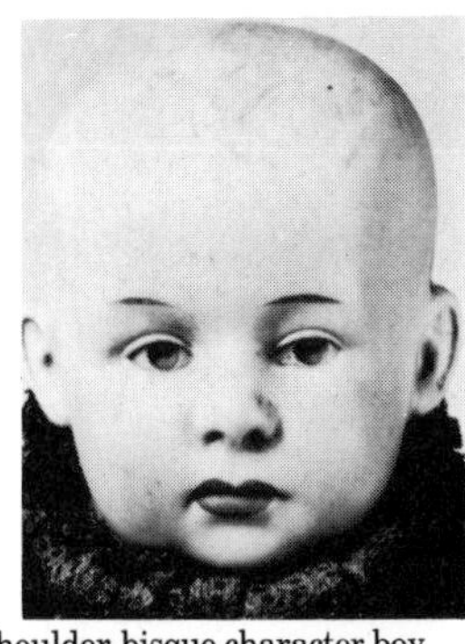

A shoulder-bisque character boy doll impressed 2, stuffed body with composition limbs, in original 'Beefeater' costume, left arm detached, fingers chipped, German, 11½ in. (29 cm.), c. 1910. **£200-£300** *S*

A rare bisque character boy doll, impressed 1428 9, with blonde mohair wig, curved limb composition body, unclothed, German, 15 in. (38 cm.), c. 1910. **£500-600** *S*

A shoulder papier mâché doll with blue painted eyes, moulded black ringlets, the stuffed body with leather arms, in original dress, slight cracking, German, 14 in. (35.5 cm.), c. 1840. **£350-450** *S*

A small oriental doll in original box with wigs for different stages in one's life, c. 1920. **£50-80** *HAD*

A wax over composition doll dressed in original white dress and petticoats, 20 in. high, c. 1880. **£150-250** *HAD*

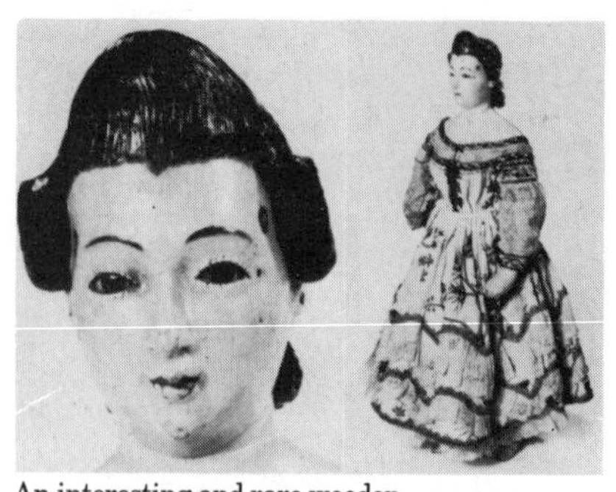

An interesting and rare wooden doll, with painted red lips, paperweight glass eyes with brown spiral pupils and pierced ears, the torso well-carved with sophisticated pegged joints, in original skirt, right arm and left fingers missing, slight scuffing to face, probably Spanish Colonial, 14½ in. (36 cm.), mid 18th C. **£1,200-1,500** *S*

The costume of this doll is of interest in that the blouse is Spanish, c. 1760. The hair style is not European and there are holes for some sort of headdress or mantilla. The doll may well have been made for the South American market. The superb body carving suggests she was made to be undressed and admired, and could have been modelled on a specific character.

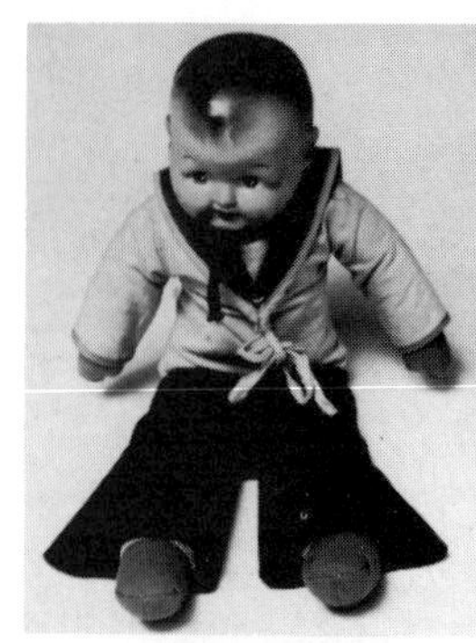

A composition-headed sailor doll, 16 in. high, c. 1920. **£15-25** *HAD*

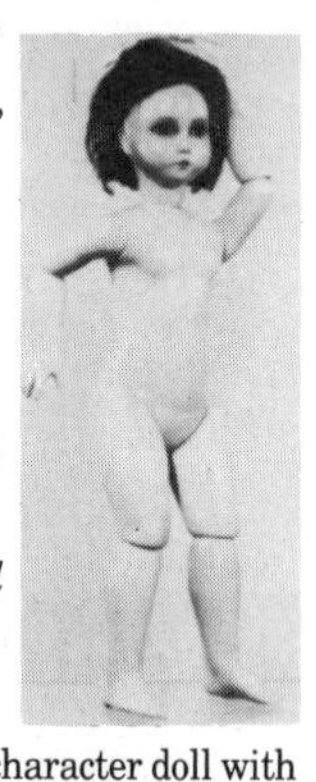

A composition character doll with brown painted eyes and well made jointed composition body with spring joints, 20 in. high. **£110-£150** *CSK*

An autoperipatetikos walking doll with bisque head and original box, 10 in. high. **£400-600** *HAD*

A Japanese doll made as a gift to honoured guests, 16 in. high. **£40-£80** *HAD*

An 18th C. religious 'procession' doll, Spanish, in original black cloak, 28 in. high. **£200-300** *HAD*

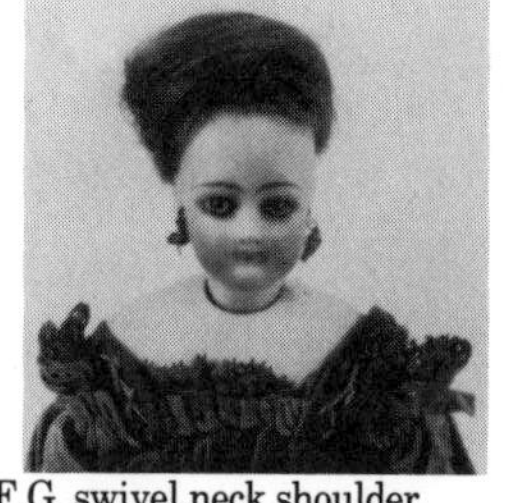

An F.G. swivel neck shoulder bisque doll, the head and shoulder-plate impressed 3/0, with pale blue eyes and original wig, with fabric body and white kid arms, in later dress, 11 in. high (28 cm.), c. 1870. **£300-350** *S*

A very fine pedlar doll, the china shoulder head with moulded black hair and painted features and the cloth body with china lower limbs, in original clothes, carrying a basket of assorted wares including a bone ivory egg timer, a chatelaine, enamelled buttons, baskets, glassware, table and kitchen wares, toys and games, 20 cm. **£900-1,000** *P*

A wooden doll modelled as an old crone with white hair and original pedlar costume of brown dress, carrying wares including lace, skeins of wool, needles, cottons, a pipe, baskets, teething rings, bellows, onion chopper, ribbons, under dome, with a label reading Betty Tramp, Licensed Hawker, no. 1765, no legs, 11½ in. high. **£100-£150** *CSK*

A bisque Belton shoulder head doll with blonde mohair wig, fixed blue paperweight eyes and closed mouth, with gussetted kid body with bisque lower arms dressed in original clothes, 38 cm. **£500-600** *P*

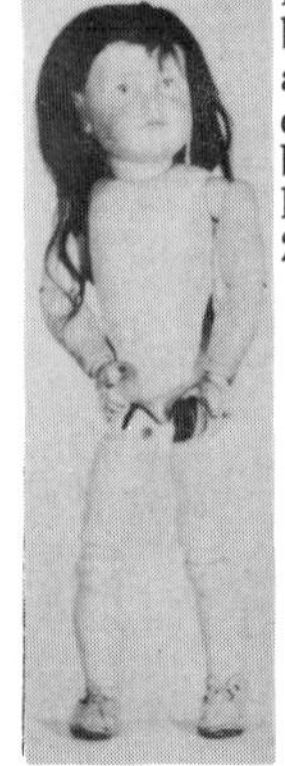

A bisque-headed character child doll with painted blue eyes, brown wig and jointed composition body wearing white shoes, marked K*R 114 43, 16½ in. high. **£1,500-£1,700** *CSK*

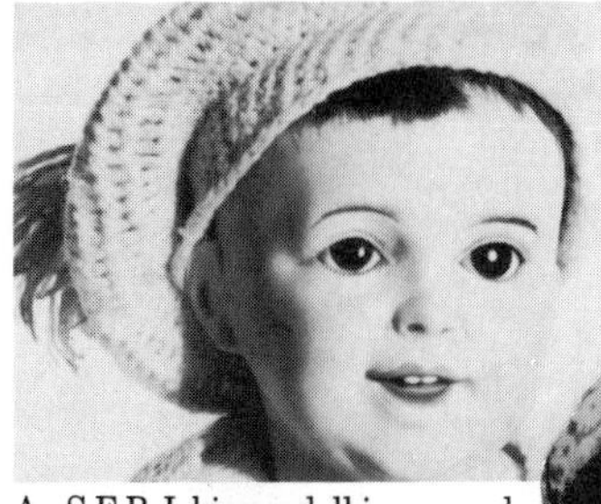

An S.F.B.J. bisque doll impressed 236 10, with open/closed mouth with 2 teeth, weighted black pupilless eyes, sparse auburn real hair wig and curved limb composition body, stringing loose, German, 18½ in. (47 cm.), c. 1910. **£400-£500** *S*

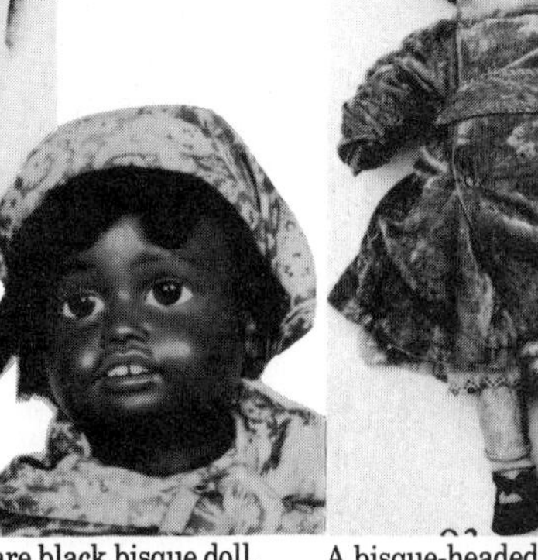

A fine and rare black bisque doll, probably by S.F.B.J. in association with Paris Bébé, the head impressed 634-30, with sleeping brown eyes, gap-fronted teeth, good jointed composition body, card pate, in original clothes and box, bearing the rising Phoenix trademark, French, 23 in. high (58 cm.), c. 1900. **£2,500-2,700** *S*

A bisque-headed character doll, the mouth with 2 moulded upper teeth, blue sleeping eyes, short brown wig and with jointed composition and wood body, marked 21 SFBJ 251 Paris 6, 17 in. high. **£400-500** *CSK*

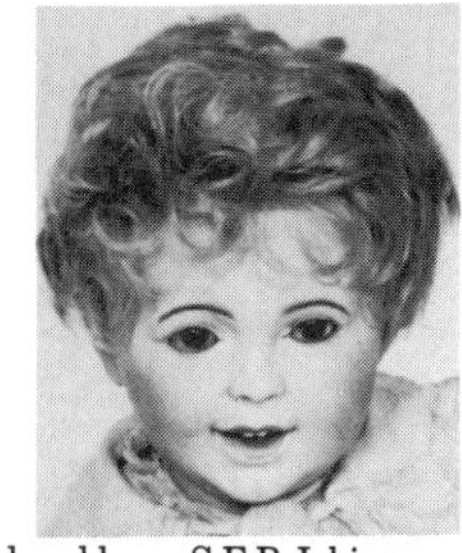

A good and large S.F.B.J. bisque character doll, impressed 236, with sleeping blue eyes, open/closed mouth, modern wig, with composition curved limb body, in contemporary clothes, 27 in. high (69 cm.), c. 1900. **£500-600** *S*

An S.F.B.J. bisque character doll impressed 236 -6-, with open/closed mouth and 2 teeth, weighted blue glass eyes, now fixed, mohair wig and curved limb composition body, French, 15 in. (38 cm.), c. 1910. **£350-400** *S*

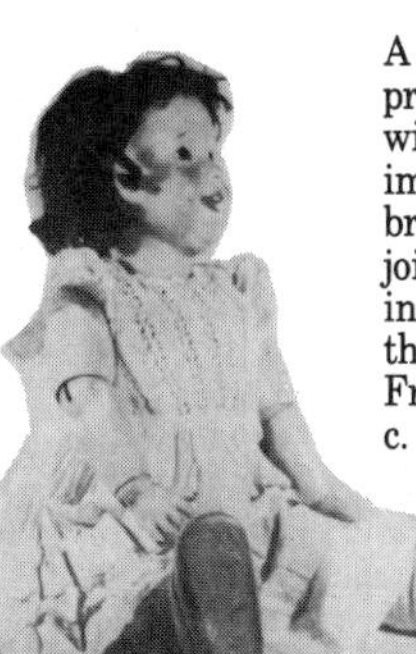

A bisque-headed character child doll with blue sleeping eyes, smiling open/closed mouth, 2 teeth and with jointed toddler body, wearing linen frock, marked SFBJ 236 Paris 12, 27 in. high. **£400-£500** *CSK*

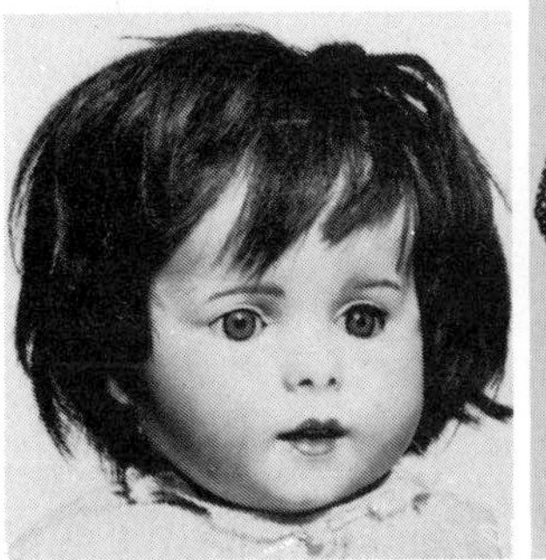

An S.F.B.J. character doll, the head impressed 247 11, lashed sleeping blue eyes, replacement auburn wig, and good curved limb composition body, re-set eyes, French, 24 in. high (61 cm.), c. 1910. **£1,100-£1,300** *SC*

A bisque-headed character doll with blue sleeping eyes, open mouth, pierced ears, hair wig and jointed composition body, marked S&H 127 9 DEP 13, 24½ in. high. **£1,000-1,200** *CSK*

A turned and carved painted wooden doll with inset enamel eyes, stitched brows and lashes, red painted cheeks with original hair wig, with painted wooden jointed legs and kid arms, wearing a silk gauze dress and petticoat, 16½ in. high, early 19th C. **£600-700** *CSK*

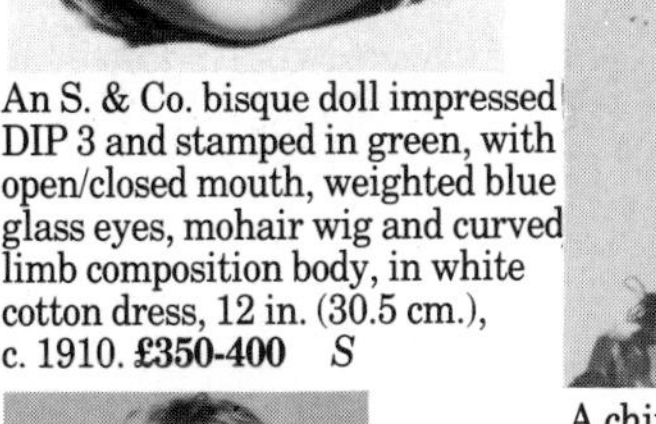

An S. & Co. bisque doll impressed DIP 3 and stamped in green, with open/closed mouth, weighted blue glass eyes, mohair wig and curved limb composition body, in white cotton dress, 12 in. (30.5 cm.), c. 1910. **£350-400** *S*

A china shoulder-headed doll with moulded hair, wearing orange silk frock trimmed with braid, 10 in. high, under dome. **£400-600** *CSK*

A bisque-headed clockwork walking doll with blue sleeping eyes, blonde hair and jointed wooden composition arms with metal body and legs containing the mechanism, with printed metal boots, marked W S K 2/0, S & H, 3½ in. high. **£300-400** *CSK*

Firdonen Imhof took out a patent for a similar metal clockwork walking doll in 1900.

A bisque shoulder-headed boy doll, with moulded curls, closed mouth, inset blue glass eyes and with kid body in original Scottish uniform, 13 in. high. **£140-160** *CSK*

A Lenci felt doll with 'Lucia' face, the all-felt stiffened body jointed at the shoulders and hips, in original box, 14 in. (35.6 cm.), c. 1920. **£280-£340** *S*

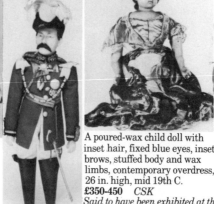

A part Schoenhut circus comprising a rare composition and wood-headed clown, and 3 others, 2 clowns in original clothes, also another painted wooden clown, a composition-headed artiste, 6½ in. high, and a ladder. **£100-150** *CSK*

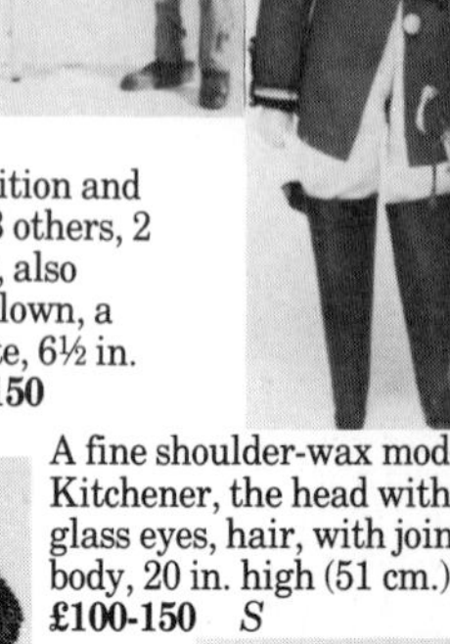

A fine shoulder-wax model of Lord Kitchener, the head with inserted glass eyes, hair, with jointed fabric body, 20 in. high (51 cm.), c. 1914. **£100-150** *S*

A poured-wax child doll with inset hair, fixed blue eyes, inset brows, stuffed body and wax limbs, contemporary overdress, 26 in. high, mid 19th C. **£350-450** *CSK*
Said to have been exhibited at the Paris exhibition of 1851.

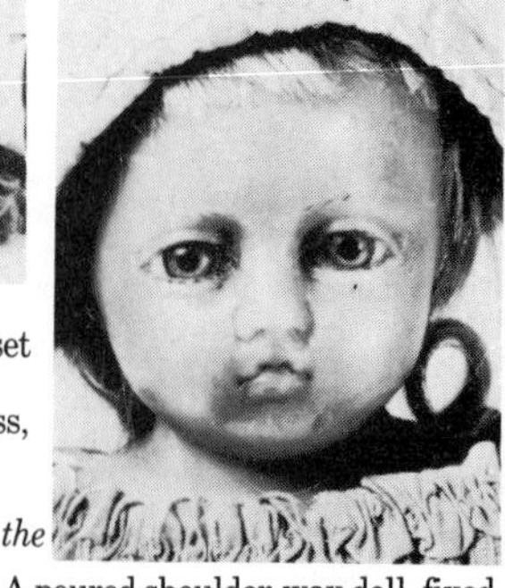

A poured shoulder-wax doll, fixed blue glass eyes, inserted eyebrows and eyelashes, the hand-stitched body with wax lower limbs in original dress, right leg replaced, repaired on shoulder, 15½ in. (39.5 cm.), c. 1860. **£180-240** *S*

A shoulder-wax over composition boy doll, inset with blue paperweight eyes, the fabric body with composition lower limbs, dressed, lacking pate, wax segment missing behind head, 17 in. high (43 cm.). **£180-220** *S*

A bisque doll, the head impressed 30934, with sleeping blue eyes, open mouth, short blonde wig, the articulated kid body with composition lower limbs, dressed, 15 in. high (38 cm.). **£200-300** *S*

A jointed wooden doll with chiselled hair, with brown painted eyes and unusual carved top of the body with painted trailing acorns and leaves, ball jointed with painted hands and legs, with contemporary black dress, 20 in. high. **£400-450** *CSK*

A dolls' house copied exactly from an original family house, the sides opening on 4 hinged doors, later furniture, 33 in. high by 39½ in. wide (84 by 100 cm.). **£400-500** *S*

A wooden miniature shop with goods including miniature bott jars and packets, a pair of scales and blue paper cones, entitled G. Jones & Co., Grocers, Provisions, 16½ in. wide. **£180-£240** *CSK*

A Victorian painted dolls' house, opening to reveal 4 rooms, a hallway, staircase and landing, each room with a fireplace, the sides with carrying handles, glass on windows broken, English, 32½ in. high by 37½ in. wide (82 by 95 cm.), c. 1890. **£250-300** *S*

A large dolls' house, with 'bricked' facade, hinged front panel with opening oak door, and comprising 4 rooms and a hallway, good condition, 32 by 37 in. (81 by 94 cm.), early 20th C. **£150-200** *S*

A large dolls' house divided in 2 sections and enclosing 8 rooms, a staircase and landing, with a garage at one side, English, 45 in. high by 73 in. long (114.5 by 185.5 cm.), c. 1930. **£200-300** *S*

An unusually large model of a typical moated house built by a country squire at the beginning of the 16th C., the model is complete with numerous items of furniture and furnishings, built 1930-70, 8 ft. high. **£750-850** *WSW*

A set of printed paper on wood dolls' house furniture decorated with garlands of flowers. **£280-£340** *CSK*

A Georgian dolls' house, containing 4 rooms, including a kitchen with range, embroidered carpets, good condition, together with a small assortment of dolls' house furniture including tinplate and gilt furniture, 28 by 30 in. (71 by 76 cm.), c. 1830. **£500-550** *SC*

A late Victorian dolls' house, the front opening in 2 sections to reveal 4 rooms, hall, staircase and landing, 25 in. high by 35 in. wide (63.5 by 89 cm.), c. 1890. **£400-£500** *S*

A miniature kidney-shaped writing desk attributed to Fred Early, 5 in. wide. **£35-45** *CSK*

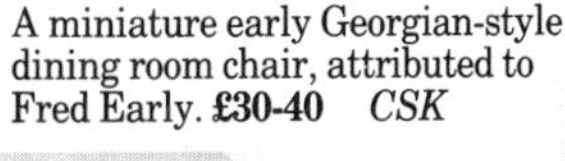

A miniature early Georgian-style dining room chair, attributed to Fred Early. **£30-40** *CSK*

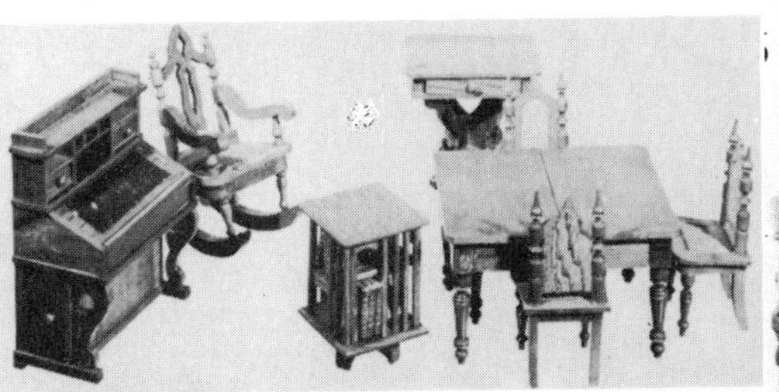

A set of Victorian Gothic-style dolls' house furniture. **£250-300** *CSK*

A miniature William and Mary-style chest on stand, attributed to Fred Early, 6¼ in. high. **£90-120** *CSK*

A Bing clockwork model of a Mercedes 90 touring car with opening doors, lamps, rubber-tyred wheels and handbrake, marked GBN, 32 cm. **£2,500-3,000** *P*

A Citröen 1923 clockwork 5CV clover leaf tourer with steerable wheels, gear shift, brake and windscreen, marked Automobile Méchanique André Citröen Made in France, 31 cm. **£450-550** *P*

A painted wood and tin model of an omnibus with glazed windows and all-wood spoked wheels, fitted with clockwork motor, finished in navy blue and cream, German, 23 in. long, c. 1910. **£150-200** *CSK*

A Meccano constructor car, with adjustable front-wheel steering and clockwork motor housed in the tail, also a quantity of spare parts (with instruction booklet), 13¼ in. long. **£180-240** *CSK*

A good Marklin constructor racing car no. 7, finished in scarlet, suspension and clockwork mechanism linked to rear axle by drive shaft, 14½ in. long (37 cm.), c. 1935. **£500-550** *S*

A Bing clockwork limousine with brake lever and opening doors, finished in dark green and black with yellow lining, one headlamp missing, 32 cm. **£300-350** *P*

A Marklin constructor streamlined 2-seater coupe, finished in pale green and beige, with suspension, adjustable front axle and clockwork mechanism linked to rear axle by drive shaft, German, 14¼ in. long (36 cm.), c. 1935. **£350-450** *S*

A good Tipp Mercedes 'Fuhrenwagen', with clockwork mechanism, 4 Hauser seated Nazi soldiers within, German, 9¼ in. long (23.5 cm.), c. 1938. **£400-500** *S*

A Bing clockwork model of a De Dion Bouton 4-seater touring car with rubber-tyred steerable wheels, with a searchlight, headlamps, tail-lamp and with handbrake, 28 cm., c. 1904. **£2,300-2,800** *P*

(l.) A Coca-Cola tinplate delivery lorry, with clockwork mechanism driving the rear axle, probably American, 7¾ in. long (19.5 cm.), c. 1935. **£120-180** *S*

(r.) A Tri-ang tinplate sentinel steam delivery lorry, with clockwork mechanism driving the rear axle and opening rear doors, English, 8½ in. long (21.5 cm.), c. 1935. **£140-180** *S*

A rare Lehmann sweep and pretzel boy, the clockwork mechanism causes the sweep and pretzel boy to beat each other alternately, and the tricycle to proceed forwards, while the bell rings, German, 5½ in. long (14 cm.), c. 1908. **£700-£800** *SC*

A Stevens & Brown tricyclist, with delicately painted composition head, brass plate hands and feet with articulated legs, cast iron tricycle, the mechanism casing painted and marked at one side 'Pat'd Jan...& Feb. 1st 1870', the figure re-clothed, American, 10½ in. long (26.5 cm.), c. 1880. **£300-400** *S*

A Gunthermann vis-a-vis horseless carriage, with rubber-tyred wheels, fitted with clockwork motor, partially repainted, 10 in. long, c. 1900. **£900-1,000** *CSK*

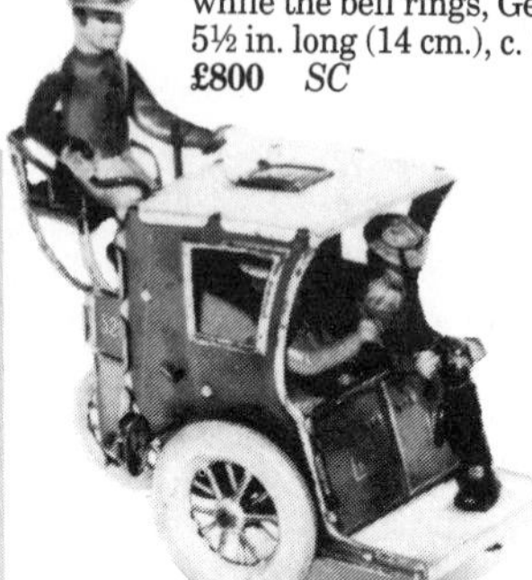

A Lehmann Li-La, with 2 women beating a begging poodle with their umbrellas, while the driver steers the vehicle from side to side, very good condition, German, 6 in. high (15 cm.), c. 1908. **£400-450** *SC*

A Gunthermann tram, with glazed windows, hinged pick-up arm, axle activated bell, clockwork mechanism, good condition, German, 9½ in. long (24 cm.), 1920's. **£250-300** *S*

A good Lehmann Auto-Onkel, no. 345, the lithographed tricycle with seated figures waving top hat and twirling an umbrella, clockwork mechanism, in original cardboard box, German, 5¼ in. wide (13.5 cm.), c. 1920. **£300-350** *S*

A Lehmann stubborn donkey, the clockwork mechanism causes the bucking beast to spin the cart and the clown to rise and fall, German, 7 in. long (18 cm.), c. 1908. **£90-120** *SC*

A Dinky 28 series van, finished in orange with transfers to each side 'Ensign Lukos Films' and 'Ensign Cameras'. **£210-250** *SC*

A large model of the 1,000 h.p. Sunbeam car which achieved the World Record of 203 m.p.h. at Daytona in 1927, red enamel. **£600-£700** *P*

A Dinky 28 series delivery van, finished in yellow with transfers to each side, 'Meccano Engineering for Boys', c. 1935. **£180-220** *SC*

A Dinky pre-war 28g delivery van, yellow body, blue wheels and tinplate radiator. **£400-450** *P*

A Dinky 22D series delivery van, in orange and blue, metal wheels and nickel-plated radiator, Hornby series, Liverpool, partially repainted, English, 3¼ in. long (8.3 cm.), c. 1933. **£120-180** *S*

A Dinky 25D series petrol tanker, green with black chassis, tinplate radiator, 'Wakefield Castrol Motor Oil' transfer in red and black, very good condition, English, 4½ in. long (10.7 cm.), c. 1939. **£110-150** *S*

A Dinky 28M series delivery van, type 2, bearing original 'Wakefield Castrol Motor Oil' to both sides, die cast radiator, white rubber tyres, metal fatigue, English, 8.1 cm. long, c. 1935. **£80-120** *S*

A Burnett tinplate construction kit car, clockwork mechanism operating rear axle, English, 9¾ in. long (25 cm.), mid 1920's. **£100-£150** *SC*

A good Carette tinplate landaulette, with bevel glass windows, opening rear doors, gear lever and handbrake, side lamps missing, the clock mechanism driving the rear axle, dark green with red details and yellow lining, 41 cm. **£1,300-£1,600** *P*

A Moko clockwork 6-cylinder saloon, the mechanism oscillating the pistons, with gear lever for forward and neutral, complete with uniformed chauffeur, clockwork mechanism defective, German, 9½ in. long (24 cm.), c. 1918-20. **£250-300** *S*

A good Lehmann 'gala' tinplate limousine, with 4 hinged doors, lithographed chauffeur, clockwork mechanism, lacking a headlight, German, 12½ in. long (32 cm.), c. 1930. **£500-550** *S*

A Dinky pre-war 34a Royal Air Mail Service Car, slight fatigue. **£80-100** *P*

A Dinky pre-war No. 16 'Silver Jubilee' train set, in original box. **£50-70**

A Lehmann 'Tut Tut' novelty car, with outsized driver holding trumpet to mouth, steers erratic course while driver blows horn, one lamp missing, one stub axle broken, in its original box, 17 cm. long. **£280-360** *SS*

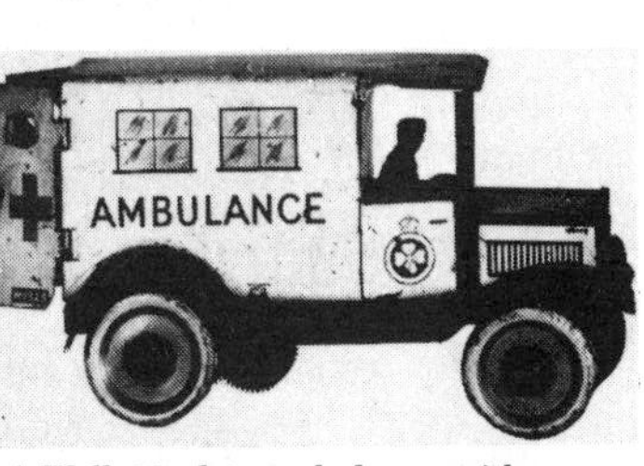

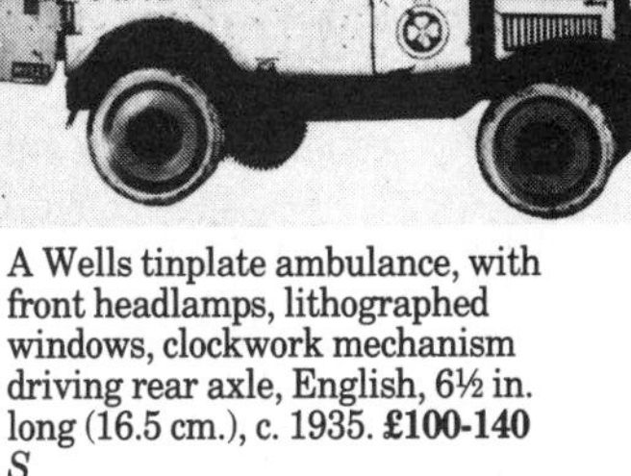

A Wells tinplate ambulance, with front headlamps, lithographed windows, clockwork mechanism driving rear axle, English, 6½ in. long (16.5 cm.), c. 1935. **£100-140** *S*

A Gunthermann double decker bus, lithographed in red and white with blue advertisements, uniformed driver, clockwork activated rear axle, lacking a wheel, German, 9½ in. long (24 cm.), c. 1930. **£350-400** *S*

A Dinky pre-war 42 police box, motor cycle patrol and policeman set, in original box, slight fatigue. **£140-180** *P*

A William Britain army staff car, in box, black rubber tyres, very good condition. **£180-220** *SC*

A Bing tinplate open truck, steering wheel and clockwork mechanism driving the rear axle, German, 9¼ in. long (23 cm.), c. 1923. **£300-350** *S*

A Chad Valley games van, brightly lithographed with various illustrations of games to the roof panel, clockwork mechanism, slight damage to paintwork on one side, English, 10¼ in. long (26 cm.), c. 1930. **£150-180** *S*

An unusual Distler for Essdee riot squad van, lithographed red and lined in yellow, roof catch releases side panels revealing policemen within, and 2 crouching machine gunners, side catch raises and lowers the aerial, lacking wheels and clockwork mechanism, German, 9½ in. long (24 cm.), c. 1925-35. **£100-140** *S*

A Bing K 200 printed tinplate motor bus, with clockwork motor, finished in London General red and cream livery, with advertisements and signboard for Route 77, 7 in. long, c. 1920, and a cast metal figure of a driver, 2 in. high. **£300-£400** *CSK*

A Meccano construction car no. 2, the tinplate body finished in cream with red mudguards, seats, etc., contained in original box, lacking one wheel, scratched paintwork, 12 in. (30.5 cm.). **£180-220** *S*

A good tinplate double-decker bus, finished in cream and red with original box, good condition, English, 10½ in. long (27 cm.), c. 1930. **£150-200** *SC*

An unusual André Citröen tinplate delivery van, lacking one roof support and rear doors, French, 14 in. long (35.5 cm.), c. 1925. **£500-£600** *S*

A tinplate '8 CYL' saloon, details including battery powered headlights, lithographed chauffeur, sliding sunroof, clockwork mechanism, complete with original box, English, 14 in. long (36 cm.), c. 1938. **£150-200** *S*

A Jouets De Paris painted tinplate de Lage saloon, fitted with steering wheel-operated front-wheel steering, gear lever, battery-operated spotlight, clockwork motor powering the rear wheels through a driveshaft mechanism, 13 in. long, c. 1925. **£400-500** *CSK*

An unusual Carette hand-painted limousine with opening rear doors and folding seats, steering wheel linked to front axle, lacks clockwork mechanism, German, 15¾ in. long (40 cm.), c. 1911. **£2,000-2,500** *S*

A Victor Bonnet & Cie tinplate vehicle and trailer, with covered cab, steering wheel and driver, with clockwork mechanism, pulling khaki cloth-covered wagon behind, French, 14 in. long (36 cm.), c. 1920. **£100-150** *S*

A hand-painted tinplate boy on scooter, with articulated right leg and clockwork mechanism below, German, 7¾ in. high (19.5 cm.), c. 1910. **£400-450** *S*

A hand-enamelled tinplate horse-drawn hansom cab, fitted with clockwork motor and finished in black and gold, probably German, 8½ in. long, c. 1900. **£80-110** *CSK*

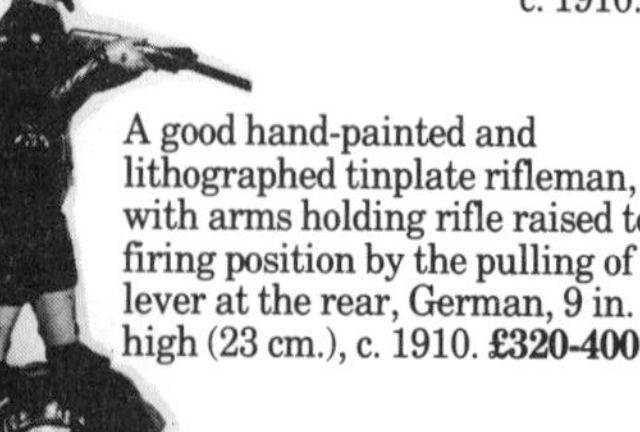

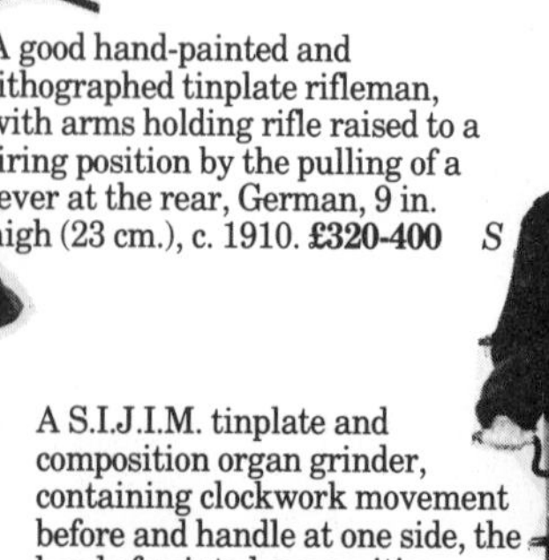

A good hand-painted and lithographed tinplate rifleman, with arms holding rifle raised to a firing position by the pulling of a lever at the rear, German, 9 in. high (23 cm.), c. 1910. **£320-400** *S*

A hand-painted tinplate Indian, with bow and arrow beneath one arm and articulated at the waist, standing on painted lead feet, German, 7 in. high (18 cm.), c. 1910. **£200-300** *S*

An unusual tinplate hand-painted Oriental balancing figure, balancing a revolving ball on his nose, the clockwork mechanism concealed within, rocking the articulated body, German, c. 1902. **£300-400** *S*

A S.I.J.I.M. tinplate and composition organ grinder, containing clockwork movement before and handle at one side, the head of painted composition, French, 8½ in. high (21.5 cm.), c. 1910. **£250-300** *S*

A printed tinplate rack-rod operated spinning top, modelled as a ballerina, dressed in pink tutu, with gold-painted slippers, German, 6 in. high, c. 1920. **£150-£180** *CSK*

(l.) An E. Cardini tinplate and cardboard horse race carousel, Italian, assembled diameter 19 in. (48 cm.), c. 1925. **£300-400** *S*

(r.) An E. Cardini tinplate and cardboard aeroplane carousel, Italian, diameter 19 in. (48 cm.), c. 1925. **£500-600** *S*

A 'Pete & The Monk' tinplate toy, probably by Distler, the internal clockwork mechanism activating a small musical movement, with dancing tinplate monkey, lacking an arm, poor condition, German, 6 in. long (15 cm.), c. 1923. **£80-£100** *S*

(l.) A small hand-painted and lithographed tinplate gunboat, possibly by Falk, with clockwork mechanism within, German, 7 in. long (18 cm.), c. 1915. **£120-150** *S*

(c.) A 3-funnel hand-painted liner, possibly by Falk, with clockwork mechanism within, German, 10½ in. long (26.5 cm.), c. 1915. **£120-180** *S*

(r.) A small hand-painted tinplate gunboat, German, 9 in. long (23 cm.), c. 1908. **£120-150** *S*

A horizontal tinplate stationary steam engine and fairground toy, German, 11¼ in. long (28.5 cm.), c. 1912. **£200-250** *S*

(l.) A Marklin hand-painted tinplate line side hut, German, 4 in. high (10 cm.), c. 1904. **£100-£150** *S*

(c.) A Marklin hand-painted tinplate central station, in English livery, for Gauge One layout, German, 11¼ in. wide (28.5 cm.), c. 1921. **£300-400** *S*

(r.) A Marklin hand-painted tinplate goods station, for Gauge 'O' layout, German, 9¾ in. wide (22 cm.), c. 1912. **£150-200** *S*

A tinplate 'Royal Trick' elephant bank, brightly lithographed, lacks tail, German, 5¾ in. long (14.5 cm.), c. 1930. **£400-500** *S*

A Meccano constructor car kit, for building M1, M2, M3, M4 vehicles, with original instructions and box, lacking windscreen and driver, English, 12 in. long (31 cm.), 1930's. **£400-450** *SC*

A good Hess tinplate dreadnought carpet battleship and convoy, powered by clockwork driving concealed wheels and linked by wire triangles to 3 smaller unpowered vessels, in original box, German, 11¼ in. wide (28.5 cm.), c. 1911. **£400-500** *S*

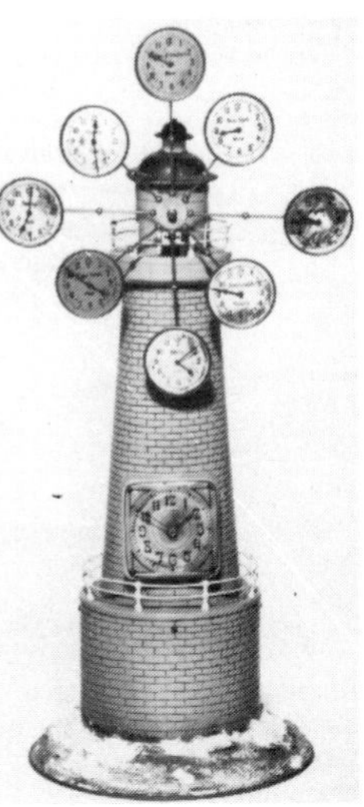

A tinplate lighthouse clock, the internal mechanism causing a wheel to revolve bearing dials for various capital cities, repainted, probably German, 23 in. high (58 cm.), c. 1910. **£400-450** *SC*

A large trestle rocking horse, together with original stirrups, on wooden trestle, English, 60 in. long (152 cm.), c. 1900. **£400-500** *SC*

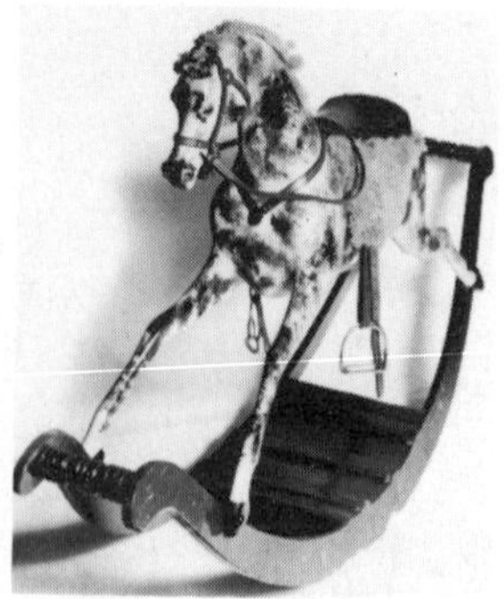

A Victorian dappled-grey rocking horse, 72 in. long over rockers. **£400-500** *HB*

A large painted dappled-grey rocking horse, with horsehair m and tail, some paint flaked, English, 46 in. high by 51 in. lo (117 by 129.5 cm.), c. 1920. **£40 £600** *S*

A Marklin Continental 4-way traffic signal, hand-painted in yellow with black trim, electrically operated, German, 7 in. high (18 cm.), c. 1930. **£150-180** *S*

A painted wooden rocking horse, with glass eyes that change colour as the horse rocks back and forth, leather saddle and bridle and remains of horsehair mane, 55 in. long by 46 in. high. **£550-650** *CSK*

A Marklin coastal defence gun on revolving gantry, handles to each side to traverse and elevate the brass barrel, lacks ammunition gantry, German, 8 in. high (20.5 cm.), c. 1910-12. **£180-220** *S*

A group comprising the Queen of Love and Beauty on her throne, presiding over a typical mediaeva tournament, with marshal, knights, squires, herald and spectators. **£2,000-3,000** *P*

A de-contamination squad, probably by William Britain, 6 figures finished in cream and black, good condition. **£60-70** *SC*

A good 'always did spise a mule' cast-iron money bank, the jockey with coin slot mouth, the bucking action of the mule causing the coin to be deposited in aperture at base, American, bridle section missing, 10 in. long (25.5 cm.), c. 1880. **£100-£150** *S*

A child's pedal driven toy jeep, 38 in. long by 18 in. high by 16 in. wide. **£40-50** *KS*

A group of figures, depicting famous personalities in action at the battle of Crecy, 1346, 69 pieces. **£3,500-4,500** *P*

From the private collection of Frederick Ping.

A large Mignot display box of models of the French Army, First World War, G-F, box P, many swords, rifles, etc. gone, 1925. **£350-£400** *P*

An interesting collection of 'Slush Cast' American made toy military vehicles and guns, to go with 'Dime Store' figures. **£40-50** *P*

Eight standing figure Kobi toys, Japanese, the largest 5⅛ in. high (13 cm.), c. 1919. **£350-400** *S*

A Disney celluloid of Donald Duck, framed and glazed, 10 by 12¼ in. (26.5 by 31 cm.), 1950's. **£150-180** *S*

A large plush-covered Mickey Mouse soft toy, possibly by Steiff, partly restored, 37½ in. high, c. 1933. **£300-350** *S*

A tinplate 'Mickey Mouse' drummer, with articulated forearms resting on a snare-drum, when the plunger at the rear is depressed the lid rattles against the drumsticks, German, 6⅜ in. high (16.8 cm.), c. 1930. **£100-£150** *S*

(1.) An American cast-iron 'Uncle Sam' mechanical money bank, painted in colours, 11 in. high. **£40-£50** *PWC*

(2.) A good tinplate model of a steam driven open roadster on 4 rubber-tyred spoked wheels, damaged, 9½ in. wide. **£550-600** *PWC*

(3.) A Bassett Lowke 0-gauge clockwork 0-4-0 tank engine, 7 in. wide. **£90-100** *PWC*

(4.) A good German vertical model hot air engine with cast-iron base, 12 in. **£90-100** *PWC*

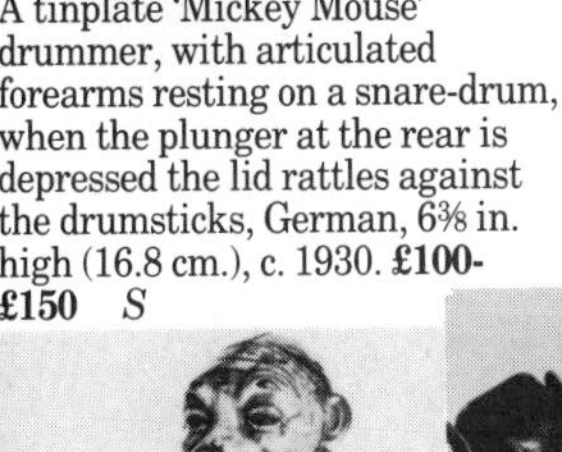

An amusing Hoytlife picture, the internal clockwork mechanism causing the negro figure to open and close his eyes, smile, original instructions to the rear, worn, complete with key, late 19th C. **£400-500** *SC*

A Disney celluloid of Little Hiawatha, framed and glazed, 8½ by 8¾ in. (21.5 by 22 cm.), c. 1938. **£75-85** *S*

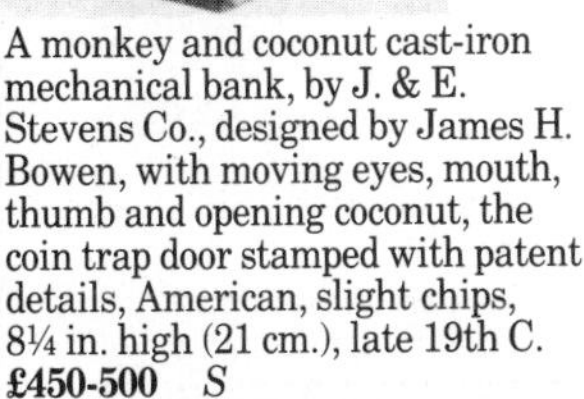

A monkey and coconut cast-iron mechanical bank, by J. & E. Stevens Co., designed by James H. Bowen, with moving eyes, mouth, thumb and opening coconut, the coin trap door stamped with patent details, American, slight chips, 8¼ in. high (21 cm.), late 19th C. **£450-500** *S*

Schoenhut circus animals, accessories and catalogue, of 'Schoenhut's Marvellous Toys', American, the largest 9½ in. long (24 cm.), c. 1910. **£150-200** *S*

A Disney celluloid of Mickey Mouse from 'Fantasia', the Sorcerer's Apprentice, framed and glazed, 10 by 12¼ in. (25.5 by 31 cm.), c. 1940. **£200-250** *S*

A metal dolls' kitchen of half-moon shape, English, 14½ in. high by 15¼ in. wide (37 by 39 cm.), c. 1880. **£600-700** *S*

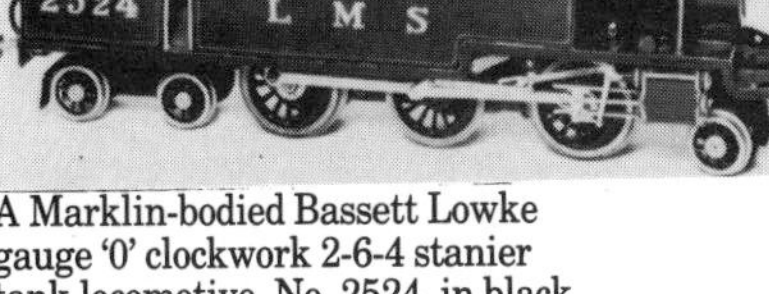

A Marklin-bodied Bassett Lowke gauge '0' clockwork 2-6-4 stanier tank locomotive, No. 2524, in black livery lined red, German and English, 1930's. **£400-500** *S*

A fine Bing boxed set comprising a 250 volt 4-4-0 locomotive and tender, 3 passenger coaches with interior lighting, a voltage reducer, track figures and 3 light bulbs, in original box. **£350-450** *P*

A Bing for Bassett-Lowke '0' gauge clockwork train set, comprising a 4-4-0 George V clockwork locomotive and tender, number 2263, and two 8-wheeled passenger coaches and a guards van number 1985, in original box, very good condition, German, c. 1910. **£250-300** *SC*

A Hornby Metropolitan electric 0-4-0 engine, with 2 teak-effect 8-wheeled bogie passenger coaches, transformer, track, and original box, excellent condition. **£350-£400** *SC*

A Hornby 0-gauge 4-6-2 locomotive and 6-wheel tender 'Princess Elizabeth', complete with centre rail pick-up, and sprung buffers in L.M.S. red livery No. 6201, in original fitted case. **£400-500** *CSK*

Miller's is a price GUIDE Not a price LIST.
The price ranges given reflect the average price a purchaser should pay for similar items. Condition, rarity of design or pattern, size, colour, provenance, restoration and many other factors must be taken into account when assessing values.

A Hornby 4-4-0 clockwork locomotive and tender, no. 2711, paintwork scratched. **£100-150** *SC*

An 0-gauge model of a Compagnie International Des Wagons Lits sleeping car, and a similar dining car, both by Marcel Darphin. **£180-£220** *CSK*

A fine gauge '0' engineered electric model of GWR 4-6-0 compound locomotive, No. 1004 'County of Somerset', with 7-pole 12v electric motor within, on small section of track. **£280-360** *S*

An '0' gauge Bassett-Lowke 2-6-0 spirit-fired locomotive and tender, no. 42980, in L.N.W.R. black livery, chipped, in original box, together with 4 L.M.S. 8-wheeled bogie passenger coaches, a G.W. bogie passenger coach, good condition, together with a large quantity of track and spares. **£350-£400** *S*

A Marklin gauge 'one' spirit-fired 4-4-0 L.N.W.R. locomotive, finished in black lined red and yellow, with matching 6-wheeled tender, German, c. 1912. **£500-600** *S*

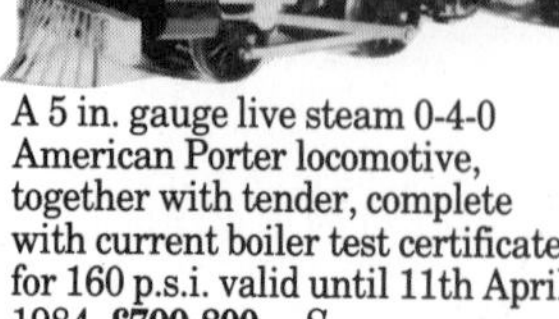

A 5 in. gauge live steam 0-4-0 American Porter locomotive, together with tender, complete with current boiler test certificate for 160 p.s.i. valid until 11th April, 1984. **£700-800** *S*

A Marklin gauge I clockwork 0-6-0 side tank locomotive in L.M.S. red livery, repainted, with Ramsbottom safety valve, whistle, steps and hand irons, with cab-operated controls. **£200-300** *CSK*

A good 5 in. gauge G.W.R. 2-6-2 Prairie Tank locomotive No. 4577, 'Firefly', built to the design of Martin Evans, with coal-fired copper boiler complete with test certificate to 120 p.s.i. valid to 2.4.83, overall length 40 in. (102 cm.). **£2,000-3,000** *S*

A 2½ in. gauge L.N.E.R. Pacific 4-6-2 locomotive and tender, No. 4472, the coal-fired boiler with outside cylinders and Walschaerts valve gear, complete, 39 in. long (99 cm.). **£650-750** *S*

An extremely rare gauge 4, live steam, spirit-fired Continental type 4-4-0 locomotive and tender No. E III by Marklin, and another, damaged, chassis finished in original paintwork, some damage but no over-painting, 2 gauge 4 open trucks, one missing 2 wheels, and a fine L.S.W.R. twin bogie full brake, in original livery, by Bing, early 20th C. **£4,500-5,500** *CSK*

A rare Bassett-Lowke electric '0' gauge 2-6-0 mogul locomotive, first version, complete with tender, no. 13000, L.M.S. maroon, with headlamps, excellent condition, 11½ in. long (29 cm.). **£200-300** *S*

A shipbuilder's model of the Freighter S.S. 'Vechtdyk', built at Sunderland Shipbuilding Co. at South Dock, Sunderland, English, 1920, built for The Holland America Line, Rotterdam, 55 in. long. **£3,000-3,500** *WW*

A Napoleonic prisoner-of-war boxwood and bone Ship Model, 61 cm. high by 72 cm. long. **£2,500-£3,000** *P*

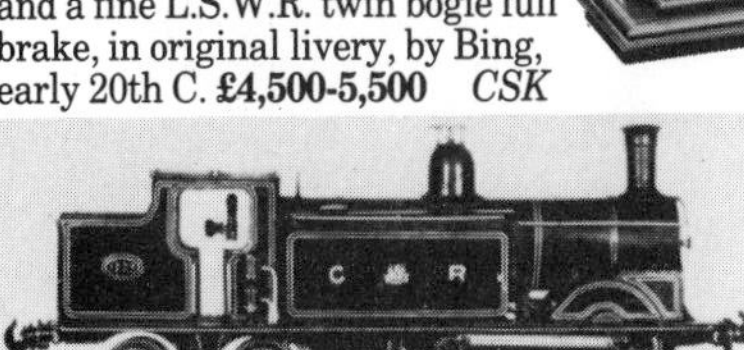

A clockwork 0-6-0 side tank locomotive in Caledonian black livery No. 784, and a clockwork 0-4-4 side tank locomotive in Caledonian blue livery No. 1227. **£280-360** *CSK*

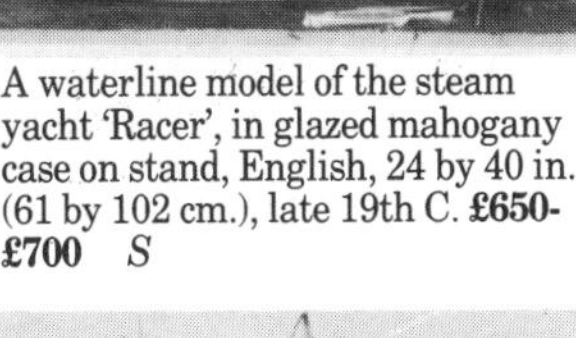

A waterline model of the steam yacht 'Racer', in glazed mahogany case on stand, English, 24 by 40 in. (61 by 102 cm.), late 19th C. **£650-£700** *S*

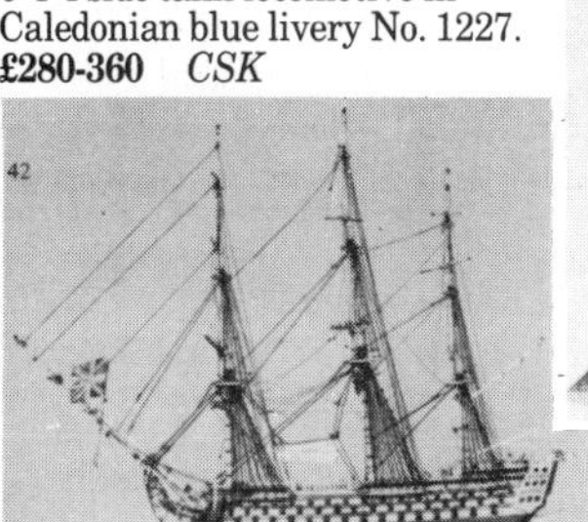

A fine French bone prisoner-of-war work model of a Royal Navy 4-masted man of war, 12½ in., early 19th C. **£2,000-2,500** *CSK*

A ship's model of a ketch, the 'Irene', built c. 1900, recently restored, 28 in. long (71 cm.). **£180-£250** *SC*

A prisoner-of-war bone model of an 88-gun third-rate ship-of-the-line, on wood and bone stand, 20 by 27 in. (51 by 69 cm.), early 19th C. **£2,000-3,000** *S*

A bone prisoner-of-war 114-gun first class ship-of-the-line, on bone stand, the base with string for operating the retractable guns on 3 decks, on later mahogany oval base under glass dome, 9 by 12 in. (23 by 30.5 cm.), early 19th C. **£2,000-£2,500** *S*

A Jean Schoenner zinc-plate spirit-fired river boat, mechanism replaced, paint poor, German, 13¾ in. long (35 cm.), c. 1902. **£250-£300** *S*

A waterline model of the steam yacht 'Victoria', with raked masts, lifeboats, ventilators and deck houses, in glazed case with painted seascape, English, 33 in. wide (84 cm.), late 19th C. **£700-800** *S*

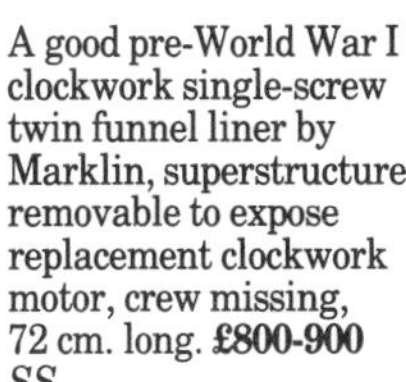

A good pre-World War I clockwork single-screw twin funnel liner by Marklin, superstructure removable to expose replacement clockwork motor, crew missing, 72 cm. long. **£800-900** *SS*

A Jean Schoenner zinc-plate steam pinnace, lacks rear flag, paintwork poor, some parts replaced and restored, German, 18½ in. long (47 cm.), c. 1902. **£250-300** *S*

A Bing live-steam, spirit-fired battleship, the engine with burner and funnel, powering a single screw, on wheeled stand, 22 in. long, c. 1905. **£800-1,000** *CSK*

A shipbuilder's model of the general cargo vessel S.S. P.L.M. 24 of Le Havre, 51½ in. long. **£1,400-£1,600** *AG*

A Bing tinplate 3-funnel liner, having lifeboats, ventilators, steering wheel, handrails and bridge, the clockwork mechanism concealed, 50 cm. **£350-400** *P*

A Schoenner live steam oscillating cylinder 2-2-0 floor train, 70 cm. gauge, German, c. 1900. **£300-£400** *S*

A late 19th C. scale model of an undertype compound steam engine, base plate bearing a brass plaque inscribed 'R.A. Illingworth, Maker, 1888-9', 26¾ in. long, 16 in. high by 11¾ in. wide. **£650-750** *Bea*

A professionally built-in wood scale model of a Shand & Mason horse-drawn fire appliance, with coal-fired vertical boiler, wooden base, overall length 82 cm. **£3,500-£4,000** *P*

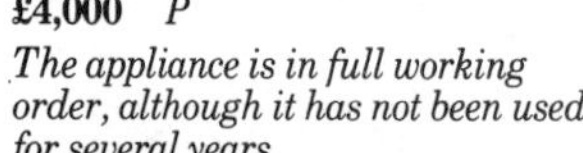

The appliance is in full working order, although it has not been used for several years.

A Bassett-Lowke ¾ in. scale traction engine, spirit fired boiler, with single cylinder, good condition, 15 in. long (38 cm.). **£280-340** *SC*

A gas-fired working model of a mid 19th C. woodworking machine shop, 29½ in. wide (75 cm.). **£400-£500** *S*

A coal-fired live steam traction engine, the 'Cheshire', 40 in. long. **£750-850** *SC*

A 19th C. brass model steam driven flat bed engine, 10 in. wide. **£80-£100** *CLA*

A large and early Ernst Plank spirit-fired tinplate fire pumper, with brass boiler, twin cylinders, brass flywheel and pump, lacks seat and burner, hand-painted body poor, some parts replaced, cast lead alloy wheels, German, 15 in. long (38 cm.), c. 1895. **£1,000-1,200** *S*

A large Bing tinplate vertical steam engine, spirit-fired, lacks burner, the base stamped 'GB 1048', German, 19 in. high (48 cm.), c. 1910. **£200-250** *S*

A vertical hot air engine, possibly by Carette, German, 12½ in. high (32 cm.), c. 1904. **£100-150** *SC*

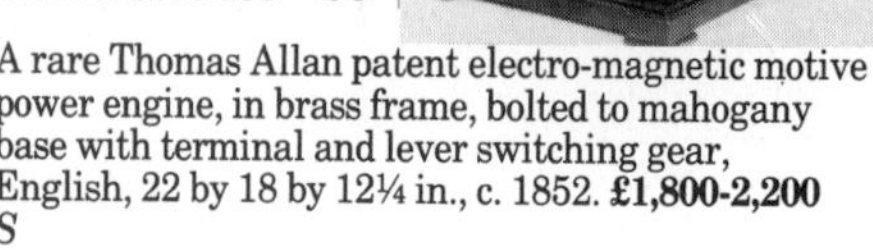

A rare Thomas Allan patent electro-magnetic motive power engine, in brass frame, bolted to mahogany base with terminal and lever switching gear, English, 22 by 18 by 12¼ in., c. 1852. **£1,800-2,200** *S*

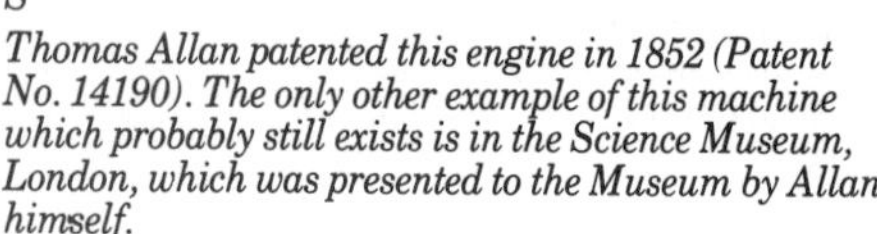

Thomas Allan patented this engine in 1852 (Patent No. 14190). The only other example of this machine which probably still exists is in the Science Museum, London, which was presented to the Museum by Allan himself.

A Chinese ivory chess set, red and natural, each piece as a member of the Chinese court, 2 balls slightly damaged, 6.5 to 13.5 cm., and a leather chess and backgammon case, 45 cm., mid 19th C. **£150-£200** *S*

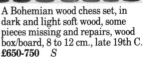

A Bohemian wood chess set, in dark and light soft wood, some pieces missing and repairs, wood box/board, 8 to 12 cm., late 19th C. **£650-750** *S*

A Delhi chess set, natural ivory and horn, the knights carved as horses' heads, the kings and queens with pierced crown tops, 2 to 4½ in. high (11.7 to 5.2 cm.), mid 19th C. **£250-300** *S*

A Chinese carved ivory chess set, white and sepia, as members of the Imperial Court, in contemporary fitted folding case/board, 3 to 4 in. high (7.3 to 10.3 cm.), 20th C. **£300-£350** *S*

A Spanish bone chess set, sepia and natural, some small chips, 5 to 8 cm., late 18th C. **£500-600** *S*

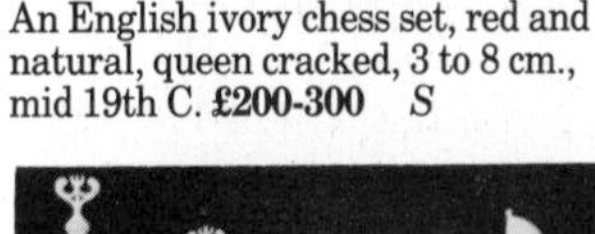

An English ivory chess set, red and natural, queen cracked, 3 to 8 cm., mid 19th C. **£200-300** *S*

A tournament-size ivory chess set of Staunton pattern, red and natural, 5.5 to 11.5 cm., mid 19th C. **£500-650** *S*

An English ivory chess set, red and natural, some small chips, 3.5 to 8 cm., mid 19th C. **£180-220** *S*

A Dieppe ivory chess set, stained red, blue and natural, 6 to 8.5 cm., early 19th C. **£600-700** *S*

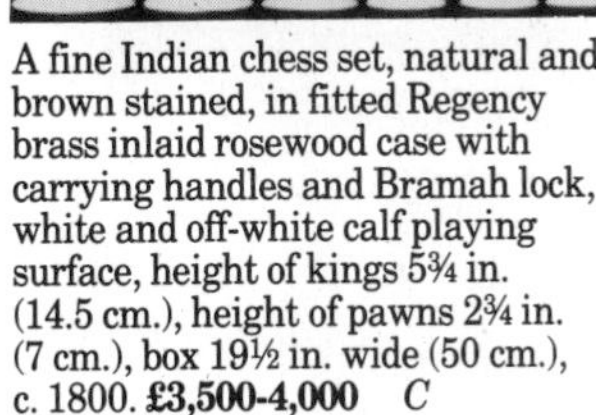

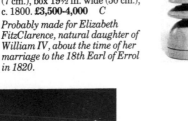

A fine Indian chess set, natural and brown stained, in fitted Regency brass inlaid rosewood case with carrying handles and Bramah lock, white and off-white calf playing surface, height of kings 5¾ in. (14.5 cm.), height of pawns 2¾ in. (7 cm.), box 19½ in. wide (50 cm.), c. 1800. **£3,500-4,000** *C*

Probably made for Elizabeth FitzClarence, natural daughter of William IV, about the time of her marriage to the 18th Earl of Errol in 1820.

An English ebony and boxwood chess set, each piece turned, one pawn scratched, 4 to 10.5 cm., mid 19th C. **£150-250** *S*

An unusual Indian chess set, the red or black stained bases decorated with eyelet ornament, finial to black king damaged, probably early 19th C., height of kings 2¼ in. (5.8 cm.), height of pawns 1½ in. (3.8 cm.). **£3,200-£3,400** *C*

A large Chinese ivory chess set, red and natural, each piece carved as a member of the Chinese court, some pawns with swords or lances missing, 10 to 18 cm., mid 19th C. **£750-850** *S*

A fine and rare 19th C. Russian silver and silver-gilt chess set with board, the gilt characters modelled as Boyars, the silver characters modelled as peasants, the knights as horses and the castles as cauldrons upon log fires, mostly by Ivan Chlebnikov, some pieces by Julius Rappoport, St. Petersburg, 45.5 cm. square, c. 1890. **£4,000-£4,500** *P*

An Indian ivory and tortoiseshell inlaid chess and backgammon board/box, 40.5 by 40.5 cm. open, c. 1840. **£400-500** *S*

An Austrian walnut marquetry games board, the interior for backgammon, inlaid with pewter and marquetry panels, the exterior with a chequer board and 9 men's morris with inlaid dice, perhaps Vienna, 17 in. square closed (43 cm.), early 18th C. **£4,500-£5,500** *S*

An early 19th C. brass inlaid cribbage board, 10½ in. **£50-60** *MPA*

The History of Little Fanny, exemplified in a Series of Figures, a printed booklet, with hand-coloured engraved figures of Fanny, the girl's head interchangeable, published by S. & J. Fuller, Temple of Fancy, Rathbone Place, London, 1811, in slipcase. **£100-150** *CSK*

A tartanware cribbage board with pegs, 8 in. **£20-25** *HA*

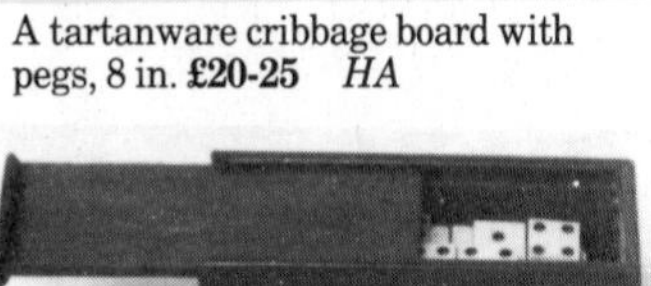

A late Victorian miniature domino set, 2 in. **£30-35** *HA*

A horn lidded dice shaker with wooden dice. **£18-22** *HA*

A 19th C. mah-jongg box, complete, 9½ in. wide. **£120-140** *HA*

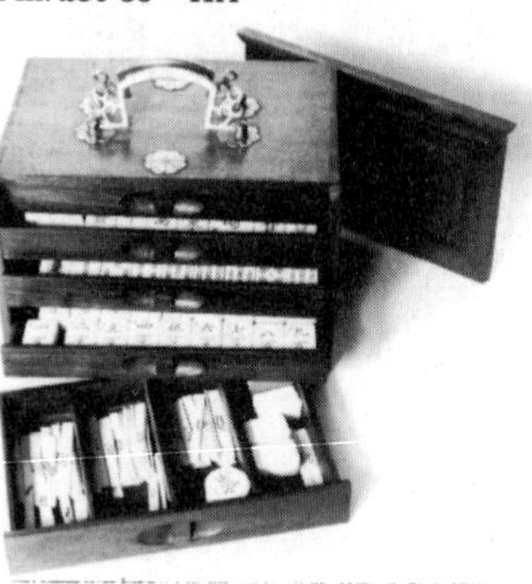

A 19th C. mah-jongg box, 8¾ in. wide. **£100-130** *HA*

A treen solitaire board with stone balls, 8½ in. diam. **£15-20** *HA*

A 19th C. demonstration device, showing 2 joined cones apparently running uphill in defiance of gravity. **£200-300** *HAD*

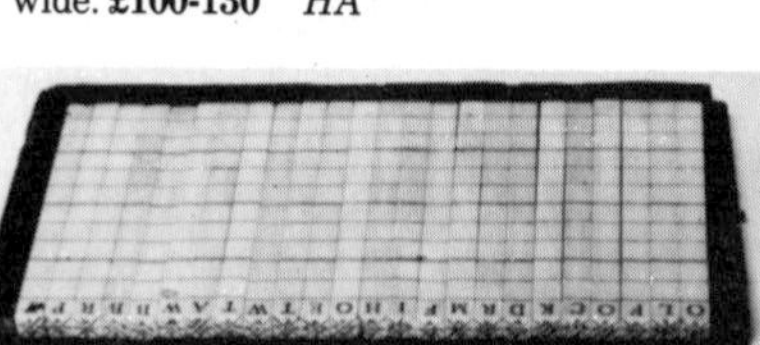

A 17th C. cased cryptographic device, with concealed cypher of Charles II. **£3,000-5,000** *HAD*

A Zuleger Tanzbar paper-roll concertina, the 16-key instrument in stained wood case, with 17 rolls, German, early 20th C. **£550-650** *S*

A polyphon disc machine, with coin slots on 2 sides, with sublime harmony comb arrangement, periphery drive motor, German, pediment, partially replaced, good working order, with 17 discs, 52 in. high (132 cm.), c. 1900. **£1,600-£1,800** *S*

A composite one-keyed ivory flute, the lower middle and foot joints by Charles Bizey, Paris, stamped Bizey, silver mounts, one nickel replacement, the end-cap engraved James Hogg, Altrine, the single key a later nickel replacement with square cover, sounding length 21 in. (53.3 cm.), 18th C. **£1,000-£1,500** *S*

James Hogg (1770-1835) is better known as the 'Ettrick Shepherd'. His poetry was published in Blackwood's Magazine in the early 19th C. Hogg was also known as a musician.

A 4-keyed boxwood flute by Wafford, London, stamped Wafford on all joints, ivory mounts, silver keys with bevelled square covers, in original mahogany case, sounding length 20 13/16 in. (52.9 cm.), c. 1775. **£600-700** *S*

A French single action pedal harp, by Cousineau, the soundboard painted with pastoral scenes, seven pedals, 37 strings, extreme height 63¾ in. (161.9 cm.), c. 1775. **£2,000-£2,500** *C*

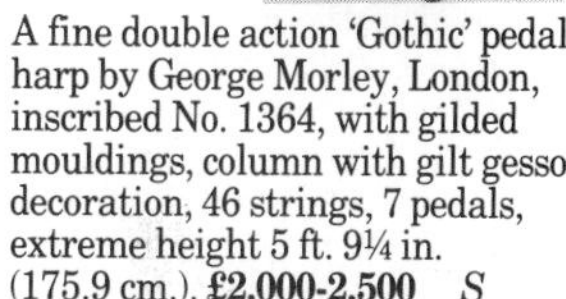

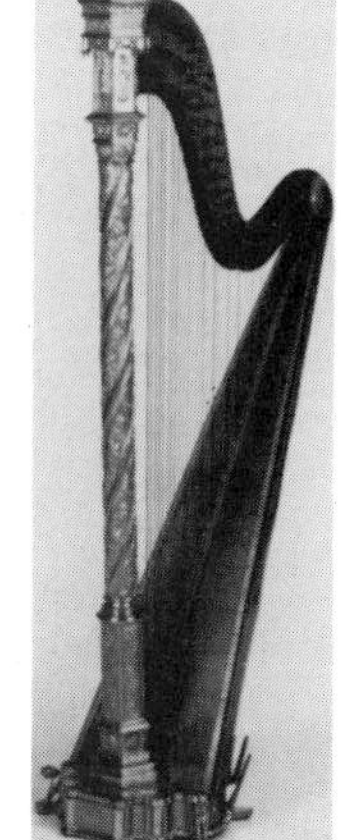

A rare French brass hunting horn by R. Cretien, Vernon, inscribed R.C. with the device of a stag, later mouthpiece, total length 31¾ in. (80.7 cm.), mid 17th C. **£2,500-£3,000** *S*

A fine double action 'Gothic' pedal harp by George Morley, London, inscribed No. 1364, with gilded mouldings, column with gilt gesso decoration, 46 strings, 7 pedals, extreme height 5 ft. 9¼ in. (175.9 cm.). **£2,000-2,500** *S*

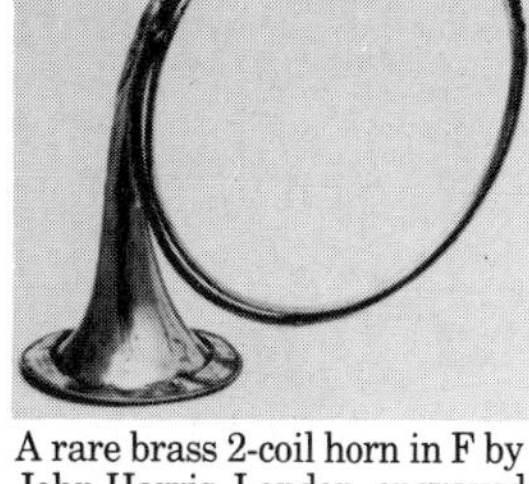

A rare brass 2-coil horn in F by John Harris, London, engraved on the garland Iohn Harris in Barwick Street, Old Soho, Londini Fecit, shank and mouthpiece absent, tube length 12 ft. 5 in. (378 cm.), diam. of coil 19½ in. (49.5 cm.), diam. of bell 9⅜ in. (23.8 cm.), early 18th C. **£1,000-1,500** *S*

A brass euphonium, stamped 'patent clear bore', maker J. Higham, 127 Strangeways, Manchester, No. 42198, 23½'. **£120-160** *DDM*

An ornate walnut late Victorian organ by the 'Bell Guelph' Organ & Piano Co. Ltd., complete with patented Feb. 24th 1887 mouse proof foot pedals. **£225-275** *Fr*

A reed barrel organ playing 8 airs in mahogany case, with label of A. Varetto & Sons, Manchester, 20 in. wide. **£1,200-1,400** *CSK*

A small George III English chamber organ by William Phillips, Little Tower Hill, London, playing 10 dance airs, with 4 stops and 14 keys, with boxwood inlaid mahogany case, 46 in. high by 20½ in. wide by 15 in. deep. **£2,000-£2,400** *B*

A table barrel organ with 14 keys and wood pipes in rosewood case, the 9-air barrel inscribed J. Sanders, No.6, Wilson St. Moorfields, 18½ in. high, the barrel 11¾ in. long. **£700-800** *CSK*

A fine English bureau chamber organ, the case of panelled mahogany with shaped brass hinges and brass handles, 4½ octave keyboard, with ebony naturals and ivory overlaid accidentals, 5 stops, pedal operated bellows, 3 ft. 8¼ in. wide by 3 ft. 6½ in. high (112.4 by 108 cm.), c. 1760. **£7,500-8,500** *S*

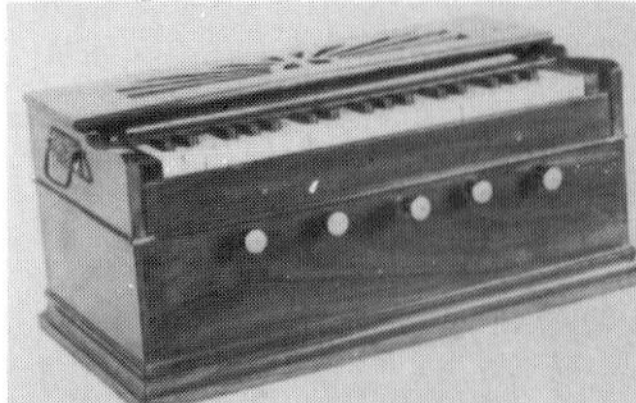

An Edwardian hand pumped table organ. **£25-30** *JMW*

A Jean-Marc Mouligne book-playing organ, the 24-note instrument with 4 racks of wooden pipes, together with 9 books of music, some incomplete, French, modern, 25 by 22 by 19 in. (63.5 by 56 by 48 cm.). **£450-550** *S*

A 22-key Benjamin Dobson church or chamber barrel organ, on base containing five 55 cm. barrels each playing 10 sacred or secular tunes, English, 70 by 29 by 22 in. (178 by 74 by 56 cm.), c. 1799. **£900-1,100** *S*

A Bechstein Arts and Crafts movement piano 'The Mediaeval Upright Grand' designed by Walter Cave. **£800-900** *EH*

A Gem roller organ, the 16 cm. pinned wooden cob operating 20 keys with handle at the front, together with 6 wooden cobs, American, 14½ in. wide (37 cm.), c. 1890. **£500-550** *S*

An American harmonium by Story & Clark of Chicago, 42 in. wide, c. 1900. **£225-275** *Ph*

An Italian ottavino, inscribed on the reverse of the nameboard Pasquinus Quercius Florentinus F. MDCVI, decorated with ivory studs, the 3½ octave keyboard, with boxwood naturals and rosewood accidentals, the later outer case of deal overlaid with red velvet, the interior of the lid painted with Classical motifs, 2 ft. 9³⁄₁₆ in. long (84.3 cm.). **£1,800-£2,200** *S*

The style of the decoration on the interior of the lid of the outer case bears a strong resemblance to that found on many of the keyboard instruments which passed through the hands of Leopoldo Franciolini, listed in his catalogues.

A double-manual harpsichord, the nameboard inscribed Jacobus et Abraham Kirckman Londini Fecerunt 1777; the figured mahogany case cross-banded with interior of burr-walnut, on a modern trestle stand with pedal, 94 in. long by 37½ in. wide (239 by 95 cm.). **£12,000-15,000** *C*

A Keith Prowse barrel piano playing 10 tunes including Dambuster's March and Colonel Bogey, with hand cart with wood wheels and hubcaps by Day & Day, Clacton, 89 in. overall. **£1,200-£1,400** *CSK*

A rare Victoria orchestrionette, the 24-note instrument with tracker bar, winding handle at the side, with 12 bands of music, German, 19 in. high (48 cm.), c. 1895. **£700-£800** *S*

A Klepetar 36-note barrel piano orchestrion with coin-slot mechanism, gravity motor, mandolin attachment, 2 drums, cymbal and triangle, with spare barrel in base, 100 in. high. **£2,000-£2,500** *CSK*

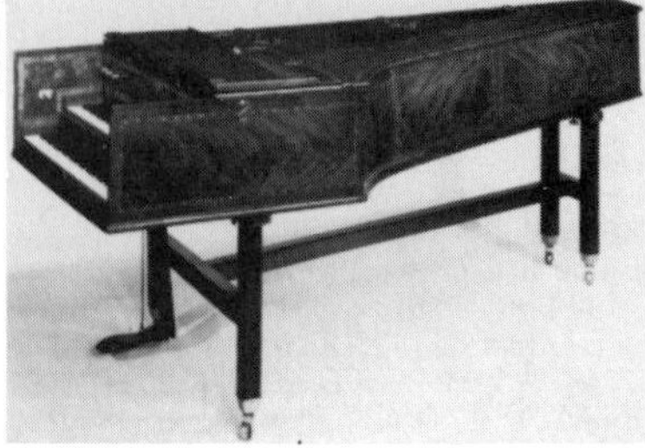

A Collard & Collard burr-walnut grand piano, the iron frame with a sounding board, stamped Collard & Collard 1870 and numbered in ink 75602, 1870's. **£500-700** *S*

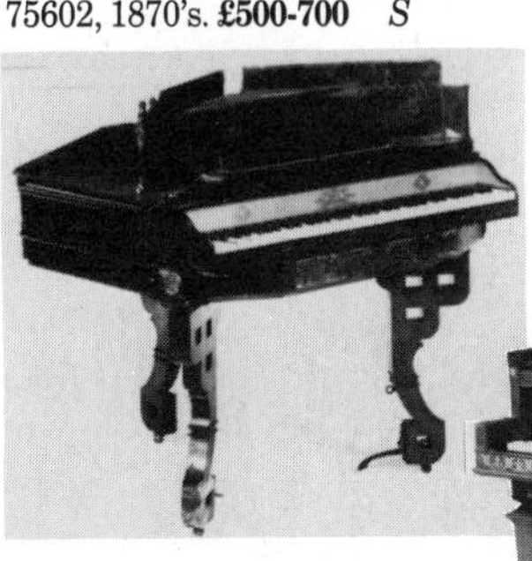

An hexagonal table piano by Jean-Henri Pape, Paris, inscribed in incised gilt letters on the nameboard, also labelled together with maintenance instructions, the mahogany case with applied chinoiserie mouldings, retractable 6 octave keyboard, with ivory naturals and ebony accidentals, 3 ft. 8 in. wide (111.8 cm.), c. 1850. **£700-800** *S*

The patent for this type of piano was taken out by Pape in 1845.

A child's upright pianoforte by H. Vogelsangs, Brussels, inscribed in brass inlay, the ebonised case with 2 gilt-metal candlesticks, 6 octave keyboard, 3 ft. 4¼ in. high by 3 ft. 2⅞ in. wide (102.2 by 98.8 cm.), late 19th C. **£400-600** *S*

An Italian grand pianoforte by Domenico Perrotta, inscribed within a gilt-metal frame, the case of mahogany, 6 octave keyboard, with ivory naturals and ebony accidentals, Viennese action, 2 knee-levers (genouillere), 7 ft. 4½ in. long by 3 ft. 7¾ in. wide (224.8 by 111.1 cm.), c. 1795. **£2,100-2,400** *S*

A walnut boudoir grand pianoforte by John Broadwood & Sons, London, 1897, inscribed, serial number 44774, the case inlaid, 7 octave keyboard with ivory naturals and ebony accidentals, 2 pedals, 6 ft. 3½ in. long by 4 ft. 7⅜ in. wide (191.8 by 140.6 cm. **£3,000-4,000** *S*

A baby grand piano by J. Broadwood & Sons, No. 253630, in a walnut-veneered case with tapering square legs and brass castors, 4 ft. 4 in. long. **£1,000-£1,200** *Bea*

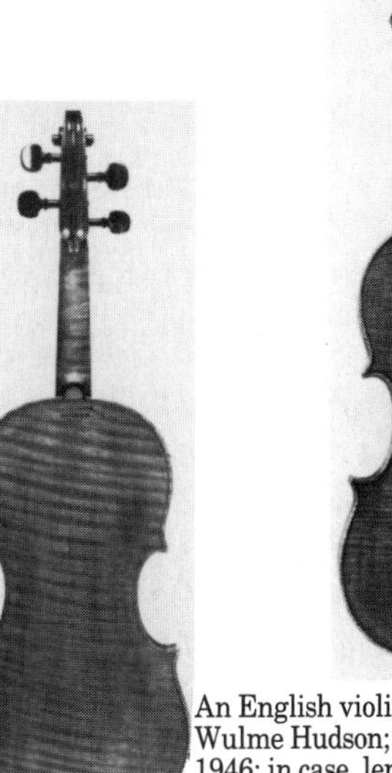

An English violin labelled Geo. Wulme Hudson; fecit/London anno 1946; in case, length of back 14 in. (35.5 cm.). **£1,200-1,600** *C*

An English violin by Lockey Hill, London, 1791, labelled Lockey Hill, Maker, Islington, 1791, and stamped Longman Lukey & Co., No. 26 Cheapside, London, beneath the button, length of back 13¹⁵⁄₁₆ in. (35.4 cm.), and a violin bow, in shaped case with outer canvas cover. **£1,200-1,500** *S*

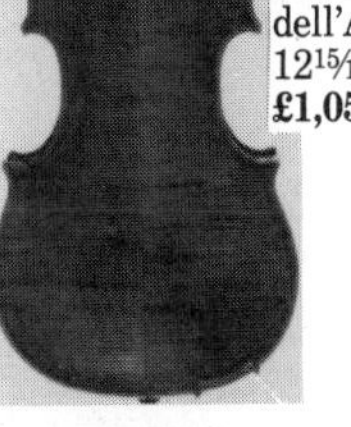

A composite violin labelled Leopold Widhalm, with 2 violin bows in case, length of back 13¹⁵⁄₁₆ in. (35.4 cm.). **£650-750** *S*

An Italian child's violin labelled Carlo Guiseppe Testore in Contrada Larga de Milano Segno dell'Aquila 1729, length of back 12¹⁵⁄₁₆ in. (32.8 cm.), in case. **£1,050-1,250** *S*

An English clavichord, by Thos. Tomkinson, London, inscribed Thos. Tomkinson, Dean Street, Soho, mahogany case with ebony stringing, 4½ octave range, ivory naturals and ebony accidentals, 67¾ in. long by 25 in. wide (172 by 63.5 cm.). **£200-300** *L*

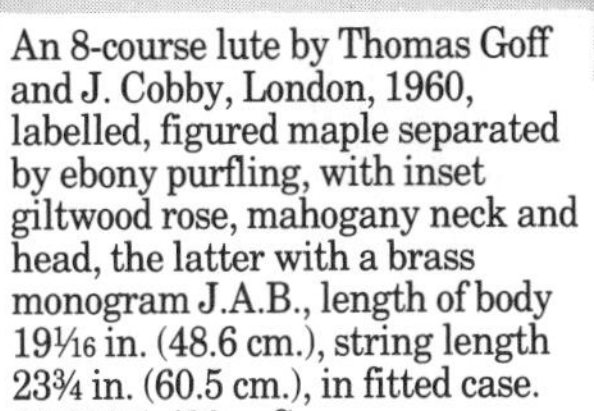

An 8-course lute by Thomas Goff and J. Cobby, London, 1960, labelled, figured maple separated by ebony purfling, with inset giltwood rose, mahogany neck and head, the latter with a brass monogram J.A.B., length of body 19¹⁄₁₆ in. (48.6 cm.), string length 23¾ in. (60.5 cm.), in fitted case. **£1,200-1,400** *S*

A French guitar, unlabelled, one-piece back, ebony overlaid neck, 34½ in. long (87.6 cm.), c. 1850, in case. **£150-200** *S*

A Moroccan 'Ud, labelled Mustapha Harakat, 615, Rue de Goulima — Casablanca, the body of 15 mahogany ribs, decorated with inlay of stained wood and white composition, 5 double courses and 1 single course, 33½ in. long (85 cm.). **£300-400** *S*

A guitar, unlabelled, School of Panormo, London, the 2-piece back and ribs of rosewood, brass machine heads by Rance with ivory pegs, 37 in. long (94 cm.), c. 1850, in case. **£300-350** *S*

A good English violin by William Atkinson, Tottenham, length of back 14 in. (35.5 cm.), 1889. **£1,050-£1,250** *S*

A silver-mounted violin bow by A. Vigneron, the stick with an ivory face, weight 59 grams. **£900-£1,200** *C*

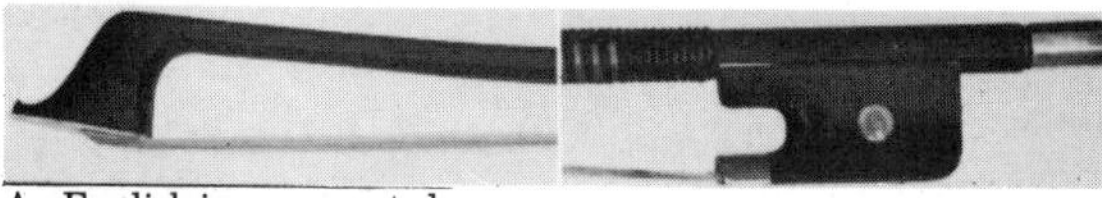

An English ivory-mounted violoncello bow by Dodd, London, open ivory frog, ivory button, 71 grams, and a German silver-mounted violin bow, stamped Dodd, the ebony frog inlaid with silver rings enclosing pearl eyes (one absent), silver overlaid ebony button, 57 grams. **£600-650** *S*

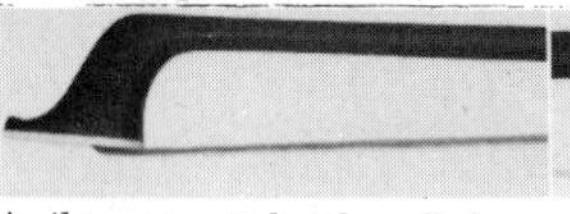

A silver-mounted violoncello bow by Dodd, London, the later ebony frog inlaid with pearl eyes, silver overlaid ebony button, 85 grams, in bow box. **£400-450** *S*

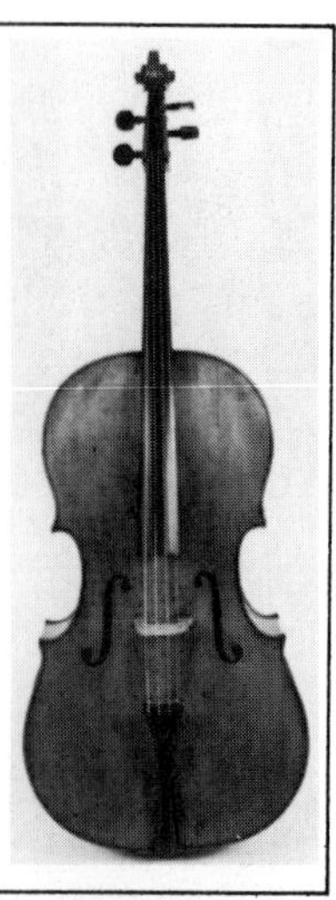

A superb Italian violoncello bearing the label: Io Bap Rogerius Bon: Nicolai Amati De Cremona Alumnus Brixiae Fecit Anno Domini 1690. LOB 28 in. with a fitted wood case by W. E. Hill & Sons. **£60,000 +** *P*

The instrument came from a private owner and is known in the music world as the 'Lancashire Strad' — because it has been in various ownerships in the north of England and was believed in the 19th C. to be the work of Stradivarius. Rogeri worked with Stradivarius at Cremona. In 1877 the cello sold in the salerooms of Puttick and Simpson (later part of Phillips) for £370 when it appeared in a quartette of instruments attributed to Stradivarius.

A fine violin by Arthur Richardson, bearing the maker's signed label in Crediton, Devon, dated 1935, No. 220. L.O.B. 13$^{15}/_{16}$ in. (354 mm.), in case. **£1,200-1,400** *P*

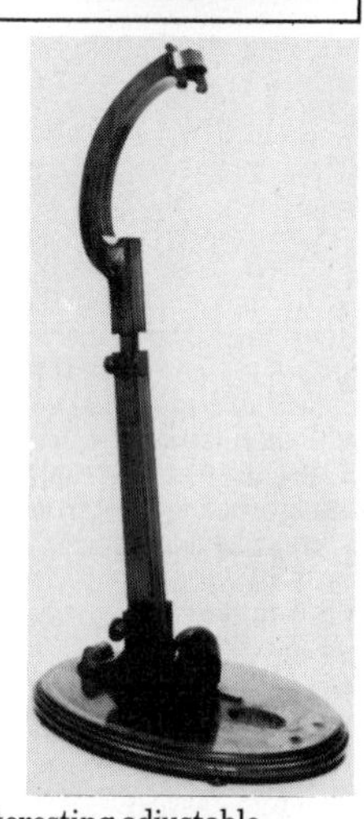

An interesting adjustable violoncello stand of mahogany, inlaid with boxwood and ebony stringing, late 18th C. **£600-800** *S*

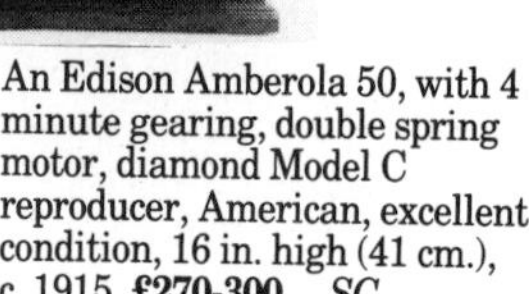

A Sublime Harmony interchangeable cylinder musical box with double-spring motor, tune selector, tune indicator, speed control, instant check and zither attachment, 30 in. wide, the cylinders 13¼ in., the three cylinders contained in grained case. **£1,000-1,200** *CSK*

A fine Aeolion Vocalion gramophone in Chinese Chippendale-style case on stand, Graduola internal and remote tone control, Aeolion Vocalion soundbox, 54½ in. high. **£400-500** *CSK*

A musical box playing 8 airs, accompanied by 18-key organ and 6 bells with automaton strikers, 24 in. wide, the cylinder 13 in. **£700-900** *CSK*

An Edison Amberola 50, with 4 minute gearing, double spring motor, diamond Model C reproducer, American, excellent condition, 16 in. high (41 cm.), c. 1915. **£270-300** *SC*

An Edison Amberola 30, with single spring motor, diamond C reproducer, stained oak body, louvred panel to the front, American, good condition, 13½ in. high (34 cm.), c. 1915. **£180-220** *SC*

A forte piano musical box by J. H. Heller, playing 12 airs (2 per turn), with separate zither attachments for each comb, 27 in. wide, the cylinder 15 by 3 in. diam. **£1,200-£1,500** *CSK*

A good coin operated 11⅞ in. symphonion disc musical box, with 'sublime harmonie' comb arrangement, in stained wood case, German, 33 in. high (84 cm.), late 19th C., together with 16 discs. **£1,000-1,200** *SC*

An interchangeable cylinder musical box, the 33 cm. cylinders each playing 8 airs, with tune indicator and zither attachment, probaby Swiss, 38½ in. long (98 cm.), c. 1870. **£1,200-1,400** *SC*

An Edison Amberola 75, with 4 minute gearing, diamond C reproducer, double-spring motor, tinplate horn concealed, American, excellent condition, c. 1915. **£400-£500** *SC*

A fine Excelsior buffet-style musical box by Mojon Manger & Co., playing 8 airs accompanied by drum and 6 bells with double spring motor, tune indicator and separate tune sheet, in walnut-veneered case, 27 in. wide, the cylinder 13 in. **£2,000-2,500** *CSK*

A fine Jerome Thibouville Lamy flute 'voix celestes' cylinder musical box, the 42 cm. cylinder playing 12 tunes, 17 reed organ concealed below the ebonised fretwork base board, French, excellent condition, 29½ in. long (75 cm.), c. 1865. **£1,600-1,800** *SC*

An early key-wound overture cylinder musical box, No. 8384, the 18.5 cm. cylinder playing 3 overtures on comb with 115 teeth, Swiss, 13¼ in. wide (33.5 cm.), c. 1830. **£1,000-1,200** *S*

A bells and drum in sight cylinder musical box, possibly by John Manger & Co., the 28 cm. cylinder playing 8 airs, stamped J.M. & Co., Swiss, 22½ in. long (57 cm.), c. 1865. **£600-700** *SC*

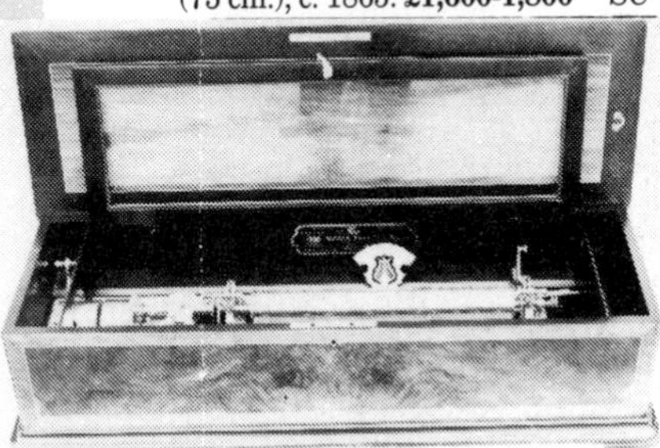
A late 19th C. music box by Nicole Freres, No. 52306, the burr-walnut case with boxwood line and satinwood edging, containing a 3-comb sublime harmony movement interchangeable cylinder, 17 in. long, with speed controller and tune indicator, the case 41 in. wide. **£1,000-1,300** *B*

An 11¾ in. Abrahams 'The Britannia' disc musical box, with 49 metal discs, Swiss, 25 in. wide (63.5 cm.), c. 1900. **£450-500** *S*

An unusual bells in sight cylinder musical box, No. 6221, made for the Chinese market, the 16 cm. cylinder playing 6 airs, Swiss, 24½ in. high (62 cm.), late 19th C. **£1,100-1,500** *S*

(l.) A Swiss cylinder musical box to play 12 airs, in banded walnut case with bird marquetry lid, cylinder 13 in. **£500-£550** *RBB*

(r.) A table polyphon with metal disc in walnut case, 13 in. **£160-200** *RBB*

A Nicole Freres overture cylinder musical box, No. 40857, the 24 cm. cylinder playing 3 overtures, cylinder in need of repinning, also lacking tune sheet and glass cover, the comb in need of redamping and cleaning, Swiss, 18½ in. wide (47 cm.), c. 1865. **£1,200-1,500** *S*

An interchangeable cylinder musical box with double-spring motor, zither attachment and 6 cylinders playing 6 airs each, in burr-walnut case with inlaid lid, 33 in. wide, the cylinders 13 in. **£1,600-1,800** *CSK*

A key-wind overture box by Nicole Freres, playing 4 overtures, Gamme No. 721, in grained case with endflap and inlaid lid, 18½ in. wide, the cylinder 12 by 3¼ in. diam. **£3,300-3,600** *CSK*

An 11 in. coin-in-slot upright polyphon disc musical box, with 16 discs, 21½ in. high. **£600-800** *CSK*

A 24⅝ in. upright polyphon disc musical box with top-wind motor, lacking cover, with 12 discs, 79 in. high. **£2,500-3,000** *CSK*

A Celestina organette, with 11 paper rolls, American, 15 in. wide (38 cm.), c. 1890. **£500-£550** *S*

A street barrel organette, the carved wooden casing with crank wound and worm driven central barrel, with detachable metal tune roll, complete with 17 metal tune sheets, partially restored, English, 17½ in. wide (45 cm.), c. 1840, contained in wooden box. **£400-£500** *S*

A singing bird box and stand, silver coloured metal, unmarked, probably German, with key, 4½ in. high (11.8 cm.), early 20th C. **£500-£600** *S*

A 15⅝ in. polyphon table disc musical box with 'comb-and-a-half' movement, with 26 discs. **£800-£900** *CSK*

A good Samuel Troll nightingale song box, Swiss, 7¼ in. square (18.5 cm.), c. 1900. **£350-450** *S*

An Edison 'Triumph' phonograph, model B, with 2 minute gearing, model C reproducer, the speaker arm fitted with shaving device, recording head, 16 cylinders, American, very good condition, 17 in. long (43 cm.), c. 1906. **£350-£400** *S*

A brightly enamelled gilt-metal singing bird box, the cover painted with a girl on a swing after 'Fragonard', with panels of dark blue and cream enamel, maker's mark EB in an oval incuse, Continental, with key, 4 in. long (10.3 cm.), mid 20th C. **£900-£1,000** *S*

A fine Edison opera phonograph, no. 1524, Type SM, Model A, with sapphire stylus, on mahogany base, original instruction booklet, and a quantity of sapphires, complete with brown mahogany cygnet horn, American, excellent condition, 18 in. long overall (46 cm.), c. 1912. **£2,000-3,000** *S*

An Edison diamond disc phonograph, serial no. L53 5094, with standard play mechanism, in mahogany cabinet with fretwork panel to the front, American, repair to tone arm, 20 in. high (51 cm.), c. 1925. **£200-250** *SC*

An Edison Bijou coin-slot phonograph with Gem mechanism, 'B' reproducer and oak case with curved glass lid and coin drawer in base, lacks reproducer connecting tube, horn and carriage return spring. **£1,200-1,400** *CSK*

An early 'handmade' E.M.G. gramophone, bearing E.M.G. label for 11 Grape St., Shaftesbury Avenue, W.C.1, with 12 in. turntable, 20 in. long, (51 cm.), complete with papier mâché goose neck horn, 23¾ in. diam. (60 cm.), good condition, English, late 1920's. **£300-400** *S*

An unusual cabinet gramophone, with 12 in. turntable, and Pathé concert reproducer, contained in elaborate bowfronted mahogany cabinet, with tulipwood and boxwood banding, winding handle to one side, 35 in. high (89 cm.). **£250-300** *S*

A Columbia Twentieth Century Premier phonograph with sound magnifying reproducer and massive triple-spring motor, in oak case with large brass horn, 53 in. long. **£400-500** *CSK*

(l.) An Edison opera phonograph with patents from 1896-1910, serial no. 2887, type SM, model A, 12 by 18 in., with self supporting Music Master laminated wooden horn, 22 in. diam. and variable speed gear. **£1,500-1,700** *AGr*

(r.) A Gramophone and Typewriter Ltd. gramophone with 10 in. turntable, carved wooden case, 12 by 12 in., with flower-shaped tinplate horn, 24 in. diam. and five 10 in. diam., 78 r.p.m. records. **£450-500** *AGr*

A Columbia type AT graphophone, no. 250829, with aluminium Q reproducer and recorder, small nickelled trumpet horn, lacking winding handle, American, 11¼ in. long (28.5 cm.), c. 1898. **£200-250** *SC*

An early 20th C. oak-cased phonograph labelled 'Edison Bell Gem' bearing patent label of Thomas Edison and A. Tainter Bell, registration number S 27575, with a collection of wax cylinders, in poor condition, 9 by 7 in. **£200-£250** *DDM*

A rare hand-driven Berliner gramophone with 5 in. diam. turntable, with 2 sets of hearing tubes, lacking sound box and hearing tube sphere, German, 13 in. long (33 cm.), c. 1893. **£800-£1,200** *S*

The gramophone was invented by Emile Berliner, a German emigré living in America in 1887-89. When visiting his native land in 1889, the toy and doll manufacturer Kammer & Reinhardt secured the rights to his invention and soon after produced a toy gramophone of similar design to the above.

A horn gramophone with 10 in. turntable, aluminium tone arm with Windsor sound box, stop mechanism defective, probably English, 20 in. diam. of horn (51 cm.), c. 1910. **£150-200** *SC*

A zonophone horn gramophone, with 10 in. turntable, stepped oak base, 14 in. wide (36 cm.), with a black enamelled horn, English, c. 1925. **£200-250** *SC*

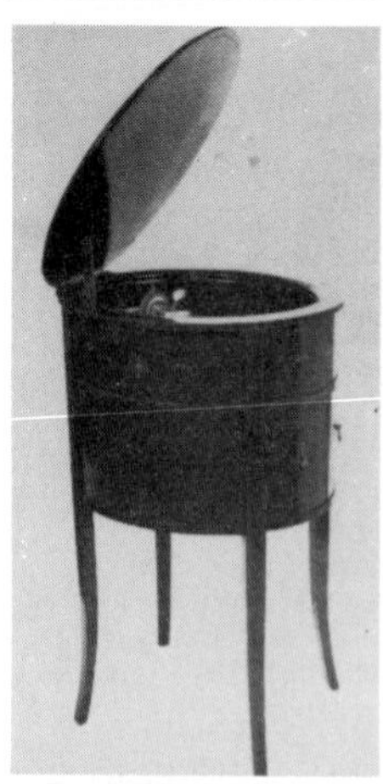

A Tyrela cabinet gramophone, the Sheraton-style cabinet concealing the 11¾ in. turntable with Tyrela soundbox, good condition, 30 in. high (77.5 cm.), c. 1925. **£100-150** *SC*

A rare Champion typewriter, the type-wheel class mechanism with indicator, selector connected by gears to the type-wheel, curved index, shift key and inking by ribbon, lacking cover, American, c. 1895. **£600-700** *S*

The People's model with inking by roller was patented in 1891 by C. J. A. Sjoberg of Brooklyn and assigned to the Garvin Machine Co. of New York. The later Champion model with inking by ribbon was patented in 1893.

A Williams typewriter, with grasshopper action, inking by pads, on stained oak wooden base, one roller distressed, American, 13½ in. long (34 cm.), c. 1895. **£350-£400** *S*

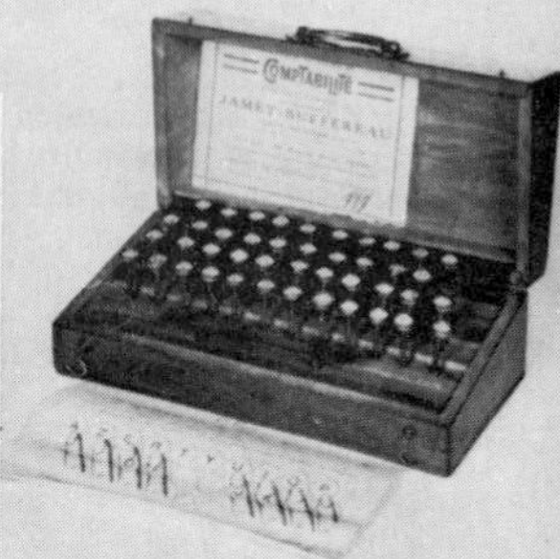

A Jamet. Billiard & Cie typewriting teaching aid, with 2 sets of instructions, French, 10½ in. wide (268 mm.), c. 1900. **£150-200** *S*

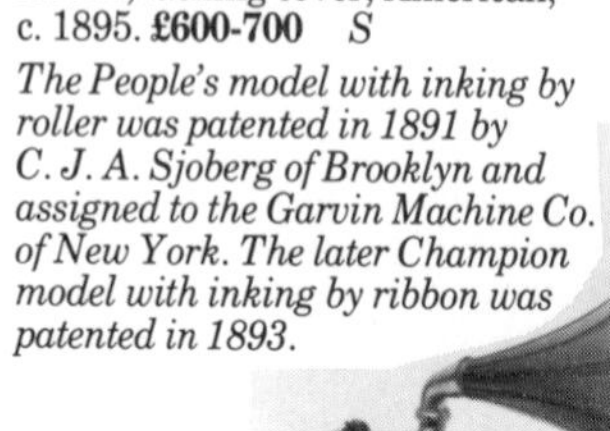

An H.M.V. mahogany table top gramophone with large wood horn. **£450-500** *M*

An early 20th C. folding typewriter. **£80-120** *HAD*

A Gramophone & Typewriter Ltd. Senior Monarch gramophone with triple-spring motor, G. & T. Exhibition soundbox and green Morning Glory horn. **£400-500** *CSK*

Locate the source

The source of each illustration in Miller's can be found by checking the code letters below each caption with the list of contributors on page 12. In view of the undoubted differences in price structures from region to region, this information could be extremely valuable to everyone who buys and sells antiques.

An early loud-speaking telephone receiver, the turned walnut stand with metal mouthpiece, electro-magnet and 2 terminals, 10 in. high (255 mm.), and a wood and metal petal horn, English, early 20th C. **£200-250** *S*

Illustrated as fig. 10 in Telephones Their Construction and Fittings by F. C. Allsop, published 1900.

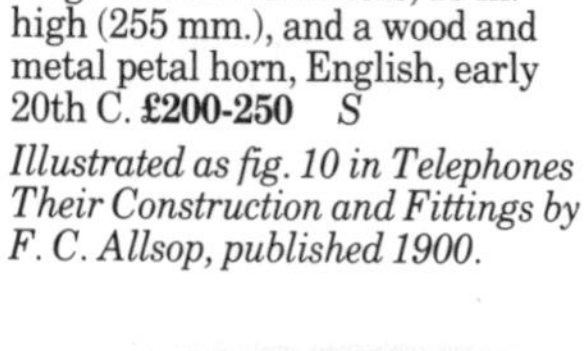

A Wheatstone telegraphic ink tape recorder, make unknown, with brass frame, 12 in. wide (30.5 cm.), c. 1870. **£120-160** *P*

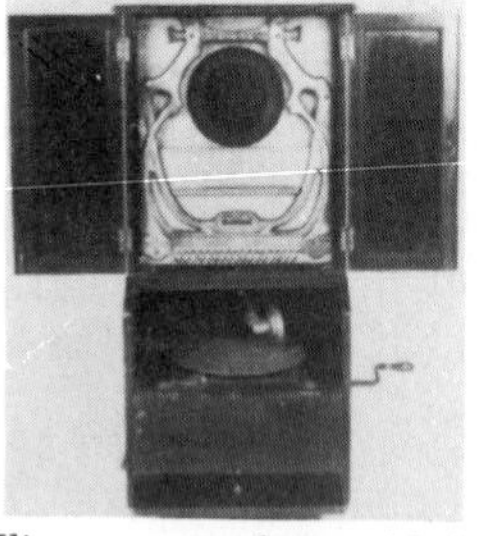

A Klingsor gramophone, with Art Nouveau-style doors opening to reveal the 32 string harp, above the 9½ in. turntable, Klingsor soundbox, German, 33½ in. high (85 cm.), c. 1920. **£250-300** *SC*

A 19th C. Breguet design dial telegraph. **£300-500** *HAD*

A rare and early model of a hand-knitting frame, the wood and steel moving model with painted gesso and wood articulated figure, the treadle movement with comb, piece of cloth and small brass padlock at the side, English, 6½ in. high (165 mm.), probably early 18th C. **£900-1,000** *S*

This type of hand-knitting frame was invented by William Lee of Leicester in 1589.

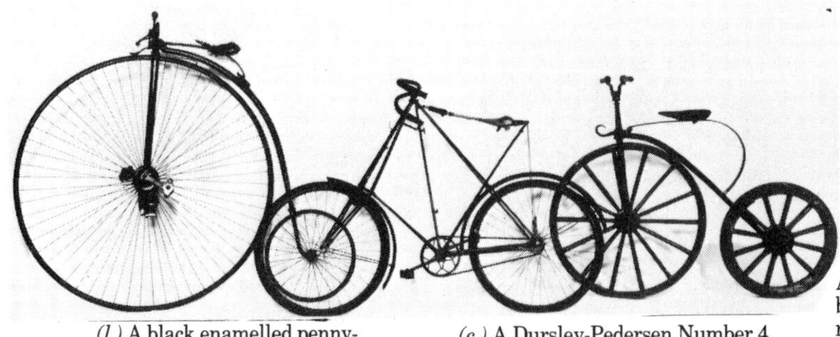

(l.) A black enamelled penny-farthing (ordinary) Victorian bicycle, having unusual duplex twin-tubular front forks, with a very rare hub oil-lamp fitted inside the front wheel marked 'Lucas's Patent No. 2493', the whole bicycle being very original throughout and dating around the 1882-88 period, front wheel diam. 50 in. **£1,200-£1,400** *P*

(c.) A Dursley-Pedersen Number 4 gentleman's bicycle, c. 1900. **£450-£550** *P*

(r.) A blacksmith produced Victorian wrought-iron and wooden-wheeled boneshaker bicycle having a front wheel diam. of approx. 30½ in. (76.5 cm.), 1870's. **£300-400** *P*

An ordinary or penny farthing bicycle, front wheel diam. 52 in., rear wheel 13 in., each with solid rubber tyres, c. 1872-85. **£180-£220** *A*

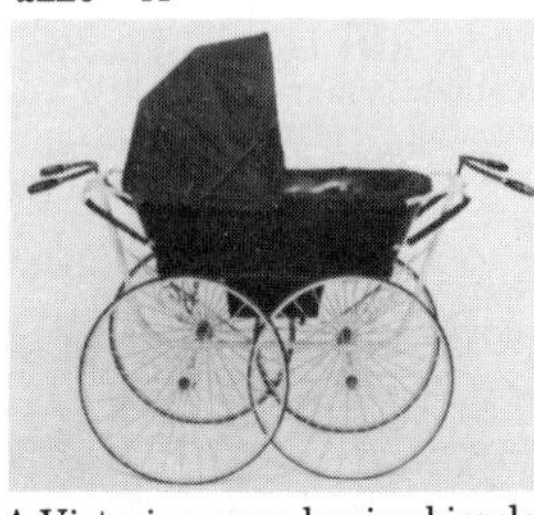

A Victorian pram having bicycle-type handlebars at each end, the pram having a suspended and sprung body, 126 cm. tall overall. **£350-400** *P*

This pram, which was originally known as the 'bicycle pram' was intended for one or two children.

(l.) A black painted early 'Imperial Rover' lady's bicycle. **£300-400** *P*

(c.) An early Dursley-Pedersen gentleman's bicycle, with Pedersen rear wheel hub gears operated by the frame fitted gear lever, handlebar-operated rear brake, brass front fork-fitted name badge, etc., complete with a Lucas 'Silver King' period brass oil headlamp. **£900-1,000** *P*

(r.) A black painted penny-farthing (ordinary) bicycle, the front wheel diam. being approx. 120 cm., the overall height being approx. 138 cm. **£1,200-1,400** *P*

(l.) A wrought-iron framed early 'Boneshaker-Velocipede' bicycle, the front wheel diam. being approx. 88 cm., 1870's. **£900-1,000** *P*

(r.) A penny farthing (ordinary) bicycle, in black enamel and gold pencil-lined finish, the front wheel diam. approx. 136 cm., the frame having been repaired just behind the saddle spring mounting. **£1,000-1,200** *P*

A velocipede or 'bone-shaker', bears brass trade plate of MICHAUX 'ANCie MAISON MICHAUX & Cie. Cie PARISIENNE, 27 RUE JEAN GOUJON, PARIS', diam. of front wheel 34 in., diam. of rear wheel 28 in., c. 1865. **£1,400-£1,600** *A*

The first bicycle with rotary crank was the invention of Pierre Lalliment, a workman employed by M. Michaux, of 29 Avenue Montaigne, Paris.

A decorative wickerwork mail cart with velvet upholstered interior, replaced, marked Bon Marche Ltd, Brixton SW, 134 cm. **£150-200** *P*

A Victorian bathchair with wicker basket seat, 2 large spoked wheels with solid tyres and a long handled steering front wheel. **£150-200** *DDM*

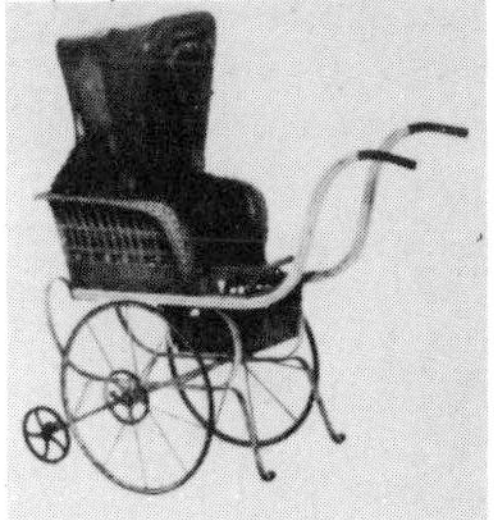

A painted wooden and decorative wickerwork mail cart of small size with fully upholstered fawn leatherette interior, deepening footwell, fringed hood and brass fittings, 92 cm. long. **£250-300** *P*

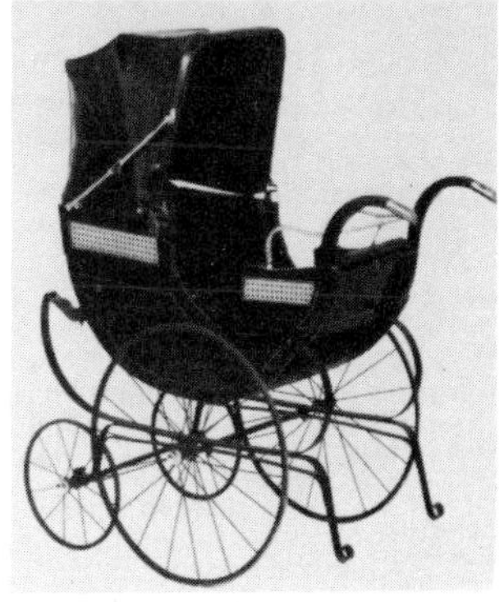

A painted wooden mail cart with leatherette interior, with footwell and second folding seat, 113 cm. long. **£130-180** *P*

A Gipsy caravan, the panelled sides painted maroon and ribbed yellow, the interior with carved wooden beading, sliding doors to the 2 sleeping compartments, cast iron pot stove, bevelled mirrored panels to the cupboards and walls and frosted glass windows, the majority of the wood in sound condition, 179 in. long (454 cm.), c. 1920. **£2,000-3,000** *SC*

The Norseman, a blue painted aluminium train headboard, 33 in. long (84 cm.). **£250-300** *CSK*

The Norseman was the weekday train running between Kings Cross and Newcastle to meet the Bergen and Oslo ferry service.

Etona, a Great Western Railway cast brass nameplate, Bulldog class, number 3323, 17 by 26 in. (43 by 65 cm.). **£2,300-2,500** *CSK*

This nameplate is one of seven of its type. The class was built in 1899 and withdrawn in 1935.

Saint Johnstoun, a London and North Eastern Railway cast brass nameplate, Thompson Pacifics Class A1, number 60162, 71 in. long (180 cm.). **£1,100-1,300** *CSK*

Sir Launcelot, a pair of Southern Railway cast brass nameplates, King Arthur Class Number 455. **£1,500-2,000** *CSK*

These plates were given to Lord Tennyson by Southern Railway on the locomotive's withdrawal between 1959 and 1962.

Lord Hawke, a Southern Railway cast brass nameplate, Lord Nelson Class No. 860. **£800-1,000** *CSK*

This nameplate became B.R. 30850 and the class was withdrawn between 1961 and 1962.

A mint metal enamelled advertising sign for the 3-speed 1912 'New Hudson' motorcycle, the sign approx. 44 cm. high by 57 cm. wide. **£55-65** *P*

A mint metal enamelled advertising sign, American origin, approx. 34 cm. high by 60.5 cm. wide. **£50-60** *P*

A Midland Railway, Wolverhampton Exhibition 1902, colour lithograph poster by Wyman & Sons, publishers, 40 by 25 in. (101 by 64 cm.). **£100-120** *CSK*

Nord Express, Chemin de Fer du Nord, colour lithograph poster by A. M. Cassandra, 29 by 42 in. **£400-£500** *CSK*

A nickel-plated Hispano Suiza Cigogne Volante, 6 in. high (15 cm.). **£280-340** *CSK*

A good nickel-plated Rolls Royce vintage Spirit of Ecstasy mascot, with the usual company name, date and signature around the base, as fitted to the late 'Phantom One' range of cars, approx. 15 cm. tall. **£180-220** *P*

A silvered brass vintage mascot of a standing cockerel, mounted on a period onyx and black marble presentation base. **£45-65** *P*

This mascot was believed to have been adopted by the Courage Brewery Company for use on their delivery vehicles for many years.

Three-plated vintage American Mack Bulldog mascots. **£180-220**

An Edwardian vintage mascot by Lejeune, stamped 'AEL Copyright', recently replated in bright nickel, overall height approx. 22 cm. **£90-£120** *P*

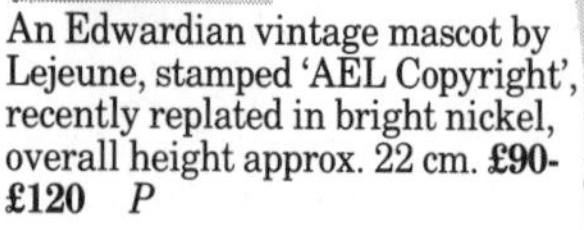

A mascot, of a winged Cupid, vintage period, inscribed 'J. Dunach', chrome-plated on brass, 17 cm. high. **£50-70** *P*

Avondale Castle, a Great Western Railway cast brass and steel name plate, Collett 4-cylinder no. 7010. **£1,300-1,600** *CSK*

A vintage chrome-plated Eagle mascot, having a large wingspan of approx. 27.5 cm. and stamped by the maker 'Finnigan's London'. **£50-60** *P*

A nickel-plated bronze Minerva 'Goddess' mascot. **£120-150** *P*

Left to right:—

(1.) A scarce multi-coloured enamelled 'Automobile Club of Pittsburgh Pennsylvania Motor Federation AAA' badge offering 'a reward of 25 U.S. dollars for arrest and conviction of anyone stealing or injuring a member's car!'. **£50-£60** *P*

(2.) A brass Royal Automobile Club full member's car badge by Elkington of Regent Street, London. **£40-50** *P*

(3.) An unusual brass and blue/white/red enamelled badge, dated 1895, for the 'Touring Club de Belgique'. **£25-30** *P*

(4.) A scarce Royal Automobile Club Associate badge, all brass, with good circular enamelled Union Jack flag, no. N65932. **£60-£70** *P*

(5.) A scarce pre-war Triumph Motor Club badge in plated brass. **£25-30** *P*

A 1920 Delage D.E.4 saloon, Paris 'Salon' show car, restored. **£10,000-£12,000** *CCC*

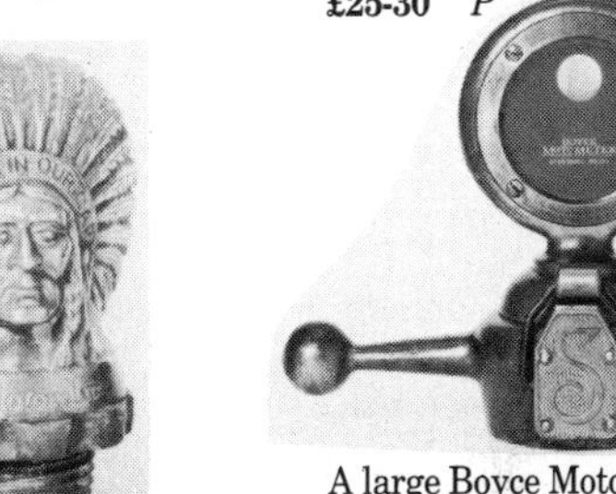

An alloy Indian Head mascot on the correct radiator cap, stamped by the makers 'Guy Motors Ltd.' and 'Feathers in our Cap' around the head-dress. **£35-40** *P*

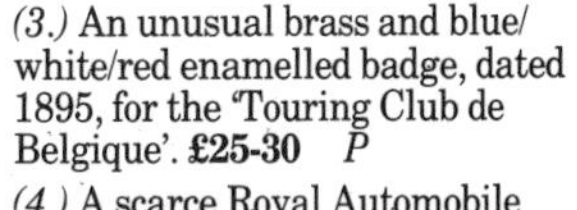

A large Boyce Moto-Meter American radiator calometer and hinged cap, as fitted to the Simplex touring car of the late Edwardian period. **£60-70** *P*

A 1923 Rolls 20 tourer, split screen, 3 speed, centre gear change model, totally rebuilt. **£17,000-19,500** *CCC*

A 1959 T.R.3A, good condition. **£2,500-3,500** *CCC*

In mint condition £4,000-5,000

A 1930 Austin 7 special. **£2,100-£2,500** *CCC*

Many specials were based on the mass produced Austin 7.

A 1951 Alvis T.C. 21/100 'Grey Lady' drophead, good condition. **£3,000-5,000** *CCC*

A 1935 Talbot 4 seater tourer, replica bodywork. **£4,000-4,250** *CCC*

An Alvis speed 20 special, converted to road use from racing model. **£5,000-5,250** *CCC*

A 1920 model T Ford TT, long wheelbase commercial, twin speed axle, 1½ ton capacity. **£4,000-£6,000** *CCC*

A 1959 Mercedes Benz 300 S.L. roadster, completely restored. **£15,500-20,000** *CCC*

The much rarer gullwing version is worth considerably more.

A 1937 M.G. Tickford V.A. 4 seater open tourer, good original condition. **£5,000-6,000** *CCC*

A 1935 Railton Straight 8, with Hudson terraplane engine; this car has a special body by Sergeant. **£7,000-8,500** *CCC*

A 1972 V.12 E. type Jaguar, 2+2, 50,000 miles from new, mint condition. **£5,500-7,000** *CCC*

The 2+2 versions are worth roughly half as much as the roadsters.

A 1960 Rover 100 P.4., one owner, original condition. **£800-1,100** *CCC*

A 1920 Ford model T, 4 seater ope tourer, in maroon and black, original specification. **£4,500-£5,250** *CCC*

The first mass produced car

A 1929 Bentley speed 6, special body by Souchet, nearly all trim is silver plated. **£35,000 +** *CCC*

A 1966 Lotus Cortina Mk. 1, twin cam., 1558 c.c., very good original condition. **£1,950-2,450** *CCC*

A 1967 Morris Minor 1000, 1098 c.c., low mileage, original condition. **£2,500-3,000** *CCC*

A 1968 Mini Cooper S, 1071 c.c., mint condition. **£1,400-1,700** *CCC*

The 1071 c.c. was thought to be the fastest Cooper S in production form.

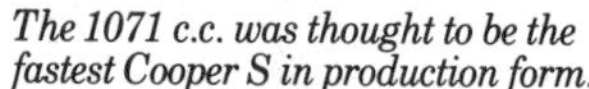

A 1969 Wolseley 16/60, original condition, one of the last few made. **£800-1,200** *CCC*

Austin cars made the similar 'Cambridge' model, Morris the 'Oxford', the main difference between these cars was in the shape of the radiator grille and standards of internal trim.

An Avro Anson Mk. 19 Series II, G-AGPG, in poor condition. **£3,000-£3,500** *P*

A Percival P 31 Proctor IV NP 303/G-ANZJ, now somewhat neglected and requiring a complete re-build and restoration. **£2,500-£3,000** *P*

A 1949 Jaguar XK 120 Roadster, early chrome sidelight model, totally restored. **£7,500-9,000** *CCC*

An Avro type 694 Lincoln B2 RF 342/G-APRJ, appears relatively sound for restoration. Corrosion is evident on the flaps, wings, main spar and undercarriage. **£8,500-£9,000** *P*

A Fiat G-46-4b Trainer NC 71 MM 53211, this fine looking rare aircraft appears in generally sound condition. **£3,500-4,000** *P*

A 1958 M.G.A. Roadster, 1600 c.c., fully restored. **£3,500-£4,000** *CCC*

The original cars had a twin-cam. engine; spares for these are now almost impossible to find.

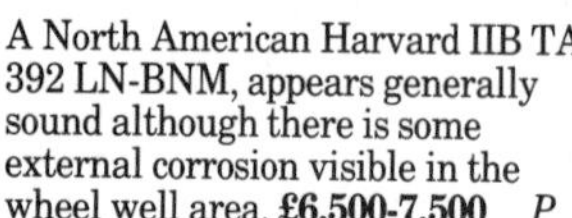

A North American Harvard IIB TA 392 LN-BNM, appears generally sound although there is some external corrosion visible in the wheel well area. **£6,500-7,500** *P*

A 19th C. boulle liqueur cabinet, 11 in. high. **£500-600** *McCMB*

A decanter cabinet, 12 in. wide, c. 1850. **£265-300** *CDE*

A late Georgian travelling set, with 4 trumpet shaped beakers with separate carrying facility, c. 1830. **£300-400** *SS*

A mahogany Sheraton period knife box with boxwood stringing and crossbanded inlay, having original interior fittings. **£250-300** *BHW*

An ebonised perfume bottle box with brass and mother-of-pearl inlay, 6 in. wide, c. 1880. **£60-70** *IHA*

A walnut brass-bound decanter box, with inset handles, containing 4 plain square decanters, with canted edges and flute cut necks, cut ball stoppers, 250 mm. high by 215 mm. square, c. 1850. **£250-£280** *Som*

An oak tantalus with cut glass decanters, 15½ in. wide, c. 1920. **£200-300** *BP*

An 'Easy' signmarker box, patent dated 1894, 19 in. **£30-40** *HA*

A Victorian oak tantalus, containing 3 cut glass decanters, with a spring loaded rising top and a drawer below, 1 ft. 3 in. wide (38 cm.), c. 1895. **£300-400** *SS*

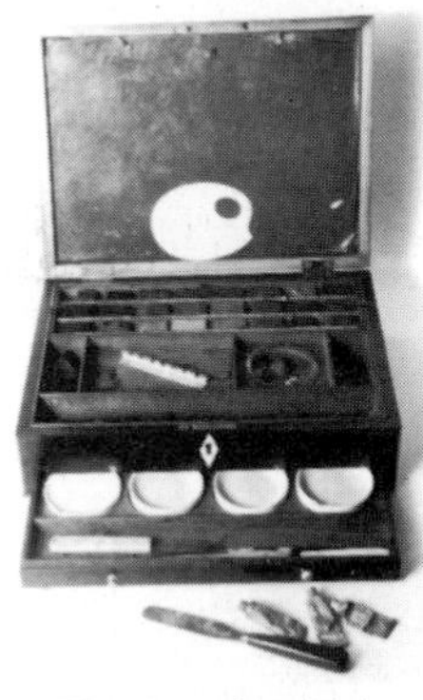

A George IV rosewood artists box by Reeves, Woodyer & Reeves, 12 in. wide, c. 1825. **£190-220** *HA*

A brass-bound walnut bridge box, 11 in. wide, c. 1860. **£80-100** *BP*

A Georgian cutlery box, 16 in. wide. **£45-50** *FF*

An inlaid mahogany card box with painted view, 10½ in., c. 1820. **£100-150** *IHA*

A gentleman's dressing box, 10 in., c. 1830. **£130-160** *HA*

An ebonised toilet case with brass and mother-of-pearl inlay, with fitted interior, period silver tops, c. 1800. **£350-450** *IHA*

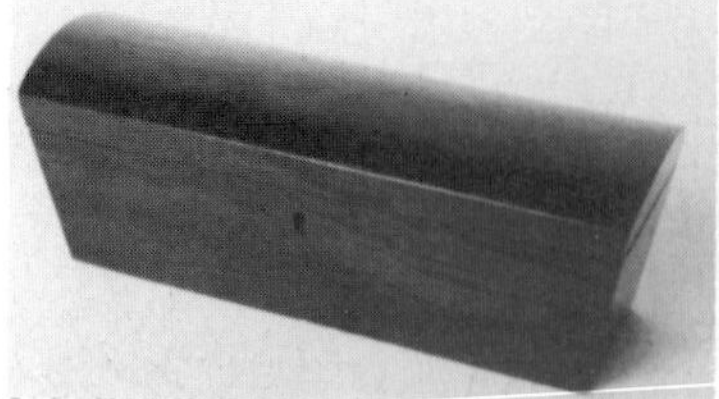

A Victorian yew-wood glove box.
£30-40 *HA*

A mahogany instrument box, 10 in., c. 1910. **£20-25** *Ph*

An early 19th C. oak instrument box, 11 in. square. **£35-40** *HA*

A mid 19th C. Continental multi-drawered jewel box, 9 in. high. **£65-£70** *HA*

A fruitwood tea caddy in the form of a pear, stalk missing, 6 in. high, early 19th C. **£350-400** *S*

A fruitwood apple-shaped tea caddy with turned stalk and iron escutcheon, German, 4¾ in. high, early 19th C. **£600-700** *S*

A George III fruitwood tea caddy in the form of a gourd, the body stained in mottled green, 5¼ in. high, c. 1800. **£600-700** *SS*

A mid Victorian jewel casket, with original silk lining, 9 in. **£60-70** *HA*

A Regency leather-covered trinket box on brass feet, 5½ in. **£50-60** *HA*

A George III rolled paperwork tea caddy, covered in gilt and coloured scrolls, 7½ in. wide (19 cm.), c. 1790. **£400-500** *S*

A velvet-covered jewel box with brass fittings, 7 in. **£20-30** *HB*

An ebony-veneered ivory and English enamel tea caddy, with 3 fitted tea containers, the front, sides and back set with 6 Liverpool or Birmingham enamel plaques, each transfer-printed in black, 9½ in. wide (24 cm.), c. 1760. **£1,300-1,500** *S*

A George IV rosewood and cut brass inlaid jewellery box, on brass ball feet, 10¼ in. wide (26 cm.), c. 1825. **£500-550** *SS*

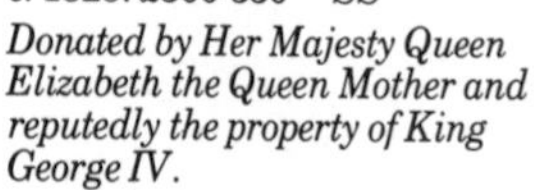

Donated by Her Majesty Queen Elizabeth the Queen Mother and reputedly the property of King George IV.

A mid Victorian coromandel wood jewel box, 12 in. **£60-70** *HA*

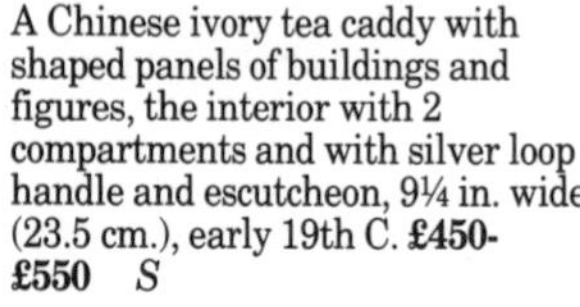

A Chinese ivory tea caddy with shaped panels of buildings and figures, the interior with 2 compartments and with silver loop handle and escutcheon, 9¼ in. wide (23.5 cm.), early 19th C. **£450-£550** *S*

A small tea caddy, 8½ in., c. 1790. **£45-50** *HA*

A mid Victorian papier mâché tea caddy, inlaid with mother-of-pearl, 6¼ in. **£60-70** *HA*

A George III amboyna tea caddy, inlaid with shell paterae, the interior now with one tin tea cannister, 5 by 9½ in. (13 by 24 cm.), mid 18th C. **£80-120** *SC*

A burr-yew tea box, with canted sides, inlaid with pearlwood lines, 5 in. square (12 cm.), late 18th C. **£50-70** *SC*

A mid Victorian papier mâché caddy with mother-of-pearl inlay, 8½ in. **£120-130** *HA*

A Regency lacquer penwork caddy with chinoiserie decoration, 12 in. wide. **£170-190** *HA*

A Georgian mahogany tea caddy with brass feet and original interior, 8 in. high, c. 1830. **£100-£135** *NP*

A good walnut and calamander combined encrier and writing slope by Mechi and Bazin, opening to reveal ink wells and an inset velvet writing surface, bearing a maker's plaque, the lock stamped Mordan and Co., 6 by 12½ in. (15 by 32 cm.), mid 19th C. **£150-200** *SC*

A Victorian leather covered stationery box, 9 in. **£40-50** *HA*

An Edwardian oak slope fronted stationery cabinet, 15 in. wide. **£65-£70** *HA*

A Victorian walnut writing slope with secret compartment, 15½ in. wide. **£120-160** *FD*

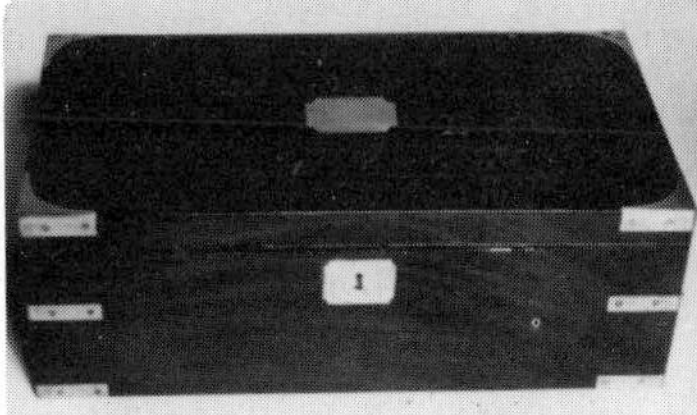
A brass-bound mahogany writing slope, 20 in. wide, c. 1880. **£80-£100** *IHA*

A bird's-eye maple tea caddy, 14 in. wide, c. 1860. **£100-120** *IHA*

A Victorian writing slope in satinwood, rosewood and ebony, 16 in. **£95-110** *HA*

A mahogany military writing box with brass banding, 20 in., c. 1810. **£120-150** *HB*

A late Regency mahogany tea caddy/apprentice piece in the form of a sideboard, 14½ in. **£300-400** *HB*

A mid 19th C. fernwork writing slope, 12 in. wide. **£140-170** *HA*
It is most unusual to find such a large piece of fernwork.

A George III rolled paperwork tea caddy dated 1799, 2 panels inset with mezzotints, with pearwood bandings, 7¼ in. wide (18.5 cm.). **£1,000-1,200** *S*

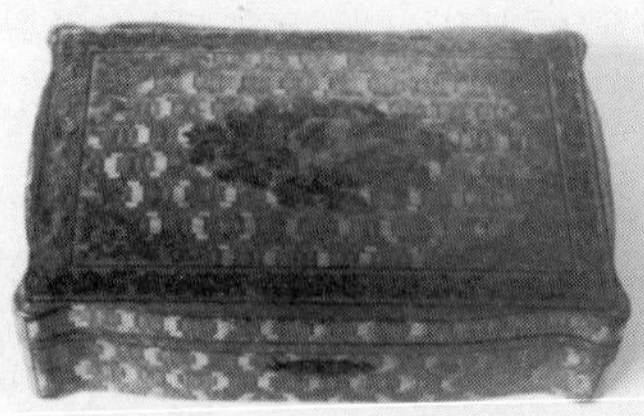
A Napoleonic prisoner-of-war straw-work box, 10 in. **£190-220** *HA*

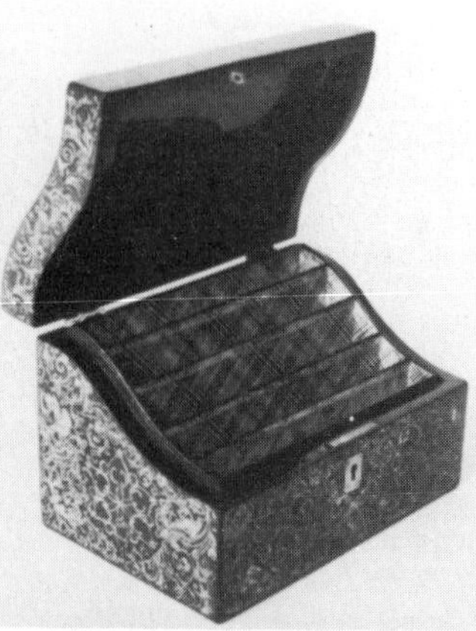
A Regency papier mâché stationery box, in original condition, 6¼ in., c. 1815-20. **£70-80** *HA*

A George III ivory-veneered decagonal tea caddy with gabled lid, the front with silver escutcheon plate and oval, 5 in. high. **£400-£500** *CSK*

A Victorian burr-elm and ebonised stationery cabinet, the interior partially veneered with coromandel, bearing presentation inscription, 1 ft. 5 in. wide (43 cm.), c. 1895. **£250-300** *SS*

An Edwardian mahogany writing box, 11 in. wide. **£50-60** *Ph*

A George III rolled paperwork tea caddy, covered in floral scrolls in different colours within beechwood bandings, the front with a roundel of Cupid and Venus, 6¾ in. wide (17 cm.). **£350-400** *S*

A black and lacquer and gilt writing box with pen drawer in base, 14½ in. wide, c. 1890. **£75-£100** *Ph*

A Regency leather-covered small sewing box, 5½ in. **£50-60** *HA*

A late Victorian inlaid writing box, 9 in. wide. **£60-80** *BP*

A French straw-work workbox formed as a book and with a hinged lid opening to reveal a watercolour inscribed A View of Beaufort Castle, with lidded compartmented interior, 12¾ in. **£100-120** *CSK*

A rosewood writing slope inlaid with brass and mother-of-pearl, 15 in. wide, c. 1840. **£100-140** *CDE*

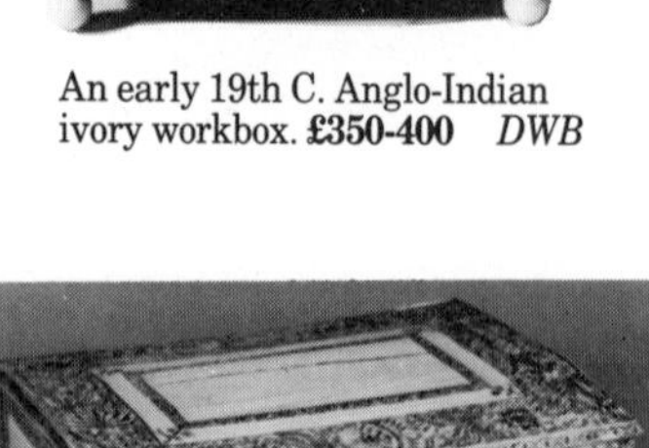
An early 19th C. Anglo-Indian ivory workbox. **£350-400** *DWB*

A straw-work box, the lid with floral inlay, the interior with 2 compartments at either side, with drawer below, 10¼ in., 19th C. **£50-£70** *CSK*

A fine Indo-Portuguese ivory and sandalwood box with hinged cover, the interior with small hinged compartment, cracked, some ivory rising, 16 by 11 by 4½ in. (41 by 28 by 11 cm.), 19th C. **£500-600** *C*

A silver-mounted tortoiseshell casket mounted with pierced foliate angles, sides similarly mounted with elaborately pierced angles, hinges and borders, possibly Batavian, 9¾ in. wide (25 cm.), 18th C. **£700-800** *C*

A rare New Zealand marquetry box by Antoine Seuffert, containing a collection of native ferns, inlaid in various native woods, 1 ft. 7¼ in. wide (49 cm.), c. 1872. **£1,300-£1,500** *S*

The box bears the trade label of A. Seuffert Cabinet Maker to His Royal Highness the Duke of Edinburgh, Elliott St, Auckland, New Zealand.

An ormolu-mounted boulle casket of Louis XIV design, the lid inset with a panel of Berrainesque designs enclosing a mahogany-lined interior, 12 in. wide, 19th C. **£300-£350** *CEd*

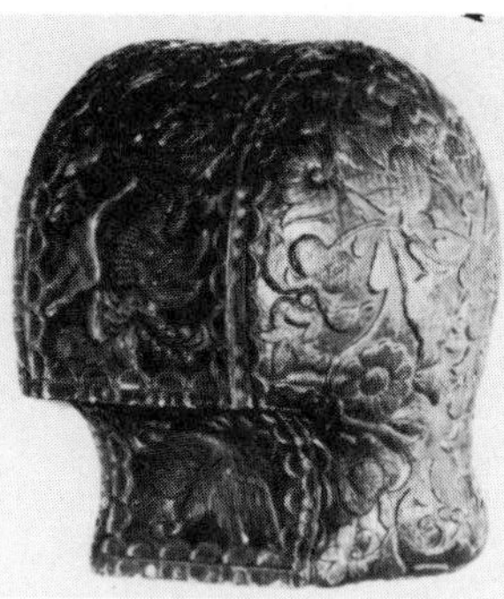

An unusual European influence Indian carved padouk box in the form of a scallop shell, 8 in. high (20 cm.), 18th C. **£200-250** *S*

A Georgian mahogany box, 9 in. high, c. 1830. **£30-45** *NP*

A rare German walnut marquetry casket in the manner of Johann Martin Reinecke, the lid inlaid, the interior now fitted as a cellaret, the interior of the lid with a hinged panel inlaid with a musician, the date Anno 1769 and names, with gilt-metal carrying handles, 1 ft. 11½ in. high by 2 ft. 3½ in. wide (60 by 70 cm.), c. 1740. **£7,000-8,000** *S*

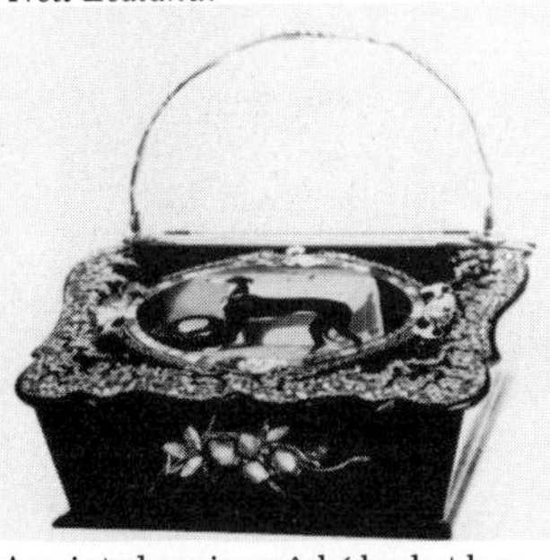

A painted papier mâché basket box with pierced gilt-metal handle, the twin panelled sloping lid painted with a greyhound and black retriever, 7¼ in. high (18.5 cm.), c. 1850. **£350-400** *S*

An American painted band box, the top painted with a scene in a chateau park of 2 ladies, 2 ft. 2 in. wide (66 cm.), c. 1840. **£500-600** *S*

A coromandel wood casket in Gothic style, 9½ in. wide, late 19th C. **£45-60** *STR*

An Anglo-Indian ivory tortoiseshell and hardwood table box, veneered with square and rectangular tortoiseshell panels contained by etched ivory bands, the interior fitted with hinged wells, drawers and a mirror, 3¾ by 11½ (9.5 by 29 cm.), 19th C. **£100-150** *SC*

An Indo-Portuguese table cabinet inlaid with foliage and stylised flowerheads, with brass corner mounts, carrying handles and lock, the interior with 7 drawers with bone facings, 19½ by 15 by 13 in. (49.5 by 38.5 by 33 cm.), late 18th/early 19th C. **£650-750** *L*

A German marquetry box in the manner of David Roentgen, the sliding lid and drawer in the side operated by concealed spring catches, 6¾ in. wide (17 cm.), c. 1780. **£600-700** *C*

A Victorian burr-yew wood box with painted top, 3 in. diam. **£20-£25** *HA*

A small Victorian tortoiseshell box, 3 in. **£25-30** *HA*

A Victorian tortoiseshell toothpick box, 2½ in. **£40-50** *HA*

A tartanware patch box with stamp on front, 1½ in. **£20-25** *HA*

A Victorian tortoiseshell purse, 3 in. **£30-40** *HA*

A 19th C. horn snuff box, 3¾ in. **£10-12** *MPA*

Miller's is a price GUIDE Not a price LIST.
The price ranges given reflect the average price a purchaser should pay for similar items. Condition, rarity of design or pattern, size, colour, provenance, restoration and many other factors must be taken into account when assessing values.

A Flemish late 17th C. tortoiseshell casket, the top 16 by 11⅜ in. **£800-£1,000** *T*

A German marquetry box in the manner of David Roentgen, with striped tambour lid enclosing a divided interior and steel catches operating a drawer in the base, bordered with tulip-wood and brass, 10½ in. wide (27 cm.), c. 1780. **£2,200-2,400** *C*

The sharply contrasted pictorial marquetry, particularly the illusionistic device of swagged drapery entwined with flowers, the striped tambour shutter (often found on the internal drawers of games tables and bureaux) and complex locking mechanism are all distinctive features characteristic of Roentgen's oeuvre of the 1770's.

A Victorian papier mâché snuff shoe, 3 in. **£28-34** *HA*

A Victorian papier mâché snuff box, 3¼ in. **£25-30** *HA*

A large ormolu-mounted boulle casket of Louis XIV design, 24 in. wide, 19th C. **£1,000-1,200** *CEd*

A small 19th C. box, 3½ in. **£5-10** *HA*

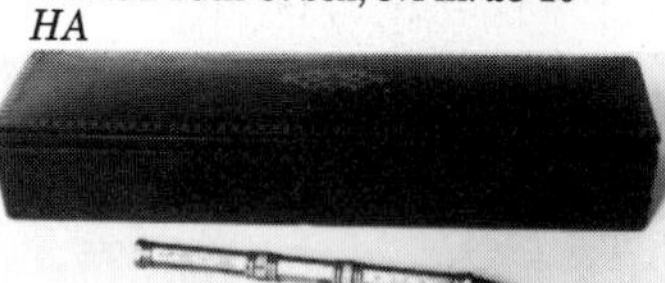

A Victorian papier mâché pen box, with pencil, 8 in. long. **£15-20** *HA*

A Georgian rent box, 9 in. **£40-50** *HA*

A Georgian painted wooden snuff box with scenes on all sides. **£110-£130** *HA*

A Victorian horn table snuff box with cairngorm set in top, 4 in. **£34-£38** *HA*

A Victorian horn and tortoiseshell snuff box, 3 in. **£22-28** *HA*

A boulle inkstand, 10 in. wide, c. 1870. **£180-200** *NSN*

A late Georgian pen tray in ebony with mother-of-pearl inlay, the inkwells with silver tops, 12½ in. wide, c. 1830. **£100-125** *STR*

A boulle standish, 14 in. wide, c. 1870. **£240-275** *STR*

A fine boulle desk set, probably English, the casket 10¼ by 14 in. (26 by 36 cm.), c. 1870. **£800-900** *S*

Similar sets were retailed by Asprey & Co.

An early Victorian horn snuff box. **£60-70** *HA*

A Spanish wooden box, of pyramid shape, 28 cm. wide, late 17th C. **£450-500** *SZ*

A French polychrome carved head, 16 in. high, 16th C. **£300-350** *RVA*

A pair of carved oak Gothic angels, 15 in. high, early 16th C. **£700-£900** *RVA*

A Franco-Netherlandish polychrome wood figure of Christ as The Good Shepherd, original colour, 40½ in. high (103 cm.), c. 1460-80. **£4,500-5,000** *S*

A Spanish polychrome and giltwood tabernacle door, carved with the Virgin and Child surrounded by symbols of the 4 Evangelists, some polychrome and gilding repainted, 19 in. high (47.2 cm.), late 15th C. **£2,200-£2,500** *S*

A South German wood relief of St. Catherine, the oval frame with red and gold acanthus, original polychroming and gilding, 30 in. high (76 cm.), early 18th C. **£1,700-£1,900** *S*

A pair of late Elizabethan carved figures, 29 in. high, c. 1600. **£350-£400** *RVA*

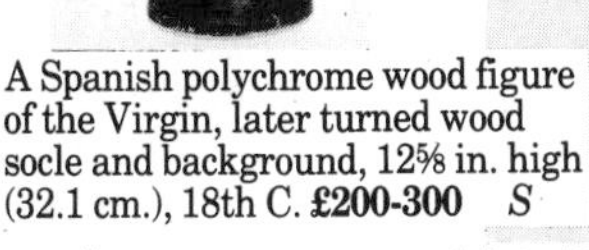
A Spanish polychrome wood figure of the Virgin, later turned wood socle and background, 12⅝ in. high (32.1 cm.), 18th C. **£200-300** *S*

A late 19th C. carved walnut eagle by H. Staehli, 14 in. high. **£180-£220** *CC*

A pair of Venetian carved wood blackamoor figures on circular marbled and gilt bases, each adapted for electricity, 38 in. **£800-£900** *GSP*

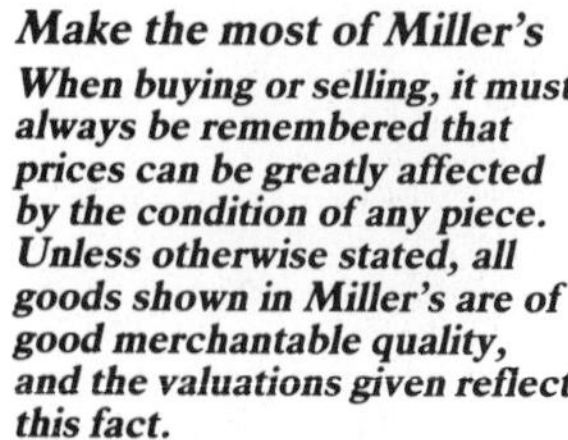

Make the most of Miller's

When buying or selling, it must always be remembered that prices can be greatly affected by the condition of any piece. Unless otherwise stated, all goods shown in Miller's are of good merchantable quality, and the valuations given reflect this fact.
Pieces offered for sale in exceptionally fine condition or in poor condition may reasonably be expected to be priced considerably higher or lower respectively than the estimates given herein.
Unless otherwise stated, any description which refers to 'a set' or 'a pair' includes a valuation for the entire set or the pair, even though the illustration may show only a single item.

A pair of carved and giltwood wall brackets, later wired, 24 in., late 18th C. **£400-500** *WHL*

An Alpine Crucifix figure of pine, finely carved with exaggerated rib cage, hands defective and toes lacking, 22½ in. (57 cm.), c. 1500. **£700-800** *S*

A polychrome and giltwood carving of a saint, 22 in. high, late 17th/early 18th C. **£500-550** *NP*

A Malines polychrome walnut group of Anna Selbdrit, wearing a gilded cloak, stamped M, with polychrome flowering hems, on contemporary base, 11¼ in. high (28.5 cm.), early 16th C. **£3,500-£4,000** *S*

An 18th C. Scottish wood carving of a saint, 40 in. **£450-£500** *LG*

A late 15th or early 16th C. Malines polychrome and giltwood bust of a young woman, the flesh parts painted naturalistically, the elaborate coiffure and moulded base gilt, 29 cm. high. **£4,000-£4,500** *C*

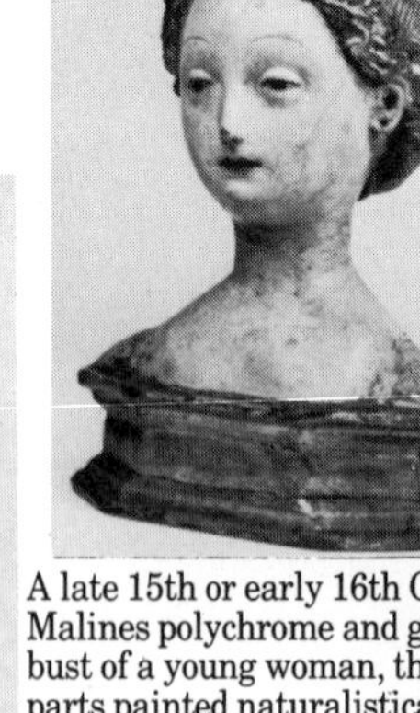

A pair of 17th C. Austrian polychrome and giltwood statues of St. Barbara and another female saint, the latter with 2 separately carved hands, one missing, surface abraded, some edges damaged, 110 cm. high. **£1,100-1,300** *C*

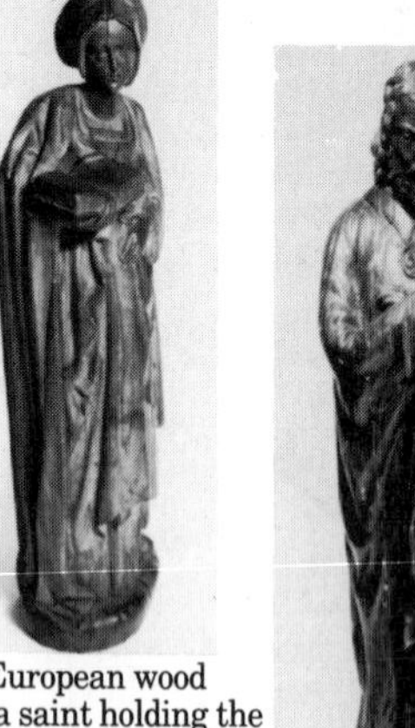

A Nothern European wood statuette of a saint holding the Bible, 23 in. high, 15th/16th C. **£1,800-2,000** *RVA*

An 18th C. carved wooden figure of an unnamed saint, Scottish, 40 in. **£450-500** *LG*

A rare North Italian wood carving of the Nativity, traces of original polychroming, 14th C. **£1,400-£1,600** *RVA*

A pair of giltwood wall brackets, 17 in. (43 cm.), c. 1870. **£500-600** *S*

An 18th C. South German carved and polychromed figure, by the Bavarian Master, of a friar, most likely that of St. Francis, 59 cm. high. **£350-400** *P*

A French walnut carving of The Nativity, 18 in. high, late 16th C. **£400-500** *RVA*

An 18th C. Flemish boxwood figure of the 'Penitent' Magdalene, 26 cm. high. **£500-600** *P*

A carved wood snuff figure of the Highlander, wearing a plumed head-dress and uniform holding a snuff mull, 24½ in. (62 cm.) early 19th C. **£300-400** *SC*

An English oak carved fragment, 50 in. long, c. 1600. **£250-300** *RVA*

A pair of French oak carved Gothic panels, 16th C. **£150-200** *RVA*

An English oak carving of the Presentation to the Temple, 11 in. high, 16th C. **£350-450** *RVA*

A large oak Gothic screen, 60 in. high, late 15th C. **£1,000-1,200** *RVA*

A pair of Romayne panels, 18 in. high, mid 16th C. **£250-300** *RVA*

An English oak carving of The Annunciation, 11 in. high, 16th C. **£350-450** *RVA*

A Gothic oak carving, English, 56 in. long, 15th/16th C. **£250-£300** *RVA*

A pair of French Romayne panels, 21 in. high, 16th C. **£500-600** *RVA*

Make the most of Miller's

When buying or selling, it must always be remembered that prices can be greatly affected by the condition of any piece. Unless otherwise stated, all goods shown in Miller's are of good merchantable quality, and the valuations given reflect this fact.

Pieces offered for sale in exceptionally fine condition or in poor condition may reasonably be expected to be priced considerably higher or lower respectively than the estimates given herein.

Unless otherwise stated, any description which refers to 'a set' or 'a pair' includes a valuation for the entire set or the pair, even though the illustration may show only a single item.

A Gothic panel carved with a bird and grapes, 12 in. high, early 16th C. **£150-200** *RVA*

A South German miniature boxwood relief, allegorical of the Mocking of Man by Woman, in the manner of Hans Sebald Beham, (1500-50), 3½ in. long (9 cm.), mid 16th C. in glazed wood frame. **£2,000-2,200** *S*

A fine English limewood relief of putti with a goat, 79 by 148 cm., 19th C. **£700-800** *C*

A Gothic oak pew end, 37 in. high, 16th C. **£450-500** *RVA*

An unusual jewel casket by Thomas Barton, the top inlaid with cube pattern within a geometric border, with a geometric pattern handle, with a T. Barton late Nye paper label, 7½ in. (19 cm.), c. 1870. **£200-250** *S*

An unusual Tunbridgeware basket 7 in. wide, c. 1875-80. **£160-200** *STR*

A Tunbridgeware rosewood stationery box, with a view of Tonbridge Castle, 9¾ in. wide (24.5 cm.), c. 1870. **£300-350** *S*

A good Tunbridgeware walnut tea caddy, inlaid with a view of Malvern Abbey, 10 in. wide (25.5 cm.), c. 1860. **£300-400** *S*

A Tunbridgeware domed caddy 7½ in., c. 1870. **£100-130** *SA*

A rosewood Tunbridgeware casket with a view of Hever Castle, 10 in. wide. **£290-340** *STR*

A Tunbridgeware trinket box in rosewood, 3¼ in. wide. **£50-60** *STR*

A Tunbridgeware rosewood jewellery case, inlaid with a view of Penshurst Place, 10½ in. wide (26.5 cm.), c. 1870. **£120-160** *S*

A Tunbridgeware satin-birch sewing box, inlaid with a rare view of Gibraltar Cottage, with a fitted tray and numerous spools, 9¼ in. wide (23.5 cm.), c. 1860. **£250-£300** *S*

A Tunbridgeware cigarette box with local trader's mark, 4½ in. wide. **£35-40** *STR*

A Tunbridgeware cotton box with hinged lid, 6 in. square. **£65-75** *STR*

A fine Tunbridgeware jewel box in maple wood, 9 in. wide. **£200-250** *STR*

A Tunbridgeware rosewood stationery box, with a view of Muckross Abbey on a boxwood ground, 10 in. wide (24.5 cm.), c. 1860. **£200-300** *S*

A Tunbridgeware jewel box, 9 in. wide, c. 1870. **£80-100** *SA*

A Tunbridgeware pen box with original Edmund Nye label, c. 1840-50. **£90-120** *STR*

A Tunbridgeware tea caddy, the inner lid compatibly decorated, 5½ in. wide. **£70-90** *STR*

A Tunbridgeware trinket box with hinged lid, 6½ in. wide, c. 1850. **£45-55** *STR*

A Tunbridgeware trinket box with hinged lid, 3½ in. wide. **£35-45** *STR*

An early Tunbridgeware box in walnut with geometric pattern, 4½ in. wide. **£45-55** *STR*

A Tunbridgeware box with chestnut and Tunbridge border, 6 in. square, c. 1870. **£70-80** *SA*

A rosewood box with Tunbridgeware decoration, 4 in. wide. **£40-50** *STR*

A Tunbridgeware pencil box, 3½ in. wide, c. 1850. **£45-55** *STR*

An early 19th C. Tunbridgeware tea caddy, 9½ in. **£60-70** *TA*

A Tunbridgeware trinket box, 2¼ in. square. **£40-50** *STR*

A Tunbridgeware work box with fitted interior, 10 in. wide. **£190-£225** *STR*

Use the Index!
Because certain items might fit easily into any of a number of categories, the quickest and surest method of locating any entry is by reference to the index at the back of the book. This has been fully cross-referenced for absolute simplicity.

A Tunbridgeware box with hinged lid, 5½ in., c. 1900. **£40-50** *STR*

A fine quality Tunbridgeware box with hinged lid, 4 in. square. **£50-£65** *STR*

A Tunbridgeware sewing box with a view of Eridge Castle, the fitted interior with lift-out tray, 11 in. wide. **£275-325** *STR*

A Tunbridgeware trinket box, 3¾ in. wide. **£30-40** *STR*

An amboyna-veneered Tunbridgeware work box, the top with an old abbey ruin, within floral borders, fitted interior, 10 in., 19th C. **£170-230** *WHL*

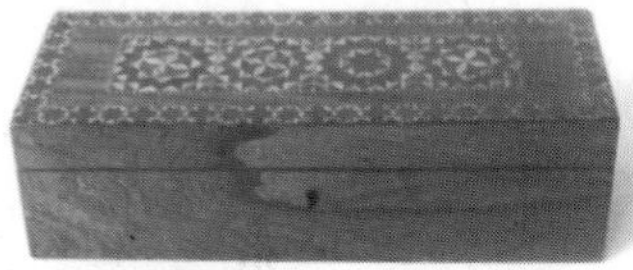
An early stickwork Tunbridgeware rosewood box, 9 in., c. 1850. **£45-£55** *HA*

A Tunbridgeware box with floral pattern, 2½ in. long. **£30-40** *STR*

A small Tunbridgeware box, cube pattern, 3½ in., c. 1850. **£20-25** *HA*

A fine Tunbridgeware stamp box, the top with an estimated 1,600 pieces making the pattern, 1½ by 1¼ in. **£65-80** *STR*

A Tunbridgeware box with early geometric pattern, 2¼ in. wide. **£40-45** *STR*

A rare Tunbridgeware puzzle box, 2 in. square. **£50-60** *STR*

A Tunbridgeware sovereign case with turned body. **£30-40** *STR*

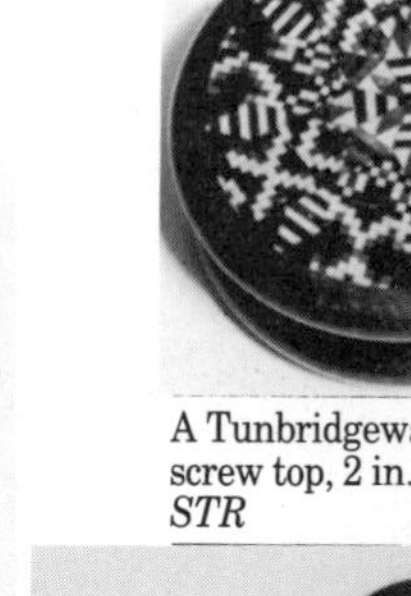

A Tunbridgeware pill box with screw top, 2 in. diam. **£35-45** *STR*

A fine Tunbridgeware stickware sovereign case, c. 1840. **£40-50** *STR*

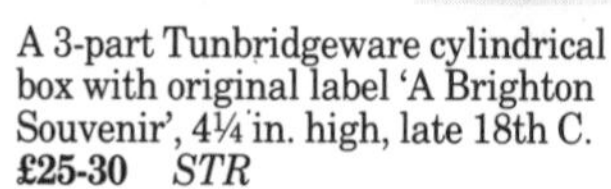

A 3-part Tunbridgeware cylindrical box with original label 'A Brighton Souvenir', 4¼ in. high, late 18th C. **£25-30** *STR*

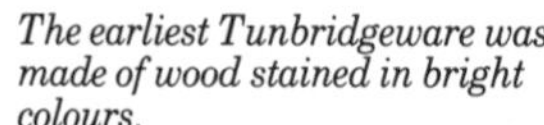

The earliest Tunbridgeware was made of wood stained in bright colours.

A Tunbridgeware counter box, with counters, c. 1870. **£30-35** *SA*

Two Tunbridgeware sovereign cases. **£35-45** each *STR*

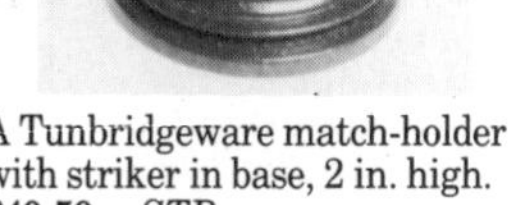

A Tunbridgeware match-holder with striker in base, 2 in. high. **£40-50** *STR*

A Tunbridgeware candleholder, 2¼ in. high, c. 1885. **£50-60** *STR*

Three Tunbridge taper sticks, c. 1870. **£30-35** each *SA*

A Tunbridgeware 'stickware' taper holder, 1 in. high. **£35-40** *STR*

An adjustable candle holder with clamp, Tunbridgeware decoration on hinges, 23 in. fully extended. **£100-150** *STR*

An ash Tunbridgeware dressing table box with the label of T. Barton, the hinged pin cushion flanked by scent bottles with stoppers, 9 in. wide (23 cm.), c. 1870. **£150-200** *S*

A rosewood parquetry and mosaic ink stand with a cut glass bottle flanked by stamp boxes, 8¾ in. wide (22 cm.), c. 1870. **£130-160** *S*

A Tunbridgeware standish with 2 stamp boxes, 8½ in. wide. **£150-£175** *STR*

A Tunbridgeware standish, 10 in. wide, c. 1870. **£110-140** *STR*

An early 19th C. Tunbridgeware desk rack, probably by Edmund Nye, 7½ in. wide, c. 1840. **£110-£135** *STR*

A Tunbridgeware cribbage box/ score board, with ivory pegs, 9¾ in., c. 1880. **£70-90** *STR*

A Tunbridgeware stickware napkin ring. **£18-22** *STR*

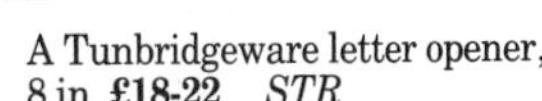

A Tunbridgeware letter opener, 8 in. **£18-22** *STR*

A Tunbridgeware floral ruler, 9 in. **£25-30** *STR*

An early cube design Tunbridgeware cribbage box complete with ivory pegs and packs of cards, 14 in. long. **£70-90** *STR*

A Tunbridgeware 'geometric' ruler, 9 in. **£20-25** *STR*

A Tunbridgeware picture frame, 9 in. high. **£40-50** *STR*

A very rare gypsy table with Tunbridgeware top and laburnum wood legs, 24 in., c. 1830. **£600-£800** *STR*

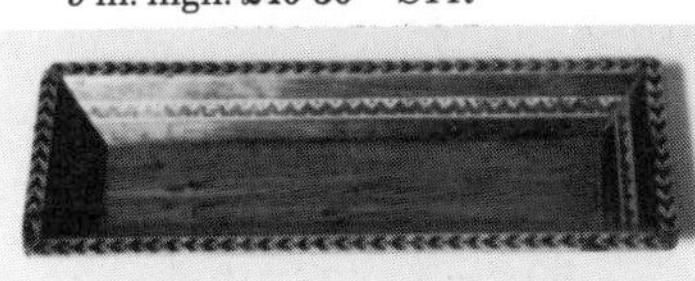

A Tunbridgeware pen tray, 9½ in., c. 1900. **£30-35** *Ph*

A Tunbridgeware nutmeg grater, 1¼ in. high. **£20-30** *STR*

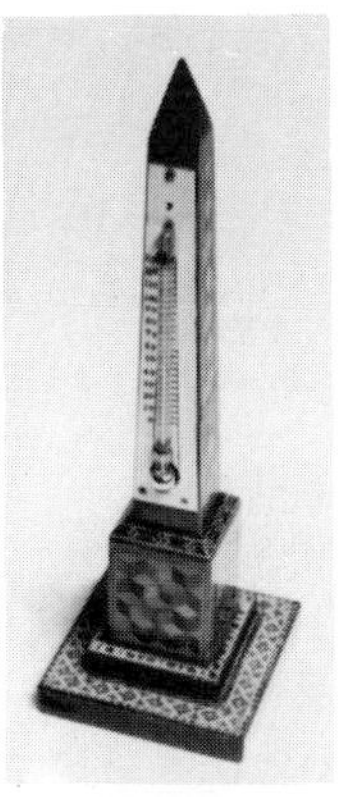

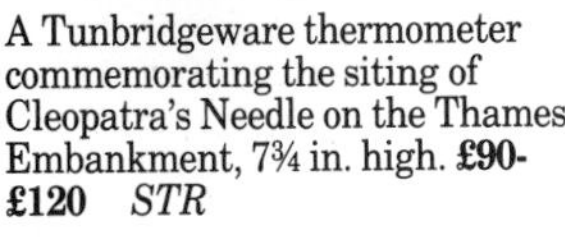

A Tunbridgeware thermometer commemorating the siting of Cleopatra's Needle on the Thames Embankment, 7¾ in. high. **£90-£120** *STR*

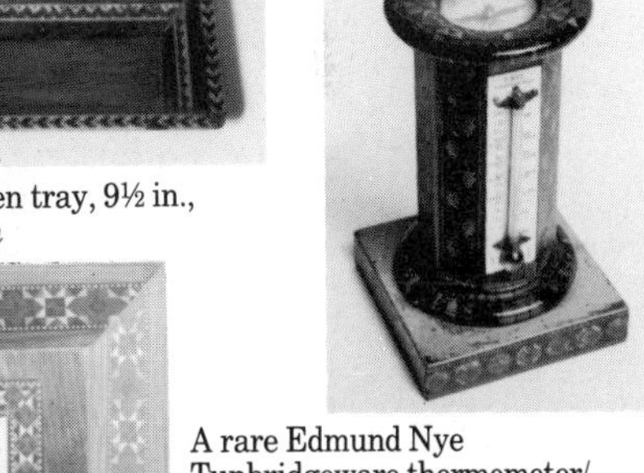

A rare Edmund Nye Tunbridgeware thermometer/ compass with early geometric pattern, 5½ in. high, c. 1845. **£250-£300** *STR*

A Tunbridgeware pen tray, 9¾ in. wide. **£65-95** *STR*

A Tunbridgeware cotton waxer with pin cushion top, 1¼ in. high. **£25-30** *STR*

A Tunbridgeware waxer and pin cushion with original tape measure, 2½ in. high. **£35-45** *STR*

A Tunbridgeware 'stickware' pin cushion, 2¼ in. **£35-40** *STR*

A Tunbridgeware double pin cushion, 1¼ in. long. **£25-30** *STR*

Three Tunbridgeware pin cushions, c. 1870. **£18-22** each *HA*

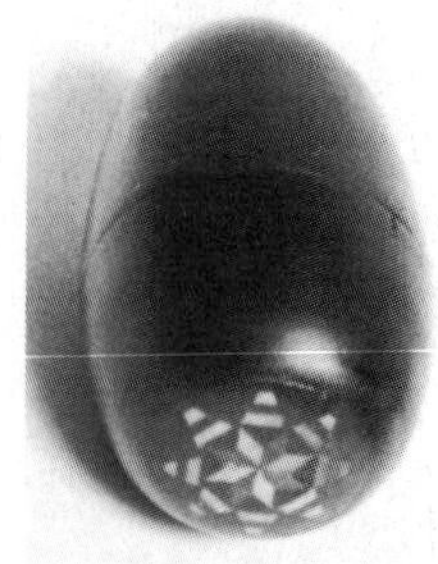

A Tunbridgeware thimble case, 1½ in. long. **£40-50** *STR*

An early Tunbridgeware sewing clamp. **£22-26** *HA*

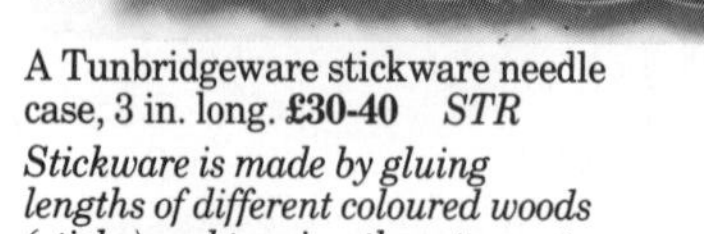

A Tunbridgeware stickware needle case, 3 in. long. **£30-40** *STR*
Stickware is made by gluing lengths of different coloured woods (sticks) and turning them to create new patterns.

Two Tunbridgeware needle cases, 2½ by 1½ in. **£30-45** each *STR*

A Tunbridgeware etui, 2¼ in. high. **£55-65** *STR*

A pin cushion with views of Carisbrook Castle and Osborne House. **£2-4** *HA*

A 19th C. bone pin cushion, 2 in. **£8-10** *HA*

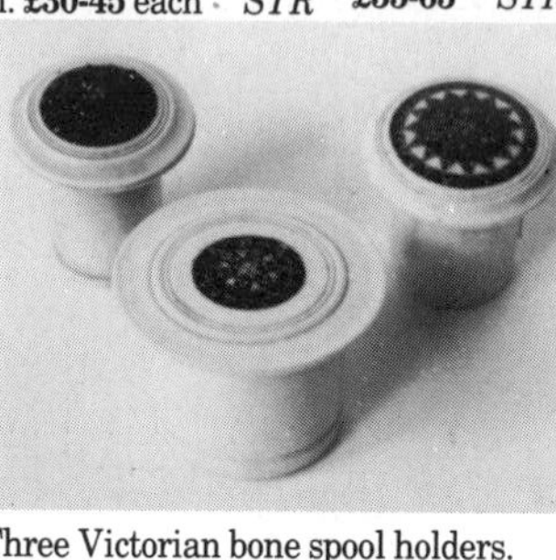

Three Victorian bone spool holders. **£6-8** each *HA*

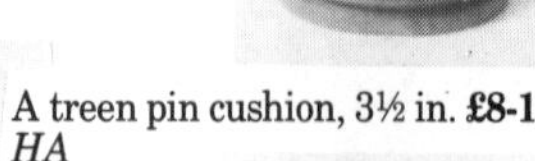

A treen pin cushion, 3½ in. **£8-12** *HA*

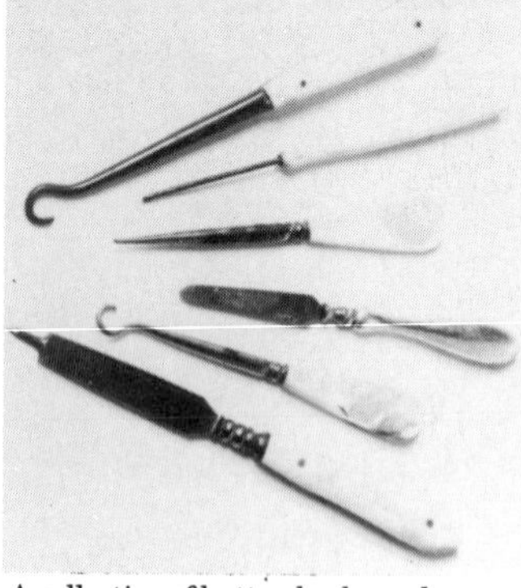

A collection of button hooks and manicure tools. **£2-4** each *HA*

Three late Victorian Mauchlineware pin cushions. **£16-£20** each *HA*

A Victorian horseshoe thimble holder, silver-mounted with silver thimble. **£22-28** *HA*

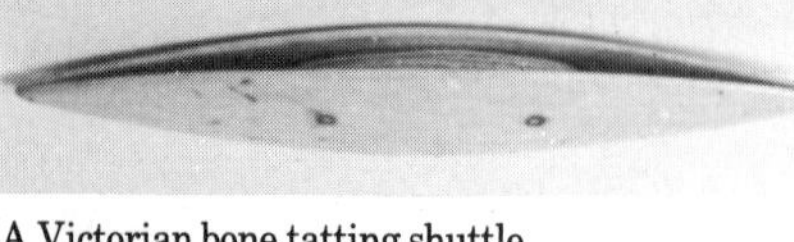

A Victorian bone tatting shuttle. **£6-8** *HA*

A mid Victorian bone sewing clamp, 4¼ in. **£32-36** *HA*

A tartan ware thimble holder and thimble. **£14-18** *HA*

A Victorian silver thimble and purse holder. **£20-25** *HA*

A comprehensive collection of 194 thimbles contained in a lined fitted oak box including 4 gold, many silver-gilt and enamelled examples, together with the collector's own detailed notes on each thimble. **£1,400-1,600** *P*

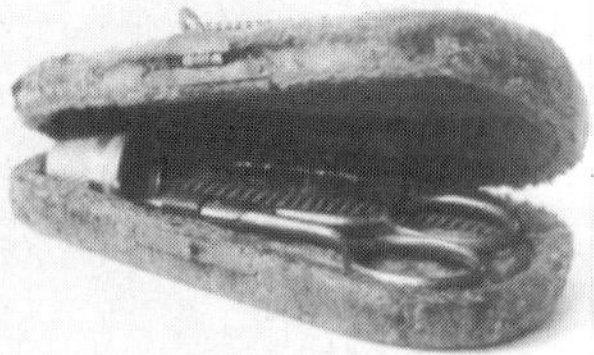

A Victorian etui with scissors and thimble, 4½ in. long. **£10-14** *HA*

Two packets of pins. **£2-4** each *HA*

A 19th C. ivory pin box. **£9-12** *HA*

A late Victorian leather needle case with needles, 2¾ in. **£12-15** *HA*

A Victorian ebonised hairpin box with Bangor Cathedral transfer. **£4-6** *HA*

An English necessaire, fitted with 2 striated agate scent flasks, each with chained gold stopper cast and enamelled as a bird and a King Charles spaniel, scroll-chased gold mirror case and gold spoon, some damage to enamel, 2 in. high (5 cm.), c. 1760. **£500-600** *S*

A Victorian treen tape measure, 1 in. diam. **£25-30** *HA*

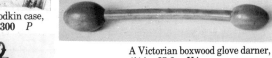

A Victorian mother-of-pearl pin cushion, an ivory pin cushion, a mother-of-pearl waxer. **£5-10** each *HA*

A Victorian tapestry sewing case with scissors and needles, 9 in. long. **£15-20** *HA*

A French 2-colour gold bodkin case, 9 cm. long, c. 1790. **£250-300** *P*

A Victorian boxwood glove darner, 4½ in. **£5-8** *HA*

A rare Alberta sewing machine by Wight & Mann, Ipswich, of Wheeler and Wilson type with mother-of-pearl inlay. **£2,200-£2,500** *CSK*

An early Grover and Baker treadle sewing machine, with decoratively cast iron foot treadle below, with original instruction booklet, American, 29 in. wide (73.5 cm.), c. 1850. **£300-400** *S*

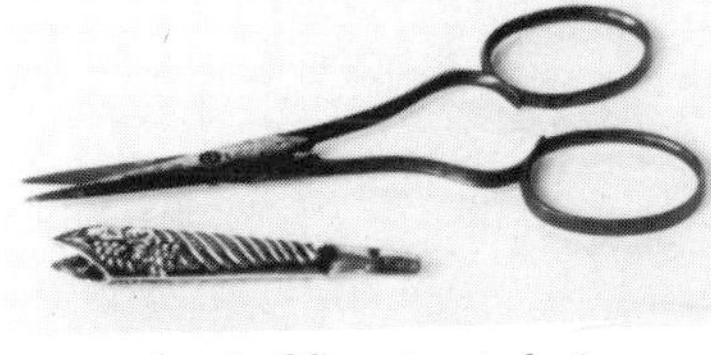

A pair of Georgian steel scissors, with silver sheath, 3¾ in. **£15-18** *HA*

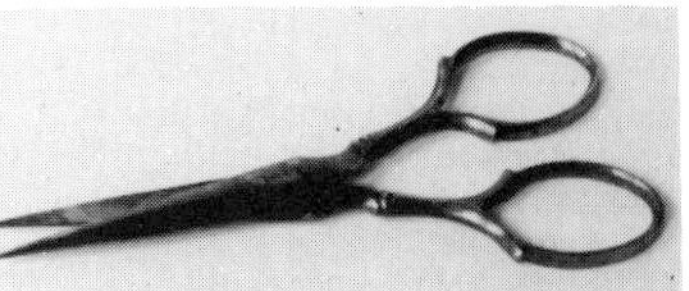

A pair of Georgian steel scissors, 3 in. **£8-12** *HA*

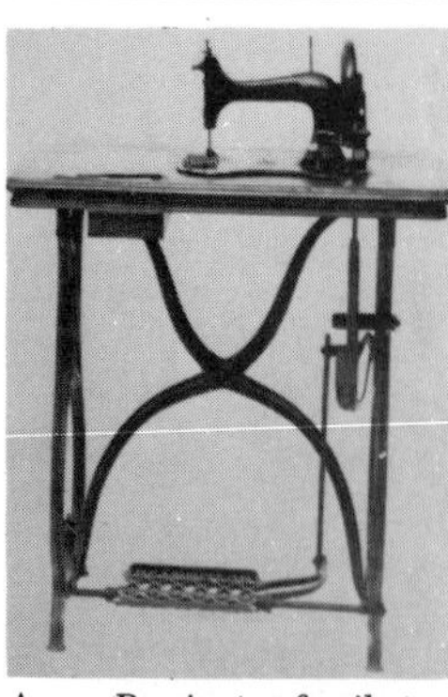

A rare Remington family treadle machine with accessories including instruction book and Remington spanner. **£800-1,000** *CSK*

When Remington undertook the manufacture of the Sholes and Glidden typewriter in 1873, they mounted it in a base using the same castings as the sewing machine treadle, with a single-foot pedal operating the carriage return.

A coco-de-mer basket, 11 in. wide, c. 1890. **£40-60** *NP*

A pole turned sycamore bowl, 17 in. **£70-100** *WHA*

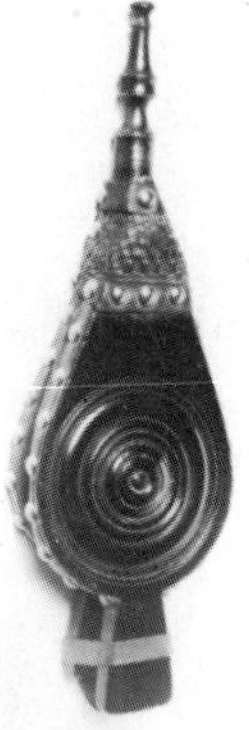

A pair of treen miniature mahogany bellows, 10 in., c. 1810. **£80-£100** *FF*

A rare English 19th C. treen basket cut out from a tree root, 9 in. **£300-350** *SA*

A pokerwork decorated wooden bowl, 16 in. diam., c. 1910. **£30-£40** *IHA*

A 19th C. wooden bowl, 12½ in. **£80-85** *FF*

A late 19th C. turned sycamore bowl, 8 in. diam. **£30-35** *MPA*

A silver-mounted coconut cup, struck with indistinct maker's mark and 2 lion passants, English, 5¼ in. high (13.5 cm.), c. 1720. **£400-450** *S*

A turned dice cup with ribbed interior, 3½ in. **£8-£10** *MPA*

A Norwegian polychrome and carved wood ale bowl, chip carved with stylised mediaeval motifs, inscribed Gunderson on the lip and dated 1759, the base carved with the initials AHS 1749 and HOSH 1756, 6 in. high (15.2 cm.), mid 18th C. Setesdal. **£2,500-3,000** *S*

A late 19th C. sycamore bowl, 17½ in. **£100-125** *TA*

A Nuremburg cup and cover of turned ebonised wood, ivory stem and decoration, 7 in. (18 cm.), 17th C. style. **£200-300** *S*

A pewter embellished coconut cup, c. 1800. **£30-40** *MPA*

An 18th C. Scandinavian juniper wood beaker, 5 in. **£60-80** *FF*

A silver-mounted coconut cup on turned wood base and baluster stem, the interior of the bowl engraved with a cockerel and an inscription, maker's mark only EI, 7¾ in. high (19.7 cm.), mid 17th C. **£800-900** *C*

An ebony bottle box, complete with bottle, 4 in. **£10-14** *HA*

A late 17th C. treen wassail cup in lignum vitae, 7 in. **£400-480** *SA*

A leather string box with scissors and movable calendar, 3½ in. **£14-£18** *HA*

A treen wafer box, 3½ in. **£10-14** *HA*

A treen barrel money box, 3¼ in. high. **£18-22** *MPA*

A Victorian beechwood stamp box, 2½ in. **£5-10** *HA*

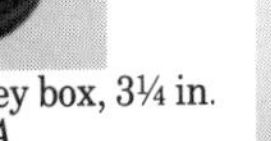

A wooden hatstretcher. **£25-£30** *CGC*

A Mauchline ware paper knife with American transfer, 10½ in. **£5-7** *HA*

A late Victorian Mauchline ware string box, 5 in. **£8-12** *HA*

A lignum vitae string box. **£30-35** *CGC*

A Victorian Mauchline ware casket with 'Edinburgh Castle from Princes Street', 3¼ in. **£10-14** *HA*

A beech auctioneer's gavel, 5 in. long. **£4-6** *MPA*

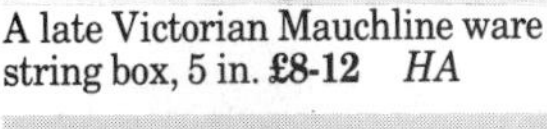

A 19th C. knitting sheath, 4½ in. **£10-12** *FF*

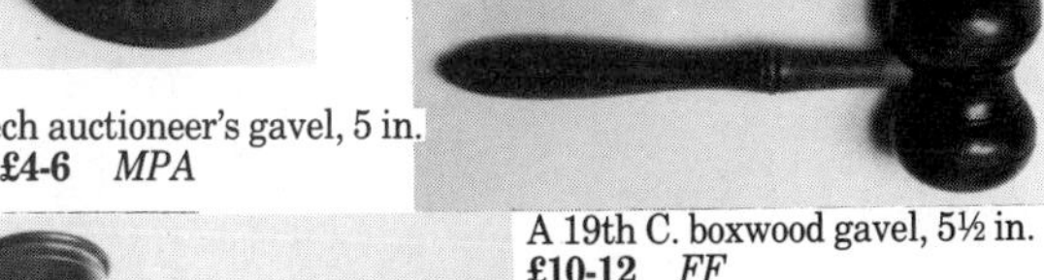

A 19th C. boxwood gavel, 5½ in. **£10-12** *FF*

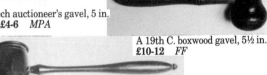

A Georgian gavel, 9¼ in. **£20-25** *MPA*

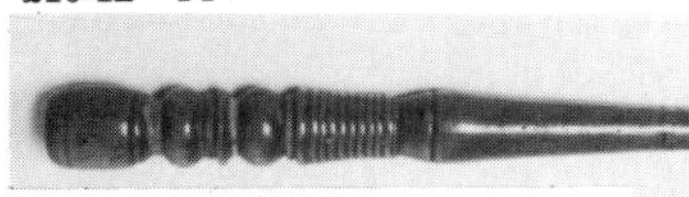

A 19th C. knitting sheath, 5½ in. **£12-14** *FF*

An early 19th C. vet's fleam hammer, 10½ in. **£20-25** *FF*

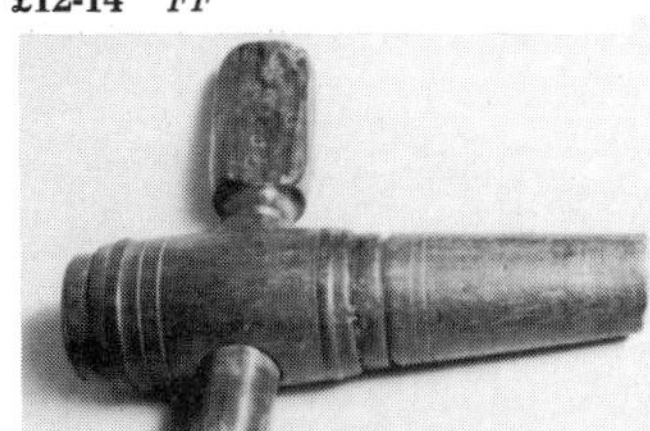

A large early 20th C. wooden vat tap, 10 in. long. **£8-10** *MPA*

A late Victorian Sorrento ware box, 2½ in. **£12-16** *HA*

Often known as 'poor man's Tunbridgeware'.

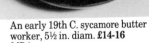

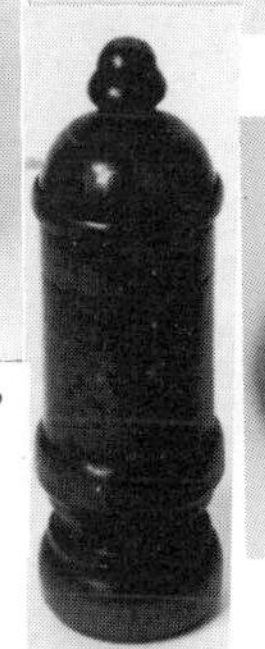

A Victorian treen hairgrip holder. **£10-13** *FD*

An early 19th C. sycamore butter worker, 5½ in. diam. **£14-16** *MPA*

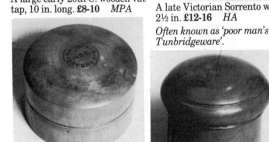

A boxwood screw top pot, 2¼ in. diam. **£8-10** *MPA*

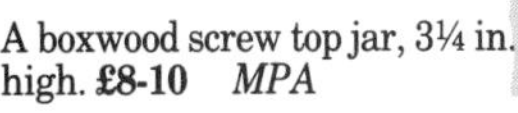

A boxwood screw top jar, 3¼ in. high. **£8-10** *MPA*

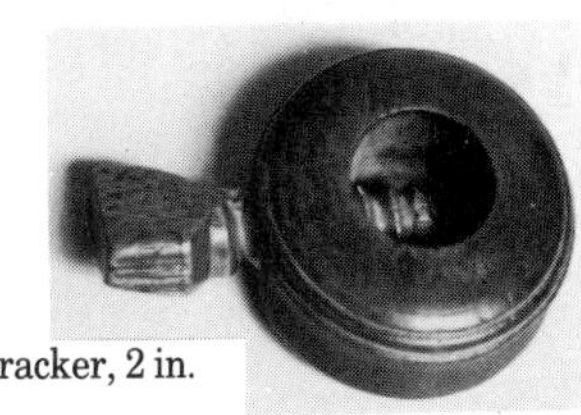

A late Georgian nut cracker, 2 in. diam. **£18-22** *MPA*

A 19th C. lignum vitae stable chuck, 3½ in. diam. **£12-16** *MPA*

An 18th C. carved wooden jar, 6 in. high. **£28-32** *MPA*

A 19th C. treen straw mill, 18½ in. **£70-80** *FF*

A pair of 18th C. turned oak candlesticks, 10 in. high. **£30-36** *MPA*

A Georgian mahogany boat-shaped trencher or cheese coaster. **£150-£200** *M*

A 19th C. English cotton reel stand, 7 in. **£85-95** *SA*

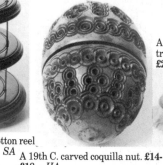

A 19th C. carved coquilla nut. **£14-£18** *HA*

A mahogany dumb-waiter, 18 in. diam., c. 1800. **£90-120** *JMW*

A wrought iron rush light holder on original elm base, 12 in. high, 17th C. **£120-150** *RVA*

A Victorian vegetable ivory rouge pot. **£10-14** *HA*

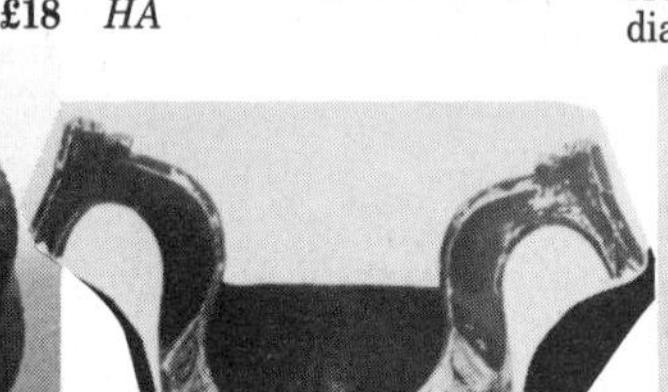

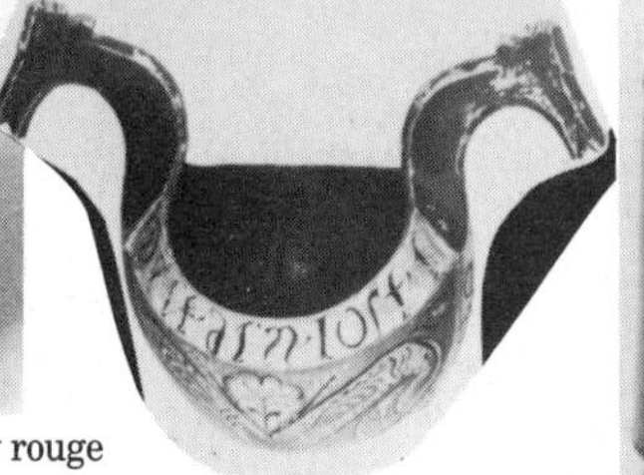

A Norwegian wood skala with horses' head handles, the exterior with polychrome decoration, dated 1841, 17.9 cm. **£650-750** *S*

An early 18th C. Norwegian treen tankard, 8 in. high. **£550-650** *HP*

A Norwegian polychrome wood skala, the exterior with polychrome decoration with indecipherable inscription below the lip, 14¾ in. (37.5 cm.), late 18th C. **£900-£1,000** *S*

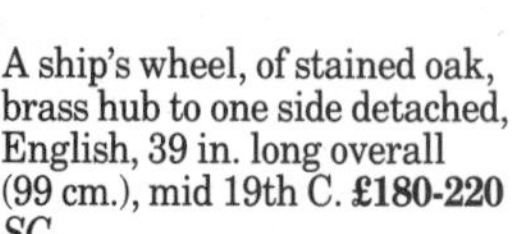

A Norwegian birch wood tankard, the lid carved in relief with the Royal Norwegian Lion, 8½ in. (21.5 cm.), late 18th/early 19th C. **£500-600** *S*

A rosewood and bamboo bird cage, white porcelain seed and waterpots incised with dragons, 9¾ in. square (25 cm.). **£250-350** *S*

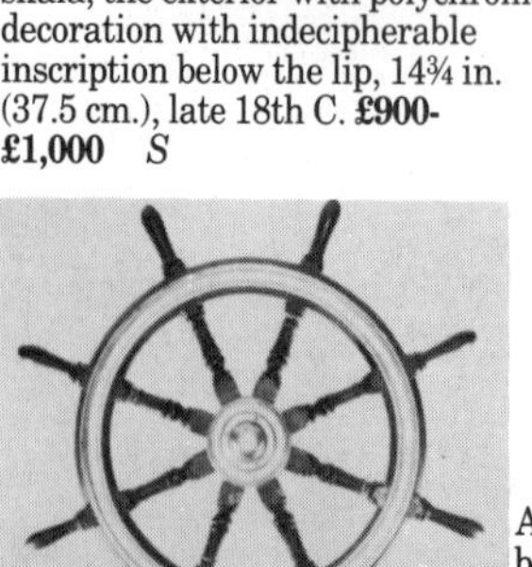

A ship's wheel, of stained oak, brass hub to one side detached, English, 39 in. long overall (99 cm.), mid 19th C. **£180-220** *SC*

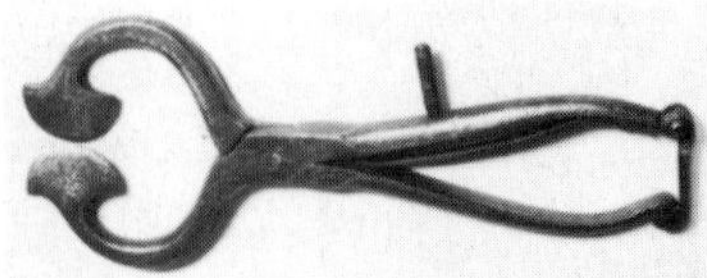

A pair of 18th C. sugar nips, 8 in. long. **£14-16** *MPA*

A black and red tea tin, 14 in. high, c. 1900. **£10-14** *AL*

A green tea tin with original decorations, 12 in. high, c. 1900. **£15-18** *AL*

An unusual George III mahogany inlaid bird cage, on white ceramic feet, 1 ft. 8 in. square (51 cm.), c. 1800. **£400-500** *S*

A 19th C. butter churn, 27½ in. high. **£200-250** *T*

A 19th C. large tin coffee pot, 12 in. high. **£85-95** *MPA*

A pair of 19th C. Georgian-style bellows, leather replaced, 21 in. long. **£28-34** *MPA*

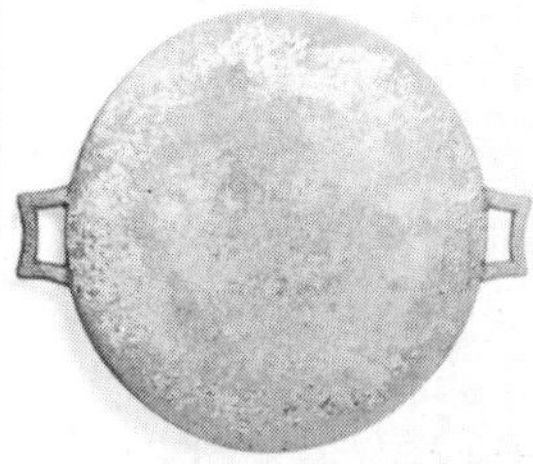

An iron griddle, 19 in. diam., c. 1850. **£13-16** *AL*

A pair of 19th C. leather, wood and iron bellows, 23 in. **£20-25** *LG*

A 'Spong' No. 1 chopping machine. **£12-15** *WHA*

A complete butter mould, 7 in. long. **£20-30** *WHA*

A Victorian butter churn in elm, 16½ in. diam., c. 1870. **£65-75** *AL*

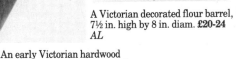

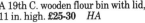

A 19th C. cheese mould, 8 in. diam. **£35-45** *FF*

A Victorian decorated flour barrel, 7½ in. high by 8 in. diam. **£20-24** *AL*

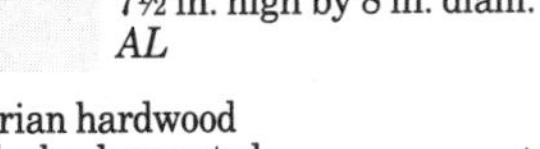

An early Victorian hardwood brass-mounted wheel-operated bellows. **£350-400** *WW*

A 19th C. wooden flour bin with lid, 11 in. high. **£25-30** *HA*

A pine washboard, 20 by 12 in., c. 1900. **£5-7** *AL*

A Victorian flour barrel with original decorations, lined with red silk as a workbox, 9 in. high by 9 in. diam., c. 1870. **£35-40** *AL*

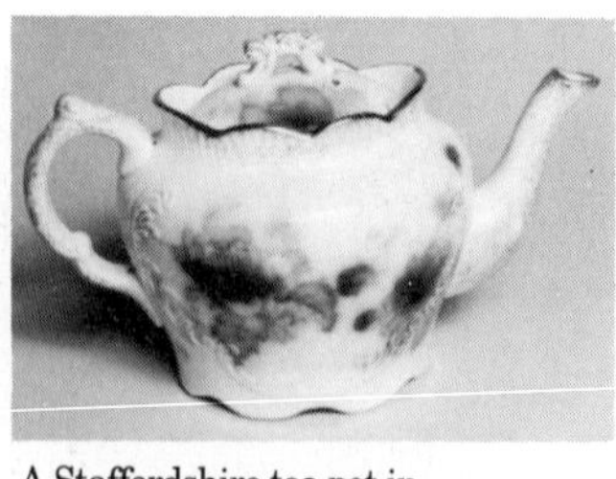

A Staffordshire tea pot in underglaze blue and gilt, 6½ in. high, c. 1880-1900. **£15-20** *BP*

A 19th C. Doulton earthenware milk pail. **£65-75** *JMW*

A Nailsworth Brewery beer bottle of dark green metal, 7½ in. high. **£4-5** *BP*

A clear glass oil lamp, 9 in. high. **£30-35** *STR*

A glazed Minton game dish with liner, 12½ in., c. 1865. **£75-85** *TA*

A coffee grinder, 'Le Parfait Broyeur'. **£12-15** *WHA*

A 19th C. Peugeot Frères coffee grinder in wood and brass, 9 in. **£30-35** *TA*

A pair of Kenrick & Sons coffee mills, 6 by 8 in. and 4½ by 6½ in. **£55-60** *AL*

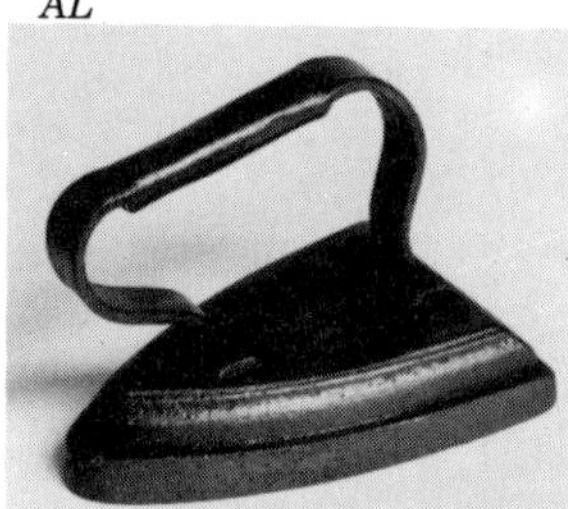

A small smoothing iron, 'Hilltop No. 6', 5½ in. **£2-4** *BP*

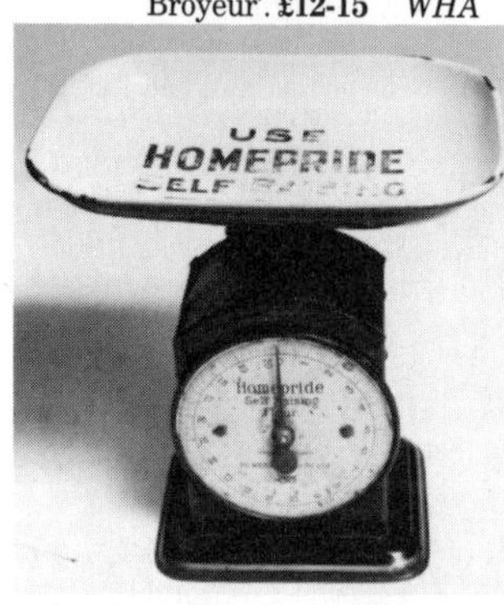

A pair of advertising scales, to weigh 20 lb., 10½ in. high, c. 1920. **£25-30** *AL*

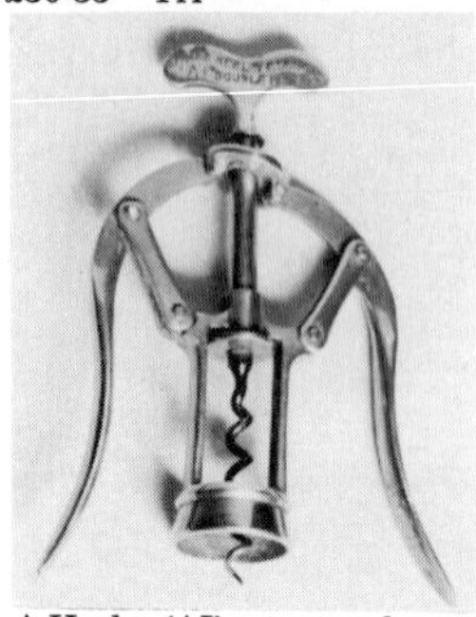

A Heeley 'AI' patent corkscrew, chrome plated. **£40-50** *MPA*

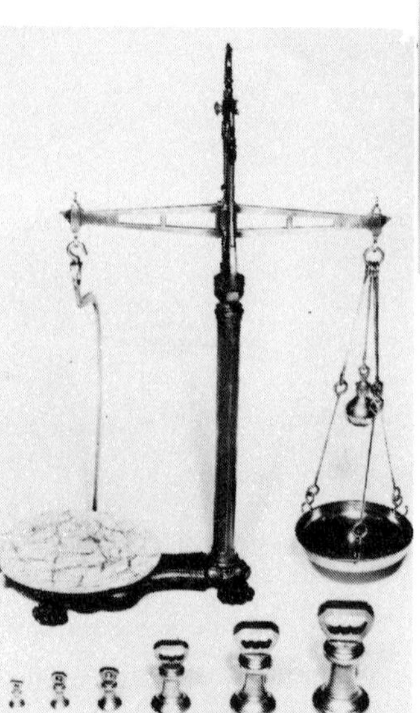

A set of Sutcliffe & Co. cast iron and brass scales, with a veined ceramic plate opposed by a brass weights tray, base stamped 'Patent Agate Balance to Weigh 10 lbs', with a set of 6 brass bell-shaped weights, 7 lb. 2 oz., 35 in. overall (89 cm.), late 19th C. **£200-300** *SC*

A set of scales with pan and weights, 20 lb. **£55-75** *WHA*

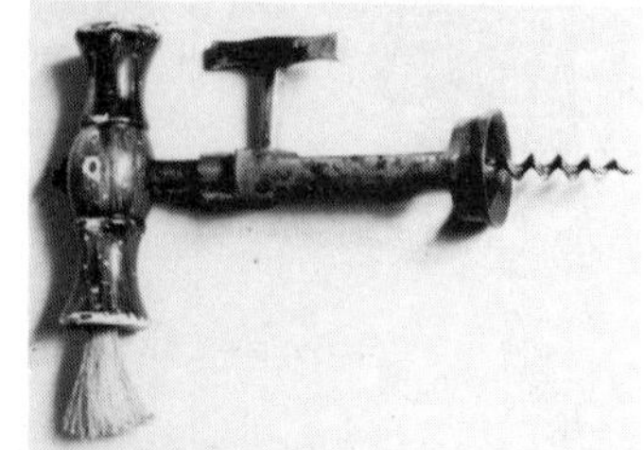

A 19th C. 'London Rack' corkscrew. **£15-18** *MPA*

A set of 19th C. beam scales, the brass lattice beam with swivel hangers, fitted with a porcelain plate and brass pan, the cast iron and brass pillar 43 in. high (90.2 cm.), with an original Avery transferred trade label and 8 brass bell weights. **£200-250** *P*

A J. C. Cox patent change machine in mahogany and brass, 16 in. high, c. 1810. **£170-200** *CDE*

A fine brass parcel scale, attributed to S. Mordan, with 3 brass dishes containing 6 brass stack weights, English, 17 in. long overall (43 cm.), c. 1886. **£150-200** *S*

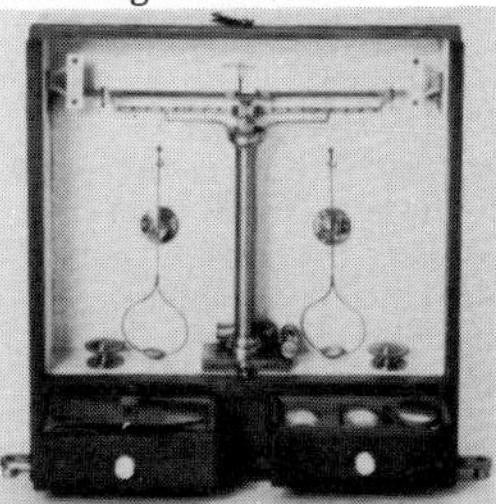

A late 19th C. jeweller's beam balance, the base of the brass pillar stamped L. Oertling Ltd, London, E.C., and numbered 22895, with weights and accessories, the folding cover forming the platform base, the case 8¾ in. square (22.2 cm.). **£300-400** *P*

An oak cake stand, 36 in. high, c. 1930. **£30-40** *Ph*

An elm toffee cutter, 24 by 12 in., c. 1920. **£6-8** *AL*

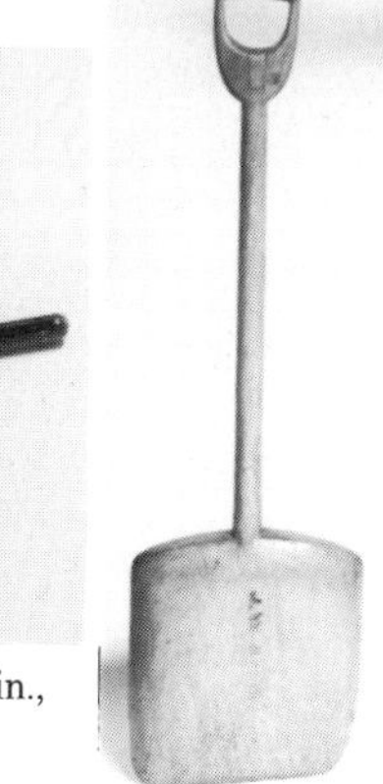

An elm grain shovel, 48 in. long, c. 1830. **£35-40** *AL*

A Victorian flail with original fittings, 70 in. long. **£35-40** *AL*

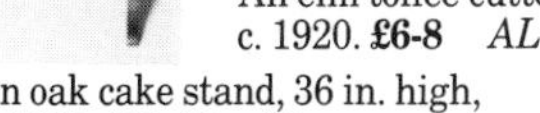

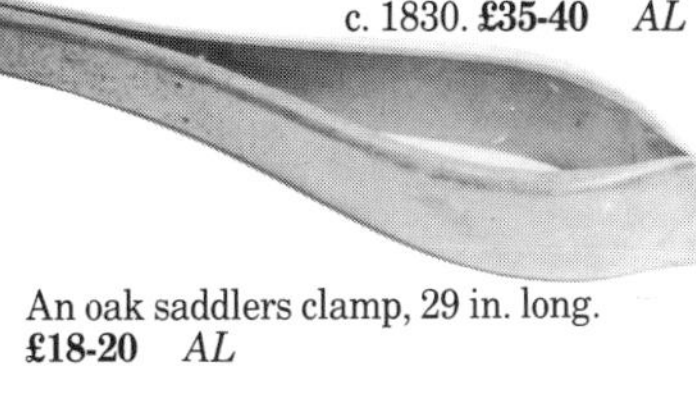

An oak saddlers clamp, 29 in. long. **£18-20** *AL*

A Victorian hay rake, 75 in. long. **£18-20** *AL*

A cast iron chimney ornament, 8½ in. high, c. 1850. **£15-20** *AL*

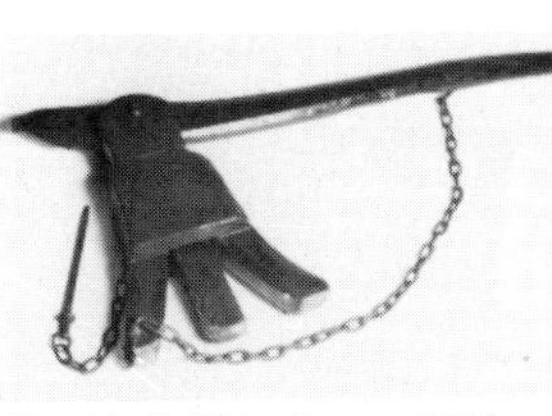

A cart jack, 50 in. long, c. 1840. **£45-50** *AL*

A 19th C. mahogany wool-winder, 3 ft. 8 in. high. **£50-70** *JMW*

A 19th C. beech and brass plough plane, 8 in. long. **£25-30** *MPA*

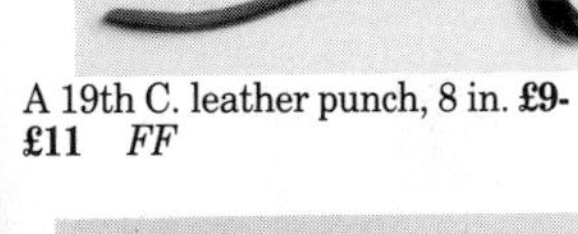

A 19th C. leather punch, 8 in. **£9-£11** *FF*

A brass tide recorder by Palatine Engineering Co. Ltd., Liverpool, with weight-driven clock and glazed cover, base length 33 in., and a wood stand. **£300-350** *CSK*

A brass spirit level, 12 in., c. 1850. **£20-30** *CLA*

A 19th C. shoemaker's last, 32 in. **£10-15** *LG*

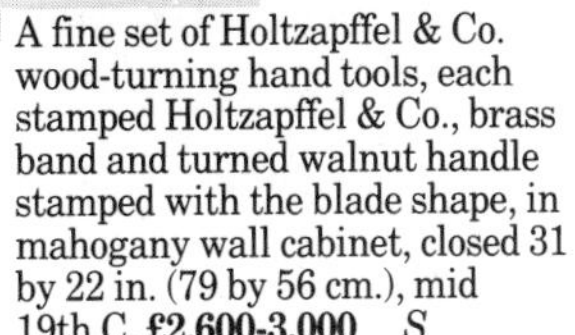

A fine set of Holtzapffel & Co. wood-turning hand tools, each stamped Holtzapffel & Co., brass band and turned walnut handle stamped with the blade shape, in mahogany wall cabinet, closed 31 by 22 in. (79 by 56 cm.), mid 19th C. **£2,600-3,000** *S*

A brass and steel topping tool, hand operated with a 7 in. flywheel, with sliding stage, with lateral and horizontal adjustment, 10 in. long (25 cm.), complete with separate case containing assorted ferrels and cutters, English, late 19th C. **£300-350** *SC*

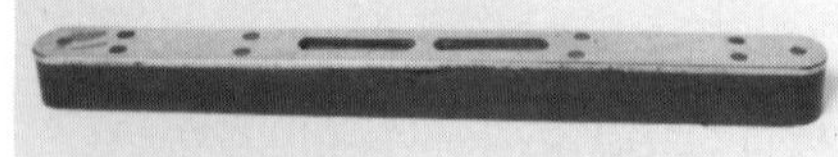

A Victorian brass-mounted spirit level, 11½ in. **£20-25** *CLA*

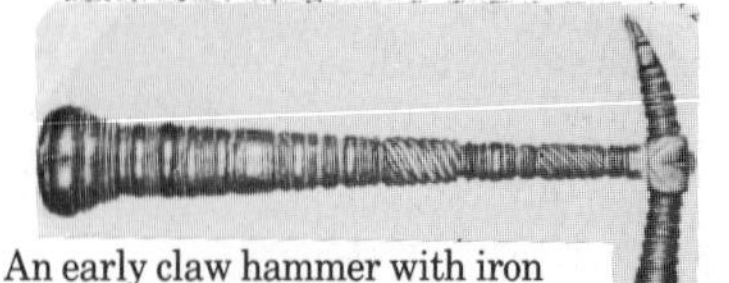

An early claw hammer with iron head and handle with lignum vitae cap to the handle and indistinct name stamp, loseph? Rooker, 18½ in. long. **£600-700** *CSK*

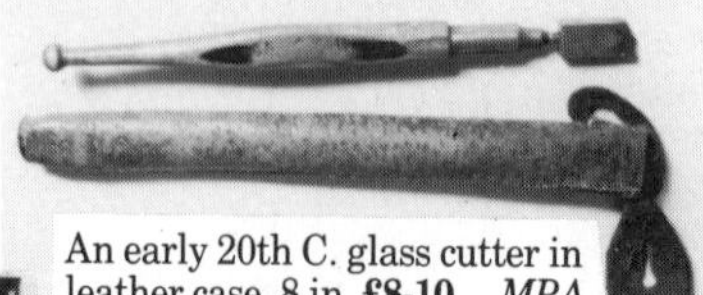

An early 20th C. glass cutter in leather case, 8 in. **£8-10** *MPA*

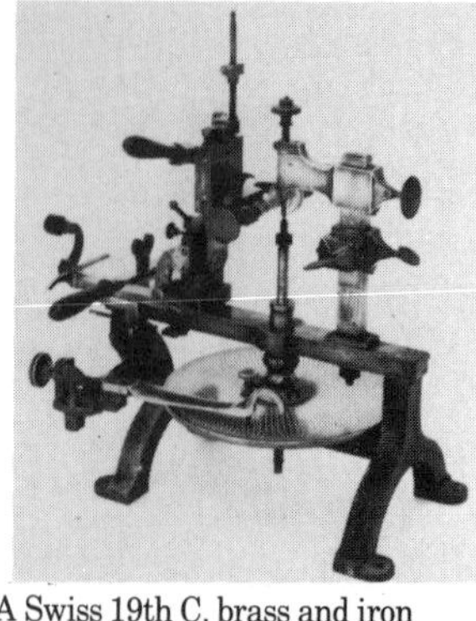

A Swiss 19th C. brass and iron wheel engine, the frame with brass disc for the divisions including 365, 366 and 360, located by a spring index, length of bed 320 mm. **£700-£800** *S*

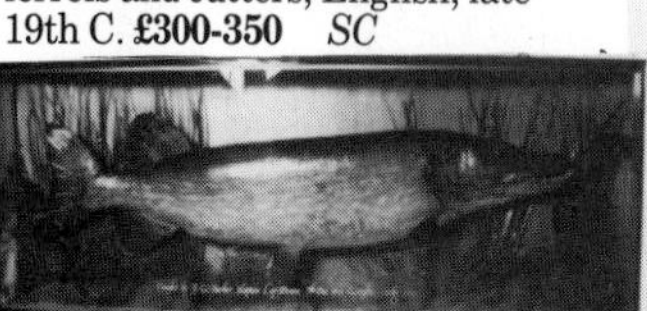

A superb stuffed pike by J. Cooper & Sons, caught by 'J.W. Barber, Slapton ley Devon', 7th December, 1919, wt. 24 lb. 5 oz., 41 in. fish, perspex bowfronted case 50 by 18 by 10 in. **£150-190** *NML*

FISHING TACKLE INTRODUCTION

FISHING TACKLE is the latest addition to the GUIDE and the market has enjoyed a growing popularity within the last 2 or 3 years with the main emphasis for the collector, being on reels.

The majority of fishing tackle was produced from the early 19th C. onwards and items before the 1830's are rare. Early brass reels, in good original condition and complete, command good prices.

The main market for collectors is reels by Hardy Brothers who dominated the tackle market when they established their works at ALNWICK in 1872. They produced, at first, split cane rods and then basic BIRMINGHAM-style reels. Their great innovation was the introduction of the 'PERFECT' REEL in 1891.

This reel, in different models, is still produced today. Other notable Hardy reels for the collector include:– 'SILEX', 'BARTON', 'UNIQUA', 'CASCAPEDIA', 'BOUGLE', 'SUNBEAM', 'DAVY', 'SAINT GEORGE' and 'SAINT JOHN'. All these reels were available in various size combinations.

Other notable makers were CHARLES FARLOW, LONDON; S. ALLCOCK, REDDITCH; ALFRED ILLINGWORTH (who produced the first true fixed spool reel in 1905); P. D. MALLOCH, PERTH, SCOTLAND; and OGDEN SMITH, LONDON.

A metal cast of an 8 lb. brown trout mounted by P. D. Malloch, Perth, Scotland, caught by Franklin Hollond on Loch Cama, 8th September, 1907, cast and flies also mounted, bowfronted case, 30 in. long by 12 in. high. **£170-200** *NML*

A pair of roach by J. Cooper & Sons, London, caught by E. P. Phipps at Hurley, River Thames, 6th January and 9th March, 1946, bowfronted glass with gilt lettering and edges, wt. 1 lb. 12¾ oz. and 2 lb., 18 in. long by 12 in. high. **£70-£90** each *NML*

A small 9½ oz. stuffed rudd, mounted by W. F. Homer, caught by H. W. Hutchins at Roydon, 15th August, 1920, bowfronted glass case, 14 in. long by 9 in. high. **£70-£90** *NML*

A mounted tench by J. Cooper & Sons, caught by E. P. Phipps at Batchworth Lake, 6th October, 1935, wt. 1 lb. 13 oz., bowfronted case, gilt edges and lettering, 18 in. long. by 10 in. high. **£70-90** *NML*

A good stuffed roach by J. Cooper & Sons, London, caught by T. A. Davis at Amberley, 16th June, 1913, wt. 1 lb. 8½ oz., bowfronted glass case, gilt edges and lettering, 19 by 12 in. **£70-100** *NML*

FISH TROPHIES NOTES

Bowfronted glass cases with gilt edges and lettering describing the history of the fish are most desirable as is the taxidermists name.

J. Cooper & Sons, London, were most prominent and fine experts of the art.

Fish in poor condition, broken glass, especially bowfronts and badly retouched examples greatly detract from the value.

A fine barbel by J. Cooper & Sons, caught by E. P. Phipps, 11th November, 1951, at Woolhampton, River Kennet, wt. 6 lb. 6 oz., bowfronted case, gilt edges and lettering, 30 in. long by 15 in. high. **£125-150** *NML*

A finely decorated leather late 19th C. tackle case with original scissors and pliers, various parchment pockets and a 4-sectional rosewood cast winder with sliding centre for lead shot, etc., 7 in. wide by 4 in. high, **£80-120** *NML*

Various leather cast cases with sectional pockets and leaves, 1910-37. **£5-15** each *NML*

An expanding japanned tin tackle case complete with traces, artificial baits, lures and reels, etc., as illustrated in 'Pike and Perch' by Alfred Jardine, 1898, 9¾ in. long by 5 in. wide by 6 in. deep. **£100-£150** *NML*

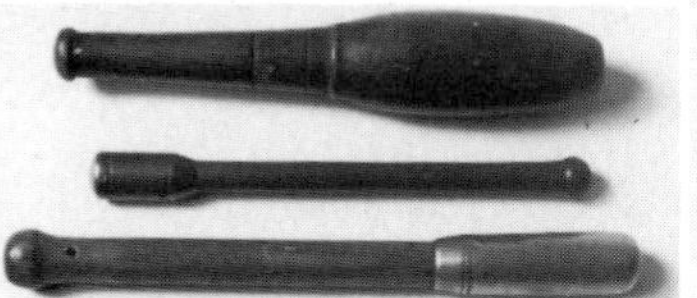

Three various fisherman's 'priests', 8 to 10 in. long. **£5-10** each *NML*

A fisherman's 'priest' is the club or mallet used to kill fish ('to administer the last rites').

A finely carved and hand-turned boxwood cast winder, the outer drum with 12 'fins' for casts and centre section with compartmented boxes for lead shot, hooks and spare line, 5¾ in. high, in leather-covered case, c. 1810. **£110-140** *NML*

Three various cast winders, c. 1930. **£2-5** each *NML*

A leather tackle case by E. Allen, 37 The Strand, London, with a pair of rosewood cast winders with bone pillars and compartments, sliding lid, 8 in. long by 4 in. wide, c. 1870. **£50-90** *NML*

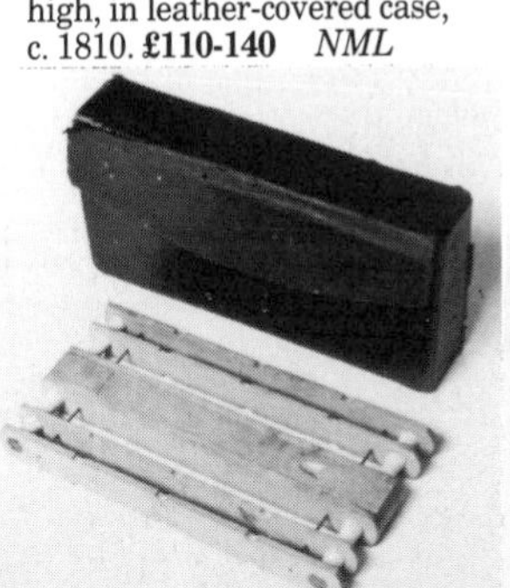

A boxwood cast and tackle winder by J. Cheek, 132 Oxford St., London, comprising 4 sections with sliding compartment between, with leather box, 8 in. long, c. 1860. **£15-£35** *NML*

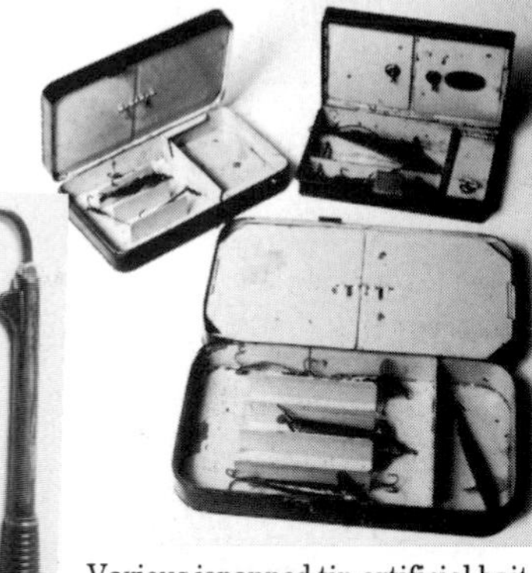

Various japanned tin artificial bait and spinning boxes with phantom baits and minnows, c. 1920. **£5-25** each *NML*

A small Hardy Bros. 'Neroda' trout fly box, 4 in. long, 2½ in. wide, c. 1937. **£5-10** *NML*

A Hardy Bros. Alnwick 3-sectional brass and steel telescopic salmon gaff, with turned rosewood handle, 16 in. long by 36 in. extended, c. 1900. **£35-50** *NML*

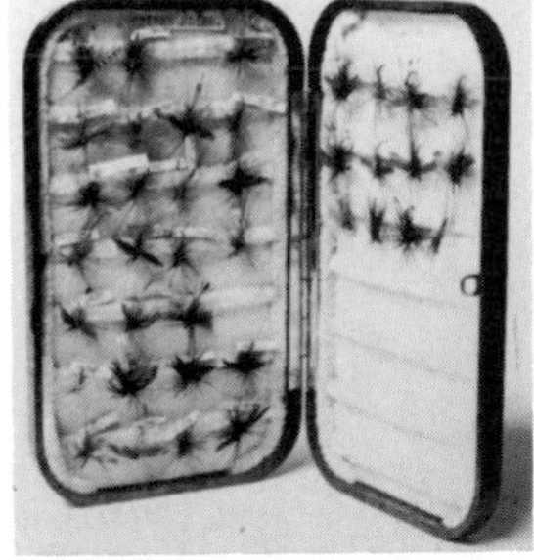

A Hardy Bros. Alnwick 'Neroda' trout fly box containing approx. 40 'parachute' flies, 6 by 4 in., c. 1937. **£15-25** *NML*

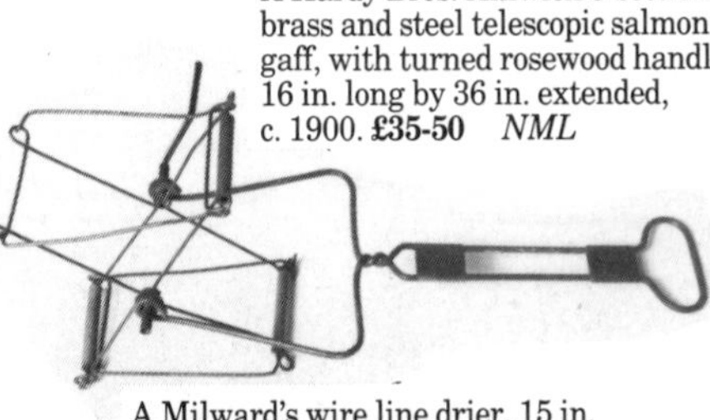

A Milward's wire line drier, 15 in. long, c. 1940. **£2-5** *NML*

Various small trout fly boxes in japanned tin with compartments for flies, c. 1930. **£5-15** each *NML*

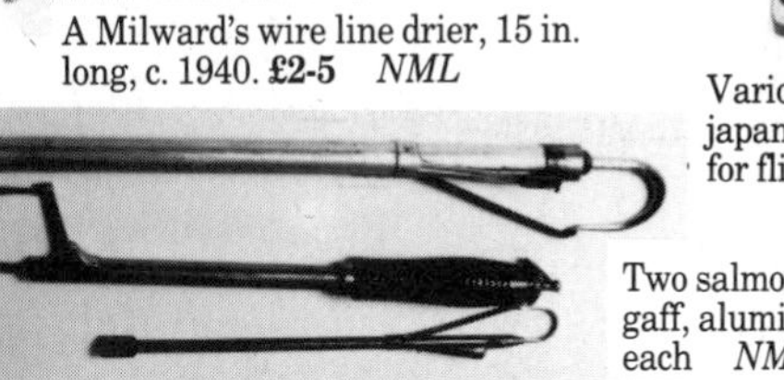

Two salmon gaffs and a small trout gaff, aluminium and brass. **£10-20** each *NML*

A 3-sectional brass and steel telescopic salmon gaff, 2 in. gape and fixed brass hook guard, turned rosewood handle inscribed 'R. Dugard, Abol, and Capt. C.B. Fisher 25 Albyn Place', 14 in. long by 35½ in. extended, c. 1870. **£50-£70** *NML*

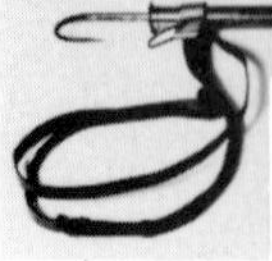

A Hardy Bros. Alnwick, steel and cane 'New Zealand' gaff with brass fittings and leather strap, 27 in. long by 49 in. extended, c. 1900. **£30-60** *NML*

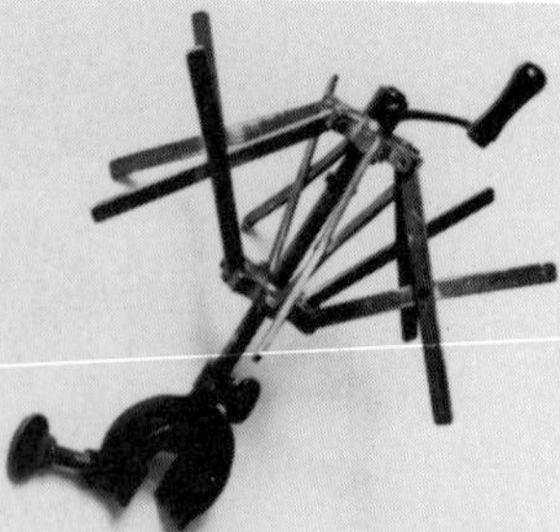

A folding line drier, with heavy brass G-clamp base, steel axle and hinged alloy 'X'-shaped frames, 11 in. diam. by 11½ in. high, c. 1890. **£30-45** *NML*

A Farlow's stained wicker creel, leather-bound with brass mounts, leather shoulder strap, 16 in. wide by 10½ in. deep, c. 1909. **£20-40** *NML*

A brass and steel fly tying vice with 'G' clamp base and sprung steel jaws, 10 in. long, c. 1890. **£5-£15** *NML*

As illustrated in the Badminton Library book on 'Fishing' by H. Cholmondeley-Pennell, 1893, p. 121.

A Hardy 'Compact' line drier, alloy construction with reel fitting handle, 6 in. between vanes, c. 1950. **£10-25** *NML*

Various wicker creels, c. 1930. **£10-£25** each *NML*

A Hardy Bros. bakelite circular cast box containing 2 cast holders of cork and felt, decorated lid with flies, c. 1930. **£10-15** *NML*

A Hardy Bros. 'drainoil' dry fly drier and oiler, nickel silver watch case, 1¾ in. diam. felt and armadou pads, c. 1937. **£2-7** *NML*

Various late Victorian zinc bait cans with perforated lids. **£3-15** each *NML*

A Farlow's 'Gye' slip landing net with brass fittings and sliding ash ring, marked with Farlow's 'Holdfast' logo, c. 1909. **£15-30** *NML*

Two oval zinc bait cans with removable perforated interiors, approx. 12 by 7 by 6 in., c. 1900. **£5-£15** each *NML*

The Art of Angling, by Charles Bowlker of Ludlow in the form of a hand-tooled leather wallet, with many internal pockets for actual flies with descriptions for use, hand-coloured frontis of flies, 6 by 4 in., 1829. **£60-100** *NML*

Various Hardy's Anglers' Guides, dating from 1911-37, size 8¼ by 5½ in. Price range **£10-80** depending on year. *NML*

Hardy's Anglers' Guides are much sought after by tackle collectors as reference books. As with most books the condition is of paramount importance. Most guides have been well thumbed as a price list in the past and hence a fine copy of any particular year is hard to find and will command a higher price. Pre-First World War editions are rare.

A C. Farlow & Co. Ltd. fishing tackle catalogue and price list, 206 pp., 1909, 6½ by 4½ in. **£30-£60** *NML*

A leather-framed case of various gut-eyed salmon flies and including 10 Hardy Bros. 'Aaro' salmon flies with spinners, 11 in. long by 7 in. wide, c. 1925. **£10-25** *NML*

A fine Hickory travelling rod by William Blacker, 54 Dean St., Soho, London, each 18 in. section complete with ivory and brass ferrule cap, the butt end with turned brass reel fittings, several spare tips in whole cane, 16 ft. 6 in. when erected, c. 1860. **£80-120** *NML*

A Hardy 'Silex' salmon spinning reel, aluminium double crank with ivory handles, optional check is marked on reel, 'The Silex' Hardy's patent, finish worn, 1½ in. wide by 4½ in. diam., c. 1899. **£40-70** *NML*

GENERAL POINTS

- **unused or mint condition reels are scarce**
- **generally reels with maker's name or mark are more desirable than those without**
- **avoid highly polished reels as original finish has been removed**
- **cheaply constructed reels can be grossly over-priced by general antique dealers**
- **value can be affected by engraved or scratched owners initials**

A Hardy Bros. alloy 'Perfect' fly reel, strapped tension screw, perforated drum face, 1896 patent mechanism, ivory handle, steel ball bearings, smooth brass foot, marked 'W. 18' on inside drum plate and 'Hardy's Alnwick Patent' on wind plate, 1⅛ in. wide by 3⅜ in. diam., c. 1910. **£50-70** *NML*

Two Hardy Bros. 'Palakona' split cane fly rods, alloy reel fittings, 3-sectional, 9 ft. 6 in. long, c. 1950. **£25-45** each *NML*

The Hardy reels are in date order. This section is followed by general reels by other makers again in date order.

A Hardy Bros. 'Perfect' trout fly reel, perforated drum, Hardy's patent line guard, Mark I type check mechanism, marked 'Hardy's Alnwick Patent' and E. 19 inside (maker's initial) complete with spare spool and fitted leather case, diam. of reel 2⅞ in., c. 1920. **£70-£90** *NML*

A Hardy Bros. 'Eureka' bottom fishing reel, aluminium construction with perforated drum, twin black composition handles, on/off check lever in rim, inside stamped 'TA', 9⁄16 in. wide by 3½ in. diam., c. 1928. **£30-50** *NML*

A Hardy 'Sunbeam' fly reel, duplicated Mk. II, complete with maker's box, brass wire line guard, black composition handle and riveted pressed brass foot, virtually unused, ⅝ in. wide by 3 in. diam., c. 1937. **£35-50** *NML*

A Hardy 'Super Silex' extra wide salmon spinning reel, twin ebonite handles, perforated drum face, ivory-handled crank lever and adjustable dial indicator for control, 3¾ in. diam., c. 1930. **£40-£80** *NML*

A Hardy Bros. all brass Birmingham-type 'Hercules' reel, with fixed check under raised front plate, the plate with ivory handle, oval Hardy logo and 'Rod in Hand' trademark, 1⅛ in. wide by 4 in. diam., c. 1890. **£50-80** *NML*

A Hardy Bros. brass-faced and alloy salmon 'Perfect' reel with strapped tension screw, 1896 check mechanism, bronze ball-bearings, ivory handle marked 'Hardy Pat. Perfect Reel' and Hardy Bros. Makers Alnwick, locking screw missing, 2⅛ in. wide by 4¼ in. diam., c. 1903. **£80-120** *NML*

A Hardy 'Perfect' salmon fly reel, heavy duty type check mechanism, ventilated drum, roller bearings, covered tension screw, Hardy's patent line guard, marked 'S' (maker's initial) and '4', finish slightly worn, 1½ in. wide by 4½ in. diam., c. 1913. **£50-90** *NML*

A Hardy Silex No. 2 aluminium spinning reel, lever type adjustable drag, twin ivory handles, open rim for control, ventilated drum, marked Hardy Bros. Alnwick outside and 'W' (maker's initial) inside, diam. 3¼ in., c. 1920. **£30-£60** *NML*

A Carswell's modified 'Illingworth' reel, with alloy foot and spool, black enamelled brass gears, handle frame and automatic half bale arm, c. 1915. **£40-60** *NML*

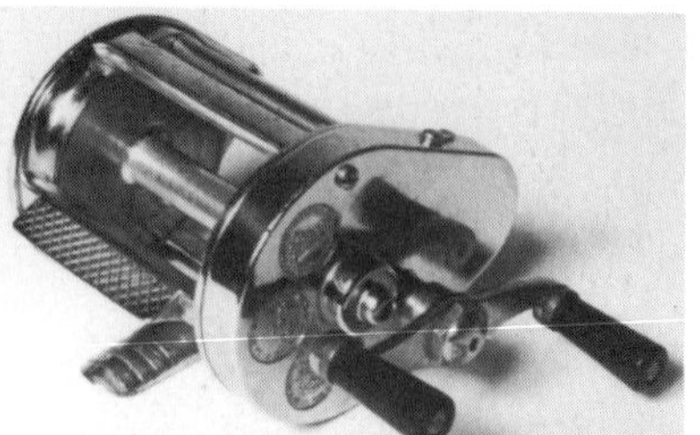

A Hardy 'Elarex' bait-casting multiplying reel, level wind, black composition handles on double 'S' crank, chromium-plated finish, 4 to 1 gear ratio, spool size 1⅝ in. wide by 1½ in. diam., c. 1960. **£5-20** *NML*

A small brass fly winch of riveted construction, turned endplates, riveted bone cranked handle, clamp fitting and screw missing, 1¼ in. diam., c. 1830. **£15-25** *NML*

A fine brass and steel fly winch by Long of Dublin, bone handled 'C' crank, turned endplates with riveted and screwed pillars and bridge with square shanked steel pin, no check mechanism, wing nut and washer missing, ⅞ in. wide by 2⅜ in. diam., c. 1825. **£120-150** *NML*

CONDITION

When assessing reels, especially finely engineered examples, i.e. Hardy Bros., the condition of the item will affect its value considerably. Obviously with rarer reels the condition is not as important as the more common varieties. The main points which reduce commercial value are:—

- **overall wear to the leaded or bronzed finish**
- **cracked or bent frames and drum rims; reels are easily dropped**
- **non-original parts:– different levers, line guards and handles**
- **worn drum bearings, handles and filed rod fittings**
- **condition internally:– wear to check and drag mechanisms**

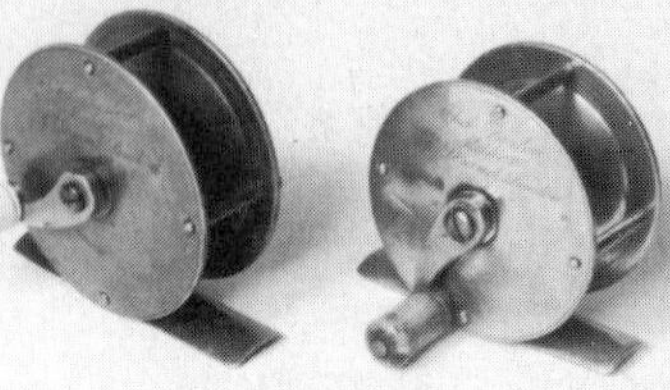

Two fine brass trout reels by C. Farlow, maker, 191 Strand, London, each with turned ivory crank handle, external raised check housing, riveted brass foot, 2½ in. diam., c. 1850. **£20-30** each *NML*

A brass crank wind salmon fly reel with folding handle, riveted brass foot and external check housing, no maker's name, 1½ in. wide by 3½ in. diam., c. 1850. **£25-40** *NML*

Two small brass multiplying reels, each with ivory handle and brass riveted foot, 2¼ and 2 in. diam., c. 1850. **£20-35** each *NML*

A small brass trout fly reel, with bone handle, fixed check mechanism, retaining most of the original finish, 1¾ in. wide by 2¾ in. diam., c. 1880. **£10-15** *NML*

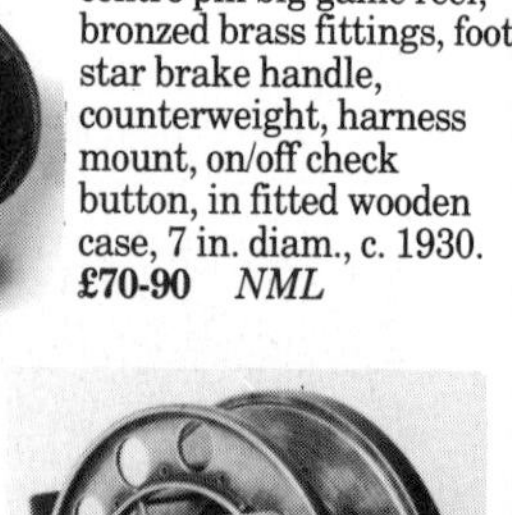

A C. Farlow & Co. Ltd. centre pin big game reel, bronzed brass fittings, foot star brake handle, counterweight, harness mount, on/off check button, in fitted wooden case, 7 in. diam., c. 1930. **£70-90** *NML*

A brass Mallochs sidecasting reel, optional ratchet check, reversible drum, horn handle, 3¼ in. diam., c. 1895. **£10-25** *NML*

Various plate wind reels, c. 1900. **£5-10** each *NML*

A Farlow's 'Mystic' spinning reel, alloy construction, twin ivorine handles, adjustable drag mechanism, brass foot with 'Holdfast' trade mark, 3½ in. diam., c. 1900. **£25-35** *NML*

An S. Allcock's, Redditch, 'Aerial' aluminium reel with perforated frontplate, ivory handles, optional check and riveted brass foot, 4½ in. diam., c. 1920. **£40-60** *NML*

An Afshar rug, the stepped indigo field with faded red centre floral medallion and boteh motifs, main mid blue border closely filled with many flowers and floral faded red narrow guards, plaited cotton kelim ends, 6 ft. 5 in. by 4 ft. 9 in. (1.95 by 1.45 m.). **£450-500** *WW*

A rare Bidjar bag face, indigo ground, the ivory border with a design of leaves, with single guard stripes, condition: fair, 2 ft. 4 in. by 1 ft. 9 in. (71 by 53 cm.), c. 1900. **£300-400** *S*

A Chinese carpet, beige field with an inner vine border and an outer border of foaming waves, 9 ft. 6 in. by 7 ft. 10 in. (290 by 239 cm.), c. 1920. **£1,000-1,200** *S*

SOME PERSIAN CARPET CLASSIFICATION

Afshar	**Tribal rugs from south of Kerman.**
Ainabad	**Kurdish rugs woven in this village in north-west Persia. Often referred to in the trade as Bibikabads.**
Bakshaish	**Rugs of a Kurdish type woven in this village near Herez.**
Bakhtiari	**Tribal, semi-nomadic rugs, woven near Isfahan.**
Birjand	**Trade name for coarse rugs marketed through Meshed.**
Dorukhsh (Dorosh)	**Good early 19th century pieces, modern carpets have none of the quality, area in the Kainat in east Persia.**
Gorovan	**Poor quality rugs woven in the villages near Herez.**
Herat	**Town now in Afghanistan.**
Herez	**Major weaving centre in north-west Persia.**
Isfahan	**For modern pieces, this term can denote either rugs woven in the town itself or rugs of a certain quality sold in Meshed.**
Kashan	**Major weaving centre in central Persia.**
Kashgai	**Tribal and village rugs of south Persia (Fars) — note Fars lion rugs.**
Kerman	**Major centre in central Persia — sometimes written Kirman.**
Khorassan	**Generic name, much abused by dealers, for carpets woven in the eastern province of Persia.**
Kum	**City of central Persia, significant modern weaving industry.**
Kurdish	**Generic name given to weavings of a tribal type from north-west Persia.**
Malayer	**Village near Arak; fine Kurdish weaving.**
Mehreban	**Area near Herez, sometimes used by dealers to denote a particular quality of rug.**
Meshed	**Capital city of Khorassan.**
Nain	**City in central Persia; large number of modern pieces from here.**
North-west Persian	**Trade name for carpets in Kurdish-Caucasian style.**
Saraband	**Trade name for rugs woven in Arak.**
Saruk	**Kurdish rugs of north-west Persia.**
Senneh	**Town near Hamadan, fine Kurdish weaving.**
Serab (Sarab)	**Rugs woven in this village near Herez.**
Tabriz	**Capital of Persian Azerbaijan, north-west Persia.**

A Bakhtiari Kelleh, the indigo ground with trees and floral shrubs, the madder border with rosettes and flowerheads, with triple guard stripes, condition: fair, 12 ft. 6 in. by 4 ft. 9 in. (381 by 145 cm.), c. 1895. **£2,200-2,500** *S*

A Chinese carpet, camel field with an inner pearl border and an outer fret border, all decorated in shades of pale indigo, 9 ft. 5 in. by 8 ft. (287 by 244 cm.), c. 1930. **£1,500-1,700** *S*

An Afshar rug, ivory field with stylised cypresses, shrubs and flowerheads, aubergine border, single floral guard stripe, condition: fair, 5 ft. 1 in. by 3 ft. 11 in. (155 by 119 cm.), c. 1920. **£350-450** *S*

An Amritzar rug, the ivory field with 4 pole medallions containing couplets of verse, in shades of aubergine, pale indigo and indigo, the border with inscription cartouches, condition: fair, slight wear, 7 ft. 8 in. by 6 ft. 6 in. (234 by 198 cm.), c. 1900. **£550-650** *S*

A Bessarabian carpet, woven with an ivory ground, framed by shell cartouches containing birds, swans, a ship and landscape vignettes with brown-ground borders, 8 ft. 2 in. by 11 ft. 9 in. (2 m. 48 cm. by 3 m. 57 cm.). **£1,350-1,450** *C*

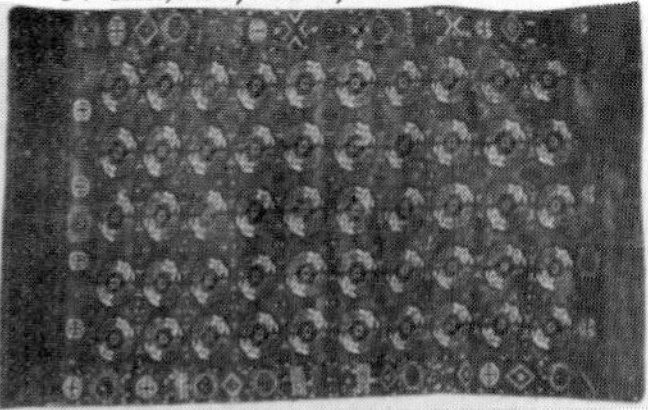

A Bokhara carpet, the madder border with hooked and stepped guls separated by bands of chevrons, combs and jewellery, stylised plant skirts, condition: fair, slight wear, 10 ft. 9 in. by 6 ft. 3 in. (328 by 190 cm.), early 19th C. **£1,500-1,200** *S*

A Derbend small carpet, in tones of blue, brown and ivory on a dark blue ground, 10 ft. 3 in. by 5 ft. 5 in. **£1,100-1,300** *GC*

A Chinese rug, beige field and in shades of indigo, saffron and grey, 4 ft. 5 in. by 7 ft. 1 in. (135 by 216 cm.), c. 1920. **£600-800** *S*

An Esfahan prayer rug, in shades of ivory, madder, green and walnut, beige border, single guard stripes, 6 ft. 10 in. by 4 ft. 4 in. (208 by 132 cm.), c. 1910. **£1,800-£2,100** *S*

A Fars lion rug, the shaded chocolate-brown field with a large ice-blue and orange marked lioness, in a broad ivory and steel-grey flowering vine border, a short kilim strip at either end, 6 ft. by 5 ft. 9 in. (183 by 152 cm.). **£2,200-2,500** *C*

A Ghashghai rug, pale indigo field with an ivory triple pole medallion, ivory border with flowerheads and leaves, twin guard stripes, condition: fair, 7 ft. 2 in. by 4 ft. 8 in. (218 by 142 cm.), c. 1900. **£400-500** *S*

A pair of Kashan rugs, the ivory field decorated with an overall design, 7 ft. by 4 ft. 2 in. (223 by 127 cm.) and 6 ft. 10 in. by 4 ft. 4 in. (208 by 132 cm.), modern. **£900-1,200** *S*

A Derbend rug, the indigo field with 3 plain cross motifs in ivory and red, inner cross motifs in ivory and mid blue, tasselled kelim ends, holed and slight damage on selvedge, 5 ft. 9 in. by 3 ft. 10 in. (1.76 by 1.17 m.). **£300-400** *WW*

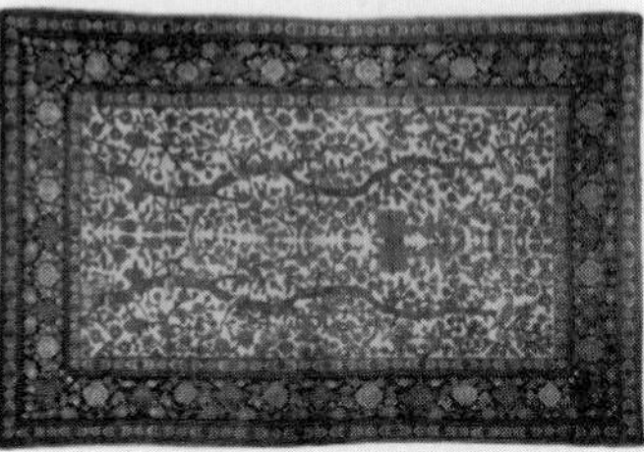

An Esfahan rug, ivory field, indigo border, 2 inner and 3 outer guard stripes, 6 ft. 10 in. by 4 ft. 7 in. (208 by 140 cm.), c. 1910. **£1,300-1,600** *S*

An Esfahan rug, ivory field, madder border with single guard stripes, 6 ft. 10 in. by 4 ft. 9 in. (208 by 145 cm.), c. 1930. **£900-£1,200** *S*

A fine silk Kashan rug with an arched cream ground field, 81 by 52 in. **£4,800-5,500** *GSP*

A Kazak rug, 6 ft. by 3 ft. 8 in. **£350-400** *PWC*

An Esfahan rug, pale indigo field with madder and indigo medallion and ivory and beige spandrels, madder border, and single guard stripes, condition: fair, 5 ft. 5 in. by 3 ft. 6 in. (165 by 107 cm.), modern. **£1,000-1,200** *S*

A Hamadan rug, the off-white field with large spaced floral figured palmettes within a lattice framework, with plain indigo outer band, 6 ft. 6 in. by 4 ft. 6 in. (198 by 137 cm.). **£600-700** *WW*

A Gorovan carpet, madder ground with an indigo medallion, indigo border, ivory floral guard stripes, condition: fair, 9 ft. by 6 ft. 4 in. (274 by 193 cm.), c. 1900. **£850-£950** *S*

A Kashan rug, with an indigo ground, the madder border with palmettes, leaves and flowerheads, condition; fair, 7 ft. 1 in. by 4 ft. 4 in. (216 by 132 cm.), c. 1930. **£850-1,050** *S*

A pair of Kashan part silk rugs, ivory and shades of beige, with twin guard stripes, both 6 ft. 9 in. by 4 ft. 5 in. (206 by 135 cm.), c. 1940. **£2,300-2,500** *S*

A Kazakh Karatchoph double-ended prayer rug, indigo field with ivory and madder medallions, ivory border and single guard stripes, 6 ft. 8 in. by 4 ft. (203 by 122 cm.), c. 1880. **£1,200-2,000** *S*

A Kazakh Karatchoph rug, with a central ivory medallion with 2 smaller ivory-hooked medallions, condition: fair, slight wear, damaged, 6 ft. 4 in. by 5 ft. 4 in. (193 by 162 cm.), c. 1880. **£1,000-£1,200** *S*

A Luri Bakthiari rug, the ivory field scattered with stylised birds, animals, mounted horsemen and human figures, in an indigo flowering vine border between 'kotchak' and polychrome barber-pole stripes, slight overall wear, 6 ft. 6 in. by 3 ft. 9 in. (198 by 114 cm.). **£1,800-2,000** *C*

A Melas rug, madder field with saffron border and an outer ivory border, 3 inner floral guard stripes, 5 ft. 6 in. by 3 ft. 6 in. (168 by 107 cm.), c. 1830. **£1,600-2,000** *S*

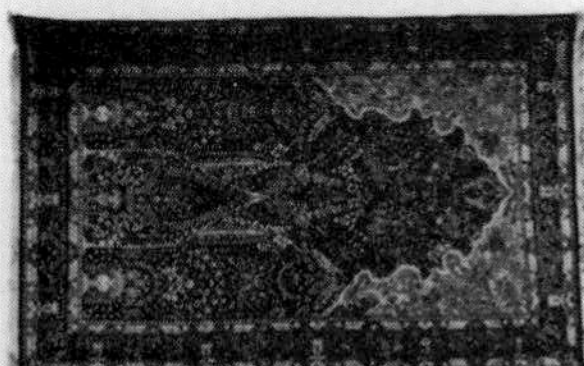
A Kerman prayer rug, the indigo mehrab surrounded by floral shrubs, all in shades of madder, pale indigo, ivory and green, condition: fair, 7 ft. 7 in. by 4 ft. 10 in. (231 by 147 cm.), c. 1920. **£850-950** *S*

A Sewan Kazakh rug, with an eagle medallion on a madder ground, in ivory and aubergine, with reciprocal trefoil guard stripes, condition: fair, 7 ft. by 5 ft. 4 in. (213 by 162 cm.), c. 1920. **£950-1,050** *S*

A Turkish Kelim prayer rug, brick mihrab with double sunbird, black and white reciprocal frame, wide faded orange border of linked sunburst motifs, 6 ft. by 4 ft. 3 in. (183 by 129 cm.). **£250-300** *WW*

A Kerman rug, ivory-lobed medallion, blue field with foliate arabesques, the main border red, condition: good, 5 ft. 11 in. by 4 ft. 7 in. (181 by 140 cm.). **£500-600** *L*

A Portuguese needlework carpet, ivory field with design of diagonal vines, flowers and leaves in vine green, saffron and rose, with a similar border, condition: fair, 7 ft. by 7 ft. (213 by 213 cm.), 18th/19th C. **£400-500** *S*

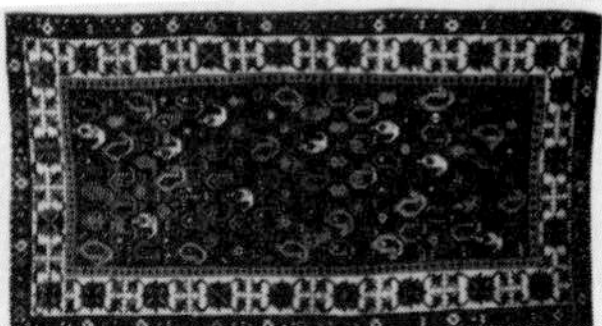
A Kazakh rug, pale indigo field with saffron, pale madder, ivory and green, ivory border and single guard stripes, 7 ft. 5 in. by 4 ft. 1 in. (226 by 124 cm.), c. 1880. **£900-1,100** *S*

A Lori-Pambakrug, the rust-red field around 3 large ivory, green and blue radiating floral medallions, 8 ft. 5 in. by 5 ft. 1 in. (256 by 155 cm.). **£2,200-2,800** *C*

A Malayir rug, the pistachio-green field with a very fine lattice of ivory cruciform lozenges, overall wear, 6 ft. 8 in. by 4 ft. 5 in. (204 by 135 cm.). **£2,000-2,500** *C*

A Nain rug, ivory field with a pale indigo pole medallion and spandrels, indigo border, twin guard stripes, condition: fair, 6 ft. 1 in. by 3 ft. 6 in. (185 by 107 cm.), modern. **£750-850** *S*

A needlework carpet, madder field with medallions enclosing stylised flowerheads, all within a pearl border, the pale green border with flowers and leaves, condition: fair, 8 ft. 2 in. by 6 ft. 3 in. (249 by 190 cm.), 19th C. **£900-1,000** *S*

An usual Mereze carpet, indigo ground, madder border with single guard stripes, condition: fair, slight wear, 10 ft. 9 in. by 5 ft. 10 in. (328 by 178 cm.), c. 1880. **£850-950** *S*

A Pirbedil rug, with an overall design on an indigo ground, condition: fair, slight wear, 6 ft. by 4 ft. (183 by 122 cm.), c. 1900. **£800-1,200** *S*

A good Qum silk rug, with fawn medallion on a gold ground, with deep blue border, 6 ft. 10 in. by 4 ft. 6 in. **£2,300-2,600** *GSP*

A Qashqai Kilim, with 5 broad bands containing crenellated motifs divided by minor ivory bands of stylised lozenges, bands of lappets at either end, 9 ft. by 5 ft. 7 in. (274 by 170 cm.). **£650-£750** *C*

A Sarough rug, camel field with indigo pole medallion, rose spandrels with large green leaves and flowers, indigo border, two inner and one outer guard stripes, condition: fair, 6 ft. 10 in. by 4 ft. 1 in. (208 by 124 cm.), c. 1900. **£700-800** *S*

A fine Senneh rug, the plain indigo field with an ivory medallion and spandrels, all with the herati pattern, twin guard stripes, condition: fair, slight wear, tinted, 6 ft. 10 in. by 4 ft. 8 in. (208 by 142 cm.), c. 1880. **£1,700-2,000** *S*

A Serapi runner, lined camel field, medallions containing stylised flowerheads and vines, ivory border, single guard stripes, condition: fair, slight wear, 14 ft. 11 in. by 3 ft. 7 in. (455 by 109 cm.), c. 1880. **£500-600** *S*

A Shiraz cane rug, in shades of saffron, madder, ivory, walnut and pale indigo, one inner and two outer guard stripes, 4 ft. 9 in. by 2 ft. 11 in. (145 by 89 cm.), c. 1900. **£1,300-1,500** *S*

An unusual Shirvan rug, pale madder field, slate border, ivory floral guard stripes, 5 ft. by 4 ft. (152 by 122 cm.), c. 1900. **£500-£600** *S*

A Serapi rug, pale indigo with floral medallions in ivory and madder, surrounded by guls and flowerheads, the ivory border with guls, vines and flowerheads, condition: fair, 7 ft. 6 in. by 3 ft. 8 in. (229 by 112 cm.), c. 1880. **£700-900** *S*

A Shirvan runner, the indigo ground with 3 medallions, stylised animals and peacocks, in saffron, ivory and pale indigo, condition: fair, guard stripe missing at one end, 9 ft. 9 in. by 3 ft. 9 in. (297 by 114 cm.), c. 1880. **£1,000-1,200** *S*

A pair of Shrinigar rugs, the indigo field with rose madder boteh, pale green border, one inner and two outer guard stripes, both 6 ft. 8 in. by 5 ft. 1 in. (203 by 155 cm.), c. 1940. **£750-850** *S*

A Tabriz carpet, ivory field, madder border with flowers in shades of green, pale madder, pale indigo and ivory, twin floral guard stripes, 14 ft. 6 in. by 11 ft. 2 in. (442 by 340 cm.), c. 1930. **£1,800-2,000** *S*

A Talysh rug, pale indigo field with a design in saffron, walnut and madder, ivory border, two inner and one outer guard stripes, 7 ft. 5 in. by 3 ft. 1 in. (226 by 94 cm.), c. 1880. **£550-650** *S*

A Tabriz carpet, ivory field, indigo border, with single guard stripes, 12 ft. 1 in. by 9 ft. 9 in. (368 by 297 cm.), c. 1920. **£1,600-1,800** *S*

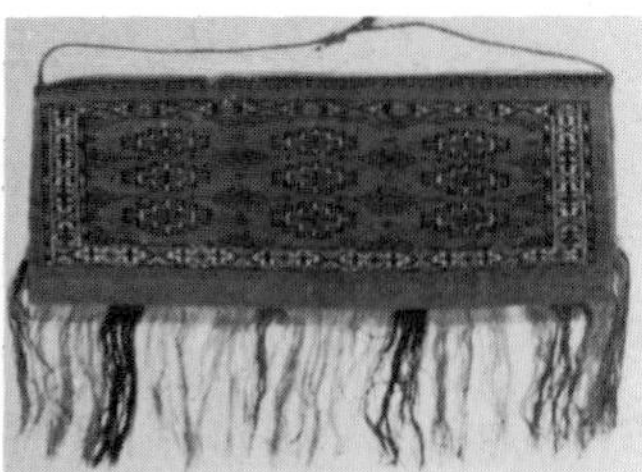

A pair of Tekke Turkoman Torbas, each with a red field, fringed skirts, condition: good, but some moth damage, 1 ft. 4 in. by 3 ft. 5 in. (41 by 104 cm.). **£200-250** *L*

A Yomud Hatchlu, the liver-brown field with guls within a serrated leaf and trellis border, condition: good, 5 ft. 8 in. by 4 ft. 2 in. (173 by 127 cm.). **£400-450** *L*

A Persian Yomut carpet, madder field, ivory border, 10 ft. by 6 ft. 5 in. (305 by 196 cm.), c. 1920. **£1,100-1,400** *S*

A Rajasthan valance of red cotton embroidered with birds and lotus flowers in orange, blue, red and ivory silks, having mirror insets, 0.93 by 4.16 m., late 19th C. **£115-£140** *P*

A Teheran prayer rug, the ivory field with shades of rose madder, pale indigo and saffron, triple floral guard stripes, 7 ft. by 4 ft. 9 in. (213 by 145 cm.), c. 1910. **£950-1,050** *S*

GLOSSARY

Abrash	**Variations of density in a colour seen in a carpet by irregular horizontal washes, can greatly add to the value.**
Aniline	**Chemical dye, a derivative of coal-tar, first produced in the 1860's, most common in the red-blue-purple range, colours tend to fade (orange-pink, for instance can fade to walnut-brown).**
Boteh	**Widespread pattern of Persian origin (original meaning 'cluster of leaves'), used in Europe in the Paisley pattern.**
Ch'ang	**Chinese endless knot, the inextricable knot of destiny.**
Chrome dye	**A fast synthetic dye now used in all the major rug weaving areas, colours do not fade.**
Gol Henai Pattern	**Floral pattern associated with Persian rugs, mainly found on Hamadan rugs.**
Hejira (or Hijra)	**The beginning of the Muhammedan calendar, 16 July, A.D. 622.**
Herati Pattern	**Also called the mahi or fish pattern. This common pattern originated in East Persia.**
Jufti	**'False' knot, either Turkish or Persian, whereby the knots are tied to four, not two, warp threads.**
Kelim	**Also spelled kilim, gilim, gelim. Principally from Anatolia.**
Madder	**Deep red-brown dye.**
Palas	**Caucasian name for kelim.**
Palmette	**A flowerhead of heart-shape with many radiating lobes or petals.**
Sileh	**A corruption of a now lost Caucasian place name. A form of Soumak, sileh pieces tend to be woven with rows of large S-motifs.**
Soumak	**Sumak, Summak, Sumacq, Sumakh, thought to be a corruption of Shemaka, town in south east Caucasus.**
Spandrels	**Architectural term for the space between the curve of an arch and the enclosing mouldings.**
Swastika	**A hooked cross. Chinese symbol for 10,000 (wan) and happiness.**
Tiraz	**Official weaving factory usually set up under Royal patronage.**

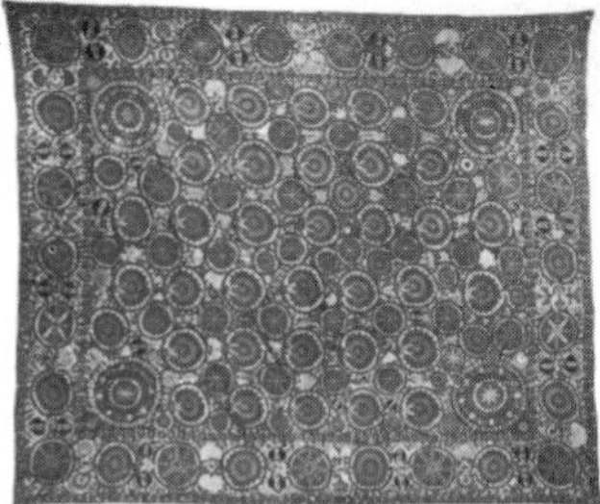

A Turkoman Susani, the ivory field with blooms surrounded by green leaves, condition: good, 6 ft. 10 in. by 5 ft. 7 in. (208 by 170 cm.). **£350-£400** *L*

A Yomut carpet, madder field with dyrnak guls, ivory border and stylised rams' horns skirts, condition: fair, 11 ft. 10 in. by 7 ft. 1 in. (361 by 216 cm.), c. 1900. **£900-1,000** *S*

A Yomut Ensi, the pale madder ground with an overall design of guls with an ivory stylised bird border, indigo gliding falcon elems, condition: fair, 5 ft. 5 in. by 4 ft. 5 in. (165 by 135 cm.), c. 1880. **£1,300-1,600** *S*

A patchwork coverlet of sunburst design, in printed cotton and chintz, lined, 2.28 m. square, 19th C. **£300-400** *P*

A cover of fine lawn worked in whitework and cutwork with the royal coat-of-arms as used by the Kings of Hanover, each corner embroidered with a verse from a poem in German, 77 by 107 in., c. 1830-40. **£150-200** *CSK*

A patchwork quilt of undyed linen, the centre applied with printed chintz and embroidered with initials R.D., fringed, probably Irish, 2.10 by 2.06 m., early 19th C. **£500-600** *P*

A rare cover composed of various patterns of net applied with a trellis of point de rose, Italian, fragile, 44 by 52 in., early 18th C. **£200-250** *CSK*

A silkwork panel, the whole in coloured silks and silver thread, probably the lid of a casket, 12½ by 8½ in., early 17th C. **£1,100-£1,300** *CSK*

A fine Uzbek silk Ikat panel, with bands of lobed concentric lozenges of yellow and burgundy on a purple ground, 6 ft. 3 in. by 5 ft. 6 in. (191 by 168 cm.). **£500-600** *C*

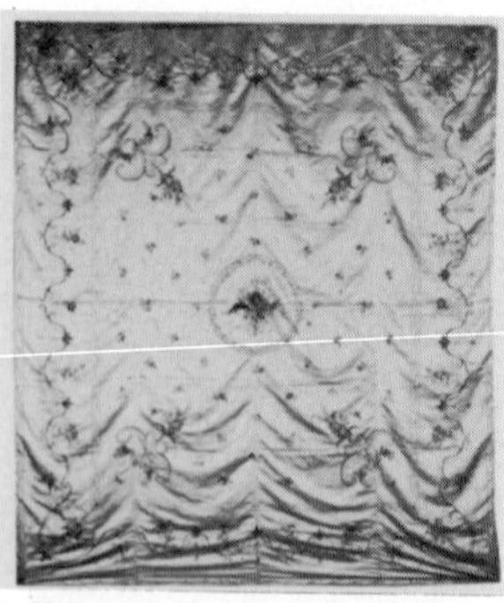

A Chinese bedcover made for the European market, embroidered in shaded red, pink, yellow, blue and green twisted silks on an eau-de-nil satin ground, the outer border of bronzed satin, 11 ft. by 9 ft. 7 in. (335 by 293 cm.), early 19th C. **£950-1,050** *S*

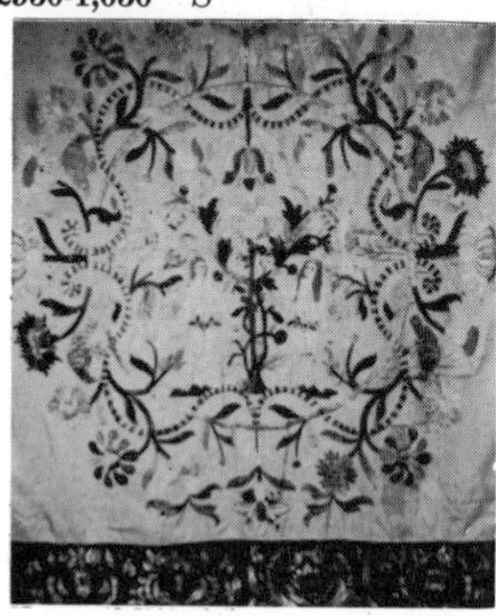

A coverlet or hanging of salmon pink silk worked in coloured silk with Adam and Eve, Portuguese, 97 by 67 in., late 17th C. **£750-£950** *CSK*

The embroidery is double sided but the borders are backed with pink silk.

An embroidered and couched yellow satin chair panel, embroidered with clouds, dragons, bats, Buddhist and Daoist symbols, all in apricot, shaded blue, green and yellow silk, 4 ft. 1 in. by 3 ft. 9 in. (125 by 114 cm.), 18th C. **£750-850** *S*

A panel of emerald green satin woven with sprays of ivory silk flowers, labelled the 'Queen's Bedroom' and 'Chosen', 29½ in. wide with selvedges, 20½ in. long. **£50-70** *CSK*

A Uzbek Nurata Suzani, the linen ground worked in basma stitch with coloured silks, 2.26 by 2 m., 19th C. **£500-600** *P*

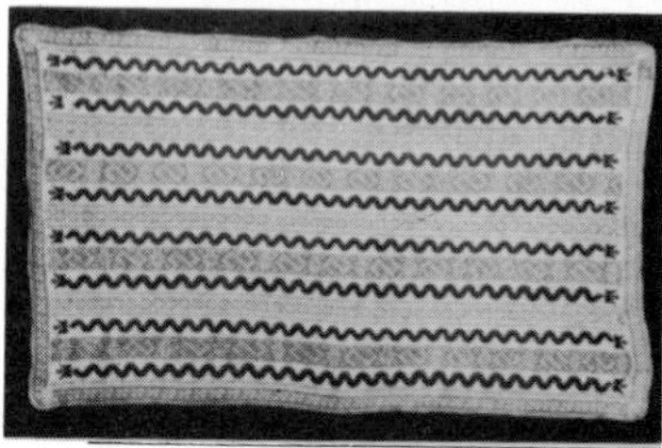

A linen coverlet with drawn-thread work, bobbin lace insertions and trim, having pink and blue silk applique, 2.42 by 1.32 m., 18th C. **£150-180** *P*

A curtain of woven wool worked with the pattern Ispahan by Morris & Co., 81 by 72 in., 1889. **£250-£350** *CSK*

A pair of Morris & Co. printed linen curtains, designed by William Morris, 'Corncockle' pattern, in pale pink, blue and green, on a natural ground, each 274 by 171.5 cm., 1883. **£400-500** *S*

Three linen curtains embroidered in ivory, lime green, brown and rust coloured crewel wools, worked by the Royal School of Needlework to designs by William Morris, one of 100 in. drop by 47 in. wide, another 118 in. drop by 48 in. wide, and the third 78 in. drop by 39 in. wide. **£700-900** *CSK*

A Japanese wall-hanging of applied cord in coloured silks and gold thread, bordered and lined, 19th C., 90 by 76 cm., 19th C. **£200-£250** *P*

An Ottoman Bursa velvet panel, with burgundy panels of feathery leafy plants, in a broad ivory border, 2 panels backed, wear and damage, 4 ft. 8 in. by 4 ft. (142 by 122 cm.), 17th C. **£500-600** *C*

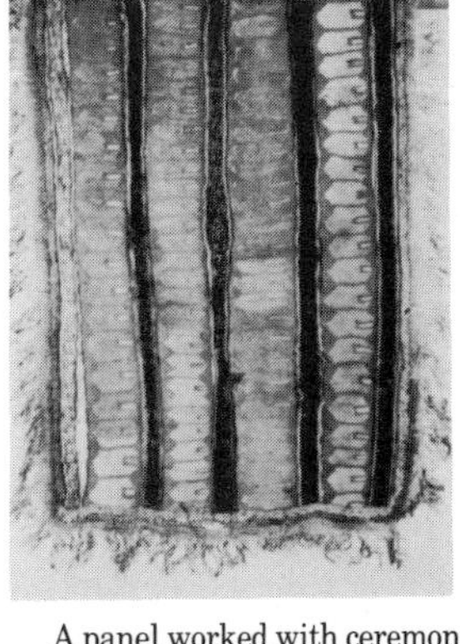

A panel worked with ceremonial head-dresses in yellow on a pink ground, with waves in black on pink within an orange, red and yellow fringed border, Chancay culture, approx. 17 in. wide by 21 in. long. **£300-400** *CSK*

A large mezzara or wall-hanging of chintz, stamped M.A., Italian, 129 by 86 in., late 18th/early 19th C. **£1,000-1,200** *CSK*

A Japanese wall-hanging of applied coiled thread and pastel silks, mainly in shades of brown, 1.99 by 1.38 m., mounted on a frame and with printed cotton backing, 19th C. **£650-750** *P*

A chintz hanging or mezzara printed in crimson, green and purple, stamped 4 USCCRI in a segmented circle, Italian, 137 by 98 in., late 18th/early 19th C. **£1,400-1,600** *CSK*

A fine set of crewel work hangings worked in pink, green, yellow and blue wools, comprising two pairs of curtains and three panels, one pair 78 by 66 in., the other pair 79 by 48 in., one joined border 18 by 52 in., another 9½ by 240 in., and another 15 by 160 in., early 18th C. **£2,500-3,000** *CSK*

A piece of 'Strawberry' pattern wool and cotton cloth, designed by C. F. A. Voysey, in yellow, green and red, 178 by 183 cm., c. 1900. **£100-150** *S*

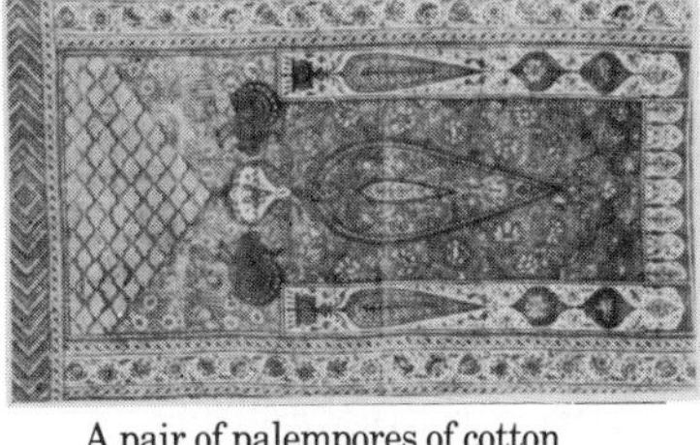

A pair of palempores of cotton printed, lined with Provencal floral cotton, Indian, 44 by 80 in., 19th C. **£450-550** *CSK*

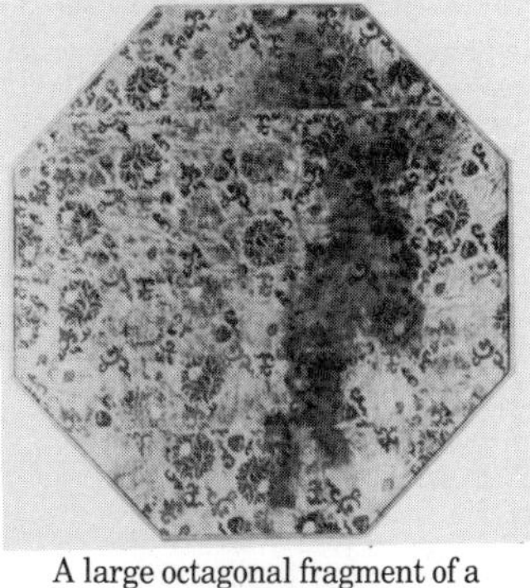

A large octagonal fragment of a textile, kesi, blue, red, yellow and green lotus heads amongst foliage on a yellow ground (with considerable wear), Ming Dynasty framed and glazed, 114 cm. wide. **£400-500** *C*

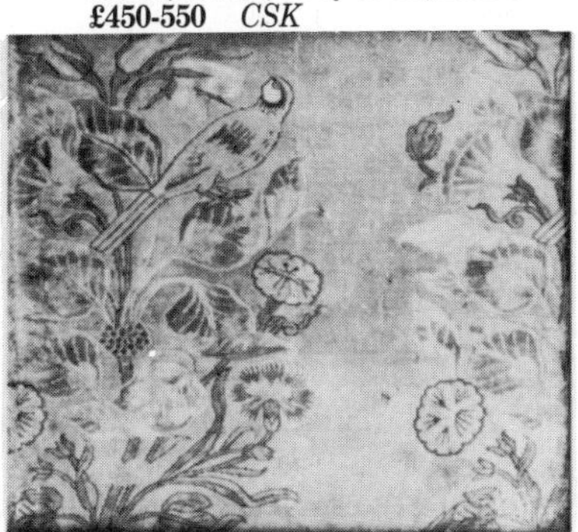

A fine Persian silk and metal thread textile fragment, on a silver ground, framed and glazed, 7¼ by 8¼ in. (18.5 by 21 cm.). **£400-500** *C*

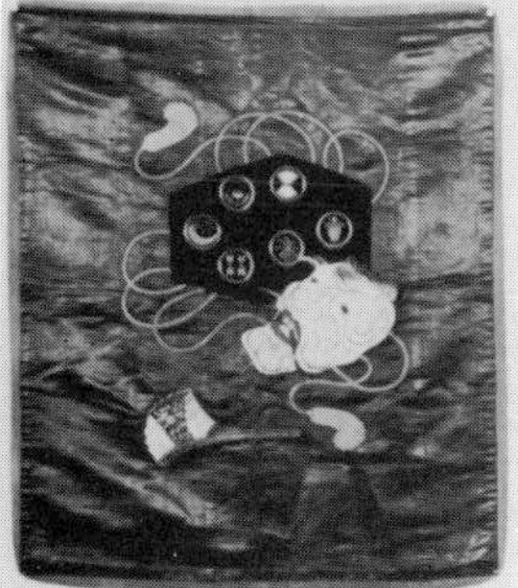

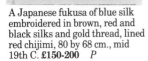

A Japanese fukusa of blue silk embroidered in brown, red and black silks and gold thread, lined red chijimi, 80 by 68 cm., mid 19th C. **£150-200** *P*

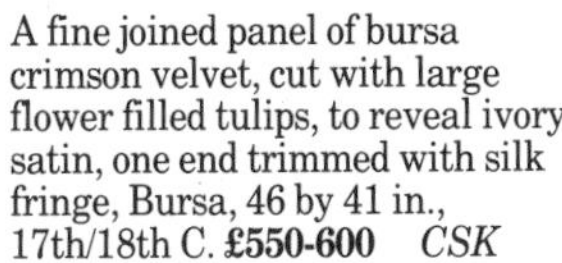

A fine joined panel of bursa crimson velvet, cut with large flower filled tulips, to reveal ivory satin, one end trimmed with silk fringe, Bursa, 46 by 41 in., 17th/18th C. **£550-600** *CSK*

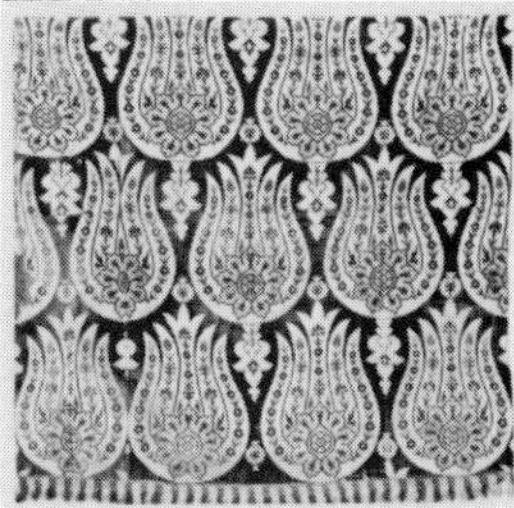

A silkwork picture, probably English, 8 by 9 in., late 17th C. **£800-1,000** *CSK*

A Charles II stumpwork picture, 12 by 17½ in. **£500-600** *PWC*

A needlework picture, the ivory silk ground worked mainly in yellow, green and blue silks in needlepoint and satin stitches designed with a Lady, flowers, insects and the traditional devices, framed and glazed, 19 by 22 cm., c. 1660's. **£350-400** *P*

A petit-point picture designed with Juno being drawn in a chariot in the clouds above the Temple, mounted, framed and glazed, 52.5 by 44 cm., mid 18th C. **£500-600** *P*

A petit-point picture worked in coloured wools and designed with The Four Seasons, 84 by 58.5 cm., within a giltwood frame, mid 18th C. **£500-600** *P*

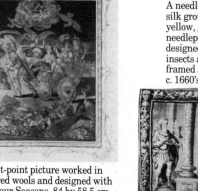

A pair of Flemish tapestries, cut and shut, minor repairs, 9 ft. 3 in. by 5 ft. 8 in. and 9 ft. 6 in. by 5 ft. 11 in., 17th C. **£3,000-4,000** *C*

A good Danish embroidered and painted silk picture of Gravensteen I det Slesvig Holsteenske by J. Petersen worked in coloured silks, framed and glazed, 31 by 38 cm., early 19th C. **£400-500** *P*

A long sampler worked by Elizabeth Smart, daughter of William and Anne, born on January 10th, 1734, framed and glazed, 17 by 4½ in. **£150-200** *CSK*

An early 19th C. needlework sampler by Harriot May, 1825, embroidered and darned in coloured silks, framed and glazed, 37 by 33 cm. **£200-250** *P*

A needlework picture embroidered mainly with needlepoint and tent stitches in coloured silks, worked in silver thread, framed and glazed, 20 by 24 cm., c. 1660's. **£500-550** *P*

A mid 19th C. needlework sampler by Helenor Stocks, aged 11, 1841, designed with Adam and Eve, worked in coloured wools on a linen ground, framed and glazed, 44 by 45 cm. **£350-450** *P*

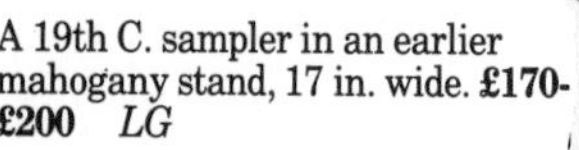

A 19th C. sampler in an earlier mahogany stand, 17 in. wide. **£170-£200** *LG*

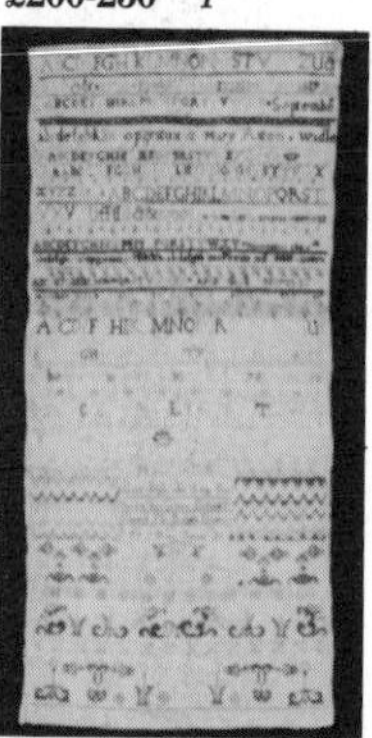

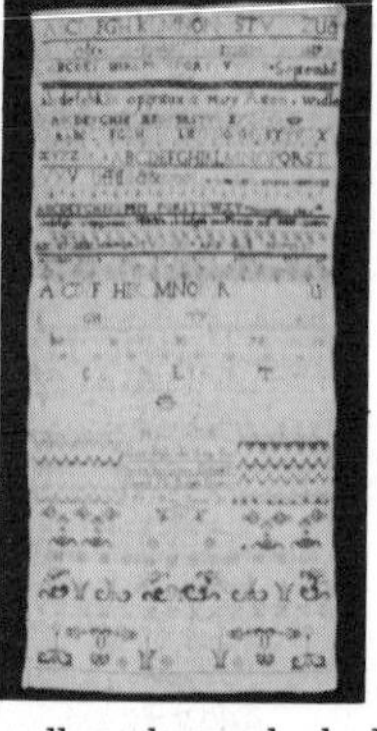

A needlework sampler by Mary Aston, 1721, designed with the alphabet, numerals, geese and a unicorn in coloured silks, 45 by 21 cm., early 18th C. **£300-400** *P*

A mid 19th C. needlework sampler by Hannah Oakes, aged 9 years, 1834, worked mainly in green and red wools on a linen ground, framed and glazed, 44.5 by 31 cm. **£500-600** *P*

A rectangular tapestry worked in greens, amber and black, with brown borders, monogram JA, mounted on board, 87 by 103.5 cm. **£180-240** *C*

A Paris tapestry woven with Diana the Huntress, with attendant maidens and hounds, the dark blue ground border woven with putti, with Mannerist cartouche, areas of repair and restoration, 10 ft. 8 in. by 10 ft. (3 m. 24 cm. by 3 m. 5 cm.), 17th C. **£4,500-5,000** *C*

An Aubusson tapestry, designed by E. Grekoff, autumnal colours, designer's credit within the design, 'E. Grekoff' and workshop mark in border 'Aubusson', 175 by 165 cm., c. 1950. **£400-450** *S*

An Oudenarde verdure tapestry woven in blues and greens, the broad borders with flowerheads, birds and shell angles, later selvedge, 5 ft. 4 in. by 9 ft. 7 in. (163 by 291 cm.), 17th C. **£900-£1,000** *C*

A rare beadwork purse, dated 1623, embroidered with yellow, green, blue, brown and white beads, 5 by 6 in. **£1,500-1,700** *CSK*

A linen pocket with whitework embroidery of a bowl of flowers, mounted in a glazed frame, c. 1620's. **£150-200** *P*

Reputed to have belonged to George Villiers, First Duke of Buckingham, b. 1592, d. 1628, and worked by The Duchess.

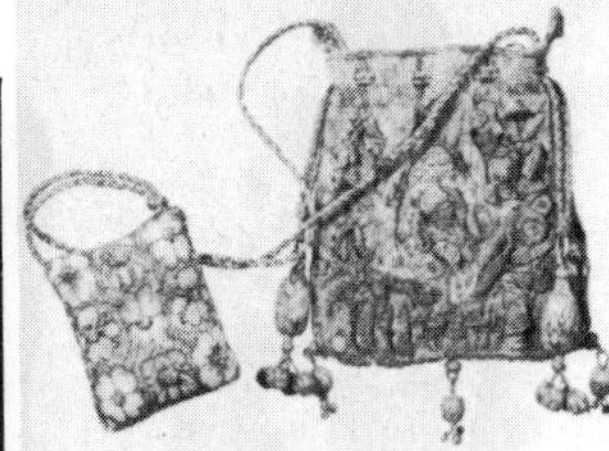

A purse in raised work, with embroidered baubles and with a small embroidered pincushion, the whole worked in coloured silks and silver and gold thread, c. 1610. **£1,200-1,400** *CSK*

A late 19th C. pincushion, worked with coloured silks and sequins on an ivory silk ground, trimmed with ribbons and lace, 15 by 18 cm. **£50-£70** *P*

Reputed to have once been the sachet made for each guest at the marriage of Czar Nicholas II, b. 1868, d. 1918, and Czarina Alexandra, b. 1872, d. 1918, in St. Petersburg on 26 November, 1894.

A casket of ivory silk, embroidered in coloured silks, the whole bound in woven silver thread, the interior with a silk lining, mirror and perfume bottles, 27 by 36 by 14 cm., c. 1650's. **£1,100-1,300** *P*

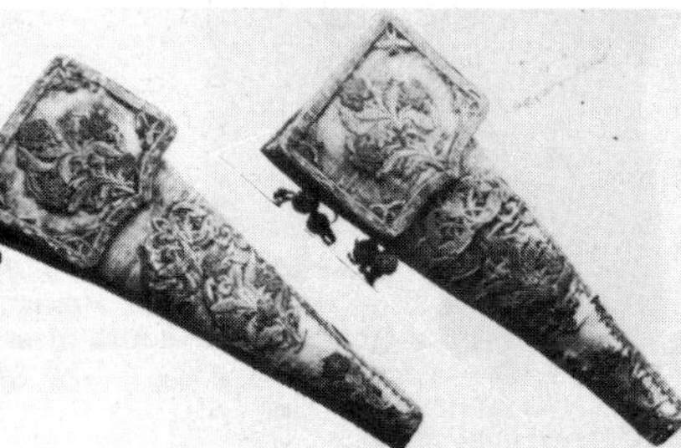

A pair of saddle holsters of crimson velvet embroidered in silver thread, one opening to reveal a small silk-covered purse, 16 in. long, late 17th C. **£550-600** *CSK*

A gentleman's nightcap of linen, embroidered in brightly coloured silks and gold thread, in display case, c. 1600. **£2,000-2,500** *CSK*

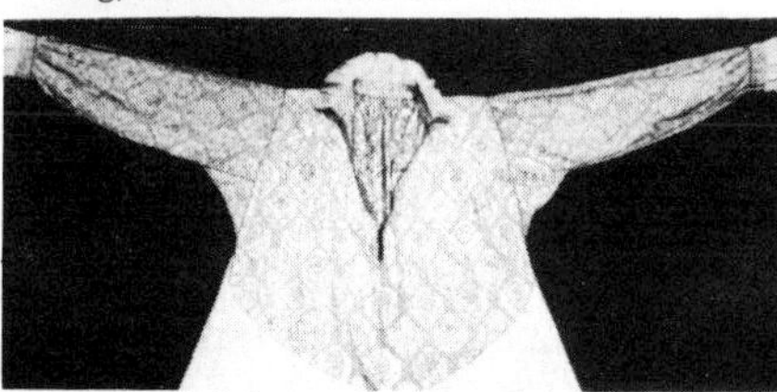

A rare lady's smock, embroidered front and back with red silk with a trellis of lovers' knots, each compartment containing a Tudor rose, a primula or a carnation, English, c. 1610. **£1,800-2,000** *CSK*

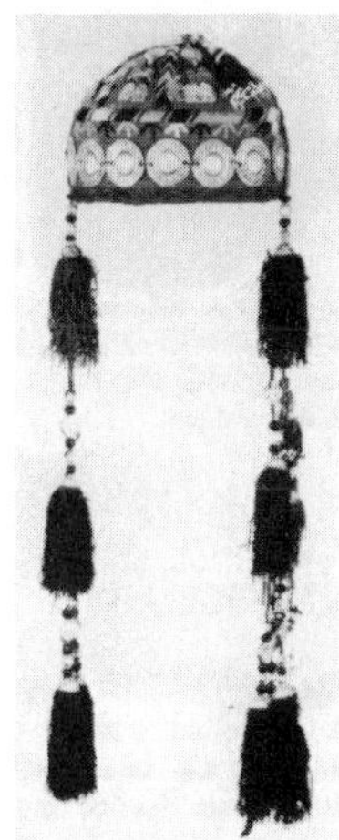

A Qirgiz hat (pamie) of embroidered cord quilted cotton and silver metal applique, with bead decorated tassels. **£110-140** *P*

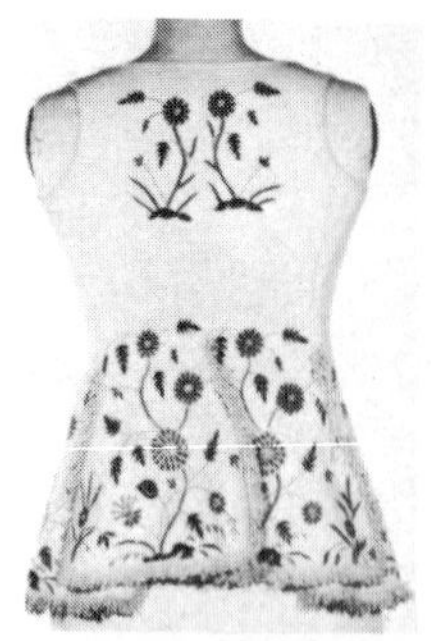

A young girl's waistcoat of wool, embroidered in green and orange crewels, c. 1730. **£3,200-4,000** *CSK*

A christening cap with Hollie point forehead and back panel insertion, with Buckinghamshire lace trim, and the matching vest, c. 1710. **£180-220** *P*

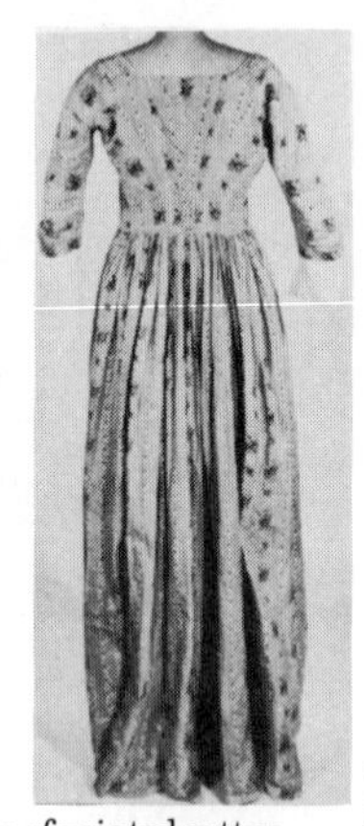

An open robe of printed cotton, printed in maroon, blue and green, slightly altered, c. 1785. **£350-£400** *CSK*

A sack-backed open robe and petticoat, of ivory striped and figured silk, brocaded with small sprays of red, blue and purple flowers, slightly altered at the sleeves, only one detached cuff, altered, English, c. 1770. **£900-£1,100** *CSK*

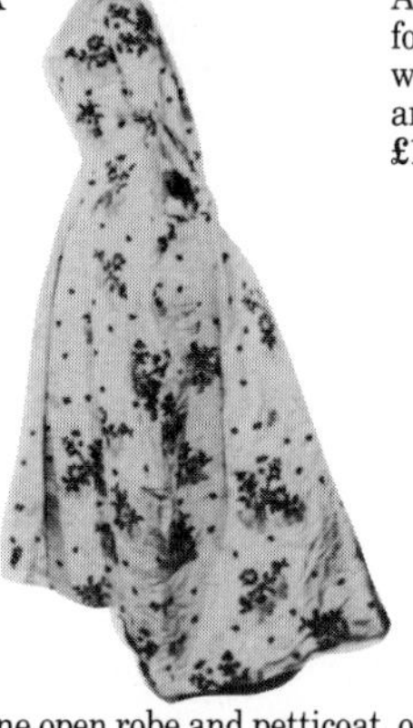

A fine open robe and petticoat, of ivory ribbed silk, brocaded with sprays of brightly coloured flowers and buds with green and gold coloured leaves, the bodice is boned and laced up at the back, the silk c. 1760, the dress probably altered c. 1770, condition very fresh except for some holes in the petticoat. **£3,500-4,500** *CSK*

A bodice and skirt of brown and blue striped shot silk, c. 1815. **£450-550** *CSK*

A rare frock coat of light blue wool, c. 1760. **£1,000-1,400** *CSK*

A gown of striped blue and green brocade silk, c. 1840's. **£150-200** *P*

Silk for the dress manufactured by T. R. & W. Cockayne Ltd., Sheffield, established 1829.

A suit of snuff coloured silk, the bodice embroidered with exotic flowers, green, pink and blue, comprising coat, breeches and waistcoat of ivory, c. 1770. **£2,200-£2,500** *CSK*

A coat of black velvet, trimmed with buttons of crimson tinsel, embroidered with silver thread, with wig bag, c. 1760. **£400-500** *CSK*

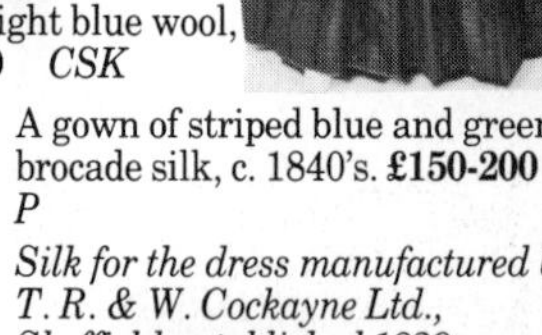

A sleeved waistcoat of ivory silk, embroidered in gold thread and tinsel, with wig bag, c. 1740. **£200-£300** *CSK*

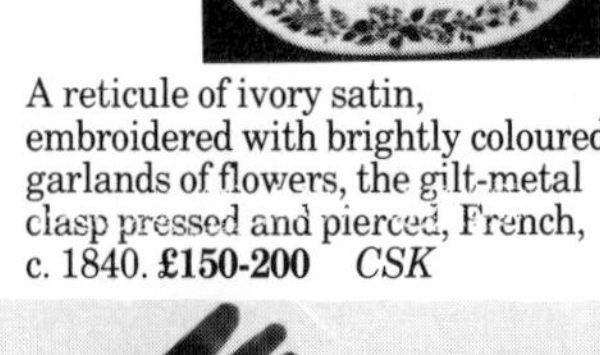

A reticule of ivory satin, embroidered with brightly coloured garlands of flowers, the gilt-metal clasp pressed and pierced, French, c. 1840. **£150-200** *CSK*

A pair of shoes, with unbleached linen uppers, the pointed toe caps of dark blue morocco bound with lilac silk ribbon, with leather soles and yellow kid stitched to protect the heels, c. 1795. **£60-80** *CSK*

A pair of lady's shoes, of lilac coloured kid, laced with silk ribbon, by Samson Boot & Shoemaker equal to London, Gloucester and engraved with his trademark: a beehive on a plinth, labelled 'My Aunt Hannah Barnard', c. 1830. **£300-350** *CSK*

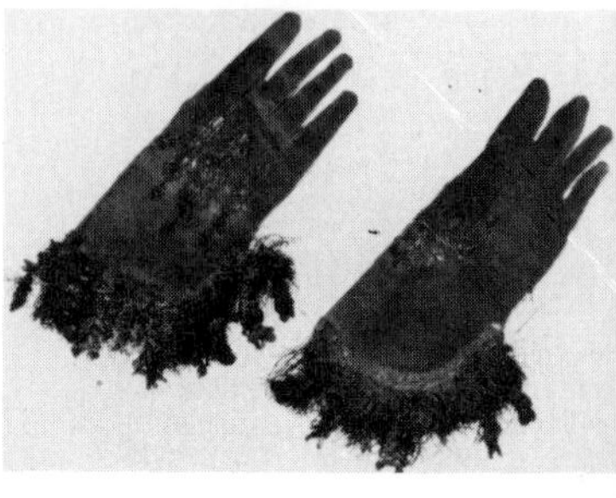

A pair of brown leather gauntlets, with gold and silver thread embroidery to the back, the cuff with coiled gold thread tassels, lined yellow silk, c. 1670's. **£400-£450** *P*

A finely embroidered and couched brilliant yellow satin Dragon robe (Qifu), gilt and shades of red, blue, green, pink and yellow, 18th C. **£650-700** *S*

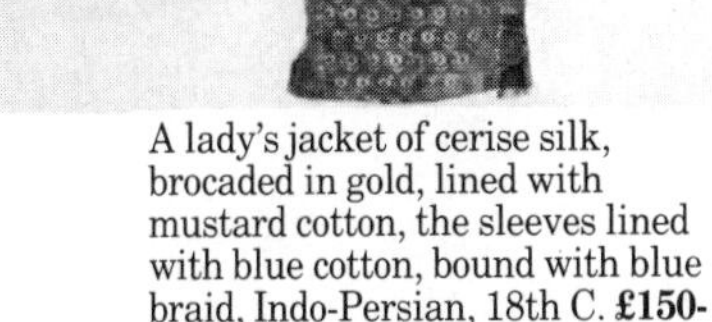

A lady's jacket of cerise silk, brocaded in gold, lined with mustard cotton, the sleeves lined with blue cotton, bound with blue braid, Indo-Persian, 18th C. **£150-£250** *CSK*

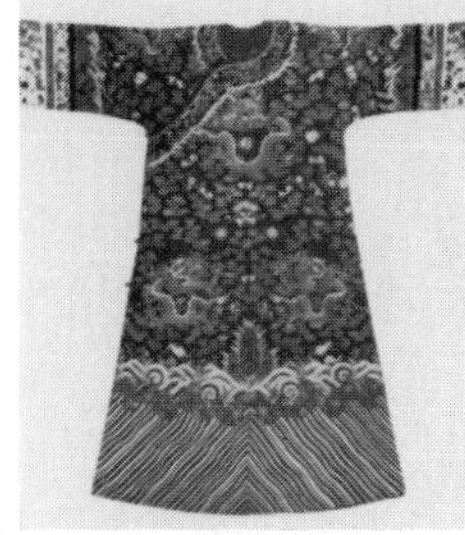

A Chinese robe of K'o-ssu, in coloured silks and gold thread, having a mid-blue silk ground and with embroidered sleeve bands, 19th C. **£450-500** *P*

A Mechlin edging, designed with carnations and butterflies, altered, 0.07 by 1.56 m., c. 1750's. **£80-£100** *P*

A 17th C. reticella border, having Genoese bobbin lace edge, 0.17 by 4 m. **£70-90** *P*

A length of Valenciennes, designed with sprays of flowers and leaves, having oeil de perdrix fillings, 7 by 904 cm., c. 1720's. **£120-150** *P*

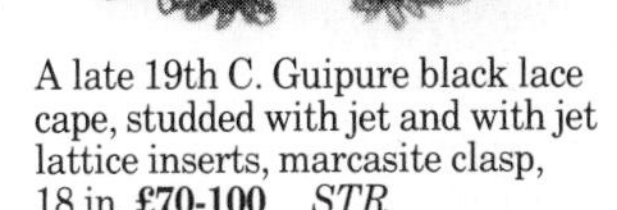

A late 19th C. Guipure black lace cape, studded with jet and with jet lattice inserts, marcasite clasp, 18 in. **£70-100** *STR*

A lacquered brise Japanese fan, 7½ in., c. 1820. **£55-75** *STR*

A Chinese export fan, the silver gilt filigree sticks enamelled with blue and green, the paper and silk leaf brightly painted, 11 in. long (28 cm.), mid 19th C. **£300-350** *S*

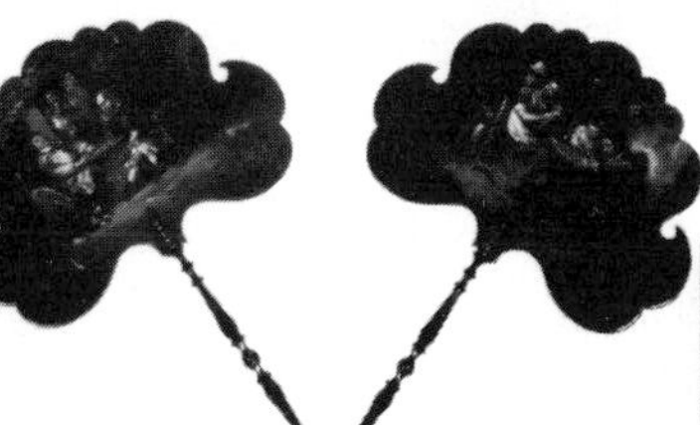

A pair of Victorian papier mâché hand screens, on turned wood handles, 10¾ in. **£220-260** *CSK*

A bone brise fan, further decorated with applied gilt foliage and flowers, French, re-ribboned and restored, 7½ in. long (19 cm.), c. 1730. **£200-250** *S*

An Italian pierced ivory fan, the chickenskin leaf with a sepia landscape between panels of neo-classical decoration, 10¼ in. long (25.5 cm.), c. 1820. **£180-220** *S*

A late Victorian fan, with hand-painted gauze leaf, 13 in. **£20-30** *STR*

A good Victorian fan with hand-painted leaf and mother-of-pearl sticks, 11 in. **£55-75** *STR*

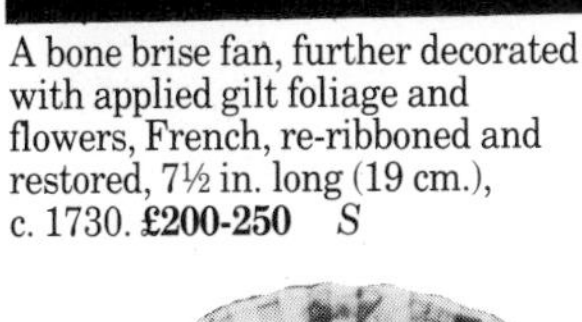

A French fan, the mother-of-pearl sticks carved, pierced and gilded, the chickenskin leaf painted with lads and lasses around a travelling theatre advertising romantic plays, 30 cm. long, c. 1840. **£400-450** *P*

A delicately pierced ivory brise fan, 6 in., c. 1840. **£30-40** *STR*

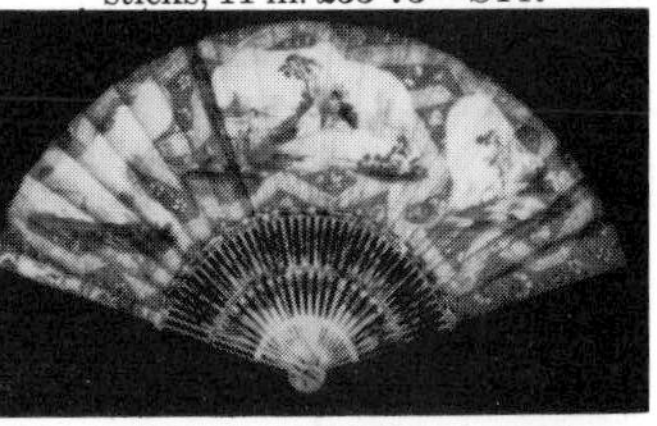

A French ivory fan, the guards carved and painted, the paper leaf painted with vignettes against a blue ground, enriched with trompe l'oeil lace ribbons, 11⅝ in. long (29.5 cm.), c. 1760. **£500-600** *S*

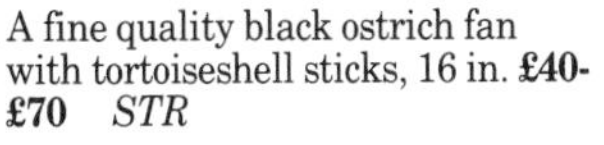

A fine quality black ostrich fan with tortoiseshell sticks, 16 in. **£40-£70** *STR*

A cloisonné scent bottle, with silver wire decoration on a pale yellow ground within a geometric border, attributed to Namikawa Yasuyuki, 6.5 cm., late 19th C. **£600-700** *S*

An unusual cloisonné enamel bottle, decorated on the overall white ground in tones of lapis-blue and turquoise, the rim encircled by a band of tassels, 14⅞ in. (37.6 cm.), Guangxu. **£750-850** *S*

A Japanese cloisonné dish, 30 cm., late 19th C. **£100-150** *SS*

A large cloisonné enamel and gilt-bronze tripod censer and domed cover, area of body restored, 52 cm. high, 18th/early 19th C. **£800-£1,000** *C*

A Japanese cloisonné enamel urn, 9 in. high, c. 1900. **£850-950** *T*

An unusual large cloisonné enamel globular jar and cover, 36.5 cm. high, late 19th C. **£900-1,000** *C*

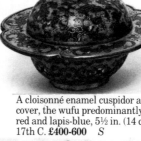

A cloisonné enamel cuspidor and cover, the wufu predominantly in red and lapis-blue, 5½ in. (14 cm.), 17th C. **£400-600** *S*

A pair of cloisonné enamel censers and covers, decorated with a horizontal band of overlapping blades, dragon scrolls, key-fret and with foliate motifs, 10¾ in. (27.3 cm.), Qianlong. **£1,500-£2,000** *S*

A cloisonné enamel vessel, 4 character mark of Xuande, Qianlong, 5⅛ in. (13 cm.). **£550-£650** *S*

A Japanese cloisonné bowl, 9½ in. diam., c. 1860. **£250-300** *TP*

A pair of cloisonné ewers and covers, enamelled with mille-fleur, 29 cm., Guangxu. **£500-550** *S*

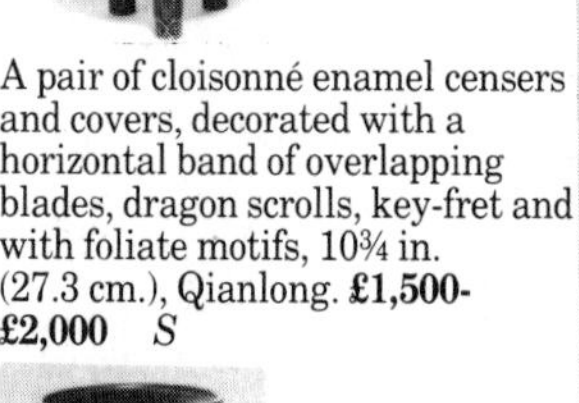

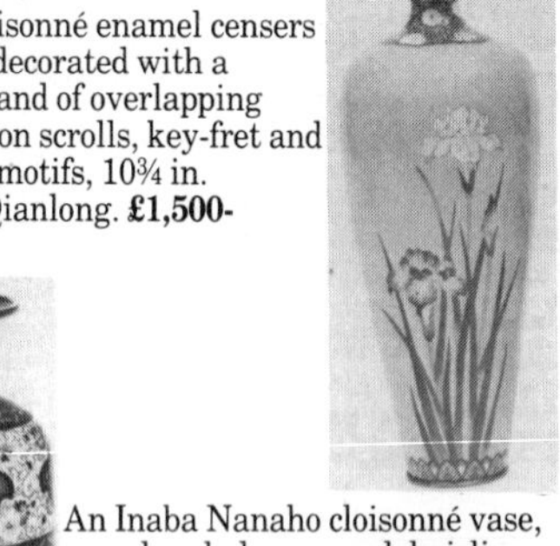

An Inaba Nanaho cloisonné vase, on pale celadon ground, hairline cracks, 17.9 cm., late 19th C. **£250-£300** *SS*

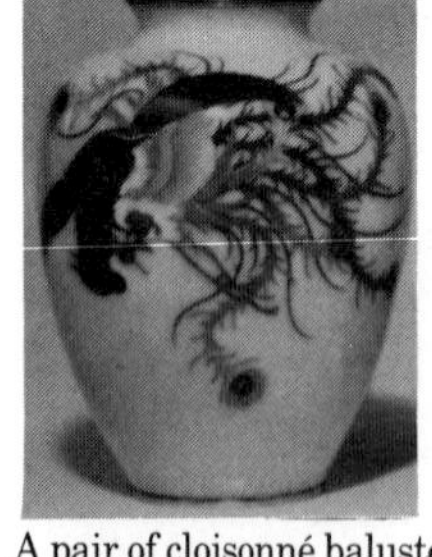

A pair of cloisonné baluster vases, in polychrome enamels on a yellow ground, 15.5 cm. high, Taisho period. **£500-600** *C*

A pair of Japanese cloisonné vases, both damaged, 37 in., c. 1900. **£700-900** *SC*

A pair of Kumeno Teitaro cloisonné vases, decorated in silver wire, on a pale green ground, silver rim and foot, mark of Kumeno Teitaro, 13.5 cm., c. 1900. **£400-600** *S*

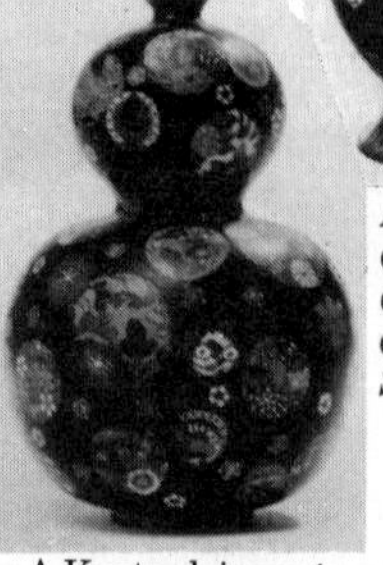

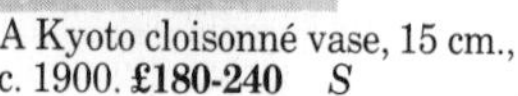

A Kyoto cloisonné vase, 15 cm., c. 1900. **£180-240** *S*

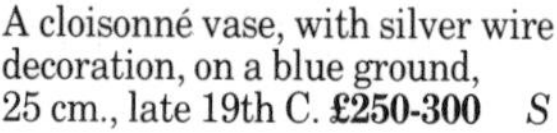

A cloisonné vase, with silver wire decoration, on a blue ground, 25 cm., late 19th C. **£250-300** *S*

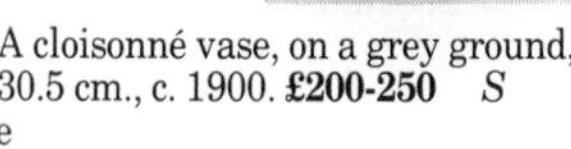

A cloisonné vase, on a grey ground, 30.5 cm., c. 1900. **£200-250** *S*

A pair of cloisonné vases, on a grey ground, 21.5 cm., c. 1900. **£750-£850** *S*

A cloisonné vase, on a midnight blue ground, 30.5 cm., c. 1900. **£500-600** *S*

A cloisonné vase, silvered foot and rim, 18.5 cm., c. 1900. **£600-700** *S*

A pair of cloisonné vases, one with slight cracks, 40 cm., c. 1900. **£750-£850** *S*

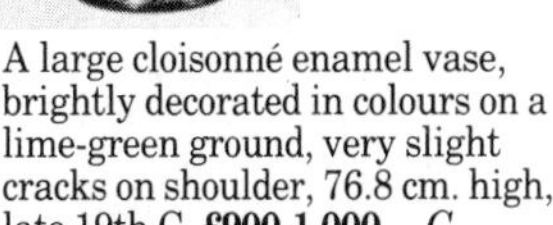

A large cloisonné enamel vase, brightly decorated in colours on a lime-green ground, very slight cracks on shoulder, 76.8 cm. high, late 19th C. **£900-1,000** *C*

A pair of cloisonné on porcelain vases, 36 cm., c. 1880. **£450-500** *S*

A cloisonné vase, with silver wire decoration of a flowering cherry branch, 37 cm., c. 1900. **£500-550** *S*

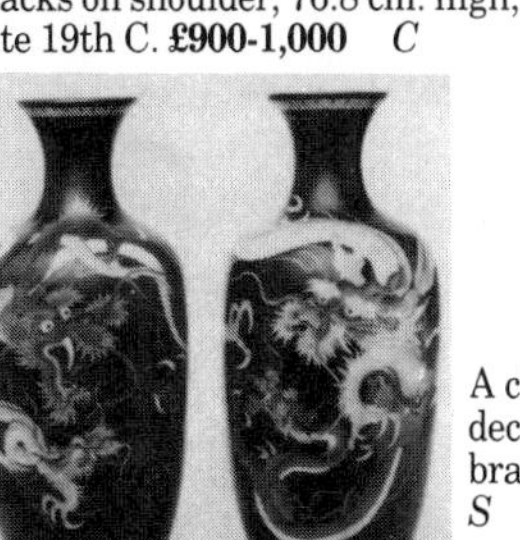

A pair of cloisonné vases, on a dark blue ground, one small chip, 46.5 cm., c. 1900. **£750-850** *S*

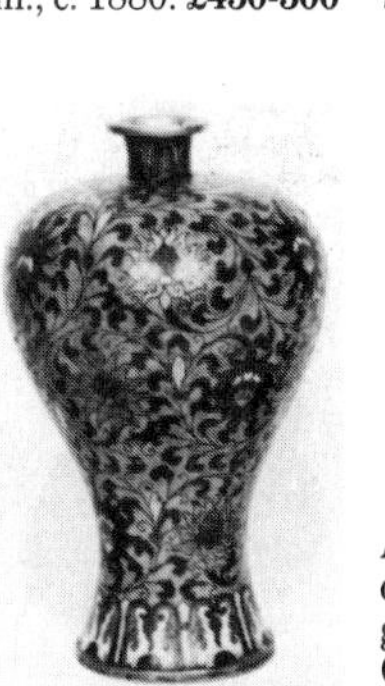

An unusual cloisonné enamel vase, decorated in tones of blue on a pale green ground, 7⅛ in. (18.2 cm.), Qianlong. **£400-600** *S*

A cloisonné enamel meiping, on a turquoise ground, 9½ in. (24.2 cm.), 17th C. **£800-900** *S*

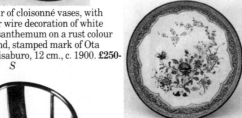

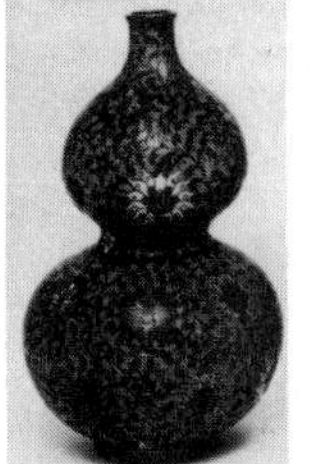

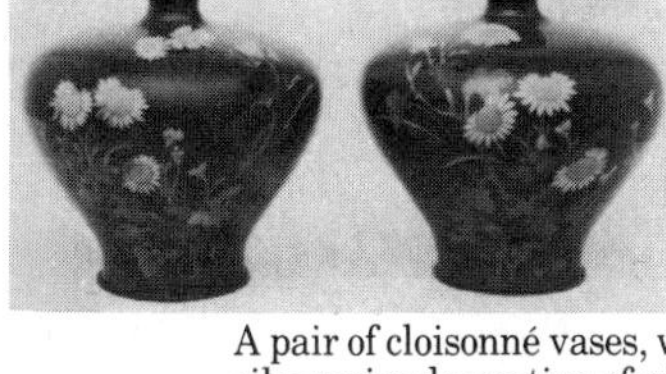

A pair of cloisonné vases, with silver wire decoration of white chrysanthemum on a rust colour ground, stamped mark of Ota Kichisaburo, 12 cm., c. 1900. **£250-£350** *S*

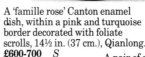

A cloisonné enamel double-gourd vase, decorated in bright colours on a turquoise ground, with red, blue, yellow, white, aubergine, green and mottled pink, 4 character mark of Jingdai, 12⅜ in. (31.4 cm.), 17th C. **£950-1,050** *S*

A 'famille rose' Canton enamel dish, within a pink and turquoise border decorated with foliate scrolls, 14½ in. (37 cm.), Qianlong. **£600-700** *S*

A pair of cloisonné enamel hat-stands, on turquoise grounds, with removable pierced gilt-bronze medallions of floral design, 11⅛ in. (28.2 cm.), Qianlong. **£800-900** *S*

A Chinese hardwood open armchair. **£550-650** *C*

An Anglo-Burmese hardwood davenport, 2 ft. wide (61 cm.), c. 1880. **£450-550** *S*

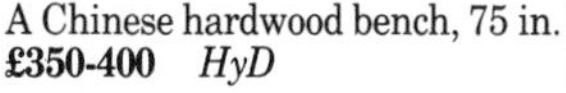

A Chinese hardwood bench, 75 in. **£350-400** *HyD*

A pair of mother-of-pearl inlaid rosewood armchairs, Guangxu. **£500-600** *S*

A Japanese gilt lacquered hardwood cabinet, 62 in. **£900-£1,100** *GSP*

A Chinese rosewood cabinet, 37 by 39 in. (94 by 99 cm.), 20th C. **£300-£375** *SC*

A red lacquer cabinet, details in yellow and black lacquer, some panels damaged, 143 cm., c. 1900. **£350-400** *S*

A small red lacquer display cabinet, decorated with shrines in mountainous landscapes, the borders with flowers and key fret, 91 by 68 cm., late 19th C. **£500-£600** *S*

A hardwood day bed, 7 ft. 1½ in. (219 cm.), base 18th C. but altered, upper part late 19th C. **£600-700** *S*

A Chinese padouk and beechwood display cabinet, inlaid with ivory and marquetry panels, 46½ in. **£1,000-1,200** *CSK*

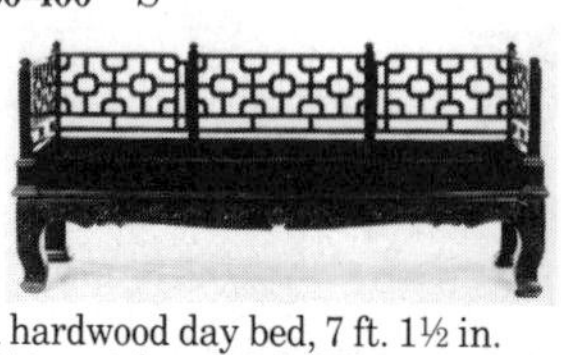

A Chinese export lacquer and parcel gilt toilet mirror, 29 by 19 in. (74 by 48 cm.), early 20th C. **£120-160** *SC*

A Chinese red lacquer urn stand, 36 in. high by 27 in. wide, 19th C. **£200-300** *Bea*

A rare Huahuangli travelling bergere suite, comprising a settee and 2 armchairs, Chinese in the English style. **£800-1,000** *S*

A Chinese rosewood toilet mirror, 51 by 20 in. (130 by 51 cm.), 20th C. **£180-220** *SC*

A Chinese rosewood urn stand, 36 by 16 in. (92 by 41 cm.), early 20th C. **£150-200** *SC*

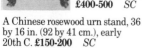

A Chinese rosewood altar table, 36 by 48 in. (92 by 122 cm.), 20th C. **£400-500** *SC*

A Chinese export occasional table, 25 in. square. **£120-140** *DS*

A Chinese black and gold lacquer table stand, 20½ in. square (52 cm.), 18th C. **£1,200-1,300** *C*

An Anglo-Indian padouk tripod table, 30 by 24 in. (76 by 61 cm.), late 19th C. **£190-240** *SC*

A pair of Chinese hardstone table screens, 40 cm. high, 19th C. **£425-£475** *SS*

An ivory box and cover, engraved Seishi, slight chip, 16 cm., late 19th C. **£400-500** *S*

A silver-mounted ivory vessel and domed cover, inlaid in Shibayama style, signed on the base Ichiraku and Baiyu, some inlay missing, 20.6 cm. high, late 19th C. **£900-£1,000** *C*

An Oriental carved ivory junk, 30 in. high. **£700-800** *AGr*

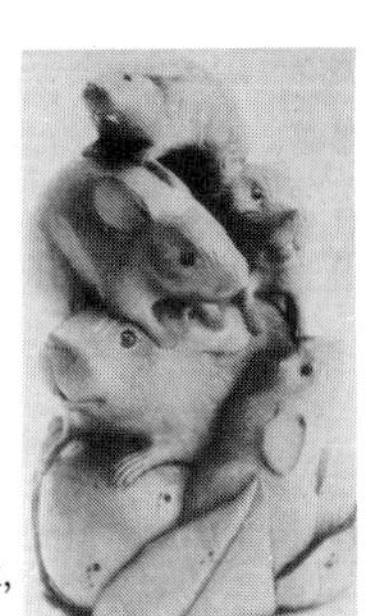

A Hokyudo Itsumin carved wood group of rats, 4½ in. **£200-300** *Bea*

An ivory okimono, signed Ono Ryomin and kakihan, 4.5 cm., c. 1870. **£250-300** *S*

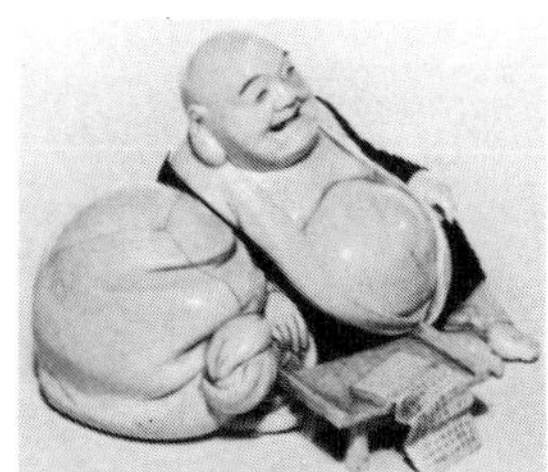

A wood and ivory group of Hotei, signed Shoko, 12 cm., c. 1900, wood stand. **£500-600** *S*

An ivory okimono, details engraved and lightly stained, signed Seiko, 6.5 cm., c. 1900. **£400-500** *S*

An ivory okimono of a saramuwashi, signed Mitsutsugu, 5.5 cm., c. 1900. **£300-350** *S*

A Japanese carved ivory market group. **£500-600** *CDC*

An ivory okimono of Tokiwa Gozen, engraved seal, 11 cm., c. 1870. **£150-200** *S*

A Japanese carved ivory sportsman figure. **£250-300** *CDC*

An ivory okimono, signed on a red seal Gyokusho. **£500-600** *L*

An ivory figure of Kwannon, the ivory stained, signed Seimin, 28 cm., late 19th C. **£200-250** *S*

An elaborate ivory okimono, depicting the Fox Spirit, in lightly stained ivory, signed Gyokuho (?), 7.5 cm. **£300-350** *S*

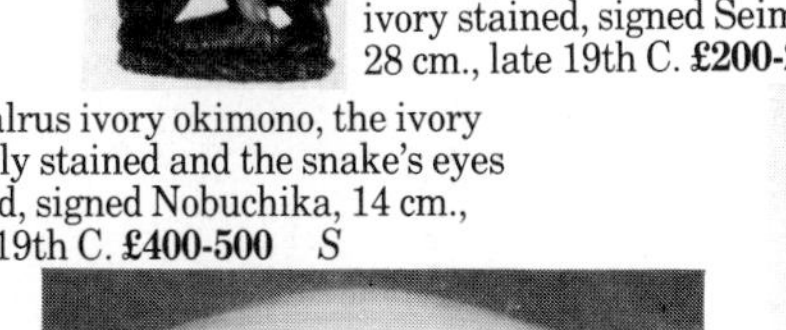

A walrus ivory okimono, the ivory lightly stained and the snake's eyes inlaid, signed Nobuchika, 14 cm., late 19th C. **£400-500** *S*

A delicately carved okimono, depicting a skeleton, unsigned, 11.6 cm., late 19th C. **£250-300** *S*

An ivory netsuke of a Karako, signed. **£200-250** *L*

An ivory shell, in the form of a clam, engraved Oho, 12.5 cm., c. 1900. **£150-250** *S*

There have been a large number of ivorine fakes of these shells, which has tended to adversely affect their value.

A Japanese carved ivory okimono of a pedlar and his son, signed 8½ in., c. 1900. **£350-400** *SC*

A sectional carved ivory okimono, 11 in., c. 1900. **£250-300** *SC*

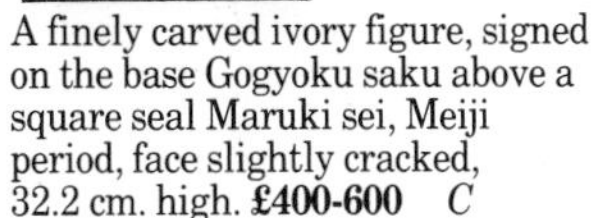

A finely carved ivory figure, signed on the base Gogyoku saku above a square seal Maruki sei, Meiji period, face slightly cracked, 32.2 cm. high. **£400-600** *C*

A large ivory carving of a caparisoned elephant, inlaid in Shibayama style, a few small pieces of inlay missing, signed Masayuki, wood stand, 42 cm. long, late 19th C. **£4,000-5,000** *C*

A fine ivory carving of a Chinese sage, signed Shuzan, 21.1 cm. high, late 19th C. **£350-450** *C*

An ivory okimono of a tanuki, 10.8 cm. high, late 19th C. **£400-£500** *C*

An ivory and inlaid hardwood figure, signed Saisen on mother-of-pearl plaque, foot chipped. **£250-£300** *S*

A fine okimono of Handaka Sonja, signed Kogetsu, slight chips, 20 cm., late 19th C. **£750-850** *S*

A rare figure of Ono No Tofu, standing at the back of a huge toad, signed in an oval reserve Masatsugu. **£300-350** *S*

An ivory study of a rat on a candle, wooden wick, in slightly worn ivory, the muzzle slightly recarved and the eyes inlaid, unsigned, 18th C. **£450-500** *S*

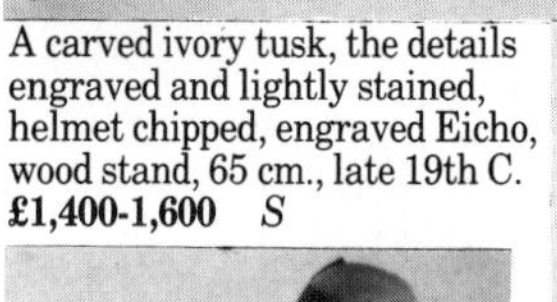

A carved ivory tusk, the details engraved and lightly stained, helmet chipped, engraved Eicho, wood stand, 65 cm., late 19th C. **£1,400-1,600** *S*

An ivory warrior, sword and lance ends missing, engraved Kodo to, 22 cm., c. 1900. **£700-800** *S*

An ivory okimono of a seated wood seller. **£400-450** *L*

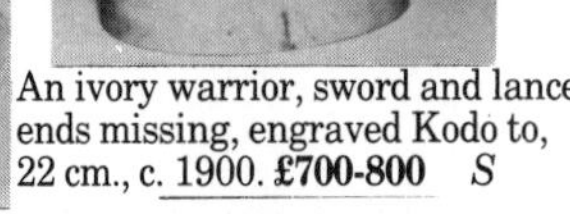

An ivory bridge group, minor chips, wood stand, 50 cm., c. 1900. **£900-£1,000** *S*

An ivory group of a fisherman and his son, stump replaced, engraved Toshinobu on lacquer reserve, 13.5 cm., c. 1900. **£1,000-1,200** *S*

A large ivory figure of an Immortal, wearing a jewelled bodice, base plate missing, 75 cm., early 20th C. **£1,200-£1,400** *S*

An ivory okimono of Bijin, reading a book, signed, 9 cm., late 19th C. **£250-300** *S*

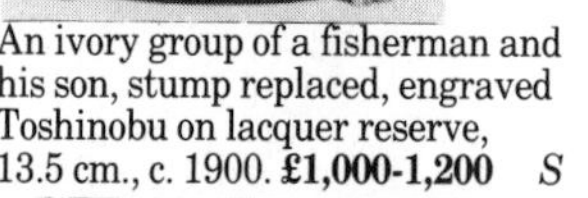

A small ivory group of a Dutchman and his son, slight restoration, unsigned, early 19th C. **£200-250** *S*

An ivory group, the details engraved and lightly stained, engraved Tomomasa on a lacquer reserve, wood stand, 25 cm., c. 1900. **£400-500** *S*

A small ivory figure of a mermaid with her child, unsigned, 19th C. **£700-800** *S*

A rare study of Abura Akango, the oil-drinking one-eyed bakemono, emerging from an oil funnel, of staghorn with natural hair still adhering, its eye of inlaid shell with a dark horn pupil, signed Kyosai zu. **£700-800** *S*

A Gyokusen ivory group of Daikoku, the details inlaid in mother-of-pearl, engraved Gyokusen on a lacquer reserve, wood stand, 21 cm., c. 1900. **£450-£550** *S*

A Gyokushu ivory group of Daikoku, light sepia, chip, engraved Gyokushu, 11 cm., c. 1900. **£250-300** *S*

An ivory group of a family of rats, the eyes inlaid in horn and the details engraved, 13 cm., late 19th C. **£250-300** *S*

A set of 4 ivory figures, engraved 4 character mark, fitted box, 25 cm., 20th C. **£350-450** *S*

An ivory group, late 19th C. **£250-£350** *S*

An ivory okimono of the Takarabune, containing the seven Gods of Good Fortune, signed Tosai, 15 cm., c. 1900. **£400-450** *S*

A collection of 19th C. turned ivory. **£5,500-6,000** *McCMB*

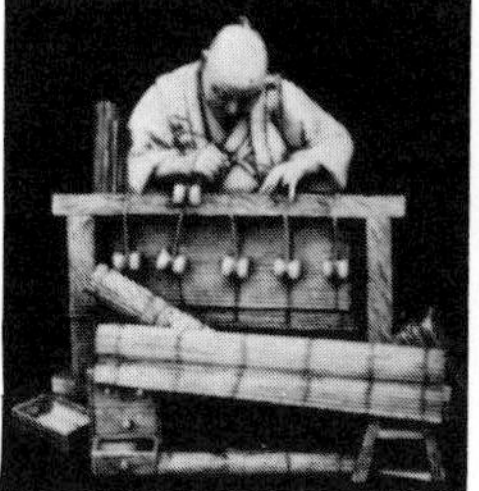

A well-carved ivory okimono of craftsmen making sudare, signed Tangasai Yoshinobu, 8 cm. wide, late 19th C. **£300-400** *C*

A sectional ivory carving of a woodcutter, slightly damaged, signed Tomei, 26.5 cm. high, late 19th C. **£450-500** *C*

An ivory okimono of a kneeling drum-seller, signed Hoshin, Meiji period, 9 cm. high. **£400-450** *C*

A Shunmei ivory, silver and Shibayama vase, inlaid in stained ivory, mother-of-pearl and hardstone, some inlay missing, handles added, engraved Shunmei, 26 cm., c. 1900. **£400-450** *S*

A Gyokuzan Shibayama vase and cover, applied with silver mounts, handle missing, slight inlay missing, signed Gyokuzan, 19 cm., c. 1900. **£600-700** *S*

A Shibayama vase, the ivory tusk decorated with a warrior beneath a flowering tree, the reverse with birds and flowers, some inlay missing, inlaid Shibayama Masayoshi, 45 cm., c. 1900. **£1,000-£1,200** *S*

An ivory tusk vase, signed Jo-O, 21.8 cm., late 19th C. **£600-700** *S*

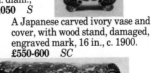

A marbled lacquer box and shallow domed cover, restored, wood box with inscription, 19 cm. diam., Ming Dynasty. **£950-1,050** *S*

A Japanese carved ivory vase and cover, with wood stand, damaged, engraved mark, 16 in., c. 1900. **£550-600** *SC*

A carved cinnabar lacquer bowl, glass liner, 15¼ in. (38.7 cm.), Qianlong. **£600-650** *S*

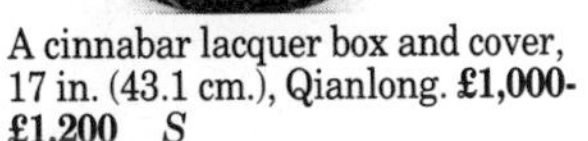

A cinnabar lacquer box and cover, 17 in. (43.1 cm.), Qianlong. **£1,000-£1,200** *S*

A lacquer box and cover in the form of a pheasant, slight chip, 19 cm., c. 1900. **£500-600** *S*

A black lacquered domed chest, decorated in gold and brown hiramakie and inlaid in shell, engraved kanagu, considerable old wear and damage, Momoyama period, 45.1 cm. wide. **£600-700** *C*

A lacquer box in the form of a teahouse with a detachable roof, decorated in gold takamakie, hiramakie and togidashi, one riser damaged, 14.9 by 11.3 by 12.1 cm., mid 19th C. **£1,600-1,800** *S*

A rounded rectangular Kinji Tebako, 16 cm. long, 18th/19th C. **£1,100-1,300** *C*

A set of 5 laque burgaute dishes, with brown lacquer ground, all in mother-of-pearl with engraved details, 5⅜ in. (13.8 cm.), 17th C. **£600-800** *S*

A pair of lacquer vases, the ground with togidashi dragons amongst flames, some damage, 26 cm., c. 1880. **£1,200-1,400** *S*

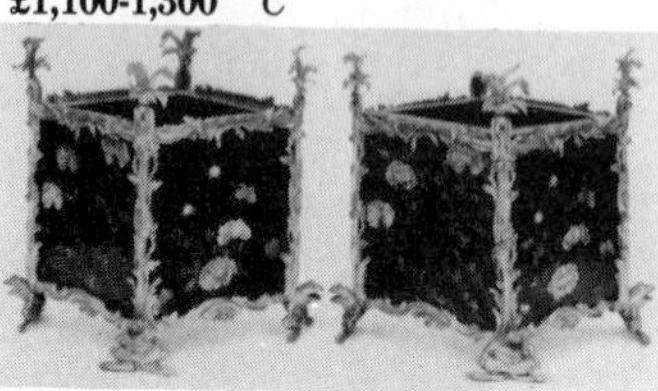

A pair of gilt-bronze mounted Japanese lacquer stands, the metalwork Paris, 32 by 28 cm., c. 1870. **£1,700-1,800** *S*

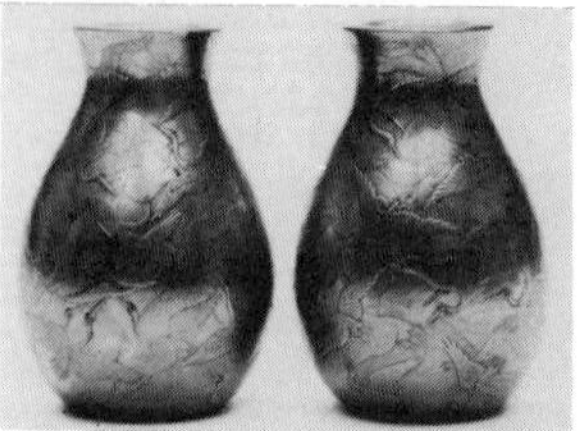

A pair of lacquer bottles each decorated in gold takamakie, rims chipped, one base cracked, signed Heishutei, 9 cm., 19th C. **£500-£600** *S*

A Japanese lacquered box and cover, late Edo, chips, loose guard, 42 by 60 by 34 cm. **£1,500-1,700** *SS*

A rare Ordos gilt-bronze applique cast in the form of a tiger, 15.5 cm., Warring States. **£4,500-5,500** *S*

An Archaic bronze covered food vessel (ding), the patina with patches of green and brown and some azurite encrustations, 14¼ in. (36.5 cm.), Eastern Zhou Dynasty. **£3,000-4,000** *S*

An archaic bronze oval globular bowl, the water patina with areas of shallow encrustation, Eastern Zhou Dynasty, 15.5 cm. wide. **£1,500-2,500** *C*

A bronze censer and cover, 14⅛ in. (36 cm.), Jiaqing. **£300-400** *S*

A rare gilt-bronze archaistic wine vessel (jue), the gilding with malachite and azurite encrustation, 12.7 cm., Ming Dynasty. **£1,600-£1,900** *S*

A dated Ming gilt-bronze figure of Zhen Wu, a long inscription on the reverse, 15⅝ in. (37.3 cm.), Jiajing. **£900-1,000** *S*

A large bronze incense burner and cover, 27½ in. (70 cm.), Jiaqing. **£1,200-1,400** *S*

A bronze of Hotei, cast signature, 16½ in., late 19th C. **£400-£500** *SC*

An early 19th C. Chinese bronze crane on a turtle, 33 in. **£2,700-£3,200** *SA*

A pair of bronze figures of geese, 17¾ in. (45 cm.). **£1,000-1,200** *S*

A patinated bronze and silvered metal group of a peacock and peahen, signed Hidehisa, Meiji period, pierced wood base, overall length 44 cm. **£650-750** *C*

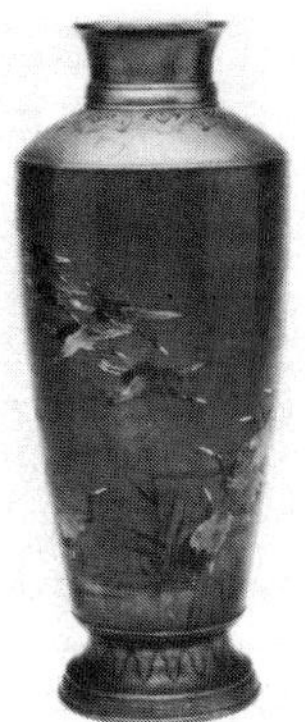

A bronze tray inlaid in silver, gilt and ivory, tarnished, 53 cm., late 19th C. **£200-280** *S*

A large bronze group of Shoulao, 18⅜ in. (46.6 cm.) high, 19th C. **£600-700** *S*

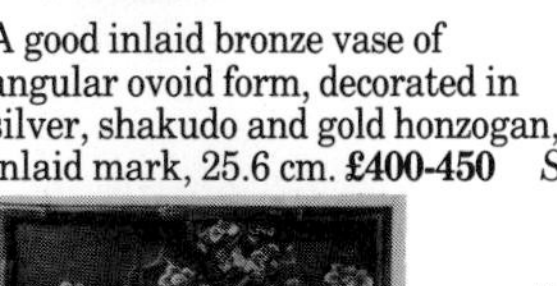

A good inlaid bronze vase of angular ovoid form, decorated in silver, shakudo and gold honzogan, inlaid mark, 25.6 cm. **£400-450** *S*

A pair of Chinese bronze pricket candlesticks, 96 cm., Guangxu. **£400-500** *Bea*

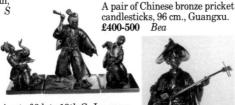

A set of 3 late 19th C. Japanese bronze figures, 20¼ and 12½ in. high respectively. **£1,200-1,400** *PK*

A Tmakimo Tokyo school bronze figure, the base cast Tmakimo and other mark, 19 cm., c. 1900. **£400-£600** *S*

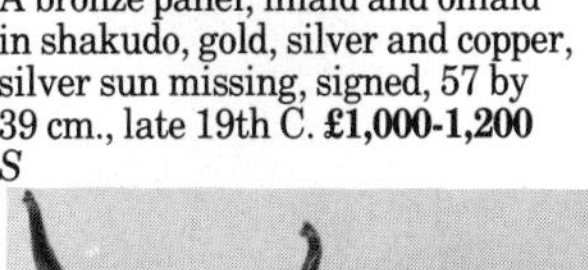

A bronze panel, inlaid and onlaid in shakudo, gold, silver and copper, silver sun missing, signed, 57 by 39 cm., late 19th C. **£1,000-1,200** *S*

A large Genryusai Seiya Tokyo school bronze figure of a musician, cast Genryusai Seiya sei, wood stand, 70 cm., c. 1900. **£1,500-£2,000** *S*

A bronze peasant woman, piece from bucket missing, engraved mark, 40 cm., c. 1900. **£250-300** *S*

A pair of bronze elephants, one trunk repaired, cast mark, 32 and 28.5 cm., c. 1900. **£250-300** *S*

A Gyoko bronze fisherman, fixed wooden stand, stand damaged, cast Gyoko, 49 cm. overall, c. 1900. **£250-300** *S*

A silver model of a palanquin, signed, 30.2 cm. wide, late 19th C. **£800-900** *S*

An Etsu Shibayama and silver box, inlaid in mother-of-pearl, stained ivory and horn, stamped Etsu, 8 cm., c. 1900. **£280-360** *S*

A Shakudo Nanako set decorated in iroe-takazogan, details in silver and gilt, unsigned. **£70-90** *S*

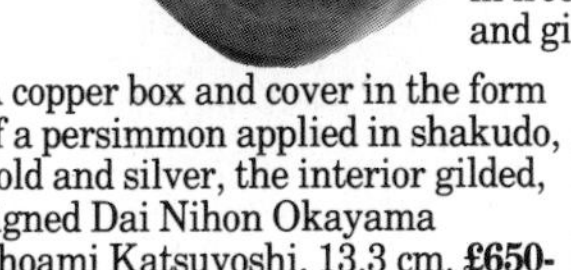

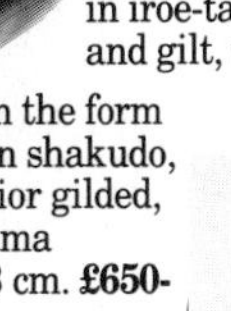

A copper box and cover in the form of a persimmon applied in shakudo, gold and silver, the interior gilded, signed Dai Nihon Okayama Shoami Katsuyoshi, 13.3 cm. **£650-£750** *S*

A Chinese silver bowl, stamped Chiuchi, 27.5 cm., Guangxu, 1,460 gm. **£500-600** *S*

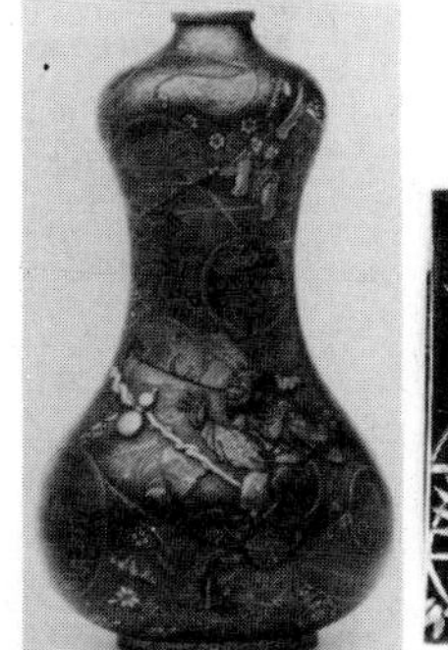

A Shakudo set, details in silver, shakudo and 2 shades of gilt, unsigned. **£150-180** *S*

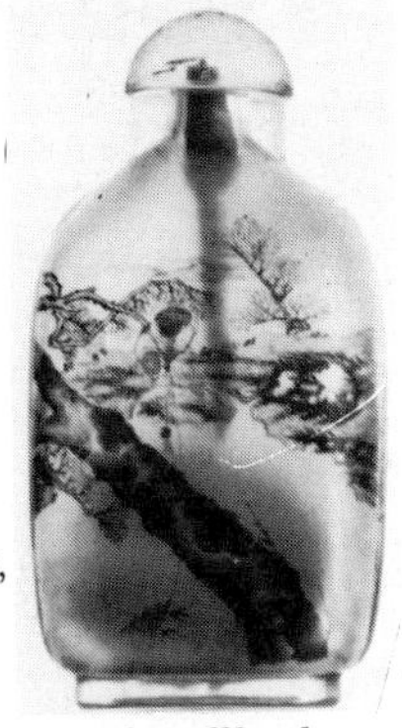

An agate bottle carved as a seated frog, the coral stopper as its tongue, inlays slightly incomplete. **£250-£350** *C*

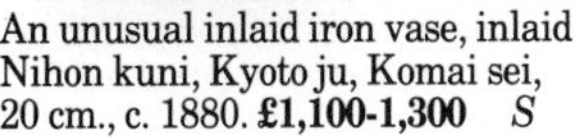

An unusual inlaid iron vase, inlaid Nihon kuni, Kyoto ju, Komai sei, 20 cm., c. 1880. **£1,100-1,300** *S*

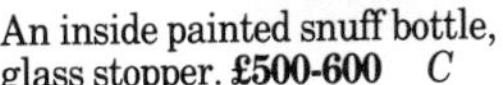

An inside painted snuff bottle, glass stopper. **£500-600** *C*

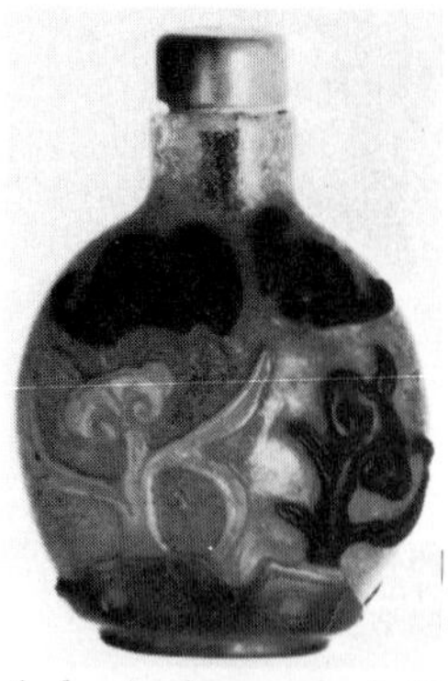

A glass 5 colour overlay bottle, the hefengdi (snowstorm) ground carved with red and green lotus, green jade stopper. **£300-350** *C*

A rock crystal bottle, quartz stopper. **£200-250** *C*

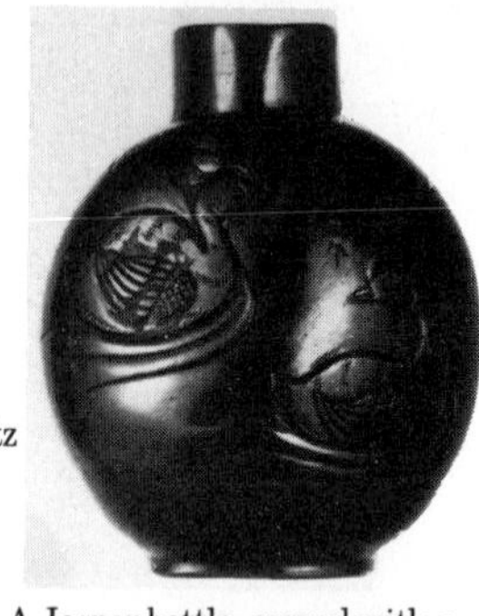

A Jasper bottle, carved with a shallow relief duck in green facing another in the brown body, rim slightly polished. **£150-250** *C*

A mottled white jade pebble bottle, with traces of the rich russet skin remaining, flecked apple and white stopper. **£150-250** *C*

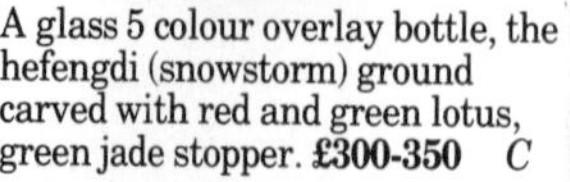

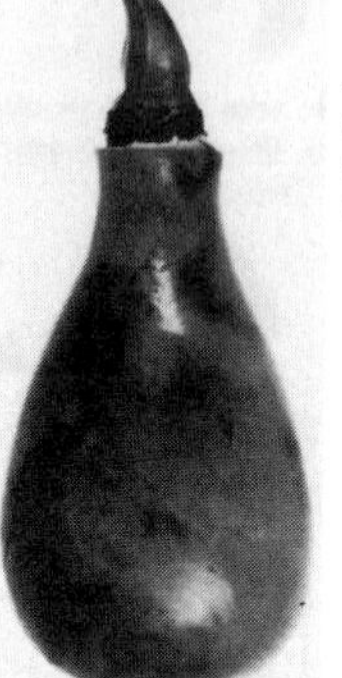

A flecked jade bottle, one side with rich apple and emerald inclusions, stopper en suite. **£250-350** *C*

An agate bottle, with flecked green jade stopper. **£400-500** *C*

An inside painted glass bottle depicting wintery scenes, and a long poem, signed Ye Zhongsan, glass stopper, incomplete. **£450-£550** *C*

Two metal bottles, one disc-shaped Canton enamel miniature pilgrim with dragons on a blue ground, stopper en suite, c. 1800, the other a dark bronze double gourd vase with metal stopper. **£250-350** *C*

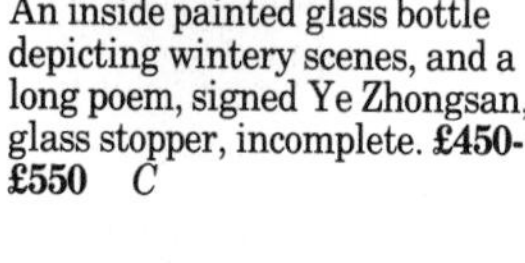

A moss agate bottle, with rich turquoise-grey inclusions, glass stopper. **£200-250** *C*

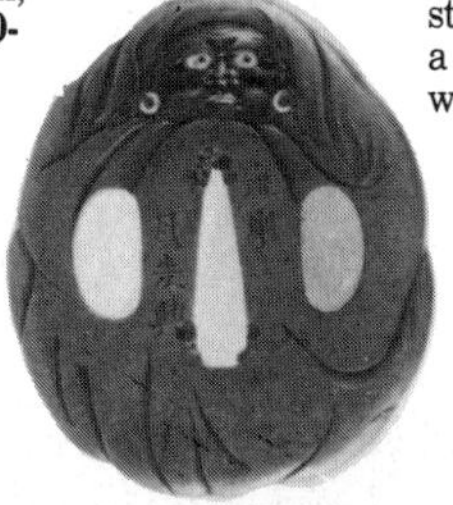

A copper tsuba fashioned in the form of Dharma, one hitsu plugged, signed Yoshu Tan Mitsuoki and dated Bunsei tsudinoe ne (Bunsei II, 1828), 6.6 cm. **£400-450** *S*

A Soten-style tsuba, of lobed mokko form, details in silver, copper and gold nunome, unsigned, 8.5 cm. **£200-250** *S*

A Jasper bottle, carved with a grasshopper on a Chinese cabbage, yellow stopper. **£600-650** *C*

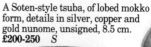

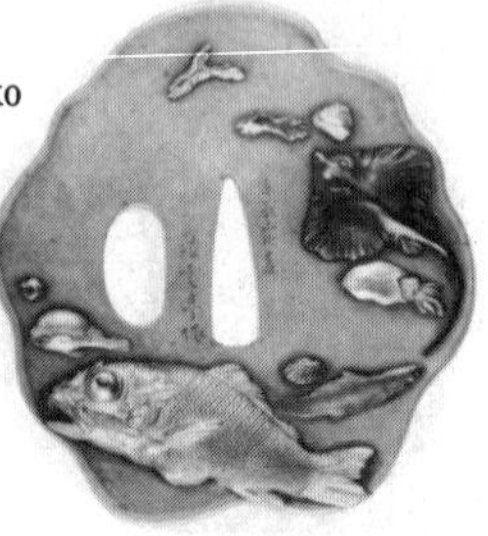

A Sentoku tsuba, details in copper, gilt, shibuichi, shakudo and silver, signed To eizan kita fumoto Ryounte saku, 9.2 cm. **£600-700** *S*

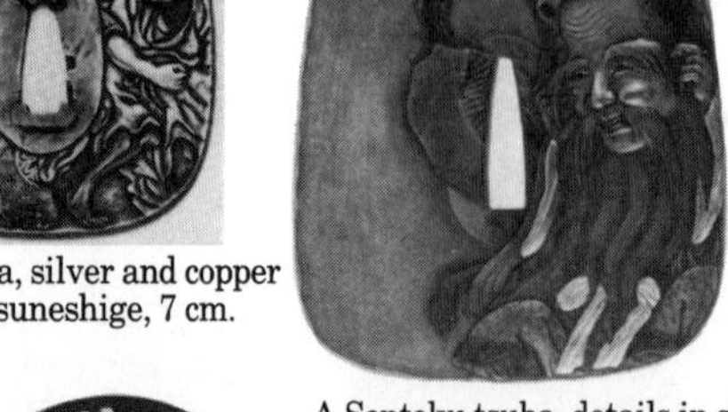

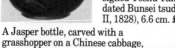

A Sentoku tsuba, silver and copper detail, signed Tsuneshige, 7 cm. **£200-250** *P*

A Shakudo Sukashi tsuba of mokko form, one hitsu plugged in sentoku, unsigned, 7 cm. **£200-£250** *S*

A Sentoku tsuba, details in silver, shibuichi, copper and gilt, signed and dated (1786) 5th year Tenmei Hamano Noriyuki, 8.9 cm. **£300-£350** *S*

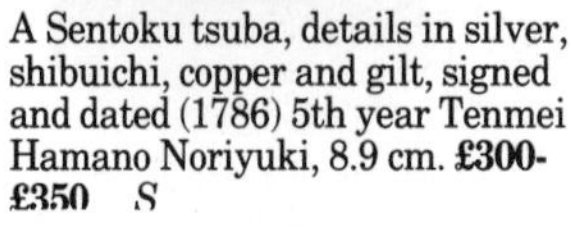

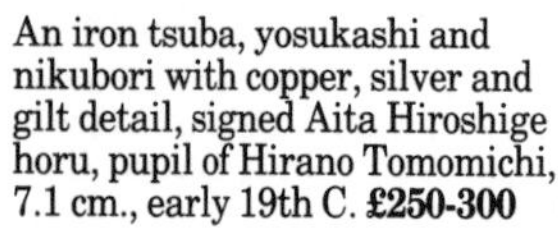

An iron tsuba, yosukashi and nikubori with copper, silver and gilt detail, signed Aita Hiroshige horu, pupil of Hirano Tomomichi, 7.1 cm., early 19th C. **£250-300** *C*

A circular Shakudo Nanako tsuba, gold, silver and copper detail, signed Soheishi Nuido Soten Sei, 7.5 cm. **£100-150** *P*

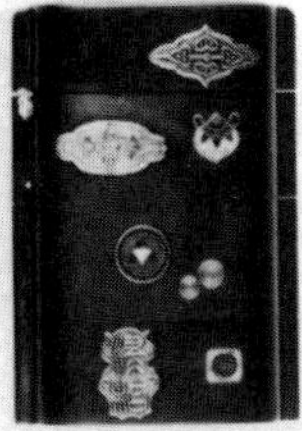

An unusual Hirata-style Shibuichi inro, of 3 cases, applied in silver, gilt and gold-wire cloisonné with jewels and reisho seals, one seal possibly intended as a signature, reading Mitsumasa, 5.7 cm., 19th C. **£500-600** *S*

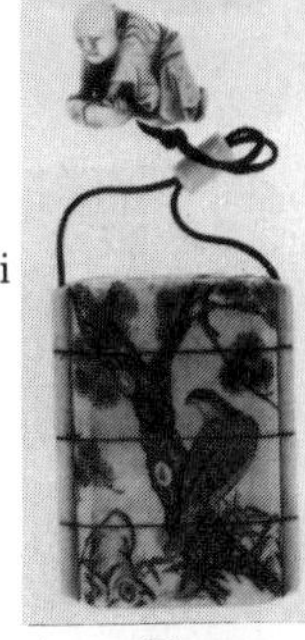

A rare ivory inro, of 3 cases, carved in shallow shishiabori, signed Shukosai with kakihan, with ivory netsuke, signed Gyokuyosai. **£400-£500** *S*

A four case inro, bearing a roiro ground all in gold takamakie and hiramakie with details of okibirame, the base of subdued nashiji and the interior of regular nashiji, one case restored, unsigned, 7.7 cm., 18th C. **£400-£500** *S*

A small wood study of a toad crouching on a discarded waraji, signed Kokei. **£500-600** *S*

A lacquered wood figure of a fisherman, fingers chipped, rod missing, glazed case, 38 cm., late 19th C. **£250-350** *S*

An unusual small 4 case inro, of inlaid aogai, the flowers of gold takamakie with details of gold and silver foil, the interior of nashiji, rubbed, unsigned, 6.9 cm., 18th C. **£600-700** *S*

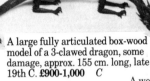

A good hardwood brushpot, 7 in. (17.8 cm.). **£850-950** *S*

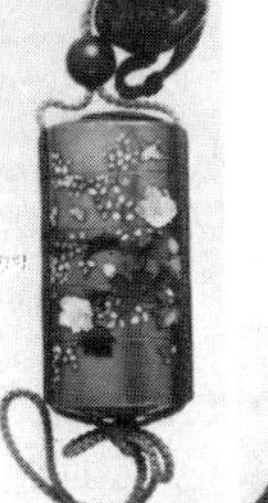

A four case Kinji inro, inlaid in Shibayama style, some inlay missing, unsigned with attached goldstone bead ojime and ebony netsuke, signed Ryomin, all 19th C. **£300-400** *C*

A large fully articulated box-wood model of a 3-clawed dragon, some damage, approx. 155 cm. long, late 19th C. **£900-1,000** *C*

A wooden netsuke formed as a deer and monkey, in slightly worn wood, the deer's eyes inlaid, the base slightly cracked, signed Shomin, 19th C. **£300-350** *S*

A carved wood group of Hotei, the details well engraved, 20 cm., late 19th C. **£400-500** *S*

An ivory netsuke of Hotei, his robe stained green, partly inlaid, the details are finely rendered and unworn, signed on a red lacquer tablet Hoko. **£1,100-1,300** *S*

An ivory netsuke of an eagle with a captured fox, details in stained ivory, partly etched black, the bird's eyes inlaid with gilt-metal, signed in a wavy reserve Hidechika, 19th C. **£650-750** *S*

NETSUKE

Most of the netsuke shown in this section are of reasonable quality, many by known artists from recognised schools. We have been asked about lower price exampes — there are many reasons why a netsuke which may look quite similar to those shown could be much cheaper

- **simply not good quality**
- **unskilful artist**
- **boring**
- **not good subject**
- **badly worn or chipped**
- **very new**

Fakes
Most people have become aware of ivorine or fake ivory and a certain nervousness has been witnessed in the buying public. This has probably been exaggerated but the 'hot needle test' is still a safeguard against the unscrupulous.

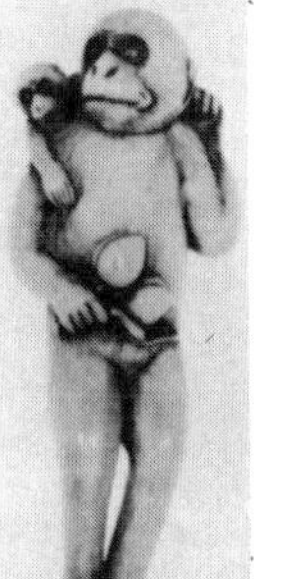

An ivory netsuke of an amusing study of a monkey, the ivory slightly worn and of a good colour, unsigned, 18th C. **£280-340** *S*

A wooden netsuke of a badger priest, the eyes inlaid with glass, signed Gyokusai, 19th C. **£300-£350** *S*

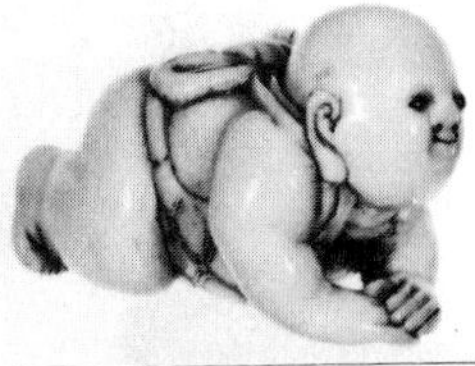

An ivory netsuke of a baby boy crawling on hands and knees, in slightly worn and well toned ivory, the eyes inlaid with dark horn, signed Masamitsu, mid 19th C. **£350-400** *S*

An ivory netsuke of a rat, in lightly stained ivory, the rat's eyes inlaid with brown horn, signed Masayoshi. **£300-350** *S*

An elaborate model of a snake and human skull, in stained ivory, 5.8 cm., late 19th C. **£380-460** *S*

A small ivory netsuke of a Karako, the ivory slightly worn and of a good colour, unsigned, 19th C. **£250-300** *S*

An ivory netsuke of a group of 3 shells, the ivory slightly worn and bearing a good patina, one small chip, unsigned, 18th C. **£180-240** *S*

An ivory netsuke of a monkey, in slightly worn and well-toned ivory, the eye pupils inlaid with dark horn, unsigned, late 18th C., Kyoto school. **£300-350** *S*

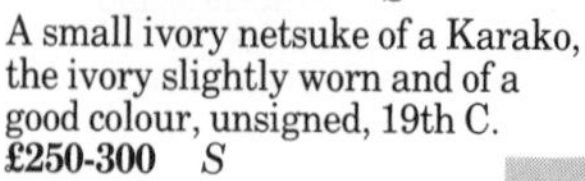

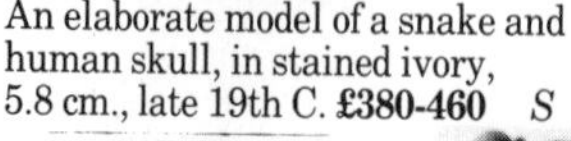

An ivory netsuke of gama sennin, signed below Hidemasa. **£550-£600** *L*

An ivory netsuke of a sennin. **£550-£600** *L*

An ivory manju netsuke, inlaid in mother-of-pearl, stained ivory and horn, minute chip, signed Shibayama, 4.5 cm., c. 1900. **£280-£360** *S*

An ivory manju netsuke, inlaid in mother-of-pearl, signed Shibayama, 4.5 cm., c. 1900. **£250-£300** *S*

An ivory netsuke of a fox dancer, the finely carved details are slightly worn in well-toned ivory, the ears chipped and one foot restored, unsigned, 18th C. **£200-£250** *S*

A 19th C. Japanese compass netsuke. **£200-300** *HAD*

A study of a biwa fruit, with slight cracks, signed in an oval reserve Mitsuhiro. **£800-£900** *S*

A Gandhara stucco head, the hair arranged in thick tresses, traces of polychrome, old damage, wood block base, 7½ in. high (17.5 cm.), 3rd/5th C. **£350-400** *C*

An ivory netsuke of a musician, the details engraved and stained, signed Hokusai, 5 cm., c. 1870. **£250-300** *S*

A pair of Shibayama vases, each with an enamelled silver body, some inlay missing, 2 handles missing, engraved mark, 26 cm., c. 1900. **£1,000-1,200** *S*

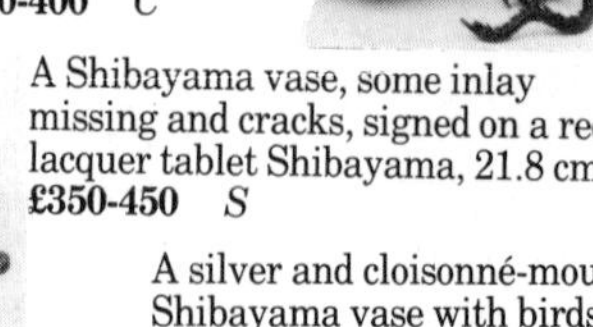

A Shibayama vase, some inlay missing and cracks, signed on a red lacquer tablet Shibayama, 21.8 cm. **£350-450** *S*

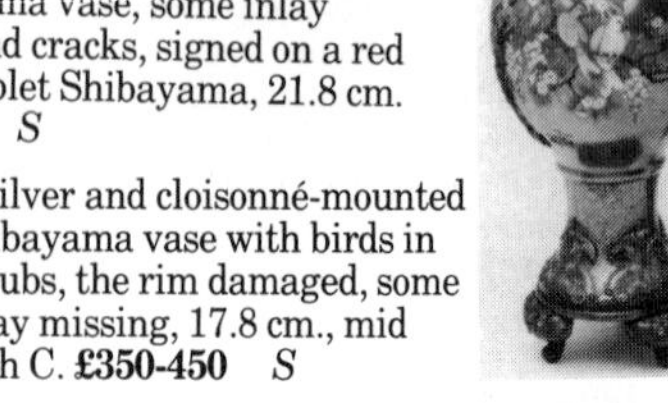

A silver and cloisonné-mounted Shibayama vase with birds in shrubs, the rim damaged, some inlay missing, 17.8 cm., mid 19th C. **£350-450** *S*

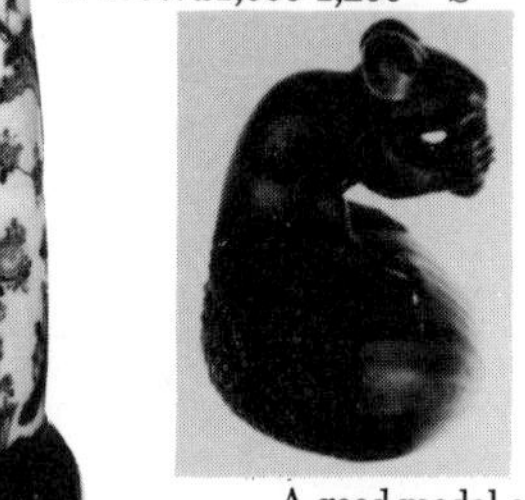

A Shibayama vase, some inlay missing, 28 cm., c. 1900. **£750-£850** *S*

A good model of a rat seated on top of a large chestnut eating a nut, the details well carved, the wood stained for effect and the eyes inlaid, signed Masanao. **£350-£400** *S*

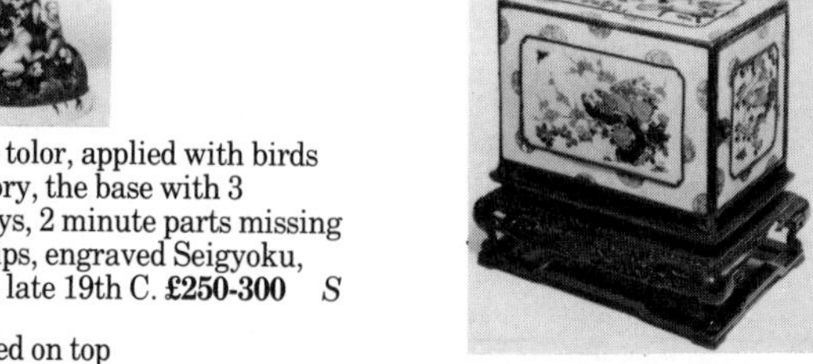

A bone tolor, applied with birds and ivory, the base with 3 monkeys, 2 minute parts missing and chips, engraved Seigyoku, 17 cm., late 19th C. **£250-300** *S*

A Shibayama Kodansu, the interior lacquered in hiramakie with foliage on a roiro ground, some inlay missing, wood stand, 17 by 23 cm., c. 1900. **£800-900** *S*

A Shibuichi Kozuka applied in relief with cranes, details in silver and shibuichi, unsigned. **£200-£250** *S*

A jade cong, the greenish-brown stone toning to brown, 1¾ in. (4.5 cm.), Han Dynasty. **£500-600** *S*

A Suzuribako, decorated in shades of gold takamakie, hiramakie, togidashi, mura-nashiji and kirigane, the interior rim with some chips, 26.4 by 24.1 by 5 cm., late Edo/Meiji period. **£2,000-£2,500** *S*

A Shakudo Kozuka applied on the nanako plate, details in copper, shibuichi gilt and silver, unsigned, Goto School. **£120-180** *S*

A pair of Pekin glass vases, the translucent metal decorated in carved overlay of bright turquoise, 9¾ in. (24.7 cm.), 19th C. **£650-£700** *S*

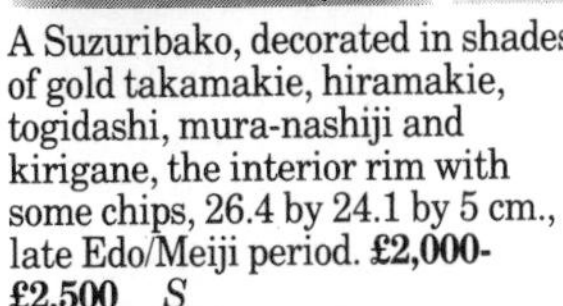

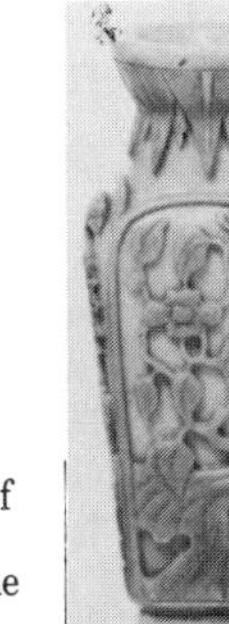

An unusual spinach-green jade covered bowl, the stone of good colour with paler mottling and black flecking overall, 7⅛ in. (18.2 cm.). **£4,000-5,000** *S*

A rhinoceros horn libation cup of yellowish honey colour, trees extending up one side to form the handle, 5⅝ in. (15 cm.), 17th/18th C. **£2,000-2,500** *S*

A jade ritual disc (bi), mottled greenish stone with black speckling and whitish calcification, 5⅜ in. (13.7 cm.), Han Dynasty. **£1,100-1,400** *S*

A pair of turquoise-overlay pink Pekin glass vases, the metal of milky pink tone decorated in bright turquoise relief with panels of flowering trees, 7⅞ in. (20 cm.), 19th C. **£450-500** *S*

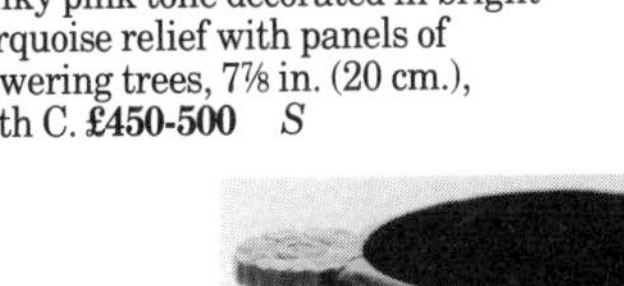

An entirely plain green jade bowl of large size, with a copper gilt stand, 10½ in. (26.7 cm.), 17th C. **£2,000-3,000** *S*

From the Collection of the Earl of Derby.

A rare dated spinach jade brushpot, Qianlong dated Imperial inscription on the rim, 6⅜ in. (16.2 cm.), Qianlong. **£5,000-£6,000** *S*

The date corresponds to the year 1795.

An unusual pair of double-handled green jade bowls, the spinach-green stone with paler clouding suffused with olive-green speckling and brownish striations, wood stands, 10½ in. (26.7 cm.), incised 4 character seal marks of Qianlong, 19th C. **£1,100-1,300** *S*

A jade carving of a goose, of pale greenish colour, 4 in. (10.3 cm.), 18th C. **£1,200-1,600** *S*

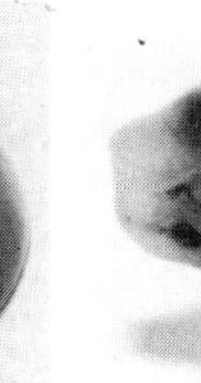

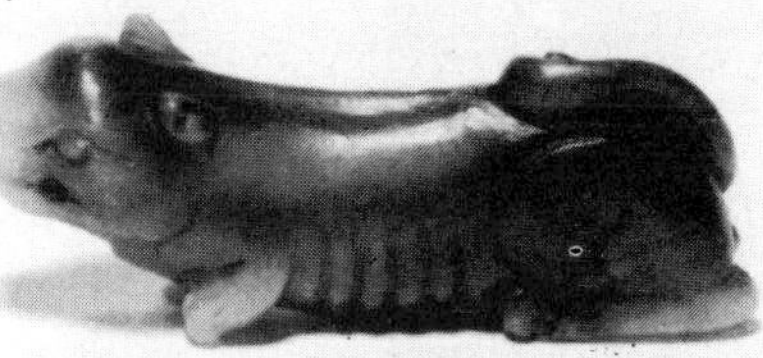

A spinach-green jade covered box, the stone of rich colour suffused with black speckling, 5¼ in. (13.3 cm.), Qianlong. **£850-950** *S*

A jade figure of a dog, the pebble of pale tone clouded with russet suffusions, 2½ in. (6.4 cm.), with box. **£300-500** *S*

A spinach-green jade censer and cover, wood stand, 7½ in. (19 cm.), Qianlong. **£3,000-3,500** *S*

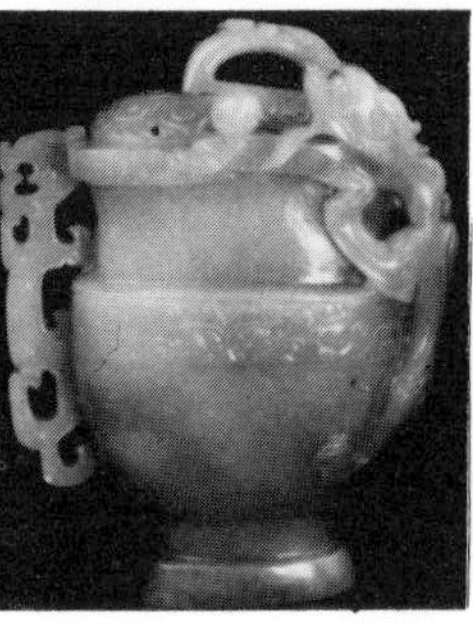

An olive celadon jade vase and cover carved as an archaic ewer, the stone yellowish green with slight russet areas, wood stand, 13.5 cm. high, 18th/19th C. **£2,500-£3,000** *C*

A very fine white jade jar and cover, the stone of even translucent tone with faint overall opaque white mottling, 8¼ in. (20.9 cm.), Qianlong. **£30,000-33,000** *S*

From the Collection of Sir Godfrey Thomas, Bart.

A jade brushwasher, the stone of pale green tone, wood stand, 5¼ in. **£300-400** *SC*

A South German ivory beaker carved with the Last Supper, mounted in silver gilt, 4¼ in. overall (10.7 cm.), 17th C. **£1,200-£1,400** *S*

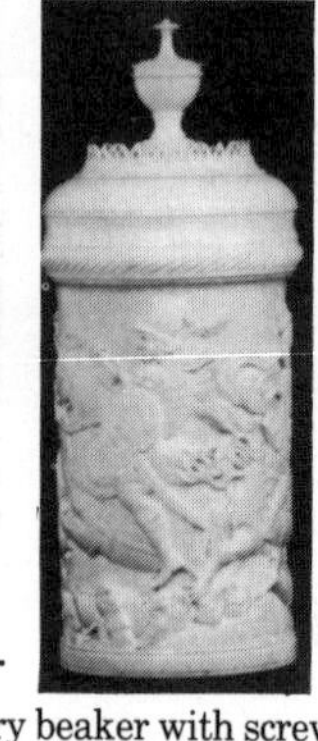
A carved ivory beaker with screw-on cover, German, 7 in. high (17.7 cm.), late 19th C. **£300-400** *S*

An ivory figure of St. Sebastian, some damage, German, 9¼ in. high (23.5 cm.), late 17th C. **£850-950** *S*

A large Dieppe ivory statuette of Louis XIV, shaft of cane missing, 47.5 cm. high, 19th C. **£2,200-£2,400** *C*

A carved ivory figure of Queen Elizabeth I, French, 13 in. high (33 cm.), late 19th C. **£1,100-£1,300** *S*

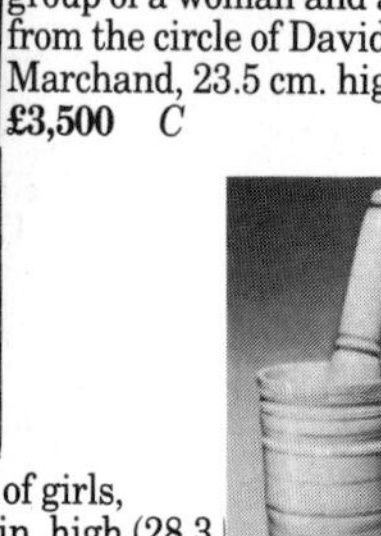
A late 17th C. Anglo-Flemish ivory group of a woman and a young boy, from the circle of David Le Marchand, 23.5 cm. high. **£3,000-£3,500** *C*

An ivory portrait bust of Napoleon I, after Canova, on ebonised wood plinth, French, 5 in. high (13 cm.), mid-late 19th C. **£350-400** *S*

A carved ivory beggar band, probably French, 6¼ in. high (16 cm.), late 19th C. **£600-700** *S*

A pair of ivory figures of girls, French, 11¼ and 10¾ in. high (28.3 and 27.4 cm.), 1890's. **£750-850** *S*

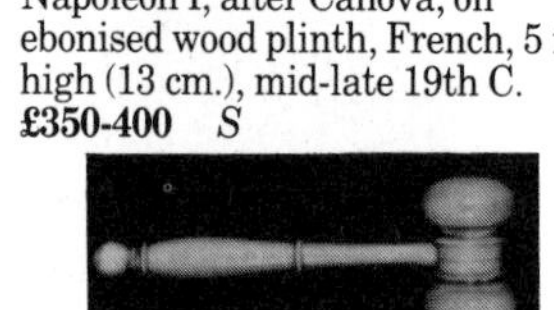
A small turned ivory gavel, 4½ in. long (11.5 cm.), late 19th C. **£140-£180** *S*

A turned ivory mortar, with pestle turned en suite, perhaps English, 7⅜ in. high (18.7 cm.), c. 1700. **£1,300-1,500** *S*

A very large and elaborately carved meerschaum pipe, by F. M. Denninger, signed, some damage, 12 in. long (30.5 cm.), 19th C. **£5,000-6,000** *C*

An ivory portrait of Christ, by N. Schrödl, signed, 6¼ in. high (16.2 cm.), c. 1850. **£700-800** *S*

A pair of pierced ivory vases, possibly Russian, 8 in. high (20.4 cm.), mid 19th C. **£1,400-£1,600** *S*

A carved ivory plaque, probably French, 14½ in. long (37 cm.), late 19th C. **£1,200-1,400** *S*

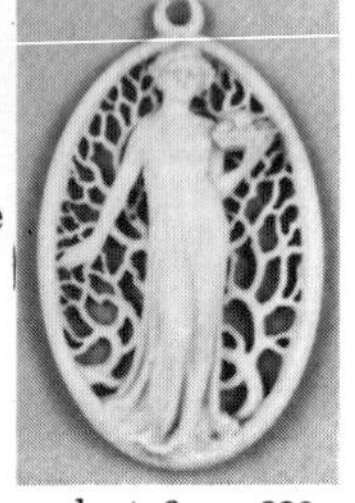
A carved ivory pendant, 6 cm. **£80-£100** *P*

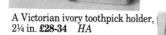

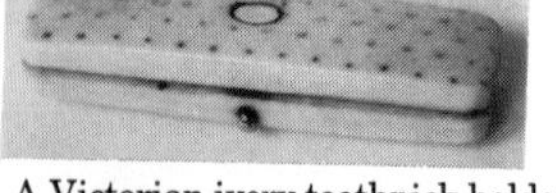
A Victorian ivory toothpick holder, 2¼ in. **£28-34** *HA*

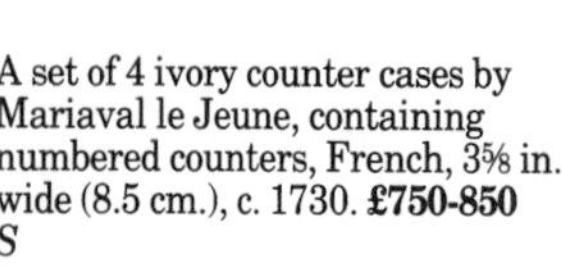

A set of 4 ivory counter cases by Mariaval le Jeune, containing numbered counters, French, 3⅝ in. wide (8.5 cm.), c. 1730. **£750-850** *S*

A Victorian ivory glove powderer, 5 in. **£35-40** *HA*

Miller's is a price GUIDE Not a price LIST.

The price ranges given reflect the average price a purchaser should pay for similar items. Condition, rarity of design or pattern, size, colour, provenance, restoration and many other factors must be taken into account when assessing values.

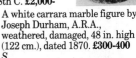

A white marble bust, inscribed T.W. Low Sc. 1873, 32 in. high. **£300-400** *CEd*

A white marble bust, signed Morelli, 30 in. high (76 cm.), c. 1880. **£1,000-1,150** *S*

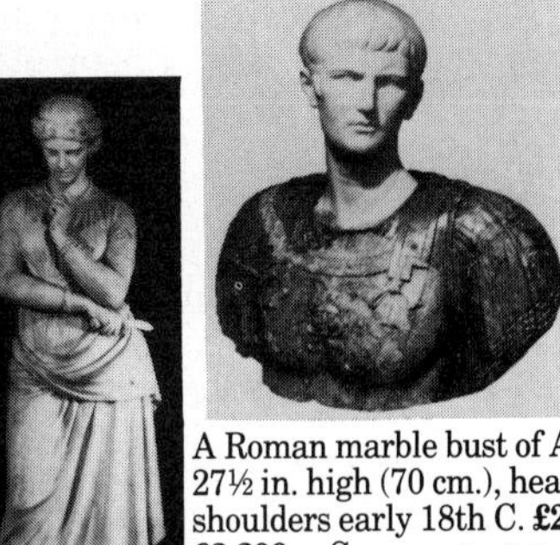

An American neo-classic marble statue of Medea, by William Wetmore Story, damaged edge of plinth, 195 cm., 19th C. **£30,000-£33,000** *C*

Medea contemplating the murder of her children was inspired by the role of Medea by the great tragedienne Adelaide Ristori, whom Story is supposed to have followed around 'like a shadow'.

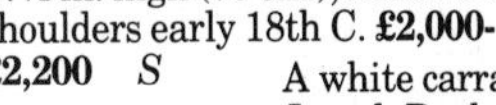

A Roman marble bust of Augustus, 27½ in. high (70 cm.), head 19th C., shoulders early 18th C. **£2,000-£2,200** *S*

A white carrara marble figure by Joseph Durham, A.R.A., weathered, damaged, 48 in. high (122 cm.), dated 1870. **£300-400** *S*

A pair of late 17th C. English marble putti, in the style of Arnold Quellin, damaged, 103 cm. high. **£1,200-£1,400** *C*

A terracotta statuette of St. Sebastian, traces of original colour, Italian, 32 in. high, early 16th C. **£2,500-3,000** *RVA*

A pair of Swedish porphyry urns, 10 in. diam. (25.5 cm.). **£1,500-£2,000** *C*

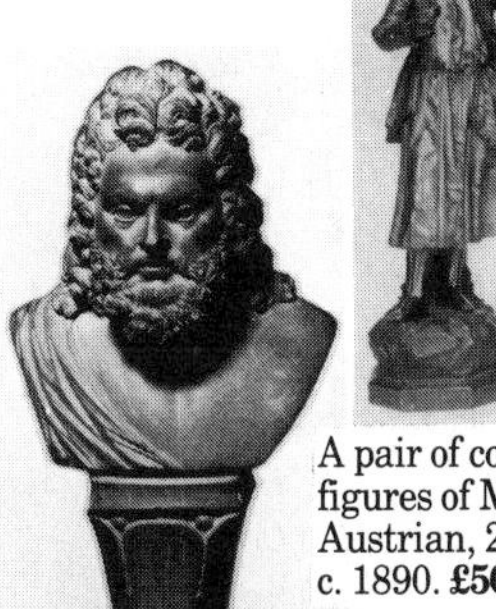

A pair of cold-painted white clay figures of Moroccans, probably Austrian, 22 in. high (56 cm.), c. 1890. **£500-600** *S*

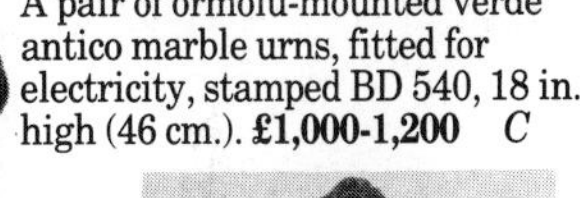

A pair of ormolu-mounted verde antico marble urns, fitted for electricity, stamped BD 540, 18 in. high (46 cm.). **£1,000-1,200** *C*

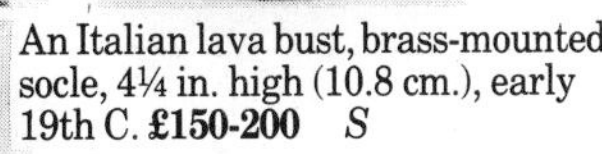

An Italian lava bust, brass-mounted socle, 4¼ in. high (10.8 cm.), early 19th C. **£150-200** *S*

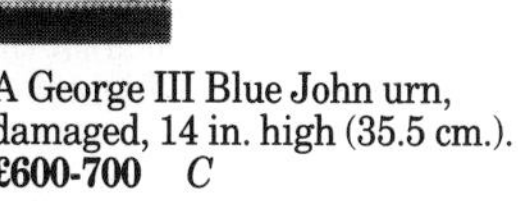

A George III Blue John urn, damaged, 14 in. high (35.5 cm.). **£600-700** *C*

A terracotta bust of Pallas Athene, 22 in., c. 1820-40. **£200-250** *BP*

A 19th C. French or English terracotta bust known as 'Roubiliac's Daughter', 22.5 cm. high. **£300-400** *C*

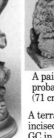

A French terracotta bust of a young lady, possibly Rose Dantier, in the style of Jean Jacques Caffieri, turned marble socle, 58 cm. high, 1770. **£1,200-1,400** *C*

BLUE JOHN

- **a type of fluorspar found in Derbyshire**
- **translucent — mainly dark purple and violet though also found in brown and yellow**
- **main period of popularity from 1745**
- **especially popular in France where it was called 'bleu-jaune'**
- **most collectable pieces — candelabra by Matthew Boulton**

A pair of stone lions sejant, probably English, 28 in. high (71 cm.), 17th C. **£1,300-1,500** *S*

A terracotta group, signed Canette, incised on underside with initials GC in an oval, 22 in. high. **£350-£400** *PWC*

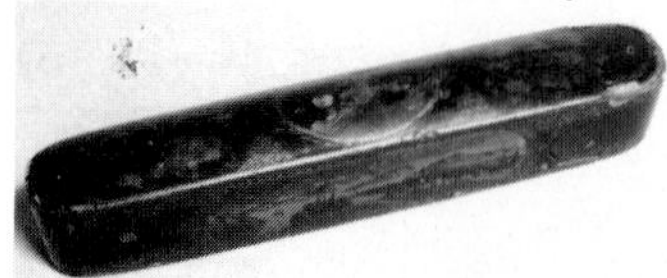

A 19th C. papier mâché and lacquer pen box, 9½ in. **£30-35** *TA*

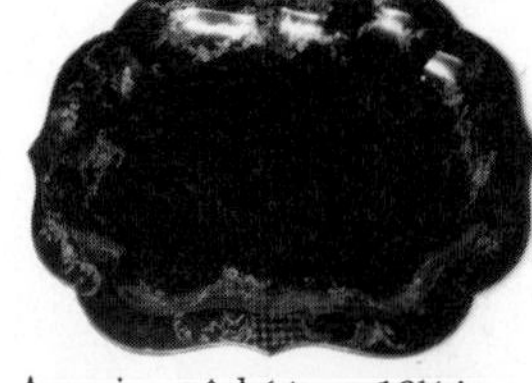

A papier mâché tray, 16½ in., c. 1880. **£50-60** *Ph*

A lacquer tray, 22 in., c. 1900. **£45-£50** *Ph*

A French blonde tortoiseshell snuff box, gold mounts, mark of Jean-Baptiste Fouache, Paris, 1774-80, 2¼ in. **£200-£300** *S*

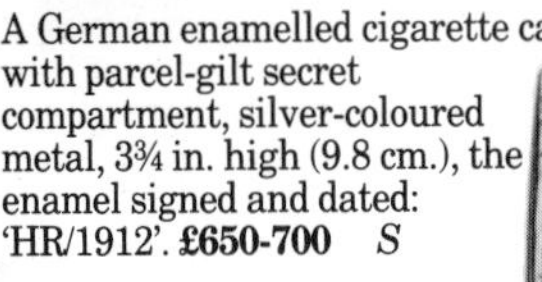

A German enamelled cigarette case with parcel-gilt secret compartment, silver-coloured metal, 3¾ in. high (9.8 cm.), the enamel signed and dated: 'HR/1912'. **£650-700** *S*

An Austrian enamel pill box, 5.25 cm. long. **£50-70** *P*

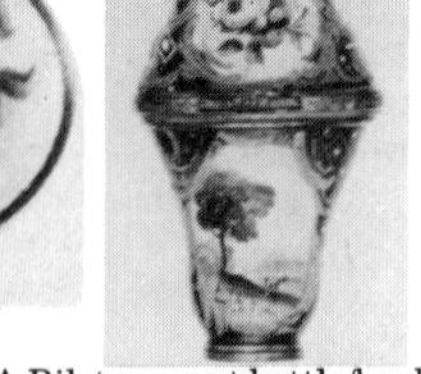

A Bilston scent bottle/bonbonniere, with gilt-metal mounts, 10 cm. long, c. 1770. **£400-500** *S*

An Indian gold and red enamel scent bottle, 7 cm. long, probably early 18th C. **£300-350** *P*

A white-ground snuff box with Les Amours Pastorales, some damage, 8 cm. wide, c. 1765. **£550-650** *S*

A Bilston dog bonbonniere, reeded metal mounts, restored, 6 cm. wide, c. 1770-75. **£300-400** *S*

A toilet box, gilt-metal reeded mounts and foot rim, 9 cm. diam., c. 1755. **£800-900** *S*

A pair of jewelled and enamelled models, Hungarian, 5 and 4 in. high (12.7 and 10.3 cm.), mid 20th C. **£900-1,000** *S*

A pair of Limoges enamel candlesticks, 15 cm. high, 19th C. **£500-600** *C*

A Russian enamel box in pink, green, yellow, mauve and blue, by Maria Semenova, 8.25 cm. long by 3.6 cm. high by 6 cm. wide, 7 oz., c. 1890. **£700-800** *P*

A George III gold and enamel pill box, in the manner of Moser, 3.2 cm., c. 1780. **£350-450** *Bon*

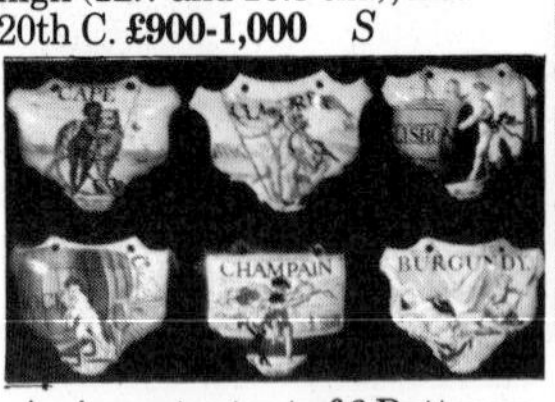

An important set of 6 Battersea enamel wine labels, transfer-printed and painted with scenes engraved by Simon Ravenet, in fitted leather case, each approx. 2½ to 3 in. long (6.3 to 7.6 cm.), c. 1755. **£7,000-8,000** *C*

The Mother of God 'Quick to Listen', 31 by 27 cm., maker's mark I.A.A., Moscow, 1899-1905. **£1,500-£1,800** *S*

The Smolensk Mother of God, 30.5 by 25.3 cm., late 19th C., encased in an earlier silver-gilt oklad, 35 by 25.5 cm., maker's mark E.B. and IM (Latin), St. Petersburg 1774. **£600-700** *S*

The Kazan Mother of God, 18th C.; encased in a later ornate silver-gilt oklad, 31 by 27 cm., maker's mark of Michail Vasilievitch Borodulin, St. Petersburg, 1843. **£800-900** *S*

A Veneto-Cretan icon of The Virgin and Child, on a gold ground, 32.8 by 24.3 cm., 17th C. **£450-£550** *S*

The Tikhvin Mother of God, applied with seed pearls and pastes, 49.8 by 39 cm., maker's mark N.F., St. Petersburg, 1834. **£2,400-2,700** *S*

The Kazan Mother of God, heightened with gold, 31 by 27 cm., 19th C. **£400-500** *S*

An icon of Christ Pantocrator, by Saztkov, on a gold ground, 31 by 26.7 cm., the maker's mark stamped beneath the Imperial Eagle Warrant, Moscow, 1870. **£900-1,100** *S*

The Theotokos, some overcleaning and restoration, 60 by 46.5 cm., 17th C. **£950-£1,150** *S*

The Grebnevskaya Mother of God, 37 by 30 cm., maker's mark indistinct, Moscow, 1798. **£800-£900** *S*

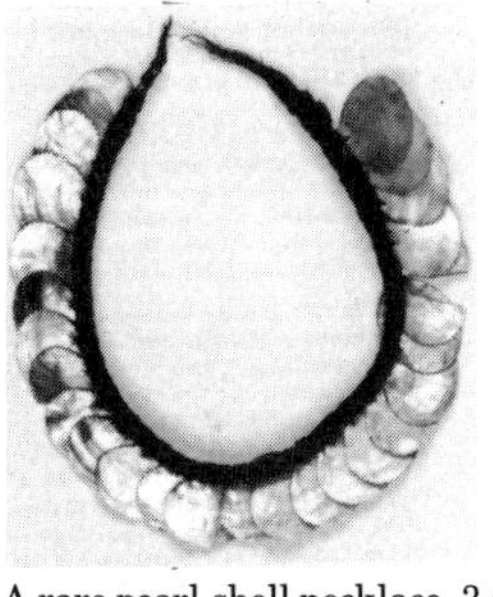

A rare pearl-shell necklace, 3 discs broken, Tahiti or the Austral Islands. **£2,200-2,800** *C*

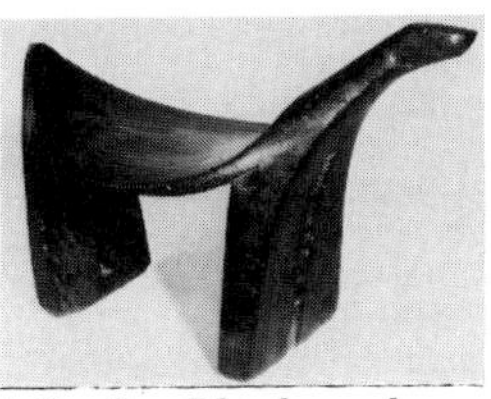

A Caroline Islands wood coconut-grater stool, 25½ in. long (65 cm.). **£1,700-1,900** *C*

A Senufo wood mask, kpelie, glossy dark brown patina, the bridge of the nose eroded, 12½ in. high (32 cm.). **£1,400-1,800** *C*

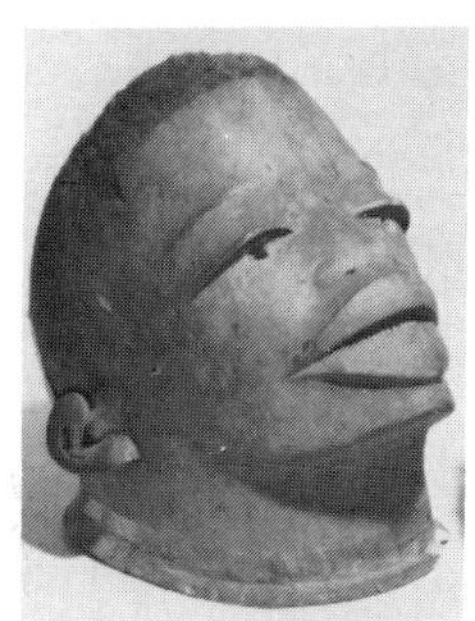

A Makonde wood helmet mask, set with human hair, chips to neck, repaired, 10 in. high (25.5 cm.), c. 1930-40. **£1,800-2,000** *C*

A Papua Gulf barkcloth mask, slight damages, Elema, 22 in. high (56 cm.). **£1,100-1,300** *C*

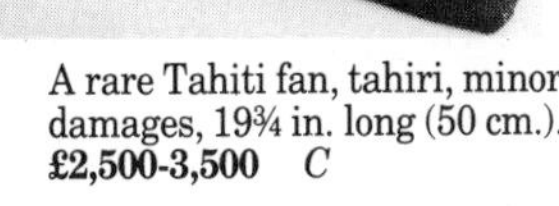

A fine Makonde wood mask, reddish brown patina, 8 in. high (20 cm.), c. 1900. **£3,000-5,000** *C*

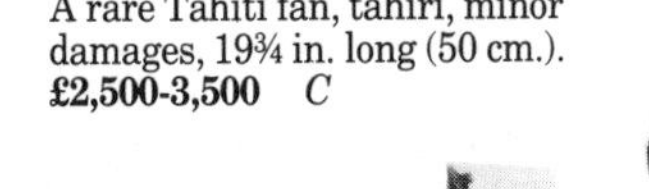

A rare Tahiti fan, tahiri, minor damages, 19¾ in. long (50 cm.). **£2,500-3,500** *C*

A Maori wood tinder box, 7⅜ in. long (18.8 cm.). **£450-550** *C*

A Vere knife and sheath, 15½ in. long (39.5 cm.). **£250-300** *C*

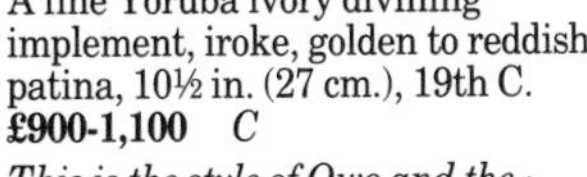

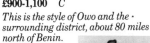

A fine Yoruba ivory divining implement, iroke, golden to reddish patina, 10½ in. (27 cm.), 19th C. **£900-1,100** *C*

This is the style of Owo and the surrounding district, about 80 miles north of Benin.

A pair of Yoruba wood twin figures, one foot mended, north central Yorubaland, 9½ in. high (25 cm.). **£500-600** *C*

A fine Baule wood female figure, crack at back and base, 17 in. high (43 cm.). **£2,200-2,800** *C*

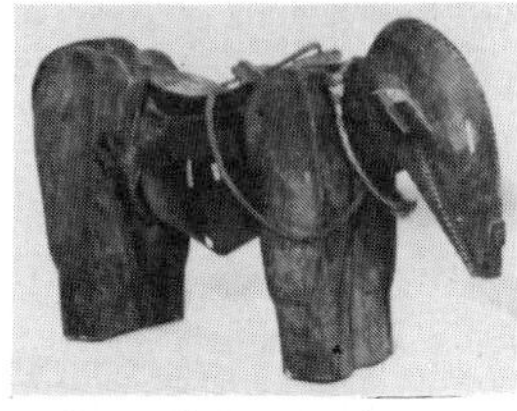

A Senufo wood horse, cracks, native mends, 17 in. high (43 cm.). **£600-800** *C*

This hobby horse was used in a dance called guro in the village of Poundiou in the Boundiali area, the culmination of a 7-year cycle of initiation for the boys, cholole. The hobby horses are carried by the boys in some of the dances during the guro.

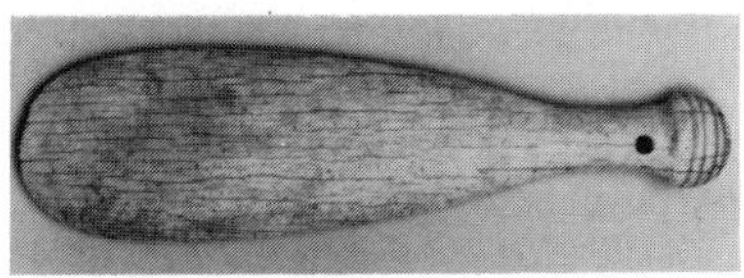

A Maori bone hand club, patu paraoa, creamy patina, shallow chip to edge, 18 in. long (46 cm.), 18th/19th C. **£1,100-1,400** *C*

An Akan wood comb, 9½ in. high (23.5 cm.). **£120-180** *C*

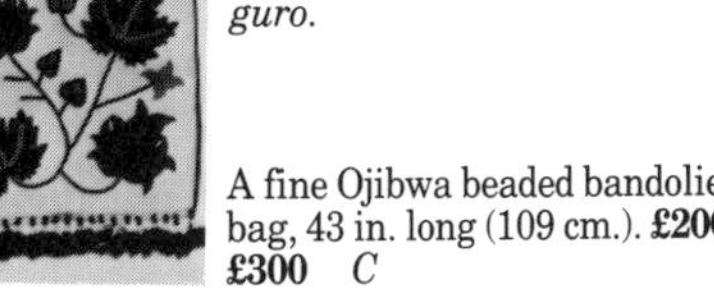

A fine Ojibwa beaded bandolier bag, 43 in. long (109 cm.). **£200-£300** *C*

EPHEMERA

As nostalgia for the past grows there is an ever increasing interest in its ephemera — Christmas cards, Valentines, scraps, cigarette cards and postcards. A favourite pastime of the Victorians was to fill scrap books with poems, greeting cards, drawings and brightly coloured 'scraps'.

At the end of the last century collecting postcards became popular. The message on many cards is 'Here is another postcard for your collection' or 'do you have this one?'. The first cigarette cards appeared in 1886. But the fashion for this kind of collecting (as well as postcard collecting) died down by the 1920's, and today's 'boom' in these ephemera started again in the mid-60's. Most collectors specialise in a particular type of ephemera.

Postcard collectors often limit their collections to certain categories — comic cards, artist designed cards, topography, etc. According to the IPM price index postcards had their largest overall price growth in 1976 (58.72%) and had an overall 47.96% growth in 1979. Since then the price growth has levelled out and it was only 2.74% overall in 1982. However, some categories of cards sell better than others. Real photographs of social history showing disasters, high streets with activity and transportation, shop fronts and railway stations are much sought after. Recently a postcard never seen before fetched £76 in the saleroom. Subject cards have maintained their prices but they have advanced very little in the past two years. Romantic cards, though amusing and colourful, do not move at the present but one can never tell what the fashion may be next year.

Cigarette cards dated up to 1905 are in demand and even when they are in only fair condition they sell well. If they are in very good condition they can command very high prices. Pre-first world war cigarette cards also sell well but those from the 1930's were printed in millions and there is little market for them.

Mid 19th century Christmas cards are desirable but the later Victorian cards only sell for a pound or two. Early Valentines in their original envelopes and post marked are sought after. Later elaborate Valentines can usually be bought for anything from £5 to £25.

In London there are monthly postcard sales at various hotels and special ephemera fairs. Postcard catalogues which are illustrated give price *guides* which can be no more than that because condition, the date of the card and other such factors make a large difference in price

The sale rooms have specialist postcard sales and interesting lots are to be found. Be sure to check the condition of the cards — bent corners or other such damage will affect the worth of the card. Notice whether the cards are all addressed to the same family. This is an indication that the cards are from a private collection and are not a made-up dealer's lot of cards he could not sell. Buying collections in the sale room, if done with care, can be a reasonable way of starting a collection. The cards that are of no interest to you can be re-sold in the sale room. The postmarks on the cards can be of considerable interest but this is a specialist field more related to philately than to postcard collecting.

A chromo-litho undivided back advertisement for Kalodont toothpaste, with Snow White and the Seven Dwarfs. **£8-12** *PC*

A C.W.S. advertising card for Luto. **£3-4** *PC*

'The Flower Girl' is worth 50 pence on her own, but the reverse is an advertisement for 'Woman's Life (for Maid and Wife)'. **£2-3** *PC*

An advertising card for 'Ewbank' carpet sweeper, 1907. **£2-3** *PC*

A 'Clifton' hand coloured postcard. **£10-12** *PC*

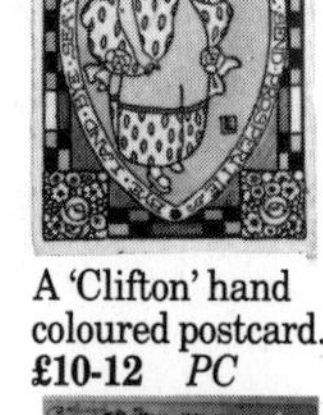

An Art Nouveau card, unsigned, 1900. **£7-£9** *PC*

A Nestle's advertising card, 1917. **£2-3** *PC*

A 1907 advertising card. **£3-5** *PC*

An embossed chromo-litho card, undivided back, 1903. **£2-3** *PC*

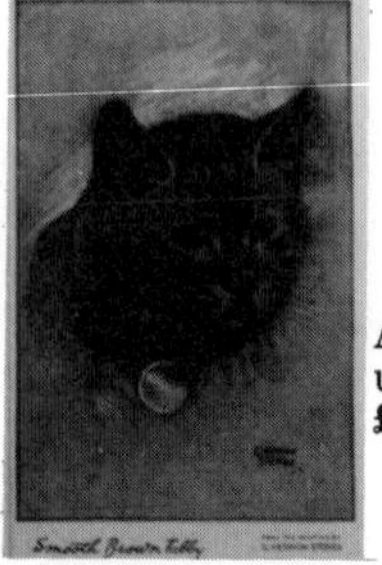

A portrait of a cat by G. Vernon Stokes, 1918. **50-75p** *PC*

In 1979 Stokes' work was catalogued at 30p a card.

A fine example of an early Raphael Kirchner, dated 1901. **£25-30** *PC*

A postcard advertising Bipex, 1981. **25-35p** *PC*

A glamour card based on a water-colour by Phillip Boileau. **£4.00-£4.50** *PC*

'Friolerie' by Raphael Kirchner, Bruton Galleries. **£10-12** *PC*

A glamorous comic card by Arthur Thiele. **£4-6** *PC*

As well as an advertisement this is a bit of social history showing what type of house could be bought for £1,000 in the 1930's. **£3-4** *PC*

A glamour postcard 'American Girl'. **£1.50-3.50** *PC*

A beautiful girl by Prati, worth more for the subject than the greeting. **£2-3** *PC*

An appealing photograph of a Victorian girl. **50p-£1** *PC*

Photographs of pretty girls only cost about **30-50p** depending on girl, costume and pose. *PC*

Louis Wain is the artist of this Raphael Tuck art postcard series, 1261. This is an early Wain valued at **£12** but Wain's prices have remained static for the last few years. Printed in Germany. *PC*

An early M. L. Attwell postcard, pre-1914. **£1-2** *PC*

This artist is much sought after. Her later cards of children (1940 on) should fetch about 25-50p.

H.M. & Co. 'Louis Wain start off!' card No. 4249. Printed in Austria. **£10-12** *PC*

A children's card by H. T. Miller published by Liberty and Co., 1915. **£2.50-3.50** *PC*

A 'Bonzo' card by G. E. Studdy, 1926. **£2.50-3.00** *PC*

A comic card by G. F. Christie. Pre-1918 **£1.50-2.00** 1918 onwards **75p-£1** *PC*

A Raphael Tuck oilette by Lance Thackery, 1909. **£3-£4** *PC*

A Donald McGill comic card, pre-1914. **£1.50-2.00** *PC*

A teddy bear card by Pillard which has double appeal, for the subject and the artist, 1909. **£2.50-3.00** *PC*

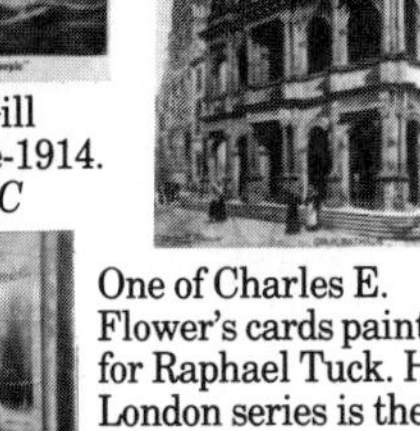

One of Charles E. Flower's cards painted for Raphael Tuck. His London series is the most sought after. **50p-£1.50** *PC*

An Edwardian comic novelty card by F.S. with pleated paper skirt that lifts up to reveal wooden legs. Publisher: L.C.V. **£3.50-5.00** *PC*

A 1904 bathing beauties card, foreign printed. **£3-4** *PC*

Postcards of children fetch as little as 30p and can make an amusing collection for little outlay. This French card is dated 1904 and would cost from **50p-£1** *PC*

A hand-coloured and decorated photograph of a child, printed in Germany, dated 1911. Because this girl is holding a doll and a bottle the card could fetch up to **£1.50** *PC*

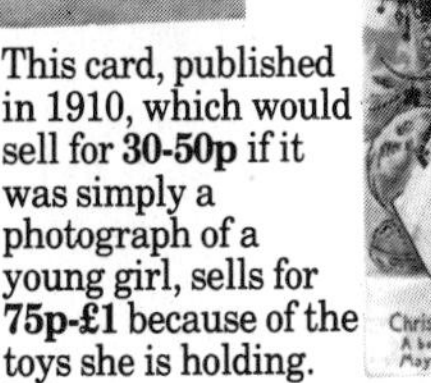

This card, published in 1910, which would sell for **30-50p** if it was simply a photograph of a young girl, sells for **75p-£1** because of the toys she is holding. *PC*

An embossed and gilded Christmas card published by Giesen Bros., London, printed in Germany. **75p-£1.25** *PC*

A comic card by F.S. (Fred Spurgin), published by Gale and Polden Ltd. **£1.00-1.50** *PC*

A 'Golliwog' card by Florence K. Upton, published by Raphael Tuck. **£8-9** *PC*

A comic type card printed in Saxony, 1908. **50-75p** *PC*

German comic 'bathing beauties' card, 1916. **£5-6** *PC*

A Bamforth pre-1918 comic card, 'Pledges' series, printed and embossed in Germany. **60-75p** *PC*

Expect to pay between **£2-4** a card for photographs of Greta Garbo, less popular stars sell for between **50p-£1.50**, 1920-39 *PC*

'At the Seaside in Dollyland' series, Raphael Tuck, published 1904. **£1.50-2.50** *PC*

Clark Gable, a favourite with collectors of film stars, 1920-39. **£1.50-£3.00** *PC*

Film star cards published in the 1930's have been attracting much interest in the sale rooms and this interest is reflected in the dealers' prices. Popular stars such as Shirley Temple sell for between **£1.50-£2.00** *PC*

An early Raphael Tuck 'Crimson & Gold' series of Christmas postcards No. 501 embossed card. **£3-6** *PC*

Christmas greetings on embossed card. Some catalogues list these cards for as little as **20p** but a more realistic price is **50-75p** *PC*

A Christmas card published by Wildt & Kray, printed in Bavaria, P.M. 1909. **75p-£1.50** *PC*

A Christmas card printed in Germany. **50-75p** *PC*

A 'Gruss Aus' hold-to-light card, 1910. **£6-£8** *PC*

An embossed 'glamour' card with glitter, 1915. **£2-3** *PC*

An embossed and gilded greeting card. **50-75p** *PC*

Embossed Italian crests with view of the Palazzo Ducale in Venice, 1918. **£1.50-£2.50** *PC*

A French greeting card, embossed and glitter applied, c. 1903-06. **75p-£1.50** *PC*

Photographic cards of military uniforms are priced between **75p-£1.50** *PC*

A fine mechanical lever card 'Movo Novelty card', P.M. 1911, reg. design 571900. **£14-16** *PC*

Bamforth series of song cards. Sets of 3: **£1.50-2.00** Sets of 4: **£2.00-2.50** Individual cards: **50p-60p** *PC*

A French hand-painted card with feather and felt, 1911. **£2.50-3.00** *PC*

British soldiers with trophies from the 1914-18 war, issued by the Y.M.C.A. Hut Fund. **£1.00-1.50** *PC*

Photographic postcard of a charabanc, worth **£3.50-4.00.** If only part of the vehicle is shown the price is in the range of **£1.00-£1.50** *PC*

A hold-to-light card of George Street, Plymouth, published by W. H. Berlin, 1903. **£3-4** *PC*

An embroidered card from Spain. **£3-4** *PC*

A hold-to-light New Year's card, printed in Germany. **£4.50-£5.50** *PC*

This Edwardian comic card showing an Edwardian gramophone is worth between **£1.50-3.50** *PC*

A card made of wood, made in Japan. **£4-£5** *PC*

A 1912 calendar card. **£1.50-2.00** *PC*

Cameras are a popular subject, this one has the added feature of pull-out views, published by Valentine, c. 1925. **£1-3** *PC*

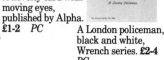

An Edwardian 'squeaker' card. **£2-£3** *PC*

These have doubled in price in the past 4 years.

A novelty card with moving eyes, published by Alpha. **£1-2** *PC*

A London policeman, black and white, Wrench series. **£2-4** *PC*

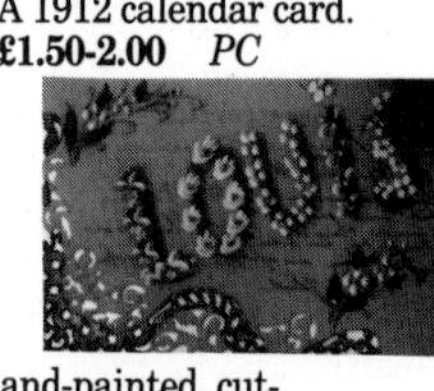

A hand-painted, cut-out celluloid card, French, 1908. **£3-5** *PC*

This card combines real hair with a ribboned hat and a dried flower. **£6-7** *PC*

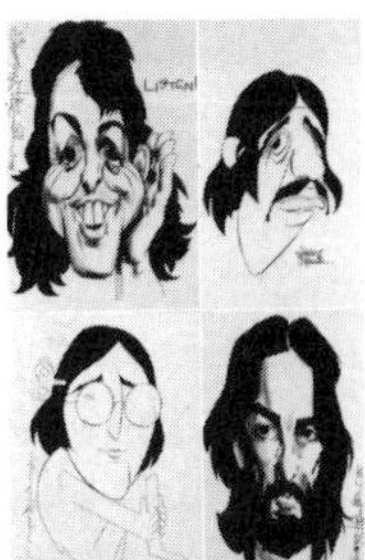

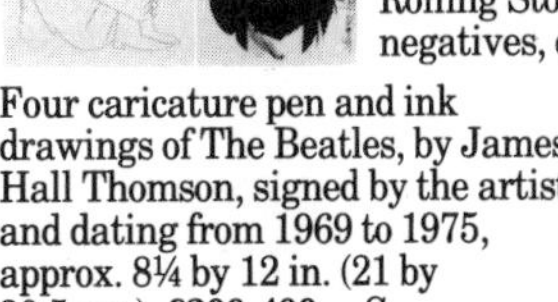

Four caricature pen and ink drawings of The Beatles, by James Hall Thomson, signed by the artist and dating from 1969 to 1975, approx. 8¼ by 12 in. (21 by 30.5 cm.). **£300-400** *S*

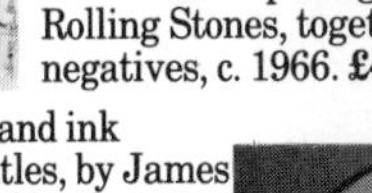

A series of 20 photographs of the Rolling Stones, together with 112 negatives, c. 1966. **£400-500** *S*

Eight photographs of the Beatles performing in 1961 in Aldershot, sold with negatives, with Pete Best on drums. **£1,200-1,300** *S*

Three early Beatles posters, 30 by 20 in. (76 by 51 cm.), 1962. **£550-£600** *S*

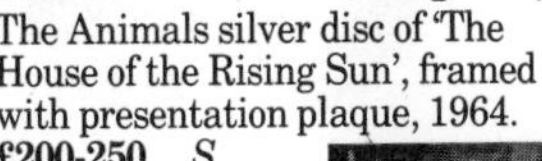

The Animals silver disc of 'The House of the Rising Sun', framed with presentation plaque, 1964. **£200-250** *S*

Eric Clapton platinum disc, for 'Backless', framed, mounted and glazed, c. 1978. **£800-900** *S*

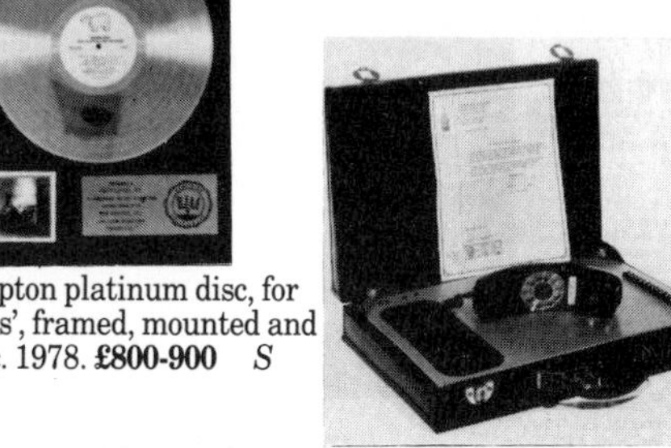

A radio-telephone, once the property of Elvis Presley, with telephone directory, contained in leather briefcase with initials EAP beneath carrying handle, with document of authenticity, 18 in. wide (46 cm.). **£700-800** *S*

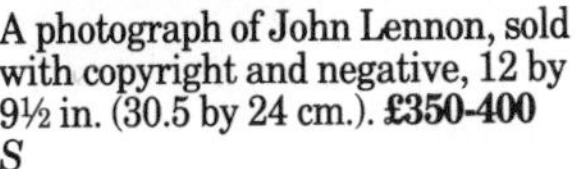

A photograph of John Lennon, sold with copyright and negative, 12 by 9½ in. (30.5 by 24 cm.). **£350-400** *S*

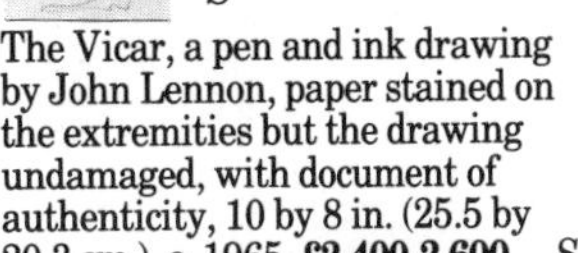

The Vicar, a pen and ink drawing by John Lennon, paper stained on the extremities but the drawing undamaged, with document of authenticity, 10 by 8 in. (25.5 by 20.3 cm.), c. 1965. **£2,400-2,600** *S*

A group of Newhaven fishwives, Calotype, by Robert Adamson and David Octavius Hill, mounted on card, 138 by 190 mm., c. 1845. **£250-300** *S*

'Woman on a Hilltop', by Heinrich Kuhn, bromoil transfer, 267 by 302 mm., c. 1910. **£600-700** *S*

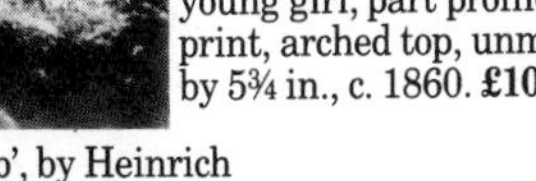

A three-quarter length portrait of a young girl, part profile, albumen print, arched top, unmounted, 7½ by 5¾ in., c. 1860. **£100-130** *C*

'Study of Ruined Abbey', albumenised salt print, 338 by 290 mm., 1850's. **£150-200** *S*

A photograph titled 'Hush, Lightly Tread', arched top, 7½ by 6½ in., published 1857. **£25-30** *C*

'Midnight in the Antarctic Summer', blue-toned silver print, by Herbert Ponting, framed and glazed, 600 by 750 mm., 1910-13. **£150-200** *S*

A photograph of a lady on horseback, possibly from a negative by Roger Fenton, salt print, 8¼ by 9 in., 1850's. **£1,300-1,500** *C*

Sir John Herschel, carbon print, by Julia Margaret Cameron, mounted on card, framed and glazed, 330 by 262 mm., c. 1870. **£400-450** *S*

'Cigarette Smoke, Greenwich Village', by Weegee, silver print, stamped photographer's credit, window matted, 355 by 280 mm., 1953. **£60-80** *S*

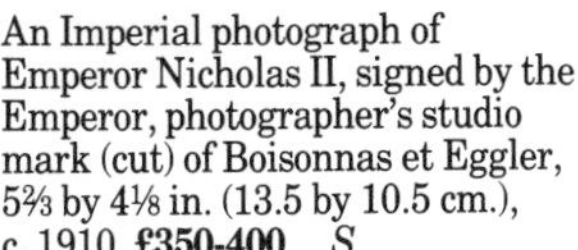

An Imperial photograph of Emperor Nicholas II, signed by the Emperor, photographer's studio mark (cut) of Boisonnas et Eggler, 5⅔ by 4⅛ in. (13.5 by 10.5 cm.), c. 1910. **£350-400** *S*

A Victorian gold bangle, set with baroque pearls and rose cut diamonds. **£550-600** *PWC*

A Murrle Bennett & Co. bracelet, set with faceted amethysts, silver coloured metal stamped M.B. & Co. and '950', 18.5 cm. **£150-200** *P*

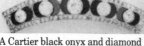

A diamond and enamel brooch. **£400-500** *L*

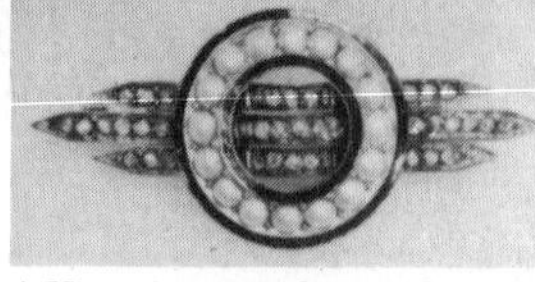

A Victorian rose diamond, split pearl and enamel circle brooch. **£180-240** *Bon*

A Victorian split pearl and diamond star. **£500-600** *Bon*

A gold and black and white enamel bow of Sevigné pattern, set with rubies, with bent pin fitment, 1¼ in. long (3.2 cm.). **£600-700** *C*

A Cartier black onyx and diamond curved brooch. **£1,700-2,000** *Bon*

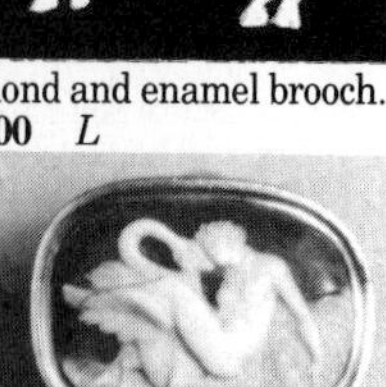

A sardonyx cameo carved with Leda and the Swan, gold ring mount, the cameo 1¼ in. long (3.2 cm.), 18th C. **£650-750** *C*

The composition of this cameo derives from a lost cartoon by Michelangelo. A variant signed by Robert Priddle is in The Hermitage, and another was executed by Burch.

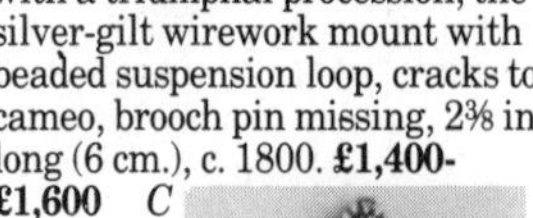

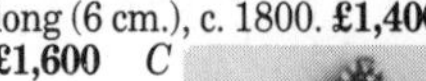

An oval sardonyx cameo, carved with a triumphal procession, the silver-gilt wirework mount with beaded suspension loop, cracks to cameo, brooch pin missing, 2⅜ in. long (6 cm.), c. 1800. **£1,400-£1,600** *C*

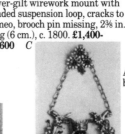

A diamond and emerald floral scroll brooch, set in 18 ct. white gold and platinum. **£1,100-1,300** *WW*

A jewelled 18 ct. gold and enamel mechanical brooch, mechanism needing repair, English, 1½ in. (4 cm.), c. 1920. **£1,200-1,500** *S*

An opal, diamond and blue enamel brooch. **£200-250** *Bon*

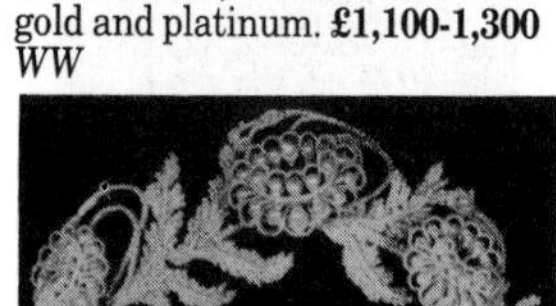

A Victorian pearl tiara. **£150-£200** *Bon*

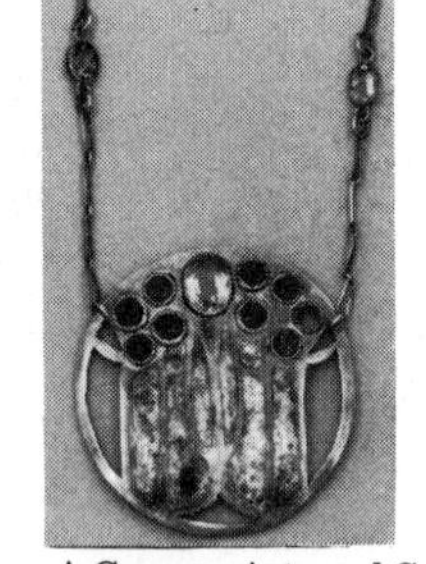

A German Arts and Crafts pendant, on chain with amethyst spacers, 4.5 cm. diam. **£180-240** *P*

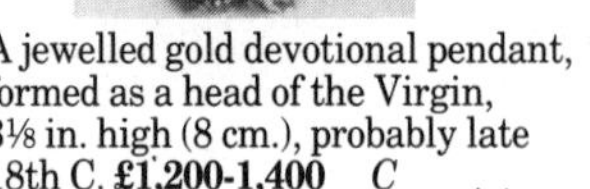

A jewelled gold devotional pendant, formed as a head of the Virgin, 3⅛ in. high (8 cm.), probably late 18th C. **£1,200-1,400** *C*

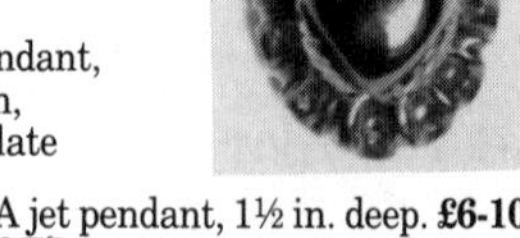

A jet pendant, 1½ in. deep. **£6-10** *STR*

A jet collar, c. 1900. **£25-30** *STR*

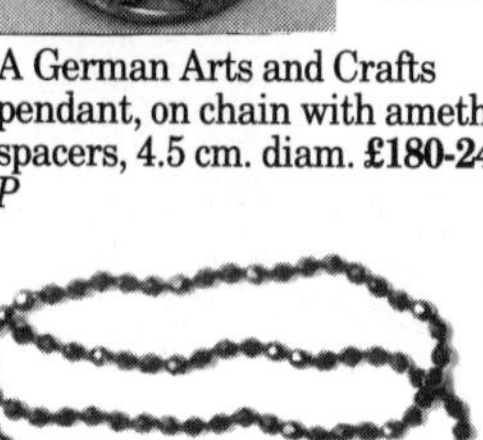

A twin string jet necklace with faceted beads, c. 1920. **£10-12** *STR*

A faceted jet choker with satin ribbon, c. 1880. **£16-20** *STR*

A jet brooch, 1½ in. diam. **£5-8** *STR*

A jet locket, 1 in. **£18-20** *STR*

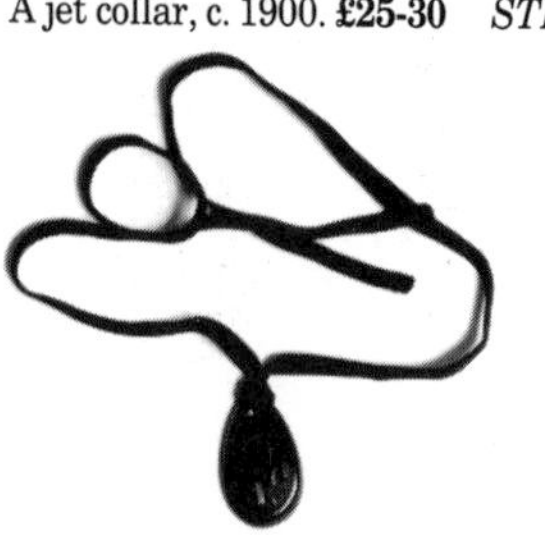

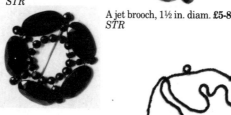

A jet pendant, 1 in. deep. **£15-20** *STR*

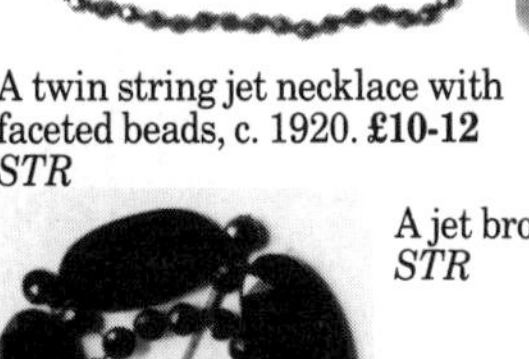

A faceted jet brooch, 2 in. diam. **£3-£5** *STR*

A jet tie-belt, 64 in. long, c. 1900. **£20-25** *STR*

A good helmet, of Savoyard type, single neck plates, some pits, early 17th C. **£1,000-1,200** *S*

A Yoko Hagi do Tosei-gusoku 60 plate hoshi-bachi kabuto, the russet iron bowl with gilded copper tehen kanemono and 3 shinodare, 5 lame ko manju shikoro, the lower plate with gilded copper kanemono, bowl signed Yoshihisa the do of nimai construction, the whole armour laced in combinations of green, red, and mauve odoshi, c. 1800, the bowl c. 1650 complete with box (kabuto only shown). **£2,500-3,000** *S*

A rare Polish Zischägge, one-piece skull with 6 radiating ribs and loop at crown, 4 lame articulated neck guard and adjustable nasal bar, late 17th C. **£900-1,000** *P*

A scarce officer's shako of the 10th Hussars, scarlet with bands of gold lace, the bosses regilt. **£750-850** *P*

Scarlet shakos were issued to the 10th Hussars in 1813 but by 1819 these had been replaced by a black shako.

A 'Spider' helmet, circular crown plate, retaining spring and 2 bars missing, probably French, 7 in. high, second half 17th C. **£600-£700** *C*

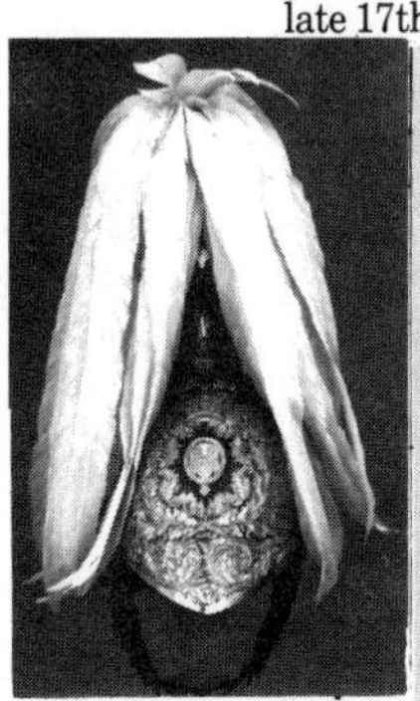

A fine helmet of the Gentleman at Arms, retaining original lining, very minor damage to chin scale, late 19th C. **£1,500-1,700** *S*

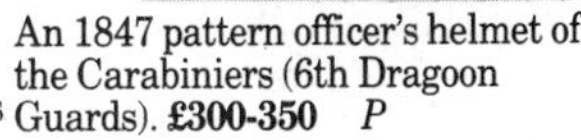

An 1847 pattern officer's helmet of the Carabiniers (6th Dragoon Guards). **£300-350** *P*

(l.) An original Nazi Old Comrades' Association peaked cap. **£30-40** *KS*

(c.) A scarce Nazi Waffen-SS peaked cap. **£165-185** *KS*

(r.) An original Nazi Luftwaffe E.M.'s peaked cap, Signals Unit Waffenfarbe. **£60-70** *KS*

An Imperial German Garde du Corps helmet, copper skull surmounted by white metal eagle, brass chin scales, slight repairs to eagle. **£350-450** *P*

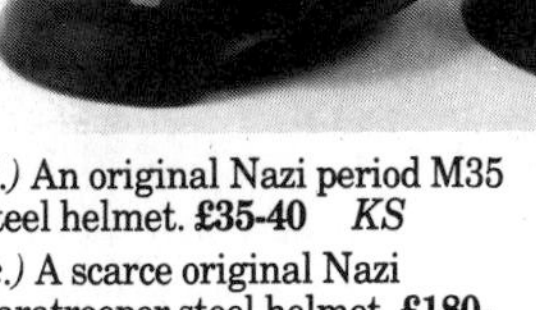

(l.) An original Nazi period M35 steel helmet. **£35-40** *KS*

(c.) A scarce original Nazi paratrooper steel helmet. **£180-£200** *KS*

(r.) An original Nazi M35 steel helmet. **£50-60** *KS*

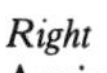

Right
A miniature suit of armour, visor a replacement, 22 in. high, 20th C. **£180-240** *S*

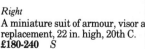

A German breast-plate, gussets repaired, the neck partly holed, 16½ in. high, c. 1530, probably Augsburg. **£550-600** *C*

Right
A full composite suit of armour. **£800-900** *PWC*

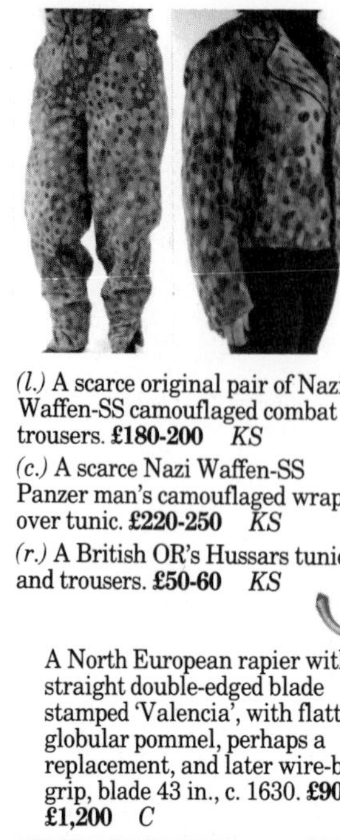

(l.) A scarce original pair of Nazi Waffen-SS camouflaged combat trousers. **£180-200** *KS*

(c.) A scarce Nazi Waffen-SS Panzer man's camouflaged wrap-over tunic. **£220-250** *KS*

(r.) A British OR's Hussars tunic and trousers. **£50-60** *KS*

A U.S. Air Force zip fronted leather 2 pocket officer's jerkin. **£50-60** *KS*

A rare couse with later haft, French or German, 22¾ in. head, late 15th C. **£1,200-1,400** *C*

A North European rapier with long straight double-edged blade stamped 'Valencia', with flattened globular pommel, perhaps a replacement, and later wire-bound grip, blade 43 in., c. 1630. **£900-£1,200** *C*

An extremely rare British early Iron Age sword and bronze scabbard, 31¾ in., c. 150 B.C.-50 A.D. **£5,000-5,500** *C*

A Dieppe ivory mounted short sword, ivory hilt, some wear to velvet, blade 48 cm., mid 19th C. **£250-300** *P*

A rare silver-gilt and enamel hilted presentation small sword with steel middle-band, point of blade repaired, by James Morisset, London, blade 32½ in., silver hallmarks for 1798. **£3,800-4,200** *C*

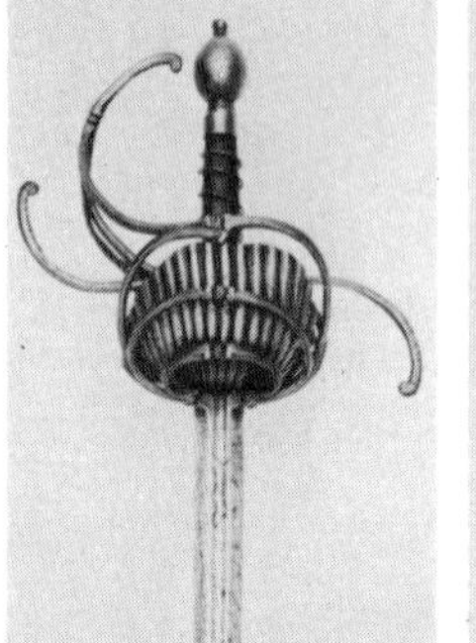

A North Italian rapier, leather covered wood grip, brazed repair to guard, 91 cm., c. 1640. **£450-500** *P*

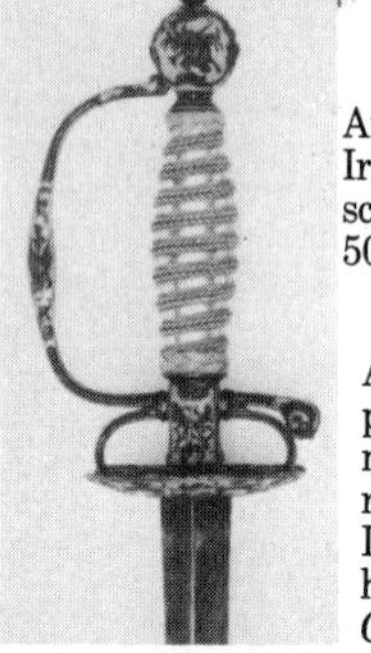

A fine French small sword, grip bound with silver-gilt wire and gold ribbon, blade 31½ in., mid 18th C. **£650-750** *C*

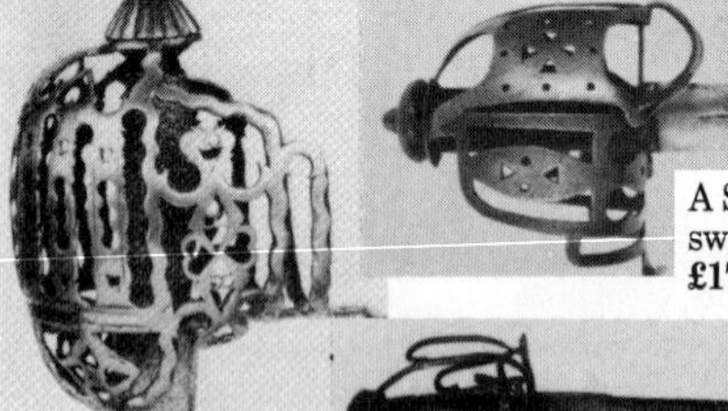

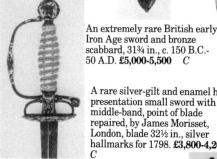

A Scottish basket hilted broad sword by J. J. Runkel, 84.5 cm. **£170-200** *L*

(l.) A Nayar temple sword, some jingles lacking, some minor rusting and pitting, 34 in., 18th C. **£120-£150** *S*

(r.) A Nayar temple sword, some pitting and rusting, 32¼ in., 18th C. **£150-200** *S*

A Scottish basket-hilted broad sword, blade with traces of inscription Andrea Ferara, re-gripped, quillon lacking, heavily worn, 33⅝ in., 18th C. **£150-200** *S*

A good signed Scottish basket hilted sword, the broadsword blade signed Andrea Ferara, signed I.G. for James Grant, blade 75 cm., mid 18th C. **£3,000-3,500** *P*

James Grant was admitted freeman of the Incorporation of Hammermen of Stirling in 1759.

A Back Sword with one broad and one narrow fuller, basket guard inscribed 3rd Bt. B.F., grip covering damaged, 42 in., late 18th C. **£300-350** *S*

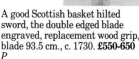

A good Scottish basket hilted sword, the double edged blade engraved, replacement wood grip, blade 93.5 cm., c. 1730. **£550-650** *P*

The fleur-de-lys in the hilt and the sun in splendour on the blade probably indicate that this sword was carried by a Scotsman in the service of France.

A Scottish regimental basket-hilted broad sword, single fuller, leather covered grip, 38⅝ in., late 19th C. **£100-130** *S*

A Scottish basket hilted sword, the broad sword blade signed Andrea Ferara, replacement wood grip, blade 81.5 cm., c. 1740. **£400-450** *P*

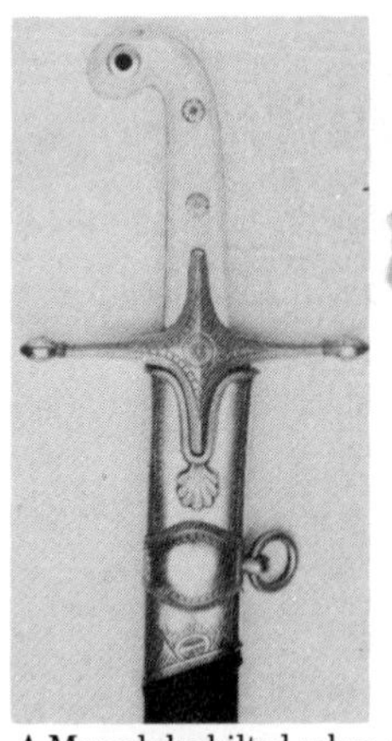

A Mameluke hilted sabre, the blade signed Hamburger Rogers & Co., 30 King St., gilt mounted hilt with ivory grips in gilt mounted leather scabbard, blade 79 cm. **£350-400** *P*

A fine Lloyd's Patriotic Fund Presentation Sword of Fifty Pounds value, the blade decorated for almost its entire length with the royal arms, Britannia, naval motifs, scrolling foliage and a presentation inscription, blade 76 cm. **£9,000-10,000** *P*

A good Indo-Persian Shamshir hilt of heavily gilded copper, a few stones replaced, 19 cm. high, early 19th C. **£750-1,000** *P*

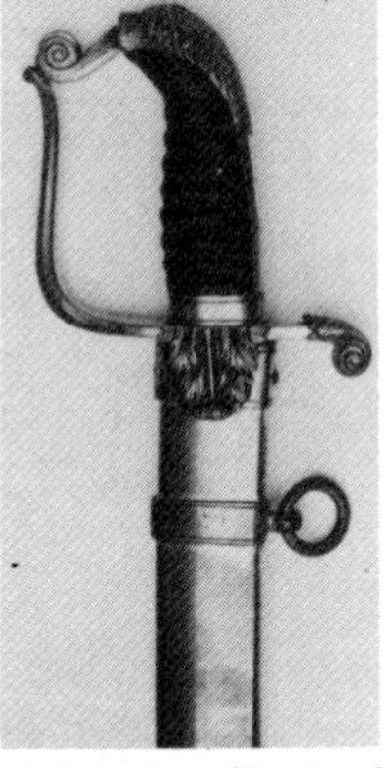

A Georgian officer's sabre, back edged blade engraved and retaining virtually all blued and gilt decoration, with maker's name Brady's, Dame St., Dublin, blade 68 cm. **£500-600** *P*

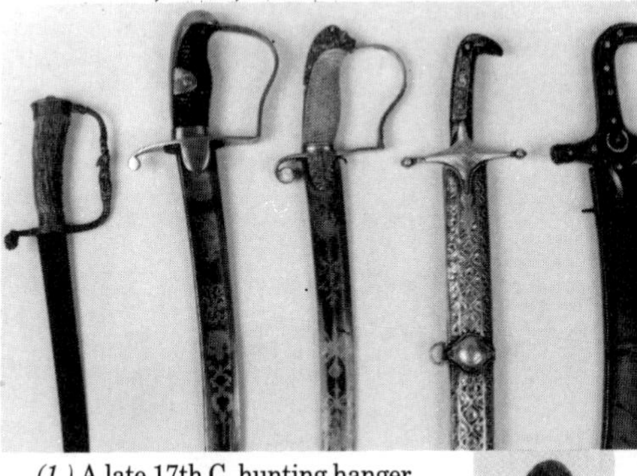

(1.) A late 17th C. hunting hanger, with curved blade bearing armourers stamp each side of man's head, blade light rust, blade 19 in. **£60-70** *KS*

(2.) A Georgian 1796 Light Cavalry officer's sword with blued and gilt blade. **£100-120** *KS*

(3.) A fine quality Georgian Light Cavalry officer's sword. **£140-160** *KS*

(4.) A scarce silver and gold mounted Turkish Shamshir with 34½ in. curved blade. **£250-300** *KS*

(5.) A scarce late 18th C. East European cavalry sabre. **£300-£350** *KS*

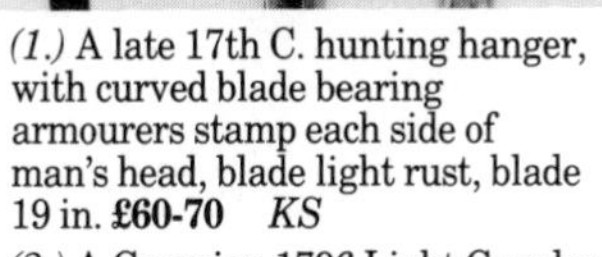

(l.) A rare Royal Air Force presentation sword with 82.5 cm. blade. **£350-400** *P*

(r.) An American Civil War presentation sabre with 80 cm. blade. **£350-400** *P*

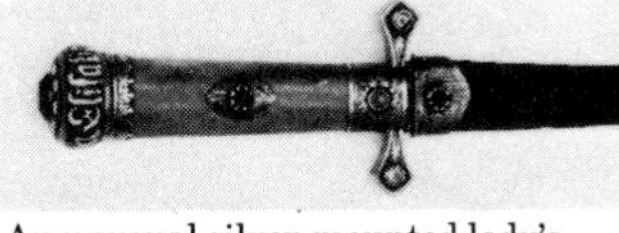

An unusual silver-mounted lady's dagger, the silver-mounted hilt inscribed Anna Elisabeth, German, blade 13 cm., c. 1600. **£550-750** *P*

A mediaeval dagger, blade of flattened diamond section inset with a copper mark, bronze quillons, chiselled iron pommel and original wire bound grip, the blade pitted, Italian ?, blade 22.5 cm., c. 1450. **£500-600** *P*

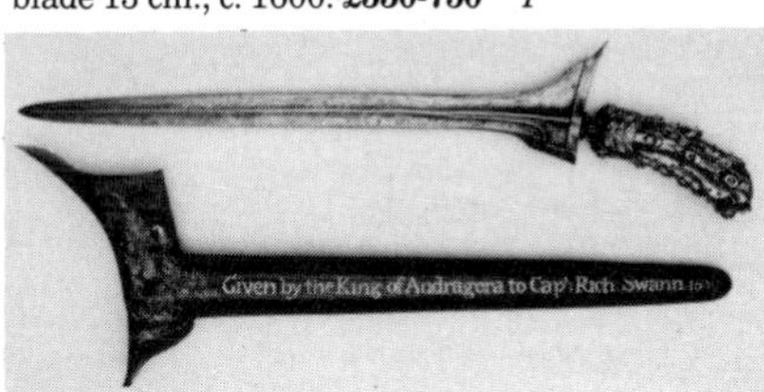

An exceptional kris, straight watered blade, gold hilt set with numerous small rubies, wooden sheath with painted decoration and inscription Given by the King of Andragera to Capt. Rich. Swann 1640, in red velvet bag, 18¼ in., 17th C. **£2,100-2,300** *S*

A silver-mounted Scottish dirk, the plain blade with back edge fuller, knife and fork en suite, the silver mounts retaining some original gilding, blade 31 cm., c. 1830. **£300-£350** *P*

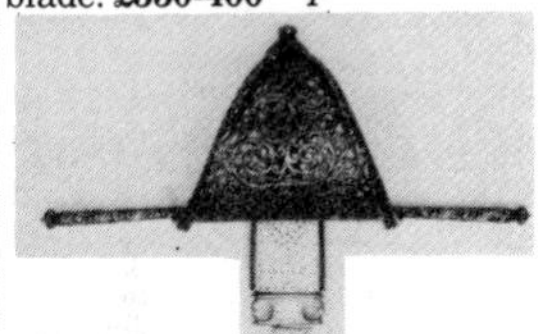

A Spanish left hand dagger, the blade pierced at the forte, the quillons and pommel decorated en suite, blade 45.5 cm., c. 1650. **£550-£750** *P*

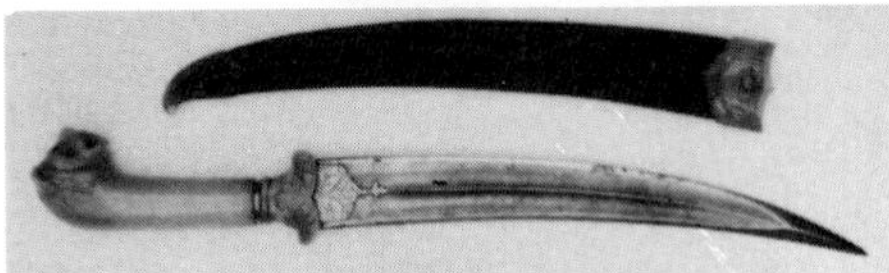

An Indian jade hilted dagger, watered steel blade, with gold koftgari scrolls, hilt set with 3 small gold-mounted rubies, velvet worn, 15⅝ in., 19th C. **£600-700** *S*

A Caucasian kindjal, 42.8 cm. **£110-140** *L*

A gold mounted kris, lower section of scabbard bound with gold wire, 20 in., 19th C. **£4,500-5,000** *S*

An Indian Khanjar with curved double-edged fullered watered blade, 13½ in., 18th/19th C. **£500-£550** *C*

An original Nazi Luftwaffe ground forces combat/boot knife. **£30-40** *KS*

An Indian Khanjar with curved double-edged fullered blade, hilt previously gold inlaid, set with foiled ruby leaves and flowers, some missing, and embossed Turkish silver-covered scabbard set with a line of turquoises, some missing, 17 in., 19th C. **£750-850** *C*

An original Nazi Luftwaffe officer's dress dagger with scabbard. **£70-£80** *KS*

A good Arab Jambiya, the horn hilt and scabbard overlaid with silver filigree decoration. **£200-250** *P*

An Irish flintlock holster pistol, twist barrel, stamped W & J Rigby Dublin, 15 in., c. 1820. **£350-400** *S*

A pair of miniature flintlock box-lock pocket pistols, by Isaac Blissett, London, Birmingham proof marks, 3¾ in., c. 1810. **£1,200-1,400** *C*

A pair of silver-mounted Queen Anne flintlock pistols, 3 stage turn-off cannon barrels, signed W. Turvey London, barrels have been lightly re-blued, 12¼ in., c. 1740. **£1,700-2,000** *S*

An unusual pair of French Empire flintlock boxlock pocket pistols, signed Boutet/Directeur/Artiste, 5⅛ in., c. 1815. **£9,000-10,000** *S*

A pair of silver-mounted flintlock pistols with barrels of Spanish form, both stocks repaired, one fore-end replaced, by Henry Hadley, London, London silver hallmarks, maker's marks JA, 12½ in., c. 1765. **£850-900** *C*

A French Model Year XIII (1804-05) halfstocked 15 bore flintlock cavalry pistol, 14 in. long. **£250-300** *WD*

A pair of all-steel flintlock highland dress pistols, unsigned, Birmingham proof marks, 10¼ in., mid 19th C. **£2,000-2,500** *C*

A Scottish flintlock pistol, signed Tho. Caddell, Doun, metal stock inlaid with silver scrolls and interlaced strapwork, with motto GANG WARILY, 14½ in., c. 1745. **£5,500-6,000** *S*

A pair of fullstocked 18 bore brass barrelled flintlock holster pistols by John Waters, 16½ in. long, c. 1770. **£850-950** *WD*

A rare flintlock 4 barrelled Duck's Foot pistol, cannon barrels numbered 1 to 4, signed Counsell, Gloucester, 11 cm. **£1,000-1,200** *P*

A Victorian percussion horse pistol by Joseph Smith, Birmingham, 14 in. **£180-220** *WW*

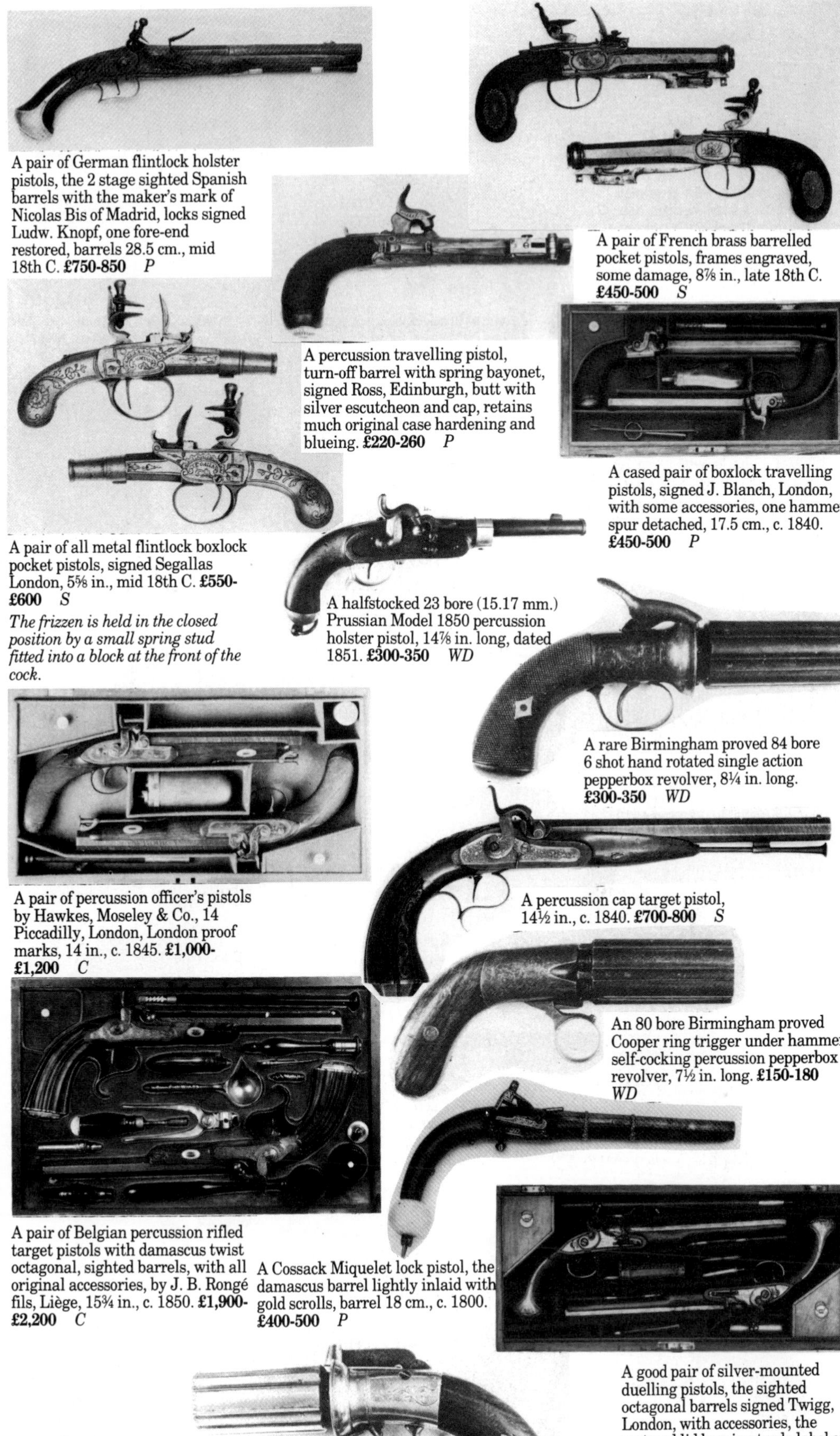

A pair of German flintlock holster pistols, the 2 stage sighted Spanish barrels with the maker's mark of Nicolas Bis of Madrid, locks signed Ludw. Knopf, one fore-end restored, barrels 28.5 cm., mid 18th C. **£750-850** *P*

A pair of French brass barrelled pocket pistols, frames engraved, some damage, 8⅞ in., late 18th C. **£450-500** *S*

A percussion travelling pistol, turn-off barrel with spring bayonet, signed Ross, Edinburgh, butt with silver escutcheon and cap, retains much original case hardening and blueing. **£220-260** *P*

A cased pair of boxlock travelling pistols, signed J. Blanch, London, with some accessories, one hammer spur detached, 17.5 cm., c. 1840. **£450-500** *P*

A pair of all metal flintlock boxlock pocket pistols, signed Segallas London, 5⅝ in., mid 18th C. **£550-£600** *S*

The frizzen is held in the closed position by a small spring stud fitted into a block at the front of the cock.

A halfstocked 23 bore (15.17 mm.) Prussian Model 1850 percussion holster pistol, 14⅞ in. long, dated 1851. **£300-350** *WD*

A rare Birmingham proved 84 bore 6 shot hand rotated single action pepperbox revolver, 8¼ in. long. **£300-350** *WD*

A pair of percussion officer's pistols by Hawkes, Moseley & Co., 14 Piccadilly, London, London proof marks, 14 in., c. 1845. **£1,000-£1,200** *C*

A percussion cap target pistol, 14½ in., c. 1840. **£700-800** *S*

An 80 bore Birmingham proved Cooper ring trigger under hammer self-cocking percussion pepperbox revolver, 7½ in. long. **£150-180** *WD*

A pair of Belgian percussion rifled target pistols with damascus twist octagonal, sighted barrels, with all original accessories, by J. B. Rongé fils, Liège, 15¾ in., c. 1850. **£1,900-£2,200** *C*

A Cossack Miquelet lock pistol, the damascus barrel lightly inlaid with gold scrolls, barrel 18 cm., c. 1800. **£400-500** *P*

A good pair of silver-mounted duelling pistols, the sighted octagonal barrels signed Twigg, London, with accessories, the restored lid bearing trade label of Henry Nock, London, barrels 25.5 cm., hallmarks for 1777. **£5,000-5,500** *P*

A rare Birmingham proved 120 bore 6 shot bar hammer self-cocking percussion pepperbox revolver, 8 in. long. **£300-350** *WD*

A pair of Catalonian Miquelet lock blunderbuss pistols, with engraved two-stage belled brass barrels, one pistol retaining its wooden ramrod, unsigned, probably Ripoll, 11 in., late 18th C. **£2,500-3,000** *C*

A pair of flintlock boxlock pocket pistols, with turn-off barrels, by John Manton, London, 6⅜ in., c. 1785. **£850-950** *C*

A nickel plated Liège proved .230 R.F. 6 shot double action revolver, case 5¾ by 3 in. **£120-150** *WD*

A rare Royal Irish Constabulary short barrelled .442 C.F. 6 shot solid frame double action revolver, barrel 2½ in. **£60-80** *WD*

A fine and rare German longwheel lock pistol, profusely inlaid with mother-of-pearl, 31¼ in., early 17th C. **£17,000-19,000** *C*

An 8 mm. squeezer palm pistol by Manufacture Francaise d'Armes des St. Etienne 'Mitrailleuse', barrel 2⅛ in. **£250-300** *SS*

A .32 calibre Smith and Wesson double action Fifth model pocket revolver, barrel 3 in. **£120-150** *WD*

A scarce .22/.32 R.F. Wheeler's patent over and under double barrelled turnover derringer, barrel 3 in. **£90-110** *WD*

A French 11 mm. model 1873 double action service revolver, manufactured at St. Etienne in 1882, in its original service holster, barrel 4½ in. **£200-250** *WD*

A .320 R.F. 6 shot Birmingham proved solid frame single action pocket revolver retailed by 'H. Allport & Sons, Cork', barrel 3½ in. **£40-50** *WD*

A nickel plated .442 C.F. 6 shot solid frame double action Webley First Model R.I.C. revolver, barrel 4½ in. **£80-100** *WD*

A 10 bore Federal Laboratories Inc. pistol truncheon, serial no. 2469, 9 in. **£80-100** *WD*

A Birmingham proved .450 C.F. 5 shot top break self-extracting double action pocket revolver, barrel 3¼ in. **£70-90** *WD*

A Birmingham proved .450 C.F. 5 shot solid frame double action pocket revolver, serial no. 30, barrel 3 in. **£160-200** *WD*

A rare London proved 6 mm. C. F. Turbiaux pattern 10 shot squeezer palm pistol, 4⅛ in. **£180-220** *WD*

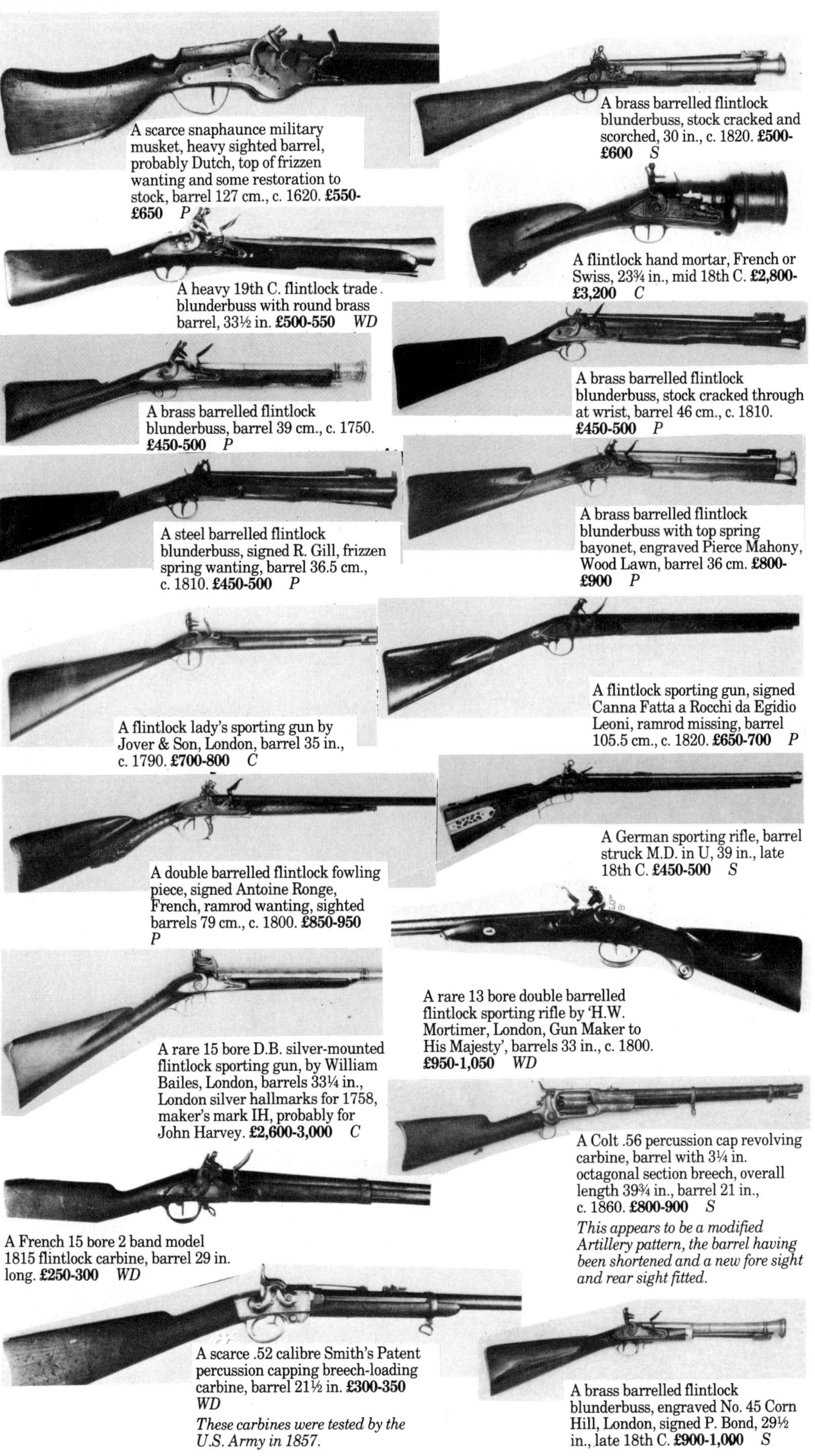

A scarce snaphaunce military musket, heavy sighted barrel, probably Dutch, top of frizzen wanting and some restoration to stock, barrel 127 cm., c. 1620. **£550-£650** *P*

A brass barrelled flintlock blunderbuss, stock cracked and scorched, 30 in., c. 1820. **£500-£600** *S*

A flintlock hand mortar, French or Swiss, 23¾ in., mid 18th C. **£2,800-£3,200** *C*

A heavy 19th C. flintlock trade blunderbuss with round brass barrel, 33½ in. **£500-550** *WD*

A brass barrelled flintlock blunderbuss, stock cracked through at wrist, barrel 46 cm., c. 1810. **£450-500** *P*

A brass barrelled flintlock blunderbuss, barrel 39 cm., c. 1750. **£450-500** *P*

A steel barrelled flintlock blunderbuss, signed R. Gill, frizzen spring wanting, barrel 36.5 cm., c. 1810. **£450-500** *P*

A brass barrelled flintlock blunderbuss with top spring bayonet, engraved Pierce Mahony, Wood Lawn, barrel 36 cm. **£800-£900** *P*

A flintlock lady's sporting gun by Jover & Son, London, barrel 35 in., c. 1790. **£700-800** *C*

A flintlock sporting gun, signed Canna Fatta a Rocchi da Egidio Leoni, ramrod missing, barrel 105.5 cm., c. 1820. **£650-700** *P*

A double barrelled flintlock fowling piece, signed Antoine Ronge, French, ramrod wanting, sighted barrels 79 cm., c. 1800. **£850-950** *P*

A German sporting rifle, barrel struck M.D. in U, 39 in., late 18th C. **£450-500** *S*

A rare 15 bore D.B. silver-mounted flintlock sporting gun, by William Bailes, London, barrels 33¼ in., London silver hallmarks for 1758, maker's mark IH, probably for John Harvey. **£2,600-3,000** *C*

A rare 13 bore double barrelled flintlock sporting rifle by 'H.W. Mortimer, London, Gun Maker to His Majesty', barrels 33 in., c. 1800. **£950-1,050** *WD*

A French 15 bore 2 band model 1815 flintlock carbine, barrel 29 in. long. **£250-300** *WD*

A Colt .56 percussion cap revolving carbine, barrel with 3¼ in. octagonal section breech, overall length 39¾ in., barrel 21 in., c. 1860. **£800-900** *S*

This appears to be a modified Artillery pattern, the barrel having been shortened and a new fore sight and rear sight fitted.

A scarce .52 calibre Smith's Patent percussion capping breech-loading carbine, barrel 21½ in. **£300-350** *WD*

These carbines were tested by the U.S. Army in 1857.

A brass barrelled flintlock blunderbuss, engraved No. 45 Corn Hill, London, signed P. Bond, 29½ in., late 18th C. **£900-1,000** *S*

A .54 calibre Burnside percussion cap breech-loading cavalry carbine, barrel 21 in. **£250-300** *WD*

A Colt .56 side-hammer 5 shot percussion revolving military rifle, London proof marks, barrel 28¼ in. long, mid 19th C. **£500-600** *C*

A 14 bore double barrelled percussion Constabulary carbine, barrels slightly shortened and some stock damage, barrels 25¼ in. **£200-250** *WD*

A Colt .56 side-hammer 5 shot percussion revolving carbine 'Patented Sept. 10th 1850', London proof marks, barrel 21 in., mid 19th C. **£1,500-1,700** *C*

A .577 3 band P53 Enfield percussion rifle, barrel 39 in. **£400-£450** *WD*

A .360 No. 5 nitro express top lever double barrelled hammer rifle by 'Army & Navy C.S.L. London', barrels 27 in. **£600-650** *WD*

An 11 mm. R.F. improved Remington pattern rolling block 2 band infantry rifle, bearing Birmingham proof marks. **£200-£250** *WD*

A double barrell 8 bore hammer shotgun by E. M. Reilly & Co., Nitro proof. **£1,000-1,200** *P*

A French 11 mm. 2 band improved Chassepot needle fire bolt action military rifle, barrel 32½ in. **£350-£400** *WD*

A Spanish Miquelet lock fowling-piece, signed Manuel Orbea, Madrid, barrel 37½ in., early 19th C. **£1,900-2,100** *C*

A pair of D.B. 12 bore sidelock extra quality Victor ejector sporting guns by Cogswell & Harrison Ltd., nitro proof. **£2,800-£3,200** *L*

A fine Spanish Madrid lock sporting gun with 2 stage barrel signed and dated in gold and inlaid with gold at the muzzle and breech, with original horn-tipped ramrod, by Joseph Cano of Madrid, barrel 38¾ in., dated 1750. **£4,000-4,500** *C*

A .303 British Bren light machine gun, serial no. D7784, dated '1940', barrel 22 in. **£180-220** *WD*

A large Flemish crossbow with steel bow, string missing, complete with windlass, strings replaced, late 17th C. **£1,200-1,400** *C*

A 7.92 mm. British Vickers MK I heavy machine gun, serial No. ET 146, on its MK IVB tripod, barrel 28½ in. **£500-550** *WD*

A scarce 9 mm. P. World War I German Bergmann MP 18 sub-machine gun, barrel 8 in. **£400-£450** *WD*

A Victorian Fifeshire Artillery volunteer officer's shako badge. **£300-350** *SS*

A Victorian militia Artillery officer's shako badge, plated, c. 1857. **£65-75** *SS*

Don Cossack Troops, central emblem below ribbon and badge of St. George, wreath around, 49 mm. high. **£350-400** *C*

A Georgian Artillery officer's shoulder belt plate, silvered, gilded and enamelled, c. 1824-33. **£130-160** *SS*

Moscow Regiment of the Imperial Guard, blue enamel cross with letters S.A.P.R. at the end of arms, 40 mm. high. **£60-80** *C*

Eighth Astrakhan Dragoon Regiment of Field Marshal Grand Duke Nicholas Nikolaevich, 48 mm. high. **£180-220** *C*

Seventeenth Chernigov Hussar Regiment of Grand Duke Michael Alexandrovich. **£120-150** *C*

Nicholas Naval Academy, Imperial Eagle on wreath of oak and laurel leaves, gilt anchors. **£160-200** *C*

Grenadier Regiment of the Imperial Guard, black enamel cross with inscription Virtuti Militari, Polish eagle in centre, 44 mm. high. **£200-250** *C*

Alexis Military School, Moscow, red enamel cross, gilt swords, double-headed eagle and monogram, 50 mm. high. **£140-£180** *C*

Headquarters of the Imperial Guard and the St. Petersburg Military District, St. Andrew's star, 45 mm. high. **£70-90** *C*

A rare Schellenbaum banner, Flying Section, 32 by 30 cm. **£550-£600** *SS*

A good post-02 R.A.M.C. officer's blue cloth helmet by D. Jones, Military Outfitters, Manchester. **£150-200** *SS*

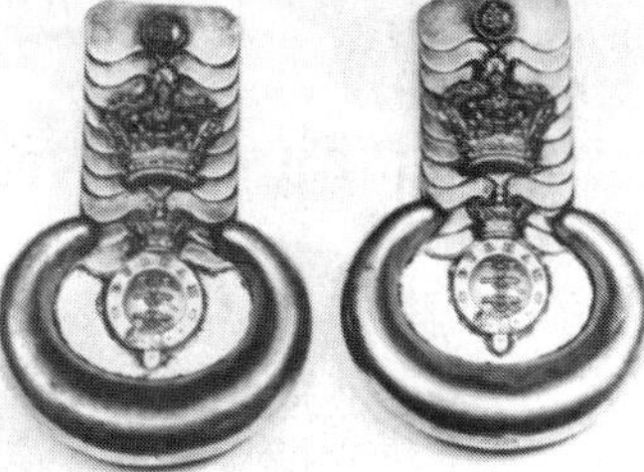

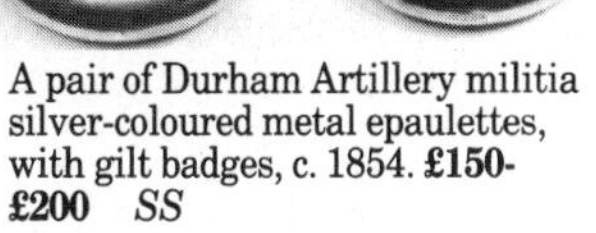

A pair of Durham Artillery militia silver-coloured metal epaulettes, with gilt badges, c. 1854. **£150-£200** *SS*

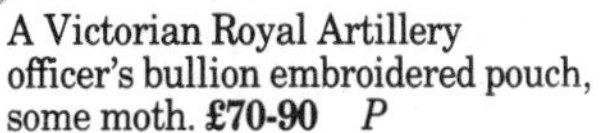

A Victorian Royal Artillery officer's bullion embroidered pouch, some moth. **£70-90** *P*

St. Petersburg Regiment of the Imperial Guard, black cross (Kulm cross), 38 mm. high. **£70-90** *C*

CRAFTS

Whereas the antiques we collect today were handmade by craftsmen and artist-craftsmen, most of the furniture, jewellery, ceramics and textiles we buy today — to be collected tomorrow — are machine-made. Mass production is the essence of our present society but it does not replace the artistic inspiration and the skill of the contemporary potter, jeweller or weaver. These artist-craftsmen are the creators of new directions and it is their work that will be the highly valued antiques of the future. They need and deserve the public support of the more adventurous collector.

Art pottery and studio ceramics are already fields that are growing in popularity and Sotheby's have successful sales in these fields. Although most such work sells in the hundreds of pounds, bowls by living potters Lucie Rie and Elizabeth Fritsch have reached several thousands of pounds. The same will undoubtedly happen with as yet unknown young potters, and the collector with a good eye can make an exciting collection in any crafts field for a relatively small amount of money. There is not yet a saleroom market in craft fields other than pottery, but it is only a matter of time before there is one.

The work of the artist-craftsman illustrated in this section has been selected from the output of leaders in their fields. Space does not permit a full inclusion. Wherever possible two photographs have been provided, with descriptions and with comparative prices of the earlier and later works. The work of the same artist-craftsman can vary in price, for like all artistic efforts some pieces are more successful than others. Like antiques, crafts are subject to fashion. There are times when the work of a new star on the horizon commands more than an established craftsman.

Creative people develop their styles and in the case of craftsmen they can also change their materials and techniques. Chances are that you will be unable to get a creative jeweller to repeat a piece or a style of the past.

There is a great satisfaction in buying the work of a living artist and there is the added advantage of being able to commission, either directly or through a gallery, a piece made expressly for you. Because these craftsmen are artistic people it can be easier, if more expensive, to commission work through a Gallery which will take on all the responsibility for the commission and its delivery. The British Crafts Council has an Index with slides of the work of all its members. There is a well-illustrated magazine, "Crafts", which features the work of young craftsmen as well as those who are well established. There are a number of craft shops and galleries throughout the country that have been approved for quality by the Crafts Council.

"Crafts" 12 Waterloo Place, Lower Regent Street, London SW1 4AU. Annual subscription £9. Single copy £1.50. **Crafts Council Gallery** 12 Waterloo Place, London SW1 4AU. Tel. 01-930 4811. **British Crafts Centre** 43 Earlham Street, London WC2H 9LD. Tel. 01-836 6993. **Victoria and Albert Museum Crafts Shop.**

'House' decorated cigarette lighters by Karel Bartosik, in silver with 18 ct., 9 ct. gold and acrylic resin decoration, 60 mm. high. **£500-700** each

Similar lighter 1975 £300-400.

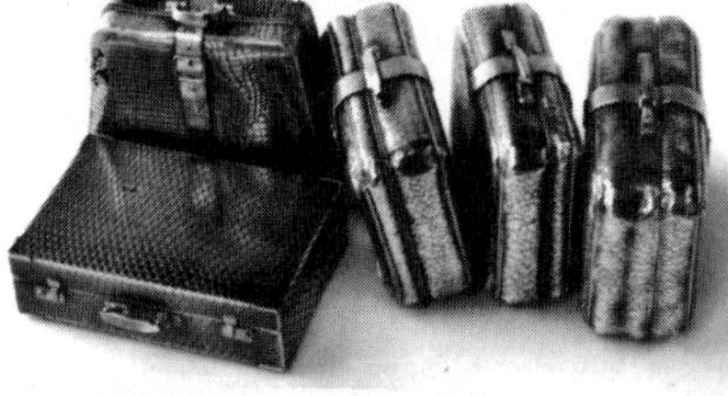

Handmade textured silver 'suitcase' pill boxes by Karel Bartosik, with gold trim, with fitted interiors. **£650-750**

Similar 'suitcase' in 1975 £200-400.

A large silver bowl by Gerald Benney, with red enamel decoration, 16 cm. diam., 1977 price **£675**

An oxidised painted red earthenware jug by Alison Britton, 1977. **£60**

A handbuilt ceramic vessel by Alison Britton, of high-fired earthenware with inlaid and painted surfaces, 1980-81. **£150-£225**

Broken and nearly broken brooches by Caroline Broadhead, in silver and ivory, 1976. **£35** each

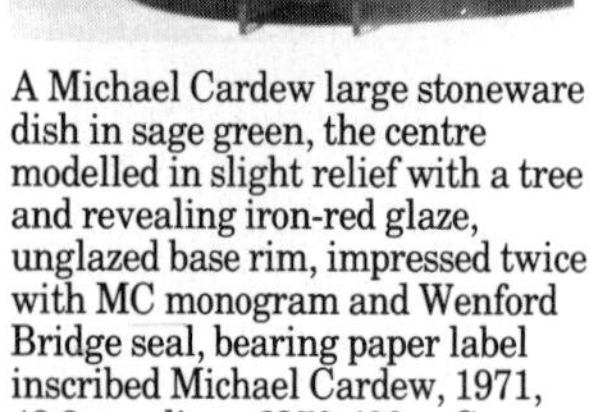

A Michael Cardew large stoneware dish in sage green, the centre modelled in slight relief with a tree and revealing iron-red glaze, unglazed base rim, impressed twice with MC monogram and Wenford Bridge seal, bearing paper label inscribed Michael Cardew, 1971, 42.2 cm. diam. **£350-400** *C*

A glazed earthenware dish by Michael Cardew, with slip trailing marks, Collection V. & A. Museum, 31.5 cm. diam., 1926-30, 1982 price **£300-400**

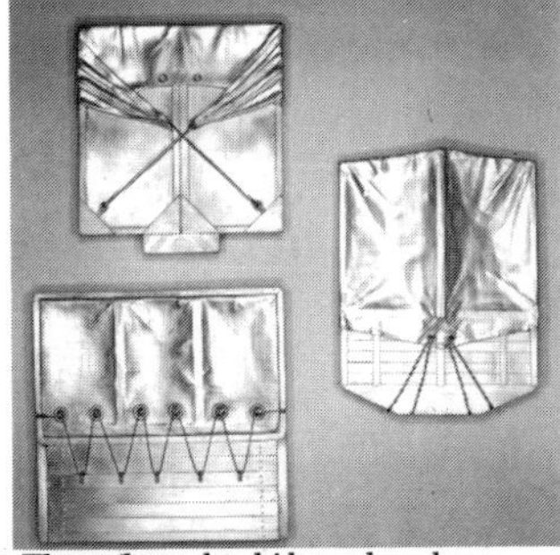

Three 'lorry back' brooches, by Rosamund Conway, fine and sterling silver with gold wires. 1974/75. **£100-150**

A flat pot with circular body, by Hans Coper, oxidised stoneware, 14¼ in. by 12 in. by 4 in., 1972 price **£60**. Current value. **£650-750**

A multi-coloured blown glass bowl by Sam Herman; in 1968 Herman's bowls sold for about £10. 1982 prices **£50-250**

A necklace and matching bracelet by Caroline Broadhead with outer silver bands containing multi-coloured threads, 1979. Necklace and bracelet **£65**

Two hand-built stoneware pots, painted with coloured slips, designed and made by Elizabeth Fritsch. 1974 price **£40-90**

A Pilgrim plate of reduced stoneware by Bernard Leach, with tenmoku glaze over dark celadon glaze, thrown, paper resist technique, 32 cm. diam., c. 1960-65. *A Pilgrim dish in Sotheby's October 1982 sale reached £1,300.*

Three triangular brooches by Rosamund Conway, silver inlaid with yellow, red, white and green gold, chased hollow bodies made in two halves and soldered together. 1978. **£120** each

A rare Hans Coper stoneware vase, tooled with spiralling rings and covered in a matt beige glaze with patches of brown, minor restoration to neck, 25 cm. high. **£1,400-£1,800** *C*

A necklace of fused silver beads and ivory beads by David Poston. 1975 **£75-125.** 1982 **£150-300**

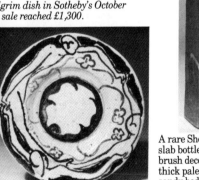

An unusual Omega workshop's pottery dish with everted rim, painted in blue, black and red, probably by Duncan Grant, impressed Omega symbol on reverse, 23 cm. diam. **£250-300** *P*

A rare Shoji Hamada stoneware slab bottle, with white and brown brush decoration on a separating thick pale grey glaze on a reddish-sandy body, 19.2 cm. high. **£1,000-£1,200** *C*

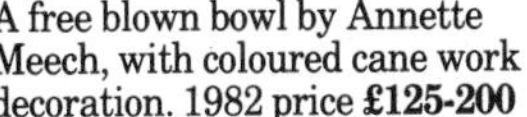

A free blown bowl by Annette Meech, with coloured cane work decoration. 1982 price **£125-200**

A handmade bowl by Jim Partridge. 1980 price **£25-30.** 1982 price **£45-£55**

A porcelain bowl by Lucie Rie, glazed in a translucent deep green, the rim banded in a lustrous bronze/brown dribbling down the sides, impressed LR seal, 10.4 cm., 1970's. **£380-460** *S*

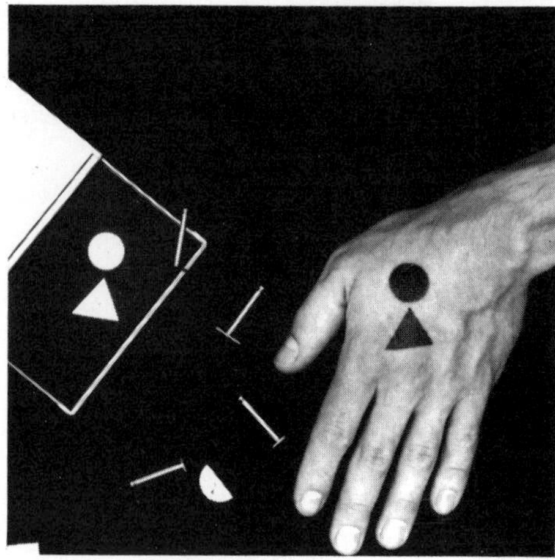

A printing set for body decoration by Wendy Ramshaw, shapes available in many variations. 1982 price **£95**

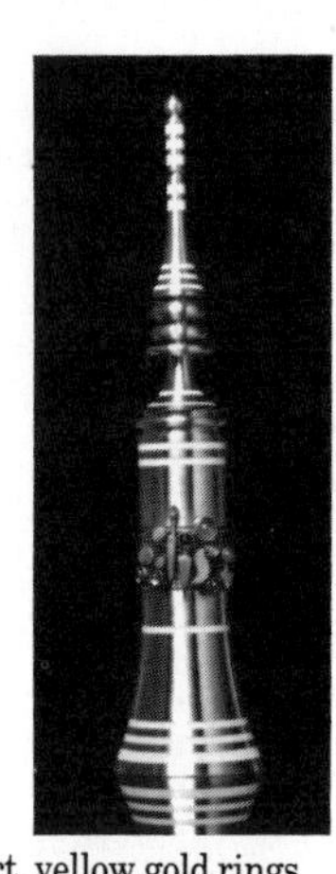

A set of 12 18 ct. yellow gold rings by Wendy Ramshaw, with blue and pink sapphires, amethysts and agate and gold shapes, mounted on a brass column inlaid with bands of white. 1981 price **£300-600.** Similar rings in the early 1970's were **£100-£200.**

A blown glass jug with 'wings' by Steven Newell. 1980 **£20.** 1983 **£30-£40**

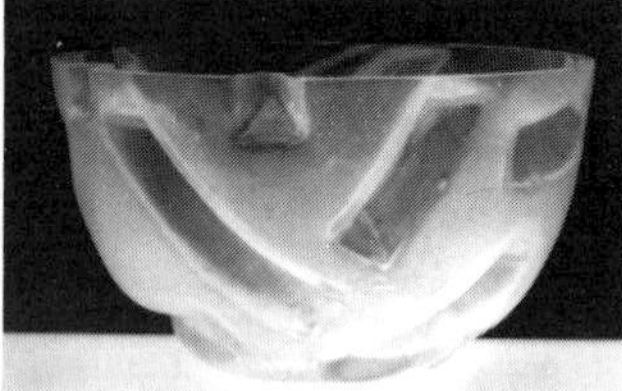

A mould blown bowl with sand blasted and acid polished surface, by Christopher Williams. 1981 price **£125.** 1982 **£200-350**

Christopher Williams also specialises in lighting fixtures, bowls and goblets.

A blown glass plate by Steven Newell, sand blasted engraving. 1982 price **£250-300**

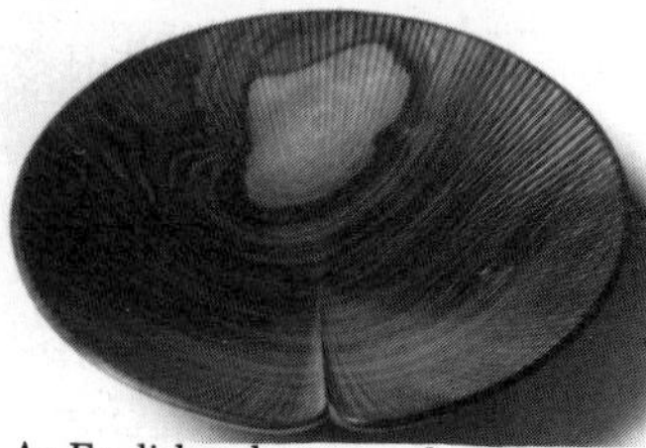

An English walnut carved wooden dish by David Pye, with radiating flutes on the inside, the outside carved and finished with a spokeshave. 1975 **£75.** 1983 **£125+**

A silver torque by Edward Delarge, with silver and titanium pendant. 1982 price **£300+**

Delarge's early necklaces sold in the range of £100-150 in the 1970's.

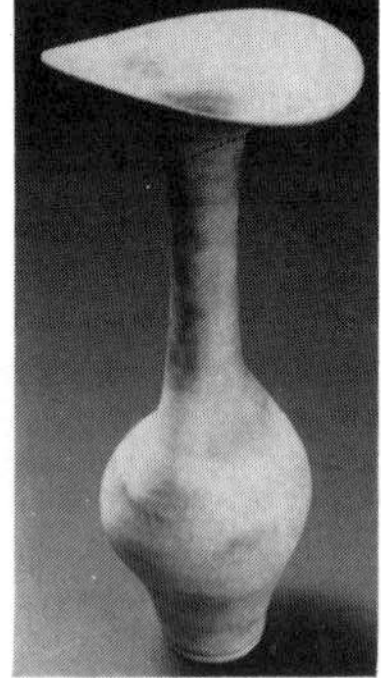

An oxidised stoneware bottle by Lucie Rie, with oxide in the body and crazed glaze, 38 cm. high, made in 1967. 1972 price **£54**

Prices for Rie's work have at least trebled in the last 20 years and her work has fetched thousands of pounds in the salerooms recently.

A hand-carved wooden bowl by David Pye, 1977 price **£54**

Pye's prices have doubled in the past 5 years.

Necklaces of hand-turned white jasper pendants suspended from nickel alloy and gold wires, made by Wendy Ramshaw in conjunction with Wedgwood, exhibited at the Victoria and Albert Museum. 1982 price **£500**

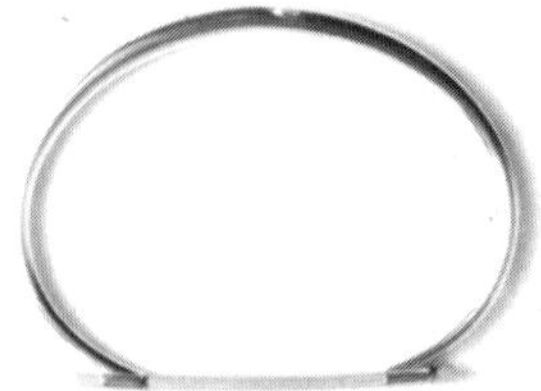

A stainless steel bracelet by David Poston, with bamboo under tension. 1979 **£80.** 1983 **£120**

DIRECTORY OF SPECIALISTS

This directory is in no way complete. If you wish to be included in next year's directory, or you have a change of address or telephone number, please could you inform us before April 1st, 1984. Finally we would advise readers to make contact by telephone before a visit is made, therefore avoiding a wasted journey, which nowadays is both time consuming and expensive.
Any entry followed by (R) denotes a specialist who undertakes restoration work.

ART DECO & ART NOUVEAU

LONDON

Antique Emporium
965 Fulham Rd., S.W.5
Tel: 01-731 2814

Butler & Wilson
189 Fulham Rd., S.W.3
Tel: 01-352 3045

Chilton
Stand A11/12, Chenil Galleries
181-183 King's Rd., S.W.3
No tel.

T. Coakley
Stand D13, Chenil Galleries
181-183 King's Rd., S.W.3
Tel: 01-351-2914

Cobra & Bellamy
149 Sloane St., S.W.1
Tel: 01-730 2823

Cobweb
2 Englands Lane, N.W.3
Tel: 01-586 4605

Ebury
89 Ebury St., S.W.1
Tel: 01-730 3341

Editions Graphiques Gallery
3 Clifford St., W.1
Tel: 01-734 3944

The Facade
196 Westbourne Grove, W.11
Tel: 01-727 2159

Galerie 1900
267 Camden High St., N.W.1
(*also at* 80 Grosvenor St., W.1)
Tel: 01-485 1001

Galerie Moderne
8 Halkin Arcade
Motcomb St., S.W.1
Tel: 01-235 8353

Gallery '25
4 Halkin Arcade, Motcomb St., S.W.1
Tel: 01-235 5178

David Gill (appointment only)
25 Palace Gate, W.8
Tel: 01-584 9184

Jones
194 Westbourne Grove, W.11
Tel: 01-229 6866

Lewis M. Kaplan Associates Ltd.
50 Fulham Rd., S.W.3
Tel: 01-589 3108

Dan Klein Ltd.
11-12 Halkin Arcade,
Motcomb St., S.W.1
Tel: 01-245 9868

Lighting Lee (Antique Forum Ltd.)
Stand 324/5 Alfie's Antique Market
13-25 Church St., N.W.8
Tel: 01-286 0859

John & Diana Lyons Gallery
47-49 Mill Lane, West Hampstead
N.W.6
Tel: 01-794 3537

Pruskin Gallery
183 King's Road, S.W.3
Tel: 01-352 9095

SURREY

Peter & Debbie Gooday
20 Richmond Hill, Richmond
Tel: 01-940 8652

SUSSEX

Armstrong-Davis Gallery
The Square, Arundel
Tel: (0903) 882752

WARKS.

Studio
Warwick Antique Centre
High St., Warwick
Tel: Warwick 41382

YORKS.

Dragon Antiques
10 Dragon Rd., Harrogate
Tel: (0423) 62037

SCOTLAND

The Rendezvous Gallery
100 Forest Ave., Aberdeen
Tel: (0224) 323247

BOXES, TREEN & WOODEN OBJECTS

LONDON

Simon Castle
38B Kensington Church St. W.8
Tel: 01-937 2268

Halcyon Days
14 Brook St., W.1
Tel: 01-629 8811

AVON

Andrew Dando
4 Wood St., Queen Sq., Bath
Tel: (0225) 22702

BERKS.

Charles Toller
20 High St., Datchet
Tel: (0753) 42903

BUCKS.

A. & E. Foster
Little Heysham, Forge Rd., Naphill
Tel: (024024) 2024

HANTS.

House of Antiques
4 College St., Petersfield
Tel: (0730) 62172

KENT

Imogen Nichols Antiques
The Farriers Cottage
St. Nicholas-at-Wade, Nr. Birchington
Tel: (0843) 81237

LEICS.

Stable Antiques
14 Loughborough Rd., Hoton
Nr. Loughborough
Tel: (0509) 880208

CAMERAS

LONDON

Sean Sexton
Stand 606, Alfie's Antique Market
13-25 Church St., N.W.8
Tel: 01-723 1370

Vintage Cameras Ltd.
254/256 Kirkdale, Sydenham, S.E.26
Tel: 01-778 5416

CLOCKS & BAROMETERS

LONDON

Asprey & Co. PLC
165-169 New Bond St., W.1
Tel: 01-493 6767

Bobinet Ltd.
102 Mount St., W.1
Tel: 01-408 0333/4

Aubrey Brocklehurst
124 Cromwell Rd., S.W.7
Tel: 01-373 0319

Camerer Cuss & Co.
17 Ryder St., St. James's, S.W.1
Tel: 01-930 1941

J. Carlton Smith
17 Ryder St., St. James's, S.W.1
Tel: 01-930 6622

The Clock Clinic Ltd.
85 Lower Richmond Rd., S.W.15
Tel: 01-788 1407

John Craggs Ltd.
15/17 King St., St. James's, S.W.1
Tel: 01-930 3817

Philip & Bernard Dombey
174 Kensington Church St., W.8
Tel: 01-229 7100

Garner & Marney Ltd.
41/43 Southgate Rd., N.1
Tel: 01-226 1535

Keith Harding, F.B.H.I. (R)
93 Hornsey Rd., N.7
Tel: 01-607 6181/2672

E. Hollander Ltd.
80 Fulham Rd., S.W.3
Tel: 01-589 7239

North London Clock Shop Ltd. (R)
72 Highbury Park, N.5
Tel: 01-226 1609

R. E. Rose, F.B.H.I.
731 Sidcup Rd., Eltham, S.E.9
Tel: 01-859 4754

Strike One (Islington) Ltd.
51 Camden Passage, N.1
Tel: 01-226 9709

Temple Brooks
12 Mill Lane, N.W.6
Tel: 01-452 9696

Volpone
12 Wynyatt St., Clerkenwell, E.C.1
Tel: 01-837 5686

AVON

The Clock Shop
9 Walcot St., Bath
Tel: (0225) 62756

Smith & Bottrill
The Clock House, 17 George St., Bath
Tel: (0225) 22809

BERKS.

Medalcrest Ltd.
Charnham House, Charnham St.
Hungerford
Tel: (0488) 84157

The Old Malthouse
15 Bridge St., Hungerford
Tel: (04886) 2209

Times Past Antiques Ltd.
59 High St., Eton
Tel: Windsor 57018

BUCKS.

The Guild Room, The Lee
Great Missenden
Tel: (024020) 463

CAMBS.

Rodney T. Firmin
16 Magdalene St., Cambridge
Tel: (0223) 67372

CHESHIRE

Peter Bosson Antiques
10B Swan St., Wilmslow
Tel: (0625) 525250/527857

Coppelia Antiques
Holford Lodge, Plumley Moor Rd.
Plumley
Tel: (056581) 2197

CORNWALL

Charles Jackson Antiques
48, 49 & 50 Market Jew St., Penzance
Tel: (0736) 4388/3774

CUMBRIA

The Old Man Antiques
Coniston
Tel: (09664) 389

DERBYS.

Derby Clocks
974 London Rd., Derby
Tel: (0332) 74996

DORSET

Tom Tribe & Son
Bridge St., Sturminster Newton
Tel: (0258) 72311

ESSEX

It's About Time
863 London Rd., Westcliff-on-Sea
Tel: (0702) 72574/205204

Littlebury Antiques
58/60 Fairycroft Rd., Saffron Walden
Tel: (0799) 27961

Simpson Antiques
44 Lower St., Stanstead Mountfichet
Tel: (0279) 813388

Tempus Fugit (appointment only)
c/o Trinity House, Trinity St., Halstead
Tel: (0787) 475409

Trinity Clocks
26 Trinity St., Colchester
Tel: (0206) 46458

GLOS.

J. & M. Bristow Antiques
28 Long St., Tetbury
Tel: (0666) 52222

Michael G. Cox (appointment only)
Avon House, Market Place, Tetbury
Tel: (0666) 52201

George Curtis
14 Suffolk Parade, Cheltenham
Tel: (0242) 513828

Colin Elliott
4 Great Norwood St., Cheltenham
Tel: (0242) 28590

Saxton House Gallery
High St., Chipping Camden
Tel: (0386) 840278

HANTS.

Charles Antiques
101 The Hundred, Romsey
Tel: (0794) 512885

E. F. P. Dobson
6 Valley Rd., Chandlers Ford
Tel: (04215) 2335

Evans & Evans
40 West St., Alresford
Tel: (096273) 2170

Gerald E. Marsh
32A The Square, Winchester
Tel: (0962) 54505

HERTS.

Country Clocks (R)
3 Pendley Bridge Cottages
Tring Station, Tring
Tel: (044282) 5090

John de Haan
12A Seaforth Drive, Waltham Cross
Tel: (0992) 763111 & (0920) 2534

KENT

Nigel Coleman Antiques
High St., Brasted
Tel: (0959) 64042

Hadlow Antiques
No. 1 The Pantiles, Tunbridge Wells
Tel: (0892) 29858

Henry Hall Antique Clocks
19 Market Square, Westerham
Tel: (0959) 62200

Imperial Antiques
1 Royal Parade, Chislehurst
Tel: 01-467 8020

The Old Clock Shop
63 High St., West Malling
Tel: (0732) 843246

Derek Roberts Antiques
24 Shipbourne Rd., Tonbridge
Tel: (0732) 358986

LEICS.

G. K. Hadfield
Blackbrook Hill House
Tickow Lane, Shepshed
Tel: (05095) 3014

MERSEYSIDE

T. Brown, Horological Restorers (R)
12 London Rd., Liverpool 3
Tel: (051709) 4048

MIDDX.

Court House Antiques
19 Market Place, Brentford
Tel: 01-560 7074 & (09322) 27186

Onslow Clocks
36 Church St., Twickenham
Tel: 01-892 7632

NORFOLK

Delawood Antiques & Clock
Restoration (R)
10 Westgate, Hunstanton
Tel: (04853) 2903

NORTHUMBERLAND

Prudhoe Cottage Antiques
15 St. Mary's Chare, Hexham
Tel: (0434) 605522 & (0661) 33421

OXON.

Peter Fell of Thame
81 High St., Thame
Tel: (084421) 4487

Laurie Leigh Antiques
36 High St., Oxford
Tel: (0865) 244197

Telling Time Antiques (R)
42 Park St., Thame
Tel: (084421) 3007

Witney Antiques
96-98 Corn St., Witney
Tel: (0993) 3902

SOMERSET

Bernard G. House, Mitre Antiques
13 Market Place, Wells
Tel: (0749) 72607

Edward A. Nowell
21-23 Market Place, Wells
Tel: (0749) 72415

Matthew Willis, Antique Clocks
22 Silver St., Glastonbury
Tel: (0458) 32103

SUFFOLK

Bullivant Antiques (R)
White Gates, Elmswell Rd.
Great Ashfield
Tel: (0359) 40040

Score Antiques
1 & 2 The Score, Beccles
Tel: (0473) 2927

SURREY

Abbott Antiques (appointment only)
158 Ember Lane, Esher
Tel: 01-398 2984

The Clock Shop
64 Church St., Weybridge
Tel: (0932) 40407/55503

Roger A. Davis
Antiquarian Horologist
19 Dorking Rd., Great Bookham
Tel: (0372) 57655/53167

Horological Workshops
204 Worplesdon Rd., Guildford
Tel: (0483) 576496

Geoffrey Stevens
26-28 Church Road, Guildford
Tel: (0483) 504075

Surrey Clock Centre
3 Lower St., Haslemere
Tel: (0428) 4547

SUSSEX

Adrian Alan Ltd.
4 Frederick Place, Brighton
Tel: (0273) 25277

Bay Tree House Ltd.
19 Middle St., Brighton
Tel: (0273) 24688

The Clock Shop
51 London Rd., St. Leonards-on-Sea
Tel: (0424) 436984

WILTS.

Andre Davis Ltd.
Church House, 26 High St.
Bromham, Chippenham
Tel: (0380) 850347

YORKS.

The Clock Shop
Hilltop House
Bellerby, Nr. Leyburn
Tel: (0969) 22596

The Dusty Miller Gallery
Low Laithe, Pateley Bridge
Tel: (0423) 780515

Windsor House Antiques (Leeds) Ltd.
18-20 Benson St., Leeds
Tel: (0532) 444666

SCOTLAND

Browns of Argyle St. Ltd.
1060 Argyle St., Glasgow
Tel: (041) 248 6760

Dareau Antique Clocks
66 Cumberland St., Edinburgh
Tel: (031) 556 0352

Christopher Wood (appointment only)
Harlaw House, Kelso
Tel: (05737) 321

WALES

Derek Rayment Antiques (R)
42 Alyn Drive, Rossett
Nr. Wrexham, Clwyd
Tel: (0244) 570869

Swansea County & W.P. Ltd.
49 St. Helen's Rd., Swansea
Tel: (0792) 53334

CRAFTS

LONDON

Amalgam
3 Barnes High St., S.W.13
Tel: 01-878 1279

Argenta Gallery
82 Fulham Rd., S.W.3
Tel: 01-584 3119

Basilisk Press
32 Englands Lane, N.W.3
Tel: 01-722 2142

British Crafts Centre
43 Earlham St., Covent Gdn., W.C.2
Tel: 01-836 6993

Casson Gallery
73 Marylebone High St., W.1
Tel: 01-487 5080

Craft Shop V & A
Victoria & Albert Museum
South Kensington, S.W.7
Tel: 01-589 5070

Craftsmen Potters Shop
William Blake House
Marshall St., W.1
Tel: 01-437 7605

Electrum
21 South Molton St., W.1
Tel: 01-629 6325

The Glasshouse
65 Long Acre, W.C.2
Tel: 01-836 9785

Innate Harmony
67 St. John's Wood High St., N.W.8
Tel: 01-722 0686

David Mellor
4 Sloane Square, S.W.1
Tel: 01-730 4259

CORNWALL

New Craftsman
24 Fore St., St. Ives
Tel: (0736) 796398

CUMBRIA

Corn Mill Galleries
The Old Town Mill, Ulverston
Tel: (0229) 54600

DEVON

Dartington Craft Shop
Dartington Cider Press Centre,
Skinners Bridge, Dartington, Totnes
Tel: (0803) 864 171

Palace Gate Gallery
1 Deanery Place, Palace Gate, Exeter
Tel: (0392) 35978

Windjammer Crafts
2 Russell Court, Salcombe
Tel: (054) 8842979

GLOS.

Chestnut Gallery
High St., Bourton-on-the-Water
Tel: (0451) 20017

HEREFORDS.

Collection
13 The Southend, Ledbury
Tel: (0531) 3581

MERSEYSIDE

Bluecoat Display Centre
Bluecoat Chambers, School Lane,
Liverpool 1
Tel: (051) 709 4014

NORTHANTS.

Four Seasons Gallery
39 St. Giles St., Northampton
Tel: (0604) 32287

OXON.

Oxford Gallery
23 High St., Oxford
Tel: (0865) 42731

Prescote Gallery
Cropredy, Banbury
Tel: (0295) 75660

SUSSEX

Barclaycraft
7 East St., Brighton
Tel: (0273) 21694

Hands Craft Gallery
150 St. Pancras, Chichester
Tel: (0243) 787645

WARWICKSHIRE

Peter Dingley
16 Meer St., Stratford-upon-Avon
Tel: (0789) 5001

Soft Surround
Studio 2, Centre Craft Yard,
Henley St., Stratford-upon-Avon
Tel: (0789) 295070

WEST MIDLANDS

Centre Crafts
169 Spon St., Coventry
Tel: (0203) 27200

DOLLS, TOYS & GAMES

LONDON

Donay Antiques
12 Pierrepont Row, N.1
Tel: 01-359 1880

Glenlea Gallery
109 Thurlow Park Rd., S.E.21
Tel: 01-670 3161

Lead Soldier, Antiquarius
135 King's Rd., S.W.3
Tel: 01-352 8734

Pete McAskie
Stand D10-12, Basement, Grays
Mews Antiques, 1-7 Davies Mews,
W.1
Tel: 01-629 2813

Carl Ridley
Stand J22, Grays Mews Antiques
1-7 Davies Mews, W.1

The Dolls House Toys Ltd.
29 The Market, Govent Gdn., W.C.2
Tel: 01-379 7243

The Singing Tree
69 New King's Road, S.W.6
Tel: 01-736 4527

Victoriana Dolls
The Knightsbridge Pavilion
Brompton Rd., S.W.7
Tel: 01-589 5908

CORNWALL

Mrs. Margaret Chesterton
33 Pentewan Rd., St. Austell
Tel: (0726) 2926

DORSET

Hobby Horse Antiques
29 & 5 (at Bridge) West Allington
Bridport
Tel: (0308) 22801

GLOS.

Antique Dolls' Shop & Dolls' Hospital
Days Stable, Sheep St.
Stow-on-the-Wold
Tel: (0451) 30381

China Doll
31 Suffolk Parade, Cheltenham
Tel: (0242) 33164

KENT

Hadlow Antiques
1 The Pantiles, Tunbridge Wells
Tel: (0892) 29858

SOMERSET

Min Lewis Antiques
Southfield House, Rode
Tel: (0373) 830531

SURREY

Curiosity Shop
72 Stafford Rd., Wallington
Tel: 01-647 5267

Doll Shop (appointment only)
18 Richmond Hill, Richmond
Tel: 01-940 6774

Past & Presents
52 High St., Thames Ditton
Tel: 01-398 0962

W. MIDLANDS

Meriden House Antiques
75 Market St., Stourbridge
Tel: (03843) 5384

YORKS.

Tim Armitage
Vintage Toyshop, 498 Bradford Rd.
Batley
Tel: (0924) 471386

SCOTLAND

The Workshop
38 Union Place, Dundee
Tel: (0382) 644950

WALES

Museum of Childhood Toys &
Gift Shop
Water St., Menai Bridge, Gwynedd
Tel: (0248) 712498

ENAMELS

LONDON

Halcyon Days
14 Brook St., W.1
Tel: 01-629 8811

EPHEMERA

LONDON

Bayly's Gallery
8 Princes Arcade, Piccadilly, W.1
Tel: 01-734 0180

Gilda Conrich Antiques
12 The Mall, 359 Upper St.
Camden Passage, N.1
Tel: 01-226 5319

Dodo
185 Westbourne Grove, W.11
Tel: 01-229 3132

Follies
Stalls M5, M6 and M7, Antiquarius
135 King's Rd., S.W.3
Tel: 01-352 7989

M. & R. Glendale
121 Gray's Antique Market
58 Davies St., W.1
Tel: 01-629 2851

David Godfrey
37 Kinnerton St., S.W.1
Tel: 01-235 7788

Pleasures of Past Times
11 Cecil Crt., Charing Cross Rd., W.C.2
Tel: 01-836 1142

Quadrille Antiques
27 Craven Terrace, W.2
Tel: 01-262 7824

Peter Stockham at Images
16 Cecil Crt., Charing Cross Rd., W.C.2
Tel: 01-836 8661

BUCKS.

Omniphil Ltd.
Germains Lodge, Fullers Hill
Chesham
Tel: (0494) 771851

Also at

Stand 110, Gray's Antique Market
Davies St., W.1
Tel: 01-629 1309

SURREY

Richmond Antiquary
28 Hill Rise, Richmond
Tel: 01-948 0583/727 4745

FURNITURE

LONDON

Antique Porcelain Co. Ltd.
149 New Bond St., W.1
Tel: 01-629 1254

Asprey & Co. PLC
165-169 New Bond St., W.1
Tel: 01-493 6767

C. W. Buckingham
301-303 Munster Rd., S.W.6
Tel: 01-385 2657
(See also under HANTS.)

John Creed Antiques Ltd.
3 & 5A Camden Passage, N.1
Tel: 01-226 8867

Zal Davar Antiques
26A Munster Rd., S.W.6
Tel: 01-736 1405/2559

John Keil Ltd.
154 Brompton Rd., S.W.3
Tel: 01-589 6454

Lee & Stacey
5 Pond St., N.W.3
Tel: 01-794 7904/452 0056

C. H. Major (Antiques) Ltd.
154 Kensington Church St, W.8
Tel: 01-229 1162

Mallett & Son (Antiques) Ltd.
40 New Bond St., W.1
Tel: 01-499 7411

M. & D. Seligmann
37 Kensington Church St., W.8
Tel: 01-937 0400

Murray Thomson Ltd.
141 Kensington Church St., W.8
Tel: 01-727 1727

William Tillman
30 St. James's St., S.W.1
Tel: 01-839 2500

O. F. Wilson Ltd.
Queen's Elm Parade, Old Church St.
S.W.3
Tel: 01-352 9554

Windsor House Antiques (Leeds) Ltd.
298 Westbourne Grove, W.11
Tel: 01-221 4883

AVON

Cottage Antiques
The Old Post Office, Langford Place
Langford, Nr. Bristol
Tel: (0934) 862597

BERKS.

Mary Bellis Antiques
Charnham Close, Hungerford
Tel: (0488) 82620

Biggs of Maidenhead
Hare Hatch Grange, Twyford
Tel: (073522) 3281

The Old Malthouse, Hungerford
Tel: (04886) 2209

Medalcrest Ltd.
Charnham House, Charnham St.
Hungerford
Tel: (0488) 84157

Charles Toller
20 High St., Datchet
Tel: (0753) 42903

BUCKS.

Bishop (Marlow) Ltd.
8 & 10 West St., Marlow
Tel: (06284) 3936

CAMBS.

W. Stockbridge & Sons Ltd.
25/26 Bridge St., Cambridge
Tel: (0223) 353500

CHESHIRE

Coppelia Antiques
Holford Lodge, Plumley Moor Rd.
Plumley
Tel: (056581) 2197

John King Antiques
157-159 London Rd. Soutn, Poynton
Tel: (0625) 873110

CLEVELAND

Margaret Bedi Antiques
5 Station Rd., Billingham
Tel: (0642) 554483

CUMBRIA

Haughey Antiques
Market St., Kirkby Stephen
Tel: (0930) 71302

Townhead Antiques
Newby Bridge
Tel: (0448) 31321

DERBYS.

Spurrier-Smith Antiques
28B & 41 Church St., Ashbourne
Tel: (0335) 43669 and
(home) (077389) 368

DEVON

Old Store Antiques
St. Marychurch Rd., Newton Abbot
Tel: (0626) 4690

DORSET

Johnsons of Sherborne Ltd.
South St., Sherborne
Tel: (0935) 812585

ESSEX

Templar Antiques
4 & 6 Stoneham St., Coggeshall
Tel: (0376) 61220

GLOS.

Duncan James Baggott
The Square, Stow-on-the-Wold
Tel: (0451) 30662
and also at
Church St., Stow-on-the-Wold
Tel: (0451) 30370

W. R. Cambridge & Son
14 Rotunda Terrace, Cheltenham
Tel: (0242) 514502

Huntington Antiques Ltd.
The Old Forge, Church St.
Stow-on-the-Wold
Tel: (0451) 30842

Peter Norden Antiques
Kingshead, Birdlip
Tel: (045282) 2299

Studio Antiques Ltd
Bourton-on-the-Water
Tel: (0451) 20352

HANTS.

Barlow Antiques
Bridge House, Stockbridge
Tel: (026481) 744

Binsted Place Antiques
Binsted, Nr. Alton
Tel: (04204) 3146

C. W. Buckingham
Twin Firs, Southampton Rd., Cadnam
Tel: (0703) 812122

Cedar Antiques
High St., Hartley Wintney
Tel: (025126) 3252

Mark Collier Antiques
1-3 Bridge St., Fordingbridge
Tel: (0425) 52555

Lita Kaye of Lyndhurst
13 High St., Lyndhurst
Tel: (042128) 2337

St. Peter's Gallery
Chesil St., Winchester
Tel: (0962) 68901

Elizabeth Viney
Jacob's House, High St., Stockbridge
Tel: (026481) 761

HEREFORDS.

Great Brampton House Antiques
Madley
Tel: (0981) 250244

HERTS.

Phillips of Hitchin (Antiques) Ltd.
The Manor House, Hitchin
Tel: (0462) 32067

KENT

Chislehurst Antiques
7 Royal Parade, Chislehurst
Tel: 01-467 1530

MIDDLESEX

Phelps Ltd.
129-135 St. Margaret's Rd.
E. Twickenham
Tel: 01-892 1778

NORFOLK

Arthur Brett & Sons Ltd.
40-44 St. Giles St., Norwich
Tel: (0603) 28171

Pearse Lukies
Bayfield House, White Hart St.
Aylesham
Tel: (026373) 4137

NORTHUMBERLAND

Prudhoe Cottage Antiques
15 St. Mary's Chare, Hexham
Tel: (0434) 605522 & (0661) 33421

NOTTS.

Matsell Antiques Ltd.
Nottingham Antique Centre
James Alexander Building
London Rd., Nottingham
Tel: ((0602) 55548/54504 and 288267

OXON.

Elizabethan House Antiques
28 & 55 High St.
Dorchester-on-Thames
Tel: (0865) 340079

Zene Walker
The Bull House, High St., Burford
Tel: (099382) 3284

Witney Antiques
96-98 Corn St., Witney
Tel: (0993) 3902

SHROPSHIRE

R. C. Cave & Sons Ltd.
17 Broad St., Ludlow
Tel: (0584) 3568

Feathers Antiques Ltd.
20-22 Bull Ring, Ludlow
Tel: (0584) 2884

Paul Smith
10 Church St., Ludlow
Tel: (0584) 2666

M. & R. Taylor (Antiques)
1 Church St., Ludlow
Tel: (0584) 4169

White Cottage Antiques
Tern Hill, Nr. Market Drayton
Tel: (063083) 222

Stanley Woolston
29 Broad St., Ludlow
Tel: (0584) 3554
and also at
Tamberlane House, The Buttercross
Ludlow

SOMERSET

Grange Court Antiques
Corfe, Nr. Taunton
Tel: (082342) 498

Trevor Micklem Antiques Ltd.
Gateway House, North St., Milverton
Tel: (0823) 400404

Edward A. Nowell
21-23 Market Place, Wells
Tel: (0749) 72415

SUFFOLK

David Gibbins Antiques
21 Market Hill, Woodbridge
Tel: (03943) 3531

Michael Moore Antiques
The Old Court, Nethergate St., Clare
Tel: (0787) 277510

Randolph
99 High St., Hadleigh
Tel: (0473) 823789

SURREY

Heath-Bullock
8 Meadrow, Godalming
Tel: (04868) 22562

Rayne Antiques
332 Brighton Rd., South Croydon
Tel: 01-680 8395

Anthony Welling Antiques
Broadway Barn, High Street, Ripley
Tel: (0483) 225384

SUSSEX

Richard Davidson
Lombard St., Petworth
Tel: (0798) 42508

The Grange Antiques
High St., Robertsbridge
Tel: (0580) 880577.

John G. Morris Ltd.
Market Square, Petworth
Tel: (0798) 42305

Village Antiques
2 & 4 Cooden Sea Rd., Little Common
Bexhill-on-Sea
Tel: (04243) 5214

WILTS.

Avon Antiques
26-27 Market St., Bradford-on-Avon
Tel: (02216) 2052

Robert Bradley
71 Brown St., Salisbury
Tel: (0722) 3677

Combe Cottage Antiques
Castle Combe, Nr. Chippenham
Tel: (0249) 782250

Michael Gray Antiques
1 St. John's Alley, Devizes
Tel: (0380) 6719

Ian G. Hastie
46 St. Ann St., Salisbury
Tel: (0722) 22957

Robert Kime Antiques
Dene House, Lockeridge
Tel: (067286) 250

Monkton Galleries
Hindon
Tel: (074789) 235

Paul Wansbrough
Seend Lodge, Seend, Nr. Melksham
Tel: (038082) 213

YORKS.

Robert Aagaard Ltd.
Frogmire House, Stockwell Rd.
Knaresborough
Tel: (0423) 864805
(Specialises in fireplaces)

Bernard Dickinson
88 High St., Gargrave
Tel: (075678) 285

W. F. Greenwood & Sons Ltd.
2 & 3 Crown Place, Harrogate
Tel: (0423) 504467

SCOTLAND

John Bell of Aberdeen Ltd.
Balbrogie, By Blackburn, Kinellar
Aberdeenshire
Tel: (0224) 79209

Paul Coutts Ltd.
101-107 West Bow, Edinburgh
Tel: (031) 225 3238

Letham Antiques
45 Cumberland St., Edinburgh
Tel: (031) 556 6565

Nicholson Antiques
3 Cranston St., Edinburgh
Tel: (031) 556 1842

Roy Sim Antiques
21 Allan St., Blairgowrie, Perthshire
Tel: (0250) 3860/3700

Unicorn Antiques
65 Dundas St., Edinburgh
Tel: (031) 556 7176

GLASS

LONDON

Asprey & Co. PLC
165-169 New Bond St., W.1
Tel: 01-493 6767

W. G. T. Burne (Antique Glass) Ltd.
11 Elystan St., S.W.3
Tel: 01-589 6074

Delomosne & Son Ltd.
4 Campden Hill Rd., W.8
Tel: 01-937 1804

Eila Grahame
97A Kensington Church St., W.8
Tel: 01-727 4132

Lloyds of Westminster
51 Kinnerton St., S.W.1
Tel: 01-235 1010

J. F. Poore
5 Wellington Terrace, W.2
Tel: 01-229 4166

R. Wilkinson & Son (R)
43-45 Wastdale Rd., Forest Hill
S.E.23
Tel: 01-699 4420

AVON

Somervale Antiques
6 Radstock Rd., Midsomer Norton
Bath
Tel: (0761) 412686

CAMBS.

Hilton Gallery
3 St. Mary's Passage, Cambridge
Tel: (0223) 356886

DORSET

Quarter Jack Antiques
The Quarter Jack, Bridge St.
Sturminster Newton
Tel: (0258) 72558

SOMERSET

Abbey Antiques
52-54 High St., Glastonbury
Tel: (0458) 31694

STAFFS.

The Old House, 47 High St., Kinver
Tel: (038483) 2985

SUFFOLK

Maureen Thompson
Sun House, Long Melford
Tel: (0787) 78252

SURREY

A. Henning
48 Walton St., Walton-on-the-Hill
Tadworth
Tel: (073 781) 3337

WORCS.

Gavina Ewart
60-62 High St., Broadway
Tel: (0386) 853371

SCOTLAND

Janet Lumsden
51A George St., Edinburgh
Tel: (031) 225 2911

William MacAdam (appointment only)
86 Pilrig St., Edinburgh
Tel: (031) 553 1364

GRAMOPHONES, PHONOGRAPHS & RADIOS

LONDON

Fagin's Phonograph Emporium
189 Blackstock Rd., N.5
Tel: 01-359 4793

Howard Hope
L.23, Gray's Mews Market
1-7 Davies Mews, W.1
Tel: 01-499 6600

Talking Machine
30 Watford Way, Hendon, N.W.4
Tel: 01-202 3473

AVON

Vintage Wireless Co.
64 Broad St., Staple Hill, Bristol
Tel: (0272) 565472

KENT

York House Antiques
37 High St., Seal
Tel: (0732) 62811

SOMERSET

Philip Knighton (R)
The Wellington Workshop
14 South St., Wellington
Tel: (082347) 7332

METALWARE

LONDON

Jack Casimir Ltd.
The Brass Shop, 23 Pembridge Rd.
W.11
Tel: 01-727 8643

Arthur Davidson Ltd.
78-79 Jermyn St., S.W.1
Tel: 01-930 6687

Gee Bee Antiques
201 Brompton Rd., S.W.3
Tel: 01-589 3317

Robert Preston
1 Campden St., W.8
Tel: 01-727 4872

Alistair Sampson Antiques
156 Brompton Rd., S.W.3
Tel: 01-589 5272

BEDS.

Christopher Sykes Antiques
The Old Parsonage, Woburn
Milton Keynes
Tel: (052525) 259/467

BERKS.

Rye Galleries
60-61 High St., Eton
Tel: (07535) 62837

BUCKS.

Albert Bartram
177 Hivings Hill, Chesham
Tel: (0494) 783271

CLEVELAND

Margaret Bedi Antiques
5 Station Rd., Billingham
Tel: (0642) 554483

CUMBRIA

Stable Antiques
Oakdene Country Hotel
Garsdale Rd., Sedbergh
Tel: (0587) 20280

GLOS.

Country Life Antiques
Sheep St., Stow-on-the-Wold
Tel: (0451) 30776

Peter Norden Antiques
Kingshead, Birdlip
Tel: (045282) 2299

OXON.

Robin Bellamy Ltd.
97 Corn St., Witney
Tel: (0993) 4793

Elizabethan House Antiques
28 & 55 High Street
Dorchester-on-Thames
Tel: (0865) 340079

Lloyd & Greenwood Antiques
Chapel House, High St., Burford
Tel: (099382) 2359

WILTS.

Combe Cottage Antiques
Castle Combe, Chippenham
Tel: (0249) 782250

Rupert Gentus Antiques
The Manor House, Milton Lilbourne
Nr. Pewsey
Tel: (06726) 3344

YORKS.

Windsor House Antiques (Leeds) Ltd.
18-20 Benson St., Leeds
Tel: (0532) 444666

MUSICAL INSTRUMENTS

LONDON

John & Arthur Beare
7 Broadwick St., W.1
Tel: 01-437 1449

Tony Bingham
11 Pond St., N.W.3
Tel: 01-794 1596

Richard Burnett (appointment only)
3 Macaulay Rd., S.W.4
Tel: 01-622 9393/4

Morley Galleries
4 Belmont Hill, Lewisham
Tel: 01-852 6151

BUCKS.

W. E. Hill & Sons
Havenfields, Great Missenden
Tel: (02406) 3655

HERTS.

Julian Thwaites & Co. (R)
7 Chalk Hill, Oxhey, Bushey
Tel: (0923) 32412

OXON.

Laurie Leigh Antiques
36 High St., Oxford
Tel: (0865) 244197

MUSICAL INSTRUMENTS — MECHANICAL

LONDON

Keith Harding, F.B.H.I. (R)
93 Hornsey Rd., N.7
Tel: 01-607 6181/2672

ESSEX

Mayflower Antiques
180-182 High St., Dovercourt
Harwich
Tel: (02555) 4079

GLOS.

Lewis of Hereford Ltd.
Corse Lawn, Gloucester
Tel: (0452) 78258

NORFOLK

Norfolk Polyphon Centre
Wood Farm, Bawdeswell, Dereham
Tel: (036 288) 230

SUSSEX

Graham Webb
59 Ship St., Brighton
Tel: (0273) 21803

PORCELAIN

LONDON

Albert Amor Ltd.
37 Bury St., St. James's, S.W.1
Tel: 01-930 2444

Antique Porcelain Co. Ltd.
149 New Bond St., W.1
Tel: 01-629 1254

Susan Becker
18 Lower Richmond Rd., S.W.15
Tel: 01-788 9082

David Brower Antiques
113 Kensington Church St., W.8
Tel: 01-221 4155

Cale Antiques
24 Cale St., Chelsea Green, S.W.3
Tel: 01-589 6146

Chester Antiques
97 Mount St., W.1
Tel: 01-499 5315

China Choice
New Cavendish St., W.1
Tel: 01-935 0184

Craven Antiques
17 Garson House, Gloucester Terrace
W.2
Tel: 01-262 4176

Delomosne & Son Ltd.
4 Campden Hill Rd., W.8
Tel: 01-937 1804

H. & W. Deutsch Antiques
111 Kensington Church St., W.8
Tel: 01-727 5984

Miss Fowler
1A Duke St., Manchester Square, W.1
Tel: 01-935 5187

Gay Antiques
1 Beauchamp Place, S.W.3
Tel: 01-584 9615

Graham & Oxley (Antiques) Ltd.
101 Kensington Church St., W.8
Tel: 01-229 1850

Grosvenor Antiques Ltd.
27 Holland St., Kensington, W.8
Tel: 01-937 8649

Harcourt Antiques
5 Harcourt St., W.1
Tel: 01-723 5919

Heirloom & Howard Ltd.
1 Hay Hill, Berkeley Square, W.1
Tel: 01-493 5868

Hoff Antiques Ltd.
66A Kensington Church St., W.8
Tel: 01-229 5516

Mercury Antiques
1 Ladbroke Rd., W.11
Tel: 01-727 5106

Raven Antiques
256 Lee High Rd., S.E.13
Tel: 01-852 5066

Edward Salti
43 Davies St., W.1
Tel: 01-629 2141

Gerald Sattin Ltd.
25 Burlington Arcade, Piccadilly, W.1
Tel: 01-493 6557

Aubrey Spiers Antiques
Shop C5, Chenil Galleries
183 King's Rd., S.W.3
Tel: 01-352 2123

Betty & Vera Vandekar at 'Walbrook'
101B Kensington Church St., W.8
Tel: 01-727 2471

Earle D. Vandekar of
Knightsbridge Ltd.
138 Brompton Rd., S.W.3
Tel: 01-589 8481/3398

Venner's Antiques
7 New Cavendish St., W.1
Tel: 01-935 0184

Joanna Warrand
99 Kensington Church St., W.8
Tel: 01-727 2333

Winifred Williams
3 Bury St., St. James's, S.W.1
Tel: 01-930 4732

AVON.

Andrew Dando
4 Wood St., Queen Square, Bath
Tel: (0225) 22702

BERKS.

The Old School Antiques
Dorney, Windsor
Tel: (06286) 3247

CORNWALL

London Apprentice Antiques
Pentewan Rd., St. Austell
Tel: (0726) 63780

DERBYS.

P. W. Gottschald Antiques
Sandyford Farm, Nr. Belper
Tel: (077382) 3305

C. B. Sheppard Antiques
(appointment only)
Hurst Lodge, Chesterfield Rd.
Tibshelf
Tel: (0773) 872419

DEVON

David J. Thorn
2 High St., Budleigh Salterton
Tel: (03954) 2448

ESSEX

Constance & Anthony Chiswell
1 Market Place, Dunmow
Tel: (0371) 2388

GLOS.

Aldbury Antiques
High St., Blockley
Nr. Moreton-in-Marsh
Tel: (0386) 700280

Hamand Antiques
Friday St., Painswick
Tel: (0452) 812310

Studio Antiques Ltd.
Bourton-on-the-Water
Tel: (0451) 20352

HANTS.

Goss & Crested China Ltd.
62 Murray Rd., Horndean
Tel: (0705) 597440

HEREFORD & WORCS.

Sabina Jennings
Newcourt Park, Lugwardine
Tel: (0432) 850752

M. Lees & Sons
Tower House, Severn St., Worcester
Tel: (0905) 26620

KENT

The Antique Porcelain Collector
High St., Shoreham Village
Nr. Sevenoaks
Tel: (09592) 3416

Bygones
Peirce Cottage, Charing, Ashford
Tel: (023371) 2494

Dunsdale Lodge Antiques
Brasted Rd., Westerham
Tel: (0959) 62160

Hop Pole Antiques
41 Pound Rd., E. Peckham, Tonbridge
Tel: (0622) 871993

Steppes Hill Farm Antiques
Stockbury, Sittingbourne
Tel: (0795) 842205

W. W. Warner (Antiques) Ltd.
The Green, Brasted
Tel: (0959) 63698

LANCS.

Burnley Antiques & Fine Arts Ltd.
336A Colne Rd., Burnley
Tel: (0282) 20143/65172

NORFOLK

T. C. S. Brooke
The Grange, Wroxham
Tel: (06053) 2644

Cromer Antiques Gallery
Church St., Cromer
Tel: (0263) 512355

OXON.

David John Ceramics
25 Oxford St., Woodstock
Tel: (0993) 812649

SHROPS.

Castle Gate Antiques
15 Castle Gate, Shrewsbury

Tudor House Antiques
33 High St., Ironbridge
Tel: (095245) 3237

SURREY

J. P. Raison (appointment only)
Sturt House, Sturt's Lane, Tadworth
Tel: (073781) 3663/3557

Elias Clark Antiques Ltd.
1 The Cobbles, Bletchingley
Tel: (0883) 843714

SUSSEX

Barclay Antiques
7 Village Mews, Little Common
Bexhill-on-Sea
Tel: (0797) 222734 (home)

Geoffrey Godden, Chinaman
17-19 Crescent Rd., Worthing
Tel: (0903) 35958

Magpie House Antiques
27 Kemp St., Brighton
Tel: (0273) 683892

McPherson & Wood
80A St. George's Rd., Kemp Town
Brighton
Tel: (0273) 681661

WILTS.

The China Hen
9 Woolley St., Bradford-on-Avon
Tel: (02216) 3369

Mark Collier Antiques
High St., Downton
Tel: (0725) 21068

Marjorie Whitworth (Antiques)
20 West St., Wilton
Tel: (072274) 2165

YORKS.

Brian Bowden
199 Carr House Rd., Doncaster
Tel: (0302) 65353

David Love
10 Royal Parade, Harrogate
Tel: (0423) 65797

Nanbooks
Undercliffe Cottage, Duke St., Settle
Tel: (07292) 3324 or (04685) 551

POTTERY

LONDON

Britannia
Gray's Market, 58 Davies St., W.1
Tel: 01-629 6772

Cale Antiques
24 Cale St., Chelsea Green, S.W.3
Tel: 01-589 6146

Gerald Clark Antiques
1 High St., Mill Hill Village, N.W.7
Tel: 01-906 0342

Richard Dennis
144 Kensington Church St., W.8
Tel: 01-727 2061

Graham & Oxley (Antiques) Ltd.
101 Kensington Church St., W.8
Tel: 01-229 1850

Jonathan Horne
66C Kensington Church St., W.8
Tel: 01-221 5658

D. M. & P. Manheim Ltd.
69 Upper Berkeley St., Portman Sq.
W.1
Tel: 01-723 6595

J. & J. May
40 Kensington Church St., W.8
Tel: 01-937 3575

Mercury Antiques
1 Ladbroke Rd., W.11
Tel: 01-727 5106

Oliver-Sutton Antiques
34C Kensington Church St., W.8
Tel: 01-937 0633

Rogers de Rin
76 Royal Hospital Rd., S.W.3
Tel: 01-352 9007

Alistair Sampson Antiques
156 Brompton Rd., S.W.3
Tel: 01-589 5272

CUMBRIA

Kendal Studio Pottery
2-3 Wildman St., Kendal
Tel: (0539) 23291

DEVON

David J. Thorn
2 High St., Budleigh Salterton
Tel: (03954) 2448

KENT

Bygones
Peirce Cottage, Charing, Ashford
Tel: (023371) 2494

Dunsdale Lodge Antiques
Brasted Rd., Westerham
Tel: (0959) 62160

W. W. Warner (Antiques) Ltd.
The Green, Brasted
Tel: (0959) 63698

LANCS.

Burnley Antiques & Fine Arts Ltd.
336A Colne Rd., Burnley
Tel: (0282) 20143/65172

SURREY

Elias Clark Antiques Ltd.
1 The Cobbles, Bletchingley
Tel: (0883) 843714

SUSSEX

Magpie House Antiques
27 Kemp St., Brighton
Tel: (0273) 683892

WILTS.

Bratton Antiques
Market Place, Westbury
Tel: (0373) 823021

Marjorie Whitworth (Antiques)
20 West St., Wilton
Tel: (072274) 2165

YORKS.

Nanbooks
Undercliffe Cottage, Duke St., Settle
Tel: (07292) 3324 or (04685) 551

SCIENTIFIC INSTRUMENTS

LONDON

Arthur Davidson Ltd.
78-79 Jermyn St., S.W.1
Tel: 01-930 6687

Mariner Antiques Ltd.
55 Curzon St., W.1
Tel: 01-499 0171

Mayfair Microscopes Ltd.
64 Burlington Arcade, W.1
Tel: 01-629 2616

Arthur Middleton Ltd.
12 New Row, Covent Garden, W.C.2
Tel: 01-836 7042/7062

Harriet Wynter Ltd.
50 Redcliffe Rd., S.W.10
Tel: 01-352 6494

BEDS.

Christopher Sykes Antique
The Old Parsonage, Woburn
Milton Keynes
Tel: (052525) 259/467

DEVON

Galaxy Arts
38 New St., Barbican, Plymouth
Tel: (0752) 667842

ESSEX

Mayflower Antiques
180-182 High St., Dovercourt
Harwich
Tel: (02555) 4079

GLOS.

Country Life Antiques
Sheep St., Stow-on-the-Wold
Tel: (0451) 30776

NORFOLK

Humbleyard Fine Art
Waterfall Cottage, Mill St.
Swanton Morley
Tel: (036283) 793

Also at

Coltishall Antiques Centre
Coltishall, Norfolk

Turret House
Wymondham
Tel: (0953) 603462

SUSSEX

Trevor Philip & Sons
2 Prince Albert St., Brighton
Tel: (0273) 202119

SCULPTURES

SUSSEX

Armstrong-Davis Gallery
The Square, Arundel
Tel: (0903) 882752

SILVER

LONDON

Asprey & Co. PLC
165-169 New Bond St., W.1
Tel: 01-493 6767

HANTS.

St. Peter's Gallery
Chesil St., Winchester
Tel: (0962) 68901

Bygones
Peirce Cottage, Charing, Ashford
Tel: (023371) 2494

Steppes Hill Farm Antiques
Stockbury, Sittingbourne
Tel: (0795) 842205

SOMERSET

Edward A. Nowell
21-23 Market Place, Wells
Tel: (0749) 72415

FAIR ORGANISERS

LONDON

Century Antique Fairs
57 Mill Lane, N.W.6
Tel: 01-794 3551

Philbeach Events Ltd.
Earl's Court Exhibition Centre
Warwick Rd., S.W.5
Tel: 01-385 1200

BERKS.

Granny's Attic Fairs
Dean House, Cookham Dean
Tel: (06284) 3658

Silhouette Fairs (inc. Newbury Antique & Collectors' Fairs)
25 Donnington Sq., Newbury
Tel: (0635) 44338

CHESHIRE

Susan Brownson, Antique Fairs North West
Brownslow House, Gt. Budworth
Northwich
Tel: (0606) 891267 & (061 962) 5629

Pamela Robertson
8 St. George's Crescent, Queens Park
Chester
Tel: (0244) 678106

CORNWALL

West Country Antiques & Collectors' Fairs (Gerry Mosdell)
Hillside, St. Issey, Wadebridge
Tel: (08414) 666

ESSEX

Stephen Charles Fairs
3 Leigh Hill, Leigh-on-Sea
Tel: (0702) 714649/556745 and (0268) 774977

Emporium Fairs
13 Abbeygate St., Colchester
Tel: (0206) 66975

Heirloom Markets
11 Wellfields, Writtle, Chelmsford
Tel: (0245) 422208

HERTS.

Bartholomew Fayres
Herts. & Essex Antiques Centre
The Maltings, Station Rd.
Sawbridgeworth
Tel: (0279) 725809 or 36603
Also in: Essex

Lima Antiques
(Mavis & George Camm)
North House, 8 Danesbury Pk. Rd.
Welwyn
Tel: (043871) 4744

HUMBERSIDE

Seaclef Fairs Ltd.
78 Humberston Ave., Humberston
Grimsby
Tel: (0472) 813858

KENT

Darent Fairs
Whitestacks Cottage, Crockenhill Lane, Eynsford
Tel: (0322) 863383

LINCS.

J.P. Antiques Fairs
286 High St., Lincoln
Tel: (0522) 29022

NOTTS.

Top Hat Exhibitions Ltd.
66-72 Derby Rd., Nottingham
Tel: (0602) 419143

OXON.

Portcullis Fairs
6 St. Peter's St., Wallingford
Tel: (0491) 39345

SHROPS.

Middleton Fairs (Stephen Middleton)
31 Ludlow Heights, Bridgnorth
Tel: (07462) 4114

SUFFOLK

Camfair (Ros Coltman)
Longlands, Kedington, Haverhill
Tel: (0440) 704632

Lorna Quick Fairs
St. John's Antique Centre
31 & 32 St. John's St.
Bury St. Edmunds
Tel: (0284) 3024

SURREY

Antiques & Collectors Club
No. 1 Warehouse, Horley Row
Horley
Tel: (02934) 72206

Cultural Exhibitions Ltd.
8 Meadrow, Godalming
Tel: (04868) 22562

Historic and Heritage Fayres
The Moorings, Molember Rd.
East Molesey
Tel: 01-398 5324

SUSSEX

Brenda Lay
Dyke Farm, West Chiltington Rd.
Pulborough
Tel: (07982) 2447

YORKS.

Bowman Antique Fairs
7 Church Hill, Bramhope, Leeds
Tel: (0532) 843333
Also in: Cheshire, Cleveland Lincolnshire, Staffordshire and Yorkshire

Castle Galleries & Fairs
31 Castlegate, York.
Tel: (0904) 27222

DIRECTORY OF AUCTIONEERS

This directory is by no means complete. Any auctioneer who holds frequent sales should contact us for inclusion in the 1985 edition. Entries must be received by April 1984. There is, of course, no charge for this listing.

LONDON

Bonhams, Montpelier Galleries
Montpelier St., Knightsbridge, S.W.7
Tel: 01-584 9161 and 01-589 4577

Borough Auctions
6 Park St., London Bridge, S.E.1
Tel: 01-407 9577 (day)
01-981 2079 (evening)

Camden Auctions
The Saleroom, Hoppers Rd.
Winchmore Hill, N.21
Tel: 01-886 1550

Christie's, Manson & Woods Ltd.
8 King St., St. James's, S.W.1
Tel: 01-839 9060

Christie's South Kensington Ltd.
85 Old Brompton Rd., S.W.7
Tel: 01-581 2231

Forrest & Co.
79-85 Cobbold Rd. Leytonstone, E.11
Tel: 01-534 2931

Stanley Gibbons Auctions Ltd.
Drury House, Russell St., W.C.2
Tel: 01-836 8444

Glendining & Co.
Blenstock House, 7 Blenheim St.
New Bond St., W.1
Tel: 01-493 2445

Harmers of London Stamp Auctioneers Ltd.
41 New Bond St., W.1
Tel: 01-629 0218

Harvey's Auctions Ltd.
14, 16 and 18 Neal St., W.C.2
Tel: 01-240 1464/5/6/7

Lefevre & Ptnrs (Auctioneers) Ltd.
The Persian Carpet Galleries
152 Brompton Rd., S.W.3
Tel: 01-584 5516

Phillips
Blenstock House, 7 Blenheim St.
New Bond St., W.1
Tel: 01-6296602

Phillips Marylebone Auction Rooms
Hayes Place, N.W.1
Tel: 01-723 2647

Phillips West 2
10 Salem Road, W.2
Tel: 01-221 5303

Rippon Boswell & Co.
The Arcade, South Kensington Station, S.W.7
Tel: 01-589 4242

Robson Lowe Ltd.
50 Pall Mall, S.W.1
Tel: 01-839 4034/5

Also at the Auction House
39 Poole Hill, Bournemouth
Tel: 0202 23235

Sotheby Parke Bernet & Co.
34-35 New Bond St., W.1
Tel: 01-493 8080

Sotheby Parke Bernet & Co.
(Grosvenor and Hodgson's Rooms)
Bloomfield Place, Off New Bond St. W.1

Sovereign Auctions Ltd.
101 Hoe St., Walthamstow, E.17
Tel: 01-521 5456 and 01-520 3215

West London Auctions
Sandringham Mews, High St.
Ealing, W.5
Tel: 01-567 6215/7096

GREATER LONDON

Bonsor Penningtons
82 Eden St., Kingston, Surrey
Tel: 01-546 0022

Croydon Auction Rooms
(Rosan & Co.)
144-150 London Rd., Croydon
Tel: 01-688 1123/4/5

Parkins
18 Malden Rd., Cheam, Surrey
Tel: 01-644 6633 and 6127

E. Reeves Ltd.
104/120 Church St., Croydon
Tel: 01-688 3136

AVON

Aldridges, Bath
The Auction Galleries
130-132 Walcot St., Bath
Tel: 0225 62830 and 62839

Davis, Champion & Payne
Chartered Surveyors
42 High St., Chipping Sodbury
Bristol
Tel: 0454 312848/313033

Hoddell Pritchard
Six Ways, Clevedon
Tel: 0272 876011

Lalonde Bros. and Parham
71 Oakfield Rd., Clifton, Bristol
Tel: 0272 734052

Osmond, Tricks & Son
Regent St., Salerooms, Clifton, Bristol
Tel: 0272 737201 and 730810

Phillips and Jolly's Auction
Rooms of Bath
1 Old King St., Bath
Tel: 0225 310609 and 310709

Taviner's Auction Rooms
Prewett Street, Redcliffe, Bristol
Tel: 0272 25996

BEDFORDSHIRE

Peacock, The Auction Centre
26 Newnham St., Bedford
Tel: 0234 66366

BERKSHIRE

Buckland & Sons
Dolphin Hotel, Slough
Tel: 0734 51370

Chancellors & Co.
31 High St., Ascot
Tel: 0990 20101

V. and V. Chattel Auctioneers
24 Greyfriars Rd., *and*
6 Station Rd., Reading
Tel: 0734 594748

Dreweatt, Watson & Barton
Donnington Priory, Donnington
Newbury
Tel: 0635 31234

Neates
8 St. Mary's Hill, Cheap St., Newbury
Tel: 0635 42961

Nicholas
13 Bridge St., Streatley, Reading
Tel: 0491 872318

Thimbleby and Shorland
31 Great Knollys St., Reading
Tel: 0734 54438

BUCKINGHAMSHIRE

Buckland & Sons
Bridgewood, East Common Rd.
Gerrards Cross. Tel: 028 13 85451

Pretty & Ellis
The Amersham Auction Rooms
125 Station Rd., Amersham
Tel: 02403 4627

CAMBRIDGESHIRE

Cheffins, Grain & Chalk
49-53 Regent St., Cambridge
Tel: 0223 358721

George Comins & Sons
3 Chequer Lane, Ely
Tel: 0353 2265

Ekins Dilley & Handley
The Salerooms, St. Ives, Huntingdon
Tel: St. Ives 0480 68144

Hammond & Co.
Cambridge Place, Cambridge
Tel: 0223 356067

Raymond Munns, F.R.I.C.S.
25 High St., Willingham
Tel: 0954 60447

Norman Wright & Hodgkinson
Abbey Rd., Bourne
Tel: 07782 2567

CHESHIRE

Brocklehursts
King Edward St., Macclesfield
Tel: 0625 27555

Andrew, Hilditch & Son
19 The Square, Sandbach
Tel: 093 67 2048 and 7246

Jackson-Stops & Staff
25 Nicholas St., Chester
Tel: 0244 28361

Frank R. Marshall & Co.
Marshall House, Church Hill
Knutsford
Tel: 0565 53461

David Morrison & Son
Central Auction Galleries
1 Market St., Altrincham
Tel: 061 928 9200

Reeds Rains
Trinity House, 114 Northenden Rd.
and Warren House, 17 Warren St.
Stockport
Tel: 061 962 9237

Phillips & Swetenhams
5 St. Werburgh St., Chester
Tel: 0244 315333

CLEVELAND

Norman Hope & Partners
2 South Rd., Hartlepool
Tel: 0429 67828

Lithgow Sons & Partners
The Auction Houses Station Rd.
Stokesley, Middlesborough
Tel: 0642 710158 and 710326

CORNWALL

Button, Menhenitt & Mutton Ltd.
Belmont Auction Rooms, Wadebridge
Tel: 020 881 2059

W. H. Cornish
Central Auction Rooms, Castle St.
Truro
Tel: 0872 2968

W. H. Lane & Son
Fine Art Auctioneers
Central Auction Rooms, Penzance
Tel: 0736 61447/8
and
Central Auction Rooms
Kinterbury House, St. Andrew's
Cross, Plymouth
Tel: 0752 669298

David Lay, A.S.V.A.
7 Morrab Rd., Penzance
Tel: 0736 68308

May, Whetter & Grose
Cornubia Hall, Par
Tel: 072 681 2271

CUMBRIA

Tissen, King, Nicholson
12 Lowther St., Carlisle
Tel: 0228 25259

Alfred Mossop & Co., F.S.V.A.
Ambleside Auction Rooms
Compston Rd., Ambleside
Tel: 09663/3015

Thomson, Roddick & Laurie
24 Lowther St., Carlisle
Tel: 0228 28939 and 39636

DERBYSHIRE

Robert E. Spark & Co.
Matlock Auction Gallery
Olde Englishe Rd., Dale Rd., Matlock
Tel: 0629 2451

DEVON

Bearnes
Rainbow, Avenue Rd., Torquay
Tel: 0803 26277

Bright & Sons
Union Lane, Brixham
Tel: 080 45 3389

Peter J. Eley, F.S.V.A.
98-100 High St., Sidmouth
Tel: 039 55 2552/3

Gribble, Booth and Taylor
West St., Axminster
Tel: 0297 32323

Charles Head & Son
113 Fore St., Kingsbridge
Tel: 0548 2352

T. D. Hussey & Son
99 High St., Honiton
Tel: 0404 2553

Phillips
Alphin Brook Rd., Alphington, Exeter
Tel: 0392 39025/6

Rendells
13 Market St., Newton Abbot
Tel: 0626 3881

John Smale & Co.
19 Cross St., Barnstaple
Tel: 0271 2000 2916

Laurence & Martin Taylor
Honiton Galleries, 63 High St.
Honiton
Tel: 0404 2404

Whitton & Laing
32 Okehampton St., Exeter
Tel: 0392 52621

John Wood & Co.
Seaton Salerooms
Harbour Rd., Seaton
Tel: 0297 20290

DORSET

S. W. Cottee & Son
The Market, East St., Wareham
Tel: 092 95 2826

Hy. Duke & Son
Fine Art Salerooms
Weymouth Ave., Dorchester
Tel: 0305 65080

John Jeffery Auctioneers
Minister House, The Commons
Shaftesbury
Tel: Shaftesbury 3331-2

Riddetts of Bournemouth
Richmond Hill, Bournemouth Sq.
Bournemouth
Tel: 0202 25686

COUNTY DURHAM

G. H. Edkins & Son
122 Newgate St., Bishop Auckland
Tel: 0388 603095

G. Tarn Bainbridge & Son
Northern Rock House, High Row
Darlington
Tel: 0325 62633 and 62553

Thomas Watson & Son
Northumberland St., Darlington
Tel: 0325 62555/9

ESSEX

Abridge Auction Rooms
High Rd., Abridge, Romford
Tel: Theydon Bois 037 881 2107

Cooper Hirst, F.R.I.C.S.
Goldlay House, Parkway, Chelmsford
Tel: 0245 58141

Spurgeon & Gilchrist
1st Floor, Tokenhouse Chambers
Rosemary Rd., Clacton-on-Sea
Tel: 0255 22472

John Stacey & Sons
Leigh Auction Rooms
86-90 Pall Mall, Leigh-on-Sea
Tel: 0702 77051

Vosts's Fine Art Auctioneers
Layer Marney, Colchester
Tel: 0206 330250

Edwin Watson & Son
1 Market St., Saffron Walden
Tel: 0799 22058

J. M. Welch & Son
Old Town Hall, Great Dunmow
Tel: 0371 2117/8

GLOUCESTERSHIRE

Bruton, Knowles & Co.
Albion Chambers, 55 Barton St.
Gloucester
Tel: 0452 21267

Cheltenham Galleries
1A Crescent Place, Cheltenham
Tel: 0242 584310

Moore, Allen & Innocent
33 Castle St., Cirencester
Tel: 0285 2862

Sandoe Luce Panes
Chipping Manor Salerooms
Wotton-under-Edge
Tel: 045 385 3193

Specialised Postcard Auctions
12 Suffolk Rd., Cheltenham
Tel: 0242 580323

HAMPSHIRE

Allen & May
18 Bridge St., Andover
Tel: 0264 3417 and 63331

Michael G. Baker, F.S.V.A.
4 Latimer St., Romsey
Tel: 0794 513331

Elliott & Green
40 High St., Lymington
Tel: 0590 77225

Fox & Sons
5 and 7 Salisbury St., Fordingbridge
Tel: 0425 52121

Hants & Berks Auctions
40 George St., Kingsclere
Tel: 0635 298181

Jacobs & Hunt
Lavant St., Petersfield
Tel: 0730 2744/5

D. M. Nesbit & Co.
7 Clarendon Rd., Southsea
Tel: 0705 820785

Ormiston, Knight & Payne
54 Southampton Rd., Ringwood
Tel: 04254 3333

Pearsons
Walcote Chambers
High St., Winchester
Tel: 0962 64444

Whiteheads
34 High St., Petersfield
Tel: 0730 2691/2

HEREFORD & WORCESTER

Banks & Silvers
66 Foregate St., Worcester
Tel: 23456

Blinkhorn & Co.
41-43 High St., Broadway
Tel: 0386 852456

Coles, Knapp & Kennedy
Tudor House, High St., Ross-on-Wye
Hereford
Tel: 0989 63553/4

Maurice Fellows
6 The Tything, Worcester
Tel: 0905 27755

Andrew Grant, F.R.I.C.S.
59/60 Foregate St., Worcester
Tel: 0905 52310

Arthur G. Griffiths & Son
57 Foregate St., Worcester
Tel: 0905 26464

J. G. Lear & Son
46 Foregate St., Worcester
Tel: 0905 25184, 25494

Phipps & Pritchard
Bank Buildings, Kidderminster
Tel: 0562 2244/6 and 2187

Russell, Baldwin & Bright
Fine Art Saleroom, Rylands Rd.
Leominster
Tel: 0568 3897

Stooke, Hill & Co.
3 Broad St., Leominster
Tel: 0568 3407

HERTFORDSHIRE

George Jackson & Son
Paynes Park House, Paynes Park
Hitchin
Tel: 0462 55212

Norris & Duvall
106 Fore St., Hertford
Tel: 0992 52249

G. E. Sworder & Sons
Chequers, 19 North St., Bishops
Stortford
Tel: 0279 52441

Watsons
Water lane, Bishops Stortford
Tel: 0279 52361/4

HUMBERSIDE NORTH

Gilbert Baitson, F.S.V.A.
'The Edwardian Auction Galleries'
194 Anlaby Rd., Hull
Tel: Hull 223355/6

Broader & Spencer
18 Quay Rd., Bridlington
Tel: 0262 70355/6

Dee & Atkinson
The Exchange, Driffield
Tel: 0377 43151

HUMBERSIDE SOUTH

Dickinson, Davy & Markham
10 Wrawby St, Brigg
Tel: 0652 53666

ISLE OF WIGHT

Way, Riddett & Co.
Town Hall Chambers, Lind St., Ryde
Tel: 0983 62255

KENT

Alberts Auctions & Co.
Maiden Lane, Crayford, Dartford
Tel: 0322 528868

B. & J. Auction Galleries
22 Mortimer St., Herne Bay
Tel: 02273 3479/66653

Bracketts
27-29 High St., Tunbridge Wells
Tel: 0892 33733

Burrows & Day
39-41 Bank St., Ashford
Tel: 0233 674485

Butler & Hatch Waterman
102 High St., Tenterden
Tel: 05806 3233/2083

Also at

86 High St., Hythe
Tel: 0303 66022/3

Geering & Colyer
Highgate, Hawkhurst
Tel: 05805 3181/3463

Hobbs Parker
9 Tufton St., Ashford
Tel: 0233 22222

John Hogbin & Son
53 High St., Tenterden
Tel: 05806 3200

Ibbett, Mosely, Card & Co.
125 High St., Sevenoaks
Tel: 0732 452246

Kent Sales
Kent House, 4 New Rd., S. Darenth
Tel: 0322 864919

Parsons, Welch & Cowell
129 High St., Sevenoaks
Tel: 0732 451211/4

Daniel Smith
24-26 Dover Rd., Folkestone
Tel: 0303 41967

Stewart, Gore
100-102 North Down Rd., Margate
Tel: 0843 21528/9

James B. Terson & Son
27-29 Castle St., Dover
Tel: 0304 202173

Worsfold's
40 Station Rd. West, Canterbury
Tel: 0227 68984

LANCASHIRE

Artingstall & Hind
378-380 Deansgate, Knott Mill
Manchester
Tel: 061-834 4559

Capes Dunn & Co.
The Auction Galleries, 38 Charles St.
Manchester
Tel: 061-273 6060

Entwistle Green
The Galleries, Kingsway, Ansdell
Lytham St. Annes
Tel: Lytham 735442

Hothersall, Forrest, McKenna & Son
Bank Salerooms, Harris Court
Clitheroe
Tel: 0200 25446/22695

J. R. Parkinson Son & Hamer
The Auction Room
Rochdale Rd., Bury
Tel: 061 761 1612/7372

John E. Pinder & Son
Stone Bridge, Longridge, Preston
Tel: 077 478 2282

LEICESTERSHIRE

Walker Walton Hanson
4 Market Place, Oakham
Tel: 0572 3377

Warner, Sheppard & Wade
The Warner Auction Rooms
16/18 Halford St., Leicester
Tel: 0533 21613

LINCOLNSHIRE

William H. Brown
31 St. Peters Hill, Grantham
Tel: 0476 66363

Earl & Lawrence
55 Northgate, Sleaford
Tel: 0529 302946

James Eley & Son
1 Main Ridge West, Boston
Tel: 0205 61687

Golding
45 High St., Grantham
Tel: 0476 5456

Thomas Mawer & Son
63 Monks Rd., Lincoln
Tel: 0522 24984 and 22215

Vergettes
38 St. Mary's St., Stamford
Tel: 0780 52136

MERSEYSIDE

Richard Baker & Thomson
9 Hamilton St., Birkenhead
Tel: 051 647 9104/5

Cobern Ball & Percival
The Grosvenor Salerooms
21 Hoghton St., Southport
Tel: Southport 36313

Kingsley Galleries
3-4 The Quadrant, Hoylake, Wirral
Tel: 051 632 5821

Outhwaite & Litherland
Kingsway Galleries
Fontenoy St., Liverpool
Tel: 051 236 6561/3

NORFOLK

Noel D. Abel
32 Norwich Rd., Watton
Tel: 0953 881204

Clowes, Nash & Thurgar
6 Tombland, Norwich
Tel: 0603 27261

Ewings
Market Place, Reepham, Norwich
Tel: 060 526 473

Thos. Wm. Gaze & Son
Roydon Rd., Diss
Tel: 0379 2291

Charles Hawkins & Sons
Lynn Rd., Downham Market
Tel: 0366 382112/3

Nigel F. Hedge
28B Market Place, North Walsham
Tel: 0692 402881

Hilham's
53 Springfield Rd., Gorleston-on-Sea
Tel: 0493 62152

James Norwich Auctions Ltd.
33 Timberhill, Norwich
Tel: 0603 24817/25369

G. A. Key
8 Market Place, Aylsham
Tel: Aylsham 3195

Long & Beck
2 Oak St., Fakenham
Tel: 0328 2231

Hanbury Williams
34 Church St., Cromer
Tel: 0263 513247

NORTHAMPTONSHIRE

Goldsmith & Bass
15 Market Place, Oundle
Tel: 08322 2349

R. L. Lowery & Partners
24 Bridge St., Northampton
Tel: Northampton 21561

Northampton Auction Galleries
Old Albion Brewery
Commercial St., Northampton
Tel: 0604 37263/4

T. W. Arnold Corby & Co.
30-32 Brook St., Raunds
Tel: Wellingborough (0933) 623722/3

Southam & Sons
Corn Exchange, Thrapston, Kettering
Tel: 08012 2409

H. Wilford Ltd.
Midland Rd., Wellingborough
Tel: 0933 222760/222762

NOTTINGHAMSHIRE

Edward Bailey & Son
17 Northgate, Newark
Tel: 0636 703141 and 77154

Furniture & General Auctions
Corn Exchange, Cattle Market
London Rd., Nottingham
Tel: 0602 866261

Neales of Nottingham
192 Mansfield Rd., Nottingham
Tel: 0602 624141

Walker Walton Hanson (Auctions)
The Nottingham Auction Mart
Byard Lane, Bridlesmith Gate
Nottingham
Tel: 0602 54272

C. B. Sheppard & Son
The Auction Gallery
Chatsworth St., Sutton-in-Ashfield
Tel: 0773 872419

Henry Spencer & Sons Ltd.
20 The Square, Retford
Tel: 0777 706767

OXFORDSHIRE

Buckell & Ballard Fine Arts
(Auctioneers)
49 Parsons St., Banbury
Tel: 0295 53197/8

Green & Co.
33 Market Place, Wantage
Tel: 023 57 3561/2

William A. Honour & Co.
112 High St., Thame
Tel: 084 421 2383/4

Mallams, Fine Art Auctioneers
24 St. Michael's St., Oxford
Tel: 0865 41358

E. P. Messenger & Son
Pevensey House Salerooms
Manorsfield Rd., Bicester
Tel: 08692 45985

Phillips Inc. Brooks
39 Park End St., Oxford
Tel: 0865 723524/5

Simmons & Lawrence
32 Bell St., Henley-on-Thames
Tel: 049 12 78301

SHROPSHIRE

Cooper & Green
3 Barker St., Shrewsbury
Tel: 0743 50081

John German Ralph Pay
43 High St., Shrewsbury
Tel: 0743 69661/4

Hall, Wateridge & Owen
Welsh Bridge Salerooms, Shewsbury
Tel: 0743 60212

McCartney, Morris & Barker
25 Corve St., Ludlow
Tel: 0584 2636

Nock, Deighton & Son
10 Broad St., Ludlow
Tel: 2364/3760

Perry & Phillips
Newmarket Salerooms
Newmarket Buildings, Listley St.
Bridgnorth
Tel: 074 62 2248

SOMERSET

Cooper & Tanner Ltd.
14 North Parade, Frome
Tel: 0373 62045

Dores
The Auction Mart
Vicarage St., Frome
Tel: 0373 62257

King, Miles & Co.
The Old Palace Saleroom
Priory Rd., Wells
Tel: 0749 73002

Lawrence Fine Art of Crewkerne
South St., Crewkerne
Tel: 0460 73041

The London Cigarette Card Co. Ltd.
Sutton Rd., Somerton
Tel: 0458 73452

Phillips, Saunders & Studds
32 The Avenue, Minehead
Tel: 0643 2281/3

Priory Saleroom
Winchester St., Taunton
Tel: 0823 77121

Wellington Salerooms
Mantle St., Wellington
Tel: 082 347 4815

STAFFORDSHIRE

Bagshaws
17 High St., Uttoxeter
Tel: 088 93 2811

Hall & Lloyd, Auctioneers
Stafford
Tel: 0785 58176

Louis Taylor & Sons
Percy St., Hanley, Stoke-on-Trent
Tel: 0782 260222

Wintertons
St. Mary's Chambers, Lichfield
Tel: 054 32 23256

SUFFOLK

H. A. Adnams
The Auction Room, St. Edmunds Rd.
Southwold
Tel: 0502 723292

Oxborrows, Arnott & Calver
14 Church St., Woodbridge
Tel: 03943 2244/5

Boardman — Fine Art Auctioneers
Station Road Corner, Haverhill
Tel: 0440 703784

Diamond, Mills & Co.
117 Hamilton Rd., Felixstowe
Tel: 03942 2281/2

Robert Dove & Partners
Dover House, Wolsey St., Ipswich
Tel: 0473 55137

Durrant's
10 New Market, Beccles
Tel: 0502 712122

Lacy Scott, Fine Art
Angel Hill, Bury St. Edmunds
Tel: 0284 63531

Neal Sons & Fletcher
26 Church St., Woodbridge
Tel: 2263/4

Notleys
Royal Thoroughfare, Lowestoft
Tel: 0502 2024/5

Olivers
23-24 Market Hill, Sudbury
Tel: 0787 72247

Spear & Sons
The James Abbott Partnership
The Hill, Wickham Market
Nr. Woodbridge
Tel: 0728 746321

Tuohy & Son
Denmark House, 18 High St.
Aldeburgh
Tel: 072 885 2066

H. C. Wolton & Son
6 Whiting St., Bury St. Edmunds
Tel: 0284 61336

SURREY

Clarke, Gammon
45 High St., Guildford
Tel: 0483 72266

Lawrences — Fine Art Auctioneers
Norfolk House, 80 High St.
Bletchingley
Tel: 0883 843323

Messenger May Baverstock
93 High St., Godalming
Tel: 048 68 23567

Wentworth Auction Galleries
21 Station Approach, Virginia Water
Tel: 09904 3711

White & Sons
104 High St., Dorking
Tel: 0306 887654

Harold Williams Bennett & Partners
2-3 South Parade, Merstham, Redhill
Tel: 073 74 2234/5

P. F. Windibank
18-20 Reigate Rd., Dorking
Tel: 0306 884556

SUSSEX — EAST

Burstow & Hewett
Abbey Auction Galleries & Granary
Salerooms, Battle
Tel: 04246 2374

Burtenshaw Walker
66 High St., Lewes
Tel: 079 16 4225

Clifford Dann & Partners
Fine Art Auction Galleries
20-21 High St., Lewes
Tel: 07916 77022

Rowland Gorringe & Co.
15 North St, Lewes
Tel: 07916 2503

Graves, Son & Pilcher
71 Church Rd., Hove
Tel: 0273 735266

Edgar Horn
47 Cornfield Rd., Eastbourne
Tel: 0323 22801/3

Raymond P. Inman
Auction Galleries
35 and 40 Temple St., Brighton
Tel: 0273 774777

Lewes Auction Rooms
(Julian Dawson)
66 High St., Lewes
Tel: 07916 78221

Meads of Brighton
St. Nicholas Rd., Brighton
Tel: 0273 202997/8

Vidler & Co.
Rye Auction Galleries
Cinque Ports St., Rye
Tel: 0797 222124

Wallis & Wallis
Regency House, Albion St. Lewes
Tel: 079 16 3137

SUSSEX — WEST

T. Bannister & Co.
Market Place, Haywards Heath
Tel: 0444 412402

Sussex Auction Galleries
Bradley & Vaughan
59 Perrymount Rd., Haywards Heath
Tel: 0444 59961

Horsham Auction Galleries
31 The Carfax, Horsham
Tel: 0403 53837

R. H. Ellis & Sons
44-46 High St., Worthing
Tel: Worthing 38999

Fox & Sons, Jordan & Cook
41 Chapel Rd., and 33 South St.
Worthing
Tel: 0903 205565

G. Knight & Son
West St., Midhurst
Tel: 073081 2456/8

Sotheby's in Sussex
Station Rd., Pulborough
Tel: 07982 3831

Stride & Son
Southdown House
St. John's St., Chichester
Tel: 0243 782626

Wyatt & Son
59 East St., Chichester
Tel: 0243 786581

TYNE & WEAR

Anderson & Garland
Fine Art Salerooms, Anderson House
Market St., Newcastle-upon-Tyne
Tel: 0632 326278

Glover, Humble & Partners
Coates Institute, Ponteland
Tel: 0661 22041

WARWICKSHIRE

Edwards, Bigwood & Bewlay
The Old School, Tiddington
Stratford-upon-Avon
Tel: 0789 69415

Henley in Arden Auction Sales Ltd.
92 High St., Henley-in-Arden, Solihull
Tel: 05642 3211

Locke & England
1 & 2 Eustace Place, Leamington Spa
Tel: 0926 27988

Seaman of Rugby
Auction House, 20 Little Church St.
Rugby
Tel: 0788 2367

WEST MIDLANDS

Allsop Sellers
No. 8 Hagley Rd., Stourbridge
Tel: 038 43 2122

Biddle & Webb
Icknield Square, Ladywood
Middleway, Birmingham
Tel: 021-455 8042

Cecil Cariss & Son
20-22 High St., Kings Heath
Birmingham 14
Tel: 021-444 5311

Codsal Antique Auctions
Codsal, Wolverhampton
Tel: 0902 66728

Collins, Son & Harvey
44 High St., Erdington, Birmingham
Tel: 021-382 8870/2

Frank H. Fellows & Sons
Bedford House, 88 Hagley Rd.
Edgbaston, Birmingham
Tel: 021-454 1261/1219

Giles Haywood
The Auction House, St. John's Rd.
Stourbridge
Tel: 03843 70891

James & Lister Lea
11 Newhall St., Birmingham
Tel: 021-236 1751

Phillips
The Old House, Station Rd.
Knowle, Solihull
Tel: 056 45 6151

Weller & Dufty Ltd.
141 Bromsgrove St., Birmingham
Tel: 021-692 1414

WILTSHIRE

Amesbury Salerooms
High St., Amesbury
Tel: 098 02 3000

Berry, Powell & Shackell
46 Market Place, Chippenham
Tel: 0249 3361

Dennis Pocock & Son
20 High St., Marlborough
Tel: 0672 53471/2

Geoffrey Taylor & Co.
30 St. John's St., Devizes
Tel: 0380 2321

Woolley & Wallis
The Castle Auction Mart
Castle St., Salisbury
Tel: 0722 27405

YORKSHIRE — NORTH

Boulton & Cooper Ltd.
Forsyth House, Market Pl., Malton
Tel: 0653 2151

H. C. Chapman & Son
The Auction Mart
North St., Scarborough
Tel: 0723 72424

Dee & Atkinson
The Exchange, Driffield
Tel: 0377 43151

Lawson, Larg
St. Trinity House, Kings Sq., York
Tel: 0904 21532

Morphets of Harrogate
4 Albert St., Harrogate
Tel: 0423 502282

M. Philip H. Scott
Church Wynd, Burneston, Bedale
Tel: 0677 23325

Renton & Renton
16 Albert St., Harrogate
Tel: 0423 61531

Stephenson & Son
43 Gowthorpe, Selby
Tel: 0757 706707

G. A. Suffield & Co.
27 Flowergate, Whitby
Tel: 0947 603433

Geoffrey Summersgill, A.S.V.A.
8 Front St., Acomb, York
Tel: 0904 791131

Tennant's
26-27 Market Place, Leyburn
Tel: 0969 23451

Ward Price & Co.
Royal Auction Rooms
Queen St., Scarborough
Tel: 0723 65455

YORKSHIRE — SOUTH

Eadon Lockwood and Riddle
2 St. James' St., Sheffield
Tel: 0742 71277

Stanilands
28 Nether Hall Rd., Doncaster
Tel: 0302 67766/27121

YORKSHIRE — WEST

Dacre, Son & Hartley
1-5 The Grove, Ilkley
Tel: 0943 600655

Eddisons
Auction Rooms, 4-6 High St.
Huddersfield
Tel: 0484 33151

Ilkley Auction Galleries
Riddings Rd., Ilkley
Tel: 0943 600456

Laidlaws
Crown Court Salerooms (off Wood St.)
Wakefield
Tel: 0924 75301

Phillips at Hepper House
17A East Parade, Leeds
Tel: 0532 448011

John H. Raby & Son
Salem Auction Rooms
21 St. Mary's Rd., Bradford
Tel: 0274 491121

Chas. E. H. Yates & Son
The Salerooms, Otley Rd.
Guiseley
Tel: 0943 74165

CHANNEL ISLANDS

Langlois Ltd.
Don St., St. Helier, Jersey
Tel: 0534 22441

F. Le Gallais & Sons
Bath St., St. Helier, Jersey
Tel: 0534 30202

SCOTLAND

John Anderson, Auctioneers
33 Cross St., Fraserburgh
Aberdeenshire
Tel: 034 62 2878

Christie's and Edmiston's Ltd.
164-166 Bath St., Glasgow,
Strathclyde
Tel: 041-332 8134/7

Frasers (Auctioneers)
28-30 Church St., Inverness
Tel: 0463 32395

J. & J. Howe
24 Commercial St., Alyth, Perthshire
Tel: 082 83 2594

Thomas Love & Sons Ltd.
St. John's Place, Perth, Perthshire
Tel: 0738 24111

John Milne
9 North Silver St., Aberdeen
Tel: 0224 50336/7

Robert Paterson & Son
8 Orchard St., Paisley
Renfrewshire
Tel: 041 889 2435

Phillips in Scotland
98 Sauchiehall St., Glasgow
Tel: 041-332 3386
Also
65 George St., Edinburgh
Tel: 031-225 2266

L. S. Smellie & Sons Ltd.
Within the Furniture Market
Lower Auchingramont Rd., Hamilton
Tel: 0698 282007

Taylor's Auction Rooms
11 Panmure Row, Montrose, Angus
Tel: 0674 2775

WALES

T. Brackstone & Co.
19 Princes Drive, Colwyn Bay, Clwyd
Tel: 0492 30481/2

R. G. Daniel & Partners
Bangor House, High St., Lampeter,
Dyfed
Tel: 0570 422550

K. Hugh Dodd & Partners, F.S.V.A.
9 Chester St., Mold, Clwyd
Tel: 0352 2552

John Francis, Thomas Jones & Son
Curiosity Salerooms, King St.
Carmarthen
Tel: 0267 33456/7

Rennie, Taylor, Miles & Escott
1 Agincourt St., Monmouth
Tel: 0600 2916

C. Wesley Haslam & Son
St. Helens Pl., High St., Rhyl, Clwyd
Tel: 0745 4467/8

THE BESTSELLERS!

Special publisher's reprint edition:

Now available as a boxed set!

- ★ Over 35,000 items described and valued
- ★ Each volume highlights different aspects of the antiques market
- ★ Many hundreds of tips and pointers to buying and selling antiques of all kinds
- ★ The most complete and visually reliable reference system — anywhere!
- ★ Fantastic value at only £24.95 post free

Wise collectors collect Miller's first.

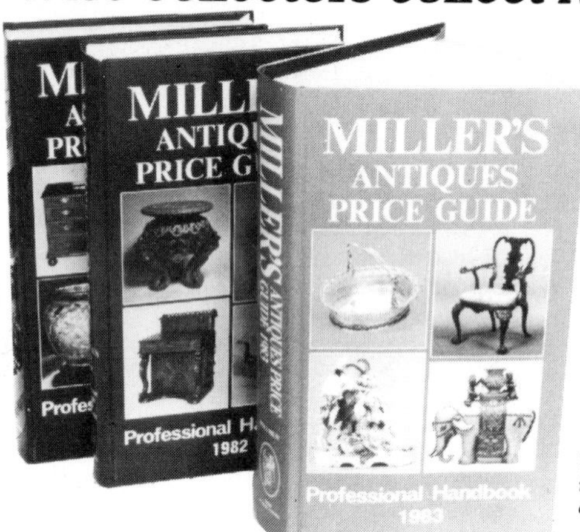

BUILDS UP FROM YEAR TO YEAR

The original Vol. I of Miller's Antiques Price Guide was purely a pilot issue which has now been deleted from our series. For ease of reference and continuity Vol. II has been renumbered Vol. I/II.

Individual volumes may be purchased at the normal price of £10.95 each, plus £1.50 towards the cost of postage and packing. Overseas rates on application.

ORDER FORM

Please send me boxed editions of Miller's Antiques Price Guide, Vols. I-IV and/or individual volumes as follows:

Vols. I-II ☐ **Vol. III** ☐ **Vol. IV** ☐

I understand that the price is only £24.95 for my boxed set, or £10.95 per individual volume plus £1.50 per volume towards the cost of postage and packing. (Overseas rates on application.)

Please debit my Access/Amex/Baclaycard account number ☐☐☐☐☐☐☐☐☐☐☐☐☐☐☐☐

NAME ______________________________

ADDRESS ______________________________

____

______________________________ SIGNATURE ______________________________

If you do not wish to deface this volume, either write the above details on a separate sheet and send it to M.J.M. Publications, The Grange, Benenden, Kent TN17 4DN, marking the envelope FREEPOST

or

Simply telephone 0580 240454

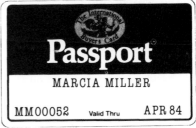

INDEX

INDEX

NOTES

NOTES

NOTES